2020

The ARRL
HANDBOOK
FOR RADIO COMMUNICATIONS

NINETY-SEVENTH EDITION

Volume 1: Introduction and Fundamental Theory — Ch. 1-4

▶ **Volume 2:** Practical Design and Principles Part 1 — Ch. 5-11

Volume 3: Practical Design and Principles Part 2 — Ch. 12-18

Volume 4: Antenna Systems and Radio Propagation — Ch. 19-21

Volume 5: Equipment Construction and Station Accessories — Ch. 22-24

Volume 6: Test Equipment, Troubleshooting, RFI, and Index — Ch. 25-28

Editor
H. Ward Silver, NØAX

Contributing Editors
Steven R. Ford, WB8IMY
Mark J. Wilson, K1RO

Editorial Assistant
Maty Weinberg, KB1EIB

Technical Consultants
Bob Allison, WB1GCM
Edward F. Hare, Jr., W1RFI
Zachary H.J. Lau, W1VT

Cover Design
Sue Fagan, KB1OKW
Bob Inderbitzen, NQ1R

Production
Michelle Bloom, WB1ENT
Jodi Morin, KA1JPA
David F. Pingree, N1NAS

Additional Contributors to the 2020 Edition
John Brooks, N9ZL
Jim Brown, K9YC
Glen Brown, W6GJB
Ralph Crumrine, NØKC

Don Daso, K4ZA
Joel Hallas, W1ZR
Bill Koch, W2RMA
Rick Lindquist, WW1ME
Glenn Loake, GØGBI
Helmut Berka, DL2MAJ
Oliver Micic, DG7XO
Carl Luetzelschwab, K9LA
Phil Salas, AD5X
Rob Sherwood, NCØB
Cory Sickles, WA3UVV
George Steber, WB9LVI
Jim Tonne, W4ENE
Paul Wade, W1GHZ

Published by:
ARRL The national association for **AMATEUR RADIO®**
225 Main Street, Newington, CT 06111-1400 USA
www.arrl.org

Copyright © 2019 by
The American Radio Relay League, Inc.

Copyright secured under the Pan-American Convention

International Copyright secured

All rights reserved. No part of this work may be reproduced in any form except by written permission of the publisher. All rights of translation are reserved.

Printed in the USA

Quedan reservados todos los derechos

ISBN: 978-1-62595-107-6 Softcover
ISBN: 978-1-62595-113-7 Six-Volume Set

Kindle eBook Editions
  ISBN: 978-1-62595-091-8 — Volume 1
  ISBN: 978-1-62595-092-5 — Volume 2
  ISBN: 978-1-62595-093-2 — Volume 3
  ISBN: 978-1-62595-094-9 — Volume 4
  ISBN: 978-1-62595-095-6 — Volume 5
  ISBN: 978-1-62595-096-3 — Volume 6

Ninety-Seventh Edition

About the cover:
The collection of components comprises the HF Packer miniHFPA2 amplifier kit. Although the kit is not featured in this 2020 edition of the ARRL Handbook, its components represent the spirit of project design and craftsmanship that has been part of Amateur Radio from the beginning.

Contents

A more detailed Table of Contents is included at the beginning of each chapter.

VOLUME 1

INTRODUCTION AND FUNDAMENTAL THEORY

1   What is Amateur (Ham) Radio?
1.1 Do-It-Yourself Wireless
1.2 Joining the Ham Radio Community
1.3 Your Ham Radio Station
1.4 Getting on the Air
1.5 Your Ham Radio "Lifestyle"
1.6 Public Service
1.7 Ham Radio in the Classroom
1.8 Resources
1.9 Glossary

2   Electrical Fundamentals
2.1 Introduction to Electricity
2.2 Resistance and Conductance
2.3 Basic Circuit Principles
2.4 Power and Energy
2.5 Circuit Control Components
2.6 Capacitance and Capacitors
2.7 Inductance and Inductors
2.8 Semiconductor Devices
2.9 References and Bibliography

3   Radio Fundamentals
3.1 AC Waveforms
3.2 Measuring AC Voltage, Current and Power
3.3 Effective Radiated Power
3.4 AC in Capacitors and Inductors
3.5 Working with Reactance
3.6 Impedance
3.7 Quality Factor (Q) of Components
3.8 Resonant Circuits
3.9 Analog Signal Processing
3.10 Electromagnetic Waves
3.11 References and Bibliography

4   Circuits and Components
4.1 Practical Resistors
4.2 Practical Capacitors
4.3 Practical Inductors
4.4 Transformers
4.5 Practical Semiconductors
4.6 Amplifiers
4.7 Operational Amplifiers
4.8 Miscellaneous Analog ICs
4.9 Analog-Digital Interfacing
4.10 Analog Device and Circuits Glossary
4.11 Heat Management
4.12 References and Bibliography

VOLUME 2

PRACTICAL DESIGN AND PRINCIPLES — PART 1

5 **RF Techniques**
  5.1 Introduction
  5.2 Lumped-Element versus Distributed Characteristics
  5.3 Effects of Parasitic (Stray) Characteristics
  5.4 Semiconductor Circuits at RF
  5.5 Ferrite Materials
  5.6 Impedance Matching Networks
  5.7 RF Transformers
  5.8 Noise
  5.9 Two-Port Networks
  5.10 RF Design Techniques Glossary
  5.11 References and Bibliography

6 **Computer-Aided Circuit Design**
  6.1 Circuit Simulation Overview
  6.2 Simulation Basics
  6.3 Limitations of Simulation at RF
  6.4 Electromagnetic Analysis of RF Circuits
  6.5 References and Bibliography

7 **Power Sources**
  7.1 Power Processing
  7.2 AC-AC Power Conversion
  7.3 Power Transformers
  7.4 AC-DC Power Conversion
  7.5 Voltage Multipliers
  7.6 Current Multipliers
  7.7 Rectifier Types
  7.8 Power Filtering
  7.9 Power Supply Regulation
  7.10 "Crowbar" Protective Circuits
  7.11 DC-DC Switchmode Power Conversion
  7.12 High-Voltage Techniques
  7.13 Batteries
  7.14 Glossary of Power Source Terms
  7.15 References and Bibliography
  7.16 Power Supply Projects

8 **DSP and SDR Fundamentals**
  8.1 Introduction to DSP
  8.2 Introduction to SDR
  8.3 Analog-Digital Conversion
  8.4 Data Converters for SDR and DSP
  8.5 Digital Signal Processors
  8.6 Digital (Discrete-time) Signals
  8.7 The Fourier Transform
  8.8 Glossary of DSP and SDR Terms
  8.9 References and Bibliography

9 **Oscillators and Synthesizers**
  9.1 How Oscillators Work
  9.2 LC Variable Frequency Oscillator (VFO) Circuits
  9.3 Building an Oscillator
  9.4 Crystal Oscillators
  9.5 Oscillators at UHF and Above
  9.6 Frequency Synthesizers
  9.7 Phase Noise
  9.8 Glossary of Oscillator and Synthesizer Terms
  9.9 References and Bibliography

10 **Analog and Digital Filtering**
  10.1 Introduction
  10.2 Filter Basics
  10.3 Passive LC Filters
  10.4 Active Audio Filters
  10.5 Digital Filters
  10.6 Quartz Crystal Filters
  10.7 SAW Filters
  10.8 Transmission Line VHF/UHF/Microwave Filters
  10.9 Helical Resonators
  10.11 Filter Projects
  10.12 Glossary of Filter Terms
  10.13 References and Bibliography

11 **Modulation**
  11.1 Introduction
  11.2 Amplitude Modulation (AM)
  11.3 Angle Modulation
  11.4 FSK and PSK
  11.5 Quadrature Modulation
  11.6 Analytic Signals and Modulation
  11.7 Image Modulation
  11.8 Spread Spectrum Modulation
  11.9 Pulse Modulation
  11.10 Modulation Bandwidth and Impairments
  11.11 Glossary of Modulation Terms
  11.12 References and Further Reading

VOLUME 3

PRACTICAL DESIGN AND PRINCIPLES — PART 2

12 Receiving
12.1 Characterizing Receivers
12.2 Heterodyne Receivers
12.3 SDR Receivers
12.4 Mixing and Mixers
12.5 Demodulation and Detection
12.6 Automatic Gain Control (AGC)
12.7 Noise Management
12.8 References and Bibliography

13 Transmitting
13.1 Characterizing Transmitters
13.2 Transmitter Architecture
13.3 Modulators
13.4 Transmitting CW
13.5 Transmitting AM and SSB
13.6 Transmitting Angle Modulation
13.7 Effects of Transmitted Noise
13.8 Microphones and Speech Processing
13.9 Voice Operation
13.10 Transmitter Power Stages
13.11 References and Bibliography

14 Transceiver Design Topics
14.1 Signal Chains in SDR Transceivers
14.2 User Interfaces
14.3 Configuration and Control Interfaces
14.4 SDR Design Tools

15 Digital Protocols and Modes
15.1 Digital "Modes"
15.2 Unstructured Digital Modes
15.3 Fuzzy Modes
15.4 Structured Digital Modes
15.5 Networking Modes
15.6 Digital Mode Table
15.7 Glossary of Digital Protocol and Mode Terms
15.8 References and Bibliography

16 Amateur Radio Data Platforms
16.1 Platform Overview
16.2 Sensors
16.3 Navigation Data and Telemetry
16.4 Payloads
16.5 High Altitude Balloon Platforms
16.6 Unmanned Aerial Vehicles (UAVs)
16.7 Rockets
16.8 Robotics
16.9 Fixed Stations
16.10 References and Bibliography

17 RF Power Amplifiers
17.1 High Power, Who Needs It?
17.2 Types of Power Amplifiers
17.3 Vacuum Tube Basics
17.4 Tank Circuits
17.5 Transmitting Tube Ratings
17.6 Sources of Operating Voltages
17.7 Tube Amplifier Cooling
17.8 Vacuum Tube Amplifier Stabilization
17.9 MOSFET Design for RF Amplifiers
17.10 Solid-State RF Amplifiers
17.11 Solid State Amplifier Projects
17.12 Tube Amplifier Projects
17.13 References and Bibliography

18 Repeaters
18.1 A Brief History
18.2 Repeater Overview
18.3 FM Voice Repeaters
18.4 D-STAR Repeater Systems
18.5 System Fusion Repeater Systems
18.6 Digital Mobile Radio (DMR)
18.7 Other Digital Voice Repeater Technologies
18.8 Glossary of FM and Repeater Terminology
18.9 References and Bibliography

VOLUME 4

ANTENNA SYSTEMS AND RADIO PROPAGATION

19 Propagation of Radio Signals
19.1 Fundamentals of Radio Waves
19.2 Sky-Wave Propagation and the Sun
19.3 MUF Predictions
19.4 Propagation in the Troposphere
19.5 VHF/UHF Mobile Propagation
19.6 Propagation for Space Communications
19.7 Noise and Propagation
19.8 Propagation Below the AM Broadcast Band
19.9 Glossary of Radio Propagation Terms
19.10 References and Bibliography

20 Transmission Lines
20.1 Transmission Line Basics
20.2 Choosing a Transmission Line
20.3 The Transmission Line as Impedance Transformer
20.4 Matching Impedances in the Antenna System
20.5 Baluns and Transmission-Line Transformers
20.6 PC Transmission Lines
20.7 Waveguides
20.8 Glossary of Transmission Line Terms
20.9 References and Bibliography

21 Antennas
21.1 Antenna Basics
21.2 Dipoles and the Half-Wave Antenna
21.3 Vertical (Ground-Plane) Antennas
21.4 T and Inverted-L Antennas
21.5 Slopers and Vertical Dipoles
21.6 Yagi Antennas
21.7 Quad and Loop Antennas
21.8 HF Mobile Antennas
21.9 VHF/UHF Mobile Antennas
21.10 VHF/UHF Antennas
21.11 VHF/UHF Beams
21.12 Radio Direction Finding Antennas
21.13 Rotators
21.13 Glossary
21.14 References and Bibliography

VOLUME 5

EQUIPMENT CONSTRUCTION AND STATION ACCESSORIES

22 Component Data and References
22.1 Component Data
22.2 Resistors
22.3 Capacitors
22.4 Inductors
22.5 Transformers
22.6 Semiconductors
22.7 Tubes, Wire, Materials, Attenuators, Miscellaneous
22.8 Computer Connectors
22.9 RF Connectors and Transmission Lines
22.10 Reference Tables

23 Construction Techniques
23.1 Electronic Shop Safety
23.2 Tools and Their Use
23.3 Soldering Tools and Techniques
23.4 Surface Mount Technology (SMT)
23.5 Constructing Electronic Circuits
23.6 CAD for PCB Design
23.7 Microwave Construction
23.8 Mechanical Fabrication

24 Assembling a Station
24.1 Fixed Stations
24.2 Mobile Installations
24.3 Portable Installations
24.4 Remote Stations

VOLUME 6

TEST EQUIPMENT, TROUBLESHOOTING, RFI, AND INDEX

25 Test Equipment and Measurements
25.1 Introduction
25.2 DC Measurements
25.3 AC Measurements
25.4 RF Measurements
25.5 Receiver Measurements
25.6 Transmitter Measurements
25.7 Antenna System Measurements
25.8 Miscellaneous Measurements
25.9 Construction Projects
25.10 References and Further Reading
25.11 Glossary of Test Equipment and Measurement Terms

26 Troubleshooting and Maintenance
26.1 Test Equipment
26.2 Components
26.3 Getting Started
26.4 Inside the Equipment
26.5 Testing at the Circuit Level
26.6 After the Repairs
26.7 Professional Repairs
26.8 Typical Symptoms and Faults
26.9 Radio Troubleshooting Hints
26.10 Antenna Systems
26.11 Repair and Restoration of Vintage Equipment
26.12 References and Bibliography

27 RF Interference
27.1 Managing Radio Frequency Interference
27.2 FCC Rules and Regulations
27.3 Elements of RFI
27.4 Identifying the Type of RFI Source
27.5 Locating Sources of RFI
27.6 Power-Line Noise
27.7 Elements of RFI Control
27.8 Troubleshooting RFI
27.9 Automotive RFI
27.10 RFI Projects
27.11 Glossary of RFI Terms
27.12 References and Bibliography

28 Safety
28.1 Electrical Safety
28.2 Antenna and Tower Safety
28.3 RF Safety

Advertiser's Index
Index
Project Index
Author's Index

DOWNLOADABLE CONTENT AND TOOLS
Space Communications
Digital Communications
Image Communications
Digital Basics
Station Accessories and Projects
2020 HF Transceiver Survey
Radio Mathematics

Contents

5.1 Introduction

5.2 Lumped-Element versus Distributed Characteristics

5.3 Effects of Parasitic (Stray) Characteristics

    5.3.1 Parasitic Inductance

    5.3.2 Parasitic Capacitance

    5.3.3 Inductors at Radio Frequencies

    5.3.4 Skin Effect

    5.3.5 RF Heating

    5.3.6 Effect on Q

    5.3.7 Self-Resonance

    5.3.8 Dielectric Breakdown and Arcing

    5.3.9 Radiative Losses

    5.3.10 Bypassing and Decoupling

    5.3.11 Effects on Filter Performance

5.4 Semiconductor Circuits at RF

    5.4.1 The Diode at High Frequencies

    5.4.2 The Transistor at High Frequencies

    5.4.3 Amplifier Classes

    5.4.4 RF Amplifiers with Feedback

5.5 Ferrite Materials

    5.5.1 Ferrite Permeability and Frequency

    5.5.2 Resonances of Ferrite Cores

    5.5.3 Ferrite Series and Parallel Equivalent Circuits

    5.5.4 Type 31 Material

5.6 Impedance Matching Networks

    5.6.1 L Networks

    5.6.2 Pi Networks

    5.6.3 T Networks

    5.6.4 Impedance Inversion

5.7 RF Transformers

    5.7.1 Air-Core Nonresonant RF Transformers

    5.7.2 Air-Core Resonant RF Transformers

    5.7.3 Broadband Ferrite RF Transformers

5.8 Noise

    5.8.1 Noise Power

    5.8.2 Signal to Noise Ratio

    5.8.3 Noise Temperature

    5.8.4 Noise Factor and Noise Figure

    5.8.5 Losses

    5.8.6 Cascaded Amplifiers

    5.8.7 Antenna Temperature

    5.8.8 Image Response

    5.8.9 Background Noise

5.9 Two-Port Networks

    5.9.1 Two-port Parameters

    5.9.2 Return Loss

5.10 RF Techniques Glossary

5.11 References and Bibliography

Chapter 5

RF Techniques

This chapter is a compendium of material from ARRL publications and other sources. It assumes the reader is familiar with the concepts introduced in the **Electrical Fundamentals**, **Radio Fundamentals**, and **Circuits and Components** chapters. The topics and techniques discussed here are associated with the special demands of circuit design in the HF and VHF ranges. The material is collected from previous editions of this book written by Leonard Kay, K1NU; *Introduction to Radio Frequency Design* by Wes Hayward, W7ZOI; and *Experimental Methods in RF Design* by Wes Hayward, W7ZOI, Rick Campbell, KK7B, and Bob Larkin, W7PUA. Material on ferrites is drawn from publications by Jim Brown, K9YC. The section on Noise was written by Paul Wade, W1GHZ, with contributions from Joe Taylor, K1JT.

Chapter 5 — Downloadable Supplemental Content

Supplemental Articles

- "Reflections on the Smith Chart" by Wes Hayward, W7ZOI
- Tuned Networks
- "Simplified Design of Impedance-Matching Networks," Parts I through III by George Grammer, W1DF
- *LTSpice* simulation files for Section 5.3, Effects of Parasitic Characteristics
- "The Galactic Background in the Upper HF Band" by Dave Typinski, AJ4CO

5.1 Introduction

When is an inductor not an inductor? When it's a capacitor! This statement may seem odd, but it suggests the main message of this chapter. In the earlier chapter, **Electrical Fundamentals**, the basic components of electronic circuits were introduced. As you may know from experience, those simple component pictures are ideal. That is, an ideal component (or element) by definition behaves exactly like the mathematical equations that describe it, and only in that fashion. For example, the current through an ideal capacitor is equal to the capacitance times the rate of change of the voltage across it without consideration of the materials or techniques by which a real capacitor is manufactured.

It is often said that, "Parasitics are anything you don't want," meaning that the component is exhibiting some behavior that detracts from or compromises its intended use. Real components only approximate ideal components, although sometimes quite closely. Any deviation from ideal behavior a component exhibits is called *non-ideal, parasitic,* or *stray.* One way of thinking about parasitic and stray effects — although this is by no means universal — is that parasitic effects are intrinsic to the component and stray effects include both parasitics and environmental effects such as coupling to nearby materials. Since most of what we'll discuss in the following sections deals with the characteristics of actual components, we'll use the term parasitic. Remember that stray and parasitic are often treated as interchangeable terms.

The important thing to realize is that *every* component has parasitic aspects that become significant when it is used in certain ways. This chapter deals with parasitic effects that are commonly encountered at radio frequencies. Knowing to what extent and under what conditions real components cease to behave like their ideal counterparts, and what can be done to account for these behaviors, allows the circuit designer or technician to work with circuits at radio frequencies. We will explore how and why the real components behave differently from ideal components, how we can account for those differences when analyzing circuits and how to select components to minimize, or exploit, non-ideal behaviors.

5.2 Lumped-Element versus Distributed Characteristics

Most electronic circuits that we use every day are inherently and mathematically considered to be composed of *lumped elements*. That is, we assume each component acts at a single point in space, and the wires that connect these lumped elements are assumed to be perfect conductors (with zero resistance and insignificant length). This concept is illustrated in **Figure 5.1**. These assumptions are perfectly reasonable for many applications, but they have limits. Lumped element models break down when:

- Circuit impedance is so low that the small, but non-zero, resistance in the wires is important. (A significant portion of the circuit power may be lost to heat in the conductors.)
- Lead and interconnection inductance is high enough (or the frequency is high enough) that the additional reactance affects circuit behavior.
- Operating frequency is high enough that the length of the connecting wires is a significant

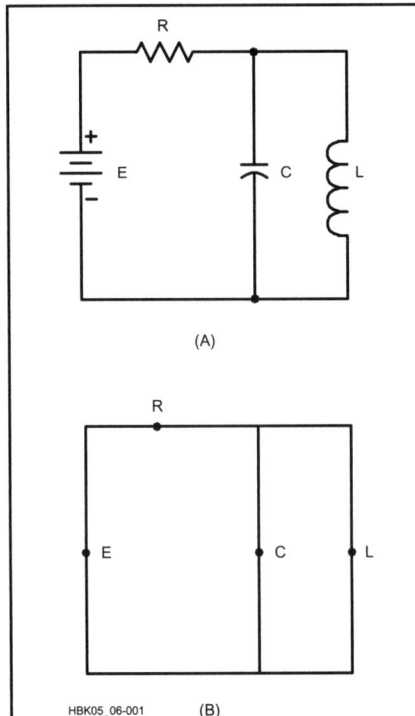

Figure 5.1 — The lumped element concept. Ideally, the circuit at A is assumed to be as shown at B, where the components are isolated points connected by perfect conductors. Many components exhibit nonideal behavior when these assumptions no longer hold.

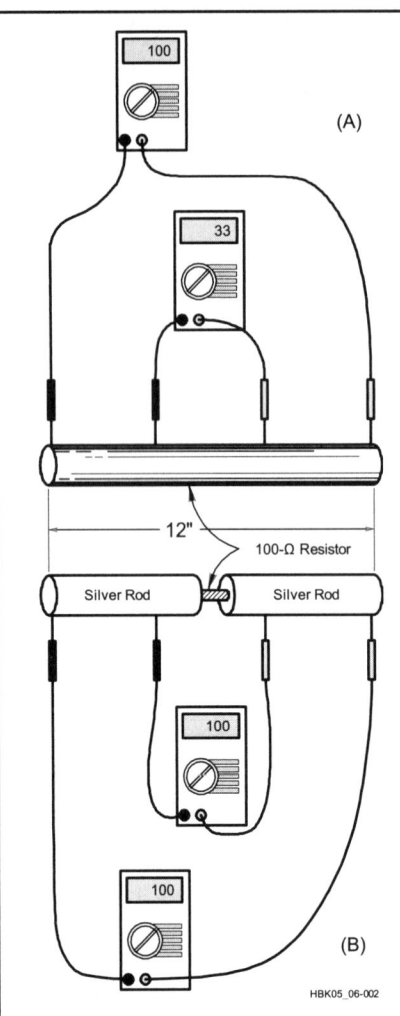

Figure 5.2 — Distributed (A) and lumped (B) resistances. See text for discussion.

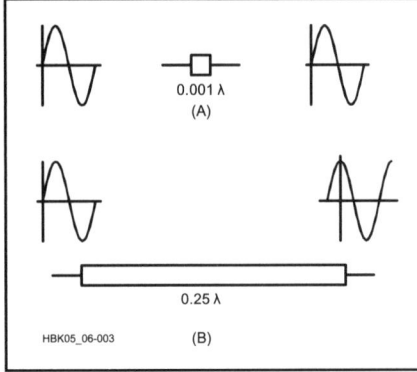

Figure 5.3 — The effects of distributed resistance on the phase of a sinusoidal current. There is no phase delay between ends of a lumped element.

fraction (>0.1) of the wavelength causing the propagation delay along the conductor or radiation from it to affect the circuit in which it is used.

- Transmission lines are used as conductors. (Their characteristic impedance is usually significant, and impedances connected to them are transformed as a function of the line length. See the **Transmission Lines** chapter for more information.)

Effects such as these are called *distributed*, and we talk of *distributed elements* or effects to contrast them to lumped elements.

To illustrate the differences between lumped and distributed elements, consider the two resistors in **Figure 5.2**, which are both 12 inches long. The resistor at A is a uniform rod of carbon. The second "resistor" B is made of two 6-inch pieces of silver rod (or other highly conductive material), with a small resistor soldered between them. Now imagine connecting the two probes of an ohmmeter to each of the two resistors, as in the figure. Starting with the probes at the far ends, as we slide the probes toward the center, the carbon rod will display a constantly decreasing resistance on the ohmmeter. This represents a distributed resistance. On the other hand, the ohmmeter connected to the other 12-inch "resistor" will display a constant resistance as long as one probe remains on each side of the small resistance and as long as we neglect the resistance of the silver rods! This represents a lumped resistance connected by perfect conductors.

Lumped elements also have the very desirable property that they introduce no phase shift resulting from propagation delay through the element. (Although combinations of lumped elements can produce phase shifts by virtue of their R, L and C properties.) Consider a lumped element that is carrying a sinusoidal current, as in **Figure 5.3A**. Since the element has negligible length, there is no phase difference in the current between the two sides of the element — *no matter how high the frequency* — precisely *because* the element length is negligible. If the physical length of the element were long, say 0.25 wavelength ($0.25\ \lambda$) as shown in Figure 5.3B, the current phase would *not* be the same from end to end. In this instance, the current is delayed by 90 electrical degrees as it moves along the element. The amount of phase difference depends on the circuit's electrical length.

Because the relationship between the physical size of a circuit and the wavelength of an ac current present in the circuit will vary as the frequency of the ac signal varies, the ideas of lumped and distributed effects actually occupy two ends of a spectrum. At HF (30 MHz and below), where $\lambda \geq 10$ m, the lumped element concept is almost always valid. In the UHF and microwave region (300 MHz and above), where $\lambda \leq 1$ m and physical component size can represent a significant fraction of a wavelength, nearly all components and wiring exhibits distributed effects to one degree or another. From roughly 30 to 300 MHz, whether the distributed effects are significant must be considered on a case-by-case basis.

Of course, if we could make resistors, capacitors, inductors and so on, very small, we could treat them as lumped elements at much higher frequencies. For example, surface-mount components, which are manufactured in very small, leadless packages, can be used at much higher frequencies than leaded components and with fewer non-ideal effects.

It is for these reasons that circuits and equipment are often specified to work within specific frequency ranges. Outside of these ranges the designer's assumptions about the physical characteristics of the components and the methods and materials of the circuit's assembly become increasingly invalid. At frequencies sufficiently removed from the design range, circuit behavior often changes in unpredictable ways.

5.3 Effects of Parasitic (Stray) Characteristics

Parasitic effects can be important at almost any frequency where performance is held to tight specifications. Stray reactances can have a big effect even at audio frequencies, for example. Lightning protection is very sensitive to grounding conductor inductance. Power connections to high-current solid-state amplifiers must have very low resistance, and so on. At HF and above (where we do much of our circuit design) these considerations become very important, in some cases dominant, in the models we use to describe our components. To understand what happens to circuits at RF we turn to a brief discussion of some electromagnetic and microwave theory concepts.

Parasitic effects due to component leads, packaging, leakage and so on are relatively common to all components. When working at frequencies where many or all of the parasitics become important, a complex but completely general model such as that in **Figure 5.4** can be used for just about any component, with the actual component placed in the box marked *. Parasitic capacitance, C_p, and leakage conductance, G_L, appear in parallel across the device, while series resistance, R_s, and parasitic inductance, L_s, appear in series with it. Package capacitance, C_{pkg}, appears as an additional capacitance in parallel across the whole device.

These small parasitics can significantly affect frequency responses of RF circuits. Either take steps to minimize or eliminate them, or use simple circuit theory to predict and anticipate changes. This maze of effects may seem overwhelming, but remember that it is very seldom necessary to consider all parasitics at all frequencies and for all applications. The **Computer-Aided Circuit Design** chapter shows how to incorporate the effect of multiple parasitics into circuit design and performance modeling. Files for the *LTSpice* simulation package that include parasitic characteristics for a resistor, capacitor and inductor are provided in the downloadable supplemental information for this *Handbook*.

5.3.1 Parasitic Inductance

Maxwell's equations — the basic laws of electromagnetism that govern the propagation of electromagnetic waves and the operation of all electronic components — tell us that any wire carrying a current that changes with time (one example is a sine wave) develops a changing magnetic field around it. This changing magnetic field in turn induces an opposing voltage, or *back EMF*, on the wire. The back EMF is proportional to how fast the current changes (see **Figure 5.5**).

We exploit this phenomenon when we make an inductor. The reason we typically form inductors in the shape of a coil is to concentrate the magnetic field and thereby maxi-

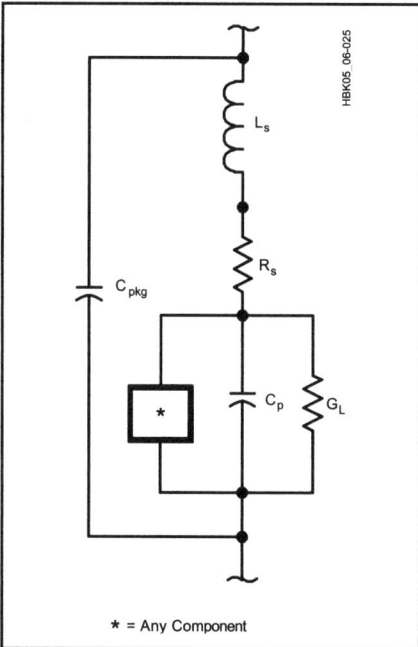

Figure 5.4 — A general model for electrical components at VHF frequencies and above. The box marked * represents the component. See text for discussion.

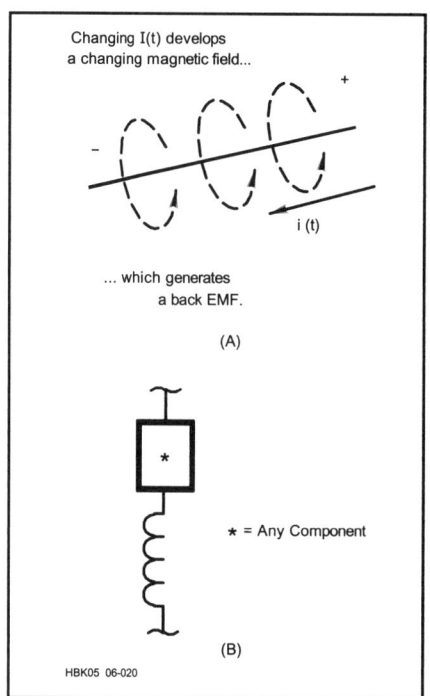

Figure 5.5 — Inductive consequences of Maxwell's equations. At A, any wire carrying a changing current develops a voltage difference along it. This can be mathematically described as an effective inductance. B adds parasitic inductance to a generic component model.

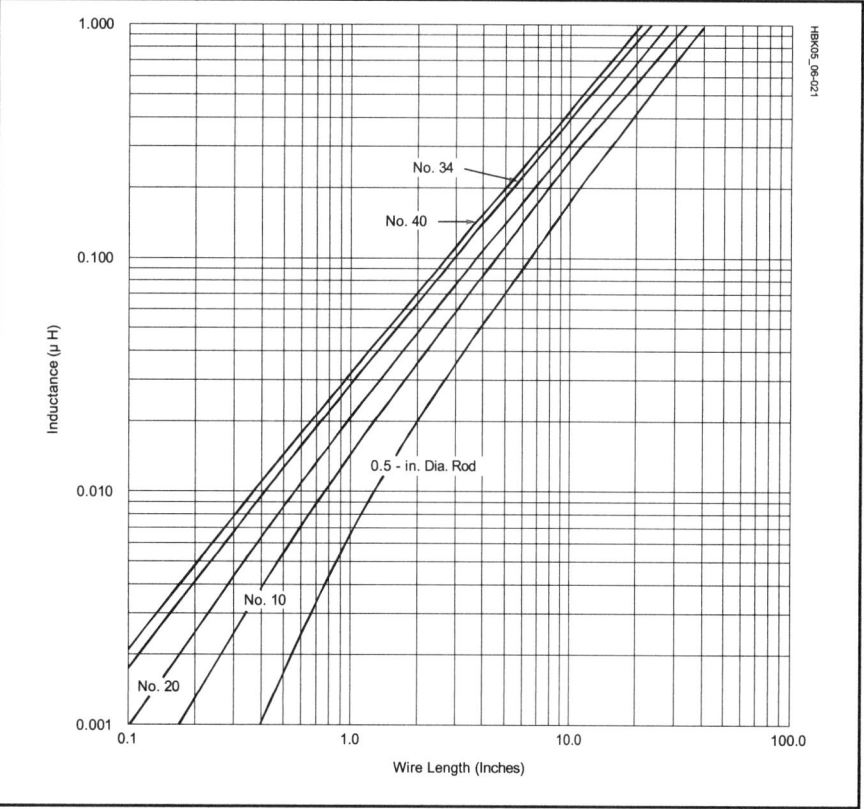

Figure 5.6 — A plot of inductance vs length for straight conductors in several wire sizes.

mize the inductance for a given physical size. However, *all* wires carrying varying currents have these inductive properties. This includes the wires we use to connect our circuits, and even the *leads* of capacitors, resistors and so on. The inductance of a straight, round, nonmagnetic wire in free space is given by:

$$L = 0.00508\, b \left[\ln\left(\frac{2b}{a}\right) - 0.75 \right] \quad (1)$$

where
L = inductance, in µH
a = wire radius, in inches
b = wire length, in inches
ln = natural logarithm (2.303 × $\log_{10}$)

Skin effect (discussed below) changes this formula slightly at VHF and above. As the frequency approaches infinity, the value 0.75 in the above equation increases to approach 1. This effect usually causes a change of no more than a few percent.

As an example, let's find the inductance of a typical #18 wire (diameter = 0.0403 inch and a = 0.0201) that is 4 inches long (b = 4):

$$L = 0.00508\,(4)\left[\ln\left(\frac{8}{0.0201}\right) - 0.75\right]$$

$$= 0.0203\,[5.98 - 0.75] = 0.106\ \mu H$$

Wire of this diameter has an inductance of about 25 nH per inch of length. In circuits operating at VHF and higher frequencies, including high-speed digital circuits, the inductance of component leads can become significant. (The #24 AWG wire typically used for component leads has an inductance on the order of 20 nH per inch.) At these frequencies, lead inductance can affect circuit behavior, making the circuit hard to reproduce or repair. Good design and construction practice is to minimize the effects of lead inductance by using surface-mount components or trimming the leads to be as short as possible.

The impact of reactance due to parasitic inductance is usually very small; at AF or LF, parasitic inductive reactance of most components is practically zero. To use this example, the reactance of a 0.106 µH inductor even at 10 MHz is only 6.6 Ω. **Figure 5.6** shows a graph of the inductance for wires of various gauges (radii) as a function of length. Whether the reactance is significant or not depends on the application and the frequency of use.

We can represent parasitic inductance in component models by adding an inductor of appropriate value in series with the component since the wire leads are in series with the element. This (among other reasons) is why minimizing lead lengths and interconnecting wires becomes very important when designing circuits for VHF and above.

PARASITIC INDUCTANCE IN RESISTORS

The basic construction of common resistor types is shown in **Figure 5.7**. The primary parasitic effect associated with resistors is parasitic inductance. (Some parasitic capacitance exists between the leads or electrodes due to packaging.) **Figure 5.8** shows some more accurate circuit models for resistors at low to medium frequencies. The type of resistor with the most parasitic inductance are wire-wound resistors, essentially inductors used as resistors. Their use is therefore limited to dc or low-frequency ac applications where their reactance is negligible. Remember that this inductance will also affect switching transient waveforms, because the component will act as an RL circuit. The inductive effects of wire-wound resistors begin to become significant in the audio range above a few kHz.

As an example, consider a 1-Ω wire-wound resistor formed from 300 turns of #24 wire closely-wound in a single layer 6.3 inches long on a 0.5-inch diameter form. What is its approximate inductance? From the inductance formula for air-wound coils in the **Electrical Fundamentals** chapter:

$$L = \frac{d^2 n^2}{18d + 40\ell} = \frac{0.5^2 \times 300^2}{(18 \times 0.5) + (40 \times 6.3)} = 86\ \mu H$$

If we want the inductive reactance to be less than 10% of the resistor value, then this resistor cannot be used above f = 0.1 / (2π × 86 µH) = 185 Hz! Real wire-wound resistors have multiple windings layered over each other to minimize both size and parasitic inductance (by winding each layer in opposite directions, much of the inductance is canceled). If we assume a five-layer winding, the length is reduced to 1.8 inches and the inductance to approximately 17 µH, so the resistor can then be used below 937 Hz. (This has the effect of increasing the resistor's parasitic capacitance, however.)

The resistance of certain types of tubular film resistors is controlled by inscribing a spiral path through the film on the inside of the tube. This creates a small inductance that may be significant at and above the higher audio frequencies.

NON-INDUCTIVE RESISTORS

The resistors with the least amount of parasitic inductance are the bulk resistors, such

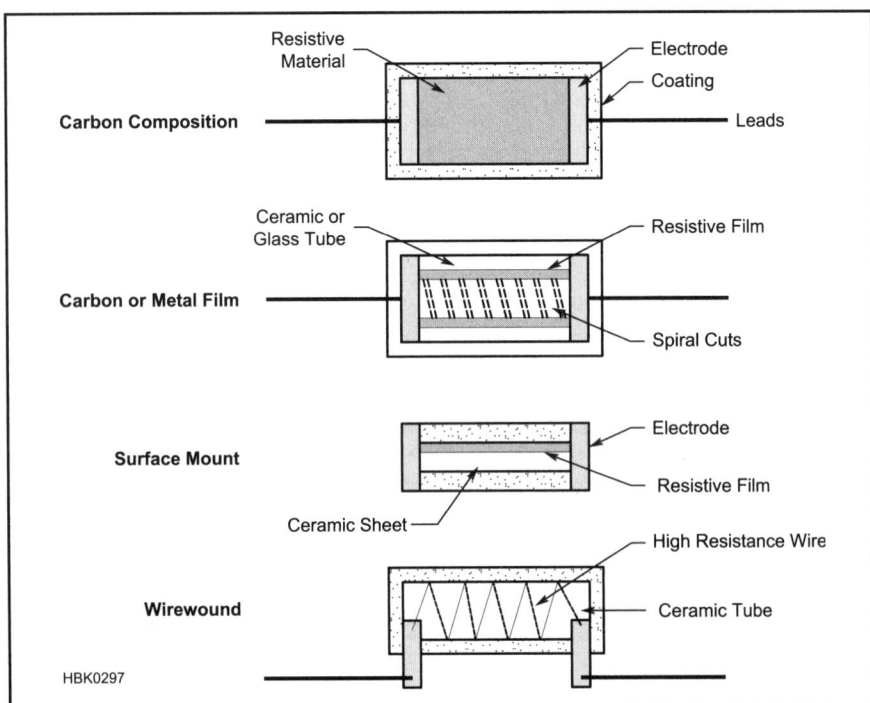

Figure 5.7 — The electrical characteristics of different resistor types are strongly affected by their construction. Reactance from parasitic inductance and capacitance strongly impacts the resistor's behavior at RF.

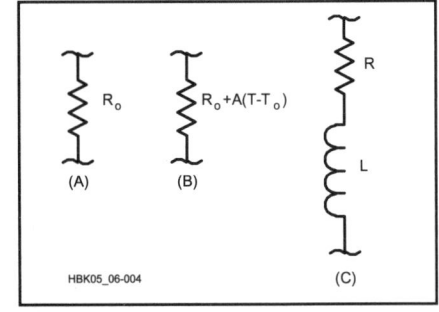

Figure 5.8 — Circuit models for resistors. The wire-wound model with associated inductance is shown at C. B includes the effect of temperature (T). For designs at VHF and higher frequencies, the model at C could be used with L representing lead inductance.

as carbon-composition, metal-oxide, and ceramic resistors. These resistors are made from a single linear cylinder, tube or block of resistive material so that inductance is minimized. Each type of resistor has a maximum usable frequency, above which parasitic capacitance and inductance begin to become significant. Review the manufacturer's data sheet for the component to learn about its performance at high frequencies.

Some resistors advertised as "noninductive" are actually wire-wound resistors with a special winding technique that minimizes inductance. These resistors are intended for use at audio frequencies and are not suitable for use at RF. If you are not sure, ask the vendor if the resistors are suitable for use in RF circuits.

Because resistors are manufactured with an insulating coating, it can be difficult to determine their internal structure and thus estimate their parasitic inductance. In cases where a surplus or used component is to be included, it is recommended that you test the component with an impedance meter or make some other type of reactance measurement if you are unable to access the manufacturer's specifications for the resistor.

PARASITIC INDUCTANCE IN CAPACITORS

The size and shape of a capacitor's plates and the leads used to connect them to circuits create parasitic inductance, often referred to as *equivalent series inductance* (ESL) by capacitor manufacturers. **Figs 5.9** and **5.10** show reasonable models for capacitors that are good up to VHF.

Figure 5.11 shows a roll-type capacitor made of two strips of very thin metal foil and separated by a dielectric. After leads are attached to the foil strips, the sandwich is rolled up and either placed in a metal can or coated with plastic. *Radial leads* both stick out of one end of the roll and *axial leads* from both ends along the roll's axis. Because of the rolled strips, the ESL is high. Electrolytic and many types of film capacitors are made with roll construction. As a result, they are generally not useful in RF circuits.

In the stack capacitor, thin sheets of dielectric are coated on one side with a thin metal layer. A stack of the sheets is placed under pressure and heated to make a single solid unit. Metal side caps with leads attached contact the metal layers. The ESL of stack capacitors is very low and so they are useful at high frequencies. Ceramic and mica capacitors are the most common stack-style capacitor.

Parallel-plate air and vacuum capacitors used at RF have relatively low parasitic inductance, but transmitting capacitors made to withstand high voltages and current are large enough that parasitic inductance becomes

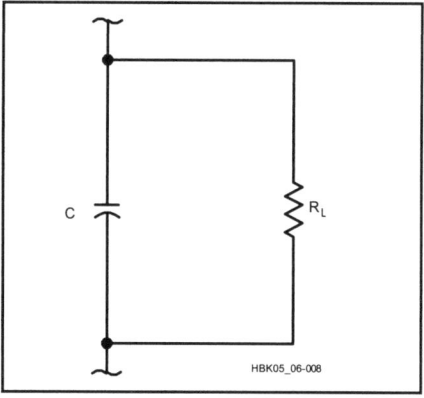

Figure 5.9 — A simple capacitor model for frequencies well below self-resonance.

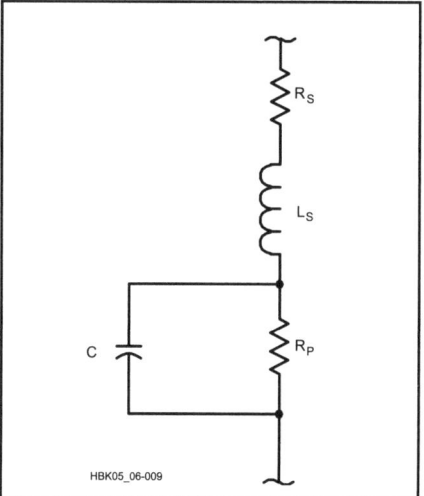

Figure 5.10 — A capacitor model for VHF and above including series resistance and distributed inductance.

significant, limiting their use to low-VHF and lower frequencies. Adjustable capacitors (air variables and compression or piston trimmer capacitors) for tuning low-power circuits are much smaller and so have correspondingly lower parasitic inductance.

It is difficult for a single capacitor to work well over a very wide frequency range, so capacitors are often placed in parallel as discussed in the section below on Bypassing and Decoupling. It is often suggested that different types of capacitors be connected in parallel to avoid the effects of parasitic inductance at different frequencies, but without testing and careful modeling the results are often unpredictable or even counterproductive as the referenced discussion shows.

5.3.2 Parasitic Capacitance

Maxwell's equations also tell us that if the voltage between any two points changes with time, a displacement current is generated between these points as illustrated in **Figure 5.12.** This *displacement current* results from the propagation of the electromagnetic field between the two points and is not to be confused with *conduction current*, which is the movement of electrons. Displacement current is directly proportional to the rate at which the voltage is changing.

When a capacitor is connected to an ac voltage source, a steady ac current can flow because taken together, conduction current and displacement current "complete the loop" from the positive source terminal, across the plates of the capacitor, and back to the negative terminal.

In general, parasitic capacitance shows up *wherever* the voltage between two points

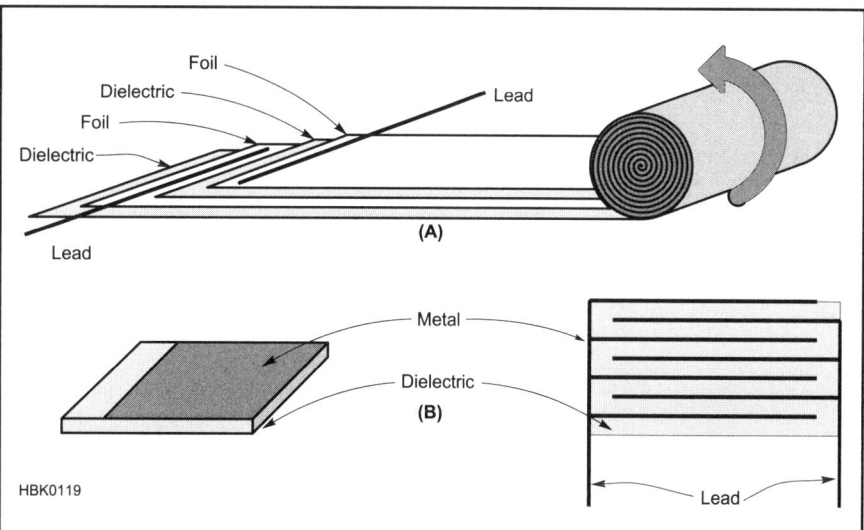

Figure 5.11 — Two common types of capacitor construction. (A) Roll construction uses two strips of foil separated by a strip of dielectric. (B) Stack construction layers dielectric material (such as ceramic or film), one side coated with metal. Leads are attached and the assembly coated with epoxy resin.

RF Techniques 5.5

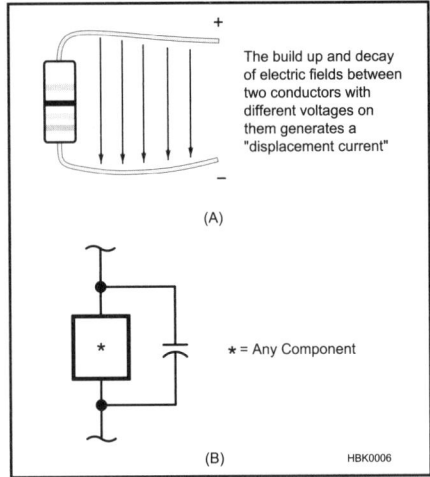

Figure 5.12 — Capacitive consequences of Maxwell's equations. A: Any changing voltage between two points, for example along a bent wire, generates a displacement current running between them. This can be treated mathematically as a capacitance. B adds parasitic capacitance to a generic component model.

is changing with time, because the laws of electromagnetics require a displacement current to flow. Since this phenomenon represents an *additional* current path from one point in space to another, we can add this parasitic capacitance to our component models by adding a capacitor of appropriate value in *parallel* with the component. These parasitic capacitances are typically less than 1 pF, so that below VHF they can be treated as open circuits (infinite reactances) and thus neglected.

PACKAGE CAPACITANCE

Another source of capacitance, also in the 1-pF range and therefore important only at

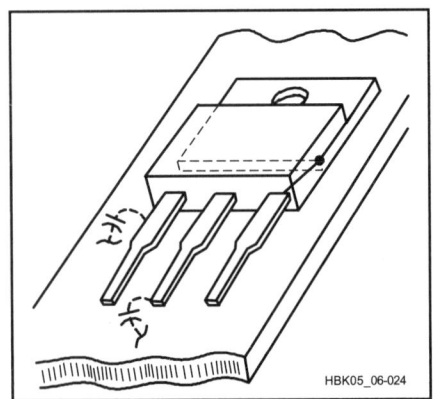

Figure 5.13 — Unexpected stray capacitance. The mounting tab of TO-220 transistors is often connected to one of the device leads. Because one lead is connected to the chassis, small capacitances from the other lead to the chassis appear as additional package capacitance at the device. Similar capacitance can appear at any device with a conductive package.

VHF and above, is the packaging of the component itself. For example, a power transistor packaged in a TO-220 case (see **Figure 5.13**), often has either the emitter or collector connected to the metal tab itself. This introduces an extra *inter-electrode capacitance* across the junctions.

The copper traces on a PC board also create capacitance with the circuit components, to other traces, and to power and ground planes. Double-sided PC boards have a certain capacitance per square inch between the layers of copper on each side of the board. (Multi-layer PC boards have higher values of capacitance due to the smaller separation between layers.) It is possible to create capacitors by leaving unetched areas of copper on both sides of the board. The dielectric constant of inexpensive PC board materials intended for use at low-frequencies is not well-controlled, however, leading to significant variations in capacitance. For this reason, the copper on one side of a double-sided board should be completely removed under frequency-determining circuits such as VFOs.

Stray capacitance (a general term used for any "extra" capacitance that exists due to physical construction) appears in any circuit where two metal surfaces exist at different voltages. Such effects can be modeled as an extra capacitor in parallel with the given points in the circuit. A rough value can be obtained with the parallel-plate formula given in the chapter on **Electrical Fundamentals**. Similar to parasitic inductance, *any* circuit component that has wires attached to it, or is fabricated from wire, or is near or attached to metal, will have a parasitic capacitance associated with it, which again, becomes important only at RF.

Stray capacitance can be difficult to account for in circuit design because it exists *between* components and other circuit structures, depending on the physical orientation of the component. Its presence may allow signals to flow in ways that disrupt the normal operation of a circuit and may have a greater affect in a high-impedance circuit because the capacitive reactance may be a greater percentage of the circuit impedance. Also, because stray capacitance often appears in parallel with the circuit, the stray capacitor may bypass more of the desired signal at higher frequencies. Careful physical design of an RF circuit and selection of components can minimize the effects of stray capacitance.

5.3.3 Inductors at Radio Frequencies

Inductors are perhaps the component with the most significant parasitic effects. Where there are many different varieties of form for capacitors and resistors, most inductors are fundamentally similar: a coil of wire on a tubular or toroidal form. As such, they are affected by both parasitic resistance and capacitance as shown in the simple inductor model of **Figure 5.14**.

While the leakage conductance of a capacitor is usually negligible, the series resistance of an inductor often is not. This is caused by the long lengths of thin wire needed to create typical inductance values used in RF circuits and the skin effect (discussed below). Consider a typical air-core inductor, with L = 33 µH and a minimum Q of 30 measured at 2.5 MHz. This would indicate a series resistance of $R_s = 2 \pi f L / Q = 17 \, \Omega$ that could significantly alter the bandwidth of a circuit. The skin effect also results in parasitic resistance in the upper HF ranges and above. To minimize losses due to the skin effect, inductors at these frequencies, particularly those intended for use in transmitters and amplifiers and that are expected to carry significant currents, are often made from large-diameter wire or tubing or even flat strap to maximize the surface area for current flow.

For coils with many turns for which large conductors are impractical, *Litz wire* is sometimes used. Litz wire is made of many fine insulated strands woven together, each with a diameter smaller than the skin depth at the expected frequency of use, thus presenting a larger surface area than a solid wire or normal stranded wire. This creates multiple resistive inductors in parallel, which reduces the total impedance. The reduction is not proportional to the number of parallel paths, however, because they are inductively coupled.

If an inductor is wound on a magnetic core, the core itself can have losses that are treated as parasitic resistance. Each type of core — iron, powdered iron or ferrite — has a frequency range over which it is designed for

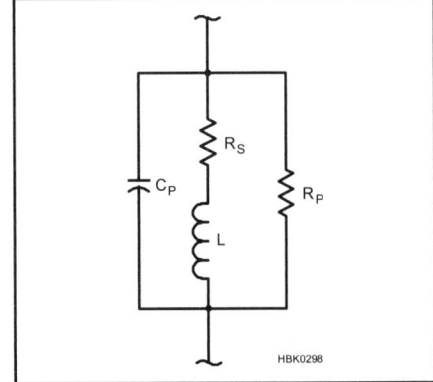

Figure 5.14 — General model for inductor with parasitic capacitance and resistance. The parasitic capacitance represents the cumulative effect of the capacitance between the different turns of wire. Parasitic resistance, R_S, depends on frequency due to the skin effect. R_P represents leakage resistance. At low frequencies, parasitic capacitance, C_P, can be neglected.

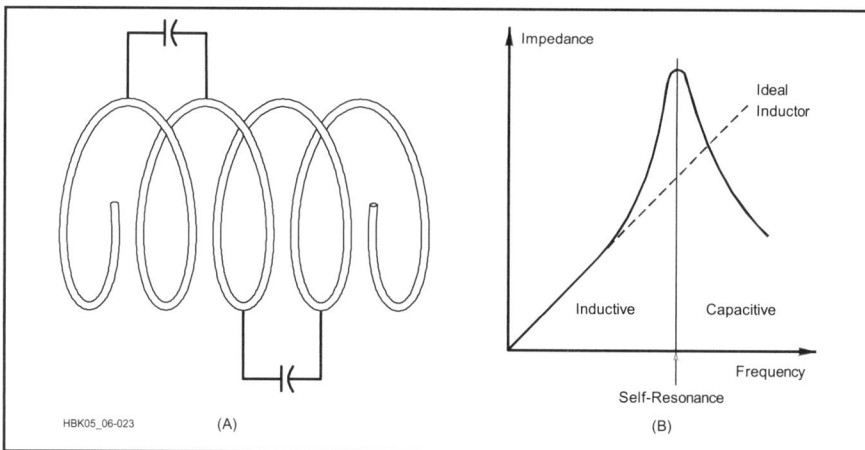
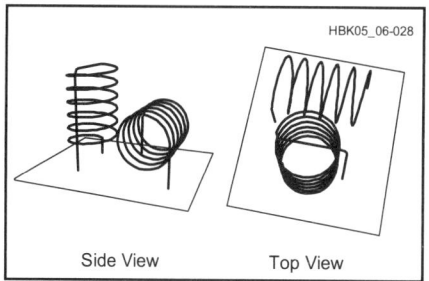

Figure 5.16 — Unshielded coils in close proximity should be mounted perpendicular to each other to minimize coupling.

Figure 5.15 — Coils exhibit distributed capacitance as explained in the text. The graph at B shows how distributed capacitance resonates with the inductance. Below resonance, the reactance is predominantly inductive which increases as frequency increases. However, above resonance, the reactance becomes predominantly capacitive which decreases as frequency increases.

maximum efficiency. Outside of that range, the core may have significant losses, raising the parasitic resistance of the inductor.

Parasitic capacitance is a particular concern for inductors because of their construction. Consider the inductor in **Figure 5.15**. If this coil has n turns, then the ac voltage between identical points of two neighboring turns is 1/n times the ac voltage across the entire coil. When this voltage changes due to an ac current passing through the coil, the effect is that of many small capacitors acting in parallel with the inductance of the coil. Thus, in addition to the capacitance resulting from the leads, inductors have higher parasitic capacitance due to their physical shape.

These various effects illustrate why inductor construction has such a large effect on performance. As an example, assume you're working on a project that requires you to wind a 5 μH inductor. Looking at the coil inductance formula in the **Electrical Fundamentals** chapter, it comes to mind that many combinations of length and diameter could yield the desired inductance. If you happen to have both 0.5 and 1-inch coil forms, why should you select one over the other? To eliminate some other variables, let's make both coils 1 inch long, close-wound, and give them 1-inch leads on each end.

Let's calculate the number of turns required for each. On a 0.5-inch-diameter form:

$$n = \frac{\sqrt{L(18d+40l)}}{d} = \frac{\sqrt{5\,[(18\times 0.5)+(40\times 1)]}}{0.5} = 31.3 \text{ turns}$$

This means coil 1 will be made from #20 AWG wire (29.9 turns per inch). Coil 2, on the 1-inch form, yields

$$n = \frac{\sqrt{5\,[(18\times 1)+(40\times 1)]}}{1} = 17 \text{ turns}$$

which requires #15 AWG wire in order to be close-wound.

What are the series resistances associated with each? For coil 1, the total wire length is 2 inches + (31.3 × π × 0.5) = 51 inches, which at 10.1 Ω/1000 ft gives $R_s = 0.043$ Ω at dc. Coil 2 has a total wire length of 2 inches + (17.0 × π × 1) = 55 inches, which at 3.18 Ω/1000 ft gives a dc resistance of $R_s = 0.015$ Ω, or about ⅓ that of coil 1. Furthermore, at RF, coil 1 will begin to suffer from skin effect at a frequency about 3 times lower than coil 2 because of its smaller conductor diameter. Therefore, if Q were the sole consideration, it would be better to use the larger diameter coil.

Q is not the only concern, however. Such coils are often placed in shielded enclosures. A common rule of thumb says that to prevent the enclosure from affecting the inductor, the enclosure should be at least one coil diameter from the coil on all sides. That is, 3×3×2 inches for the large coil and 1.5×1.5×1.5 for the small coil, a volume difference of over 500%.

INDUCTOR COUPLING

Mutual inductance (see the **Electrical Fundamentals** chapter) will also have an effect on the resonant frequency and Q of RF circuits. For this reason, inductors in frequency-critical circuits should always be oriented and with sufficient spacing to minimize coupling. For example, mount coils near each other with their axes perpendicular as in **Figure 5.16**. The use of ferrous cores also tends to keep magnetic fields within the core, reducing unwanted coupling.

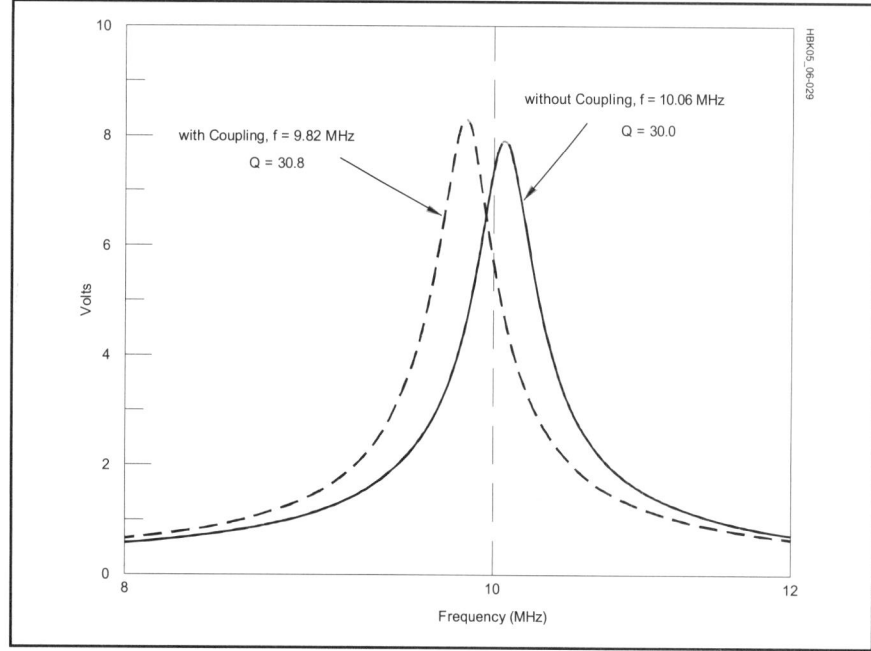

Figure 5.17 — Result of light coupling (k = 0.05) between two identical circuits of Figure 5.19A on their frequency responses.

As an example, assume we build an oscillator circuit that has both input and output resonant circuits. If we are careful to keep the two coils in these circuits uncoupled, the frequency response of either of the two circuits is shown by the solid line in **Figure 5.17**.

If the two coils are coupled either through careless placement or improper shielding, the resonant frequency and Q will be affected. The dashed line in Figure 5.17 shows the frequency response that results from a coupling coefficient of k = 0.05, a reasonable value for air-wound inductors mounted perpendicularly in close proximity on a circuit chassis. Note the resonant frequency shifted from 10.06 to 9.82 MHz, or 2.4%. The Q has gone up slightly from 30.0 to 30.8 as a result of the slightly higher inductive reactance at the resonant frequency.

Capacitance between coils can also affect a circuit's frequency response. Using shielded inductors or can-mounted coils reduces the effects of stray capacitance between components.

5.3.4 Skin Effect

The resistance of a conductor to ac is different than its value for dc because of the way ac fields interact with the conductor. As a result, thick, near-perfect conductors (such as metals) conduct ac only to a certain *skin depth*, δ, inversely proportional to the square root of the frequency of the current. Called the *skin effect*, this decreases the effective cross-section of the conductor at high frequencies and thus increases its resistance.

$$\delta = \frac{1}{\sqrt{\pi f \mu \sigma}} \quad (2)$$

where

μ is the conductor's permeability, and
σ is the conducting material's conductance.

The increase in resistance caused by the skin effect is insignificant at and below audio frequencies, but beginning around 1 MHz (depending on the size of the conductor) it is so pronounced that practically all the current flows in a very thin layer near the conductor's surface. For example, at 10 MHz, the skin depth of a copper conductor is about 0.02 mm (0.00079 inch). For this reason, at RF a hollow tube and a solid rod of the same diameter and made of the same metal will have the same resistance and the RF resistance of a conductor is often much higher than its dc resistance. A rough estimate of the frequency above which a nonmagnetic wire (one made of nonferrous metal) will begin to show appreciable skin effect can be calculated from

$$f = \frac{124}{d^2} \quad (3)$$

where
f = frequency, in MHz
d = diameter in mils (a mil is 0.001 inch)

Above this frequency, increase the resistance of the wire by 10× for every 2 decades of frequency (roughly 3.2× for every decade). For example, say we wish to find the RF resistance of a 2-inch length of #18 AWG copper wire at 100 MHz. From the wire tables in the **Component Data and References** chapter, we see that this wire has a dc resistance of 2 inches × 6.386 Ω/1000 ft = 1.06 mΩ. From the above formula, the frequency is found to be 124 / 40.3^2 = 76 kHz. Since 100 MHz is roughly three decades above this (100 kHz to 100 MHz), the RF resistance will be approximately 1.06 mΩ × 3.2^3 = 1.06 mΩ × 32.8 = 34.8 mΩ. Again, values calculated in this manner are approximate and should be used qualitatively — like when you want an answer to a question such as, "Can I neglect the RF resistance of this length of connecting wire at 100 MHz?" Several useful charts regarding skin effect are available in *Reference Data for Engineers*, listed in the References section of this chapter.

Losses associated with skin effect can be reduced by increasing the surface area of the conductor carrying the RF current. Flat, solid strap and tubing are often used for that reason. In addition, because the current-carrying layer is so thin at UHF and microwave frequencies, a thin highly conductive layer at the surface of the conductor, such as silver plating, can lower resistance. Silver plating is too thin to improve HF conductivity significantly, however.

5.3.5 RF Heating

RF current often causes component heating problems where the same level of dc or low frequency ac current may not. These losses result from both the skin effect and from dielectric losses in insulating material, such as a capacitor dielectric.

An example is the tank circuit of an RF oscillator. If several small capacitors are connected in parallel to achieve a desired capacitance, skin effect will be reduced and the total surface area available for heat dissipation will be increased, thus significantly reducing the RF heating effects as compared to a single large capacitor. This technique can be applied to any similar situation; the general idea is to divide the heating among as many components as possible.

An example is shown in the circuit block in **Figure 5.18**, which is representative of the input tank circuit used in many HF VFOs. Along with L, C$_{main}$, C$_{trim}$, C1 and C3 set the oscillator frequency. Therefore, temperature effects are critical in these components. By using several capacitors in parallel, the

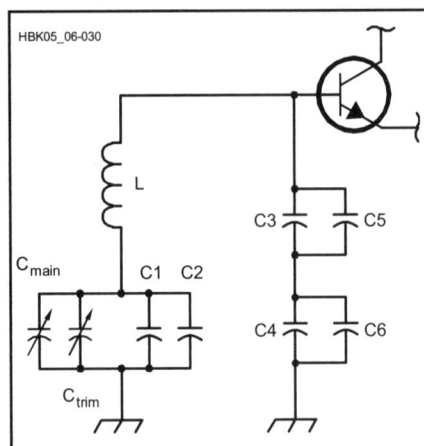

Figure 5.18 — A tank circuit of the type commonly used in VFOs. Several capacitors are used in parallel to distribute the RF current, which reduces temperature effects.

RF current (and resultant heating, which is proportional to the square of the current) is reduced in each component. Parallel combinations are used for the feedback capacitors for the same reason.

At high power levels, losses due to RF heating — either from resistive or dielectric losses — can be significant. Insulating materials may exhibit dielectric losses even though they are excellent insulators. For example, nylon plastic insulators may work very well at low frequencies, but being quite lossy at and above VHF, they are unsuitable for use in RF circuits at those frequencies. To determine whether material is suitable for use as an insulator at RF, a quick test can be made by heating the material in a microwave oven for a few seconds and measuring its temperature rise. (Take care to avoid placing parts or materials containing any metal in the microwave!) Insulating materials that heat up are lossy and thus unsuitable for use in RF circuits.

5.3.6 Effect on Q

Recall from the **Electrical Fundamentals** chapter that circuit Q, a useful figure of merit for tuned RLC circuits, can be defined in several ways:

$$Q = \frac{X_L \text{ or } X_C}{R} \quad (4)$$

$$= \frac{\text{energy stored per cycle}}{\text{energy dissipated per cycle}}$$

Q is also related to the bandwidth of a tuned circuit's response by

$$Q = \frac{f_0}{BW_{3\,dB}} \quad (5)$$

Parasitic inductance, capacitance and resis-

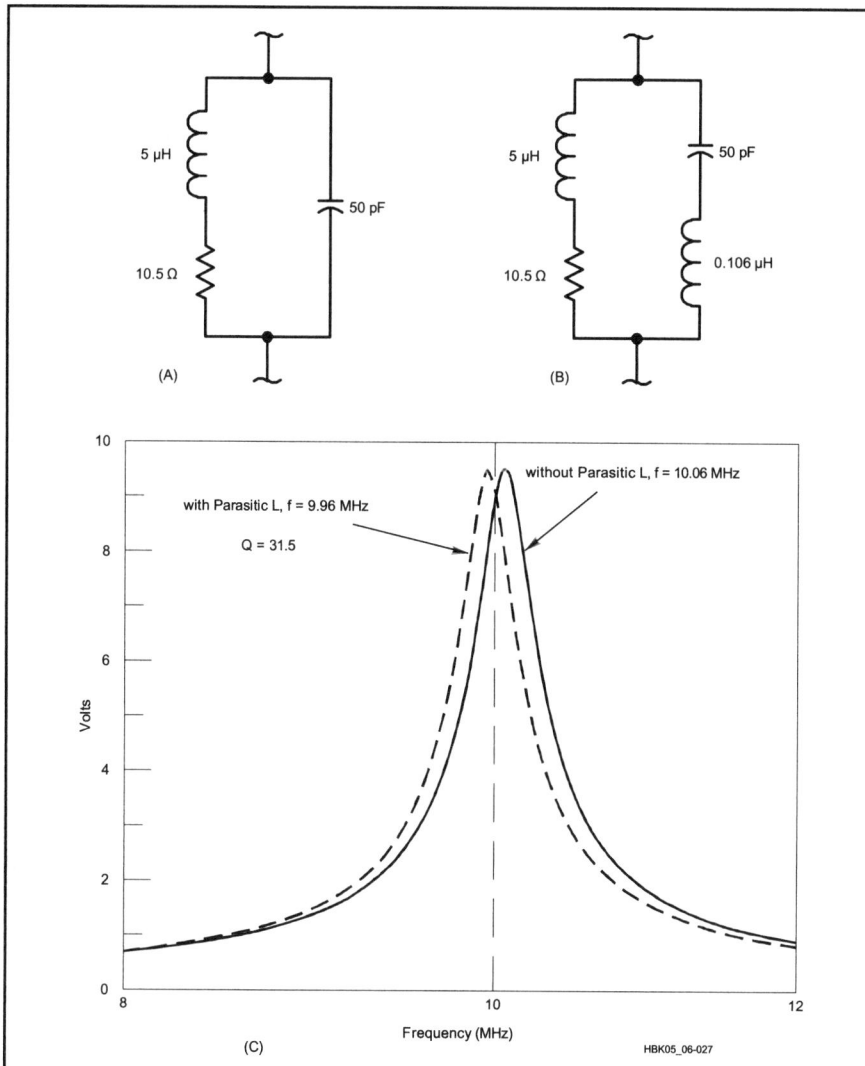

Figure 5.19 — A is a tank circuit, neglecting parasitics. B is the same circuit including L_p on capacitor. C is the frequency response curves for A and B. The solid line represents the unaltered circuit (also see Figure 5.17) while the dashed line shows the effects of adding parasitic inductance.

The results are shown in the plot in Figure 5.19C, where we can see that the parasitic circuit has an f_0 of 9.96 MHz (a shift of 1%) and a Q (measured from the −3 dB points) of 31.5. For comparison, the simulation of the unaltered circuit does in fact show f_0 = 10.06 MHz and Q = 30.

5.3.7 Self-Resonance

Because of parasitic effects, a capacitor or inductor — all by itself — exhibits the properties of a resonant RLC circuit at frequencies for which the parasitic effects are significant. Figs 5.10 and 5.14 illustrate RF models for the capacitor and inductor, which are based on the general model in Figure 5.4, leaving out the packaging capacitance. Note the slight difference in configuration; the pairs C_p-R_p and L_s-R_s are in series in the capacitor but in parallel in the inductor. This is because of the different physical structure of the components.

At some sufficiently high frequency, both inductors and capacitors become *self-resonant* when the parasitic reactance cancels or equals the intended reactance, creating a series-resonant circuit. Similar to a series-resonant circuit made of discrete components, above the self-resonant frequency a capacitor will appear inductive, and an inductor will appear capacitive.

For an example, let's calculate the approximate self-resonant frequency of a 470-pF capacitor whose leads are made from #20 AWG wire (0.032-inch diameter), with a total length of 1 inch. Using equation 1, we calculate the approximate parasitic inductance

$$L\,(\mu H) = 0.00508\,(1)\left[\ln\left(\frac{2(1)}{(0.032/2)}\right) - 0.75\right]$$

$$= 0.021\,\mu H$$

and the self-resonant frequency is roughly

$$f = \frac{1}{2\pi\sqrt{LC}} = 50.6\text{ MHz}$$

Similarly, an inductor can also have a parallel self-resonance.

The purpose of making these calculations is to provide a feel for actual component values. They could be used as a rough design guideline, but should not be used quantitatively. Other factors such as lead orientation, shielding and so on, can alter the parasitic effects to a large extent. Large-value capacitors tend to have higher parasitic inductances (and therefore a lower self-resonant frequency) than small-value capacitors.

Self-resonance becomes critically important at VHF and UHF because the self-resonant frequency of many common components is at or below the frequency where the component will be used. In this case, either special techniques can be used to construct

tance can significantly alter the performance and characteristics of a tuned circuit if the design frequency is close to the self-resonant frequencies of the components.

As an example, consider the resonant circuit of **Figure 5.19A**, which could represent the frequency-determining resonant circuit of an oscillator. Neglecting any parasitics,

$$f_0 = \frac{1}{2\pi\sqrt{LC}} = 10.06\text{ MHz}$$

As in many practical cases, assume the resistance arises entirely from the inductor series resistance. The data sheet for the inductor specified a minimum Q of 30, so assuming Q = 30 yields an R value of

$$\frac{X_L}{Q} = \frac{2\pi\,(10.06\text{ MHz})\,(5\,\mu H)}{30} = 10.5\,\Omega$$

Next, let's include the parasitic inductance of the capacitor (Figure 5.19B). A reasonable assumption is that this capacitor has the same physical size as the example from the section on Parasitic Inductance for which we calculated L_s = 0.106 µH. This would give the capacitor a self-resonant frequency of 434 MHz — well above our frequency of interest. However, the added parasitic inductance does account for an extra 0.106/5.0 = 2% inductance. Since this circuit is no longer strictly series or parallel, we must convert it to an equivalent form before calculating the new f_0.

An easier and faster way is to *simulate* the altered circuit by computer. This analysis was performed on a desktop computer using *SPICE*, a standard circuit simulation program described in the **Computer-Aided Circuit Design** chapter. The voltage response of the circuit (given an input current of 1 mA) was calculated as a function of frequency for both cases, with and without parasitics.

RF Techniques 5.9

components to operate at these frequencies, by reducing the parasitic effects, or else the idea of lumped elements must be abandoned altogether in favor of microwave techniques such as striplines and waveguides.

5.3.8 Dielectric Breakdown and Arcing

Anyone who has ever seen an arc form across a transmitting capacitor's plates, seen static discharges jump across an antenna insulator or touched a metal doorknob on a dry day has experienced the effects of dielectric breakdown.

In the ideal world, we could take any two conductors and put as large a voltage as we want across them, no matter how close together they are. In the real world, there is a voltage limit (*dielectric strength*, measured in kV/cm and determined by the insulating material between the two conductors) above which the insulator will break down.

Because they are charged particles, the electrons in the atoms of a dielectric material feel an attractive force when placed in an electric field. If the field is sufficiently strong, the force will strip the electron from the atom. This electron is available to conduct current, and furthermore, it is traveling at an extremely high velocity. It is very likely that this electron will hit another atom, and free another electron. Before long, there are many stripped electrons producing a large current, forming an *arc*. When this happens, we say the dielectric has suffered *breakdown*. Arcing in RF circuits is most common in transmitters and transmission line components where high voltages are common, but it is possible anywhere two components at significantly different voltage levels are closely spaced.

If the dielectric is liquid or gas, it will repair itself when the applied voltage is removed and the molecules in the dielectric return to their normal state. A solid dielectric, however, cannot repair itself because its molecules are fixed in place and the low-resistance path created by the arc is permanent. A good example of this is a CMOS integrated circuit. When exposed to the very high voltages associated with static electricity, the electric field across the very thin gate oxide layer exceeds the dielectric strength of silicon dioxide, and the device is permanently damaged by the resulting hole created in the oxide layer.

The breakdown voltage of a dielectric layer depends on its composition and thickness (see **Table 5.1**). The variation with thickness is not linear; doubling the thickness does not quite double the breakdown voltage. Breakdown voltage is also a function of geometry: Because of electromagnetic considerations, the breakdown voltage between two conductors separated by a fixed distance is less if the surfaces are pointed or sharp-edged than if they are smooth or rounded. Therefore, a simple way to help prevent breakdown in many projects is to file and smooth the edges of conductors. (See the **Power Sources** and **RF Power Amplifier** chapters for additional information on high voltage applications.)

Capacitors are, by nature, the component most often associated with dielectric failure. To prevent damage, the working voltage of a capacitor — and there are separate dc and ac ratings — should ideally be two or three times the expected maximum voltage in the circuit. Capacitors that are not air-insulated or have a *self-healing dielectric* should be replaced if a dielectric breakdown occurs.

Resistors and inductors also have voltage ratings associated with breakdown of their insulating coating. High-value resistors, in particular, can be bypassed by leakage current flowing along the surface of the resistor. High-voltage resistors often have elongated bodies to create a long *leakage path* to present a high resistance to leakage current. Cleaning the bodies of resistors and inductors in high-voltage circuits helps prevent arcs from forming and minimizes leakage current.

5.3.9 Radiative Losses

Any conductor placed in an electromagnetic field will have a current induced in it. We put this principle to good use when we make an antenna. The unwelcome side of this law of nature is the phrase "any conductor"; even conductors we don't intend to act as antennas will respond this way.

Fortunately, the efficiency of such "antennas" varies with conductor length. They will be of importance only if their length is a significant fraction of a wavelength. When we make an antenna, we usually choose a length on the order of $\lambda/2$. Therefore, when we *don't* want an antenna, we should be sure that the conductor length is *much less* than $\lambda/2$, no more than 0.1 λ. This will ensure a very low-efficiency antenna. This is why even unpaired 60-Hz power lines do not lose a significant fraction of the power they carry — at 60 Hz, 0.1 λ is about 300 miles!

In addition, we can use shielded cables. Such cables do allow some penetration of EM fields if the shield is not solid, but even 95% coverage is usually sufficient, especially if some sort of RF choke is used to reduce shield current.

Radiative losses and coupling can also be reduced by using twisted or parallel pairs of conductors — the fields tend to cancel. In some applications, such as audio cables, this may work better than shielding. Critical stages such as tuned circuits should be placed in shielded compartments where possible.

This argument also applies to large components — remember that a component or long wire can both radiate and receive RF energy. Measures that reduce radiative losses will also reduce unwanted RF pickup. See the **RF Interference** chapter for more information.

5.3.10 Bypassing and Decoupling

BYPASSING

Circuit models showing ac behavior often show ground connections that are not at dc ground. Bias voltages and currents are neglected in order to show how the circuit responds to ac signals. Rather, those points are "signal grounded" through bypass capacitors. Obtaining an effective bypass can be difficult and is often the route to design difficulty. The problem is parasitic inductance. Although we label and model parts as "capacitors," a more complete model is needed. The better model is a series RLC circuit, shown in **Figure 5.20**. Capacitance is close to the marked value while inductance is a small value that grows with component lead length. Resistance is a loss term, usually controlled by the Q of the parasitic inductor. Even a leadless SMT (surface-mount technology) component will display inductance commensurate with its dimensions. As shown in the Parasitic Inductance section, wire component leads have an inductance of about 1 nH per mm of length (20-25 nH per inch).

Bypass capacitor characteristics can be measured in the home lab with the test setup of **Figure 5.21**. **Figure 5.22** shows a test fixture with an installed 470-pF leaded capacitor. The fixture is used with a signal generator and spectrum analyzer to evaluate capacitors. Relatively long capacitor leads were required to interface to the BNC con-

---

Table 5.1
Dielectric Constants and Breakdown Voltages

Material	Dielectric Constant*	Puncture Voltage**
Aisimag 196	5.7	240
Bakelite	4.4-5.4	240
Bakelite, mica filled	4.7	325-375
Cellulose acetate	3.3-3.9	250-600
Fiber	5-7.5	150-180
Formica	4.6-4.9	450
Glass, window	7.6-8	200-250
Glass, Pyrex	4.8	335
Mica, ruby	5.4	3800-5600
Mycalex	7.4	250
Paper, Royalgrey	3.0	200
Plexiglas	2.8	990
Polyethylene	2.3	1200
Polystyrene	2.6	500-700
Porcelain	5.1-5.9	40-100
Quartz, fused	3.8	1000
Steatite, low loss	5.8	150-315
Teflon	2.1	1000-2000

*At 1 MHz
**In volts per mil (0.001 in.)

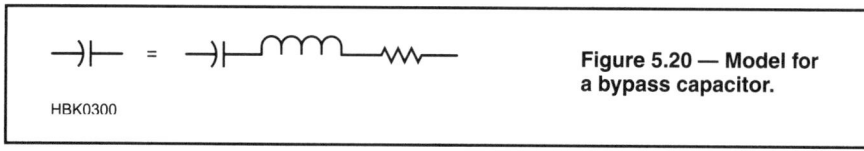

Figure 5.20 — Model for a bypass capacitor.

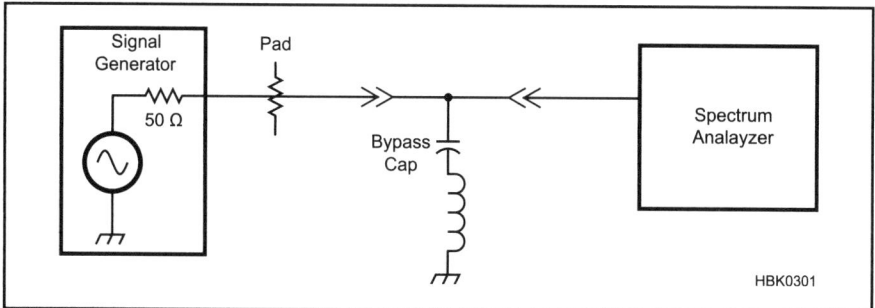

Figure 5.21 — Test set for home lab measurement of a bypass capacitor.

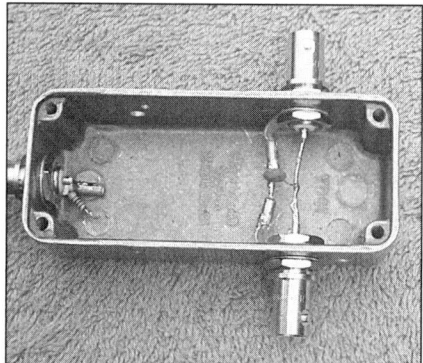

Figure 5.22 — Test fixture for measuring self-resonant frequency of capacitors.

nectors, even though the capacitor itself was small. The signal generator was tuned over its range while examining the spectrum analyzer response, showing a minimum at the series resonant frequency. Parasitic inductance is calculated from this frequency. The C value was measured with a low-frequency LC meter. Additional test instruments and techniques are discussed in the **Test Equipment and Measurement** chapter.

The measured 470-pF capacitor is modeled as 485 pF in series with an inductance of 7.7 nH. The L is larger than we would see with shorter leads. A 0.25-inch 470-pF ceramic disk capacitor with zero lead length will show a typical inductance closer to 3 nH. The measured capacitor Q was 28 at its self-resonance of 82 MHz but is higher at lower frequency. Data from a similar measurement, but with a network analyzer is shown in **Figure 5.23**. Two 470-pF capacitors are measured, one surface mounted and the other a leaded part with 0.1-inch leads.

It is often suggested that the bandwidth for bypassing can be extended by paralleling a capacitor that works well at one frequency with another to accommodate a different part of the spectrum. Hence, paralleling the 470 pF with a 0.01-µF capacitor should extend the bypassing to lower frequencies. The calculations are shown in the plots of **Figure 5.24**. The results are terrible! While the low frequency bypassing is indeed improved, a high impedance response is created at 63 MHz. This complicated behavior is again the result of inductance. Each capacitor was assumed to have a series inductance of 7 nH. A parallel resonance is approximately formed between the L of the larger capacitor and the C of the smaller. The Smith Chart plot shows us that the impedance is nearly 50 Ω at 63 MHz. Impedance would be even higher with greater capacitor Q.

Bypassing can be improved by paralleling capacitors. However, the capacitors should be approximately identical. **Figure 5.25** shows the result of paralleling two capacitors of about the same value. They differ slightly at 390 and 560 pF, creating a hint of resonance. This appears as a small perturbation in the reactance plot and a tiny loop on the Smith Chart. These anomalies disappear as the C values become equal. Generally, paralleling is the scheme that produces the best bypassing. The ideal solution is to place an SMT capacitor on each side of a printed circuit trace or wire at a point that is to be bypassed.

Matched capacitor pairs form an effective bypass over a reasonable frequency range. Two 0.01-µF disk capacitors have a reactance magnitude less than 5 Ω from 2 to 265 MHz. A pair of the 0.1-µF capacitors was even better, producing the same bypassing impedance from 0.2 to 318 MHz. The 0.1-µF capacitors are chip-style components with attached wire leads. Even better results can be obtained with multi-layer ceramic chip capacitors. Construction with multiple layers creates an integrated paralleling.

Some applications (for example, IF amplifiers) require effective bypassing at even lower frequencies. Modern tantalum electrolytic capacitors are surprisingly effective through the RF spectrum while offering high enough C to be useful at audio. In critical applications, however, the parts should be tested to be sure of their effectiveness.

DECOUPLING

The bypass capacitor usually serves a dual role, first creating the low impedance needed to generate a "signal" ground. It also becomes part of a decoupling low-pass filter that passes dc while attenuating signals. The attenuation must function in both directions, suppressing noise in the power supply that might reach an amplifier while keeping amplifier signals from reaching the power supply. A low-pass filter is formed with alternating series and parallel component connections. A parallel bypass is followed by a series impedance, ideally a resistor.

Additional shunt elements can then be added, although this must be done with care. An inductor between shunt capacitors should have high inductance. It will resonate with the

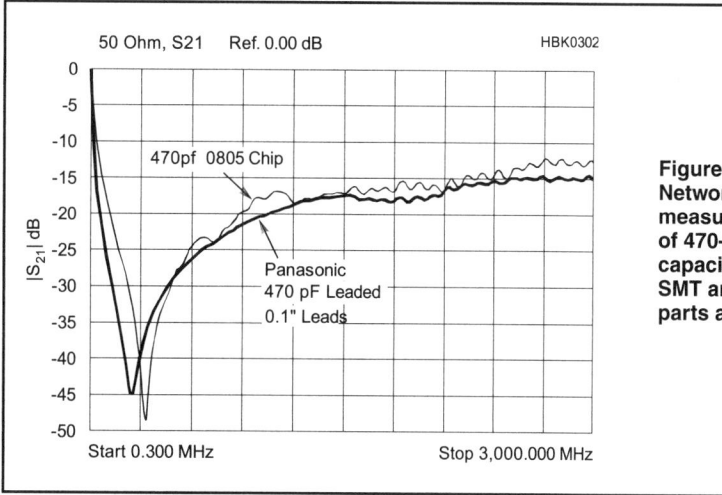

Figure 5.23 — Network analyzer measurement of 470-pF shunt capacitors. Both SMT and leaded parts are studied.

RF Techniques 5.11

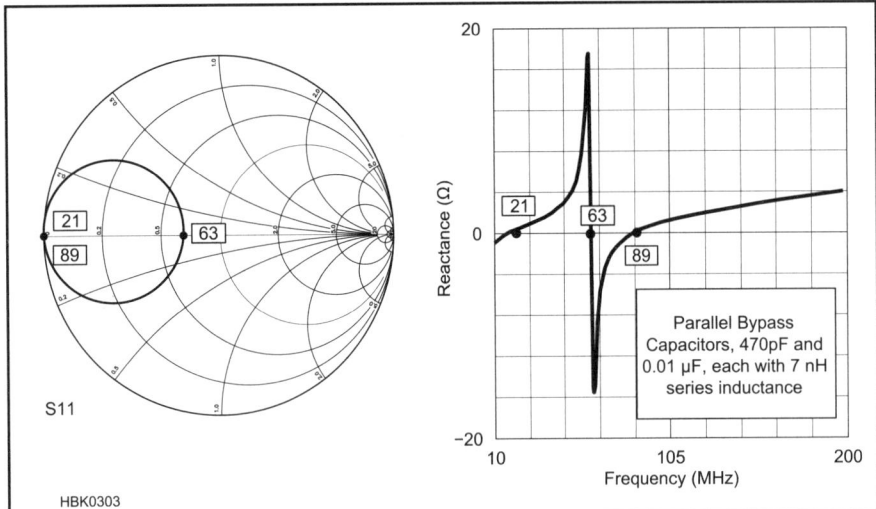

Figure 5.24 — The classic technique of paralleling bypass capacitors of two values, here 470 pF and 0.01 µF. This is a *terrible* bypass! See text.

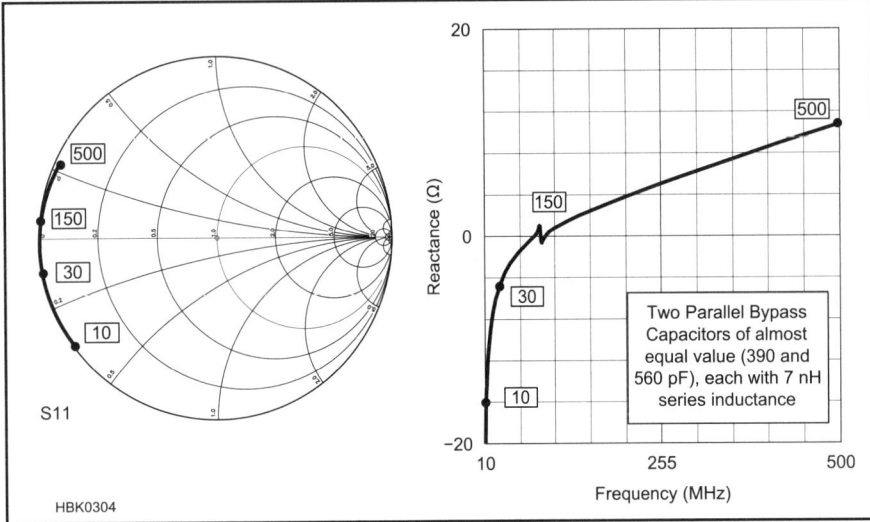

Figure 5.25 — Paralleling bypass capacitors of nearly the same value. This results in improved bypassing without complicating resonances.

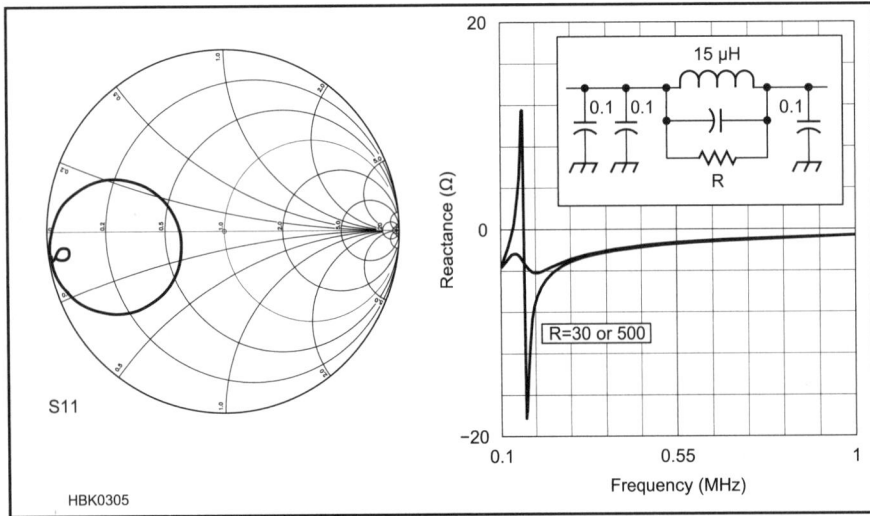

Figure 5.26 — Two different resistor values parallel a decoupling choke. The lower, 30-Ω value is more effective. See text.

shunt capacitors to create high impedances just like those that came from parasitic inductance in the bypasses. This makes it desirable to have an inductance that is high enough that any resonance is below the band of interest. But series inductors have their own problems; they have parasitic capacitance, creating their own self-resonance. As an example, a pair of typical RF chokes (RFCs) were measured (now as series elements) as described earlier. A 2.7-µH molded choke was parallel resonant at 200 MHz, indicating a parallel capacitance of 0.24 pF. The Q at 20 MHz was 52. A 15-µH molded choke was parallel resonant at 47 MHz, yielding a parallel C of 0.79 pF. This part had a Q of 44 at 8 MHz.

Large inductors can be fabricated from series connections of smaller ones. The best wideband performance will result only when all inductors in a chain have about the same value. The reasons for this (and the mathematics that describe the behavior) are identical with those for paralleling identical capacitors.

Low inductor Q is often useful in decoupling applications, encouraging us to use inductors with ferrite cores. Inductors using the Fair-Rite Type #43 material have low Q in the 4 to 10 range over the HF spectrum. One can also create low-Q circuits by paralleling a series inductor of modest Q with a resistor.

Figure 5.26 shows a decoupling network and the resulting impedance when viewed from the "bypass" end. The 15-µH RFC resonates with a 0.1-µF capacitor to destroy the bypass effect just above 0.1 MHz. A low-value parallel resistor fixes the problem.

A major reason for careful wideband bypassing and decoupling is the potential for amplifier oscillation. Instability that allows oscillations is usually suppressed by low impedance terminations. The base and collector (or gate and drain) should both "see" low impedances to ensure stability. But that must be true at all frequencies where the device can produce gain. It is never enough to merely consider the operating frequency for the amplifier. A parallel resonance in the base or collector circuits can be a disaster. When wideband bypassing is not possible, negative feedback that enhances wideband stability is often used.

Emitter bypassing is often a critical application. As demonstrated in the **Circuits and Components** chapter, a few extra ohms of impedance in the emitter circuit can drastically alter amplifier performance. A parallel-resonant emitter bypass could be a profound difficulty while a series-resonant one can be especially effective.

Capacitors also appear in circuits as blocking elements. A blocking capacitor, for example, appears between stages, creating a near short circuit for ac signals while accommodating different dc voltages on the two sides. A blocking capacitor is not as critical as a bypass, for the impedances on either side will usually be higher than that of the block.

With parasitic effects having the potential to strongly affect circuit performance, the circuit designer must account for them wherever they are significant. The additional complexity of including parasitic elements can result in a design too complex to be analyzed manually. Clearly, detailed modeling is the answer to component selection and the control of parasitic effects.

5.3.11 Effects on Filter Performance

LC bandpass filters perform a critical function in determining the performance of a typical RF system such as a receiver. An input filter, usually a bandpass, restricts the frequency range that the receiver must process. Transmitters use LC filters to reduce harmonic output. Audio and LF filters may also use LC elements. The LC filters we refer to in this section are narrow with a bandwidth from 1 to 20% of the center frequency. Even narrower filters are built with resonators having higher Q; the quartz crystal filter discussed in the **Analog and Digital Filtering** chapter is used where bandwidths of less than a part per thousand are possible. The basic concepts that we examine with LC circuits will transfer to the crystal filter.

LOSSES IN FILTERS AND Q

The key elements in narrow filters are tuned circuits made from inductor-capacitor pairs, quartz crystals, or transmission line sections. These resonators share the property that they store energy, but they have losses. A chime is an example. Striking the chime with a hammer produces the waveform of **Figure 5.27**. The rate at which the amplitude decreases with time after the hammer strike is determined by the filter's Q, which is discussed in the chapter on **Circuits and Components**. The higher the Q, the longer it takes for the sound to disappear. The oscillator amplitude would not decrease if it were not for the losses that expend energy stored in the resonator. The mere act of observing the oscillation will cause some energy to be dissipated.

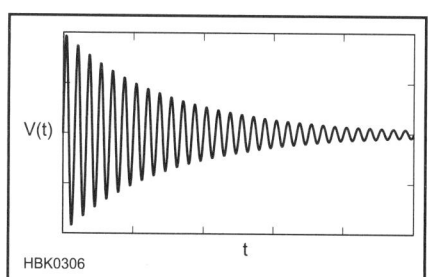

Figure 5.27 — The amplitude of a chime's ring after being struck by a hammer. Units are arbitrary.

A chime is an acoustic resonator, but the same behavior occurs in electric resonators. A pulse input to an LC circuit causes it to ring; losses cause the amplitude to diminish. The most obvious loss in an LC circuit is conductor resistance, including that in the inductor wire. This resistance is higher than the dc value owing to the skin effect, which forces high frequency current toward the conductor surface. Other losses might result from hysteresis losses in an inductor core or dielectric losses in a capacitor.

An inductor is modeled as an ideal part with a series or a parallel resistance. The resistance will depend on the Q if the inductor was part of a resonator with that quality. The two resistances are shown in **Figure 5.28**.

$$R_{Series} = \frac{2\pi f L}{Q} \quad \text{and}$$

$$R_{Parallel} = Q \times 2\pi f L \quad (6)$$

The higher the inductor Q, the smaller the series resistance, or the larger the parallel resistance is needed to model that Q. It does not matter which configuration is used. The Q of a resonator is related to the bandwidth of the tuned circuit by

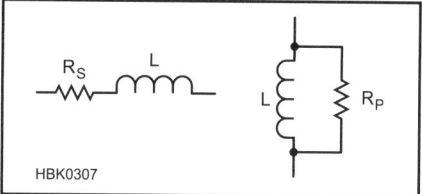

Figure 5.28 — Inductor Q may be modeled with either a series or a parallel resistance.

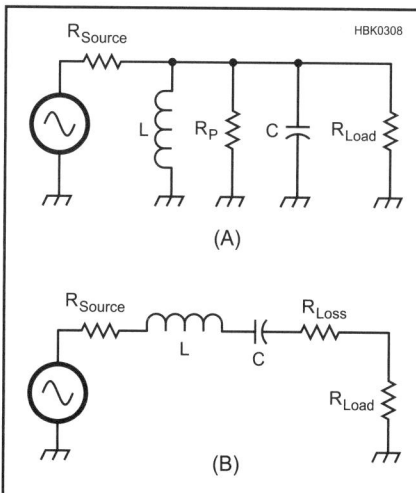

Figure 5.29 — Two simple forms of the single-tuned circuit.

$$BW = \frac{f_C}{Q} \quad (7)$$

where f_C is the tuned circuit's center frequency. This is also the Q of an inductor in a tuned circuit if the capacitor is lossless.

The single-tuned circuit is presented in two different forms in **Figure 5.29**. In the top, a parallel tuned circuit consisting of L and C has loss modeled by three resistors. The resistor R_p is the parallel loss resistance representing the non-ideal nature of the inductor. (Another might be included to represent capacitor losses.) But the LC is here paralleled by three resistors: the source, the load and the loss element. R_p would disappear if the tuned circuit was built from perfect components. The source and load remain; they represent the source resistance that must be present if power is available and a load resistance that must be included if power is to be extracted.

Equation 6 and 7 can be applied in several ways. If the resonator is evaluated with only its intrinsic loss resistance (in either series or parallel form) the resulting Q is called the *unloaded Q*, or Q_u. If, however, the net resistance is used, which is the parallel combination of the load, the source, and the loss in the parallel tuned circuit, the resulting Q is called the *loaded Q*, Q_L. If we were working with the series tuned circuit form, the loaded Q would be related to the total series R.

Consider an example, a parallel tuned circuit (Figure 5.29A) with a 2-μH inductor tuned to 5 MHz with a 507-pF capacitor. Assume the parallel loss resistor was 12.57 kΩ. The unloaded Q calculated from equation 6 is 200. The unloaded bandwidth would be 5 MHz/200 = 25 kHz. Assume that the source and load resistors were equal, each 2 kΩ. The net resistance paralleling the LC would then be the combination of the three resistors, 926 Ω. The loaded Q becomes 14.7 with a loaded bandwidth of 339 kHz. The loaded Q is also the filter Q, for it describes the bandwidth of the single-tuned circuit, the simplest of band-pass filters.

This filter also has *insertion loss* (IL). This is illustrated in **Figure 5.30** which shows the

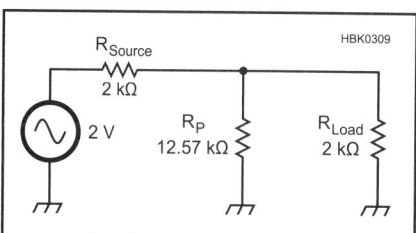

Figure 5.30 — Simplified parallel tuned circuit at resonance. The effect of loss is illustrated by removing the parallel-LC combination which at resonance has infinite impedance.

parallel-resonant LC combination removed (at resonance, the LC combination has infinite impedance), leaving only the loss resistance of 12.57 kΩ. We use an arbitrary open circuit source voltage of 2. The available power to a load is then 1 V across a resistance equaling the 2-kΩ source. If the resonator had no internal losses, this available power would be delivered to the 2-kΩ load. However, the loss R parallels the load, causing the output voltage to be 0.926 V, a bit less than the ideal 1 V. Calculation of the output power into the 2-kΩ load resistance and the available power shows that the insertion loss is 0.67 dB.

This exercise illustrates two vital points that are general for all bandpass filters. First, the bandwidth of any filter must always be larger than the unloaded bandwidth of the resonators used to build the filter. Second, any filter built from real-world components will have an insertion loss. The closer the Q of the filter approaches the unloaded resonator Q, the greater the insertion loss becomes. A parallel tuned circuit illustrated these ideas; the series tuned filter would have produced identical results. Generally, the insertion loss of a single-tuned circuit relates to loaded and unloaded Q by

$$IL(dB) = -20 \log\left(1 - \frac{Q_L}{Q_U}\right) \quad (8)$$

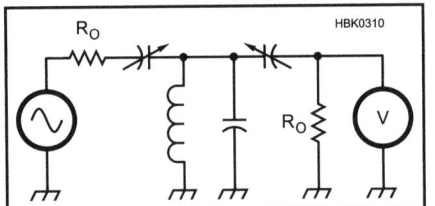

Figure 5.31 — Test setup for measuring the Q of a resonator. The source and load impedances, R_O, are assumed to be identical. The two coupling capacitors are adjusted to be equal to each other. The output signal is measured with an appropriate ac voltmeter, an oscilloscope or a spectrum analyzer.

The Q of a tuned LC circuit is easily measured with a signal generator of known output impedance (usually 50 Ω) and a sensitive detector, again with a known impedance level, often equal to that of the generator. The test configuration is shown in **Figure 5.31**. It uses equal loads and equal capacitors to couple from the terminations to the resonator. Equal capacitors, C1 and C2 guarantees that each termination contributes equally to the resonator parallel load resistance. The voltmeter across the load is calibrated in dB.

To begin measurement we remove the tuned circuit and replace it with a direct connection from generator to load. The available power delivered to the load is calculated after the voltage is measured. The resonator is then inserted between the generator and load, and the generator is tuned for a peak. The measured power is less than that available from the source, with the difference being the insertion loss for the simple filter. Capacitors C1 and C2 are adjusted until the loss is 30 dB or more. With loss this high, the intrinsic loss resistance of the resonator will dominate the loss. The generator is now tuned first to one side of the peak, and then to the other, noting the frequencies where the response is lower than the peak by 3 dB. The unloaded bandwidth, ΔF, is the difference between the two 3 dB frequencies. The unloaded Q is calculated as

$$Q_U = \frac{F}{\Delta F} \quad (9)$$

This method for Q measurement is quite universal, being effective for audio tuned circuits, simple LC RF circuits, VHF helical resonators, or microwave resonators. The form of the variable capacitors, C1 and C2, may be different for the various parts of the spectrum, but the concepts are general. Indeed, it is not even important how the coupling occurs. The Q measurement normally determines an unloaded value, but loaded values are also of interest when testing filters.

5.4 Semiconductor Circuits at RF

The models used in the **Circuits and Components** chapter are reasonably accurate at low frequencies, and they are of some use at RF, but more sophisticated models are required for consistent results at higher frequencies. This section notes several areas in which the simple models must be enhanced. Circuit design using models accurate at RF, particularly for large signals, is performed today using design software as described in the **Computer-Aided Circuit Design** chapter of this book. In-depth discussions of the elements of RF circuit design appear in Hayward's *Introduction to Radio Frequency Design*, an excellent text for the beginning RF designer (see the References section).

5.4.1 The Diode at High Frequencies

A DIODE AC MODEL

At high frequencies, the diode's behavior becomes less like a switch, especially for small signals that do not cause the diode's operating point to move by large amounts. In this case, the diode's small-signal dynamic behavior becomes important.

Figure 5.32 shows a simple resistor-diode circuit to which is applied a dc bias voltage plus an ac signal. Assuming that the voltage drop across the diode is 0.6 V and R_f is negligible, we can calculate the bias current to be I = (5 – 0.6) / 1 kΩ = 4.4 mA. This point is marked on the diodes I-V curve in Figure 5.32. If we draw a line tangent to this point, as shown, the slope of this line represents the *dynamic resistance* of the diode, R_d, experienced by a small ac signal. At room temperature, dynamic resistance is approximately

$$R_d = \frac{25}{I} \Omega \quad (10)$$

where I is the diode current in mA. Note that this resistance changes with bias current and should not be confused with the dc forward resistance discussed in the **Circuits and Components** chapter, which has a similar value but represents a different concept. **Figure 5.33** shows a low-frequency ac model for the diode, including the dynamic resistance and junction capacitance. This model should only be used when the diode's dc operating parameters can be neglected.

SWITCHING TIME

If you change the polarity of a signal applied to the ideal diode, current flow stops or starts instantaneously. Current in a real diode cannot do this, as a finite amount of time is required to move electrons and holes in or out of the diode as it changes states. Effectively, the diode junction capacitance, C_J, in Figure 5.33 must be charged or discharged. As a result, diodes have a maximum useful frequency when used in switching applications.

The operation of diode switching circuits can often be modeled by the circuit in **Figure 5.34**. The approximate switching time (in seconds) for this circuit is given by

$$t_s = \tau_p \frac{\left(\frac{V_1}{R_1}\right)}{\left(\frac{V_2}{R_2}\right)} = \tau_p \frac{I_1}{I_2} \quad (11)$$

5.14   Chapter 5

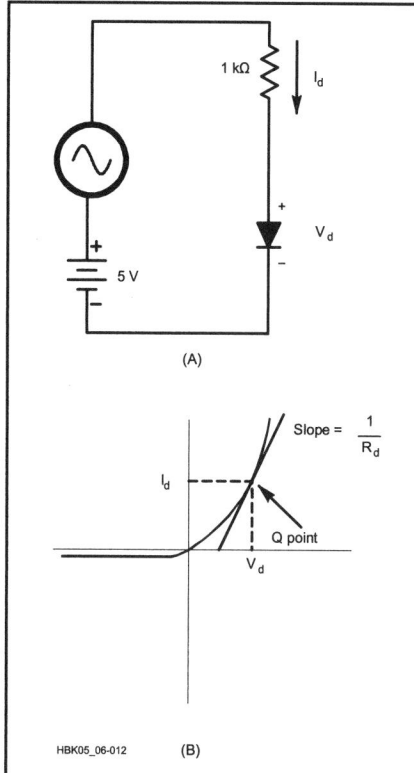

Figure 5.32 — A simple resistor-diode circuit used to illustrate dynamic resistance. The ac input voltage "sees" a diode resistance whose value is the slope of the line at the Q-point, shown in B.

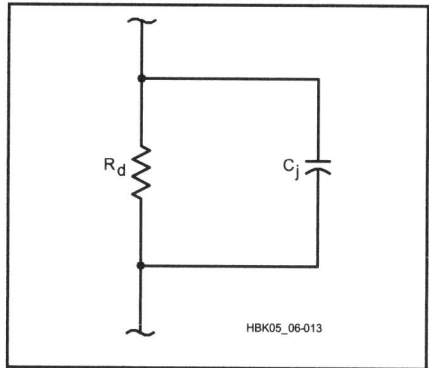

Figure 5.33 — An ac model for diodes. R_d is the dynamic resistance and C_j is the junction capacitance.

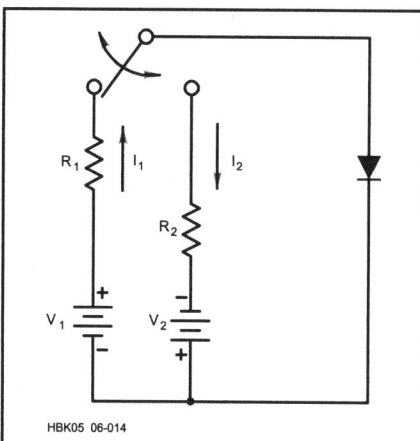

Figure 5.34 — Circuit used for computation of diode switching time.

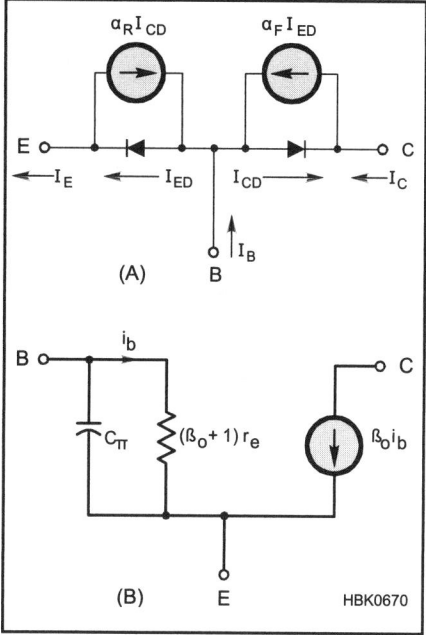

Figure 5.35 — (A) The Ebers-Moll model of the bipolar junction transistor (BJT) is used at dc and low frequencies when the transistor is in its active region. (B) The hybrid-pi model includes frequency dependence.

5.4.2 The Transistor at High Frequencies

The development and selection of suitable models for active devices at RF is an involved and nuanced process. This section presents a few of the models used for bipolar junction transistors (BJT) and field-effect transistors (FET) as examples of the issues involved. For more information on model details, start with the *SPICE* home page at **bwrc.eecs.berkeley.edu/classes/icbook/spice** and the user's manual for the simulation software you intend to use.

GAIN VERSUS FREQUENCY

The circuit design equations in **Circuits and Components** generally assumed that current gain in the bipolar transistor was independent of frequency. As signal frequency increases, however, current gain decreases. The low-frequency current gain, β_0, is constant through the audio spectrum, but it eventually decreases, and at some high frequency it will drop by a factor of 2 for each doubling of signal frequency. (The h-parameter [h_{FE}] is often substituted for β at dc and h_{FE} for ac current gain. H-parameters are discussed later in this chapter.) A transistor's frequency vs current gain relationship is specified by its *gain-bandwidth product* (GBW), or F_T, the frequency at which the current gain is 1. Common transistors for lower RF applications might have $\beta_0 = 100$ and $F_T = 500$ MHz. The frequency at which current gain equals β_0 is called F_b and is related to F_T by $F_b = F_T / \beta_0$.

The *Ebers-Moll model* for the bipolar transistor, shown in **Figure 5.35A**, is a "large signal model." It is used when the transistor is in its active mode and gives good results for dc collector and emitter currents. This would be a good model to use when designing a pass-transistor voltage regulator circuit, for example.

The frequency dependence of current gain is modeled by adding a capacitor across the base resistor of Figure 5.35B, the *hybrid-pi* model results. The capacitor's reactance should equal the low-frequency input resistance, $(\beta + 1)r_e$, at F_b. This simulates a frequency-dependent current gain.

Similar considerations affect the transconductance of FETs as the gate-to-source and gate-to-drain capacitances act to reduce high-frequency gain. Instead of F_T, most FETs designed for amplifier use specify input and output transconductance, susceptance, and power gain at different frequencies.

Recognizing that transistor gain varies with frequency, it is important to know the conditions under which the simpler model is useful. Calculations show that the simple model is valid, with $\beta = F_T / F$, for frequencies well above F_b. The approximation worsens, however, as the operating frequency (f_0) approaches F_T.

where τ_p is the minority carrier lifetime of the diode, a material constant determined during manufacture, on the order of 1 ms. I_1 and I_2 are currents that flow during the switching process. The minimum time in which a diode can switch from one state to the other and back again is therefore $2t_s$, and thus the maximum usable switching frequency is f_{sw} (Hz) $= 1/(2t_s)$. It is usually a good idea to stay below this by a factor of two. Diode data sheets usually give typical switching times and show the circuit used to measure them.

Note that f_{sw} depends on the forward and reverse currents, determined by I_1 and I_2 (or equivalently V_1, V_2, R_1, and R_2). Within a reasonable range, the switching time can be reduced by manipulating these currents. Of course, the maximum power that other circuit elements can handle places an upper limit on switching currents.

RF Techniques 5.15

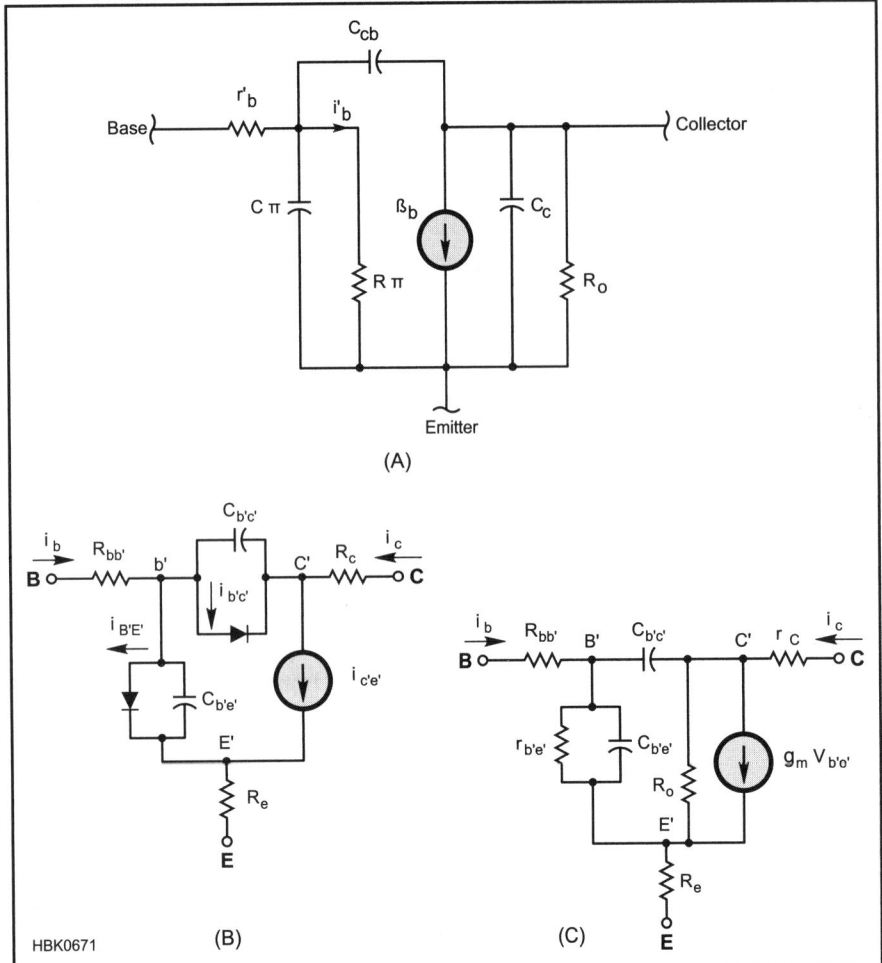

Figure 5.36 — High-frequency models for the bipolar junction transistor. (A) An improved version of the hybrid-pi model including additional device capacitances. (B) is the large-signal Gummel-Poon model used at dc and low-frequencies — the standard used for bipolar transistors by simulators based on *SPICE3* and (C) is the small-signal ac version.

SMALL-SIGNAL DESIGN AT RF

The simplified hybrid-pi model of Figure 5.35B is often suitable for non-critical designs, but **Figure 5.36A** shows a better small-signal model for RF design that expands on the hybrid-pi. Consider the physical aspects of a real transistor: There is some capacitance across each of the PN junctions (C_{cb} and C_p) and capacitance from collector to emitter (C_c). There are also capacitances between the device leads (C_e, C_b and C_c). There is a resistance in each current path, emitter to base and collector. From emitter to base, there is r_π from the hybrid-pi model and $r'b$, the "base spreading" resistance. From emitter to collector is R_o, the output resistance. The leads that attach the silicon die to the external circuit present three inductances.

Manual circuit analysis with this model is best tackled with the aid of a computer and specialized software. Other methods are presented in Hayward's *Introduction to Radio Frequency Design*. Surprisingly accurate results may be obtained, even at RF, from the simple models. Simple models also give a better "feel" for device characteristics that might be obscured by the mathematics of a more rigorous treatment. Use the simplest model that describes the important features of the device and circuit at hand.

The *Gummel-Poon model* shown in Figs 5.36B and 5.36C is the standard used by simulation software based on *SPICE3*. By adding additional parasitic elements, such as lead inductance and lead-to-package capacitances, the small-signal ac model can be used accurately at high frequencies. Note how the ac model becomes progressively more sophisticated from Figure 5.35A through 5.36C.

HIGH FREQUENCY FET MODELS

At low frequencies the FET can be treated as a simple current source controlled by the gate-to-source voltage as in Figure 3.49 in the **Circuits and Components** chapter. As frequency increases, the inter-electrode capacitances become significant and must be included, such as in the model in **Figure 5.37A**. As with

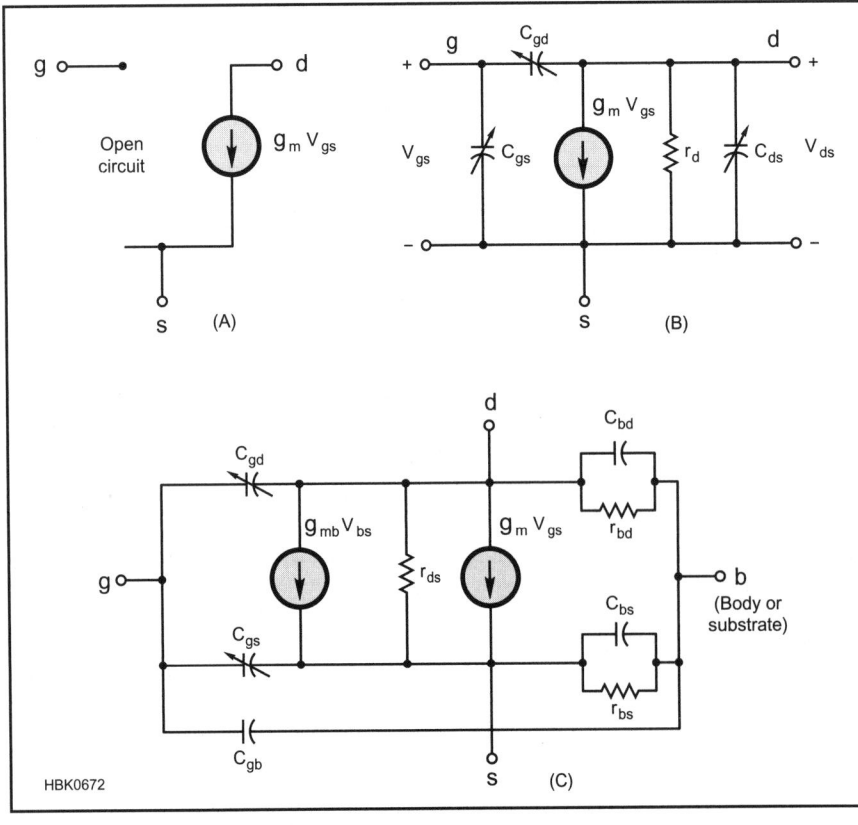

Figure 5.37 — Small-signal models for the field-effect transistor (FET). (A) is a simple low-frequency model. (B) is a common *SPICE3* large-signal model and (C) is a typical high-frequency model for the JFET.

the BJT, separate models are used for small-signal and large-signal applications. Figure 5.37B shows a small-signal *SPICE3* simulation model for the JFET. All of the model's capacitances vary with temperature and device operating characteristics. Figure 5.37C shows a typical high-frequency MOSFET model used by *SPICE3* (there are several) that includes the effect of the body or substrate elements.

The advances in CMOS integrated circuit technology have resulted in transistors (and capacitors and inductors) with sufficient performance for use in RF design work. In fact, most radio transceivers for cellular telephones, wireless LANs and similar high-volume applications are implemented almost exclusively in CMOS technology due to the high integration available. MOSFET RF design principles are similar to BJT and JFET designs, and most circuit simulators provide good models for MOSFET devices. These additional techniques are enabled by the excellent device matching available in IC technology and the ability to integrate additional circuitry at low incremental cost.

PARASITIC ELEMENTS AND NOISE

For accurate RF simulation the effects of additional parasitic elements must be included. The most significant is lead inductance — generally inserted in series with the device's external connections. Lead-to-package and lead-to-lead capacitances are also included in most high-frequency simulations. Depending on the simulation package used, the user may be required to install these parasitic elements as separate circuit elements or the simulator or manufacturer may provide special models for high-frequency simulation.

Simulation of device noise is not covered here, but many simulator packages include separate noise models for various active devices. Review the simulator's documentation for information about how to include noise in your simulation.

5.4.3 Amplifier Classes

The class of operation of an amplifier is determined by the fraction of a drive cycle during which conduction occurs in the amplifying device or for switchmode devices. (Switchmode amplifiers use different criteria.) The Class A amplifier conducts for 100% of the cycle. It is characterized by constant flow of supply current, regardless of the strength of the driving signal. Most of the amplifiers we use for RF applications and many audio circuits in receivers operate in Class A.

A Class B amplifier conducts for 50% of the cycle, which is 180 degrees if we examine the circuit with regard to a driving sine wave. A Class B amplifier draws no dc current when no input signal is applied, but current begins to flow with any input, growing with the input strength. A Class B amplifier can display good *envelope linearity*, meaning that the output amplitude at the drive frequency changes linearly with the input signal. The total absence of current flow for half of the drive cycle will create harmonics of the signal drive.

A Class C amplifier is one that conducts for less than half of a cycle. No current flows without drive. Application of a small drive produces no output and no current flow. Only after a threshold is reached does the device begin to conduct and provide output. A bipolar transistor with no source of bias for the base typically operates in Class C.

The large-signal models discussed earlier are suitable for the analysis of all amplifier classes. Small-signal models are generally reserved for Class A amplifiers. The most common power amplifier class is a cross between Class A and B — the Class AB amplifier that conducts for more than half of each cycle. A Class AB amplifier at low drive levels is indistinguishable from a Class A design. However, increasing drive produces greater collector (or drain) current and greater output.

Amplifier class letter designators for vacuum tube amplifiers were augmented with a numeric subscript. A Class AB_1 amplifier operates in AB, but with no grid current flowing. A Class AB_2 amplifier's grid is driven positive with respect to the cathode and so some grid current flows. In solid-state amplifiers, which have no grids, no numeric subscripts are used.

While wide-bandwidth Class A and Class B amplifiers are common, most circuits operating in Class C and higher are tuned at the output. The tuning accomplishes two things. First, it allows different terminations to exist for different frequencies. For example, a resistive load could be presented at the drive frequency while presenting a short circuit at some or all harmonics. The second consequence of tuning is that reactive loads can be created and presented to the amplifier collector or drain. This then provides independent control of current and voltage waveforms.

While not as common as A, B, and C, Class D and E amplifiers are of increasing interest. The Class D circuit is a balanced (two transistor) switching format where the input is driven hard enough to produce square wave collector waveforms. Class E amplifiers usually use a single switching device with output tuning that allows high current to flow in the device only when the output voltage is low. Other "switching amplifier" class designators refer to the various techniques of controlling the switched currents and voltages.

Class A and AB amplifiers are capable of good envelope linearity, so they are the most common formats used in the output of SSB amplifiers. Class B and, predominantly, Class C amplifiers are used for CW and FM applications, but lack the envelope linearity needed for SSB.

Efficiency varies considerably between amplifier class. The Class A amplifier can reach a collector efficiency of 50%, but no higher, with much lower values being typical. Class AB amplifiers are capable of higher efficiency, although the wideband circuits popular in HF transceivers typically offer only 30% at full power. A Class C amplifier is capable of efficiencies approaching 100% as the conduction cycle becomes small, with common values of 50 to 75%. Both Class D and E are capable of 90% and higher efficiency. An engineering text treating power amplifier details is Krauss, Bostian, and Raab's *Solid State Radio Engineering*. A landmark paper by a Cal Tech group led by David Rutledge, KN6EK, targeted to the home experimenter, *High-Efficiency Class-E Power Amplifiers*, was presented in *QST* for May and June, 1997.

5.4.4 RF Amplifiers with Feedback

The feedback amplifier appears frequently in amateur RF circuits. This is a circuit with two forms of negative feedback with (usually) a single transistor to obtain wide bandwidth, well-controlled gain and well-controlled, stable input and output resistances. Several of these amplifiers can be cascaded to form a high gain circuit that is both stable and predictable.

The small-signal schematic for the feedback amplifier is shown in **Figure 5.38** without bias components or power supply details. The design begins with an NPN transistor biased for a stable dc current. Gain is reduced with emitter degeneration, increasing input resistance while decreasing gain. Additional feedback is then added with a parallel feedback resistor, R_f, between the collector and base. This is much like the resistor between an op-amp output and the inverting input which reduces gain and *decreases* input resistance.

Several additional circuits are presented

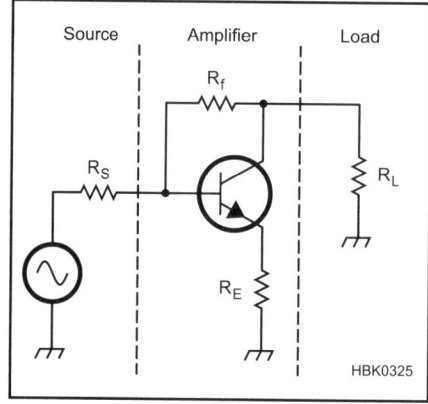

Figure 5.38 — Small-signal circuit for a feedback amplifier.

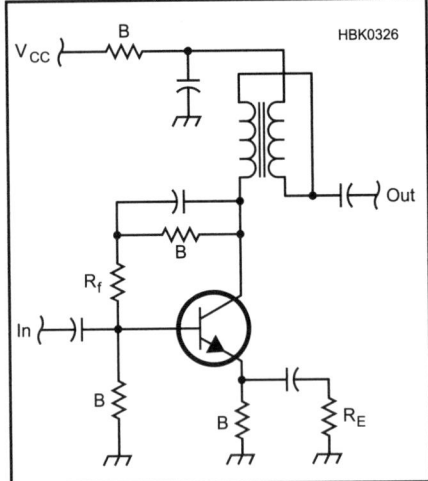

Figure 5.39 — A practical feedback amplifier. Components marked with "B" are predominantly for biasing. The 50-Ω output termination is transformed to 200 Ω at the collector. A typical RF transformer is 10 bifilar turns of #28 on a FT-37-43 ferrite toroid. The inductance of one of the two windings should have a reactance of around 250 Ω at the lowest frequency of operation.

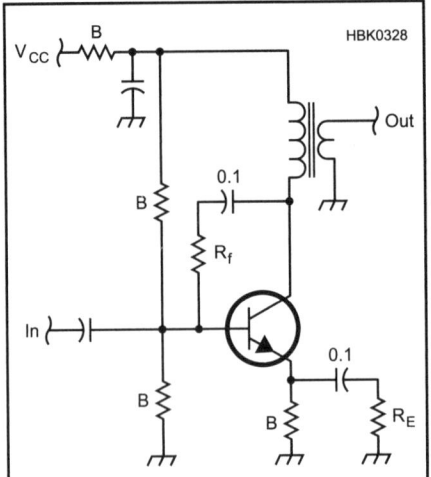

Figure 5.41 — This form of the feedback amplifier uses an arbitrary transformer. Feedback is isolated from bias components.

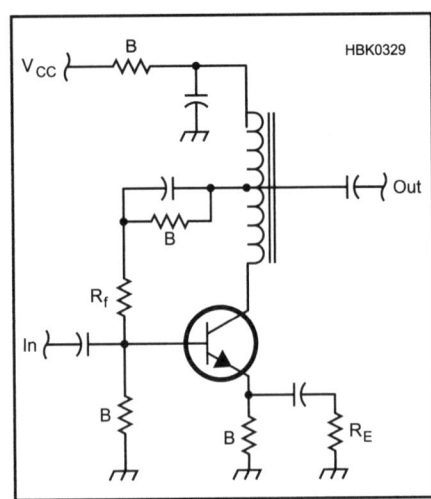

Figure 5.42 — A feedback amplifier with feedback from the output transformer tap. This is common, but can produce unstable results.

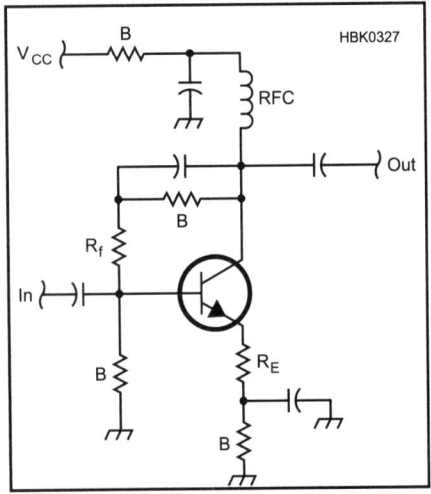

Figure 5.40 — A variation of the feedback amplifier with a 50-Ω output termination at the collector.

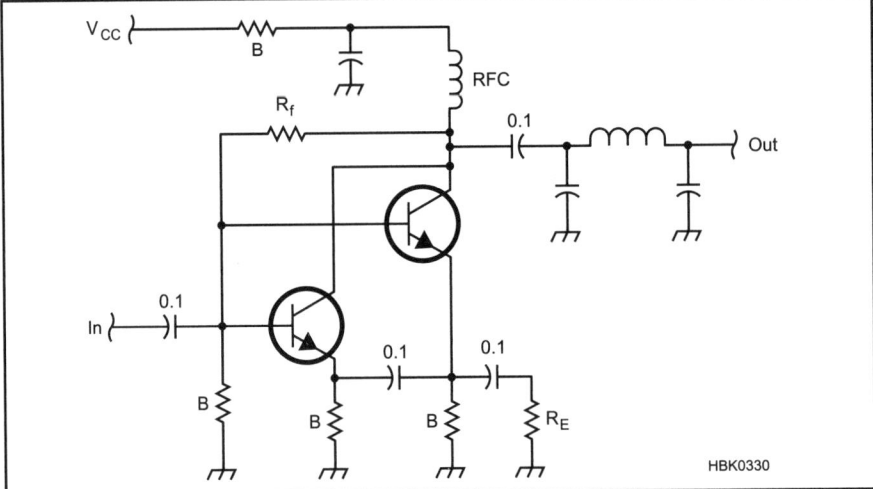

Figure 5.43 — Feedback amplifier with two parallel transistors.

showing practical forms of the feedback amplifier. **Figure 5.39** shows a complete circuit. The base is biased with a resistive divider from the collector. However, much of the resistor is bypassed, leaving only R_f active for actual signal feedback. Emitter degeneration is ac coupled to the emitter. The resistor R_E dominates the degeneration since R_E is normally much smaller than the emitter bias resistor. Components that are predominantly used for biasing are marked with "B." This amplifier would normally be terminated in 50 Ω at both the input and output. The transformer has the effect of making the 50-Ω load "look like" a larger load value, $R_L = 200$ Ω to the collector. This is a common and useful value for many HF applications.

Figure 5.40 differs from Figure 5.39 in two places. First, the collector is biased through an RF choke instead of a transformer. The collector circuit then "sees" 50 Ω when that load is connected. Second, the emitter degeneration is in series with the bias, instead of the earlier parallel connection. Either scheme works well, although the parallel configuration affords experimental flexibility with isolation between setting degeneration and biasing. Amplifiers without an output transformer are not constrained by degraded transformer performance and often offer constant or "flat" gain to several GHz.

The variation of **Figure 5.41** may well be the most general. It uses an arbitrary transformer to match the collector. Biasing is traditional and does not interact with the feedback.

Feedback is obtained directly from the output tap in the circuit of **Figure 5.42**. While this scheme is common, it is less desirable than the others, for the transformer is part of the feedback loop. This could lead to instabilities. Normally, the parallel feedback tends to stabilize the amplifiers.

The circuit of **Figure 5.43** has several features. Two transistors are used, each with a separate emitter biasing resistor. However, ac coupling causes the pair to operate as a single device with degeneration set by R_E. The parallel feedback resistor, R_f, is both a signal feedback element and part of the bias divider. This constrains the values slightly. Finally, an arbitrary output load can be presented to the composite collector through a π-type matching network. This provides some low pass filtering, but constrains the amplifier bandwidth.

5.5 Ferrite Materials

Ferrites are ceramics consisting of various metal oxides formulated to have very high permeability. Iron, manganese, manganese zinc (MnZn), and nickel zinc (NiZn) are the most commonly used oxides. Ferrite cores and beads are available in many styles, as shown in **Figure 5.44**. Wires and cables are then passed through them or wound on them.

When ferrite surrounds a conductor, the high permeability of the material provides a much easier path for magnetic flux set up by current flow in the conductor than if the wire were surrounded only by air. The short length of wire passing through the ferrite will thus see its self-inductance "magnified" by the relative permeability of the ferrite. The ferrites used for suppression are soft ferrites — that is, they are not permanent magnets.

Recalling the definition in the **Electrical Fundamentals** chapter, *permeability* (μ) is the characteristic of a material that quantifies the ease with which it supports a magnetic field. Relative permeability is the ratio of the permeability of the material to the permeability of free space. The relative permeability of nonmagnetic materials like air, copper, and aluminum is 1, while magnetic materials have a relative permeability much greater than 1. Typical values (measured at power frequencies) for stainless steel, steel and mu-metal are on the order of 500, 1000 and 20,000 respectively. Various ferrites have values from the low tens to several thousand. The permeability of these materials changes with frequency and this affects their suitability for use as an inductor's magnetic core or as a means of providing EMI suppression.

Manufacturers vary the chemical composition (the *mix* or *material "type"*) and the dimensions of ferrites to achieve the desired electrical performance characteristics. It is important to select a mix with permeability and loss characteristics that are appropriate for the intended frequency range and application. (The **Component Data and References** chapter includes tables showing the data for different types of ferrite and powdered-iron cores and appropriate frequency ranges for each.)

Fair-Rite Products Corp. supplies most of the ferrite materials used by amateurs, and their website (**www.fair-rite.com**) includes extensive technical data on both the materials and the many parts made from those materials. Much can be learned from the study of this data, the most extensive of any manufacturer. The website includes two detailed application notes on the use of ferrite materials, *How to Choose Ferrite Components for EMI Suppression* and *Use of Ferrites in Broadband Transformers*.

5.5.1 Ferrite Permeability and Frequency

Product data sheets characterize ferrite materials used as chokes by graphing their series equivalent impedance, and chokes are usually analyzed as if their equivalent circuit had only a series resistance and inductance, as shown in **Figs 5.45A** and 5.45B. (Figure 5.45 presents small-signal equivalent circuits.

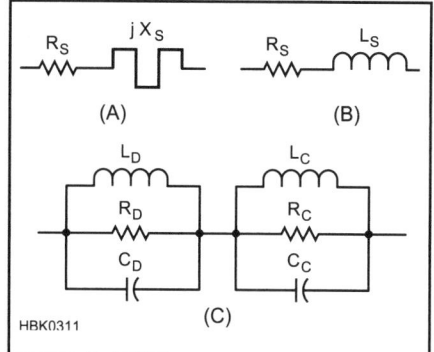

Figure 5.45 — Equivalent circuits for ferrite material. (A) shows the equivalent series circuit specified by the data sheet. (B) shows an over-simplified equivalent circuit for a ferrite choke. (C) shows a better equivalent circuit for a ferrite choke.

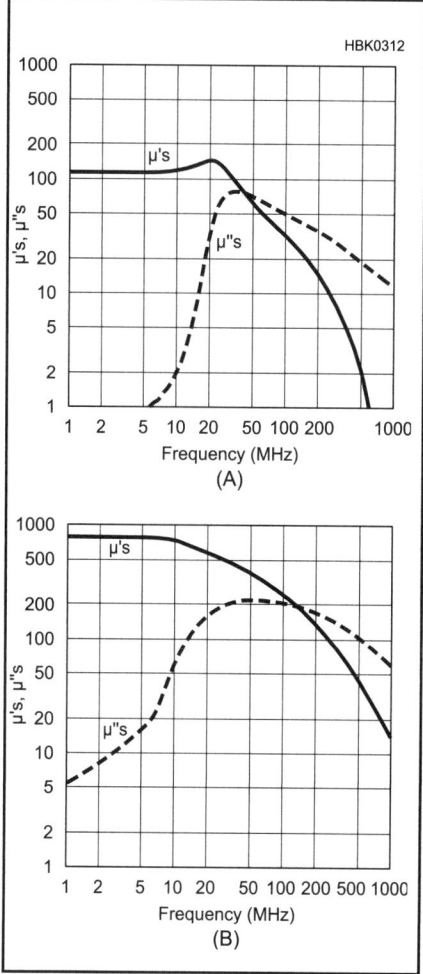

Figure 5.46 — Permeability of a typical ferrite material, Fair-Rite Type #61 (A) and of Type #43 material (B). (Based on product data published by Fair-Rite Products Corp.)

Figure 5.44 — Ferrites are made in many forms. Beads are cylinders with small center holes so that they can be slid over wires or cables. Toroidal cores are more ring-like so that the wire or cable can be passed through the center hole multiple times. Snap-on or split cores are made to be clamped over cables too large to be wound around the core or for a bead to be installed.

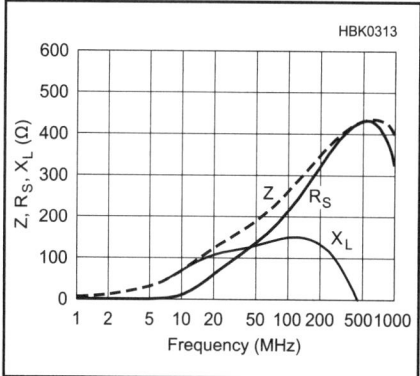

Figure 5.47 — Impedance of a bead for EMI suppression at UHF, Fair-Rite Type #61. (Based on product data published by Fair-Rite Products Corp.)

RF Techniques   5.19

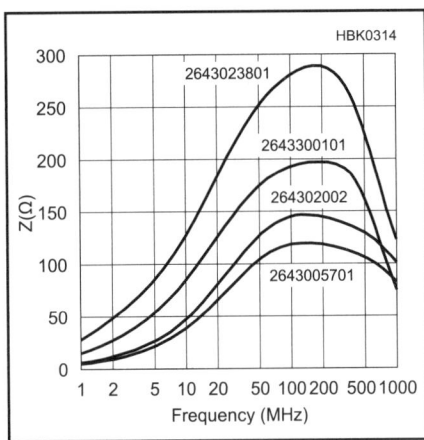

Figure 5.48 — Impedance of different length beads of Fair-Rite Type #43 material. The longer the bead, the higher the impedance. (Based on product data published by Fair-Rite Products Corp.)

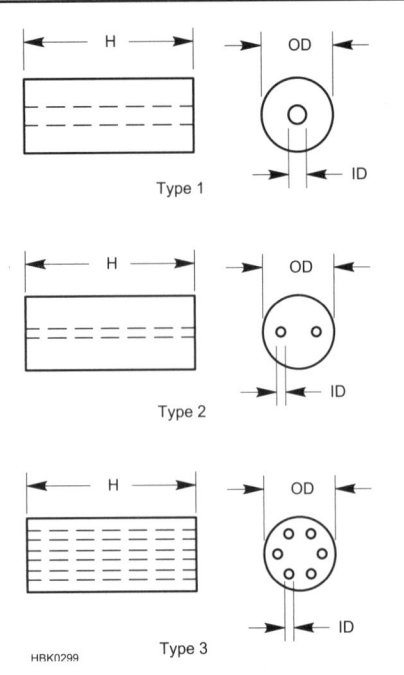

Figure 5.49 — Typical one-piece ferrite bead configurations. Component leads or cables can be inserted through beads one or more times to create inductance and loss as described in the text.

Figure 5.50 — A ferrite choke consisting of multiple turns of cable wound on a 2.4-in. OD × 1.4-in. ID × 0.5-in. toroid core.

Issues of temperature and saturation at high power levels are not addressed in this section.) The actual equivalent circuit is closer to Figure 5.45C. The presence of both inductance and capacitance creates resonances visible in the graphs of impedance versus frequency as discussed below. One resonance is created by the pair $L_D C_D$ and the other by $L_C C_C$.

Figure 5.46A graphs the permeabilities μ'_S and μ''_S for Fair-Rite Type #61 ferrite material (Fair-Rite products are identified by a material "Type" and a number), one of the many mix choices available. This material is recommended for use in inductive applications below 25 MHz and for EMI suppression at frequencies above 200 MHz.

For the simple series equivalent circuit of Figure 5.45A and B, the permeability constant for ferrite is actually complex; $\mu = \mu'_S + j \mu''_S$. In this equation, μ'_S represents the component of permeability defining ordinary inductance, and μ''_S describes the component that affects losses in the material. You can see that up to approximately 20 MHz, μ'_S is nearly constant, meaning that an inductor wound on a core of this material will have a stable inductance. Below about 15 MHz, the chart shows that μ''_S is much smaller than μ'_S, so that losses are small, making this material good for high power inductors and transformers in this frequency range.

Above 15 MHz, μ''_S increases rapidly and so do the material's associated losses, peaking between 300 and 400 MHz. That makes the inductor very lossy at those frequencies and good for suppressing EMI by absorbing energy in the unwanted signal. **Figure 5.47** shows the manufacturer's impedance data for one "turn" of wire through a cylindrical ferrite bead (a straight wire passing through the bead) made of mix #61 with the expected peak in impedance above 200 MHz. Interestingly, X_L goes below the graph above resonance, but it isn't zero. The negative reactance is created by the capacitors in Figure 5.45C.

The Type #43 mix (see Figure 5.46B) used for the beads of **Figure 5.48** is optimized for suppression at VHF (30-300 MHz). Type #43 material's μ'_S is much higher than type #61, meaning that fewer turns are required to achieve the needed inductance. But μ''_S for #43 remains significant even at low frequencies, limiting its usefulness for inductor and transformer cores that must handle high power. The figure shows the impedance data for several beads of different lengths. The longer the bead, the higher the impedance. The same effect can be obtained by stringing multiple beads together on the same wire or cable.

5.5.2 Resonances of Ferrite Cores

Below resonance, the impedance of a wire passing through a ferrite cylinder is propor-

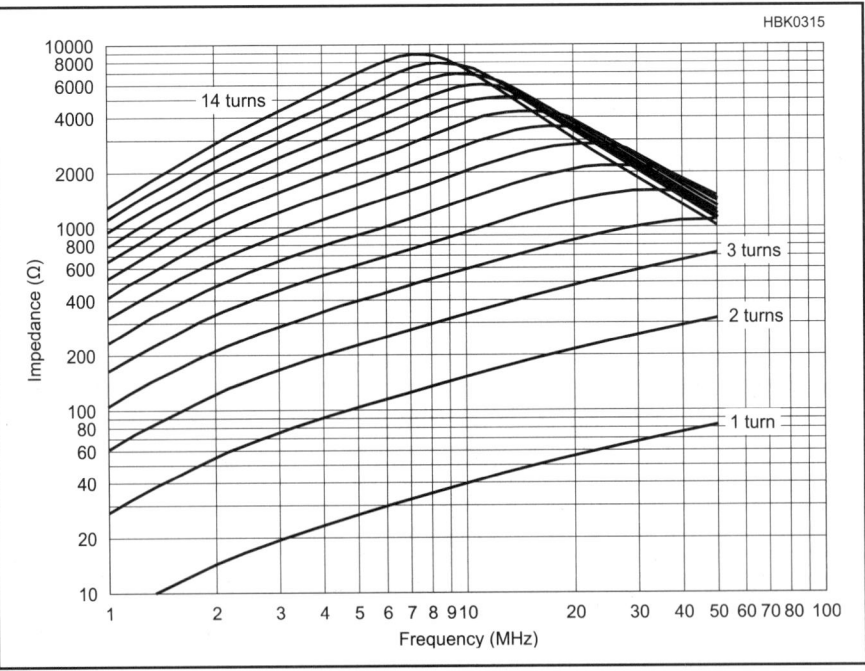

Figure 5.51 — Impedance of multi-turn choke wound on a Fair-Rite Type #43 core as shown in Figure 5.50. Type #43 material is optimized for use as a choke for the VHF range. (Measured data)

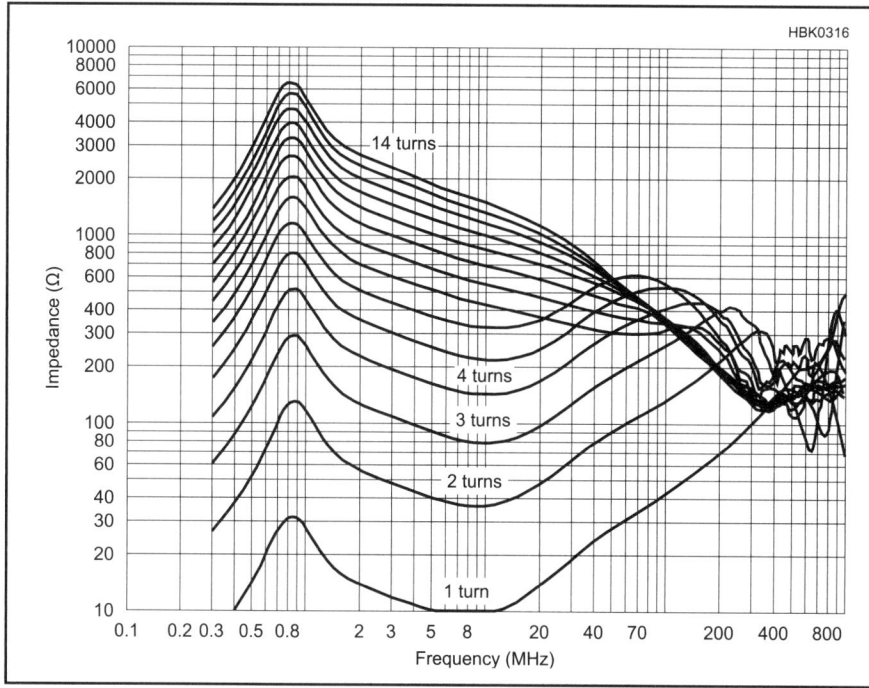

Figure 5.52 — Impedance of multi-turn choke wound on a Fair-Rite Type #78 core as shown in Figure 5.50. Type #78 material is optimized for use as a choke below 2 MHz. (Measured data)

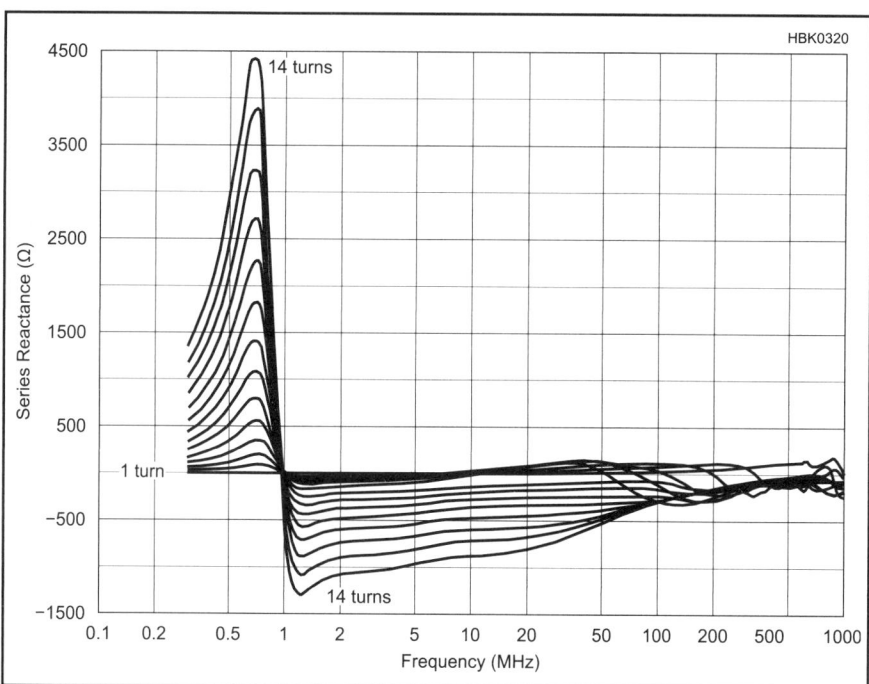

Figure 5.53 — Series reactive component of the chokes of Figure 5.52. (Measured data)

choke in Figure 5.50 made of ferrite optimized for the VHF range (30-300 MHz). The data of **Figure 5.52** are for toroids of the same size, but wound on a material optimized for use below 2 MHz.

The measured data for Figures 5.51, 5.52, and 5.53 are for chokes wound with small diameter wire. The choke of Figure 5.50 will exhibit a somewhat lower resonant frequency for the same number of turns because the larger diameter cable has more capacitance between turns. The cable in the photo is a high quality braid-shielded twisted pair with an outside diameter comparable to RG-59.

We'll study the L_D C_D resonance first. A classic text (*Soft Ferrites, Properties and Applications*, by E. C. Snelling, published in 1969), shows that there is a dimensional resonance within the ferrite related to the velocity of propagation (V_P) within the ferrite and standing waves that are set up in the cross-sectional dimensions of the core. In general, for any given material, the smaller the core, the higher will be the frequency of this resonance, and to a first approximation, the resonant frequency will double if the core dimension is halved. In Figure 5.45C, L_D and C_D account for this dimensional resonance, and R_D for losses within the ferrite. R_D is mostly due to eddy currents (and some hysteresis) in the core.

Now it's time to account for R_C, L_C and C_C. Note that there are two sets of resonances for the chokes wound around the Type #78 material (Figure 5.52), but only one set for the choke of Figure 5.51. For both materials, the upper resonance starts just below 1 GHz for a single turn and moves down in frequency as the number of turns is increased. **Figure 5.53**, the reactance for the chokes of Figure 5.52, also shows both sets of resonances. That's why the equivalent circuit must include two parallel resonances!

The difference between these materials that accounts for this behavior is their chemical composition (the mix). Type #78 is a MnZn ferrite, while Type #43 is a NiZn ferrite. The velocity of propagation (V_P) in NiZn ferrites is roughly two orders of magnitude higher than for MnZn, and, at those higher frequencies, there is too much loss to allow the standing waves that establish dimensional resonance to exist.

To understand what's happening, we'll return to our first order equivalent circuit of a ferrite choke (Figure 5.45C). L_C, and R_C, and C_C are the inductance, resistance, (including the effect of the μ of the ferrite), and stray capacitance associated with the wire that passes through the ferrite. This resonance moves down in frequency with more turns because both L and C increase with more turns. The dimensional resonance does not move, since it depends only on the dimensions V_P of the ferrite.

What is the source of C_C if there's no "coil," only a single wire passing through a cylinder?

tional to the length of the cylinder. Figure 5.48 shows the impedance of a family of beads that differ primarily in their length. There are also small differences in their cross section, which is why the resonant frequency shifts slightly as discussed below. **Figure 5.49** shows some typical ferrite bead configurations.

Like all inductors, the impedance of a ferrite choke below resonance is approximately proportional to the square of the number of turns passing through the core. **Figure 5.50** shows a multi-turn choke wound on a 2.4-inch OD × 1.4-inch ID × 0.5-inch ferrite toroid core. **Figure 5.51** is measured data for the

RF Techniques   5.21

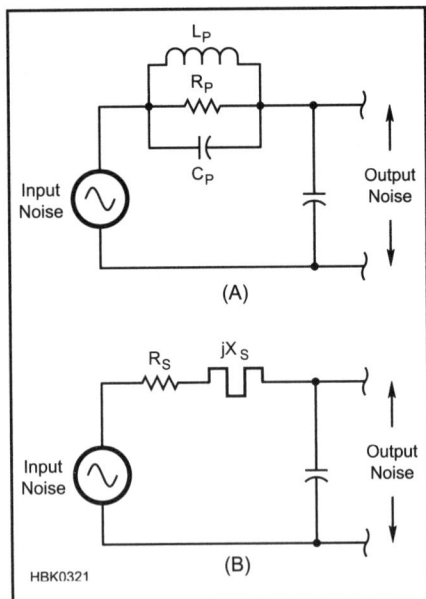

Figure 5.54 — At A, the series element of the divider is a parallel-resonant circuit. At B, the series element of the divider is the series-equivalent circuit used by ferrite data sheets.

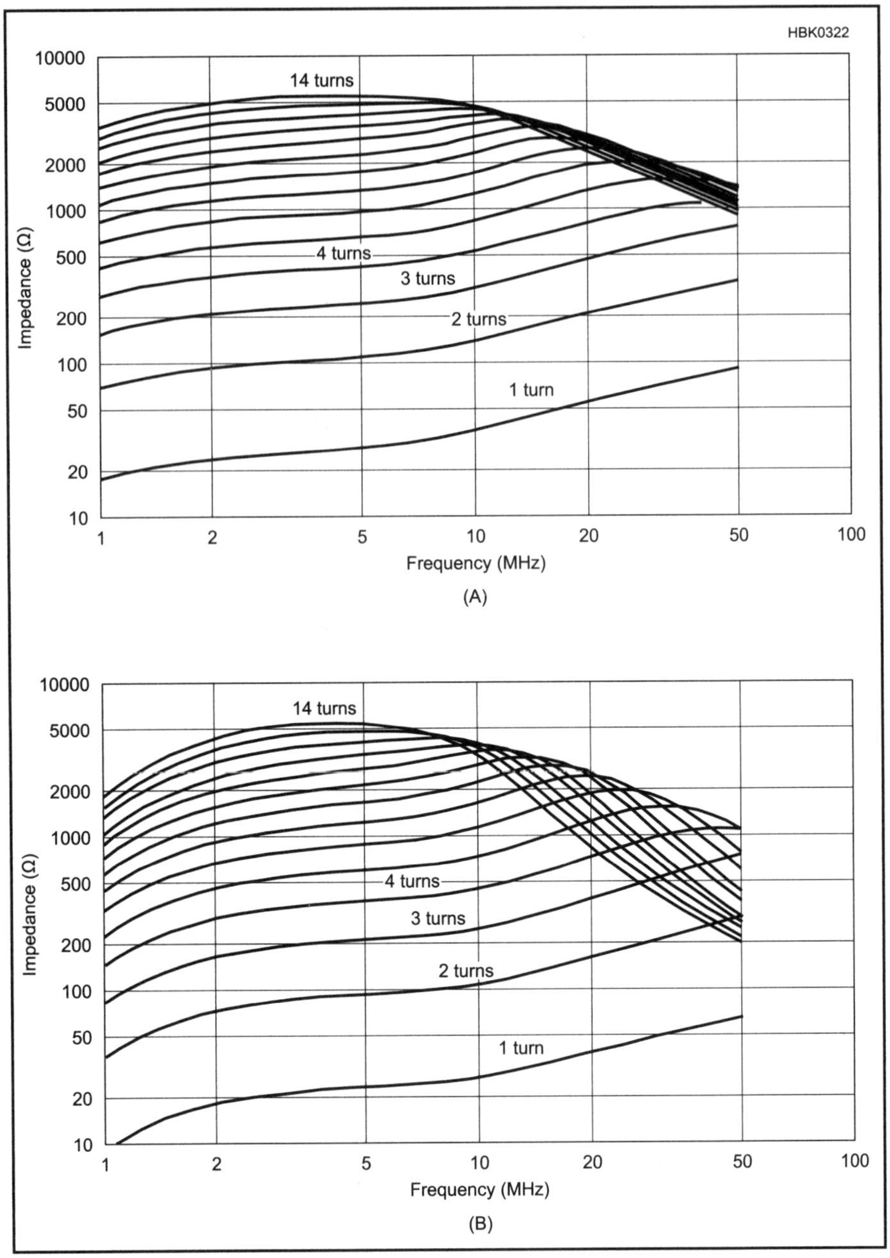

It's the parasitic capacitance from the wire at one end of the cylinder to the wire at the other end, with the ferrite acting as the dielectric. Yes, it's a very small capacitance, but you can see the resonance it causes in the measured data and on the data sheet.

5.5.3 Ferrite Series and Parallel Equivalent Circuits

Let's talk briefly about series and parallel equivalent circuits. Many impedance analyzers express the impedance between their terminals as Z with a phase angle, and the series equivalent R_S and X_S. They could just have easily expressed that same impedance using the parallel equivalent R_P and X_P but R_P and X_P will have values that are numerically different from R_S and X_S. (See the section on series-parallel impedance transformation in the **Electrical Fundamentals** chapter.)

It is important to remember that in a series circuit, the larger value of R_S and X_S has the greatest influence, while in a parallel circuit, the smaller value of R_P and X_P is dominant. In other words, for R_P to dominate, R_P must be small.

Both expressions of the impedance (series or parallel) are correct at any given frequency, but whether the series or parallel representation is most useful will depend on the physics of the device being measured and how that device is used in a circuit. We've just seen, for example, that the parallel equivalent circuit is a more realistic representation of a ferrite choke — the values of R_P, L_P, and C_P will come much closer to remaining constant as frequency changes than if we use the series equivalent. (R_P, L_P and C_P won't be precisely constant though, because the physical properties of all ferrites — permeability, resistivity and permittivity — all vary with frequency.)

But virtually all product data for ferrite chokes is presented as the series equivalent

Figure 5.55 — At A, the impedance of multi-turn chokes on a Type #31 2.4-in. OD toroidal core. At B, the equivalent series resistance of the chokes of (A). (Measured data)

R_S and X_S. Why? First, because it's easy to measure and understand, second, because we tend to forget there is stray capacitance, and third because ferrite beads are most often used as chokes to reduce current in a series circuit! **Figure 5.54A** and Figure 5.54B are both useful representations of the voltage divider formed by a ferrite choke and a small bypass capacitor across the device input. Which we use will depend on what we know about our ferrite.

If we know R_P, L_P and C_P and they are

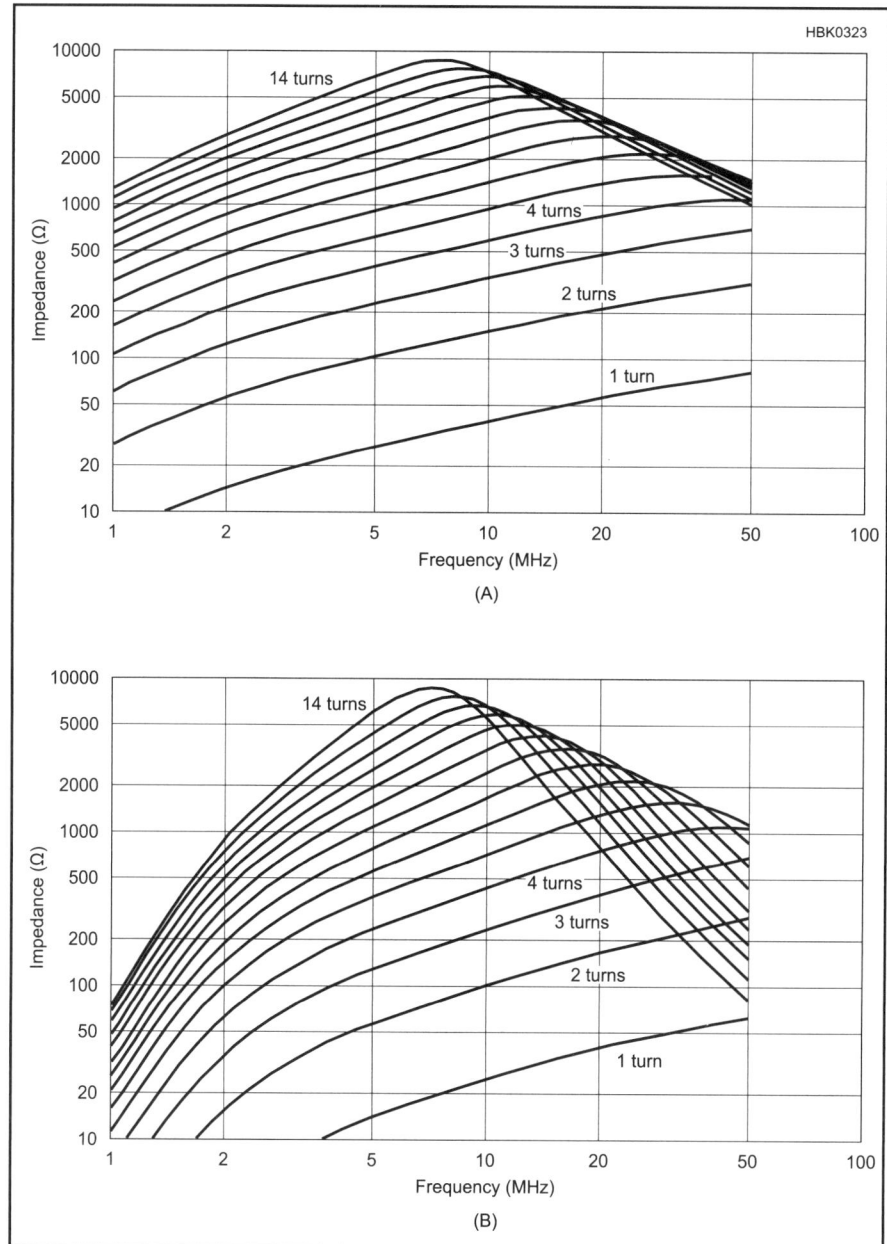

Figure 5.56 — At A, the impedance of multi-turn chokes on a Type #43 2.4-in. OD toroidal core. At B, the equivalent series resistance of the chokes of A. (Measured data).

constant over the frequency range of interest, Figure 5.54A may be more useful, because we can insert values in a circuit model and perhaps tweak the circuit. But if we have a graph of R_S and X_S vs frequency, Figure 5.54B will give us a good answer faster. Because we will most often be dealing with R_S and X_S data, the series circuit equivalents are used most often. Another reason for using R_S and X_S is that the impedance of two or more ferrite chokes in series can be computed simply by adding their R_S and X_S components, just as with any other series impedances! When you look at the data sheet plots of R_S, X_L and Z for a standard ferrite part, you are looking at the series equivalent parameters of their dominant resonance. For most MnZn materials, it is dimensional resonance, while, for most NiZn materials, it is the circuit resonance.

Values for R_P, L_P and C_P for nearly any ferrite choke can be obtained by curve-fitting the data for its parallel-resonance curve. (Self-resonance is discussed earlier in this chapter.) Because the C_P of many practical chokes is quite small and their impedance at resonance is often rather high, they are quite difficult to measure accurately, especially with reflection-based measurement systems. See the **Test Equipment and Measurements** chapter for a simple measurement method that can provide good results. More information on the use of ferrite cores and beads for EMI suppression is available in the chapter on **RF Interference** and in *The ARRL RFI Book*. A thorough treatment of the use of these ferrite materials for EMI suppression is continued in the online publication *A Ham's Guide to RFI, Ferrites, Baluns, and Audio Interfacing* at **k9yc.com/publish.htm**. The use of ferrite beads and cores for transmitting chokes is presented in the **Transmission Lines** chapter.

5.5.4 Type 31 Material

Type #31 material made by Fair-Rite Products is extremely useful as a choke core, especially if some component of your problem occurs below 5 MHz. Measured data for the new material is displayed in **Figs 5.55A** and 5.55B. Compare it with **Figs 5.56A** and 5.56B, which are corresponding plots for the older Type #43 material. By comparison, Type #31 provides nearly 7 dB greater choking impedance at 2 MHz, and at least 3 dB more on 80 meters. At 10 MHz and above, the two materials are nearly equivalent, with Type #43 being about 1 dB better. If your goal is EMI suppression or a feed line choke (a so-called "current balun"), the Type #31 material is the best all round performer to cover all HF bands, and is clearly the material of choice at 5 MHz and below. Between 5 MHz and 20 MHz, Type #43 has a slight edge (about 1 dB), and above 20 MHz they're equivalent. (Baluns are discussed more in the section below on Transmission Line Transformers and in the chapters on **Transmission Lines** and **Antennas**.)

Type #31 material is useful because it exhibits both of the resonances in our equivalent circuit — that is, the dimensional resonance of the core and the resonance of the choke with the lossy permeability of the core material. Below 10 MHz, these two resonances combine (in much the manner of a stagger-tuned IF) to provide significantly greater suppression bandwidth (roughly one octave, or one additional harmonically related ham band). The result is that a single choke on a Type #31 core can be made to provide very good suppression over about 8:1 frequency span, as compared to 4:1 for Type #43. Type #31 also has somewhat better temperature characteristics at HF.

RF Techniques   5.23

5.6 Impedance Matching Networks

An impedance transforming or matching network is one that accepts power from a generator with one characteristic impedance, the source, and delivers virtually all of that power to a load at a different impedance. The simple designs in this section provide matching at only one frequency. More refined methods discussed in the reference texts can encompass a wide band of frequencies.

Both source and load impedances are likely to be complex with both real and imaginary (reactive) parts. The procedures given in this section allow the reader to design the common impedance-matching networks based on the simplification that both the source and load impedance are resistive (with no reactive component). To use these procedures with a complex load or source impedance, the usual method is to place a reactance in series with the impedance that has an equal and opposite reactance to cancel the reactive component of the impedance to be matched. Then treat the resulting purely-resistive impedance as the resistance to be transformed. For example, if a load impedance to be matched is $120 + j\,40\;\Omega$, add capacitive reactance of $-j\,40\;\Omega$ in series with the load, resulting in a load impedance of $120 + j\,0\;\Omega$ so that the following procedures can be used. The series reactance-canceling component may then be combined with the matching network's output component in some configurations.

A set of 14 simple resonant networks, and their equations, is presented in **Figure 5.58**. Note that in these diagrams R_S is the low impedance side and R_L is the high impedance side and that the X values are calculated in the top-down order given.

The formulas for the various networks use and produce values of reactance. To convert the reactances to L and C values, use the formulas

$$C = \frac{1}{2\pi f X_c} \text{ and } L = \frac{X_L}{2\pi f}$$

The program *MATCH.EXE* with the downloadable supplemental material can perform the calculations.

You may wish to review the section on series-parallel impedance transformations in the **Electrical Fundamentals** chapter as those techniques form the basis of impedance-matching network design. There is additional discussion of L networks in the chapters on **Transmission Lines** and of Pi networks in the **RF Power Amplifiers** chapter. These discussions apply to more specific applications of the networks.

5.6.1 L Networks

Perhaps the most common LC impedance transforming network is the L network, so named because it uses two elements — one series element and one parallel — resembling the capital L on its side. There are eight different types of L networks as shown in **Figure**

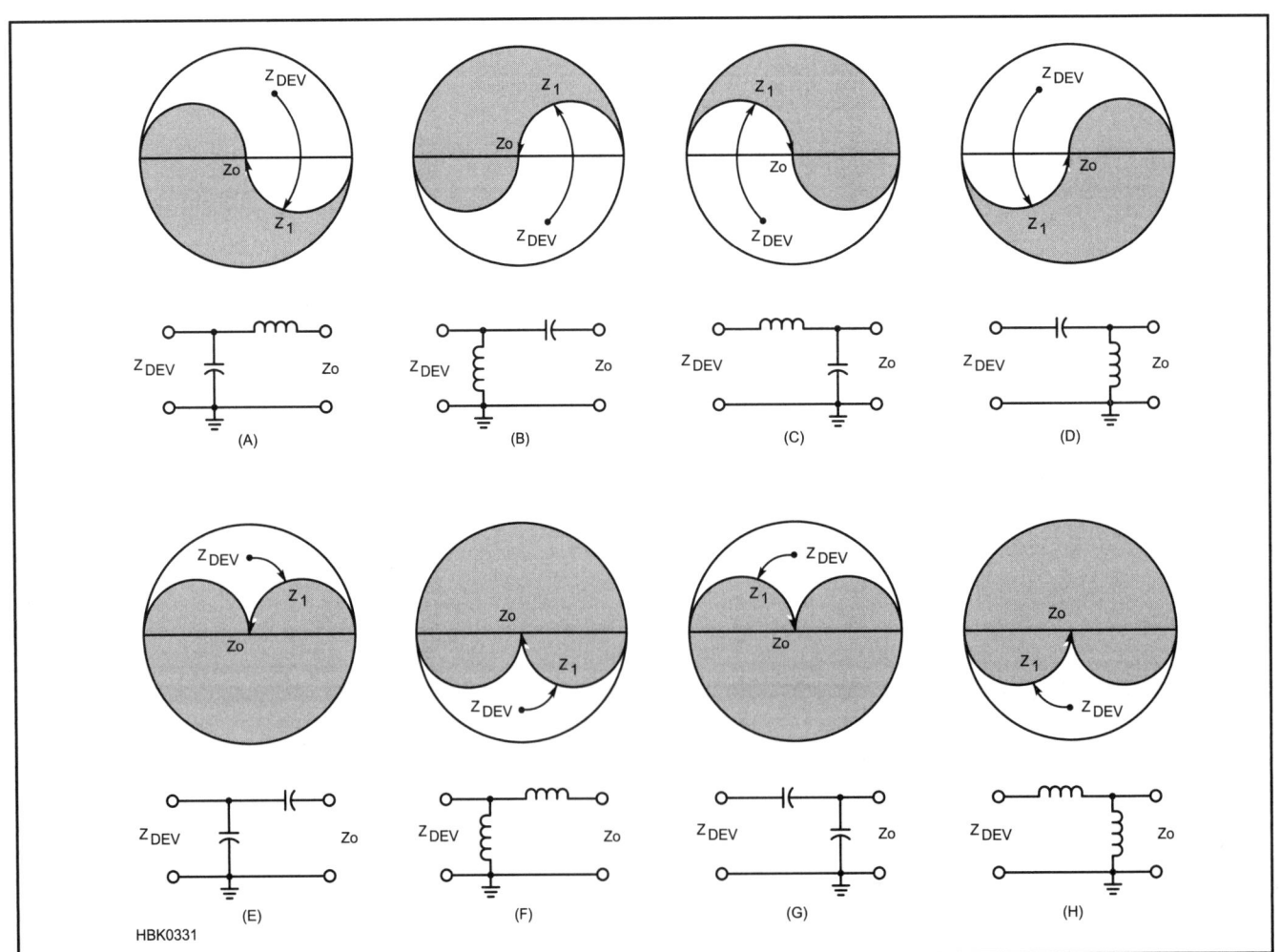

Figure 5.57 — L networks which will match a complex impedance (shown here as Z_{DEV}, the output impedance of a device) to Z_0, a resistive source or load. Impedances within the shaded portion of the simplified Smith Chart cannot be matched by the network. Z_1 represents the impedance that is transformed from Z_{DEV} by the series element.

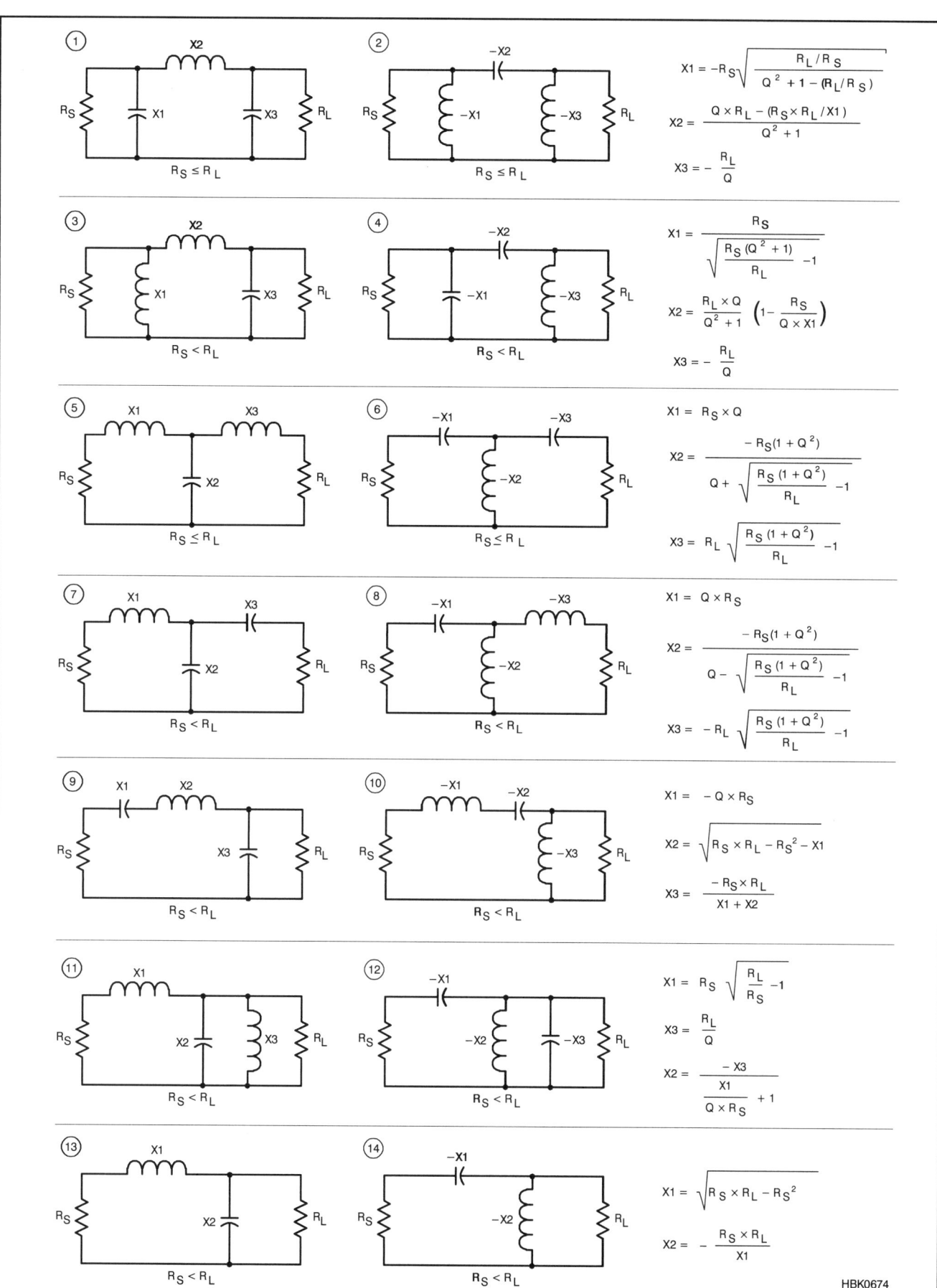

Figure 5.58 — Fourteen impedance transforming networks with their design equations (for lossless components).

5.57. (Types G and H are not as widely used and not covered here.) The simplified Smith Chart sketches show what range of impedance values can be transformed to the required impedance Z_0 and the path on the chart by which the transformation is achieved by the two reactances. (An introductory discussion of the Smith Chart is provided with the downloadable supplemental content, and a detailed treatment is available in *The ARRL Antenna Book*.) Z_{DEV} represents the output impedance of a device, such as a transistor amplifier or any piece of equipment.

The process of transformation works the same in both "directions." That is, a network designed to transform Z_{DEV} to Z_0 will also transform Z_0 to Z_{DEV} if reversed. The L network (and the Pi and T networks discussed below) is *bilateral,* as are all lossless networks.

Purely from the standpoint of impedance matching, the L network can be constructed with inductive or capacitive reactance in the series arm and the performance will be exactly the same in either case. However, the usual case in amateur circuits is to place the inductive reactance in the series arm to act as a low pass filter. Your particular circumstances may dictate otherwise, however. For example, you may find it useful that the series-C/parallel-L network places a dc short circuit across one side of the network while blocking dc current through it.

The design procedure for L network configurations A through F in Figure 5.57 is as follows:

Given the two resistance values to be matched, connect the series arm of the circuit to the smaller of the two (R_S) and the parallel arm to the larger (R_P).

Find the ratio R_P/R_S and the L network's Q:

$$Q = \sqrt{\frac{R_P}{R_S} - 1}$$

Calculate the series reactance $X_S = QR_S$
Calculate the parallel reactance $X_P = R_P/Q$

5.6.2 Pi Networks

Another popular impedance matching network is the Pi network shown in circuits 1 and 2 of Figure 5.58. The Pi network can be thought of as two L networks "back to back." For example, the Pi network in circuit 1 can be split into the L network of circuit 13 on the right and its mirror image on the left. The two inductors in series are combined into the single inductance of the Pi network. There are other forms of the Pi network with different configurations of inductance and capacitance, but the version shown is by far the most common in amateur circuits.

The use of two transformations allows the designer to choose Q for the Pi network, unlike the L network for which Q is determined by the ratio of the impedances to be matched. This is particularly useful for matching amplifier outputs as discussed in the **RF Power Amplifier** chapter because it allows more control of the network's frequency response and of component values. Q must be high enough that $(Q^2 + 1) > (R_1 / R_2)$. If these two quantities are equal, X_{C2} becomes infinite, meaning zero capacitance, and the Pi network reduces to the L network in Figure 5.57A. The design procedure for the Pi network in Figure 5.58 is as follows:

Determine the two resistance values to be matched, $R_1 > R_2$, and select a value for Q. Follow the calculation sequence for circuit 1 or 2 in Figure 5.58.

Calculate the value of the parallel reactance $X_{C1} = R_1 / Q$.

Calculate the value of the parallel reactance X_{C2}

$$X_{C2} = R_2 \sqrt{\frac{R_1/R_2}{Q^2 + 1 - R_1/R_2}}$$

Calculate the value of the series reactance X_L

$$X_L = \frac{QR_1 + R_1 R_2 / X_{C2}}{Q^2 + 1}$$

5.6.3 T Networks

Many amateur transmission line impedance matching units ("antenna tuners") use the version of the T network in circuit 6 of Figure 5.58. The circuits are constructed using variable capacitors and a tapped inductor. This is easier and less expensive to construct than a fully-adjustable version of circuit 5 in which two variable inductors are required. Circuit 5 is especially useful in matching relatively low input impedances from solid-state amplifier outputs to 50-Ω loads with low Q and good harmonic suppression due to the series inductances. Circuit 7 is also useful in solid-state amplifier design as described in the reference texts listed at the end of this chapter.

The T network shown in circuit 5 of Figure 5.58 is especially useful for matching to relatively low impedance from 50-Ω sources with practical components and low Q. Like the Pi network, Q must be high enough that $(Q^2+1) > (R_1/R_2)$. Designing the component values for this network requires the calculation of a pair of intermediate values, A and B, to make the equations more manageable.

Determine the two resistance values to be matched, $R_1 > R_2$, and select a value for Q.

Calculate the intermediate variables A and B

$$A = R_1(Q^2 + 1) \text{ and } B = \sqrt{\frac{A}{R_2} - 1}$$

Calculate the value of the input series reactance $X_{L1} = R_1 Q$.

Calculate the value of the output series reactance $X_{L2} = R_2 B$.

Calculate the value of the parallel reactance $X_C = A / (Q + B)$

Convert the reactances to component values:

$$C = \frac{1}{2\pi f X_c} \text{ and } L = \frac{X_L}{2\pi f}$$

5.6.4 Impedance Inversion

Symmetrical Pi and T networks have the useful property of *impedance inversion* when the reactances of all elements are the same at the design frequency: $X_C = X_L = |X|$, resulting in a Q of 1. For either type of network, the impedance looking into the network, Z_{IN}, will be the load impedance, Z_{OUT}, inverted about X:

$$Z_{IN} = \frac{X^2}{Z_{OUT}}$$

This is the same effect as if the network were replaced with a ¼-wavelength transmission line with $Z_0 = |X|$. Since the network is symmetrical, the inversion occurs in either direction through the network. The result is true only at the frequency for which all reactances are equal.

For example, to invert all impedances about 50 Ω, set X = 50 Ω at the design frequency. The input impedance will then be $50^2/Z_{OUT}$. If $Z = 10 + j10$ Ω is connected to one end of the network, the impedance looking into the other end of the network will be 2500 / (10 + j10) = 125 − j125 Ω.

5.7 RF Transformers

5.7.1 Air-Core Nonresonant RF Transformers

Air-core transformers often function as mutually coupled inductors for RF applications. They consist of a primary winding and a secondary winding in close proximity. Leakage reactances are ordinarily high, however, and the coefficient of coupling between the primary and secondary windings is low. Consequently, unlike transformers having a magnetic core, the turns ratio does not have as much significance. Instead, the voltage induced in the secondary depends on the mutual inductance.

In a very basic transformer circuit operating at radio frequencies, such as in **Figure 5.59**, the source voltage is applied to L1. R_S is the series resistance inherent in the source. By virtue of the mutual inductance, M, a voltage is induced in L2. A current flows in the secondary circuit through the reactance of L2 and the load resistance of R_L. Let X_{L2} be the reactance of L2 independent of L1, that is, independent of the effects of mutual inductance. The impedance of the secondary circuit is then:

$$Z_S = \sqrt{R_L^2 + X_{L2}^2} \qquad (12)$$

where
- Z_S = the impedance of the secondary circuit in ohms,
- R_L = the load resistance in ohms, and
- X_{L2} = the reactance of the secondary inductance in ohms.

The effect of Z_S upon the primary circuit is the same as a coupled impedance in series with L1. Figure 5.60 displays the coupled impedance (Z_P) in a dashed enclosure to indicate that it is not a new physical component. It has the same absolute value of phase angle as in the secondary impedance, but the sign of the reactance is reversed; it appears as a capacitive reactance. The value of Z_P is:

$$Z_P = \frac{(2 \pi f M)^2}{Z_S} \qquad (13)$$

where
- Z_P = the impedance introduced into the primary,
- Z_S = the impedance of the secondary circuit in ohms, and
- $2 \pi f M$ = the mutual reactance between the reactances of the primary and secondary coils (also designated as X_M).

5.7.2 Air-Core Resonant RF Transformers

The use of at least one resonant circuit in place of a pair of simple reactances elimi-

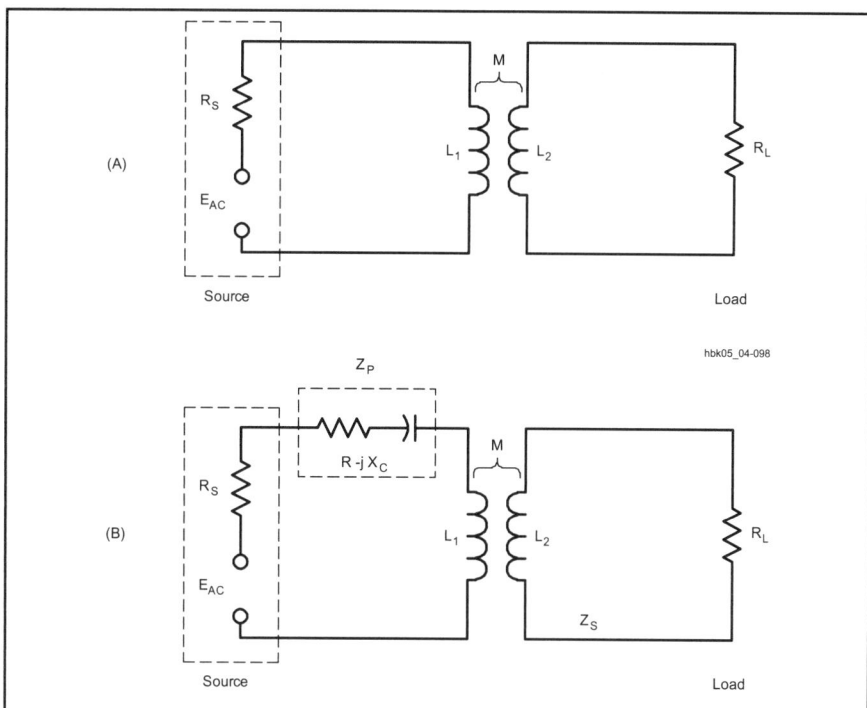

Figure 5.59 — The coupling of a complex impedance back into the primary circuit of a transformer composed of nonresonant air-core inductors.

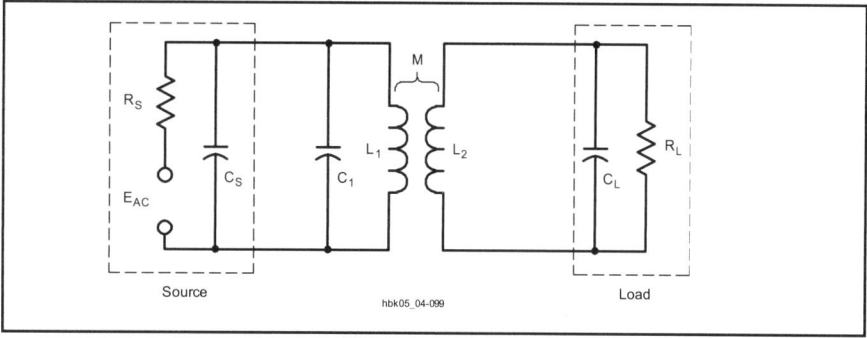

Figure 5.60 — An air-core transformer circuit consisting of a resonant primary circuit and an untuned secondary. R_S and C_S are functions of the source, while R_L and C_L are functions of the load circuit.

nates the reactance from the transformed impedance in the primary. For loaded or operating Q of at least 10, the resistances of individual components is negligible. **Figure 5.60** represents just one of many configurations in which at least one of the inductors is in a resonant circuit. The reactance coupled into the primary circuit is cancelled if the circuit is tuned to resonance while the load is connected. If the reactance of the load capacitance, C_L is at least 10 times any stray capacitance in the circuit, as is the case for low impedance loads, the value of resistance coupled to the primary is

$$R1 = \frac{X_M^2 R_L}{X_2^2 + R_L^2} \qquad (14)$$

where:
- R1 = series resistance coupled into the primary circuit,
- X_M = mutual reactance,
- R_L = load resistance, and
- X_2 = reactance of the secondary inductance.

The parallel impedance of the resonant circuit is just R1 transformed from a series to a parallel value by the usual formula, $R_P = X_2 / R1$.

The higher the loaded or operating Q of the circuit, the smaller the mutual inductance required for the same power transfer. If both the primary and secondary circuits consist of resonant circuits, they can be more loosely coupled than with a single tuned circuit for the same power transfer. At the usual loaded Q of 10 or greater, these circuits are quite selective, and consequently narrowband.

Although coupling networks have to a large measure replaced RF transformer coupling that uses air-core transformers, these circuits are still useful in antenna tuning units and other circuits. For RF work, powdered-iron toroidal cores have generally replaced air-core inductors for almost all applications except where the circuit handles very high power or the coil must be very temperature stable. Slug-tuned solenoid coils for low-power circuits offer the ability to tune the circuit precisely to resonance. For either type of core, reasonably accurate calculation of impedance transformation is possible. It is often easier to experiment to find the correct values for maximum power transfer, however.

5.7.3 Broadband Ferrite RF Transformers

The design concepts and general theory of ideal transformers presented in the **Electrical Fundamentals** chapter apply also to transformers wound on ferromagnetic-core materials (ferrite and powdered iron). As is the case with stacked cores made of laminations in the classic I and E shapes, the core material has a specific permeability factor that determines the inductance of the windings versus the number of wire turns used. (See the earlier discussion on Ferrite Materials in this chapter.)

Toroidal cores are useful from a few hundred hertz well into the UHF spectrum. The principal advantage of this type of core is the self-shielding characteristic. Another feature is the compactness of a transformer or inductor. Therefore, toroidal-core transformers are excellent for use not only in dc-to-dc converters, where tape-wound steel cores are employed, but at frequencies up to at least 1000 MHz with the selection of the proper core material for the range of operating frequencies. Toroidal cores are available from micro-miniature sizes up to several inches in diameter that can handle multi-kW military and commercial powers.

One of the most common ferromagnetic transformers used in amateur circuits is the conventional broadband transformer. Broadband transformers with losses of less than 1 dB are employed in circuits that must have a uniform response over a substantial frequency range, such as a 2- to 30-MHz broadband amplifier. In applications of this sort, the reactance of the windings should be at least four times the impedance that the winding is designed to look into at the lowest design frequency.

Example: What should be the winding reactances of a transformer that has a 300-Ω primary and a 50-Ω secondary load? Relative to the 50-Ω secondary load:

$$X_S = 4\,Z_S = 4 \times 50\,\Omega = 200\,\Omega$$

and the primary winding reactance (X_P) is:

$$X_P = 4\,Z_P = 4 \times 300\,\Omega = 1200\,\Omega$$

The core-material permeability plays a vital role in designing a good broadband transformer. The effective permeability of the core must be high enough to provide ample winding reactance at the low end of the operating range. As the operating frequency is increased, the effects of the core tend to disappear until there are scarcely any core effects at the upper limit of the operating range. The limiting factors for high frequency response are distributed capacity and leakage inductance due to uncoupled flux. A high-permeability core minimizes the number of turns needed for a given reactance and therefore also minimizes the distributed capacitance at high frequencies.

Ferrite cores with a permeability of 850 are common choices for transformers used between 2 and 30 MHz. Lower frequency ranges, for example, 1 kHz to 1 MHz, may require cores with permeabilities up to 2000. Permeabilities from 40 to 125 are useful for VHF transformers. Conventional broadband transformers require resistive loads. Loads with reactive components should use appropriate networks to cancel the reactance.

The equivalent circuit in Figure 5.45 applies to any coil wound on a ferrite core, including transformer windings. (See the section on Ferrite Materials.) However, in the series-equivalent circuit, $\mu'S$ is not constant with frequency as shown in Figure 5.46A and 5.46B. Using the low-frequency value of $\mu'S$ is a useful approximation, but the effects of the parallel R and C should be included. In high-power transmitting and amplifier applications, the resistance R may dissipate some heat, leading to temperature rise in the core. The parasitic capacitances of each winding are shown as C_{PP} and C_{SP} in parallel with the primary and secondary circuits, respectively. These capacitances act to reduce high-frequency response.

Regarding C, there are at least two forms of stray capacitance between windings of a transformer as shown in **Figure 5.61A**; from wire-to-wire through air and from wire-to-wire through the ferrite, which acts as a dielectric material. These capacitances are combined as C_W from the primary to secondary circuits. (Ferrites with low iron content have a relative dielectric constant of approximately 10 to 12.)

Figure 5.61B illustrates one method of transformer construction using a single toroid as the core. The primary of a step-down impedance transformer is wound to occupy the entire core, with the secondary wound over the primary. Conventional broadband transformers provide dc isolation between the primary and secondary circuits.

Winding-to-winding capacitance C_W reduces isolation between primary and secondary circuits. If isolation is an important characteristic of the transformer, then the windings should *not* be layered but separated on the core as in Figure 5.61C. The effect of C_W will increase with increasing frequency. This is a likely path for coupling of HF noise onto Ethernet cables if the network interface uses transformers.

A Faraday shield can be used to minimize

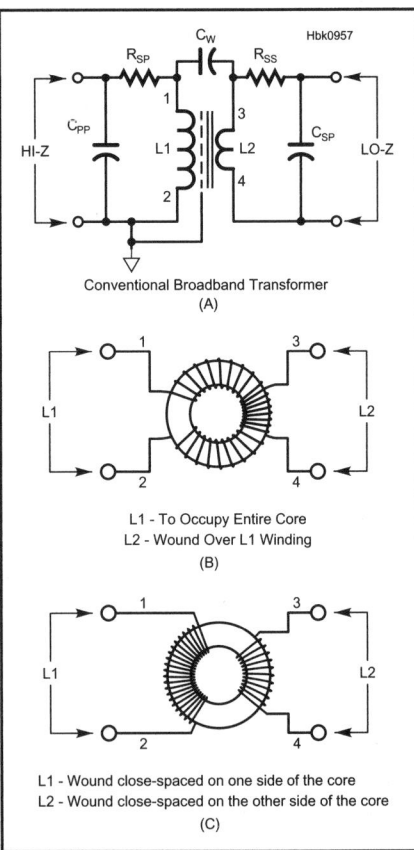

Figure 5.61 — (A) Schematic representation of a conventional broadband transformer wound on a toroid core. A Faraday shield (see text) can also be used to reduce capacitive coupling between the primary and secondary circuits. At (B) a pictorial showing the secondary winding (L2) is wound over the primary winding (L1) which provides very good coupling but low isolation. For designs emphasizing isolation over coupling, wind the transformer as in C with the primary and secondary windings separated on the core.

C_W. It is made of conductive material, such as aluminum foil, that is connected to the circuit reference as in Figure 5.61A. (Faraday shields can also be connected to the secondary circuit reference.) Faraday shields are also used between windings in transformers for use in power, data, and audio circuits to prevent capacitive coupling of noise between windings.

The high voltages encountered in high-impedance-ratio step-up transformers may require that the core be wrapped with glass electrical tape before adding the windings (as an additional protection from arcing and voltage breakdown), especially with ferrite cores that tend to have rougher edges. In addition, high voltage applications should also use wire with high-voltage insulation and a high temperature rating.

The first step in designing the transformer is to select a core of the desired permeability. Convert the required reactances determined earlier into inductance values for the lowest frequency of use. To find the number of turns for each winding, use the A_L value for the selected core and the equation for determining the number of turns:

$$L = \frac{A_L \times N^2}{1000000} \quad (15)$$

where
L = the inductance in mH
A_L = the inductance index in mH per 1000 turns, and
N = the number of turns.

Be certain the core can handle the power by calculating the maximum flux and comparing the result with the manufacturer's guidelines.

$$B_{max} = \frac{E_{RMS} \times 10^8}{4.44 \times A_e \times N \times f} \quad (16)$$

where
B_{max} = the maximum flux density in gauss
E_{RMS} = the voltage across the inductor
A_e = the cross-sectional area of the core in square centimeters
N = the number of turns in the inductor, and
f = the operating frequency in Hz.

(Both equations are from the section on ferrite toroidal inductors in the **Electrical Fundamentals** chapter and are repeated here for convenience.)

Example: Design a small broadband transformer having an impedance ratio of 16:1 for a frequency range of 2.0 to 20.0 MHz to match the output of a small-signal stage (impedance ≈ 500 Ω) to the input (impedance ≈ 32 Ω) of an amplifier.

Since the impedance of the smaller winding should be at least 4 times the lower impedance to be matched at the lowest frequency,

$$X_S = 4 \times 32\,\Omega = 128\,\Omega$$

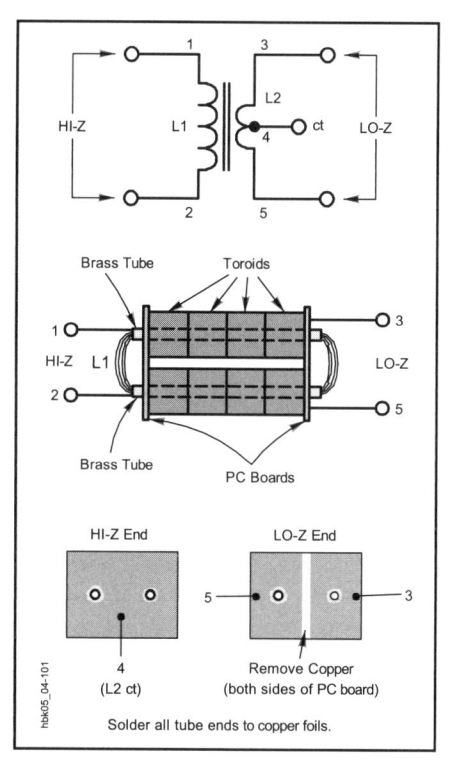

Figure 5.62 — Schematic and pictorial representation of a "binocular" style of conventional broadband transformer. This style is used frequently at the input and output ports of transistor RF amplifiers. It consists of two rows of high-permeability toroidal cores, with the winding passed through the center holes of the resulting stacks.

The inductance of the secondary winding should be

$$L_S = \frac{X_S}{2\pi f} = \frac{128}{6.2832 \times 2.0 \times 10^6\,\text{Hz}}$$

$$= 0.0101\,\text{mH}$$

Select a suitable core. For this low-power application, a ⅜ inch. ferrite core with permeability of 850 is suitable. The core has an A_L value of 420. Calculate the number of turns for the secondary.

$$N_S = 1000\sqrt{\frac{L}{A_L}} = 1000\sqrt{\frac{0.010}{420}}$$

$$= 4.88\,\text{turns}$$

A 5-turn secondary winding should suffice. The primary winding derives from the impedance ratio:

$$N_P = N_S\sqrt{\frac{Z_P}{Z_S}} = 5\sqrt{\frac{16}{1}}$$

$$= 5 \times 4 = 20\,\text{turns}$$

This low-power application will not approach the maximum flux density limits for the core, and #28 AWG enamel wire should both fit the core and handle the currents involved.

A second style of broadband transformer construction appears in **Figure 5.62**. The key elements in this transformer are the stacks of ferrite cores aligned with tubes soldered to pc-board end plates. This style of transformer is suited to high power applications, for example, at the input and output ports of transistor RF power amplifiers. Low-power versions of this transformer can be wound on "binocular" cores having pairs of parallel holes through them.

For further information on conventional transformer matching using ferromagnetic materials, see the **RF Power Amplifiers** chapter. Refer to the **Component Data and References** chapter for more detailed information on available ferrite cores. A standard reference on conventional broadband transformers using ferromagnetic materials is *Ferromagnetic Core Design and Applications Handbook* by Doug DeMaw, W1FB, published by MFJ Enterprises.

NOTES ON TOROID WINDINGS

For a toroidal (cylindrical) core, the number of turns is the number of times the conductor passes through the core. A wire passing once through a cylindrical core constitutes one turn. Likewise, a split or "clamp-on" core that is simply clamped onto a conductor forms a single-turn choke. A wire passing twice through the core is a two-turn choke, even though there is only one pass external to the core.

The inductance of a toroid can be adjusted. If the turns can be pressed closer together or separated a little, inductance variations of a few percent are possible.

In general, all of the flux associated with ferrite inductors (and chokes) is confined to the core material — for all practical purposes, there is no inductive coupling between inductors (or chokes) that are physically adjacent but wound on different cores. Coupling between adjacent coils can be eliminated by placing a Faraday shield between them as discussed earlier in this section.

Toroidal windings do exhibit a small amount of leakage flux. Toroid coils are wound in the form of a helix (screw thread) around the circular length of the core. This means that there is a small component of the flux from each turn that is perpendicular to the circle of the toroid (parallel to the axis through the hole) and is therefore not adequately linked to all the other turns. This effect is responsible for a small leakage flux and the effect is called the "one-turn" effect.

5.8 Noise

The following material was contributed by Paul Wade, W1GHZ. The section on background noise by Joe Taylor, K1JT, is reproduced from his discussion of Earth-Moon-Earth (EME) communications in this books's downloadable supplemental content. Additional discussion of noise measurement is available in the **Test Instruments and Measurements** *chapter and in the Noise Instrumentation document provided with the downloadable supplemental content.*

As anyone who has listened to a receiver suspects, everything in the universe generates noise. In communications, the goal is to maximize the desired signal in relation to the undesired noise we hear. In order to accomplish this goal, it would be helpful to understand where noise originates, how much our own receiver adds to the noise we hear, and how to minimize it.

It is difficult to improve something unless we are able to measure it. Measurement of noise in receivers does not seem to be clearly understood by many amateurs, so this section attempts to explain the concepts and clarify the techniques, and to describe the standard "measure of merit" for receiver noise performance: "noise figure." In addition, the Noise Instrumentation document with the downloadable supplemental content describes how to build your own noise generator for noise figure measurements.

A number of equations are included, but only a few need be used to perform noise figure measurements. The rest are included to as an aid to understanding supported by explanatory text.

5.8.1. Noise Power

The most pervasive source of noise is *thermal noise* (also called *Johnson* or *Johnson-Nyquist noise*), due to the motion of thermally agitated free electrons in a conductor. Since everything in the universe is at some temperature above absolute zero, every conductor must generate noise.

Every resistor (and all conductors have resistance) generates an RMS noise voltage:

$$e = \sqrt{4kTRB} \qquad (17)$$

where R is the resistance, T is the absolute temperature in kelvins (K), B is the bandwidth in hertz, and k is Boltzmann's constant, 1.38×10^{-23} joules /K (or J K^{-1}).

Converting to power, e^2/R, and adjusting for the Gaussian distribution of noise voltage, the noise power generated by the resistor is:

$$P_n = kTB \text{ (watts)} \qquad (18)$$

which is independent of the resistance. Thus, all resistors at the same temperature generate the same noise power.

Thermal noise is *white noise*, meaning that the power density does not vary with frequency, but always has a *power density* or *spectral density* of kT watts/Hz. (The corresponding noise voltage distribution is a *spectral voltage density*, measured in volts / √Hz, spoken as "volts per root hertz".) More important is that the noise power is directly proportional to absolute temperature T, since k is a constant. At the nominal ambient temperature of 290 K, we can calculate this power; converted to dBm, we get the familiar –174 dBm/Hz. Multiply by the bandwidth in hertz to get the available noise power at ambient temperature. The choice of 290 K for ambient might seem a bit cool, since the equivalent 17° C or 62° F would be a rather cool room temperature, but the value 290 makes for an easier-to-remember numeric calculation of $P_n = (1.38 \times 10^{-23} \times 290)$ B = 400×10^{-23} B.

The *instantaneous* noise voltage has a *Gaussian distribution* around the RMS value. The Gaussian distribution has no limit on the peak amplitude so at any instant the noise voltage may have any value from –infinity to +infinity. For design purposes we can use a value that will not be exceeded more than 0.01% of the time. This voltage is 4 times the RMS value, or 12 dB higher, so our system must be able to handle peak powers 12 dB higher than the average noise power if we are to measure noise without errors. (See Pettai in the Reference section.)

5.8.2. Signal to Noise Ratio

Now that we know the noise power in a given bandwidth, we can easily calculate how much signal is required to achieve a desired *signal to noise ratio*, *S/N* or *SNR*. For SSB, perhaps 10 dB SNR is required for good communications; since ambient thermal noise in a 2.5 kHz bandwidth is –140 dBm, calculated as follows:

$$P_n = kTB = 400 \times 10^{-23} \times 2500$$
$$= 1.0 \times 10^{-17} \text{ W}$$

dBm = 10 log ($P_n \times 1000$) [multiplying watts by 1000 converts to milliwatts]

The signal power must be 10 dB larger, so minimum signal level of –130 dBm is required for a 10 dB S/N. This represents the noise and signal power levels at the antenna. We are then faced with the task of amplifying the signal without degrading SNR.

5.8.3. Noise Temperature

There are many types of noise, but most have similar characteristics to thermal noise and are often added together, creating a single equivalent noise source whose output power per unit of bandwidth is P_N. The *noise temperature* of the source is defined as the temperature T = P_N / k at which a resistor would generate the same noise power per unit of bandwidth as the source. This is a useful way to characterize the various sources of noise in a communications system.

All amplifiers add additional noise to the noise present at their input. The input noise per unit of bandwidth is $N_i = kT_g$, where T_g is the noise temperature at the amplifier's input. Amplified by power gain G, the output noise is kT_gG. The additional noise contributed by the amplifier can also be represented as a noise temperature, T_n. The noise power added by the amplifier, kT_n, is then added to the amplified input noise to produce a total output noise:

$$N_o = kT_gG + kT_n$$

We can treat the amplifier as ideal and noise-free but with an additional noise-generating resistor of temperature $T_e = T_n$ / G at the input so that all sources of noise can be treated as inputs to the amplifier as illustrated by **Figure 5.63**. The output noise is then:

$$N_o = kG (T_g + T_e)$$

The noise added by an amplifier can then be represented as kGT_e, which is amplifier's noise temperature amplified by the amplifier gain. T_e is sometimes referred to as *excess temperature*.

Note that while the noise temperature of a resistor is the same as its physical temperature, the noise temperature of a device such as a diode or transistor can be many times the physical temperature.

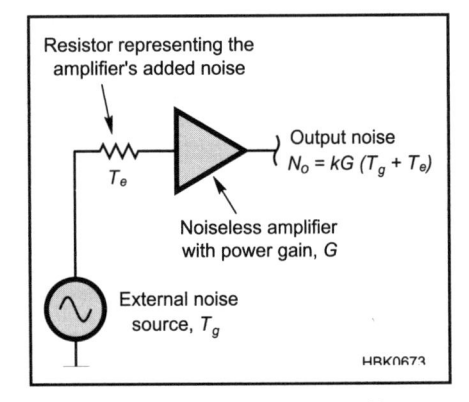

Figure 5.63 — The noise generated by an amplifier can be represented as an external resistor with a noise temperature of T_e connected at the input of a noiseless amplifier.

SINAD

Signal-to-noise and distortion ratio (SINAD) is often used to measure of the quality of a demodulated signal.

$$\text{SINAD} = \frac{P_{signal} + P_{noise} + P_{distortion}}{P_{noise} + P_{distortion}} \quad (19)$$

where P is an average power. SINAD is usually expressed in dB and is often used as a condition at which a receiver's RF sensitivity is measured. For example: a sensitivity of 0.1 μV for 12 dB SINAD. (A thorough explanation of SINAD and several related terms such as THD is provided by the Analog Devices tutorial MT-003 by Kester listed in the References section of this chapter.)

5.8.4. Noise Factor and Noise Figure

The *noise factor*, F, of an amplifier is the ratio of the total noise output of an amplifier with an input T_g of 290 K to the noise output of an equivalent noise-free amplifier. A more useful definition is to calculate it from the excess temperature T_e:

$$F = 1 + T_e / T_g, \text{ where } T_g = 290 \text{ K} \quad (20)$$

It is often more convenient to work with *noise figure*, NF, the logarithm of noise factor expressed in dB:

$$\text{NF} = 10 \log (1 + T_e / T_g) = 10 \log F \quad (21)$$

$$F = \log^{-1}(\text{NF}/10)$$

Expressed in terms of signal, S, and noise power, N, at the input and output of a device:

$$F = (S_{in}/N_{in})/(S_{out}/N_{out}) \text{ and}$$

$$F = G_{noise}/G_{signal}$$

where G_{signal} is the device's power gain and G_{noise} is the device's *noise gain*. If SNR in dB is known at the input and output:

$$\text{NF} = \text{SNR}_{in} - \text{SNR}_{out}$$

If NF or F is known, then T_e may be calculated as:

$$T_e = (F - 1) T_g$$

Typically, T_e is specified for very low noise amplifiers where the NF would be fraction of a dB. NF is used when it seems a more manageable number than thousands of K.

Noise figure is sometimes stated as *input noise figure* to emphasize that all noise sources and noise contributions are converted to an equivalent set of noise sources at the input of a noiseless device. In this way, noise performance can be compared on equal terms across a wide variety of devices.

Noise figure is particularly important at VHF and UHF where atmospheric and other artificial noise is quite low. Typical noise figures of amateur amplifiers range from 1 to 10 dB. Mixers are generally toward the high end of that range. Modern GaAsFET and HEMT preamplifiers are capable of attaining an NF of 0.1 to 0.2 dB at UHF with NF under 1 dB even at 10 GHz.

5.8.5. Losses

We know that any loss or attenuation in a system reduces the signal level. If attenuation also reduced the noise level then we could suppress thermal noise by adding attenuation. We know intuitively that this can't be true — the attenuator or any lossy element has a noise temperature, T_x, which contributes noise to the system while the input noise is being attenuated.

The output noise after a loss L (expressed as ratio) expressed as an equivalent input noise temperature is:

$$T_g' = T_g/L + [(L - 1)/L] T_x$$

If the original source temperature, T_g, is higher than the attenuator temperature, T_x, then the noise contribution is found by adding the loss in dB to the NF. However, for low source temperatures the degradation can be much more dramatic. If we do a calculation for the effect of 1 dB of loss (L = 1.26) on a T_g of 25 K:

$$T_g' = 25/1.26 + (0.26/1.26) \times 290 = 80 \text{ K}$$

The resulting T_g' is 80 K, a 5 dB increase in noise power (or 5 dB degradation of signal to noise ratio). Since noise power = kT and k is a constant, the increase is the ratio of the two temperatures, 80/25, or in dB, 10 log (80/25) = 5 dB.

It is also useful to note that for linear, passive devices, such as resistors or resistive attenuators, noise figure is the same as loss in dB. A resistive attenuator with 6 dB loss has a noise figure of 6 dB which is equal to a noise factor of 4.

5.8.6. Cascaded Amplifiers

If several amplifiers are cascaded, the output noise N_o of each becomes the input noise Tg to the next stage. We can create a single equation for the total system of amplifiers. After removing the original input noise term, we are left with the added noise:

$$N_{added} = (k\,T_{e1}G_1G_2...\,G_N) + (kT_{e2}G_2...\,G_N) + ... + (kT_{eN}G_N)$$

where N is the number of stages cascaded. Substituting in the total gain $G_T = (G_1G_2...G_N)$ results in the total excess noise:

$$T_{eT} = T_{e1} + \frac{T_{e2}}{G_1} + \frac{T_{e2}}{G_1G_2} + ... + \frac{T_{eN}}{G_1G_2...G_{N-1}}$$

with the relative noise contribution of each succeeding stage reduced by the gain of all preceding stages.

The *Friis formula for noise* (a.k.a. the Friis equation) expresses this in terms of noise factor:

$$F = F_1 + \frac{F_2 - 1}{G_1} + \frac{F_3 - 1}{G_1G_2} + ... + \frac{F_N - 1}{G_1G_2...G_{N-1}} \quad (22)$$

Clearly, if the gain of the first stage, G_1, is large, then the noise contributions of the succeeding stages become too small to be significant. In addition, the noise temperature of the first stage is the largest contributor to the overall system noise because it is amplified by all remaining stages. The effect on overall noise figure of adding a low-noise preamplifier ahead of a noisy receiver are illustrated in **Figure 5.64**, in which the system's noise figure changes from 20 dB for the receiver alone to 7.1 dB with the preamplifier added.

Any lossy component of an antenna system, such as the feed line, increases the noise figure at its input by an amount equal to the loss. As a result, it is important to concentrate noise-reduction efforts on the first amplifier or preamplifier in a system. Because noise performance is so important in early stages of cascaded systems such as receivers, low-noise VHF+ preamplifiers are usually mounted at the antenna so that their gain occurs ahead

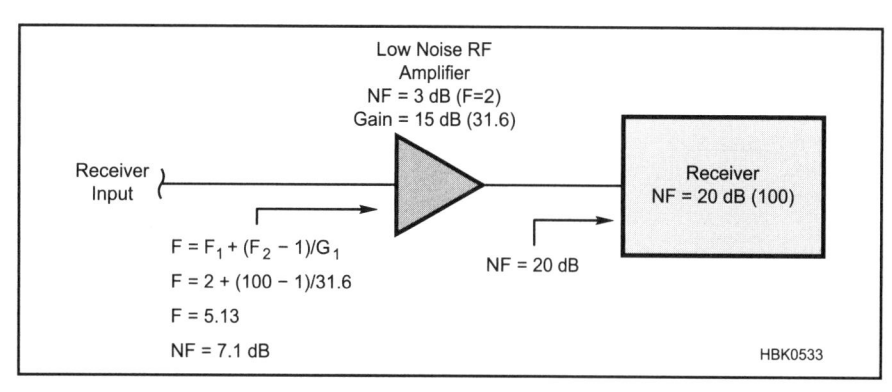

Figure 5.64 — The effect of adding a low-noise preamplifier in front of a noisy receiver system.

of the feed line loss. **Figure 5.65** compares the results of adding a preamplifier before and after 1.5 dB of feed line loss. Moving the preamplifier to the antenna improves the system's noise figure from 2.57 to 1.13 dB.

5.8.7. Antenna Temperature

Antenna temperature, T_A, is a way of describing how much noise an antenna produces. It is not the physical temperature of the antenna because the antenna gathers noise from the environment according to its radiation pattern. If the antenna is directional and looks at a warm environment, T_A will be higher than if the antenna is looking at something cooler.

For example, if a lossless dish antenna is receiving signals from space rather than the warm Earth then the background noise is much lower than the warmer ambient temperature of 290 K or so. The background temperature of the universe has been measured as about 3.2 K. An empirical temperature for a 10 GHz antenna pointing into clear sky is about 6 K, since the antenna must always look through attenuation and temperature of the atmosphere. (See Graves in the Reference section.)

If the antenna's radiation pattern has any sidelobes that must be accounted for in the total noise received by the antenna. This raises the noise temperature. If a warm body, such as the Sun, moves into the antenna's view, the additional *sun noise* will raise T_A as well. If the antenna is looking directly at the Earth, T_A will be close to ambient temperature. As an example, T_A will vary with frequency, but a good EME antenna might have a T_A of around 20 K at UHF and higher frequencies.

5.8.8. Image Response

Most receiving systems use at least one frequency converting mixer which has two responses: the desired frequency and an image frequency above and below the frequency of the local oscillator. If the image response is not filtered out, it will add additional noise to the mixer output. Since most preamps are sufficiently broadband to have significant gain (and thus, noise output) at both the desired frequency, $G_{desired}$, and at the image frequency, G_{image}, an image filter must be placed between the preamplifier and the mixer. The total NF including image response is:

$$\text{NF} = 10 \log \left[\left(\frac{1 + T_e}{T_0} \right) \left(1 + \frac{G_{image}}{G_{desired}} \right) \right] \quad (23)$$

assuming equal noise bandwidth for the desired and image responses.

Without any filtering, $G_{image} = G_{desired}$ so $G_{image}/G_{desired} = 1$, doubling the noise figure, which is the same as adding 3 dB. Thus, without any image rejection, the overall

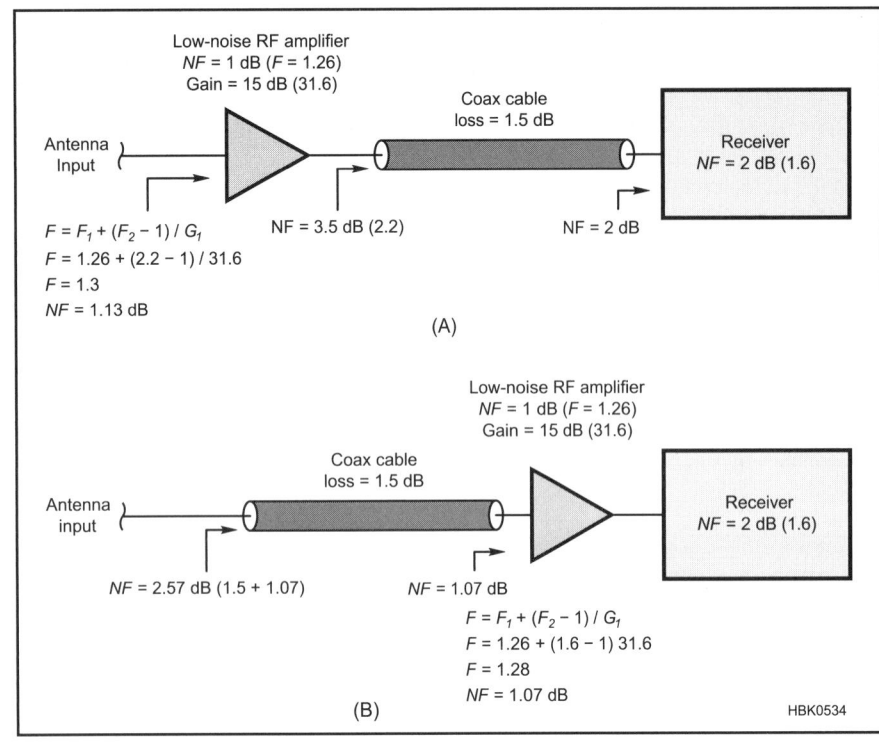

Figure 5.65 — The effect of adding a low-noise preamplifier at the antenna (A) compared to adding it at the receiver input (B).

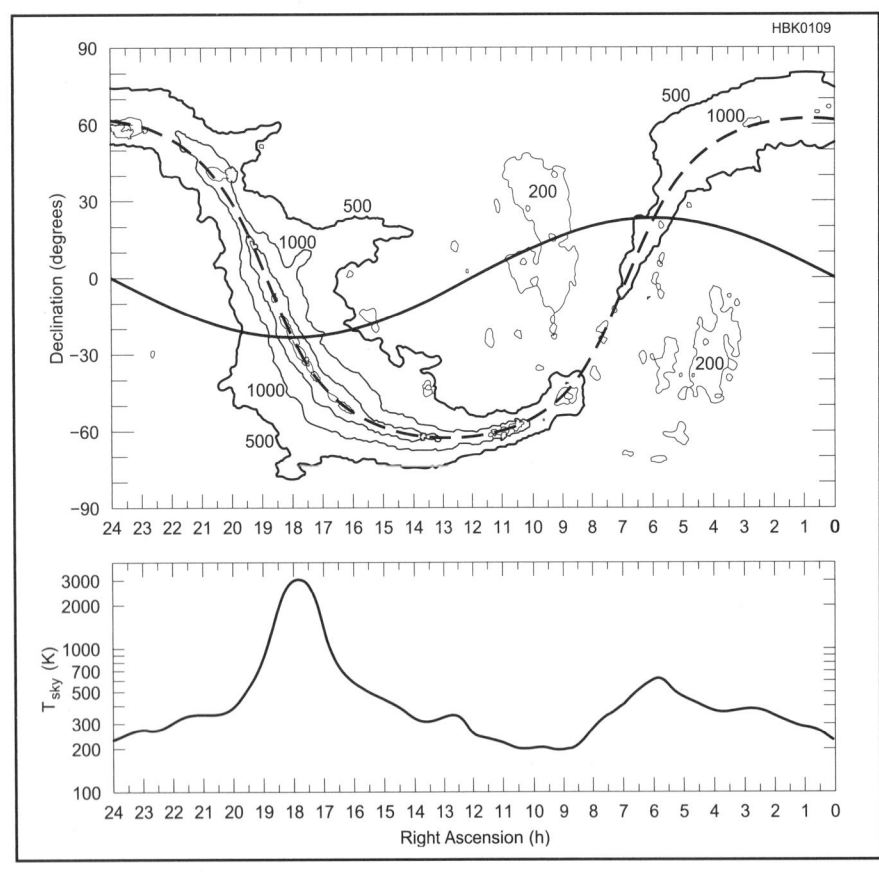

Figure 5.66 — Top: All-sky contour map of sky background temperature at 144 MHz. The dashed curve indicates the plane of our galaxy, the Milky Way; the solid sinusoidal curve is the plane of the ecliptic. The sun follows a path along the ecliptic in one year; the Moon moves approximately along the ecliptic (± 5°) each month. Map contours are at noise temperatures 200, 500, 1000, 2000 and 5000 K. Bottom: One-dimensional plot of sky background temperature at 144 MHz along the ecliptic, smoothed to an effective beamwidth of 15°.

noise figure is at least 3 dB regardless of the NF of the preamplifier. For the image to add less than 0.1 dB to the overall NF, gain at the image frequency must be at least 16 dB lower than at the operating frequency.

As the state of the art improves beyond the typical numbers in this and previous sections, system performance also improves. The very best low-noise preamplifiers today have noise figures as low as 0.2 dB, or a T_r of about 14 K, at UHF and 1296 MHz. The best EME dishes can have a T_a in the neighborhood of 20 K at 1296 MHz when pointed at clear sky. Thus the potential T_{sys} is perhaps 40 K. At these low noise temperatures any small loss or stray noise is significant — a loss of just 0.2 dB will reduce the signal to noise ratio by 1 dB, and low SNR communications such as EME rarely have many dB to spare. The preamp must be right at the antenna for optimum performance, and have sufficient gain so that subsequent stages have little effect.

5.8.9. Background Noise

A received signal at VHF and higher frequencies necessarily competes with noise generated in the receiver as well as that picked up by the antenna, including contributions from the warm Earth, the atmosphere, the lunar surface, the diffuse galactic and cosmic background and possibly the Sun and other sources, filling the whole sky. If P_n is the total noise power collected from all such noise sources expressed in dBW, we can write the expected signal-to-noise ratio of a communications link as

$$SNR = P_r - P_n = P_t + G_t + L + G_r - P_n \quad (24)$$

where P_r is received power, P_n is noise power, P_t is transmitted power, G_t of the transmitting antennas, L is *isotropic path loss*, and G_r is the gain of the receiving antennas. All powers are expressed in dBW and all gains in dBi. (Isotropic path loss is explored further in the material on Earth-Moon-Earth (EME) communications in this book's downloadable supplemental material on **Space Communications**.)

Since isotropic path loss L is essentially fixed by choice of a frequency band, optimizing the signal-to-noise ratio generally involves trade-offs designed to maximize P_r and minimize P_n — subject, of course, to such practical considerations as cost, size, maintainability, and licensing constraints.

It is convenient to express P_n (in dBW) in terms of an equivalent system noise temperature T_s in kelvin (K), the receiver bandwidth B in Hz, and Boltzmann's constant k = 1.38 × 10^{-23} J K^{-1}:

$$P_n = 10 \log (kT_sB)$$

The system noise temperature may in turn be written as

$$T_s = T_r + T_a$$

Here T_r is receiver noise temperature, related to the commonly quoted noise figure (NF) in dB by

$$T_r = 290 \, (10^{\,0.1NF} - 1)$$

Antenna temperature T_a includes contributions from all noise sources in the field of view, weighted by the antenna pattern. Sidelobes are important, even if many dB down from the main beam, because their total solid angle is large and therefore they are capable of collecting significant unwanted noise power.

At VHF the most important noise source is diffuse background radiation from our galaxy, the Milky Way. An all-sky map of noise temperature at 144 MHz is presented in the top panel of **Figure 5.66**. This noise is strongest along the plane of the galaxy and toward the galactic center. Galactic noise scales as frequency to the −2.6 power, so at 50 MHz the temperatures in Figure 5.66 should be multiplied by about 15, and at 432 divided by 17. At 1296 MHz and above

Table 5.2
Typical Contributions to System Noise Temperature

Freq (MHz)	CMB (K)	Atm (K)	Moon (K)	Gal (K)	Side (K)	T_a (K)	T_r (K)	T_s (K)
50	3	0	0	2400	1100	3500	50	3500
144	3	0	0	160	100	260	50	310
222	3	0	0	50	50	100	50	150
432	3	0	0	9	33	45	40	85
902	3	0	1	1	30	35	35	70
1296	3	0	2	0	30	35	35	70
2304	3	0	4	0	30	37	40	77
3456	3	1	5	0	30	40	50	90
5760	3	3	13	0	30	50	60	110
10368	3	10	42	0	30	85	75	160
24048	3	70	170	0	36	260	100	360

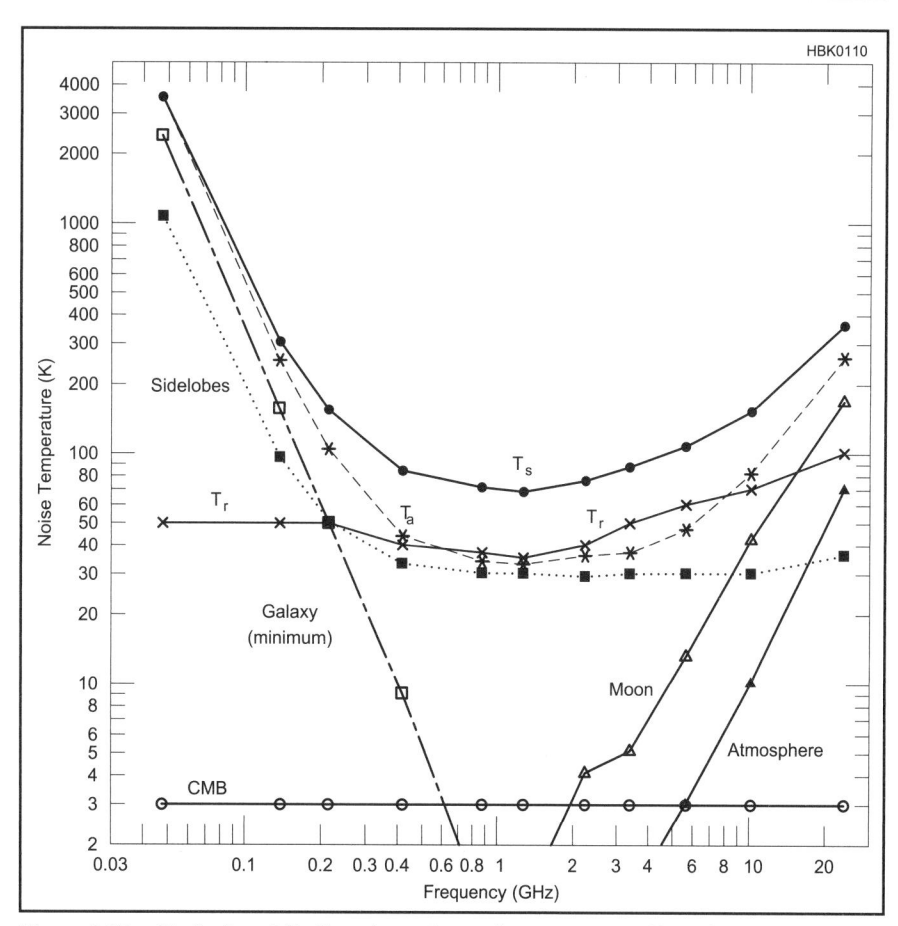

Figure 5.67 — Typical contributions to system noise temperature T_s as function of frequency. See text for definitions and descriptions of the various sources of noise.

galactic noise is negligible in most directions. (See the previously mentioned downloadable supplemental material on EME for the effects of lunar noise.)

The galactic background (GB) is a factor for HF reception as well. For daytime communications, it is less obvious due to the contributions of daytime band noise. Somewhere above 10 MHz, however, what today's quiet HF receivers hear at night becomes dominated by the GB. The frequency at which GB noise overtakes band noise depends on sunspot activity, the strength of atmospheric noise sources such as storms, geomagnetic conditions, the position of the galaxy in the sky, and the antenna's radiation pattern.

The GB has a negative spectral index, meaning it gets weaker with increasing frequency, but is still strong in the 15, 17, and 20 meter bands. Below 10 MHz the GB continues to increase, peaking around 3 MHz, but ionospheric attenuation increases with decreasing frequency, making it less of a factor than atmospheric noise. (The article "The Galactic Background in the Upper HF Band" by Dave Typinksi, AJ4CO discusses the GB at HF and is available with this book's downloadable supplemental content.)

By definition the Sun also appears to an observer on Earth to move along the ecliptic, and during the day solar noise can add significantly to P_n if the antenna has pronounced sidelobes. At frequencies greater than about 5 GHz the Earth's atmosphere also contributes significantly. An ultimate noise floor of 3 K, independent of frequency, is set by cosmic background radiation that fills all space. A practical summary of significant contributions to system noise temperature for the amateur bands 50 MHz through 24 GHz is presented in Table 5.2 and Figures 5.67 and 5.68.

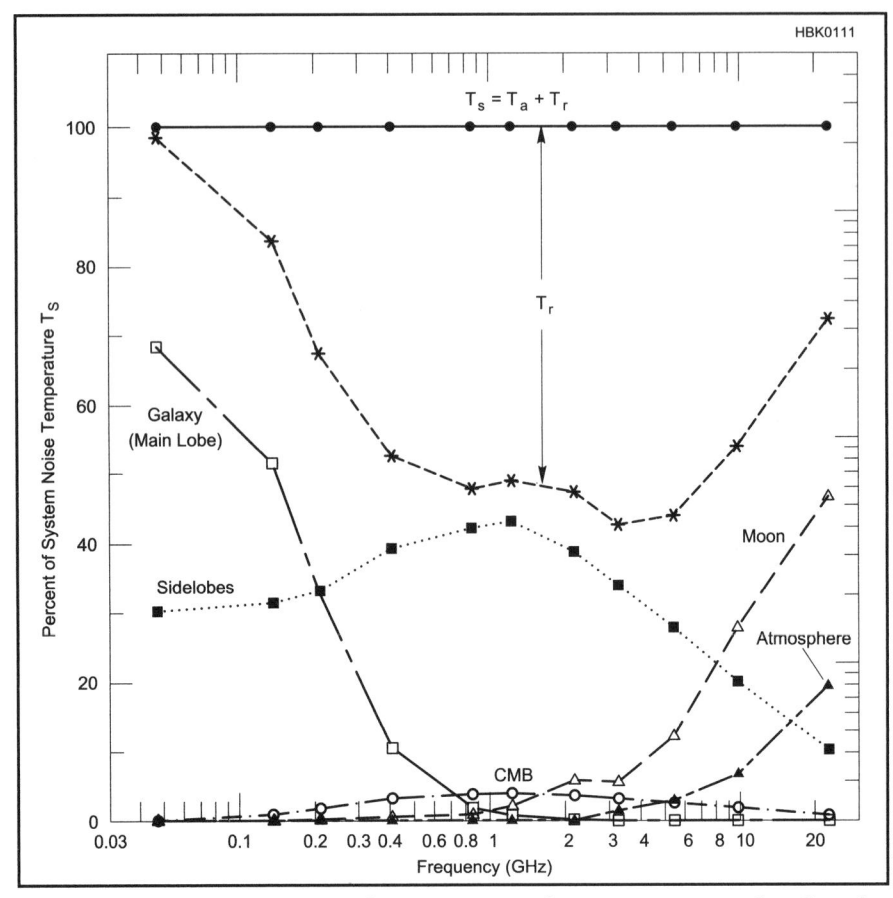

Figure 5.68 — Percentage contributions to system noise temperature as a function of frequency.

5.9 Two-Port Networks

A *two-port network* is one with four terminals. The terminals are arranged into pairs, each being called a *port*. The general network schematic is shown in **Figure 5.69**. The input port is characterized by input voltage and current, V_1 and I_1, and the output is described by V_2 and I_2. By convention, currents into the network are usually considered positive.

Many devices of interest have three terminals rather than four. Two-port methods are used with these by choosing one terminal to be common to both input and output ports. The two-port representations of the common emitter, common base and common collector connections of the bipolar transistor are shown in **Figure 5.70**. Similar configurations may be used with FETs, vacuum tubes, ICs or passive networks.

The general concepts of two-port theory are applicable to devices with a larger number of terminals. The theory is expandable to any number of ports. Alternatively, the

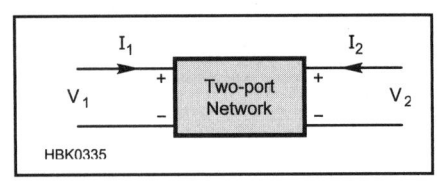

Figure 5.69 — General configuration of a two-port network. Note the voltage polarities and direction of currents.

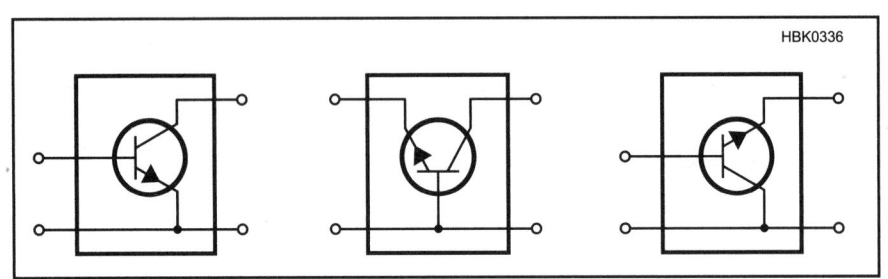

Figure 5.70 — Two-port representations of the common emitter, common base and common collector amplifiers.

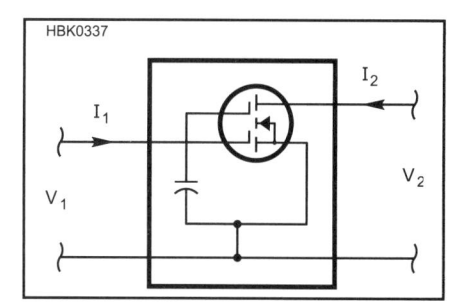

Figure 5.71 — A dual-gate MOSFET treated as a three-terminal device in a two-port network.

bias on some terminals can be established with attention fixed only upon two ports of a multi-element device. An example would be a dual-gate MOSFET in a common-source configuration as shown in **Figure 5.71**. The input port contain the source and gate 1 while the output port contains the source and drain leads. The fourth device terminal, gate 2, has a fixed bias potential and is treated as an ac ground. Signal currents at this terminal are ignored in the analysis.

5.9.1 Two-Port Parameters

There are four variables associated with any two-port network; two voltages and two currents. These are signal components. Any two variables may be picked as independent. The remaining variables are then dependent variables. These are expressed as an algebraic linear combination of the two independent quantities. The following overview are intended for definition purposes. A complete discussion of the use of two-port parameters can be found in the reference texts at the end of this chapter and examples of their use in RF circuit design in Hayward's *Introduction to Radio Frequency Design*.

Y AND Z PARAMETERS

Assume that the two voltages are chosen as independent variables. The two currents are then expressed as linear combinations of the voltages, $I_1 = K_a V_1 + K_b V_2$ and $I_2 = K_c V_1 + K_d V_2$. The constants of proportionality, K_a through K_d, have the dimensions of admittance. The usual representation is

$I_1 = y_{11} V_1 + y_{12} V_2$
$I_2 = y_{21} V_1 + y_{22} V_2$

The independent and dependent variable sets are column vectors, leading to the equivalent matrix representation

$$\begin{pmatrix} I_1 \\ I_2 \end{pmatrix} = \begin{pmatrix} y_{11} & y_{12} \\ y_{21} & y_{22} \end{pmatrix} \begin{pmatrix} V_1 \\ V_2 \end{pmatrix} \quad (25)$$

The y matrix for a two-port network uniquely describes that network. The set of y_{11} through y_{22} are called the two-port network's *Y parameters* or *admittance parameters*. Consider the y parameters from an experimental viewpoint. The first y parameter, y_{11}, is the input admittance of the network with V_2 set to zero. Hence, it is termed the *short-circuit input admittance*. y_{21} is the *short-circuit forward transadmittance*, the reciprocal of transconductance. Similarly, if V_1 is set to zero, realized by short circuiting the input, y_{22} is the *short-circuit output admittance* and y_{12} is the *short-circuit reverse transadmittance*.

The matrix subscripts are sometimes replaced by letters. The set of y parameters can be replaced by y_i, y_r, y_f, and y_o where the subscripts indicate respectively input, reverse, forward, and output. The subscripts are sometimes modified further to indicate the connection of the device. For example, the short circuit forward transfer admittance of a common emitter amplifier would be y_{21e} or y_{fe}.

The y parameters are only one set of two-port parameters. The open-circuited *Z parameters* or *impedance parameters* result if the two currents are treated as independent variables

$$\begin{pmatrix} V_1 \\ V_2 \end{pmatrix} = \begin{pmatrix} z_{11} & z_{12} \\ z_{21} & z_{22} \end{pmatrix} \begin{pmatrix} I_1 \\ I_2 \end{pmatrix} \quad (26)$$

The parameter sets describe the same device; hence, they are related to each other. If the KVL equations are multiplied by y_{12} and the resulting equations subtracted, the result is the input voltage as a function of the currents

$$V_1 = \frac{I_1 y_{22} - y_{12} I_2}{y_{11} y_{22} - y_{12} y_{21}}$$

A similar procedure is used to find the output voltage as a function of the currents, leading to the general relationships

$z_{11} = \dfrac{y_{22}}{\Delta y} \quad z_{12} = \dfrac{-y_{12}}{\Delta y}$

$z_{21} = \dfrac{-y_{21}}{\Delta y} \quad z_{22} = \dfrac{y_{11}}{\Delta y}$

where Δy is the determinant of the y matrix, $y_{11} y_{22} - y_{12} y_{21}$. The inverse transformations, yielding the y parameters when z parameters are known, are exactly the same except that the y_{jk} and z_{jk} values are interchanged. The similarity is useful when writing transformation programs for a programmable calculator or computer.

H PARAMETERS

The *H parameters* or *hybrid parameters* are defined if the input current and output voltage are selected as independent variables

$$\begin{pmatrix} V_1 \\ I_2 \end{pmatrix} = \begin{pmatrix} h_{11} & h_{12} \\ h_{21} & h_{22} \end{pmatrix} \begin{pmatrix} I_1 \\ V_2 \end{pmatrix} \quad (27)$$

The input term, h_{11}, is an impedance, while h_{22} represents an output admittance. The forward term, h_{21}, is the ratio of the output to the input current, beta for a bipolar transistor. The reverse parameter, h_{12}, is a voltage ratio. The mixture of dimensions accounts for the "hybrid" name of the set.

SCATTERING (S) PARAMETERS

The two-port parameters presented above deal with four simple variables; input and output voltage and current at the ports. The variables are interrelated by appropriate matrices. The choice of which matrix is used depends upon which of the four variables are chosen to be independent.

There is no reason to limit the variables to simple ones. Linear combinations of the simple variables are just as valid. The more complicated variables chosen should be linearly independent and, ideally, should have some physical significance.

A transformation to other variables is certainly not new. For example, logarithmic transformations such as the dB or dBm are so common that we used them interchangeably with the fundamental quantities without even mentioning that a transformation has occurred. Such a new viewpoint can be of great utility in working with transmission line when an impedance is replaced by a reflection coefficient, $\Gamma = (Z - Z_0) / (Z + Z_0)$.

Scattering parameters or *S parameters* are nothing more than a repeat of this viewpoint. Instead of considering voltages and currents to be the fundamental variables, we use four "voltage waves." They are interrelated through an appropriate matrix of s parameters.

Figure 5.72 shows the traditional two-port network and an alternate one with voltage

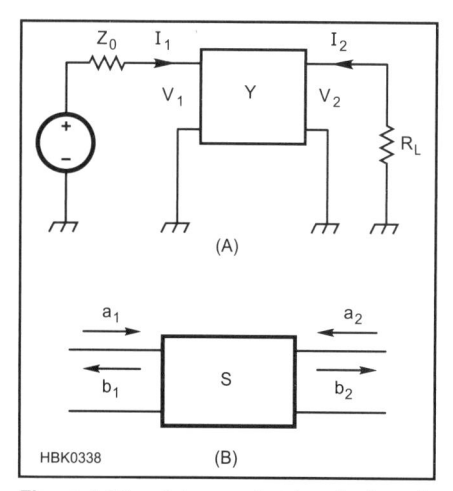

Figure 5.72 — A two-port network viewed as being driven by voltages and currents (A) or voltage waves (B). The voltages and currents are related by Y parameters while the voltage waves are related by scattering or S parameters.

RF Techniques 5.35

waves incident on and reflected from the ports. The voltage waves are defined with the letters a_1, b_1, a_2, and b_2. The a waves are considered to be incident waves on the parts and are the independent variables. The b waves are the result of reflection or "scattering" and are the dependent variables. The waves are related to voltages and currents and defined with respect to a characteristic impedance, Z_0.

The scattered waves are related to the incident ones with a set of linear equations just as the port currents were related to the port voltages with y parameters. The relating equations are

$$b_1 = S_{11}a_1 + S_{12}a_2$$
$$b_2 = S_{21}a_1 + S_{22}a_2$$

or, in matrix form

$$\begin{pmatrix} b_1 \\ b_2 \end{pmatrix} = \begin{pmatrix} S_{11} & S_{12} \\ S_{21} & S_{22} \end{pmatrix} \begin{pmatrix} a_1 \\ a_2 \end{pmatrix} \qquad (28)$$

Consider the meaning of S_{11}. If the incident wave at the output, a_2, is set to zero, the set of equations 27 reduce to $b_1 = S_{11}a_1$ and $b_2 = S_{21}a_1$. S_{11} is the ratio of the input port reflected wave to the incident one. This reduces, using the defining equations for a_1 and b_1 to

$$S_{11} = \frac{Z - Z_0}{Z + Z_0} \qquad (29)$$

This is the *input port reflection coefficient*. Similarly, S_{21} is the voltage wave emanating from the output as the result of an incident wave at the network input. In other words, S_{21} represents a forward gain. The other two S parameters have similar significance. S_{22} is the *output reflection coefficient* when looking back into the output port of the network with the input terminated in Z_0. S_{12} is the reverse gain if the output is driven and the signal at the input port detected.

The reflection coefficient nature of S parameters makes them especially convenient for use in design and specification and even more so when displayed on a Smith Chart.

5.9.2 Return Loss

Although SWR as described in the **Transmission Lines** chapter is usually used by amateurs to describe the relationship between a transmission line's characteristic impedance and a terminating impedance, the engineering community generally finds it more convenient to use *return loss, RL*, instead.

Return loss and SWR measure the same thing — how much of the incident power, P_{INC}, in the transmission line is transferred to the load and how much is reflected by it, P_{REFL} — but state the result differently.

$$\text{Return Loss(dB)} = -10 \log\left(\frac{P_{REFL}}{P_{INC}}\right) \qquad (30)$$

Because P_{REFL} is never greater than P_{FWD}, RL is always positive. The more positive RL, the less the amount of power reflected from the load compared to forward power. If all the power is transferred to the load because $Z_L = Z_0$, RL = ∞ dB. If none of the power is transferred to the load, such as at an open- or short-circuit, RL = 0 dB. (You may encounter negative values for RL in literature or data sheets. Use the absolute magnitude of these values — the negative value does not indicate power gain.)

RL can also be calculated directly from power ratios, such as dBm (decibels with respect to 1 mW) or dBW (decibels with respect to 1 watt). In this case, RL = $P_{INC} - P_{REFL}$ because the logarithm has already been taken in the conversion to dBm or dBW. (Ratios in dB are computed by subtraction, not division.) For example, if P_{INC} = 10 dBm and P_{REFL} = 0.5 dBm, RL = 10 - 0.5 = 9.5 dB. Both power measurements must have the same units (dBm, dBW, and so on) for the subtraction to yield the correct results — for example, dBW can't be subtracted from dBm directly.

Since SWR and RL measure the same thing — reflected power as a fraction of forward power — they can be converted from one to the other. Start by converting RL back to a power ratio:

$$\frac{P_{REFL}}{P_{INC}} = \log^{-1}(-0.1 \times RL) \qquad (31)$$

Now use the equation for computing SWR from forward and reflected power (see the **Transmission Lines** chapter):

$$SWR = \frac{\left[1 + \sqrt{\frac{P_{REFL}}{P_{INC}}}\right]}{\left[1 - \sqrt{\frac{P_{REFL}}{P_{INC}}}\right]} \qquad (32)$$

SWR can also be converted to RL by using the equation for power ratio in terms of SWR:

$$\frac{P_{REFL}}{P_{INC}} = \left[\frac{SWR - 1}{SWR + 1}\right]^2 \qquad (33)$$

Then convert to RL using equation 30.

5.10 RF Techniques Glossary

Arc — Current flow through an insulator due to breakdown from excessive voltage.

Balun — A device that transfers power between *bal*anced and *un*balanced systems, sometimes transforming the impedance level as well (see also **unun**).

Bead — Hollow cylinder of magnetic material through which a wire is threaded to form an inductor.

Bilateral — A network that operates or responds in the same manner regardless of the direction of current flow in the network.

Choke balun — see **current balun**.

Core — Magnetic material around which wire is wound or through which it is threaded to form an inductor.

Current balun — A balun that transfers power from an unbalanced to a balanced system by forcing current flow in the balanced system to be balanced as well (also called a **choke balun**).

Dielectric strength — The rated ability of an insulator to withstand voltage.

Distributed element — Electronic component whose effects are spread out over a significant distance, area or volume.

Dynamic resistance — The change in current in response to a small change in voltage.

Equivalent Series Inductance (ESL) — A capacitor's parasitic inductance.

Ferrite — A ferromagnetic ceramic.

Gain-bandwidth product — The frequency at which a device's gain drops unity. Below that frequency the product of the device's gain and frequency tends to be constant.

Hybrid-pi — High-frequency model for a bipolar transistor.

Impedance inversion — Dividing a characteristic impedance by the ratio of the impedance to be inverted to the

characteristic impedance. For example, 25 Ω inverted about 50 Ω is 100 Ω and 200 Ω inverted about 50 Ω is 12.5 Ω.
Insertion loss (IL) — The loss inherent in a circuit due to parasitic resistance.
Inter-electrode capacitance — Capacitance between the internal elements of a semiconductor or vacuum tube.
Lumped element — Electronic component that exists at a single point.
Mix — The chemical composition of a ferrite or powdered-iron material (also called **type**).
Noise — Any unwanted signal, usually refers to signals of natural origins or random effects resulting from interfering signals.
Noise factor (F) — The amount by which noise at the output of a device is greater than that at the input multiplied by the gain of the device. A measure of how much noise is generated by a device.
Noise figure (NF) — 10 log (noise factor).
Noise gain — Circuit output noise power divided by the available input noise power. This is not always equal to signal gain, depending on the source of the noise and the location of the noise source in the circuit.
Nonideal — Behavior that deviates from that of an ideal component (see also **parasitic**).
Nonlinear — A component that acts on a signal differently depending on the signal's amplitude.
Parasitic — Unintended characteristic related to the physical structure of a component.
Permeability — The ability of a material to support a magnetic field.
Return loss (RL) — The difference in dB between forward and reflected power at a network port.
Self-resonant — Resonance of a component due to parasitic characteristics.
Simulate — Model using numerical methods, usually on a computer.
Skin effect — The property of a conductor that restricts high-frequency ac current flow to a thin layer on its surface.
Skin depth — The depth of the layer at the surface of a conductor to which ac current flow is restricted (see **skin effect**).
Spectral Power Density — The amount of power per unit of bandwidth, usually "root-Hz" or √Hz, the square root of the measurement bandwidth.
Stray — see **parasitic.**
Toroid (toroidal) — A ring-shaped continuous core.
Two-port network — A network with four terminals organized in two pairs, each pair called a port.
Two-port parameters — A set of four parameters that describe the relationship between signals at the network's two ports.
Unun — A device that transfers power between two unbalanced systems, usually performing an impedance transformation (see also **balun**).

5.11 References and Bibliography

Alley, C. and Atwood, K., *Electronic Engineering* (John Wiley & Sons, New York, 1973)
Brown, J., K9YC, "Measured Data For HF Ferrite Chokes," **k9yc/publish.htm**
Brown, J., K9YC, "A Ham's Guide to RFI, Ferrites, Baluns, and Audio Interfacing," **k9yc/publish.htm**
Carr, J., *Secrets of RF Circuit Design* (McGraw-Hill/TAB Electronics, 2000)
Counselman, C., W1HIS, "Common-Mode Chokes," **www.yccc.org/Articles/W1HIS/CommonModeChokesW1HIS2006Apr06.pdf**
DeMaw, D., *Practical RF Design Manual* (MFJ Enterprises, 1997)
Dorf, R., Ed., *The Electrical Engineering Handbook* (CRC Press, 2006)
Grammer, G., W1DF, "Simplified Design of Impedance-Matching Networks," *QST*, Part I, Mar 1957, pp 38-42; Part II, Apr 1957, pp 32-35; and Part III, May 1957, pp 32-35.
Hayward and DeMaw, *Solid-State Design for the Radio Amateur* (ARRL, out of print)
Hayward, Campbell, and Larkin, *Experimental Methods in Radio Frequency Design* (ARRL, 2009)
Hayward, W., *Introduction to RF Design* (ARRL, 1994)
Kaiser, C., *The Resistor Handbook* (CJ Publishing, 1994)
Kaiser, C., *The Capacitor Handbook* (CJ Publishing, 1995)
Kaiser, C., *The Inductor Handbook* (CJ Publishing, 1996)
Kester, W., "Understand SINAD, ENOB, SNR, THD, THD + N, and SFDR so You Don't Get Lost in the Noise Floor,", Analog Devices, MT-003 Tutorial, **www.analog.com/media/en/training-seminars/tutorials/MT-003.pdf**
Maxwell, Walt W2DU, "Reflections III," *CQ Communications*, 2010
Pettai, R., *Noise in Receiving Systems*, (Wiley, 1984)
Pozar, D., *Microwave Engineering*, Fourth Edition (John Wiley & Sons, 2012)
Terman, F., *Electronic and Radio Engineering* (McGraw-Hill, New York, 1955)
Van Valkenburg, M., *Reference Data for Engineers* (Newnes, 2001)
Zavrel, R., W7SX, *Antenna Physics: An Introduction* (ARRL, 2016)

Contents

6.1 Circuit Simulation Overview

    6.1.1 Hobby versus Professional Circuit Simulation Tools

    6.1.2 The Design Cycle

    6.1.3 Schematic Capture and Simulation Tools

6.2 Simulation Basics

    6.2.1 *SPICE* — History

    6.2.2 Conventions

    6.2.3 Types of Simulations

    6.2.4 RF-Fluent Simulators

6.3 Limitations of Simulation at RF

    6.3.1 *SPICE*-based Simulators

    6.3.2 Harmonic Balance Simulators

    6.3.3 Contrasts in Results

    6.3.4 RF Simulation Tools

6.4 Electromagnetic Analysis of RF Circuits

    6.4.1 Historical Background

    6.4.2 Types of Electromagnetic Analysis

6.5 References and Bibliography

**Chapter 6 —
Downloadable Supplemental Content**

- "The Dangers of Simple Usage of Microwave Software" by Ulrich Rohde, N1UL and Hans Hartnagel
- "Using Simulation at RF" by Ulrich Rohde, N1UL
- "Mathematical Stability Problems in Modern Non-Linear Simulation Programs" by Ulrich Rohde, N1UL and Rucha Lakhe
- Examples of Circuit Simulation by David Newkirk, W9VES
- SON and data files for Electromagnetic Analysis of RF Circuits section
- Full color images for the Electromagnetic Analysis of RF Circuits section

Chapter 6

Computer-Aided Circuit Design

This chapter provides an overview of computer-aided design (CAD) for electronic design and PCB layout. These tools enable the hobbyist to harness some of the circuit simulation power employed by professional electronic and RF engineers in the product and system design cycle.

Material originally contributed by David Newkirk, W9VES, addresses generic circuit simulation tools. Dr Ulrich Rohde, N1UL, surveys issues associated with linear and nonlinear RF simulation and contributes three extensive papers with the downloadable supplemental content. Jim Rautio, AJ3K, presents an overview of electromagnetic (EM) simulation.

The purpose of this chapter is not to provide detailed instructions for using any particular software package, but to explain the basic operations, limitations and vocabulary for circuit and RF design software. Software to aid design and analysis in specialized areas, for example filter design, switchmode power supplies, transmission lines, and RF power amplifiers, is covered in other chapters.

6.1 Circuit Simulation Overview

Mathematics can predict and analyze the action of electromagnetic signals and the radio-electronic circuitry we build to produce and process them. Program an electronic computer — which, at base, is a generic math machine — to do the radio/electronics math in practically applicable ways, and you're ready to do computer-aided design (CAD) of radio and electronic circuits. (Program a computer to do radio-electronics math *in real time*, and you're ready to replace radio-electronics hardware with software, as described by this book's coverage of DSP and software-defined radio technology.)

6.1.1 Hobby versus Professional Circuit Simulation Tools

Professional grade circuit simulation software exists to facilitate the construction of tightly packaged, highly integrated, no-tweaking-required modern electronics/RF products. These products work predictably well even when reproduced by automated processes in large quantities — quantities that may, with sufficient marketing success and buyer uptake, exceed millions of units.

Manufacturers of specialized *electronic design automation* (*EDA*) software serve the engineering needs of this industry. Through comprehensive CAD suites, one may proceed from graphical component level circuit and/or IC design (*schematic capture*), through simulation of circuit and IC behavior (often using a variant of the simulator called *SPICE*, but increasingly with non-*SPICE* simulators more fluent in issues of RF and electromagnetic design), through design of PC board and IC masks suitable for driving validation, testing and production. Comprehensive EDA CAD reduces costs and speeds time to market with the help of features that can automatically modify circuits to achieve specific performance goals (*optimization*); predict effects of component tolerances and temperature on circuit behavior across large populations of copies (*Monte Carlo analysis*); and generate bills of materials (BOMs) suitable for driving purchasing and procurement at every step of the way.

Demonstration or student versions are available for some EDA CAD products at no or low cost (see **Table 6.1**), and a subset of these are especially useful for hobby purposes. Although these *demoware* tools come to us with a large-scale-production pedigree, they are greatly (and strategically) feature-limited. Only a relatively few components, often representing only a subset of available component models, may be used per simulation. Monte Carlo analysis, optimization, BOM generation and similar enhancements are usually unavailable. The licenses for these packages often limits the use of the software to noncommercial applications. Demoware is intended to drive software purchasing decisions and serve as college level learning aids — learning aids in college study toward becoming electronics/RF professionals who will each day work with the unlimited, full versions of the demoware. *Freeware* versions of simulation and layout software with considerable power are also available and may also have some restrictions. In either case, read the licensing agreement to become aware of any obligations on your part.

The radio hobbyist's circuit simulation needs are much simpler than the professional. Most of us will build only one copy of a given design — a copy that may be lovingly tweaked and refined to our hearts' content far beyond "good enough." Many of us may build as much with the intent of learning about and exploring the behavior of circuits as achieving practical results

Table 6.1
Some Sources of Freeware/Demoware Electronic CAD Software

Source	Address	Resource
Ansoft (now Ansys)	www.ansys.com	*Ansoft Designer SV 2* (schematic, linear RF simulator, planar electromagnetic simulator, layout [PCB] design), more. No longer available but older copies of the program may be available
Autodesk	www.autodesk.com	*EAGLE* schematic and layout design
Cadence Design Systems	www.orcad.com	*OrCAD* (schematic, *SPICE* simulator, layout [PCB] design)
gEDA	www.gpleda.org	GPLed suite of electronic design automation tools
Kicad	kicad-pcb.org/	GPLed full-function schematic and layout design
Linear Technology Corp	www.linear.com	*LTSpice* (schematic, *SPICE* simulator enhanced for power-system design)

with them. A demoware circuit simulator can accelerate such self-driven exploration and education in electronics and RF.

6.1.2 The Design Cycle

The components we use to build real circuits always operate to the full extent of their actual properties, regardless of our relative ignorance of what those properties may be and how and why they operate the way they do. *No real-world component operates ideally.* So it is that we may set out to design, build and publish an amplifier circuit only to discover at power-up that we have instead built a persistent oscillator. Or if the prototype is an oscillator, that for 3 out of every 100 subsequent reader-builders the circuit does not oscillate at all!

The electrical and electronic components available in circuit simulators are only mathematical *models* of real world components — because every modeled behavior of a component is only an approximation relative to the behaviors of its real world counterpart. Simulated component characteristics and behaviors approach those of real world components only as closely as science may allow and only as closely as the model's description of the real world behavior.

Were this chapter a textbook, or part of a textbook, on computer-aided circuit design, we might begin exploring simulation by reviewing the basics of what electronic circuits are and do, following this with a discussion of what computerized circuit simulation is and how it works. An excursion into the arcane world of active device modeling — the construction and workings of mathematical electrical equivalents to the transistors, diodes and integrated circuits that await us at our favorite electronics suppliers and in our junk boxes — might follow. Finally, we might systematically proceed through a series of simulation examples from the basic to the more complex, progressively building our store of understood, trustworthy and applicable-to-future-work concepts as we go.

But this is a chapter in a handbook, not a textbook, and following a sequence of abstract basics to concrete practice very likely does not reflect the process most of us have followed, and follow yet, in learning and using what we know about electronics and radio. More realistically, our approach is more like this: We find ourselves in need of a solution to a problem, identify one, and attempt to apply it. If it works, we move on, likely having learned little if we have not had to troubleshoot. If the solution does *not* work, we may merely abandon it and seek another, or — better, if we are open to learning — we may instead seek to understand why, with the happily revised aim of understanding what we need to understand to make the solution work. Even if we must ultimately abandon the solution as unworkable in favor of another, we do not consider our time wasted because we have further accelerated our deepening intuition by taking the initiative to understand why.

There is no smell of burning resistor or overheated transistor in a simulation. The placement of components on the screen has no effect on the behavior of the circuit, so a high gain stage whose input is too close to its output will never break into oscillation. The dc power sources are free of ripple and noise. These effects and many more can only be experienced (and remedies learned) by building real circuits.

Figure 6.1 shows the process by which you really learn circuit design from concept to finished project. The first step is to select a type of circuit and describe what it is supposed to do — these are the *performance requirements*. For example, an amplifier will need to achieve some level of gain over some frequency range. You may need a certain input impedance and output impedance. Armed with that information, choose a circuit and come up with a preliminary set of component values by using pencil and paper or a computer design tool. This is your *design*.

Next, *simulate* the circuit's performance. If the result satisfies your performance requirements, you can move to the next step. If not, change the circuit in some way (or change your requirements) until you are satisfied.

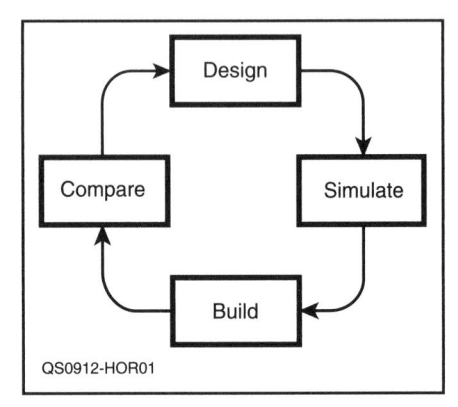

Figure 6.1 — Getting the most out of circuit simulation requires that you compare what the simulator predicts with how the actual circuit behaves.

Now *build* your design as a real world collection of components and verify that the circuit works. This is where the real fun begins as the effects of construction and actual component variation take effect. Are you done? Not yet!

To soak up every bit of design experience and know-how, go back and *compare* your actual measured performance to what the simulator predicted, particularly near the limits of the circuit's function. Look for *design sensitivities* by substituting different parts or values. If the circuit's behavior diverges from the simulator's predictions, now is the time to take a closer look. You may not be able to say exactly why differences are present, but you'll be aware they exist.

This continual *design cycle* simultaneously builds your knowledge of how real circuits and components behave, how your simulation tools work, and — most importantly — the circumstances for which the two are likely to be different.

The downloadable supplemental content includes a number of design examples developed by the original author of this section, David Newkirk, W9VES. In these examples, he creates real world circuits, simulates their behavior, compares it to actual performance, and explains why there are differences. Later in this chapter, a section by Ulrich Rohde, N1UL, discusses the differences among the different types of simulation tools used at RF — there are even differences among the different tools!

6.1.3 Schematic Capture and Simulation Tools

Almost any circuit-simulation program or electronic design automation (EDA) suite that uses schematic circuit capture can serve as a first rate schematic editor. (See Table 6.1) Although demoware component library limitations usually restrict the types of components you can use — in CAD-speak, *place* — in a design, *part count* limitations usually operate only at simulation time. Restrictions in physical size of the output drawing and layer count will likely apply to whatever layout design facilities may be available. After all, the main purpose of demoware is to let students and potential buyers taste the candy without giving away the store.

Excellent simulation-free schematic capture and layout design products exist, of course. The schematic style long standard in ARRL publications comes from the use of Autodesk *AutoCAD*, a fully professional product with a fully professional price. Long popular with radio amateurs and professionals alike is AutoDesk *EAGLE*, a schematic capture and layout design product available in freeware and affordable full version forms. You can even export *EAGLE* schematics to a *SPICE* simulator and back with Beige Bag Software's *B2 Spice* (**www.beigebag.com**). The full function freeware schematic and PCB layout application *Kicad* and the EDA suite *gEDA* come to us from the open source community.

The basic drawing utility included with your computer's operating system, such as *Paint* which comes with *Windows*, can also serve as a limited do-it-yourself schematic capture tool. The ARRL also provides a limited set of schematic symbols that can be used with *PowerPoint* at the Hands-On Radio web page, **www.arrl.org/hands-on-radio**. Cutting, copying, moving and pasting components snipped from favorite graphical schematic files and adding new connections as graphical lines is enough to create a picture of the schematic but without any of the underlying tools or facilities of a true schematic capture tool.

CAD Software and Your Computer's Operating System

The *OrCAD 16.0* and *Ansoft Designer SV 2* demoware packages used in this chapter, and most other CAD products you're likely to use, are compiled to run under Microsoft *Windows*. So what if you want to run RF and electronics CAD software under *Linux* or on the Mac?

You're in luck. *EAGLE* schematic and layout software is available in native versions for *Windows*, *Linux*, and the Macintosh. The GPLed EDA application suite, *gEDA*, are primarily developed on *Linux*, but are intended to run under, or at least be portable to, *POSIX*-compliant systems in general. The GPLed schematic and layout editor *Kicad* runs natively under *Windows* and *Linux*, and has been tested under *FreeBSD* and *Solaris*. Further, the great strides made in the *Wine* translation layer (**www.winehq.com/**) allow many applications written for *Windows* to run well under the operating systems supported by *Wine*, including *Linux* and the Macintosh.

MicroSim *DesignLab 8* (a widely distributed precursor to *OrCAD 16* that can run all of the *SPICE* examples described in this chapter) and Ansoft *Serenade SV 8.5* (a precursor to *Ansoft Designer SV 2*) can be run in *Wine* under *Linux* with few artifacts and their expected schematic capture and simulation capabilities intact. Cursor handling in *OrCAD 16* installs under *Wine* readily enough, but cursor handling artifacts in its schematic editor, at least in the computers tried, seems to preclude its use under *Wine* for now. *Ansoft Designer SV 2* installs but does not properly start.

All things considered, however, especially as *Wine* and CAD applications continue to strengthen and mature, running your favorite *Windows* based applications under *Wine* is well worth a try. You may also consider purchasing an inexpensive used computer that runs one of the later versions of *Windows*, such as XP, and dedicating it to running the simulation

---

6.2 Simulation Basics

This section is a collection of notes and illustrations that address various important circuit simulation concepts. In this section, conventional *SPICE* notation and vocabulary are used unless specifically noted differently. Not all simulation tools use exactly the same words and phrases to label and explain their features. When in doubt, refer to the software's user manual or HELP system. There are a number of excellent textbooks about using *SPICE*-based simulators Widely used simulation tools almost always have online communities of users, all of whom were beginners once, too. Joining one of these groups is highly recommended.

Simulation tool users groups frequently develop and maintain a library of tutorials, Frequently Asked Questions (FAQ), accessory programs and utilities, even models and complex circuit models. Before you ask questions, consult the available resources, such as searchable message archives, to see if your question has been answered before — it usually has! The other users will appreciate your diligence before asking the entire group.

6.2.1 SPICE — History

SPICE — *Simulation Program with Integrated-Circuit Emphasis* — originates from the Electrical Engineering and Computer Sciences Department of the University of California at Berkeley and first appeared under its current name as *SPICE1* in 1972. "*SPICE*," write the maintainers of the official *SPICE* homepage at **http://bwrcs.eecs.berkeley.edu/Classes/IcBook/SPICE** "is a general-purpose circuit simulation program for nonlinear dc, nonlinear transient, and linear ac analyses. Circuits may contain resistors, capacitors, inductors, mutual inductors, independent voltage and current sources, four types of dependent sources, lossless and lossy transmission lines (two separate implementations), switches, uniform distributed RC lines, and the five most common semiconductor devices: diodes, BJTs, JFETs, MESFETs, and MOSFETs."

That *SPICE* is "general-purpose" does not mean that its usefulness is unfocused, but rather that it is well established as a circuit simulation mainstay of comprehensive power. A wide, deep *SPICE* community exists as a result of decades of its daily use, maintenance and enhancement by industrial, academic and hobby users. Many excellent commercial versions of *SPICE* exist — versions that may be improved for workhorse use in particular sub-disciplines of electronics, power and RF design.

6.2.2 Conventions

SCALE FACTORS

SPICE's use of unit suffixes — *scale factors* in *SPICE*-speak — differs from what we are generally accustomed to seeing in electrical schematics, and that we have multiple options for specifying values numerically using integer and decimal floating point numbers. The scale factors available in *SPICE* include:

- F (femto) — 1E–15
- G (giga) — 1E9
- K (kilo) — 1E3
- M (milli) — 1E–3
- MEG (mega) — 1E6
- MIL (0.001 inch) — 25.4E–6 meter
- N (nano) — 1E–9
- P (pico) — 1E–12
- T (tera) — 1E12
- U (micro) — 1E–6

Specifying the value of a resistor as 1M would cause *SPICE* to assign it the value of 1 milliohm (0.001 Ω). This would probably create a wildly different result than expected! Specifying the value of R1 as 1MEG or 1000K would be correct alternatives. *SPICE* scale factors are case insensitive. Until you are thoroughly familiar with using circuit simulation, take the time to double-check component and parameter values. It will save you a lot of time tracking down errors caused by mistaken component values.

Notice that *SPICE* assumes unit *dimensions* — ohms, farads, henrys and so on — from component name context; in specifying resistance, we need not specify ohms. In parsing numbers for scale factors, *SPICE* detects only scale factors it knows and, having found one, ignores any additional letters that follow. This lets us make our schematics more readable by appending additional characters to values — as long as we don't confuse *SPICE* by running afoul of existing scale factors. We may therefore specify "100pF" or "2.2uF" for a capacitance rather than just "100p" or "2.2u" — a plus for schematic readability. (On the reduced readability side, however, *SPICE* requires that there be *no space* between a value and its scale factor — a limitation that stems from programming expediency and is present in many circuit-simulation programs.)

SOURCES

There are two basic types of sources used in simulation models — voltage sources and current sources — as discussed in the **Electrical Fundamentals** chapter. Sources can be *independent* with an assigned value or characteristic that does not change, or *dependent* with a value or characteristic that depends on some other circuit value. An example of an independent source would be a fixed voltage power supply (dc) or a sinusoidal signal source (ac). An example of a dependent source is a bipolar transistor model's collector current source that has a value of βI_B.

COMPONENT MODELS

All *real* inductors, capacitors, and resistors — all real components of any type — are non-ideal in many ways. For starters, as **Figure 6.2** models for a capacitor, every real *L* also exhibits some *C* and some *R*; every real *C*, some *L* and *R*; every real *R*, some *L* and *C*. These unwanted qualities may be termed *parasitic*, like the parasitic oscillations that sometimes occur in circuits that we want to act only as amplifiers. The **RF Techniques** chapter discusses parasitics for various components.

For simulating many ham-buildable circuits that operate below 30 MHz, the effects of component parasitic R, L and C can usually be ignored unless guidance or experience suggests otherwise. In oscillator and filter circuits and modeled active devices, however, and as a circuit's frequency of operation generally increases, neglecting to account for parasitic L, C and R can result in surprising performance shortfalls in real world *and* simulated performance. In active device modeling realistic enough to accurately simulate oscillator phase noise and amplifier phase shift and their effects on modern, phase-error-sensitive data communication modes, device-equivalent models must even include *nonlinear* parasitic inductances and capacitances — Ls and Cs that vary as their associated voltages and currents change.

Figuring out what the circuit of an appropriate model should be is one thing; measuring and/or realistically calculating real world values for R_S, L_S and R_P for application in a circuit simulator is a significant challenge. How and to what degree these parasitic characteristics may cause the electrical behavior of a component to differ from the ideal depends on its role in the circuit that includes it and the frequency at which the circuit operates.

Designers aiming for realism in simulating power circuits that include magnetic core inductors face the additional challenge that all real magnetic cores are nonlinear. Their magnetization versus magnetic field strength (*B-H*) characteristics exhibit hysteresis. They can and will saturate (that is, fail to increase their magnetic field strength commensurately with increasing magnetization) when overdriven. Short of saturation, the permeability of magnetic cores varies, hence changing the inductance of coils that include them, with the flow of dc through their windings. These effects can often be considered negligible in modeling ham-buildable low power circuits.

As active device operation moves from small signal — in which the signals handled by a circuit do not significantly shift the dc bias points of its active devices — to large signal — in which applied signals significantly shift active device dc bias and gain — the reality of *device self-heating* must be included in the device model. Examples: When amplitude stabilization occurs in an oscillator or gain reduction occurs in an amplifier as a result of voltage or current limiting or saturation.

While manufacturers often provide detailed models for their devices, avoid the temptation to assume that models will behave in a simulation just as an actual component will behave in a real circuit. *Absolutely every desired behavior exhibited by a simulated device must be explicitly built into the model*, mathematical element by mathematical element. A simulated device can reliably simulate real world behavior only to the extent that it has been programmed and configured to do so. A 1N4148 diode from your junk box "knows" exactly what to do when ac is applied to it, regardless of the polarity and level of the signal. Mathematically *modeling* the forward and reverse biased behavior of the real diode is almost like modeling two different devices. Realistically modeling the smooth transition between those modes, especially with increasing frequency, is yet another challenge.

Mathematical transistor modeling approaches the amazingly complex, especially for devices that must handle significant power at increasingly high frequencies, and especially as such devices are used in digital communication applications where phase relationships among components of the applied signal must be maintained to keep bit error rates low. The effect of nonlinear reactances — for instance, device capacitances that vary with applied signal level — must be taken into account if circuit simulation is to accurately predict oscillator phase noise and

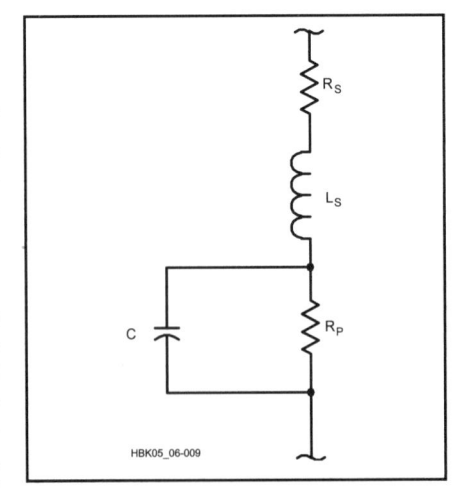

Figure 6.2 — A capacitor model that aims for improved realism at VHF and above. R_S models the net series resistance of the capacitor package; L_S, the net equivalent inductance of the structure. R_P, in parallel with the capacitance, models the effect of leakage that results in self-discharge.

effects of the large signal phenomenon known as *AM-to-PM conversion*, in which changes in signal amplitude cause shifts in signal phase. In effect, different aspects of device behavior require greatly different models — for instance, a dc model, a small signal ac model, and a large signal ac model. Of *SPICE*'s bipolar-junction-transistor (BJT) model, we learn from the *SPICE* web pages that "The bipolar junction transistor model in *SPICE* is an adaptation of the integral charge control model of Gummel and Poon introduced in the **RF Techniques** chapter. This modified Gummel-Poon model extends the original model to include several effects at high bias levels. The model automatically simplifies to the simpler Ebers-Moll model when certain parameters are not specified."

As an illustration of device model complexity, **Figure 6.3** shows as a schematic the BIP linear bipolar junction transistor model from *ARRL Radio Designer*, a linear circuit simulator published by ARRL in the late 1990s. This model worked well at audio and relatively low radio frequencies. The model must be even more complex for accurate results in the upper HF and higher frequency ranges.

Especially in the area of MOSFET and MESFET device modeling, and large signal device modeling in general (of critical importance to designers of RF integrated circuits [RFICs] for use at microwave frequencies), *SPICE* and RF-fluent non-*SPICE* simulators include active device models home experimenters are unlikely to use. Help in deciding on what version of a model is appropriate for your application is another reason to join your simulation tool's users group.

Most of us will go (and need go) no further into the arcanities of device modeling than using *SPICE*'s JFET model for FETs such as the 2N3819, J310, and MPF102, and *SPICE*'s BJT model for bipolar transistors such as the 2N3904. *OrCAD 16* includes preconfigured 1N914, 1N4148, 2N2222, 2N2907A, 2N3819, 2N3904 and 2N3906 devices, among many others, and these will be sufficient for many a ham radio simulation session. Getting the hang of the limitations and quirks of these models may well provide challenge enough for years of modeling exploration.

To get parameters for other devices, especially RF devices and specialty components like transformers, we must search the Internet in general and device manufacturer websites in particular to find the data we need. The manufacturer sites listed in **Table 6.2** will get you started. Because the use of simulation and *SPICE* models is so widespread, manufacturers routinely make those models available at no cost. The usual place to find them is via the device's online data sheet through a hyperlink or in a special model library on the manufacturer's website — enter "models" into the site's search function if you can't find the models.

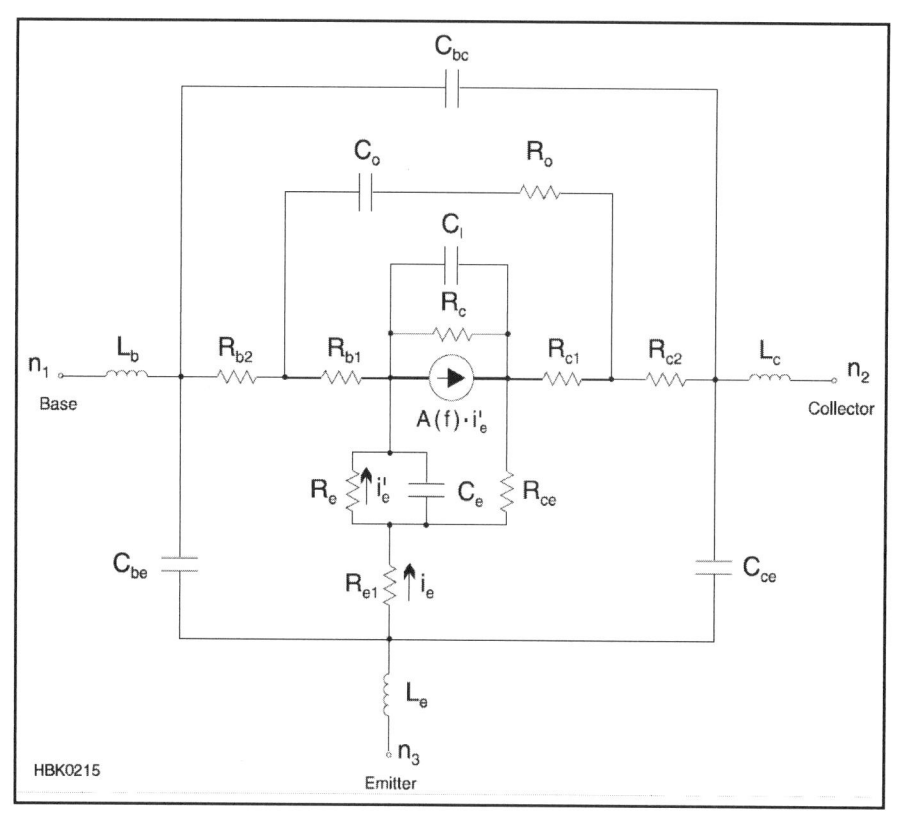

Figure 6.3 — The linear BJT model, BIP, from *ARRL Radio Designer*, a now-discontinued circuit simulation product published by ARRL in the late 1990s.

Table 6.2
Device Parameter Sources

Source	Address	Resource
Cadence Design Systems	www.cadence.com/products/orcad/pages/downloads.aspx#cd	OrCAD-ready libraries of manufacturer-supplied device models
California Eastern Laboratories	www.cel.com	Data and models NEC RF transistors
Duncan's Amp Pages	www.duncanamps.com/spice.html	*SPICE* models for vacuum tubes
Infineon	www.infineon.com	Data and models for Siemens devices
Fairchild Semiconductor	www.fairchildsemi.com	Device data and *SPICE* models
National Semiconductor and Texas Instruments	www.ti.com	Data and *SPICE* models for National and Texas Instruments op amps
NXP	www.nxp.com/models/index.html	Data and models for Philips devices
Freescale	www.freescale.com	Data and models for Freescale (previously Motorola) devices
On Semiconductor	www.onsemi.com	Data and models for On Semiconductor (previously Motorola) devices

Models for any particular device are generally available through a link on the online version of the device's data sheet. Internet searches for the device's part number and "model" usually works, as well.

```
              2N2222
              NPN
       IS     14.340000E-15
       BF     255.9
       NF     1
       VAF    74.03
       IKF    .2847
       ISE    14.340000E-15
       NE     1.307
       BR     6.092
       NR     1
       RB     10
       RC     1
       CJE    22.010000E-12
       MJE    .377
       CJC    7.306000E-12
       MJC    .3416
       TF     411.100000E-12
       XTF    3
       VTF    1.7
       ITF    .6
       TR     46.910000E-09
       XTB    1.5
       CN     2.42
       D      .87

.model Q2N2222 npn (IS=2.48E-13 VAF=73.9 BF=400 IKF=0.1962 NE=1.2069
+ ISE=3.696E-14 IKR=0.02 ISC=5.00E-09 NC=2 NR=1 BR=5 RC=0.3
CJC=7.00E-12
+ FC=0.5 MJC=0.5 VJC=0.5 CJE=1.80E-11 MJE=0.5 VJE=1 TF=4.00E-10
+ ITF=2 VTF=10 XTF=10 RE=0.4 TR=4.00E-08)
```

Figure 6.4 — A list of parameters specified for the Gummel-Poon model of a 2N2222A transistor and the condensed form usually seen in available model files.

A typical *SPICE* model is shown in **Figure 6.4**. This particular model is for the familiar 2N2222A NPN bipolar transistor. Each parameter in the vertical list (IS, BF, NF and so forth) is one element of the Gummel-Poon model for the generic transistor used by *SPICE* simulation programs. Typically, the model is provided as plain ASCII text in the compressed form at the bottom of the figure with several parameters per line. Every parameter between the opening and closing parentheses defines some element of the underlying mode. (See the *SPICE* references listed at the end of this chapter for detailed information about the syntax of *SPICE* models.)

NETLISTS

A *netlist* is a specialized table that names a circuit's components, specifies their electrical characteristics, and maps in text form the electrical interconnections among them. Uniquely numbered nodes or *nets* — in effect, specifications for each of the connections in the simulated circuit — serve as interconnects between components, with each component defined by a statement comprising one or more netlist lines.

The netlist served as the original means of circuit capture for all simulators known to the writer, including *SPICE*; *schematic capture* as we imagine it today, using graphic symbols, came later. Further reflecting *SPICE*'s pre-graphical heritage is the fact that, to this day a *SPICE* netlist may be referred to by long-time *SPICE* users as a *SPICE deck*, as in "deck of Hollerith punch cards." In *SPICE*'s early days, circuit definitions and simulation instructions (netlist statements that begin with a period [.]) were commonly conveyed to the simulation engine in punched-paper-card form. Netlists are still the means of conveying circuit topology and simulation instructions to most simulators, although they are text files today.

In the models and netlists that you will encounter, statements that must span multiple lines include *continuation characters* (+) to tell the netlist parser to join them at line breaks. Asterisk (*) or other non-alphanumeric characters denote comments — informational-to-human lines to be ignored by the simulator.

SUBCIRCUITS

Figure 6.5 illustrates the level of detail involved in more accurate device modeling typical for devices used at VHF and UHF. The device is a California Eastern Labs NE46134, a surface mount BJT intended to serve as a broadband linear amplifier at collector currents up to 100 mA and collector voltages up to 12.5 V.

This manufacturer supplied model for the NE46134 embeds an unpackaged device chip (NE46100, shown as Q1 in the figure) within a *subcircuit*. (Note the .SUBCKT label on the first non-comment line of the model which indicates that the following information defines a subcircuit.) The subcircuit includes Q1 plus the parasitic reactances contributed by the transistor package, such as CCBpkg — a collector-to-base package capacitance. The chip leads themselves are modeled as transmission lines, TB and TE.

Following the lines that define of all of the subcircuit's component values that represent the parasitic reactances, the NE46100 transistor model is provided, beginning with the line .MODEL NE46100 NPN. That information will be used to define Q1 when referenced in the subcircuit model above.

The overall model then appears to the external circuit like a regular three terminal transistor with a base, emitter and collector. In this fashion nested subcircuits can be used to create arbitrarily complex models that can be used as components by the designer.

Figures 6.6A and 6.6B show a schematic of a typical RF circuit — a 7 MHz double-tuned filter. Figure 6.6A is the usual depiction you would see in a magazine or book article about the circuit. It has the usual symbols and variable capacitors of a tunable filter. Figure 6.6B shows the circuit after schematic capture by the *OrCAD Capture CIS* tool. An ac voltage source, V1, is placed at the input with a 50 Ω series resistor, R1, to create a 50 Ω signal source impedance. The transformers TX1 and TX2 actually contain subcircuits consisting of primary and secondary inductances and a coupling element with 0.22 Ω resistors that simulate loss resistance. The paralleled fixed and variable capacitors are combined into single fixed value capacitors. A 50 Ω load, R2, has been attached to the output. Ground symbols now have a 0 nearby to indicate zero voltage.

TIME STEP

Simulators are *discrete time* devices — calculations are performed throughout the circuit and results obtained, then time is changed by a fixed amount (the *time step*) and the calculations run again. The size of the time step can be automatically chosen by the simulator (a usually reasonable value based on a default setting or some evaluation of the circuit component values) or set to specific values by the user.

While using very small time steps makes for a smooth looking output and wide frequency ranges, it makes the simulation run slower (less of an issue as computers get faster) and makes the output data files quite a bit bigger (less of an issue as hard drives get

```
*  FILENAME:         NE46134.CIR
*  from http://www.cel.com/pdf/models/ne46134.cir
*  NEC PART NUMBER: NE46134
*  LAST MODIFIED:    11/97
*  BIAS CONDITIONS: Vce=5V, to 12.5V,  Ic=50mA to 100mA
*  FREQ RANGE:       0.1GHz TO 2.5GHz
*
*                                        CCBpkg
*                               .-------||--------.
*                               |       CCB       |
*                               |    .--||---.    |
*   BASE                        |    |       |    |         COLLECTOR
*                       __Tb__  |    |       |    |
*   o---------|      |-o-LB---o--|Q1      |    /----o-o--------o----o
*             |_____|           |  B  \        |         |
*                                --       --              --  CCE
*                           -- CBEpkg  E o----'           --CCEpkg
*                                |       |                |
*                                |       LE               |
*                                `-----------o------------'
*                                            |
*                                            -
*                                           | | Te
*                                           | |
*                                            -
*                                            |
*                                            o EMITTER
*
*      CCB    = 0.03 pF      LB  = 1.2nH         Tb/Te:
*      CCE    = 0.5  pF      LE  = 1.2nH         z=60 ohms
*      CCBpkg= 0.18pF                            l=50 mils
*      CCEpkg= 0.18pF                            a=0.0001
*      CBEpkg= 0.01pF                            f=0.9GHz
*
*                   c b e
.SUBCKT NE46134/CEL 2 1 3
Q1 2 6 7 NE46100
CCB  6 2 0.03E-12
CCE  2 7 0.5E-12
LB   4 6 1.2E-9
LE   7 5 1.2E-9
TB 1 0 4 0 Z0=60 TD=9.63E-12
TE 5 0 3 0 Z0=60 TD=9.63E-12
CCBPKG 4 2 0.18E-12
CCEPKG 2 5 0.18E-12
CBEPKG 4 5 0.01E-12
.MODEL NE46100 NPN
+(  IS=8.7e-16     BF=185.0      NF=0.959     VAF=30.0      IKF=0.20
+  ISE=5.70e-13    NE=1.80       BR=5.0       NR=1.0        VAR=12.4
+  IKR=0.018       ISC=1.0e-14   NC=1.95      RE=0.630      RB=6.0
+  RBM=4.0         IRB=0.004     RC=3.0       CJE=4.9e-12   VJE=0.60
+  MJE=0.450       CJC=2.50e-12  VJC=0.830    MJC=0.330     XCJC=0.20
+  CJS=0.0         VJS=0.750     MJS=0.0      FC=0.50       TF=12.9e-12
+  XTF=1.60        VTF=19.9      ITF=0.40     PTF=0.0       TR=1.70e-8
+  EG=1.11         XTB=0.0       XTI=3.0      KF=0.0        AF=1.0  )
.ENDS
*$
```

Figure 6.5 — California Eastern Laboratories model of the NE46134 linear broadband transistor. The transistor model is constructed as a subcircuit consisting of several parasitic components connected to the NE46100 transistor (Q1).

bigger). While today's computers make short work of simulations that would have brought the previous era's mainframes to a halt, there is no need to generate vastly more data than you need for the job at hand.

If you set the time step to at least 10 times smaller than the reciprocal of the highest frequency in which you're interested, that will strike a nice balance. For example, when simulating an audio circuit, you might be interested in signals out to 100 kHz so a good time step size would be 1/10 of 1/100 kHz or about 1 µs. Similarly, if the circuit was supposed to operate up to 10 MHz, the time step should be no smaller than 10 ns. Your simulation software manual will have guidelines for that particular package as well.

6.2.3 Types of Simulations

Once the circuit has been entered into the simulator via schematic capture and all error checks have been completed, simulation can begin in earnest. There are several ways in which the circuit can be simulated, corresponding to the various tests that you would run on a real circuit on the workbench. The following paragraphs are only definitions — for a complete description of these simulations and how to perform them, the reader is directed to the References section of this chapter and reminded that the software provider and associated users groups will also have a lot of information and background material.

DC OPERATING POINT OR BIAS POINT

The first step in simulation is usually to

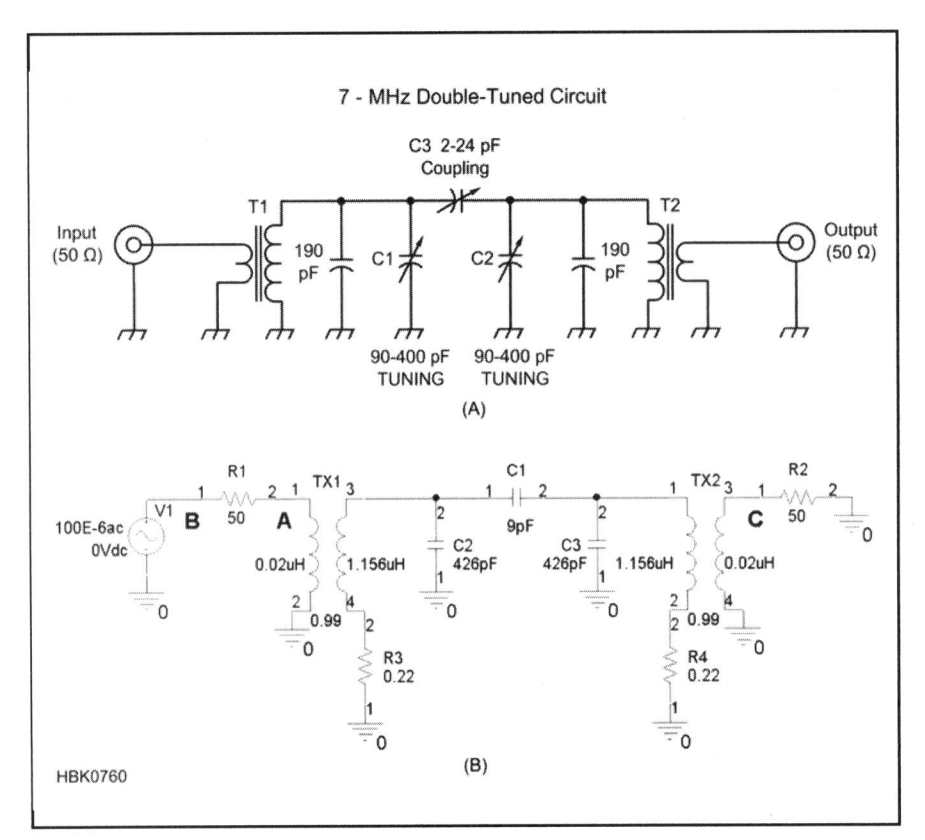

Figure 6.6 — A is a 7 MHz double-tuned filter as drawn for real world builders. B shows the filter schematic as it is typically drawn for construction and service.

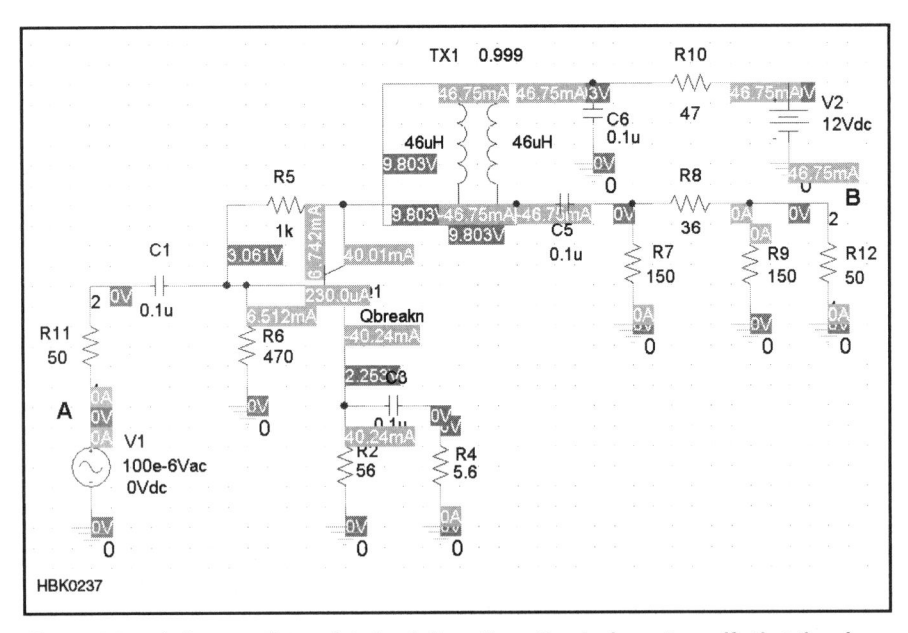

Figure 6.7 — A dc operating point simulation allows the designer to verify that the circuit biasing is realistic for all devices and that all voltages and currents are as expected.

run a *DC Operating Point* or *DC Bias Point* analysis. (Remember that terminology usually changes from program to program.) In this analysis, the simulator "applies power" to the circuit and calculates the dc voltages and currents for all circuit components.

Figure 6.7 shows the results of a typical DC Operating Point analysis for an amplifier circuit. The labels obscure the circuit elements a bit in this print image but you can see a transistor (Qbreakn) in the middle, an input voltage source at the lower left (V1), the power supply voltage source at the upper right (V2), and a variety of components making up the circuit. The darker labels show voltages such as 3.061 V (transistor base voltage) and 46.75 mA (the power supply output current). The information is generally available as a text file, as well. Most simulators also allow you to flag certain points in the circuit for which voltage and current (ac and/or dc) are displayed on screen at all times.

It is good practice, particularly for beginning and occasional modelers, to verify that the dc operating point is as expected for all circuit components before moving ahead to the more interesting ac waveform and spectrum displays. Many hours have been wasted troubleshooting a circuit's simulated ac performance when the problem is really that the dc operating point isn't right!

TIME DOMAIN VS FREQUENCY DOMAIN

Simulators can provide two primary types of ac simulation results. The time domain output displays one or more voltages or currents on an X-Y display as traces with amplitude on the vertical axis and time on the horizontal axis. In other words, it simulates an oscilloscope type display. **Figure 6.8** shows an example time domain display of an R-C oscillator starting to oscillate. The single trace is of the oscillator's ac output voltage, showing that oscillation begins about 30 ms after the simulation begins and quickly stabilizes to a steady sine wave output.

Figure 6.9 shows a frequency domain output that looks very much like a spectrum analyzer display. This particular simulation is of the same amplifier shown in Figure 6.7 with two input signals (the large components at 7 and 10 MHz) and uses a logarithmic vertical scale to show the harmonics and intermodulation products. *SPICE*-type simulators first perform time domain ac analysis to generate a waveform then use Fast Fourier Transform techniques to calculate a frequency domain output. This technique is often insufficient to obtain highly accurate frequency domain simulations, such as noise and intermodulation performance, leading to alternatives such as harmonic balance simulations that are called *RF-fluent* since they give more accurate results at high frequencies. (See the sections on RF-Fluent Simulators and Limitations of Simulation at RF in this chapter.)

TRANSIENT

Transient simulation involves putting the circuit in a stable, known state and then applying a controlled disturbance of some sort. The response to the disturbance is then calculated and displayed over some time period in either time domain or frequency domain form. Typical inputs to transient analysis are steps (a parameter changes very quickly from

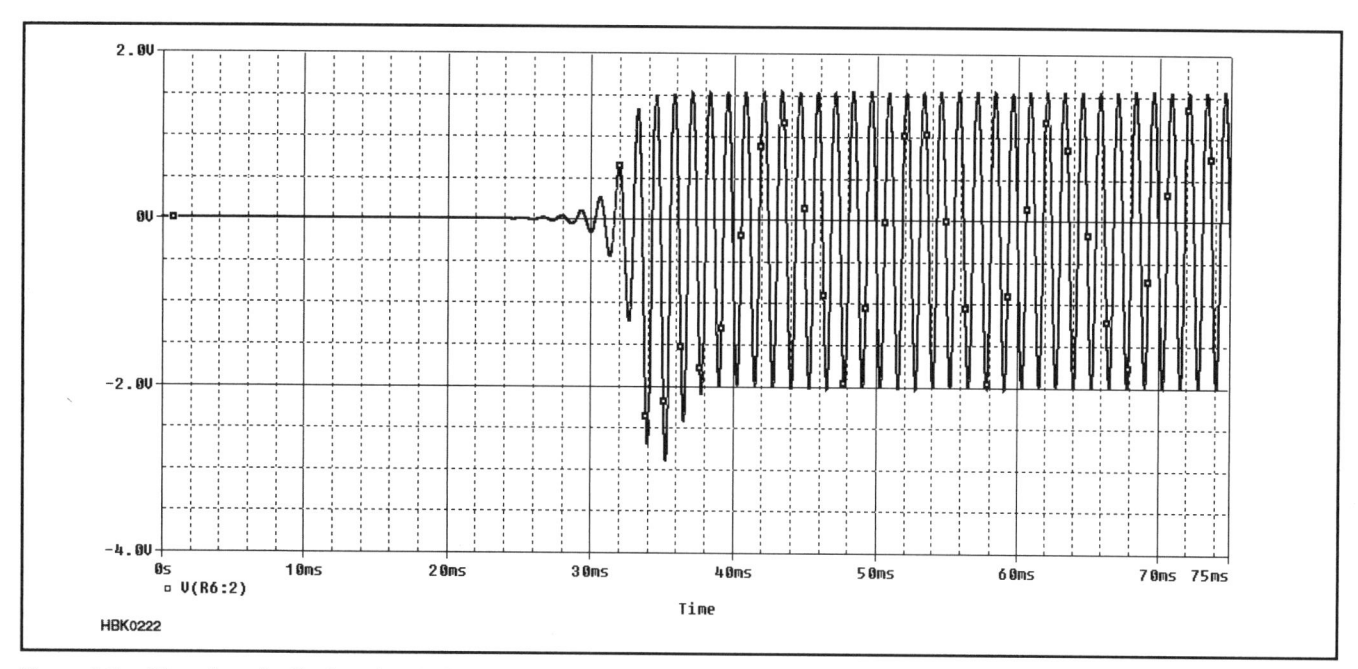

Figure 6.8 — Time domain display of an R-C oscillator startup showing voltage on the vertical axis and time on the horizontal. The display is very much like that of an oscilloscope.

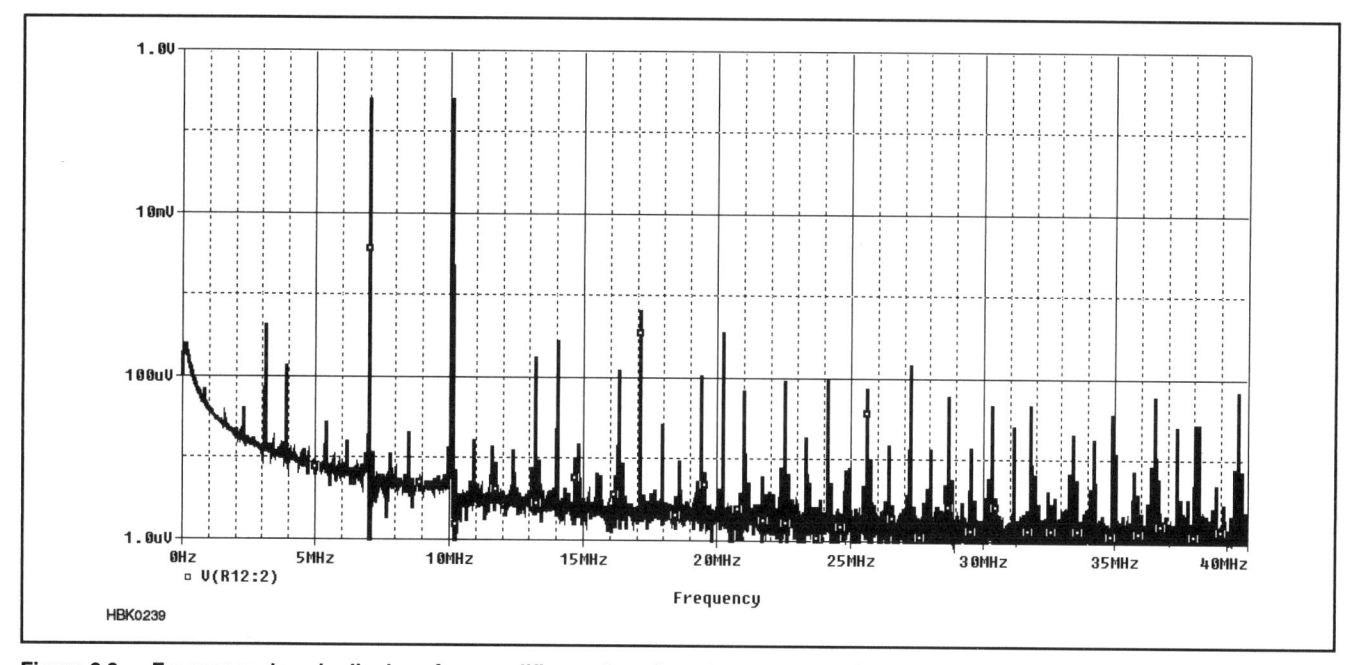

Figure 6.9 — Frequency domain display of an amplifier undergoing a two-tone test. Amplitude in dB is shown on the vertical axis and frequency on the horizontal axis. This display is very much like that of a spectrum analyzer.

DC AND AC SWEEPS

Once a circuit is working, it is useful to characterize its performance over a range of conditions, called a *sweep*: power supply voltage, input voltage, input frequency and one value to another), delta pulses (infinitely narrow pulses with some finite energy), rectangular pulses, ramps, and various other selectable waveforms.

so on. Even temperature can be swept to see how the circuit behaves in different environments. Note that this requires the behavior of components with changing temperature to be accounted for in the component models.

One of the most common swept simulations for ham radio circuits is a frequency sweep to determine the frequency response of an amplifier or filter. **Figure 6.10** shows the insertion loss and return loss (see the **RF Techniques** chapter) for the 7 MHz filter in Figure 6.6 across a range of 6.8 to 7.4 MHz. **Figure 6.11** shows the gain of the amplifier in Figure 6.7 with the input frequency swept across a range of 1 to 100 MHz.

6.2.4 RF-Fluent Simulators

SPICE-based simulators can do wonders in many classes of circuit simulation. For RF

Computer-Aided Circuit Design 6.9

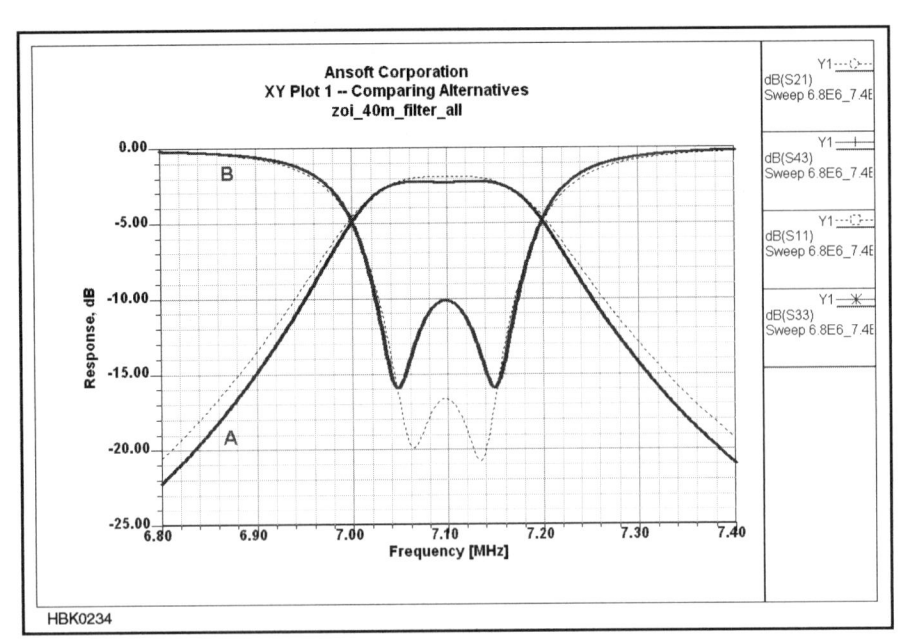

Figure 6.10 — Insertion loss (A) and return loss (B) of the 7 MHz double-tuned filter in Figure 6.6.

use, however, *SPICE* has significant drawbacks. For starters, *SPICE* is not RF-fluent in that it does not realistically model *physical* distributed circuit elements — microstrip, stripline and other distributed circuit elements based on transmission lines. It cannot directly work with network parameters (*S, Y, Z* and more — see the **RF Techniques** chapter), stability factor and group delay. It cannot simulate component *Q* attributable to skin effect. It cannot simulate noise in nonlinear circuits, including oscillator phase noise. It cannot realistically simulate intermodulation and distortion in high-dynamic-range circuits intended to operate linearly. This also means that it cannot simulate RF mixing and intermodulation with critical accuracy.

The feature-unlimited version of *Ansoft Designer* and competing RF-fluent simulation products can do these things and more excellently — but many of these features, especially those related to nonlinear simulation, are unavailable in the student/demoware versions of these packages if such versions exist.

From 2000 to 2005, the free demoware precursor of *Ansoft Designer SV 2*, Ansoft *Serenade SV 8.5*, brought limited use of nonlinear simulation tools to students and experimenters. With *Serenade SV 8.5*, you could simulate mixers, including conversion gain and noise figure of a mixer. Amplifier two-tone IMD could be simulated as in Figure 6.9. Optimization was enabled. Realistic nonlinear libraries were included for several Siemens — now Infineon — parts. You could accurately predict whether or not a circuit you hoped would oscillate would *actually* oscillate, and assuming that it would, you could accurately predict its output power and frequency. **Figu**res **6.12**, **6.13** and **6.14** give some examples of the power of RF-fluent simulation software, in this case, Ansoft (now ANSYS) *Serenade Designer SV 8.5*.

The harmonic balance techniques used by Ansoft's nonlinear solver — and by the nonlinear solvers at the core of competing RF-fluent CAD products, such as Agilent *Advanced Design System* (ADS) — allowed you to simulate crystal oscillators as rapidly as you can simulate lower-*Q* oscillators based on LC circuits. (In *SPICE*, getting a crystal oscillator to start may be impossible without presetting current and/or voltages in key components to nonzero values.)

Although these features are no longer available as student/demoware/freeware, if you're serious about pushing into RF CAD beyond what *SPICE* can do, see if you can find a used copy of *Serenade SV 8.5* or find a friend working with the professional tools who will let you use it occasionally for hobby applications.

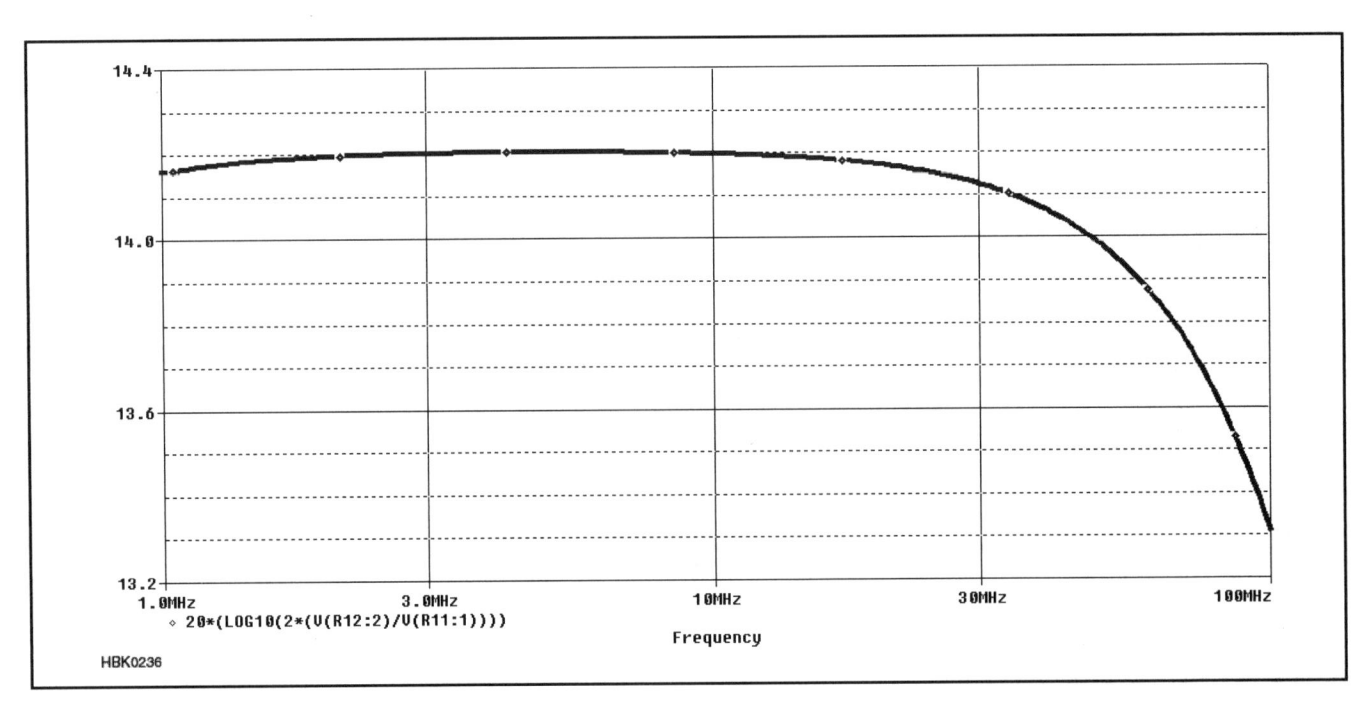

Figure 6.11 — The gain in dB of the amplifier in Figure 6.6 over a range of 1 to 100 MHz.

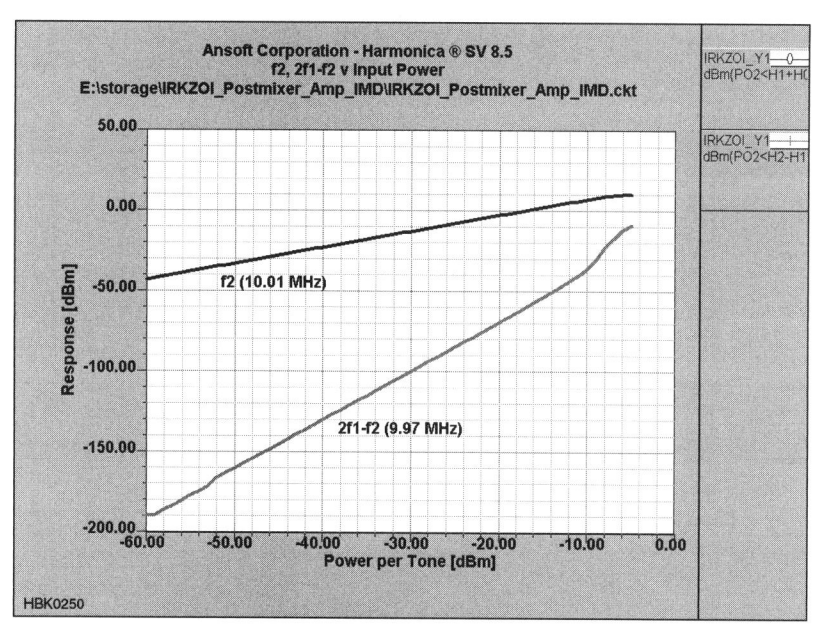

Figure 6.12 — A two-tone nonlinear simulation of third-order IMD performed by Ansoft *Serenade Designer SV 8.5*.

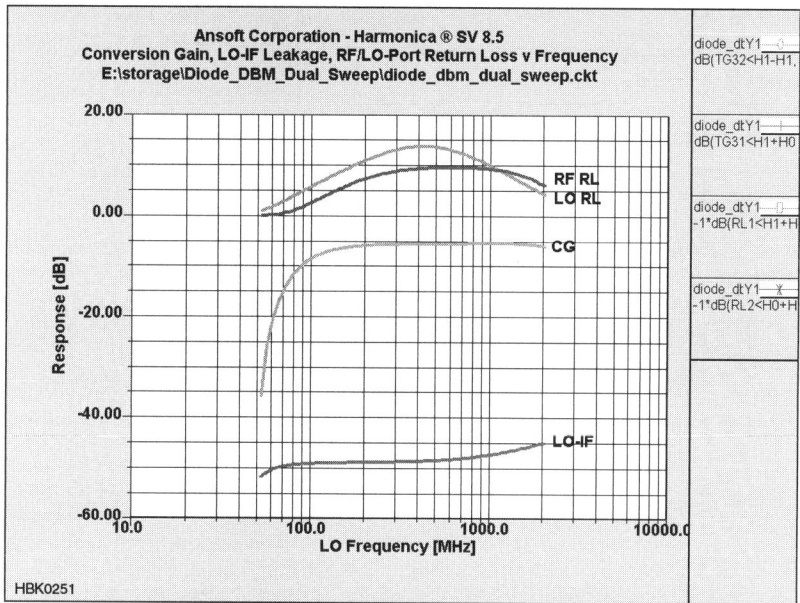

Figure 6.13 — Professional RF circuit simulators can also simulate mixing and the small signal characteristics of mixers, such as port return loss, conversion gain, and port-to-port isolation. (*Serenade SV 8.5* simulation)

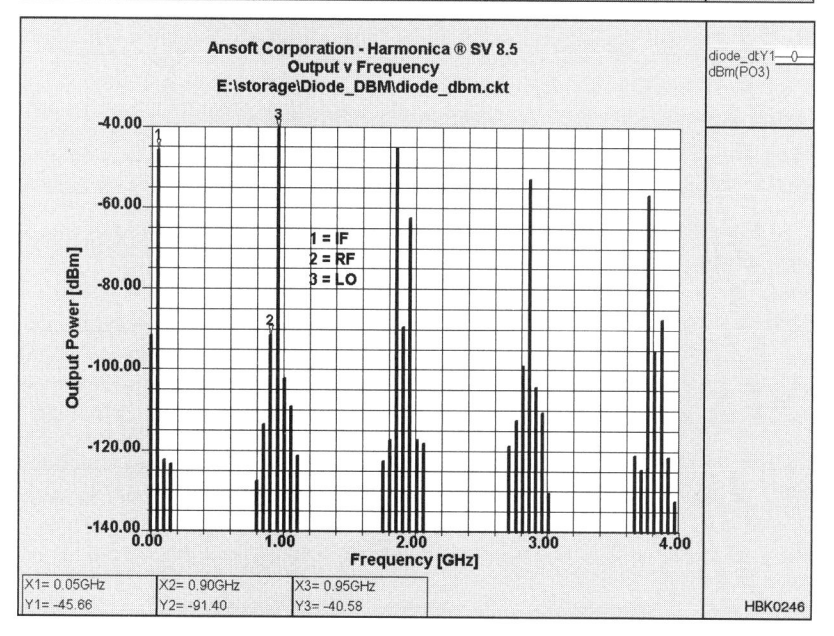

Figure 6.14 — Output spectrum of a diode-ring doubly balanced mixer as simulated by *Serenade SV 8.5*. Note the dynamic range implicit in this graph: In a simulation that includes a local oscillator (LO) signal at 7 dBm, accurate values are calculated for IMD products nearly *140 dB weaker* without encountering mathematical noise — an achievement unapproachable with *SPICE*-based simulators.

Computer-Aided Circuit Design 6.11

6.3 Limitations of Simulation at RF

[Experienced users of circuit simulation software are wary of using any software near or outside the boundaries of circuits and parameters for which it was intended and tested. RF simulation can present just such situations, leading to software failure and unrealistic results. Introduced and summarized in this section, several detailed papers by Dr Ulrich Rohde, N1UL, exploring simulation at RF are provided with the downloadable supplemental content. The papers are:

• "Using Simulation at RF" by Rohde, a survey of the issues of RF simulation and the techniques used in current modeling programs.

• "The Dangers of Simple Usage of Microwave Software" by Rohde and Hartnagel, a discussion of inaccuracies introduced by device parameter measurement and model characteristics.

• "Mathematical Stability Problems in Modern Non-Linear Simulations Programs" by Rohde and Lakhe, presenting various approaches to dealing with nonlinear circuit simulation.

In addition, there are many online resources to help you obtain trustworthy simulation results with a simulator designed for RF. For the interested reader with some technical background, the online paper "Introduction to RF Simulation and its Application" by Ken Kundert (**icslwebs.ee.ucla.edu/dejan/researchwiki/images/3/30/Rf-sim.pdf**) provides an introduction to RF simulation methods and how they account for the characteristics of RF circuits when generating common RF measurements. The website The Designer's Guide (**www.designers-guide.org**) also provides many tutorials, technical guides, models, and other resources for analog and RF simulation users.

While the precise lower bound of "RF" is ill-defined, RF effects start already at about 100 kHz. This was first noticed as self-resonance of high-Q inductors for receivers. In response, Litz wire was invented in which braided copper wires were covered with cotton and then braided again to reduce self-resonance effects.

As frequencies get higher, passive elements will show the effects of parasitic elements such as lead inductance and stray capacitance. At very high frequencies, the physical dimensions of components and their interconnections reach an appreciable fraction of the signal wavelength and their RF performance can change drastically.

RF simulators fall in the categories of *SPICE*, harmonic balance (HB) programs

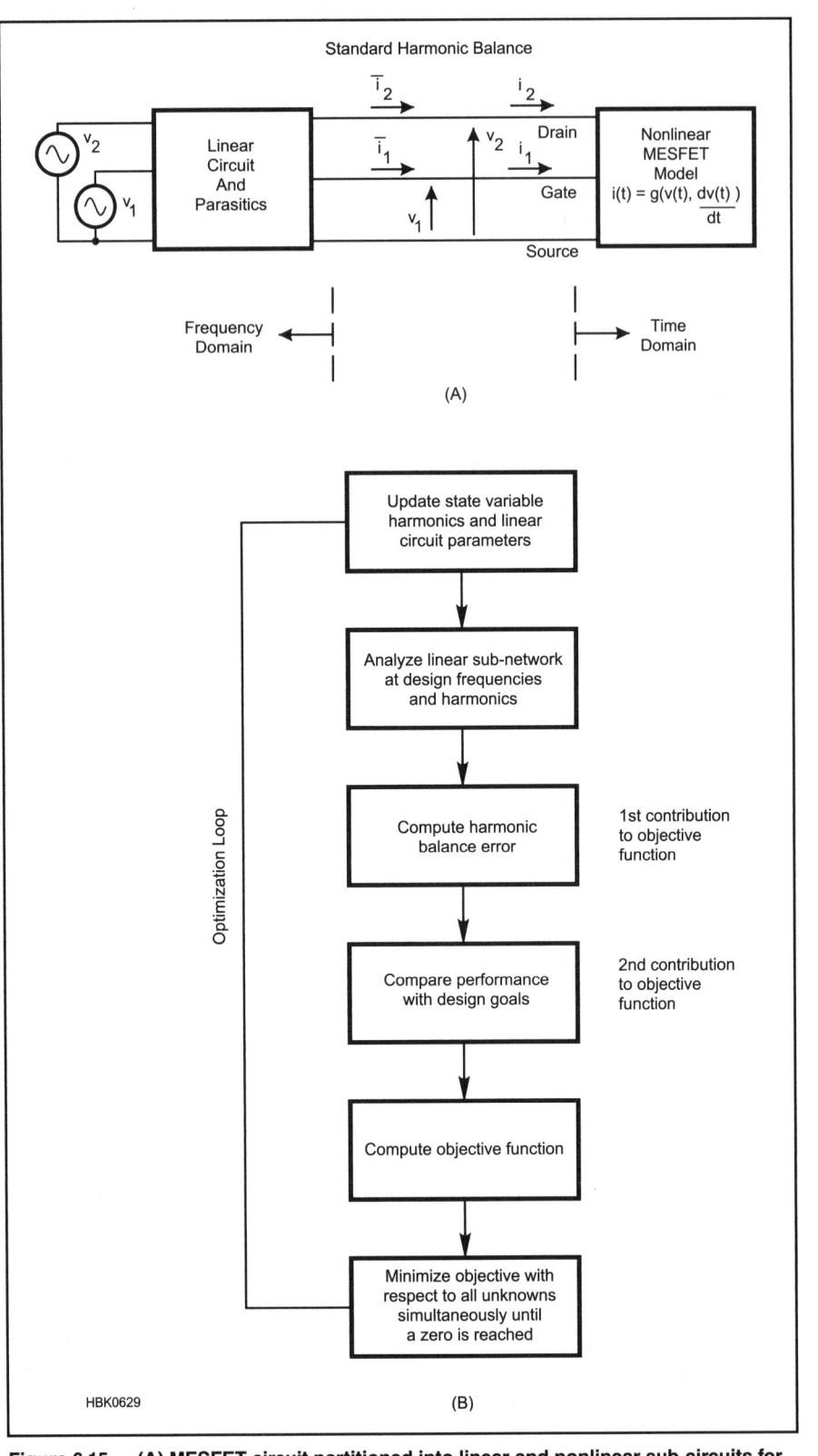

Figure 6.15 — (A) MESFET circuit partitioned into linear and nonlinear sub-circuits for harmonic balance analysis. Applied gate and drain voltages, and relevant terminal voltages and currents, are indicated. (B) Flowchart of a general purpose harmonic balance design algorithm that includes optimization.

and EM (electromagnetic) programs. The EM simulators are more exotic programs. Two types are common, the 2D (2.5) or 2-dimensional and the full 3-dimensional versions. They are used to analyze planar circuits, including vias (connections between layers) and wraparounds (top-to-ground plane connections), and solid-shapes at RF. They go far beyond the *SPICE* concept.

6.3.1 *SPICE*-based Simulators

SPICE was originally developed for low frequency and dc analysis. (Modern *SPICE* programs are based on *SPICE3* from University of California — Berkeley.) While doing dc, frequency, and time domain simulations very well, *SPICE*-based simulation has some problems. The time domain calculation uses the very complex mathematics of the Newton-Raphson solution to nonlinear equations. These methods are not always stable. All kind of adjustments to the program settings may be necessary for the calculations to converge properly. Knowledge of the specifics of different types of electronic circuits can assist the user in finding an accurate solution by specifying appropriate analysis modes, options, tolerances, and suitable model parameters. For example, oscillators require certain initializations not necessary for amplifiers and bipolar transistors may need different convergence tolerances than do MOS circuits. Generally, *SPICE* finds a solution to most circuit problems. However, because of the nonlinearity of the circuit equations and a few imperfections in the analytical device models, a solution is not always guaranteed when the circuit and its specification are otherwise correct.

The next problem at RF is that the basic *SPICE* simulator uses ideal elements and some transmission line models. As we approach higher frequencies where the lumped elements turn into distributed elements and special connecting elements become necessary, the use of the standard elements ends. To complicate matters, active elements such as diodes and transistors force the designer to more complex simulators. Adding the missing component elements leads to highly complex models and problems of convergence in which the simulator gives an error advising of a numerical problem or more likely by failing to generate a solution.

SPICE also has problems with very high-Q circuits and noise analysis. Questions of the noise figure of amplifiers or phase noise of an oscillator cannot be answered by a *SPICE*-based program accurately. Noise analysis, if not based on the noise correlation matrix approach, will not be correct if the feedback capacitance (Im(Y_{12}), the imaginary component of Y-parameter Y_{12}) is significant at the frequencies involved. Analysis of oscillators in *SPICE* does not give a reliable output frequency and some of the latest *SPICE* programs resort to some approximation calculations.

6.3.2 Harmonic Balance Simulators

Harmonic balance (HB) analysis is performed using a spectrum of harmonically related frequencies, similar to what you would see by measuring signals on a spectrum analyzer. The fundamental frequencies are the frequencies whose integral combinations form the spectrum of harmonic frequency components used in the analysis. On a spectrum analyzer you may see a large number of signals, even if the input to your circuit is only one or two tones. The harmonic balance analysis must truncate the number of harmonically related signals so it can be analyzed on a computer.

The modern HB programs have found better solutions for handling very large numbers of transistors (>1 million transistors) and their math solutions are much more efficient, leading

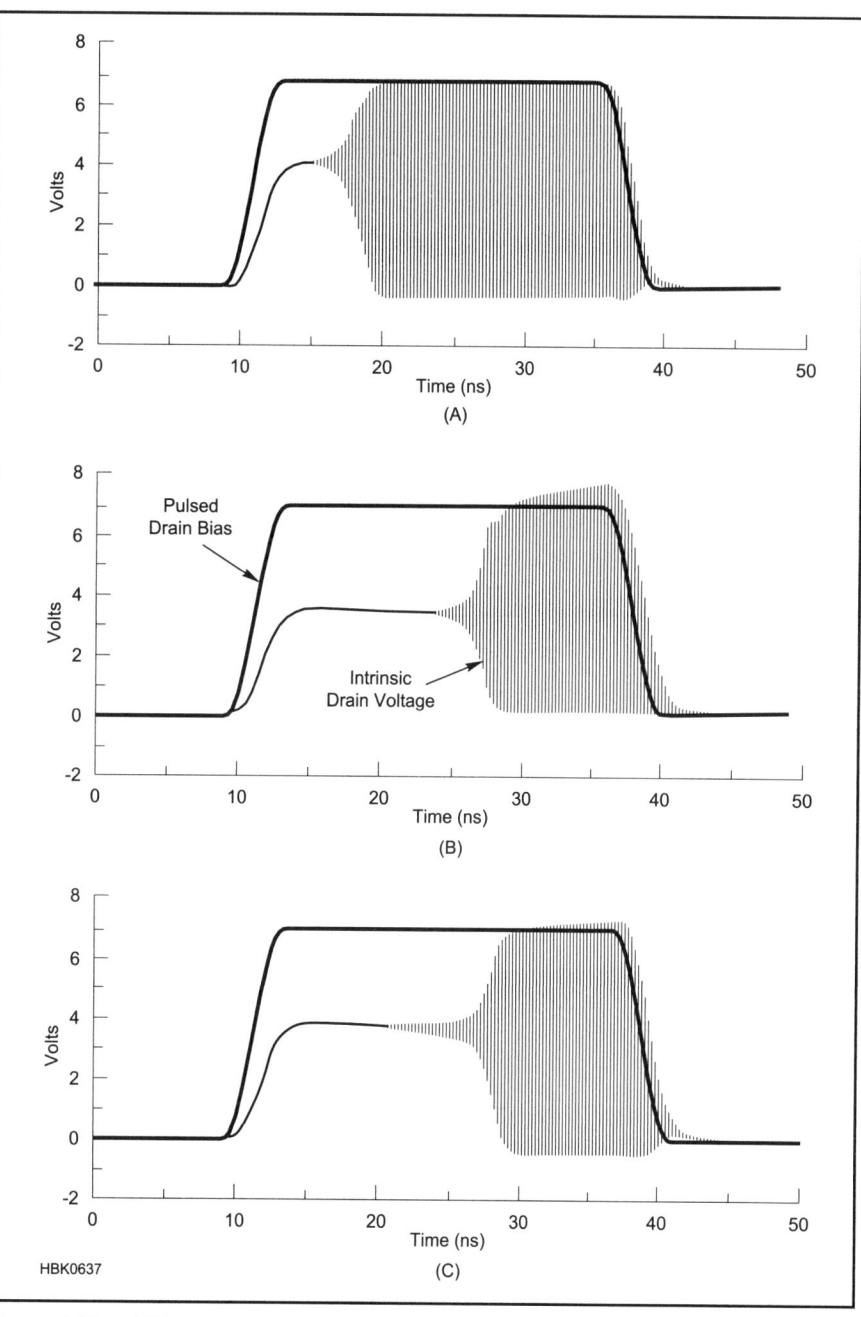

Figure 6.16 — (A) is the initial simulation of a *SPICE*-based simulator. (B) is the correct response of a pulsed microwave oscillator obtained by harmonic balance simulation using the Krylov-subspace solution. (C) is the *SPICE*-based simulation after 80 pulses of the drain voltage.

Computer-Aided Circuit Design 6.13

to major speed improvements. Memory management through the use of matrix formulations reduces the number of internal nodes and solving nonlinear equations for transient analysis are some of the key factors to this success.

HB analysis performs steady-state analysis of periodically excited circuits. The circuit to be analyzed is split into linear and nonlinear sub-circuits. The linear sub-circuit is analyzed in the frequency domain by using distributed models. In particular, this enables straightforward intermodulation calculations and mixer analysis. The nonlinear sub-circuit is calculated in the time domain by using nonlinear models derived directly from device physics. This allows a more intuitive and logical circuit representation.

Figure 6.15A diagrams the harmonic balance approach for a MESFET amplifier. Figure 6.15B charts a general purpose nonlinear design algorithm that includes optimization. Modern analysis tools that must provide accurate phase noise calculation should be based on the principle of harmonic balance.

Analysis parameters such as Number of Harmonics specify the truncation and the set of fundamental frequencies used in the analysis. The fundamental frequencies are typically not the lowest frequencies (except in the single-tone case) nor must they be the frequencies of the excitation sources. They simply define the base frequencies upon which the complete analysis spectrum is built.

6.3.3 Contrasts in Results

The following time domain analysis is a good example of differences between *SPICE* and harmonic balance simulation. A microwave oscillator is keyed on and off and a transient analysis is performed. When using the standard *SPICE* based on *SPICE3*, the initial calculation shows an incorrect response after one iteration as seen in **Figure 6.16A**. It takes about 80 pulses (80th period of the pulsed drain voltage) until the simulation attains the correct answer (Figure 6.16C) of the Krylov-subspace-based harmonic balance in Figure 6.16B.

The frequencies involved need not be in the GHz range. Oscillators, in particular, can be very difficult to analyze at any frequency as shown by simulations of a low-MHz phase shift oscillator and a 10 MHz Colpitts oscillator in the referenced papers.

Validating the harmonic balance approach, **Figure 6.17** shows a BJT microwave oscillator entered into the schematic capture module of a commercially available HB simulator (Ansoft *Serenade 8.0*); **Figure 6.18** compares this oscillator's simulated phase noise to measured data. HB analysis gives similarly accurate results for mixers.

6.3.4 RF Simulation Tools

PSPICE: OrCAD *PSPICE* is a popular version available from Cadence PCB Solutions (**www.orcad.com**) and a "Lite" version is available for free download. (The Lite version is limited in the size and complexity of designs that can be created.) AIM-spice (**www.aimspice.com**) is a PC version of *SPICE* with a revised user interface, simulation control, and with extra models.

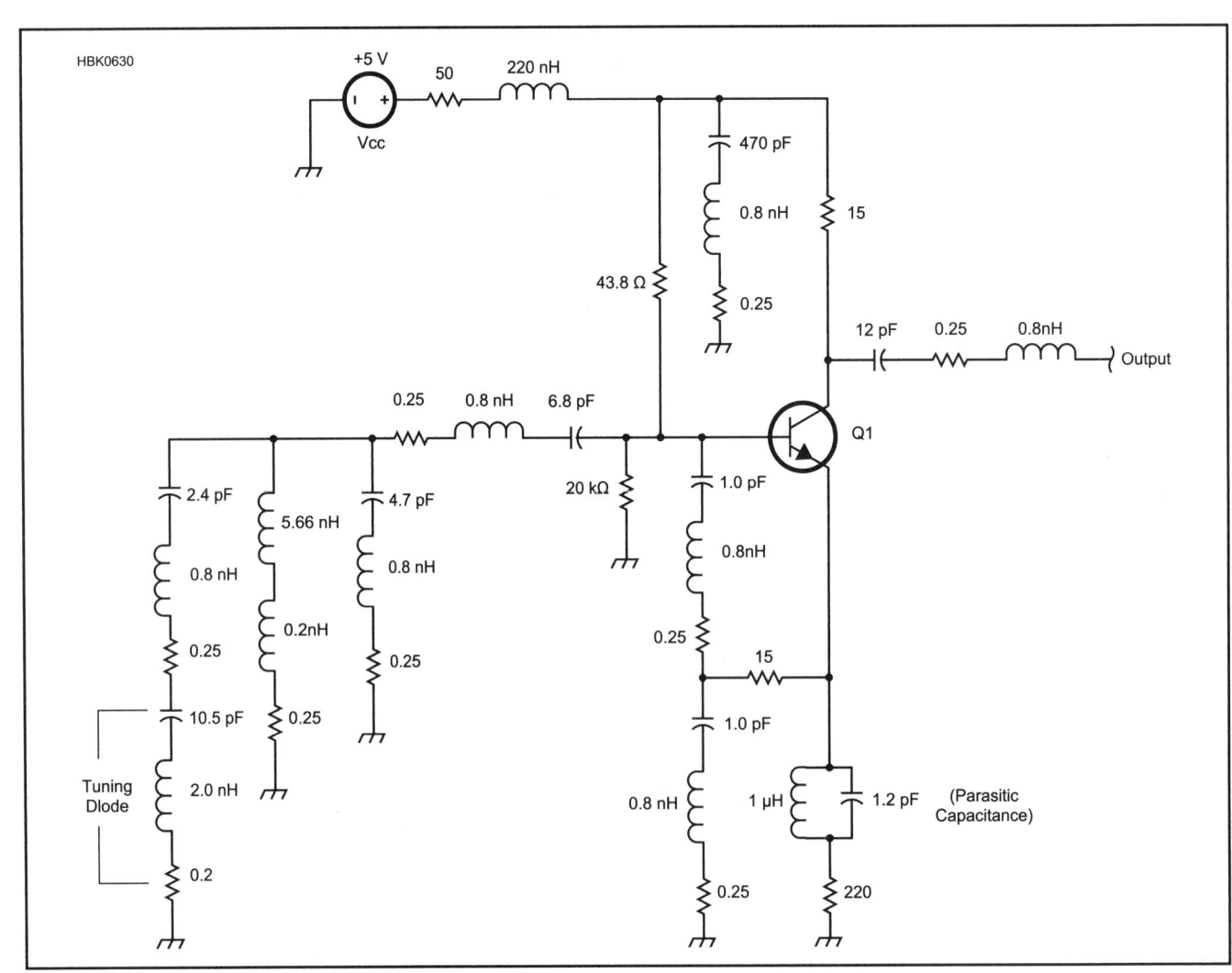

Figure 6.17 — Colpitts oscillator for 800 MHz with lumped elements modeled by their real values.

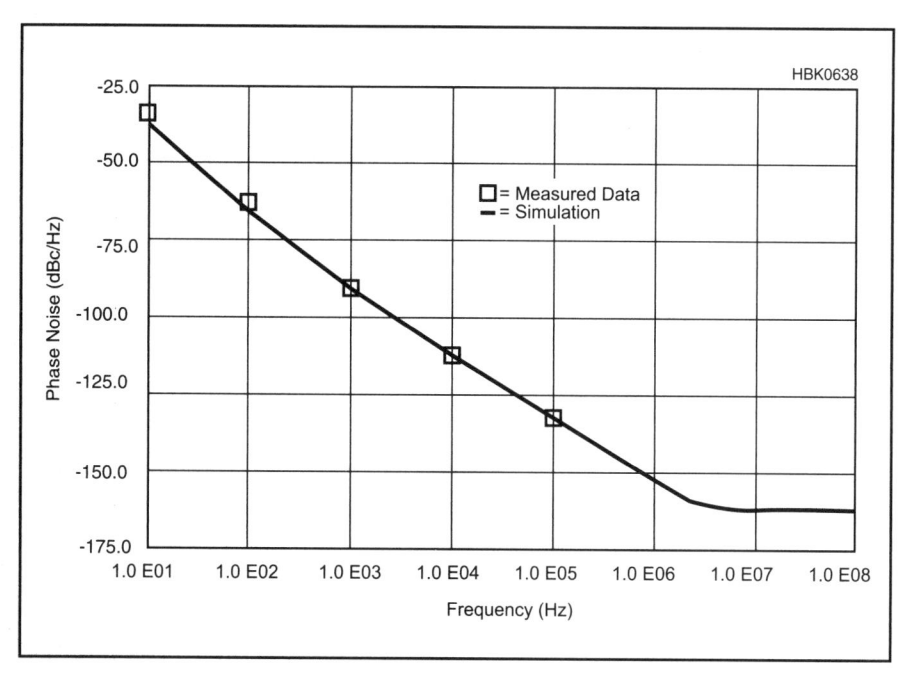

Figure 6.18 — Comparison between predicted and measured phase noise for the oscillator shown in Figure 6.17.

A student version can be downloaded. Table 6.1 earlier in this chapter shows other free *SPICE* offerings.

There are a number of PC based *SPICE* programs in the $1000 range but they are designed more for switching power supplies and logic circuits optimization than RF. *ICAP4* (www.intusoft.com/demos.htm) and *MICROCAP* (www.spectrum-soft.com/index.shtm) both have demonstration/evaluation versions available for download

Agilent, AWR, Ansys, and Synopsis offer very modern mixed-mode CAD tools and they combine the concept of *SPICE* with the advanced technologies. These are professional quality tools, but if one can arrange to make use of them through a friend or associate, the results are worth investing the time to learn their use.

Linear Technologies also offers a free version, *LTSpice*, in support of its switchmode products but handles all types of circuits and has a large number of users. (For a *QST* tutorial and a set of references and downloadable component libraries, see the Reference entries for Silver and Würth Elektronik.)

6.4 Electromagnetic Analysis of RF Circuits

Solving the equations governing electromagnetic (EM) fields first became technically feasible in the late 1970s and is now a well-developed technology. A wide variety of software is available, all developed over decades of intense research. Today, you can take advantage of the fruits of this research without learning the equations and without writing any software. This section provides some historical background, discusses different types of EM analysis techniques, and outline how electromagnetic software is used today. Then we show how you can use some of these tools for your RF designs.

6.4.1 Historical Background

In 1865, James Clerk Maxwell, **Figure 6.19**, published the equations that govern electric and magnetic fields. Maxwell's equations, as they are now called, put in solid mathematical terms the following principles:

1) A changing electric field creates a changing magnetic field that is exactly at right angles to the electric field.

2) A changing magnetic field creates a changing electric field that is exactly at right angles to the magnetic field.

Maxwell quickly recognized an important implication of his equations. If both an electric and magnetic field could somehow exist at the same time and at the same place and be exactly at right angles to each other with both changing in just the right way, each one would continually create the other and a propagating wave would result. Using his equations, he calculated the speed of that hypothetical "electromagnetic" wave. Amazingly, he saw that it was virtually identical to the mechanically measured speed of light. His conclusion was earth-shaking, "…that light is an electromagnetic disturbance propagated through the field according to electromagnetic laws." However, Maxwell felt that the chances of using electricity to actually create such a wave would be difficult if not impossible.

After Maxwell's death, almost by accident while experimenting with a spark-gap, a German professor, Heinrich Hertz, succeeded in creating and detecting electromagnetic waves. He then refined how he created and detected the waves and conducted experiments reflecting, diffracting, focusing, and polarizing electromagnetic waves. This provided definitive proof that Maxwell's equations are correct. However, Hertz felt there was little if any practical use for such waves. As we all know, an Italian entrepreneur, Guglielmo Marconi, thought otherwise and was spectacularly successful.

Science marches on and modern physics has shown us that Maxwell's equations are wrong. You may be familiar with the concept of a "photon," the particle of light. A photon is indivisible. We cannot have half of a photon. The light we see can only be composed of an integer number of photons. A sensitive photomultiplier tube can receive one photon, or two, or three, but never 2.853 photons.

Maxwell's equations form a "field" theory. There are no photons in Maxwell's equations. Mathematically, we can easily write

Figure 6.19 — James Clerk Maxwell (1831 – 1879) gave us the equations which govern the interaction between changing electric and magnetic fields. These equations can be solved on a computer, revealing how our RF and microwave circuits will perform.

The Basic Elements of Maxwell's Equations

The complete set of Maxwell's equations can be described as, "A set of four simultaneous partial differential equations operating on four vector fields in four dimensions and driven by two scalar fields." The four dimensions are the three spatial dimensions (x, y, z) and time. The four vector fields are electric, **E** and **D**, and magnetic, **H** and **B**. The two scalar fields are electric and magnetic charge. (Magnetic charge has yet to be discovered, but that does not stop the mathematics.)

You may also know these equations as laws named for scientists who originally discovered the relationships. It was Maxwell who brought them all together into one set of equations that define electromagnetics. (For an explanation of vectors, scalars, and what the various symbols mean, see the item "Radio Mathematics" in the downloadable supplemental material.)

Gauss' Law for Electric Fields: $\nabla \cdot \mathbf{D} = \rho$

Gauss' Law for Magnetic Fields: $\nabla \cdot \mathbf{B} = 0$

Faraday's Law: $\nabla \times \mathbf{E} = -\dfrac{\partial \mathbf{B}}{\partial t}$

Ampere – Maxwell Law: $\nabla \times \mathbf{H} = \mathbf{J} + \dfrac{\partial \mathbf{D}}{\partial t}$

Where ρ represents the density of electric charge and **J** represents a distribution of electric current (moving charge). There are also forms of Maxwell's Laws that are written as integrals; that incorporate relativity; that use mathematical objects known as tensors; and various other ways. The four equations above, though, are the most widely known.

J is a vector because current has a direction. A distribution of *electric* charge changing with time is exactly what makes electric current. So, for RF, we can use either current or charge (both of which can vary with time) to drive the equations. All sorts of other abstract mathematical quantities are also helpful, including some strange beasts known as vector and scalar potentials. Fortunately, we can often simplify things by assuming that **D** is proportional to **E** (**D** = ε**E**), and **B** is proportional to **H** (**B** = μ**H**). Then, we have only have two vector fields to deal with, but even that is still a big problem.

By doing this extra math, Maxwell's equations and all their vector and scalar fields are turned into a big pile of discrete numbers that can be stored on and crunched in a computer. It has only taken a couple decades with hundreds if not thousands of researchers all over the world, but it seems like today we are pretty much there.

For a detailed introduction to Maxwell's equations, if you have some calculus background, see *A Student's Guide to Maxwell's Equations* by Daniel Fleisch from Cambridge Press. It is an excellent tutorial on this important topic.

---

the equations for an electromagnetic wave with the energy of 2.853 photons. But we know that such a wave cannot exist. It is here that something called quantum electrodynamics (QED) takes over. Fortunately, for virtually everything we do, QED is not needed. The number of photons is so incredibly huge, we can just pretend that we are dealing with electric and magnetic fields. So, we use Maxwell's equations. Just as Newton's laws of motion are still useful when figuring how long it will take to get to the grocery store, Maxwell's equations are useful for our work with radio waves.

We are especially fortunate to have Maxwell's equations. In nearly all other fields of science and engineering, exact solutions to practical problems are often impossible. In contrast, given a precisely known passive RF circuit, we can use Maxwell's equations to get precise results for how it will operate. (Active circuits, typically with transistors, are with elsewhere in this book.) Appropriate circuits include filters, matching networks, couplers, power dividers, connectors, transformers, and any passive structure involved in handling RF.

All this gradually started to become possible in the 1970s. Computers were just starting to come into wide use. Large corporate timeshare computers saw some of the first EM software ever developed. The first IBM-PC put serious computing power (for the day) in front of a lot of eager, bright eyed experimenters and amateurs. We were off to the races! As with many things, there is more than one way to slice that loaf of bread. Let's see what toys we now have in our electromagnetic tool box.

6.4.2 Types of Electromagnetic Analysis

Maxwell liked to think "analogically," reasoning that completely different areas of physics and nature somehow use similar equations. For example, he suspected that incompressible fluid flow (think of a submarine powering through the ocean depths) and electrostatics (think about rubbing a balloon on your hair) use the same equations. So he derived the equations for incompressible fluid flow and found that they magically work just fine for electrostatics…absolutely mind-boggling when we think about it. That was his first step in coming up with the full set of Maxwell's equations.

We can use analogical thinking in solving Maxwell's equations on a computer, too. The problem is that we have continuous electric and magnetic fields everywhere. In contrast, a computer can only store numbers, and we must be careful that we do not overrun the computer's memory capacity. The same is true for images. To get an image into a computer, we take a picture with a camera. The camera converts the continuous image into discrete pixels. There are three numbers (red, green, and blue, colors which Maxwell was the first to figure out) for each pixel. In this form, our picture is just a bunch of numbers. We can now store the picture on any computer and use software to process the picture as we like. So, if analogical thinking works for this case, maybe we can convert our electromagnetic problem into "pixels."

And indeed we can. First, the fields and currents are *discretized*, just like an image being converted to pixels. However, an image is usually two-dimensional while EM fields are three-dimensional in space, and they vary with time. Thus, we actually have to deal with pixels in four dimensions. To make the problem worse, we have to discretize the electric field, the magnetic field, the charge (or, equivalently, the current), and even the circuit itself. That is a lot of numbers!

Fortunately, today's computers have gotten really good at storing lots of numbers. Once we have the numbers stored, then, just like when we do image processing, we can use software to do what we want with the numbers. This is where the last few decades of EM research has concentrated. There are two ways to do this: *Volume meshing* and *surface meshing*. (Meshing means to divide a volume or surface into many smaller volumes or surfaces with boundaries that are connected to each other, forming a mesh filling or covering the entire volume or surface.) We discuss each below.

VOLUME MESHING — FDTD

The easiest to understand is *finite difference time domain* (FDTD) analysis. In its simplest form, we mesh the entire volume of the RF structure into tiny rectangular hexahedral cells (six sides, for example cubes, rectangular cuboids, and similar shapes). Note that we must also mesh all of space that might have any EM fields. This includes any air (e.g., free space) surrounding the structure. You can imagine this structure as an enormous spreadsheet in which the value in each cell depends on the values of each neighboring cell.

Next we assume an initial condition. This

is like an RF input into the structure. Let's say we have 1 volt of electric field at the input right at the start (time: $t = 0$). This input is a single impulse, we put it there for only a single instant (i.e., time step). This is like hitting a bell to start it ringing.

And indeed it does ring. Changing the input voltage, which we placed on an edge of one of the hexahedrals (one face of a cube), from 0 volts to 1 volt right at the start gives us a changing electric field. In addition to meshing the structure, we also have to discretize time. So we pick a tiny time-step. Then the software uses Maxwell's equations to calculate exactly how much changing magnetic field is created by the changing electric field at the input. In addition, the software knows, because of Maxwell's equations, that this changing magnetic field must be at right angles to the changing electric field. This changing magnetic field is now created on the edges of every hexahedral surrounding the hexahedral edge that has the changing electric field input.

In the next time-step, we have both changing magnetic fields and changing electric fields near the original input. Each hexahedral edge with a changing magnetic field creates a changing electric field in all surrounding hexahedral edges. Each changing electric field creates a changing magnetic field in all surrounding edges. Using Maxwell's equations, the software calculates how much electric and magnetic field is created. And so it repeats. Imagine each cell of the spreadsheet constantly updating its value based on the value of its neighbors.

Soon (at the speed of light) electric and magnetic fields propagate throughout the entire structure. For every hexahedral in the structure, the computer now stores a list of numbers that tell us how the electric and magnetic fields change as a function of time. If there is a little bit of loss (and in real life, there is always at least a little bit of either conductor or radiation loss), the ringing electric and magnetic fields gradually die out to zero, and the solution is complete.

Often, we are not interested in the electric and magnetic fields in the entire circuit. For example, we might be interested only in an input and an output. We still need to calculate all the field information everywhere to get to the final desired result. But at any given time-step during analysis, only the last several time-steps of complete field information are needed. In this case, we discard all internal field information after it is no longer needed for calculating the next time-step. In other cases, we actually want to see the complete internal fields as they develop during the analysis and we keep that information available, usually by storing it conveniently on the computer's hard drive.
Figure 6.20 shows a typical FDTD result. Red (or bright) color indicates high electric fields as a continuous RF wave at a single frequency propagates along a complex rectangular waveguide circuit. The field strength is shown across the entire cross-section of the guide at the ports, and on a horizontal plane in the middle of the waveguide along its length. The hexahedral meshing is so fine that it is not visible in this image. The set of full-color figures is available as a PDF file in the online supplemental information for this book.

A little more detail is important. Due to problems calculating rate-of-change with time (known in calculus as a "time derivative") and rate-of-change across space (a "gradient"), there are actually two full and nearly identical discretizations of the structure being analyzed. Both discretizations cover the same volume. The only difference is one discretization is offset from the other by one-half of a hexahedral. The changing electric field is calculated on one discretization, and the changing magnetic field is calculated on the other. This means that every sample of magnetic field is midway between all adjacent samples of the electric field. Likewise, the electric field calculation is always for points that are midway between all adjacent samples of the magnetic field. Without this special modification, there can be stability problems.

In practice, the input is typically not a simple impulse. A pure impulse can cause numerical instability. So, we typically use a "gentler" input, like a Gaussian pulse. This kind of pulse is the well-known "bell curve" used to curve test grades or to represent the probability of many random processes. If we are especially interested in results over a specific band of frequencies, we can use the Gaussian pulse to modulate an RF carrier centered on the band of interest.

For most circuits, the electric and magnetic fields at a given point plotted as a function of time look just like what we would expect for a ringing bell, or a ringing resonant LC circuit, **Figure 6.21**. For this case, the input

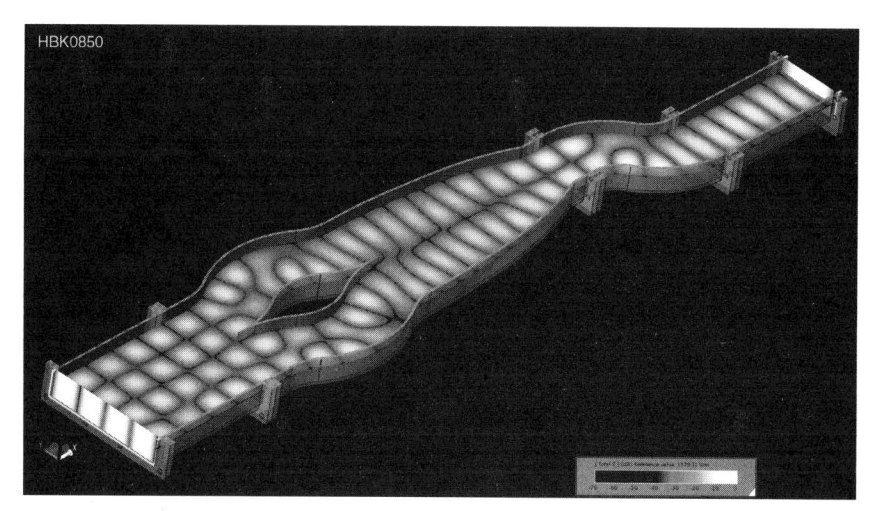

Figure 6.20 — A complex rectangular waveguide mode converter as analyzed by FDTD. Electric field is shown with red (or bright) indicating high field strength. Input is on the right. [Courtesy Remcom, used with permission]

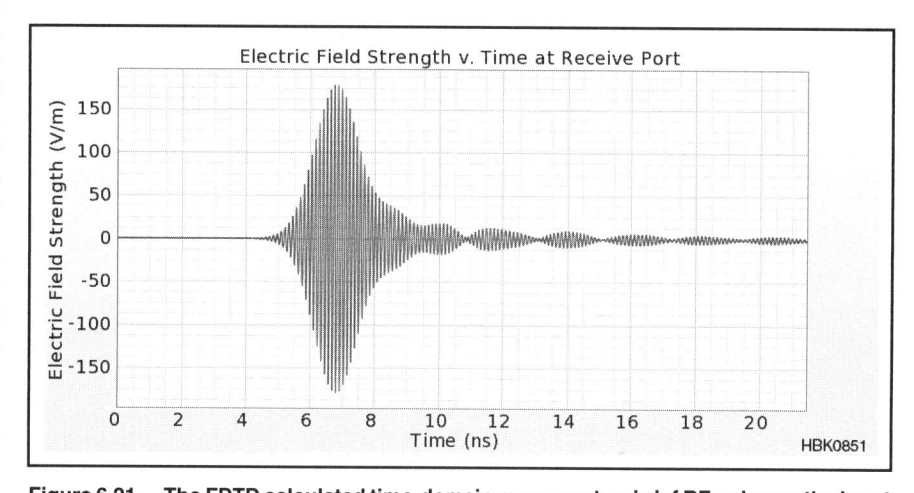

Figure 6.21 — The FDTD calculated time-domain response to a brief RF pulse on the input of the mode converter of Figure 6.20 resembles the ringing of a bell. This is called the "impulse response". [Courtesy Remcom, used with permission]

Computer-Aided Circuit Design 6.17

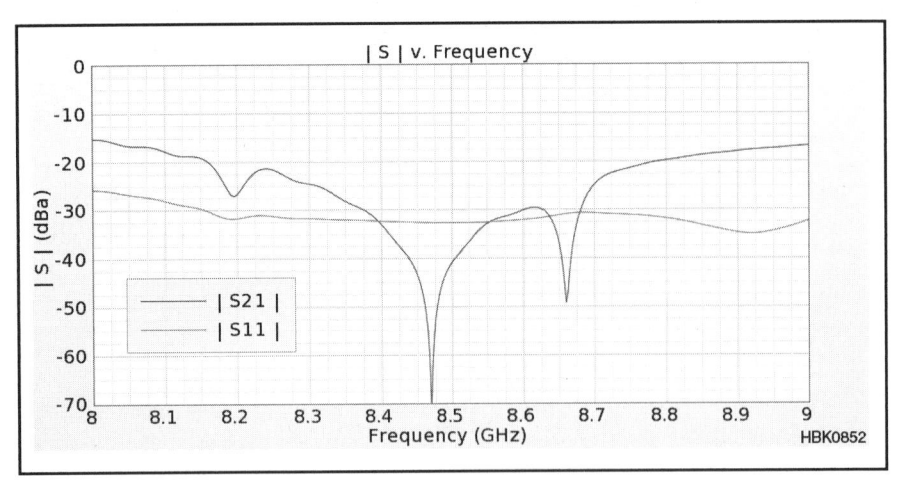

Figure 6.22 — Performing a Fourier transform on the circuit response is equivalent to using a spectrum analyzer to see the frequency domain response of the mode converter given the broad band impulse used to excite the filter. [Courtesy Remcom, used with permission]

VOLUME MESHING — FINITE ELEMENT METHOD

Mechanical engineers use the *Finite Element Method* (FEM) extensively. Materials can only take so much stress and strain before they fail. FEM allows designers to rapidly try out many different structure designs on the computer. Then they build the best one, where "best" might be based on the most strength for the least weight, or size, or cost, or other factor.

Stresses and strains are vector fields, just like electromagnetic fields. A "vector" has a magnitude and a direction. For example, an electric vector field at a given point might be "5 V/m in the x direction". A "field" means that the vector is defined over a region, like inside a waveguide, or even everywhere in all of space. So, by analogical thinking, it seems we might be able to apply FEM to our RF and microwave problems too. And indeed we can. But the devil is in the details. Like all numerical EM techniques, it has taken world class researchers several decades to reach today's high level of maturity.

FDTD is a time domain analysis. In other words, the EM analysis evaluates the EM fields as they evolve in time. We get the full frequency response by performing an FFT on the calculated impulse response.

For RF work, FEM tools typically provide frequency domain results. In this case, we specify a frequency of interest and the FEM

is a modulated Gaussian pulse modulating an RF carrier. The rapid oscillation is from the RF carrier, and the envelope is the result of the "bell" ringing. This is closely related to what professionals call the "impulse response," the impulse being a single instant of electric field that started all the fields going. While impressive, this is not of much use in designing our circuit. We typically need a frequency response.

The input pulse that started everything ringing actually has a wide band of frequencies present in it. Think about the spark gaps that Hertz and Marconi, as well as early hams, used to generate electromagnetic waves. They were very broad band. If we think of our circuit as being a filter, the output is just a filtered version of that broad band impulse we put on the input. The spectrum of that output is the filter response that we want to see. The computer can take the numbers that were calculated for the impulse response and simulate a spectrum analyzer by using a mathematical algorithm, i.e., a mathematical recipe, called a *Fourier transform*. The fastest way of doing a Fourier transform on a computer is creatively called the *fast Fourier Transform (FFT)*. (The FFT is also discussed in the chapter **DSP and SDR Fundamentals**.)

So the software simply performs an FFT on the impulse response, and we have the current and voltage output of our circuit. This output is then converted to S-parameters and plotted, **Figure 6.22**. The indicated "S21" is the ratio of the amplitude of the output voltage wave (i.e., coming out of port 2) to the amplitude of the input voltage wave (i.e., going into port 1). "S11" is the reflection coefficient, i.e., the ratio of the reflected wave to the input wave.

There are a number of time domain approaches similar to FDTD. Another approach is called the *transmission line method* or TLM in which Maxwell's equations are modeled as a fine mesh of short transmission lines. However, the basic idea of all time domain volume meshing EM tools is similar to what we describe above. The entire volume is meshed, an input pulse is applied, the time-domain response is calculated one time-step at a time, and then the output is (usually) converted from time-domain to frequency-domain.

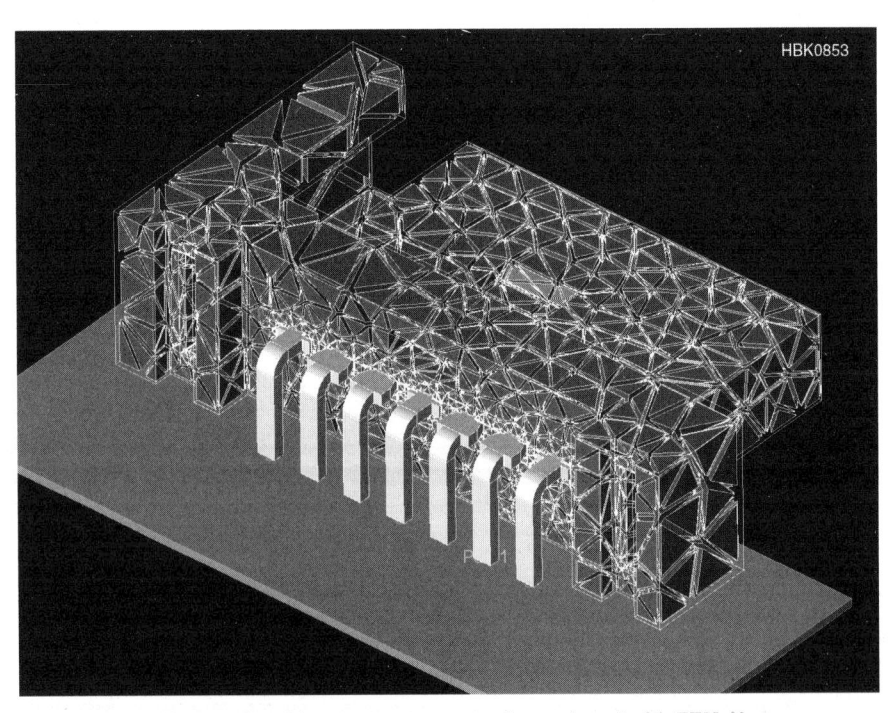

Figure 6.23 — Extremely arbitrary structures can be analyzed with FEM. Here we see the meshing for a PCB multi-pin connector. High accuracy analysis at high frequency is critical when high performance is needed. The entire volume is meshed with tetrahedra. For clarity, the tetrahedra used for meshing are outlined only where they intersect with a surface of the connector. [Courtesy Keysight, used with permission]

software analyzes the response at that frequency. Then we specify a second frequency, and repeat the analysis for the new frequency. This repeats until we have results at all frequencies of interest.

The advantage of frequency domain analysis is that we analyze only the frequencies that we want. In addition, we now need to solve only for the three spatial dimensions. We already know that the fields all vary in time with a sine wave at a given frequency. We are however, restricted to working with linear circuits. Given input at a single frequency, linear circuits have only that exactly same frequency present everywhere in the circuit. An amplifier or a mixer would have several frequencies bouncing around even if only one frequency is input. Given only one frequency is present everywhere, our EM analysis now needs to solve only for the magnitude and phase of that sine wave. The advantage of time domain analysis is that we get all the frequencies (by using the FFT on the impulse response) with a single analysis.

FEM starts just like FDTD, by discretizing the structure we are analyzing. For RF work, FEM tools mesh our structure into tetrahedral (a three-sided pyramid with a triangular base). **Figure 6.23** shows an example of a multi-pin connector meshing. The rectangular hexahedral mesh used for structures in FDTD often leaves a "staircase" appearance. The staircase can be reduced by making the mesh very fine, but this increases memory requirements and analysis time. With pictures, the pixels also give a staircase appearance too. But with today's cameras, the pixels are so tiny (and there are so many of them) that they are hard to see without magnification.

FEM can use tetrahedra of any size. Thus curving surfaces appear to be meshed into triangles (the exposed surface of each tetrahedra). This is often a better representation of the surface than is possible with the hexahedral cells of FDTD. In addition, since different size tetrahedra can be used as desired, the accuracy of the mesh can be varied. Very tiny tetrahedra can be used where the highest accuracy is needed, and large tetrahedra can be used elsewhere. In fact, an initial solution can be performed and the error estimated everywhere. Adaptive meshing then refines the mesh (makes more and smaller tetrahedra) where ever the error is too high. Thus the fine mesh, which can consume a lot of analysis time and computer memory, is only used where it is needed. Care should be taken because the region of fine mesh might require modification depending on the frequency of analysis and on how the structure is excited.

The mathematics of FEM can get very involved, and there are many different ways to implement it. High level, we must cast the problem into what is called a "variational form." For example, an equation for the energy in, say, a microwave filter, given some boundary conditions (like an RF voltage source on the input) is a variational form. FEM then finds the EM fields consistent with Maxwell's equations and the given boundary conditions that give the minimum total energy. That field is the solution.

We can intuitively see why the minimum energy solution is the correct solution. Imagine a length of a thin, moderately wide conductor on a printed circuit board. Next, we place static electric charge on the conductor. Electrons are all negative and repel each other, pushing themselves to opposite edges of the conductor as best they can. We now have the highest charge on the edges of the conductor and lower charge towards the center of the conductor. This configuration of charge gives the minimum potential energy for the charge. This is the solution that FEM finds. It makes sense, highest charge on the edges means we have the highest voltage there too. If we add too much charge, the sharp edges are where the arcs and sparks will come from (do not try this at home!).

Mathematically, the situation for RF is nearly identical. It is just that instead of charge, we have RF current flowing. The RF current flows most strongly on the edges of a planar (for example, printed circuit board, PCB) conductor. In fact, if we run too much RF current, the edges literally start evaporating. This can actually happen even with low power if the conductor dimensions are very small, for example, on a silicon RF integrated circuit (SiRFIC) as is widely used in cell phones. In this case, the evaporation process is called "electromigration." SiRFIC designers add a layer of insulator on top of the RF conductors because of this problem. Otherwise, our cell phone would quickly fail. **Figure 6.24** shows a drawing of a typical RFIC made using GaAs (instead of silicon) mounted on a carrier. This was prepared using CAD (computer aided design) software and is ready for FEM meshing.

Thus, FEM is similar to an optimization problem. As such it is often iterative. It will try an initial (usually fast, coarse mesh, high error) analysis and evaluate the error (i.e., non-minimum energy) everywhere in that solution. Then the FEM software refines the meshing and refines the solution. This process repeats until the error is below a user-specified threshold. If you feel you need a better solution, just make the error threshold smaller. For high-accuracy work, it is best to refine the solution until all FEM calculated fields and currents appear smooth (error appears as noise in the fields). Sharp edges (as in PCB and SiRFIC) should have smooth high current. However, results can be useful even if error is still apparent in the field display. **Figure 6.25** shows a high quality result for a complex coaxial connector-to-PCB transition.

As we can see above, a major strength of the volume meshing techniques, like FEM and FDTD, is that they can easily analyze just about anything no matter what shape it is. These techniques excel by being able to handle extremely arbitrary structures, provided (as with all EM analyses) the problem does not get too big for our computer memory or our willingness to wait for an answer.

Next, we consider a technique that can

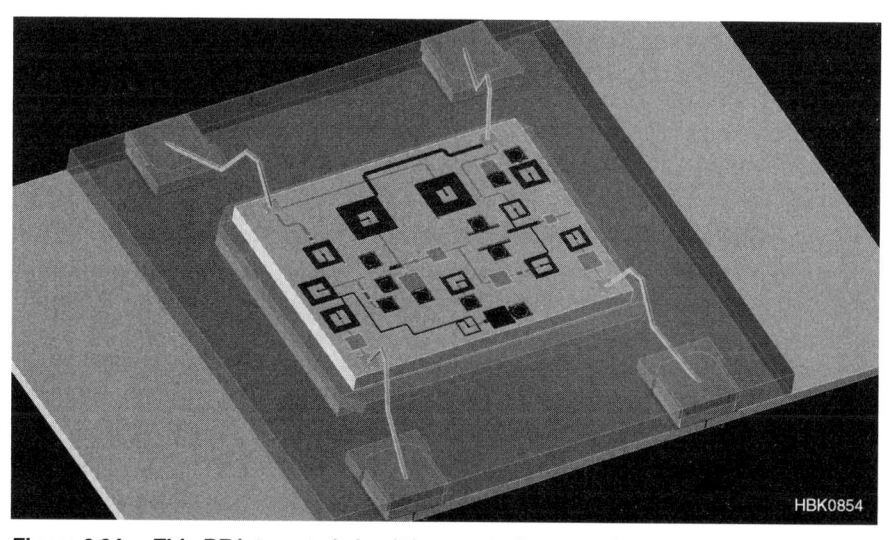

Figure 6.24 — This RF integrated circuit is mounted on a carrier with wire bonds making connections to the outside world. This is a view of the circuit prior to meshing. FEM can analyze the entire structure including all electromagnetic interactions. [Courtesy Keysight, used with permission]

Figure 6.25 — FEM has meshed a circuit with two coaxial connectors transitioning to two PCB conductors. The PCB conductors then come close to each other to form the start of a coupled line. The color coding shows current density on the conductors with red (or bright) indicating high current. This includes a ground plane on the underside, which we can see through the narrow slots between the PCB conductors and the ground plane that surrounds them on the top side of the substrate. This is known as CPW, or coplanar waveguide. Note that the current is smooth with high current on the edges, indicating a high quality result. [Courtesy Keysight, used with permission]

handle much larger problems, but only if the problem is appropriate for the technique.

SURFACE MESHING — METHOD OF MOMENTS

Like FEM and FDTD, *Method of Moments* (MoM) was developed in the 1960s. MoM was fully formalized and popularized in the West by Prof. Roger Harrington of Syracuse University. He named it after similar work that had previously been performed in Russia. The equations needed to understand Method of Moments can be difficult. Fortunately, the concept is easy to understand:

Imagine we have a planar circuit, say a filter on a printed circuit board (PCB). In the first step, we discretize (divide into small subsections) only the metal of the circuit. In contrast with volume meshing techniques, we do not mesh the substrate and we do not mesh the air around the substrate. We mesh only the metal of the circuit. Next, we put current (at a given RF frequency) on one subsection of that circuit. We calculate how much voltage that bit of RF current induces on all other subsections. We can view this as one tiny transmitting antenna (the subsection with current) and all the other subsections are tiny receiving antennas. Typically high voltage is induced on nearby subsections, and lower voltage on more distant subsections. The effect of the PCB dielectric material is included in this calculation. (This is the step where the math can get really complicated. But all that has already been done. You don't have to worry about it!)

This calculation (i.e., current on one subsection induces voltage on all other subsections) is repeated for all subsections in the circuit, one at a time. All this information is stored on the computer in the form of a matrix. Next, the computer puts current on all subsections at the same time. This, as previously calculated, induces voltage in all the subsections in the circuit. Every subsection has voltage induced in it from all the other subsections in the circuit. In fact, each subsection also has voltage induced in it due to itself. All these voltages in all of these subsections add together.

But a perfect conductor (which is our assumption for this description) cannot have any voltage at all across it! (Measure the voltage across any piece of copper. It is really close to short circuit, zero voltage. A perfect conductor would be exactly zero voltage.) So, the computer adjusts all the currents in all the subsections so that there is zero voltage in all the subsections. (In practice, this is actually done by a process called "matrix inversion.") Of course, the subsection that we are using for the input to the circuit must have some voltage across it. Otherwise, we will have zero current (and zero voltage) everywhere... no fun in that!

The currents in all the subsections that give us zero voltage everywhere that there is conductor (given an input voltage in the input subsection) is the current distribution in the conductor. That is our solution. Next, we take the now-known current on the input subsection and, given the voltage we assumed on that subsection, we can calculate the input impedance. Repeat this process for each frequency of interest and we have a plot of the input impedance as a function of frequency. We now have all this information without ever having built anything.

This implementation of the method of moments is restricted to planar circuits only. Arbitrary 3D structures, including those illustrated in the previous section, are not appropriate for this approach. The reason planar method of moments has seen widespread use is that it can handle much larger planar circuits at high levels of accuracy, provided the circuits are planar. Appropriate planar circuits can include a large number of layers. PCBs in a computer might contain as many as 28 layers. This is no problem for the method of moments. Sometimes planar problems are referred to as having 2.5 dimensions, rather than full 3D. However, full 3D fields and full 3D current are calculated (conducting vias allow current to flow vertically between layers), so describing this kind of problem as 3D planar is more accurate. Fields and currents are 3D, while the circuit is formed on layered (i.e., planar) dielectric.

RF and microwave designers usually work with S-parameters, or "Scattering-Parameters." (See the chapter on **RF Techniques** for a discussion of S-parameters.) For example, we could take the input impedance calculated above and convert it to SWR (standing wave ratio) or VSWR (voltage standing wave ratio). We can also mathematically convert either the VSWR or input impedance into a *reflection coefficient*. This gives us the voltage amplitude of the reflected wave given a 1 volt incident wave. When we include the phase of the reflected wave in the calculation, it becomes an S-parameter.

If we are dealing with a 2-port filter (an input port and an output port), we also need to know how much of that the 1 volt wave incident on the input makes it to the output. (2-port circuits are discussed in the RF Techniques chapter.) This is a *transmission coefficient*. Now, let's say, our antenna is not perfectly matched and reflects RF back to the output of our filter. In response, the filter output now generates a reflected wave that goes right back to the antenna. This is called an *output reflection coefficient*. Finally, a portion of that wave that was reflected from the antenna and is hitting the output of our filter finds its way through the filter and actually comes out of the input of the filter. This is called the *reverse transmission coefficient*. So, we have four numbers now to describe our 2-port filter.

These are all scattering parameters and for the benefit of our computer, we put them all in a 2×2 matrix.

The Method of Moments has been developed for a wide variety of problems. For example, there are a few ways to implement the Method of Moments that make it amazingly efficient for doing extremely large problems such as a radar signal illuminating an aircraft, or even an entire aircraft carrier. However, this type of implementation tends not to be as useful for, say, circuits on PCBs or other planar circuits where they can suffer reduction in speed and accuracy.

There are two widely used approaches that are preferred for MoM analysis of planar circuits. Both approaches can handle large planar circuits, even when they have multiple layers. One approach performs the required current-induces-voltage calculation assuming the planar circuit is unshielded. The other assumes the circuit is shielded. Both approaches have useful accuracy. The unshielded approach is a natural for unshielded circuits, such as antennas. The shielded approach is a natural for shielded circuits, such as a filter inside a shielding box. However, each approach can flex into the other's domain. The shielded approach benefits from a more accurate induced voltage calculation but it requires an underlying, fine pixel-like grid for meshing. The unshielded approach benefits from allowing arbitrary subsection size, which can be handy provided the required less accurate induced-voltage calculation is not of concern.

Figure 6.26 shows a typical circuit analyzed using shielded 3D planar method of moments. This is a spiral inductor on silicon, a critical component used in many places in all cell phone RF chip sets. For example, when you make a call, the cell phone computer must move the transmitter and receiver to the channel assigned by the cell site for your call. To do this, it programs a VCO (voltage controlled oscillator) that is inside a PLL (phase locked loop) to move to the required frequency. The VCO has an inductor as part of its tuned circuit. From the view point of silicon chips, inductors are gigantic. They take up a lot of space and space (or "real estate" as the RFIC designers call it) is expensive. The solution is to make the spiral turns even smaller and use more of them. However, that increases the loss. If there is too much loss, the VCO noise goes up and tuning range goes down. In the worst case, loss might be so high that the VCO does not even start oscillating.

A typical wafer fabrication ("wafer fab" for short) in which a circuit is actually etched into semiconductor material such as silicon can easily cost $1 million. We cannot build and tweak a circuit. It is critical that the VCO, and everything else on that wafer, work the first time. This is where EM analysis saves the day. The designer does all the trial and

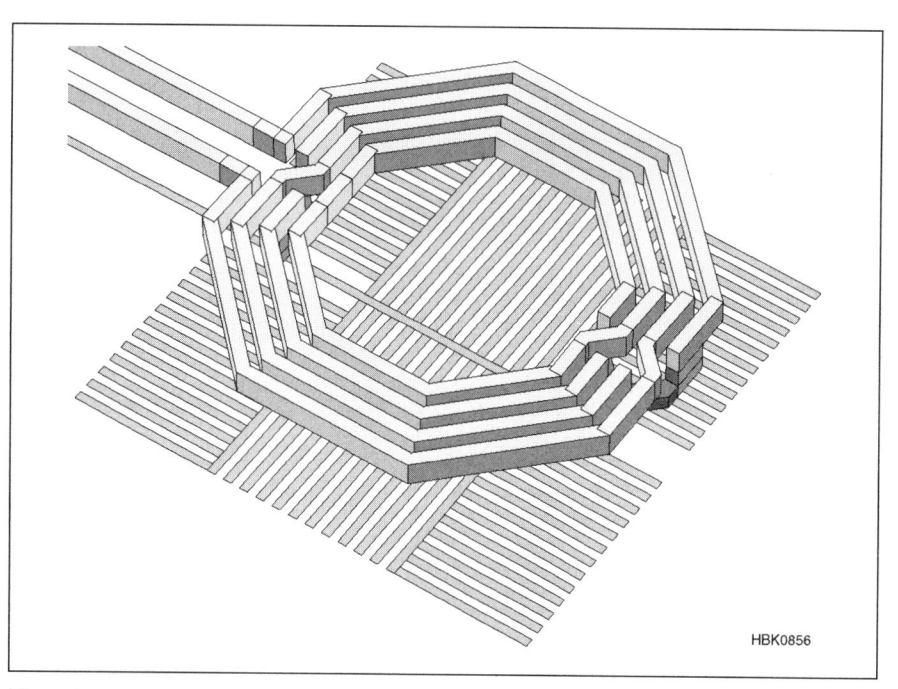

Figure 6.26 — Method of Moments can be used to analyze planar 3D circuits like this spiral inductor over silicon. Many such inductors are present in the RF chip set for every cell phone. Silicon dioxide insulator (not shown) gives some separation between the bottom of the inductor and the top of the semi-conducting silicon. To reduce inductor losses, a grid-like ground shield is placed directly on the silicon to try to keep the inductor fields out of the silicon. [Courtesy Sonnet, used with permission]

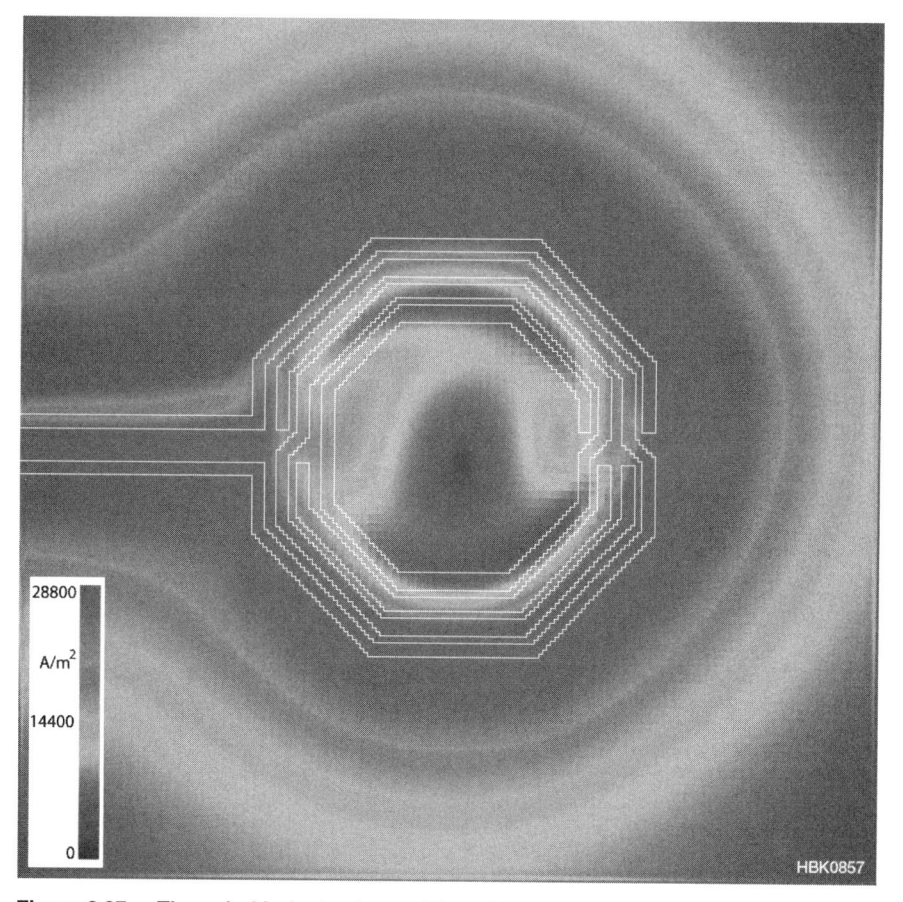

Figure 6.27 — The spiral inductor, here without the ground shield, induces current in the silicon. This current increases loss and must be minimized. [Courtesy Sonnet, used with permission]

Computer-Aided Circuit Design   6.21

A *Sonnet* Tutorial using Port Tuning

Up to this point, we have described how EM software solves what is called the "analysis" problem. In other words, we have a planar RF circuit layout and we need to analyze the RF circuit response. This was a huge advantage when it first became available because without it, we would be forced to build a circuit and then measure it. Of course, it would never work quite the way we wanted it to work. Now what do we do?

Before EM software, we would get out the razor knife and little bits of copper and start tuning the circuit. Maybe this open-circuited stub needs to be a little shorter. But if shorter makes it worse, now we realize we need to make it longer. Get out the soldering iron. High-level designers could dab on some silver epoxy. Those days are gone, thank goodness.

With EM analysis, we just make the open stub (or whatever part of the circuit you think might improve the response) a little shorter or a little longer and then repeat the analysis. This is so much better than the old days!

As you might imagine, we are never satisfied. Each time we repeat the EM analysis, it can be a long wait, especially for the larger and more complicated circuits. We want something faster.

Over the last decade, a much faster methodology has developed called *port tuning*. We can do things with EM analysis that we could never do with a circuit that we actually built. For example, a typical filter has a few resonators in it. These are often just half-wave long lengths of line, just like a dipole antenna, but often with nothing connected. If our filter has its passband a little bit low in frequency, we make the resonator shorter. If the passband is a little too high, we make it longer. It turns out that port tuning lets us do this without having to repeat the entire EM analysis each time.

The following section uses a port-tuning exercise to illustrate this using *Sonnet*. If you would like to follow along, download the free *SonnetLite* at **www.sonnetsoftware.com**. The following description is for *Sonnet Version 16*. If you have a later version, the user interface will probably be somewhat different.

After you install the software, go through the *Sonnet* tutorial by selecting HELP->GETTING STARTED from the menus at the top. Concentrate on Chapter 4, "Tutorial: A Quick Tour". It will take around one hour to do this.

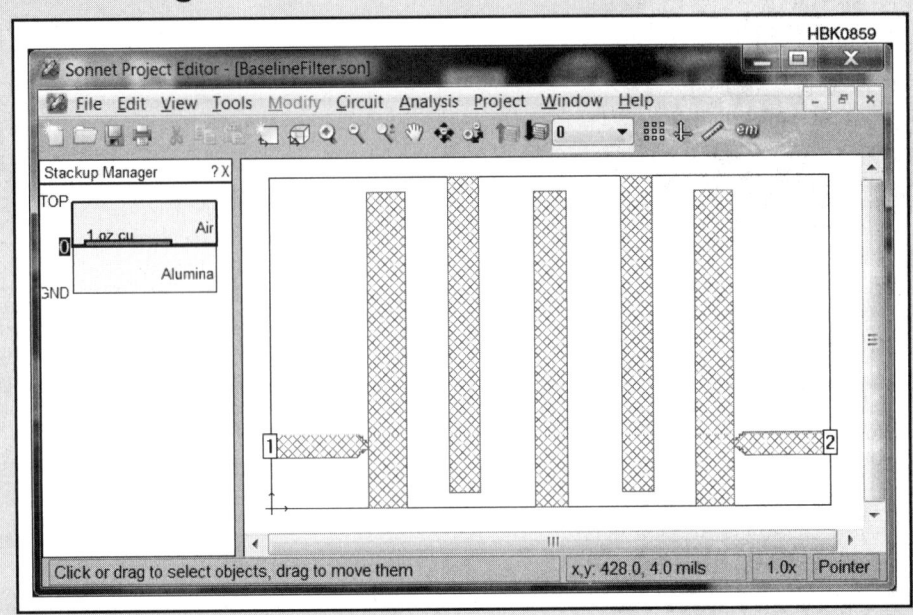

Figure A — The baseline filter that we use to illustrate port tuning is made of quarter wavelength resonators, each grounded at one end to a perfectly conducting sidewall that is present at the edge of the substrate. [Courtesy Sonnet, used with permission]

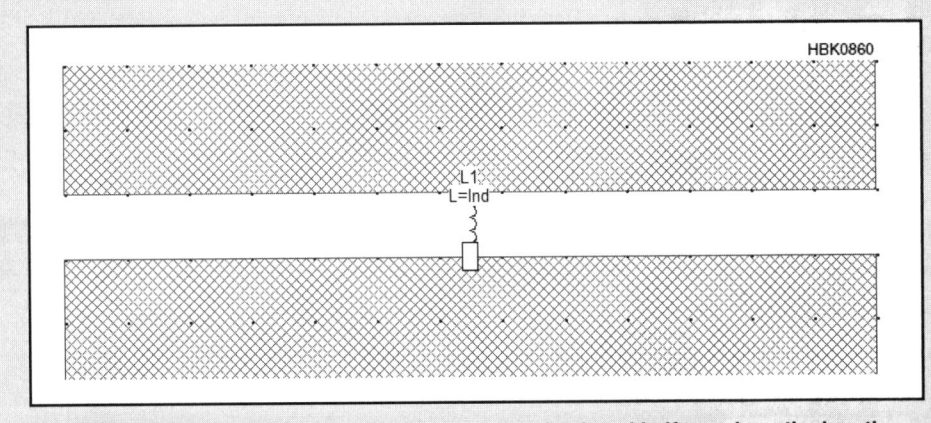

Figure B — Following instructions in the text, a gap is placed halfway along the length of the first (left) resonator. This is a zoomed detail of the inductor component that was inserted in that gap. The value of the inductance, "Ind", is a variable parameter that will be tuned. [Courtesy Sonnet, used with permission]

When you are finished, you can start your first port tuning project.

Upon completing Chapter 4 of the tutorial, you will have the layout of **Figure A** on your *Sonnet* screen. The *Sonnet* file for this filter is *BaselineFilter.son* with the downloadable supplemental content. This is an interdigital filter. The resonators are one-quarter wavelength long with one end of each resonator shorted to ground. The antenna equivalent is a quarter-wavelength vertical antenna, which also has one end shorted to ground.

Select one of the resonators to tune. For this example, we select the first (left) resonator, but any resonator can be tuned with this method. Lengthening a resonator lowers the resonant frequency and shortening a resonator increases the resonant frequency. To tune the length of the resonator you selected, we need to remove a very small portion of the resonator creating

6.22   Chapter 6

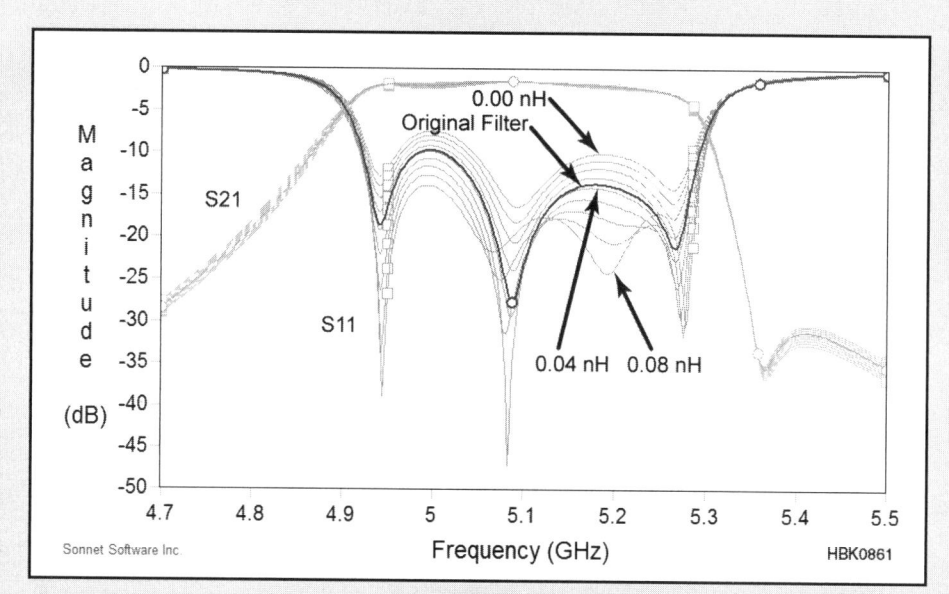

Figure C — Results of running a parameter sweep for the value of "Ind" from 0 to 0.08 nH shows that 0.04 nH gives almost the same response as the original (untuned) filter. A value of 0.08 nH gives an improved reflection coefficient ("S11") and indicates the first resonator should be made 0.002 inch longer (see text for details). [Courtesy Sonnet, used with permission]

a narrow gap. Then we replace the piece we removed with a small, ideal inductor. Repeating an EM analysis for every little change in a layout takes time. But we can change the small inductor and get nearly instantaneous analysis results.

Before proceeding, it is worth your time to read Chapter 7, about Components, of the *Sonnet Version 16 User's Manual* (HELP->MANUALS). We are inserting an "Ideal Component", an inductor. Here is step-by-step description for SonnetLite Version 16:

1) Select EDIT->DIVIDE POLYGONS.
2) Cut across the width of the desired resonator about half way along the length (the exact position is not critical).
3) Select EDIT->DIVIDE POLYGONS again.
4) Cut across the width of the resonator again, one cell away from your first cut. A "cell" is the smallest bit of metal allowed for a given analysis. The cell size is indicated by a grid of dots. For this project, the cell size was set to 0.002 inches square.
5) Select the one cell long piece of resonator and press DELETE. This leaves a narrow gap across the width of the resonator.
6) Select MODIFY->ADD COMPONENT->IDEAL. We are going to add a small inductor across the narrow gap we just cut. In the window that appears, select Inductor, and set the Terminal Width to Feedline Width. For the value of the inductor, we will use a Sonnet variable. Type in "Ind" for the name of the inductor value variable. "Ind" is variable that we will sweep, i.e., *Sonnet* will automatically change the value of the variable and repeat the analysis. Next, click OK, and you are asked for more information about the variable. Nothing more is needed, so just click OK.
7) When the information windows you were just using disappear, click in the center of one side of the gap and click a second time in the center of the other side of the gap. This places the inductor across the gap.

Your layout, zoomed to the region around the gap, should be similar to **Figure B** (*Port Tuning Example.son* with the downloadable supplemental content). As you have likely guessed, we are going to use the inductor that we added to this layout to replace the metal that we took out to make the gap in the resonator. If it turns out a little more inductance gives us a more desirable filter, then we make the resonator a little longer. A little less inductance means we should make the resonator a little shorter. Here, even negative inductors are allowed.

First, we must find out how much inductance corresponds to how much change in resonator length by using a parameter sweep. To do a parameter sweep, read Chapters 9 and 10 of the *Sonnet Version 16* User's Manual.

Figure B shows the results of the parameter sweep, sweeping the value of the port tuning inductor from 0.0 to 0.08 nH with a step of 0.01 nH. Also plotted is the original filter, the one that we started with before adding the tuning ports. The original filter reflection coefficient is highlighted. Reflection (S11) is about −10 dB. It turns out that the curve for Ind = 0.04 nH gives a very close match to the original filter. Thus we conclude that the 0.002 inch gap in the resonator is equal to about 0.04 nH.

Next notice that the curve for Ind = 0.08 nH gives a reflection that is 5 dB better, or −15 dB. This tells us that we can improve the filter return loss by 5 dB if we make the input resonator another 0.002 inch (i.e., another 0.04 nH) longer.

If we take the original filter and increase the length of that resonator by 0.002 inch, a confirming EM analysis, *FinalFilter.son* with the downloadable supplemental content, gives us almost exactly the same response as the port tuning filter with Ind = 0.08 nH. That is the filter we will build.

There are some other practical considerations when port tuning real filters. For example, in this filter the distance from the open end of the resonator to the sidewall is 0.010 inch. Making that resonator longer by 0.002 inch reduces that distance. That increases the open end capacitance, which lowers the resonant frequency a small amount. This would become critical if the resonator must be lengthened by, say, 0.008 inch. The gap to the wall would only be 0.002 inch. Lengthening the resonator by even more would require that we move the wall.

Also, in practice, we would lengthen the resonators symmetrically. In other words, if we lengthen the input resonator, we would lengthen the output resonator by the same amount. This can be done by adding an identical inductor in an identical gap in the output resonator. The inductance of the first inductor is a variable name ("Ind") so we can just use that same variable name for the output resonator tuning inductor. Then, both resonators are automatically equal.

Computer-Aided Circuit Design 6.23

error on the computer, and then builds the circuit once.

Silicon is a lossy conductor — a semiconductor. Any RF designer knows that when we put an inductor close to a lossy conductor, the inductor loss increases. To reduce the loss, we try to get the inductor as far as possible from the silicon. A given process might have a few microns of silicon dioxide, or other insulators, deposited on top of the silicon. So, the designer puts the inductor on top of all available silicon dioxide. In Figure 6.26, these insulating layers are not shown, so it looks like the inductor is floating in air.

Another trick to reduce loss is to add a ground shield. This is the grid-like conductor pattern under the inductor. It is important that the ground shield conductors are, more or less, at right angles to the spiral inductor turns above them. If the ground shield conductors are parallel, they start to act like a shorted turn in the secondary winding of a transformer, not good!

Figure 6.27 shows the current in the surface of the silicon directly under the spiral inductor when there is no ground shield. Red (or bright) is high current. At first it is a surprise that the direction of the current (not shown) is radial, flowing toward or away from the inductor. This means the current is driven by the electric field around the inductor, not by the magnetic field. The designer wants this current to be as low as possible in order to reduce loss.

Figure 6.28 shows the substrate current in the silicon under a small portion of the inductor with a ground shield. This was analyzed using *Sonnet*, a shielded 3D planar EM tool. As mentioned above, the induced voltage calculation is very accurate for shielded tools, but a fine, underlying rectangular mesh is required. If you look closely at this zoomed image, you can see the "pixelation" caused by the fine mesh.

Normally, we view only the current in the conductors of our circuit with planar EM tools. A description of how to view tangential electric fields using something called "sense metal" in planar method of moments is given in Chapter 4 of *Sonnet Version 16* user's manual (**www.sonnetsoftware.com**). By Ohm's law, the tangential electric field on the surface of the silicon substrate is proportional the current flowing in the silicon.

Professionals often use an EM analyzer, such as *Sonnet*, in conjunction with a so-called "framework." A microwave design framework includes many different interconnected microwave-related software tools including, for example, circuit theory analysis. For port-tuning, a designer using both the Keysight Technologies *ADS* framework and *Sonnet* can use any *ADS* component as a tuning element in *Sonnet*. In this case, using a transmission line model (instead of a small inductor) makes life especially easy as the designer can simply read off the required resonator change of length right from the optimized transmission line element. Figuring out how much inductance corresponds to how much resonator length is not needed. This can even be done in *Sonnet* by using a "Project" component for tuning and making a *Sonnet* netlist project with the tuning transmission line in the project.

Finally, designers also often need to tune the length of every resonator, not just one or two of them. In addition, they also need to tune the coupling between resonators (adjust the gap between resonators). **Figure 6.29** shows an example of a filter tuned in this way. All of this can be done with port tuning, but it exceeds the capability of *SonnetLite*. For those with access to a full copy of *Sonnet* and a full microwave framework (Keysight Technologies ADS, National Instruments' *Microwave Office*, or Cadence *Virtuoso*), detailed tutorials can be found at **www.sonnetsoftware.com**.

COMMERCIAL ELECTROMAGNETIC ANALYSIS TOOLS

Below we describe most of the current RF and microwave EM software vendors that concentrate on the microwave market. These vendors have all exhibited at IMS, the International Microwave Symposium which is the premier microwave conference in the world. (See **www.ims2018.org**, for example, and search for "General Exhibition Content" to see all of the EM software vendors. Our apologies to any vendors that we missed.) All product names are trademarks of the associated vendors.

Ansoft (a division of Ansys): Widely used finite element code specialized for microwave work, *HFSS* (High Frequency Structure Simulator). Ansoft provides a variety of other EM tools, including planar unshielded method of moments. All tools are integrated into a comprehensive microwave design framework with a wide variety of circuit theory and systems simulation tools. **www.ansys.com**

AWR (a division of National Instruments): Their tool, *Axiem*, uses unshielded planar method of moments integrated into a comprehensive widely used microwave design framework (*Microwave Office*) incorporating a wide variety of circuit theory and systems simulation tools. **www.awrcorp.com**

CST (a division of Dassault Systèmes): A wide range of nearly every kind of EM solver available today. Their primary tool is based on a technique closely related to FDTD providing time-domain full 3D volume meshing EM analysis. Their wide range of tools are organized into various suites. For example, CST *Microwave Studio* includes transient, frequency domain, eigenmode, resonant, integral equation, asymptotic, and TLM solvers. **www.cst.com**

EM Software and Systems (a division of Altair): Primary product is *FEKO*, based on a fast implementation of method of moments intended for very large problems. It is hybridized with several other EM techniques including finite elements, physical optics, geometric optics, and uniform theory of diffraction. Suitable for EMC, cable harnesses, antenna placement, bio-medical, microwave circuits, and other applications. **www.feko.info**

IMST: Their main software product, *Empire XPU*, provides time domain 3D volume meshing FDTD analysis of microwave structures. They also offer a tool, *MultiLib*, that provides models for planar multi-layer microwave circuits that can be used directly in the Keysight Technologies microwave design framework *ADS*. **www.imst.com**

Integrand Software: Used widely for Si RFIC design, *EMX* is a 3D unshielded method of moments analysis that is tailored specifically for RF design work on silicon, including a high degree of automation. It is fully integrated into Cadence *Virtuoso*, a widely used Si RFIC design framework. **www.integrandsoftware.com**

Keysight Technologies: Two main EM tools, unshielded 3D planar method of moments EM analysis *Momentum*, and 3D volume meshing finite elements *EMPro*. Formerly Agilent Technologies Electronic Measurement Group, they offer the largest and most widely used range of integrated microwave tools including their microwave design framework, *ADS* (*Advanced Design System*). **www.keysight.com/find/eesof**

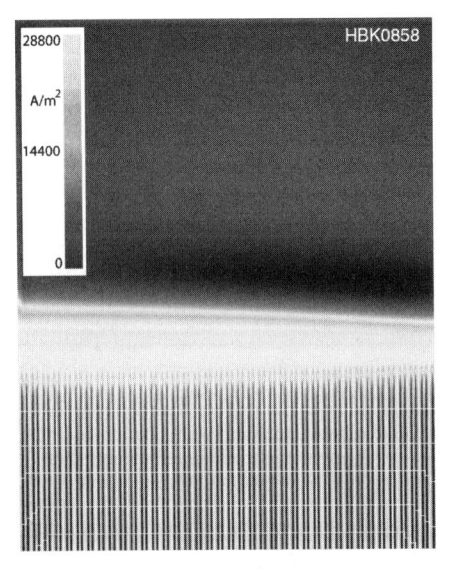

Figure 6.28 — A small section of the current in the silicon under the inductor with ground shield in place shows a strongly modified current in the silicon. Whether or not inductor loss is actually decreased, or increased, strongly

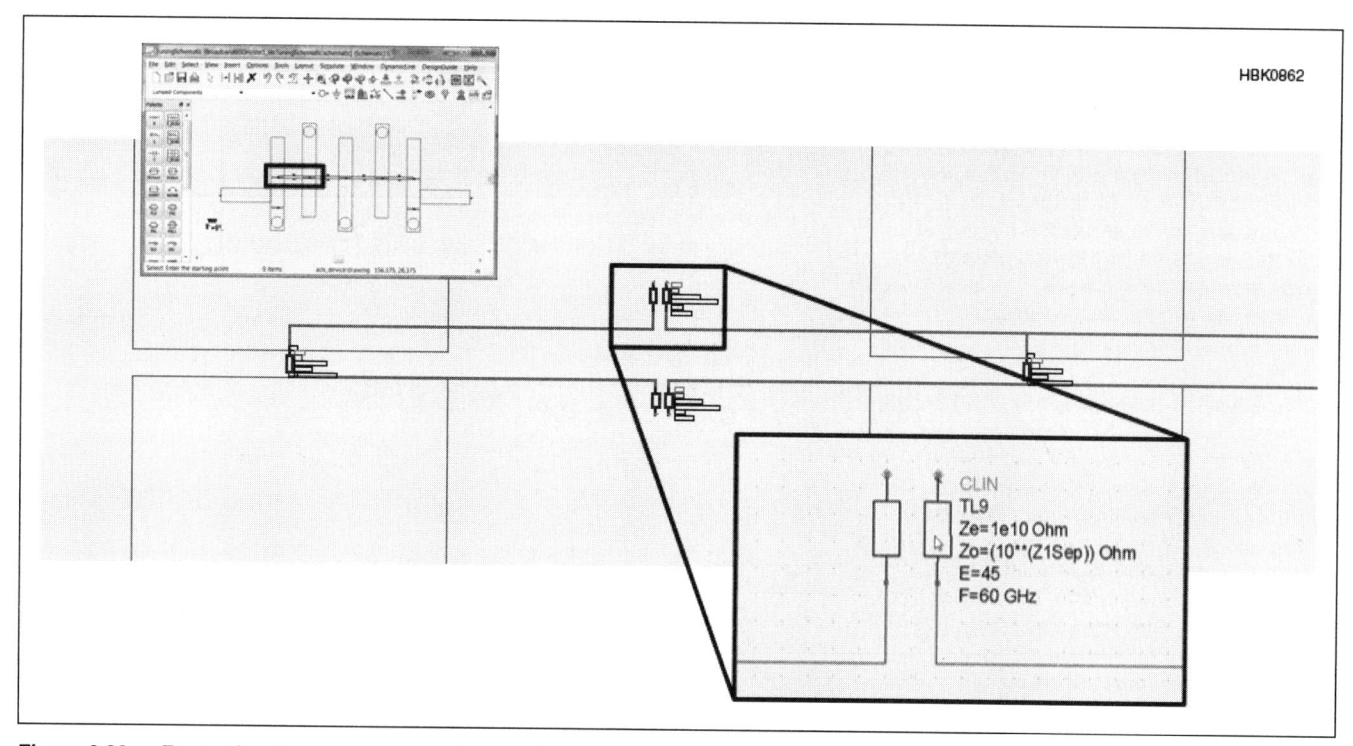

Figure 6.29 — For professional use, port tuning can be used to tune all resonator lengths and couplings between resonators in order to obtain the desired response. This illustrates a filter tuned using Keysight ADS and Sonnet EM analysis. The lower right detail illustrates a circuit theory coupled line used to fine tune the coupling between two resonators. [Courtesy Sonnet, used with permission]

Mician: Mode matching tool μWave *Wizard*, uses the fact that every finite volume structure has a finite set of characteristic modes, sometimes also called resonances. Any structure that can be decomposed into a set of simpler building blocks that have known modes solved for by any of the many different EM tools included can be analyzed by adding all modes together weighted so that all fields match at the boundaries between the blocks. Very fast and accurate analysis of waveguide filters, for example, is possible. A free version is available. **www.mician.com**

Microwave Innovation Group: Mode matching tool *WASP-NET*, uses the fact that every finite volume structure has a finite set of characteristic modes, sometimes also called resonances. Any structure which can be de-composed into a set of simpler building blocks that have known modes solved for by any of the many different EM tools included can be analyzed by adding all modes together weighted so that all fields match at the boundaries between the blocks. Very fast and accurate analysis of waveguide filters, for example, is possible. **www.wasp-net.com**

Remcom: Provider of *XFdtd*, a full wave 3D EM solver for antenna design and placement, mobile device design, biomedical, microwave, automotive radar, and so on. Other products include *Wireless InSite*, site-specific radio propagation software for analysis of wireless communication systems, and *XGtd*, a ray-based EM analysis tool for antenna placement on large structures such as ships and aircraft. **www.remcom.com**

Sonnet Software: Main tool, *Sonnet Suites*, integrates a shielded 3D planar method of moments EM analysis with plotting, modeling, and other tools. Sonnet also integrates well with Keysight Technologies *ADS*, AWR *Microwave Office*, and Cadence *Virtuoso* microwave design frameworks. A free version is available. **www.sonnetsoftware.com**

WIPL-D: A range of products all based on unshielded method of moments. Emphasis is on fast solution of very large problems. Primary applications include large antennas, including dish antennas, antenna placement, EM compatibility analysis (EMC), and microwave circuits. A free version is available. **www.wipl-d.com**

6.5 References and Bibliography

SIMULATION REFERENCES

Allen, J. Wayde "Gain Characterization of the RF Measurement Path," *NTIA Report TR-04-410* (Washington: US Department of Commerce: 2004). Available as **www.its.bldrdoc.gov/pub/ntia-rpt/04-410/04-410.pdf**.

Hayward, W. W7ZOI; R. Campbell, KK7B; and B. Larkin, W7PUA, *Experimental Methods in RF Design*, 2nd ed (ARRL: Newington, 2009).

P. Horowitz and W. Hill, *The Art of Electronics*, 2nd ed (Cambridge: Cambridge University Press, 1989).

Kundert, K., "Introduction to RF Simulation and its Application," **http://icslwebs.ee.ucla.edu/dejan/researchwiki/images/3/30/Rf-sim.pdf**

NXP Semiconductor: **www.nxp.com**

Newkirk, D. WJ1Z, "Math in a Box, Transistor Modeling, and a New Meeting Place," Exploring RF, *QST*, May 1995, pp 90-92.

Newkirk, D. WJ1Z, "Transistor Modeling with ARRL Radio Designer, Part 2: Optimization Produces Realistic Transistor Simulations," Exploring RF, *QST*, Jul 1995, pp 79-81.

Newkirk, D. WJ1Z, "ARRL Radio Designer as a Learning (and Just Plain Snooping) Tool," Exploring RF, *QST*, Nov 1995, pp 89-91.

Newkirk, D. WJ1Z, "An ARRL Radio Designer Voltage Probe Mystery: The 3-dB Pad that Loses 9 dB," Exploring RF, *QST*, Jan 1996, pp 79-80.

Newkirk, D. WJ1Z, "ARRL Radio Designer versus Oscillators, Part 1," Exploring RF, *QST*, Jul 1996, pp 68-69.

Newkirk, D. WJ1Z, "ARRL Radio Designer Versus Oscillators, Part 2," Exploring RF, *QST*, Sep 1996, pp 79-80.

Newkirk, D. W9VES, "Simulating Circuits and Systems with *Serenade SV*," *QST*, Jan 2001, pp 37-43.

Rohde, U. N1UL, "Mathematical Stability Problems in Modern Nonlinear Simulation Programs," *QEX*, Nov/Dec 2013, pp 16-26.

"The Spice Page," (**http://bwrcs.eecs.berkeley.edu/Classes/IcBook/SPICE/**). The home page for *SPICE*.

Tuinenga, Paul W., *Spice: A Guide to Circuit Simulation and Analysis Using Pspice*, 2nd ed (New York: Prentice-Hall, 1992).

Vladimirescu, Andrei, *The SPICE Book* (New York: John Wiley and Sons, 1994).

Silver, W. NØAX, "Hands-On Radio Experiments 83-85: Circuit Simulation," *QST*, Dec 2009 through Feb 2010.

Simulation in LTspice IV, **www.we-online.com/web/en/electronic_components/produkte_pb/fachbuecher/Trilogie_1.php**

Contents

7.1 Power Processing

7.2 AC-AC Power Conversion
    7.2.1 Fuses and Circuit Breakers

7.3 Power Transformers
    7.3.1 Volt-Ampere Rating
    7.3.2 Source Voltage and Frequency
    7.3.3 How to Evaluate an Unmarked Power Transformer

7.4 AC-DC Power Conversion
    7.4.1 Half-Wave Rectifier
    7.4.2 Full-Wave Center-Tapped Rectifier
    7.4.3 Full-Wave Bridge Rectifier
    7.4.4 Comparison of Rectifier Circuits

7.5 Voltage Multipliers
    7.5.1 Half-Wave Voltage Doubler
    7.5.2 Full-Wave Voltage Doubler
    7.5.3 Voltage Tripler and Quadrupler

7.6 Current Multipliers

7.7 Rectifier Types
    7.7.1 Semiconductor Diodes
    7.7.2 Rectifier Strings or Stacks
    7.7.3 Rectifier Ratings versus Operating Stress
    7.7.4 Rectifier Protection

7.8 Power Filtering
    7.8.1 Load Resistance
    7.8.2 Voltage Regulation
    7.8.3 Bleeder Resistors
    7.8.4 Ripple Frequency and Voltage
    7.8.5 Capacitor-Input Filters
    7.8.6 Choke-Input Filters

7.9 Power Supply Regulation
    7.9.1 Zener Diodes
    7.9.2 Linear Regulators
    7.9.3 Linear Regulator Pass Transistors
    7.9.4 Three-Terminal Voltage Regulators

7.10 "Crowbar" Protective Circuits

7.11 DC-DC Switchmode Power Conversion
    7.11.1 The Buck Converter
    7.11.2 The Boost Converter
    7.11.3 Buck-Boost and Flyback Converters
    7.11.4 The Forward Converter
    7.11.5 Parallel, Half and Full-Bridge Converters
    7.11.6 Building Switchmode Power Supplies
    7.11.7 Switchmode Control Loop Issues

7.12 High-Voltage Techniques
    7.12.1 High-Voltage Capacitors
    7.12.2 High-Voltage Bleeder Resistors
    7.12.3 High-Voltage Metering Techniques
    7.12.4 High-Voltage Transformers and Inductors
    7.12.5 Construction Techniques for High-Voltage Supplies
    7.12.6 Construction Practices for High-Voltage Safety

7.13 Batteries
    7.13.1 Choices of Secondary Batteries
    7.13.2 Lead Acid Batteries
    7.13.3 Nickel-based Batteries
    7.13.4 Lithium-based Batteries
    7.13.5 Charging Methods
    7.13.6 Discharge Methods
    7.13.7 Battery Handling
    7.13.8 DC-AC Inverters
    7.13.9 Selecting a Battery for Mobile Operation

7.14 Glossary of Power Source Terms

7.15 References and Bibliography

7.16 Power Source Projects
    7.16.1 Four-Output Switching Bench Supply
    7.16.2 12 V, 15 A Linear Power Supply
    7.16.3 13.8 V, 5 A Linear Power Supply
    7.16.4 Adjustable Resistive Load
    7.16.5 Inverting DC-DC Converter
    7.16.6 High-Voltage Power Supply
    7.16.7 Reverse-Polarity Protection Circuits
    7.16.8 Simple Sealed Lead-Acid Battery Float Charger and Switch
    7.16.9 Simple Adjustable Tracking Power Supply
    7.16.10 Overvoltage Protection for AC Generators
    7.16.11 Overvoltage Crowbar Circuit

Chapter 7

Power Sources

Our transceivers, amplifiers, accessories, computers and test equipment all require power to operate. This chapter illustrates the various techniques, components and systems used to provide power at the voltage and current levels our equipment needs. Topics range from basic transformers, rectifiers and filters to linear voltage regulation, switchmode power conversion, high voltage techniques and batteries. Material on switchmode conversion was contributed by Rudy Severns, N6LF and Chuck Mullett, KR6R. The section on batteries was contributed by Isidor Buchmann from his book *Batteries in a Portable World*. Alan Applegate, KØBG contributed the section on selecting batteries for mobile use. For the 2019 edition, John Boal, K9JEB, contributed a Simple Sealed Lead-Acid Battery Float Charger and Switch project.

Chapter 7 — Downloadable Supplemental Content

Projects
- Four Output Bench Supply
- 12 V, 15 A Power Supply — Article and PCB Template
- 13.8 V, 5 A Power Supply — PCB Template
- Dual Output Power Supply
- Revisiting the 12 V Power Supply
- Series Regulator Power Supply — Article and PCB Template
- Build an Inverting DC-DC Converter
- Adjustable Tracking Power Supply
- A Deluxe High Voltage Supply by James Garland, W8ZR
- A Small, Lightweight High-Voltage Switch-Mode Power Supply by Ralph Crumrine, NØKC
- Automatic Sealed Lead-Acid Battery Charger by Bob Lewis, AA4PB

Supplemental Articles
- Testing and Monitoring Batteries — Excerpts from *Batteries in a Portable World* by Isidor Buchmann
- Vacuum Tube and Obsolete Rectifiers

The title of this chapter reflects the broad assortment of methods for powering amateur equipment. More mobile and portable operation relies on power from batteries, for example. Hybrids of ac and dc power sources are becoming more common, blurring what has traditionally been known as a "power supply." (Generators are covered in the Portable Installations section of the chapter on **Assembling a Station**.)

7.1 Power Processing

Figure 7.1 illustrates the concept of a power processing unit inserted between the energy source and the electronic equipment or load. The *power processor* is often referred to as the *power supply*. That's a bit misleading in that the energy "supply" actually comes from some external source (battery, utility power and so forth), which is then converted to useful forms by the power processor. Be that as it may, in practice the terms "power supply" and "power processor" are used interchangeably.

The real world is even more arbitrary. Power processors are frequently referred to as *power converters* or simply as *converters*, and we will see other terms used later in this chapter. It is usually obvious from the context of the discussion what is meant and the glossary at the end of this chapter gives some additional information.

Power conversion schemes can take the form of: ac-to-ac (usually written

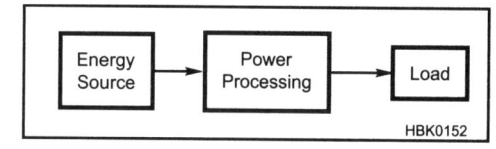

Figure 7.1 — Basic concept of power processing.

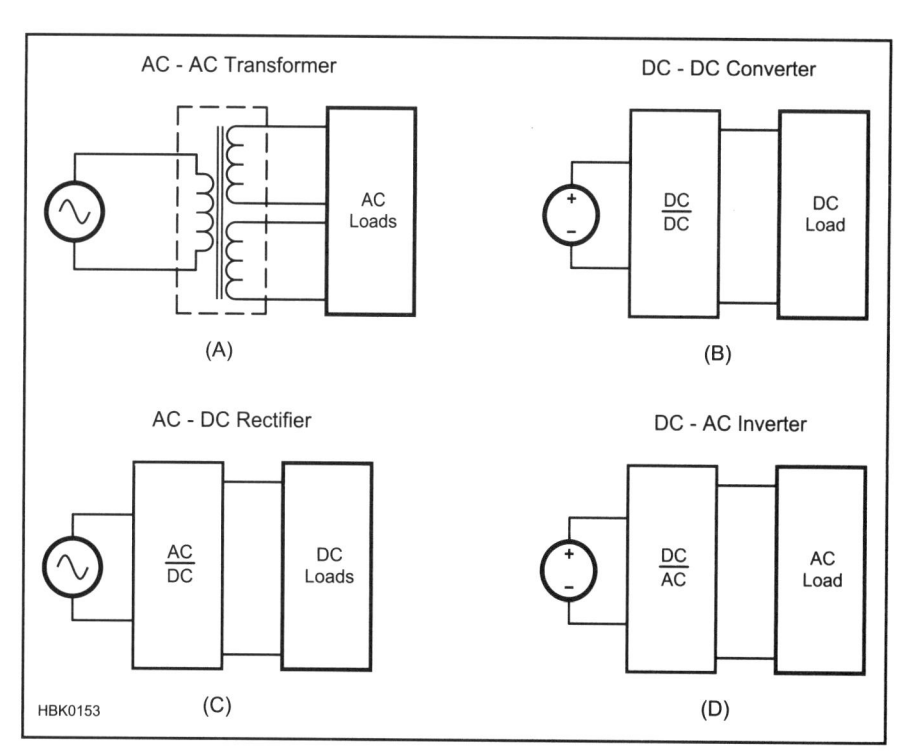

Figure 7.2 — Four power processing schemes: ac-ac, dc-dc, ac-dc and dc-ac.

ac-ac), ac-dc, dc-ac and dc-dc. Examples of these schemes are given in **Figure 7.2**. Specific names may be given to each scheme: ac-dc => rectifier, dc-dc => converter and dc-ac => inverter. These are the generally recognized terms but you will see exceptions.

Power conversion normally includes voltage and current regulation functions. For example, the voltage of a vehicle battery may vary from more than 14 V when being charged down to 10 V or less when discharged. A converter and regulator are required to maintain adequate voltage to mobile equipment at both over- and under-voltage conditions. Commercial utility power may vary from 90 to 270 V ac depending on where you are in the world. AC power converters are frequently required to handle that entire voltage range while still providing tightly regulated dc power.

7.2 AC-AC Power Conversion

In most US residences, three wires are brought in from the outside electrical-service mains to the house distribution panel. In this three-wire system, one wire is neutral and should be connected to a ground electrode. (See the **Safety** chapter for information on electrical safety.) The neutral connection to a ground rod or electrode is usually made at the distribution panel. The voltage between the other two wires is 60-Hz ac with a potential difference of approximately 240 V RMS. Half of this voltage appears between each of these wires and the neutral, as indicated in **Figure 7.3A**. In systems of this type, the 120 V household loads are divided at the breaker panel as evenly as possible between the two sides of the power mains. Heavy appliances such as electric stoves, water heaters, central air conditioners and so forth, are designed for 240 V operation and are connected across the two ungrounded wires.

Both hot wires for 240 V circuits and the single hot wire for 120 V circuits should be protected by either a fuse or breaker. A fuse or breaker or any kind of switch should *never* be used in the neutral wire. Opening the neutral wire does not disconnect the equipment from an active or "hot" line, possibly creating a potential shock hazard between that line and earth ground.

Another word of caution should be given at this point. Since one side of the ac line is grounded (through the green or bare wire — the standard household wiring color code) to earth, all communications equipment should be reliably connected to the ac-line ground through a heavy ground conductor made of strap, heavy flat-weave braid or #14 AWG or heavier wire. This safety conductor must be separate from the power wiring neutral conductor. (A properly-wired 120 V outlet with a ground terminal uses one wire for the ac hot connection, one wire for the ac neutral connection and a third wire for the safety ground connection.) This provides a measure of safety for the operator in the event of accidental short or leakage of one side of the ac line to the chassis.

Remember that the antenna system is frequently bypassed to the chassis via an RF choke or tuned circuit, which could make the antenna electrically "live" with respect to the earth ground and create a potentially lethal shock hazard. A *ground fault circuit interrupter* (GFCI or GFI) is also desirable for safety reasons, and should be a part of the shack's electrical power wiring. (See the reference item for Silver for more information on grounding and bonding.)

7.2.1 Fuses and Circuit Breakers

All transformer primary circuits should be fused properly and multiple secondary outputs should also be individually fused. To determine the approximate current rating of the fuse or circuit breaker on the line side of a power supply it is necessary to determine the total load power. This can be done by multiplying each current (in amperes) being drawn by the load or appliance, by the voltage at which the current is being drawn. In the case of linear regulated power supplies, this voltage has to be the voltage appearing at the output of the rectifiers before being applied to the regulator stage. Include the current drawn by bleeder resistors and voltage dividers. Also include filament power if the transformer is supplying vacuum tube filaments. The National Electrical Code (NEC) also specifies maximum fuse ratings based on the wire sizes used in the transformer and connections.

After multiplying the various voltages and currents, add the individual products. This is the total power drawn from the line by the supply. Then divide this power by the line voltage and add 10 to 30% to account for the inefficiency of the power supply itself. Use a fuse or circuit breaker with the nearest larger current rating. Remember that the charging of filter capacitors can create large surges of current when the supply is turned on. If fuse blowing or breaker tripping at turn on is a problem, use slow-blow fuses, which allow for high initial surge currents.

For low-power semiconductor circuits, use fast-blow fuses. As the name implies, such fuses open very quickly once the current exceeds the fuse rating by more than 10%.

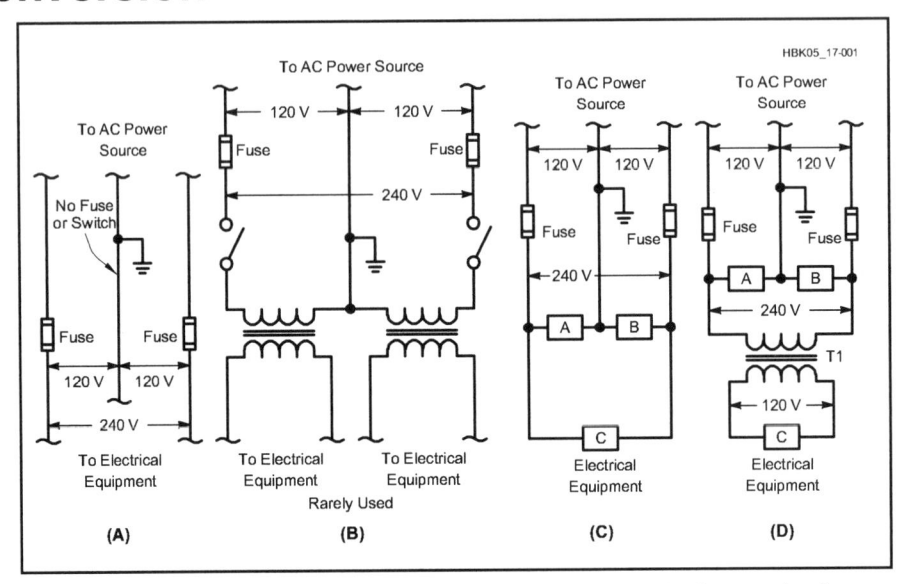

Figure 7.3 — Three-wire power-line circuits. At A, normal three-wire-line termination. No fuse should be used in the grounded (neutral) line. The ground symbol is the power company's ground, not yours! Do not connect anything other than power return wiring, including the equipment chassis, to the power neutral wire. At B, the "hot" lines each have a switch, but a switch in the neutral line would not remove voltage from either side of the line and should never be used. At C, connections for both 120 and 240 V transformers. At D, operating a 120 V plate transformer from the 240 V line to avoid light blinking. T1 is a 2:1 step-down transformer.

7.3 Power Transformers

Numerous factors are considered to match a transformer to its intended use. Some of these parameters are:

1. Output voltage and current (volt-ampere rating).
2. Power source voltage and frequency.
3. Ambient temperature.
4. Duty cycle and temperature rise of the transformer at rated load.
5. Mechanical considerations like weight, shape and mounting.

7.3.1 Volt-Ampere Rating

In alternating-current equipment, the term *volt-ampere* (*VA*) is often used rather than the term watt. This is because ac components must handle reactive power as well as real power. If this is confusing, consider a capacitor connected directly across the secondary of a transformer. The capacitor appears as a reactance that permits current to flow, just as if the load were a resistor. The current is at a 90º phase angle, however. If we assume a perfect capacitor, there will be no heating of the capacitor, so no real power (watts) will be delivered by the transformer. The transformer must still be capable of supplying the voltage, and be able to handle the current required by the reactive load. The current in the transformer windings will heat the windings as a result of the I^2R losses in the winding resistances. The product of the voltage and current in the winding is referred to as "volt-amperes," since "watts" is reserved for the real, or dissipated, power in the load. The volt-ampere rating will always be equal to, or greater than, the power actually being drawn by the load.

The number of volt-amperes delivered by a transformer depends not only upon the dc load requirements, but also upon the type of dc output filter used (capacitor or choke input), and the type of rectifier used (full-wave center tap or full-wave bridge). With a capacitive-input filter, the heating effect in the secondary is higher because of the high peak-to-average current ratio. The volt-amperes handled by the transformer may be several times the power delivered to the load. The primary winding volt-amperes will be somewhat higher because of transformer losses. This point is treated in more detail in the section on ac-dc conversion. (See the **Electrical Fundamentals** chapter for more information on transformers and reactive power.)

7.3.2 Source Voltage and Frequency

A transformer operates by producing a magnetic field in its core and windings. The intensity of this field varies directly with the instantaneous voltage applied to the transformer primary winding. These variations, coupled to the secondary windings, produce the desired output voltage. Since the transformer appears to the source as an inductance in parallel with the (equivalent) load, the primary will appear as a short circuit if dc is applied to it. The unloaded inductance of the primary (also known as the *magnetizing inductance*) must be high enough so as not to draw an excess amount of input current at the design line frequency (normally 60 Hz in the US). This is achieved by providing a combination of sufficient turns on the primary and enough magnetic core material so that the core does not saturate during each half-cycle.

The voltage across a winding is directly related to the time rate of change of magnetic flux in the core. This relationship is expressed mathematically by $V = N\, d\Phi/dt$ as described in the section on Inductance in the **Electrical Fundamentals** chapter. The total flux in turn is expressed by $\Phi = A_e B$, where A_e is the cross-sectional area of the core and B is the flux density.

The maximum value for *flux density* (the magnetic field strength produced in the core) is limited to some percentage (< 80% for example) of the maximum flux density that the core material can stand without saturating, since in saturation the core becomes ineffective and causes the inductance of the primary to plummet to a very low level and input current to rise rapidly. Saturation causes high primary currents and extreme heating in the primary windings.

At a given voltage, 50 Hz ac creates more flux in an inductor or transformer core because the longer time period per half-cycle results in more flux and higher magnetizing current than the same transformer when excited by same 60-Hz voltage. For this reason, transformers and other electromagnetic equipment designed for 60-Hz systems must not be used on 50-Hz power systems unless specifically designed to handle the lower line frequency.

7.3.3 How to Evaluate an Unmarked Power Transformer

Hams who regularly visit hamfests frequently develop a junk box filled with used and unmarked transformers. Over time, transformer labels or markings on the coil wrappings may come off or be obscured. There is a good possibility that the transformer is still useable, but the problem is to determine what voltages and currents the transformer can supply. First consider the possibility that you may have an audio transformer or other impedance-matching device rather than a power transformer. If you aren't sure, don't connect it to ac power!

If the transformer has color-coded leads, you are in luck. There is a standard for transformer lead color-coding, as is given in the **Component Data and References** chapter. Where two colors are listed, the first one is the main color of the insulation; the second is the color of the stripe.

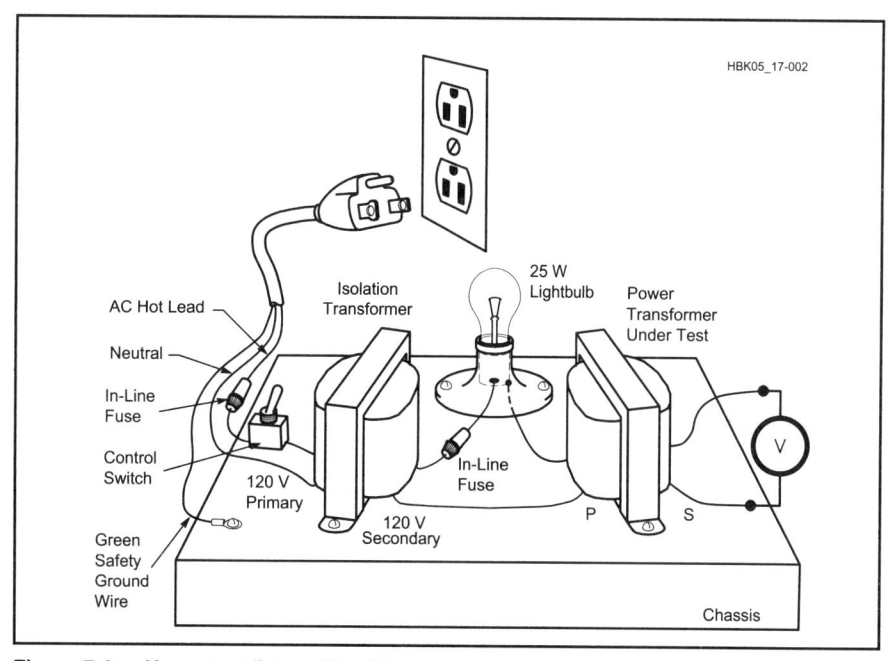

Figure 7.4 — Use a test fixture like this to test unknown transformers. Don't omit the isolation transformer, and be sure to insulate all connections before you plug into the ac mains.

Check the transformer windings with an ohmmeter to determine that there are no shorted (or open) windings. In particular, check for continuity between any winding and the core. If you find that a winding has been shorted to the core, do not use the transformer! The primary winding usually has a resistance higher than a filament winding and lower than a high-voltage winding.

Figure 7.4 shows that a convenient way to test the transformer is to rig a pair of test leads to an electrical plug with a 25 W household light bulb in series to limit current to safe (for the transformer) levels. For safety reasons use an isolation transformer and be sure to insulate all connections before you plug into the ac mains. Switch off the power while making or changing any connections. You can be electrocuted if the voltmeter leads or meter insulation are not rated for the transformer output voltage! If in doubt, connect the meter with the circuit turned off, then apply power while you are not in contact with the circuit. *Be careful! You are dealing with hazardous voltages!*

Connect the test leads to each winding separately. The filament/heater windings will cause the bulb to light to full brilliance because a filament winding has a very low impedance and almost all the input voltage will be across the series bulb. The high-voltage winding will cause the bulb to be extremely dim or to show no light at all because it will have a very high impedance, and the primary winding will probably cause a small glow. The bulb glows even with the secondary windings open-circuited because of the small magnetizing current in the transformer primary.

When the isolation transformer output is connected to what you think is the primary winding, measure the voltages at the low-voltage windings with an ac voltmeter. If you find voltages close to 6 V ac or 5 V ac, you know that you have identified the primary and the filament windings. Label the primary and low voltage windings.

Even with the light bulb, a transformer can be damaged by connecting ac mains power to a low-voltage or filament winding. In such a case the insulation could break down in a primary or high-voltage winding because of the high turns ratio stepping up the voltage well beyond the transformer ratings.

Connect the voltmeter to the high-voltage windings. Remember that transformers from vacuum tube equipment may supply as much as 800 V_{pk} or so across the winding, so make sure that your meter can withstand these potentials without damage and that you use the voltmeter safely.

Divide 6.3 (or 5) by the voltage you measured across the 6.3 V (or 5 V) winding in this test setup. This gives a multiplier that you can use to determine the actual no-load voltage rating of the high-voltage secondary. Simply multiply the ac voltage measured across the high-voltage winding by the multiplier.

The current rating of the windings can be determined by loading each winding with the primary connected directly (no bulb) to the ac line. Using power resistors, increase loading on each winding until its voltage drops by about 10% from the no-load figure. The current drawn by the resistors is the approximate winding load-current rating.

7.4 AC-DC Power Conversion

One of the most common power supply functions is the conversion of ac power to dc, or *rectification*. The output from the rectifier will be a combination of dc, which is the desired component, and ac *ripple* superimposed on the dc. This is an undesired but inescapable component. Since most loads cannot tolerate more than a small amount of ripple on the dc voltage, some form of filter is required. The result is that ac-dc power conversion is performed with a rectifier-filter combination as shown in **Figure 7.5**.

As we will see in the rectifier circuit examples given in the next sections, sometimes the rectifier and filter functions will be separated into two distinct parts but very often the two will be integrated. This is particularly true for voltage and current multipliers as described in the sections on multipliers later in the chapter. Even when it appears that the rectifier and filter are separate elements, there will still be a strong interaction where the design and behavior of each part depends heavily on the other. For example the current waveforms in the rectifiers and the input source are functions of the load and filter characteristics. In turn the voltage waveform applied to the filter depends on the rectifier circuit and the input source voltages. To simplify the discussion we will treat the rectifier connections and the filters separately but always keeping in mind their interdependence.

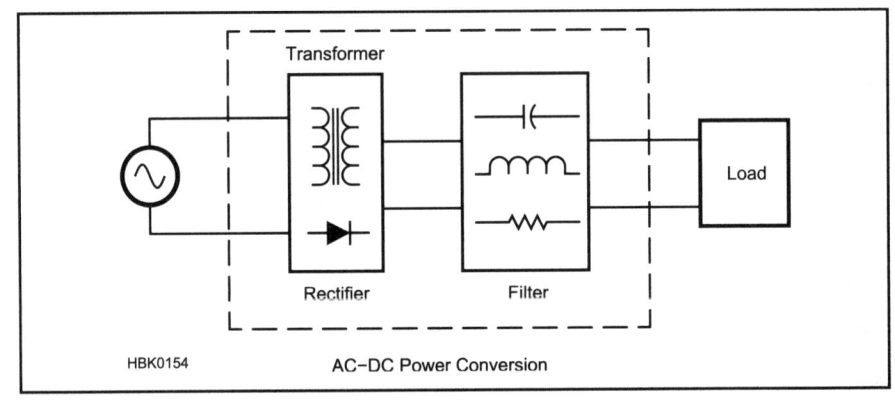

Figure 7.5 — Ac-dc power conversion with a rectifier and a filter.

The following rectifier-filter examples assume a conventional 60 Hz ac sine wave source, but these circuits are frequently used in switching converters at much higher frequencies and with square wave or quasi-square wave voltage and current waveforms. The component values may be different but the basic behavior will be very similar.

There are many different rectifier circuits or "connections" that may be used depending on the application. The following discussion provides an overview of some of the more common ones. The circuit diagrams use the symbol for a semiconductor diode, but the same circuits can be used with the older types of rectifiers that may be encountered in older equipment.

For each circuit we will show the voltage and current waveforms in the circuit for resistive, capacitive and inductive loads. The inductive and capacitive loads represent commonly used filters. We will be interested in the peak and average voltages as well as the RMS currents.

7.4.1 Half-Wave Rectifier

Figure 7.6 shows several examples of the half-wave rectifier circuit. It begins with a simple transformer with a resistive load (Figure 7.6A) and goes on to show how the output voltage and transformer current varies when a diode and filter elements are added.

Without the diode (Figure 7.6A) the output voltage (V_R) and current are just sine waves, and the RMS current in the transformer windings will be the same as the load (R) current.

Next, add a rectifier diode in series with the load (Figure 7.6B). During one half of the ac cycle, the rectifier conducts and there is current through the rectifier to the load. During the other half cycle, the rectifier is reverse-biased and there is no current (indicated by the broken line in Figure 7.6B) in R. The output voltage is pulsating dc, which is a combination of two components: an average dc value of 0.45 E_{RMS} (the voltage read by a dc voltmeter) and line-frequency ac ripple. The transformer secondary winding current is also pulsating dc. The power delivered to R is now ½ that for Figure 7.6A but the secondary RMS winding current in Figure 7.6B is still 0.707 times what it was in Figure 7.6A.

For the same winding resistance, the winding loss, in proportion to the output power, is twice what it was in Figure 7.6A. This is an intrinsic limitation of the half-wave rectifier circuit — the RMS winding current is larger in proportion to the load power. In addition, the dc component of the secondary winding current may bias the transformer core toward saturation and increased core loss.

A filter can be used to smooth out these variations and provide a higher average dc voltage from the circuit. Because the frequency of the pulses (the ripple frequency) is low (one pulse per cycle), considerable filtering is required to provide adequately smooth dc output. For this reason the circuit is usually limited to applications where the required current is small. Parts C, D and E in Figure 7.6 show some possible capacitive and inductive filters.

As shown in Figure 7.6C and D, when a capacitor is used for filtering the output dc voltage will approach

$$V_{pk} = \sqrt{2} \times E_{RMS} = 1.4 \times E_{RMS} \quad (1)$$

and the larger we make the filter capacitance, the smaller the ripple will be.

Unfortunately, as we make the filter capacitance larger, the diode, capacitor and transformer winding currents all become high-amplitude narrow pulses which will have a very high RMS value in proportion to the power level. These current pulses are also transmitted to the input line and inject currents at harmonics of the line frequency into the power source, which may result in interference to other equipment. Narrow high-amplitude current pulses are characteristic of capacitive-input filters in all rectifier connections when driven from voltage sources.

As shown in Figure 7.6E, it is possible to use an inductive filter instead, but a second diode (D2, sometimes called a *free-wheeling diode*) should be used. Without D2 the output voltage will get smaller as we increase the size of L to get better filtering, and the output voltage will vary greatly with load. By adding D2 we are free to make L large for small output ripple but still have reasonable voltage regulation. Currents in D1 and the winding will be approximately square waves, as indicated. This will reduce the line harmonic currents injected into the source but there will still be some.

Peak inverse voltage (PIV) is the maximum voltage the rectifier must withstand when it isn't conducting. This varies with the load and rectifier connection. In the half-wave rectifier, with a resistive load the PIV is the peak ac voltage ($1.4 \times E_{RMS}$); with a capacitor filter and a load drawing little or no current, the PIV is the peak ac voltage ($1.4 \times E_{RMS}$). With a capacitor-input filter (Figure 7.6C

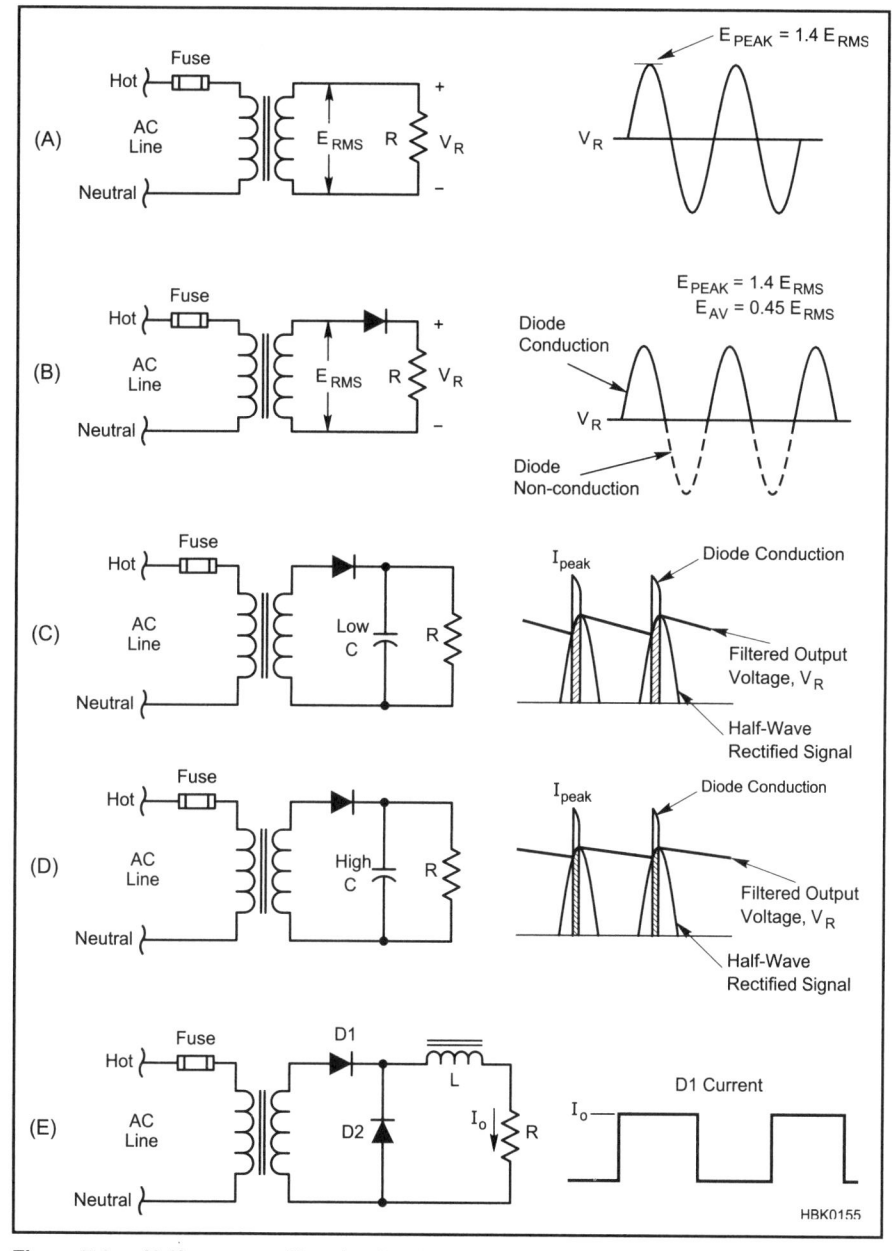

Figure 7.6 — Half-wave rectifier circuits. A illustrates the voltage waveform at the output without a rectifier. B represents the basic half-wave rectifier and the output waveform. C and D illustrate the impact of small and large filter capacitors on the output voltage and input current waveforms. E shows the effect of using an inductor filter with the half-wave rectifier. Note the addition of the shunt diode (D2) when using inductive filters with this rectifier connection.

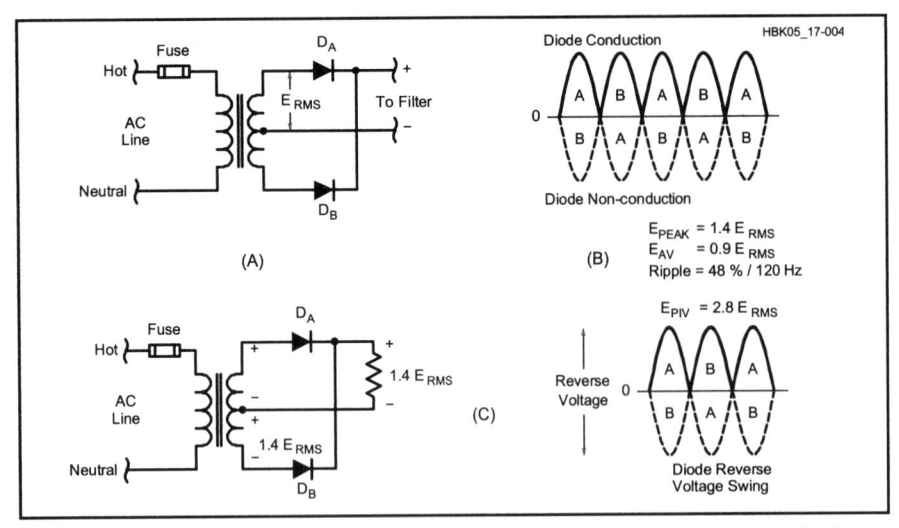

Figure 7.7 — Full-wave center-tap rectifier circuits. A illustrates the basic circuit. Diode conduction is shown at B with diodes A and B alternately conducting. The peak inverse voltage for each diode is 2.8 E_{RMS} as depicted at C.

and 7.6D), the capacitor is assumed to stay charged between the charging half-cycles. This means the rectifier output stays near 1.4 × E_{RMS} while its input reaches the full opposing peak voltage. Thus, the rectifier experiences a PIV of 2 (1.4 × E_{RMS}) = 2.8 × E_{RMS}.

7.4.2 Full-Wave Center-Tapped Rectifier

The full-wave center-tapped rectifier circuit is shown in **Figure 7.7**. The operation of this circuit can be imagined as the secondary of the transformer producing two waveforms (A and B) that are 180° out of phase that are each connected to a half-wave rectifier. The half-wave rectifier outputs are then combined so that both halves of the ac cycle are used to deliver power to the output. A transformer with a center-tapped secondary is required.

The average output voltage of this circuit is 0.9 × E_{RMS} of half the transformer secondary (the center-tap to one side); this is the maximum that can be obtained with a suitable choke-input filter. The peak output voltage is 1.4 × E_{RMS} of half the transformer secondary; this is the maximum voltage that can be obtained from a capacitor-input filter.

As can be seen in Figure 7.7C, the PIV impressed on each diode is independent of the type of load at the output. This is because the peak inverse voltage condition occurs when diode D_A conducts and diode D_B is not conducting. The positive and negative voltage peaks occur at precisely the same time, a condition different from that in the half-wave circuit. As the cathodes of diodes D_A and D_B reach a positive peak (1.4 E_{RMS}), the anode of diode D_B is at a negative peak, also 1.4 E_{RMS}, but in the opposite direction. The total peak inverse voltage is therefore 2.8 E_{RMS}. If a capacitor-input filter is used, the capacitor stays charged to nearly 1.4 × E_{RMS} during each diode's non-conducting half cycles and so the PIV is 2.8 × E_{RMS}.

Figure 7.7C shows that the ripple frequency is twice that of the half-wave rectifier (two times the line frequency). Substantially less filtering is required because of the higher ripple frequency. Since the rectifiers work alternately, each handles half of the load current. The current rating of each rectifier need be only half the total current drawn from the supply.

The problem with dc bias in the transformer core associated with the half-wave connection is largely eliminated with this circuit and the RMS current in the primary winding will also be reduced.

7.4.3 Full-Wave Bridge Rectifier

Another commonly used rectifier circuit that does not require a center-tapped transformer is illustrated in **Figure 7.8**. In this arrangement, two rectifiers operate in series on each half of the cycle, one rectifier being in the lead supplying current to the load, the other being the current return lead. As shown in Figures 7.8A and B, when the top lead of the transformer secondary is positive with respect to the bottom lead, diodes D_A and D_C will conduct while diodes D_B and D_D are reverse-biased. On the next half cycle, when the top lead of the transformer is negative with respect to the bottom, diodes D_B and D_D will conduct while diodes D_A and D_C are reverse-biased.

The output voltage wave shape and ripple frequency are the same as for the full-wave center-tapped circuit. The average dc output voltage into a resistive load or choke-input filter is 0.9 times E_{RMS} delivered by the transformer secondary; with a capacitor filter and a light load, the maximum output voltage is 1.4 times the secondary E_{RMS} voltage.

Figure 7.8C shows the PIV to be 1.4 E_{RMS} for each diode which is half that of the full-wave center-tapped circuit for the same output voltage. When an alternate pair of diodes (such as D_A and D_C) is conducting, the other diodes are essentially connected in parallel (the conducting diodes are essentially short

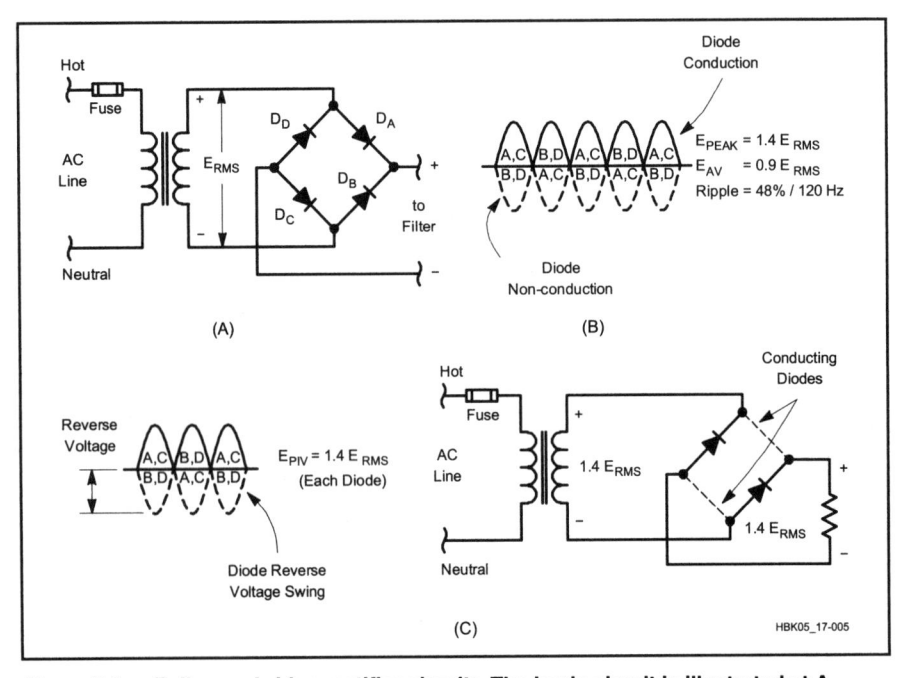

Figure 7.8 — Full-wave bridge rectifier circuits. The basic circuit is illustrated at A. Diode conduction and nonconduction times are shown at B. Diodes A and C conduct on one half of the input cycle, while diodes B and D conduct on the other. C displays the peak inverse voltage for one half cycle. Since this circuit reverse-biases two diodes essentially in parallel, 1.4 E_{RMS} is applied across each diode.

circuits) in a reverse-biased direction. This limits the diode PIV to $1.4 \times E_{RMS}$ even if a capacitor-input filter is used. Each pair of diodes conducts on alternate half cycles, with the full load current through each diode during its conducting half cycle. Since each diode is not conducting during the other half cycle the average diode current is one-half the total load current drawn from the supply.

Compared to the half-wave and full-wave center-tapped circuit, the full-wave bridge circuit further reduces the transformer RMS winding currents. In the case of a resistive load the winding currents are the same as when the resistive load is connected directly across the secondary. The RMS winding currents will still be higher when inductive and especially capacitive filters are used because of the pulsating nature of the diode and winding currents.

7.4.4 Comparison of Rectifier Circuits

Comparing the full-wave center-tapped and the full-wave bridge circuits, we can see that the center-tapped circuit has half the number of rectifiers as the bridge but these rectifiers have twice the PIV rating requirement of the bridge diodes. The diode current ratings are identical for the two circuits. The bridge makes better use of the transformer's secondary than the center-tapped rectifier, since the transformer's full winding supplies power during both half cycles, while each half of the center-tapped circuit's secondary provides power only during its positive half-cycle.

The full-wave center-tapped rectifier is typically used in high-current, low-voltage applications because only one diode conducts at a time. This reduces the loss associated with diode conduction. In the full-wave bridge circuit there are two diodes in series in conduction simultaneously, which leads to higher loss. The full-wave bridge circuit is typically used for higher output voltages where this is not a serious concern. The lower diode PIV and better utilization of the transformer windings makes this circuit very attractive for higher output voltages and higher powers typical of high voltage amplifier supplies.

Because of the disadvantages pointed out earlier, the half-wave circuit is rarely used in 60-Hz rectification except for bias supplies or other small loads. It does see considerable use, however, in high-frequency switchmode power supplies.

7.5 Voltage Multipliers

Other rectification circuits are sometimes useful, including *voltage multipliers*. These circuits function by the process of charging one or more capacitors in parallel on one half cycle of the ac waveform, and then connecting that capacitor or capacitors in series with the opposite polarity of the ac waveform on the alternate half cycle. In full-wave multipliers, this charging occurs during both half-cycles.

Voltage multipliers, particularly *voltage doublers*, find considerable use in high-voltage supplies. When a doubler is employed, the secondary winding of the power transformer need have only half the voltage that would be required for a bridge rectifier. This reduces voltage stress in the windings and decreases the transformer insulation requirements. This is not without cost, however, because the transformer-secondary *current* rating has to be correspondingly doubled for a given load current and charging of the capacitors leads to narrow high-RMS current waveforms in the transformer windings and the capacitors.

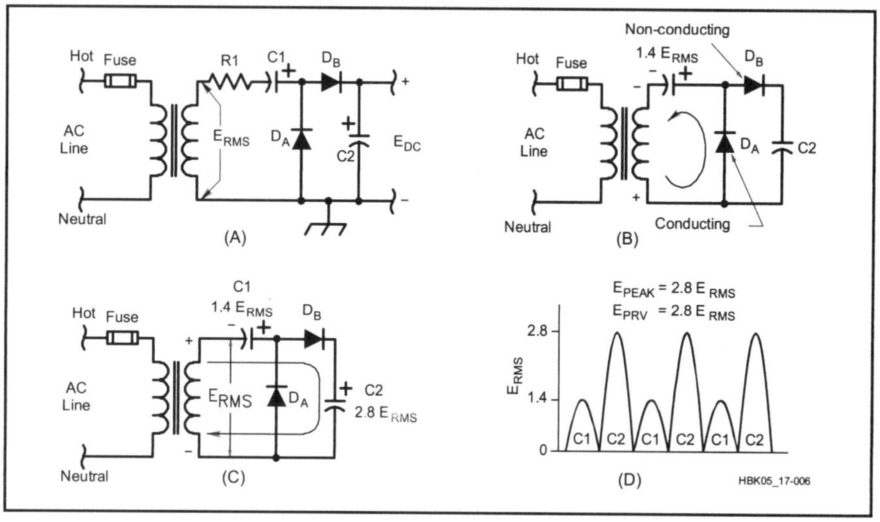

Figure 7.9 — Part A shows a half-wave voltage-doubler circuit. B displays how the first half cycle of input voltage charges C1. During the next half cycle (shown at C), capacitor C2 charges with the transformer secondary voltage plus that voltage stored in C1 from the previous half cycle. The arrows in parts B and C indicate the conventional current. D illustrates the levels to which each capacitor charges over several cycles.

7.5.1 Half-Wave Voltage Doubler

Figure 7.9 shows the circuit of a half-wave voltage doubler and illustrates the circuit operation. For clarity, assume the transformer voltage polarity at the moment the circuit is activated is that shown at Figure 7.9B. During the first negative half cycle, D_A conducts (D_B is in a nonconductive state), charging C1 to the peak rectified voltage (1.4 E_{RMS}). C1 is charged with the polarity shown in Figure 7.9B. During the positive half cycle of the secondary voltage, D_A is cut off and D_B conducts, charging capacitor C2. The amount of voltage delivered to C2 is the sum of the transformer peak secondary voltage plus the voltage stored in C1 (1.4 E_{RMS}). On the next negative half cycle, D_B is non-conducting and C2 will discharge into the load. If no load is connected across C2, the capacitors will remain charged — C1 to 1.4 E_{RMS} and C2 to 2.8 E_{RMS}. When a load is connected to the circuit output, the voltage across C2 drops during the negative half cycle and is recharged up to 2.8 E_{RMS} during the positive half cycle.

The output waveform across C2 resembles that of a half-wave rectifier circuit because C2 is pulsed once every cycle. Figure 7.9D illustrates the levels to which the two capacitors are charged throughout the cycle. In actual operation the capacitors will usually be large enough that they will discharge only partially, not all the way to zero as shown.

7.5.2 Full-Wave Voltage Doubler

Figure 7.10 shows the circuit of a full-wave voltage doubler and illustrates the circuit operation. During the positive half cycle of the transformer secondary voltage, as shown in Figure 7.10B, D_A conducts charging capacitor C1 to 1.4 E_{RMS}. D_B is not conducting at this time.

During the negative half cycle, as shown in Figure 7.10C, D_B conducts, charging capacitor C2 to 1.4 E_{RMS}, while D_A is non-conducting. The output voltage is the sum of the two capacitor voltages, which will be 2.8 E_{RMS} under no-load conditions. Figure 7.10D illustrates that each capacitor alternately receives a charge once per cycle. The effective filter capacitance is that of C1 and C2 in series, which is less than the capacitance of either C1 or C2 alone.

Resistors R1 and R2 in Figure 7.10A are used to limit the surge current through the rectifiers. Their values are based on the transformer voltage and the rectifier surge-current rating, since at the instant the power supply is turned on, the filter capacitors look like a short-circuited load. Provided the limiting resistors can withstand the surge current, their current-handling capacity is based on the maximum load current from the supply. Output voltages approaching twice the peak voltage of the transformer can be obtained with the voltage doubling circuit shown in Figure 7.10.

Figure 7.11 shows how the voltage depends upon the ratio of the series resistance to the load resistance, and the load resistance times the filter capacitance. The peak inverse voltage across each diode is 2.8 E_{RMS}. As indicated by the curves in Figure 7.11, the output voltage regulation of this doubler connection is not very good and it is not attractive for providing high voltages at high power levels.

There are better doubler connections for higher power applications, and two possibilities are shown in **Figure 7.12**. The connection in Figure 7.12A uses two bridge rectifiers in series with capacitive coupling between the ac terminals of the bridges. At the expense of more diodes, this connection will have much better output voltage regulation at higher power levels. Even better regulation can be achieved by using the connection shown in Figure 7.12B. In this example, two windings on the transformer are used. It is not essential that both windings have the same voltage, but both must be capable of providing the desired output current. In addition, the insulation of the upper winding must be adequate to accommodate the additional dc bias applied to it from the lower winding.

7.5.3 Voltage Tripler and Quadrupler

Figure 7.13A shows a voltage-tripling circuit. On one half of the ac cycle, C1 and C3 are charged to the source voltage through D1, D2 and D3. R1 represents the resistance of the transformer secondary winding, which limits the amount of current available for charging the capacitors. On the opposite half of the cycle, D2 conducts and C2 is charged

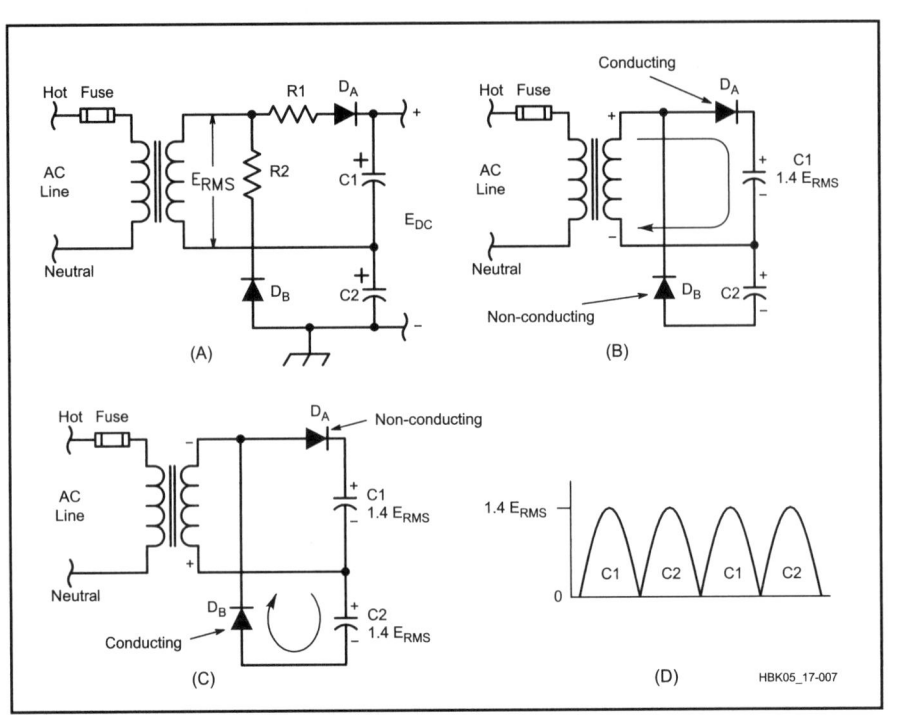

Figure 7.10 — Part A shows a full-wave voltage-doubler circuit. One-half cycle is shown at B and the next half cycle is shown at C. Each capacitor receives a charge during every input-voltage cycle. D illustrates how each capacitor is charged alternately.

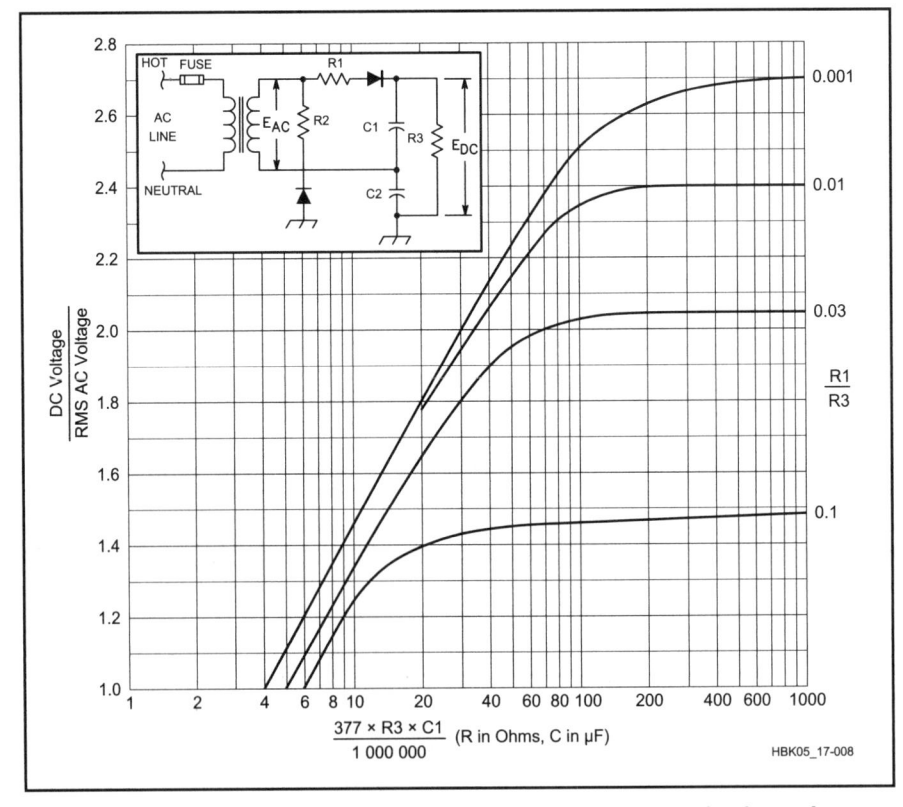

Figure 7.11 — DC output voltages from a full-wave voltage-doubler circuit as a function of the filter capacitances and load resistance. For the ratio R1 / R3 and for the R3 × C1 product, resistance is in ohms and capacitance is in microfarads. Equal resistance values for R1 and R2, and equal capacitance values for C1 and C2 are assumed. (From Schade, see References)

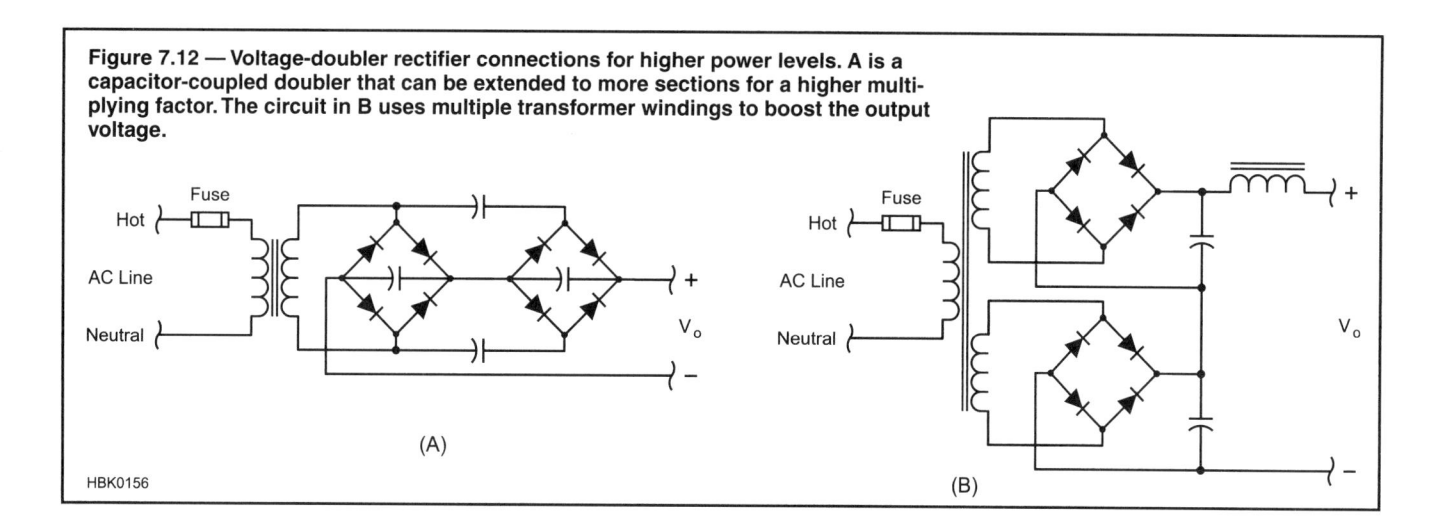

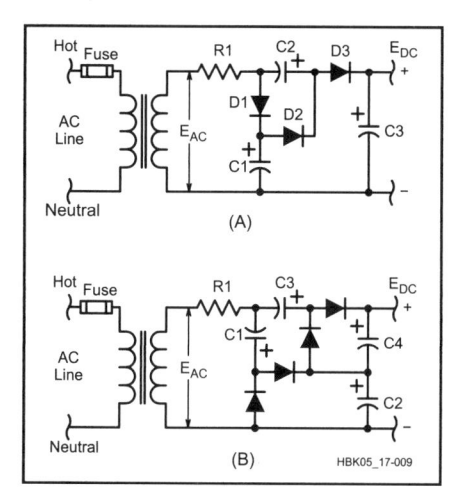

Figure 7.12 — Voltage-doubler rectifier connections for higher power levels. A is a capacitor-coupled doubler that can be extended to more sections for a higher multiplying factor. The circuit in B uses multiple transformer windings to boost the output voltage.

Figure 7.13 — Voltage-multiplying circuits with one side of the transformer secondary used as a common connection. A shows a voltage tripler and B shows a voltage quadrupler. Capacitances are typically 20 to 50 µF, depending on the output current demand. Capacitor dc ratings are related to E_{PEAK} (1.4 E_{RMS}):
C1 — Greater than E_{PEAK}
C2 — Greater than 2 E_{PEAK}
C3 — Greater than 3 E_{PEAK}
C4 — Greater than 2 E_{PEAK}
R1 — Resistance of the transformer secondary winding

to twice the source voltage, because it sees the transformer plus the charge in C1 as its source (D1 is cut off during this half cycle). At the same time, D3 conducts, and with the transformer and the charge in C2 as the source, C3 is charged to three times the transformer voltage.

The voltage-quadrupling circuit of Figure 7.13B works in similar fashion. In either of the circuits of Figure 7.13, the output voltage will approach an exact multiple of the peak ac voltage when the output current drain is low and the capacitance values are large.

The secondary resistance, R1, limits the charging current for the capacitors, and thus the maximum output voltage. This is illustrated in a complementary way by the flattening of the output voltage curve in Figure 7.11 as filter capacitance increases. Increasing R1 has the same effect. For high-voltage supplies, a low-resistance secondary is often required to reach a full multiple of the available ac voltage.

Power Sources 7.9

7.6 Current Multipliers

Just as there are voltage multiplier connections for high-voltage, low-current loads, there are current multiplier connections for low-voltage, high-current loads. An example of a current-doubler is given in **Figure 7.14A**.

To make the circuit operation easier to visualize, we can represent L1 and L2 as current sources (Figure 7.14B) which is a good approximation for steady-state operation. When terminal 1 of the secondary winding is positive with respect to terminal 2, diode D_A will be reverse-biased and therefore non-conducting. The current flows within the circuit are shown in Figure 7.14B. Note that all of the output current (I_o) flows through D_B but only half of I_o flows through the winding. At the cathode of D_B the current divides with half going to L2 and the other half to the transformer secondary. The output voltage will be one-half the voltage of the average winding voltage (0.45 E_{RMS}). This rectifier connection divides the voltage and multiplies the current! Because of the need for two inductors, this circuit is seldom used in line-frequency applications but it is very useful in high-frequency switchmode regulators with very low output voltages (<10 V) because it makes the secondary winding design easier and can improve circuit efficiency. At high frequencies, the inductors can be quite small.

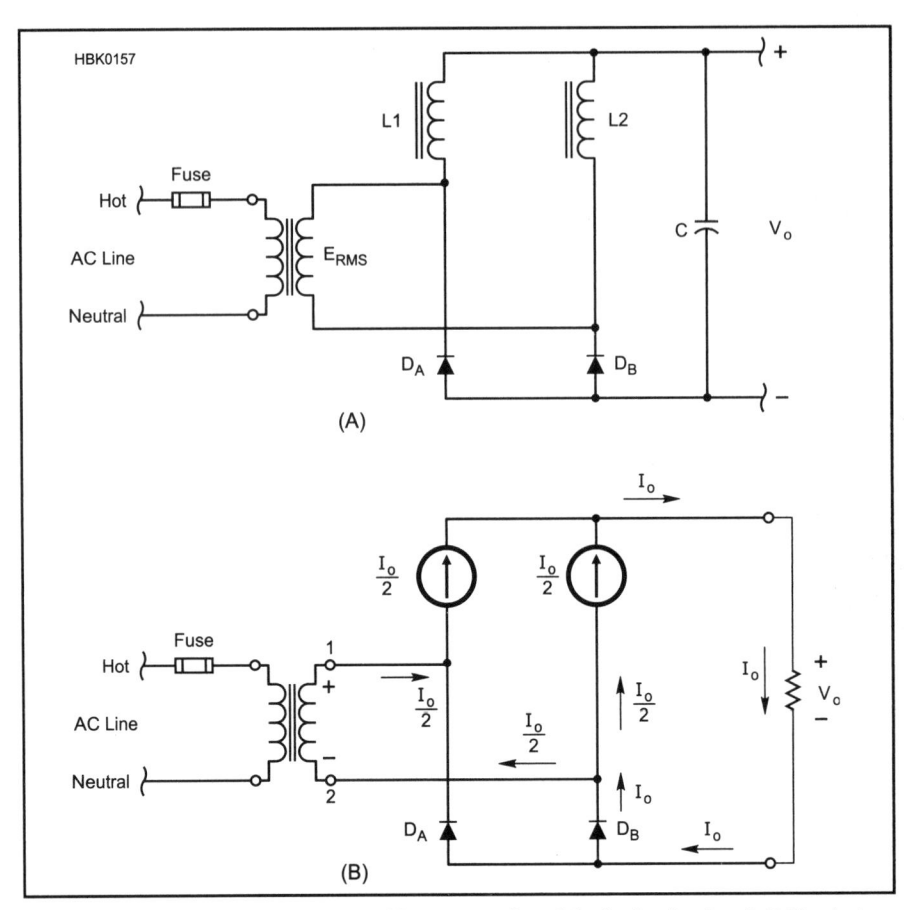

Figure 7.14 — A current doubler rectifier connection. A is the basic circuit. B illustrates current flow within the circuit.

7.7 Rectifier Types

Rectifiers have a long history beginning with mechanical rectifiers in the 1800s to today's abundant variety of semiconductor devices. While many different devices have been created for this purpose, they all have the characteristic that they block current flow in the reverse direction, withstanding substantial reverse voltage and allowing current flow in the forward direction with minimum voltage drop. The simplest rectifiers are diodes, but it is also possible to have three-terminal devices (such as a thyristor) that can be controlled to regulate the output dc in addition to providing rectification. It is also possible to use devices like MOSFETs as synchronous rectifiers with very low forward drop during conduction. This is typically done to improve efficiency for very low voltage outputs. The following is a brief description of several of the more common examples. The sections on vacuum tube and other obsolete types of rectifiers from previous editions are available as a PDF article with this book's downloadable supplemental content.

7.7.1 Semiconductor Diodes

Rectifier diodes can be made from a number of different semiconductor materials such as germanium, silicon, silicon-carbide or gallium-arsenide, and no doubt other materials will appear in the future. The choice will depend on the application and as always cost is a factor.

Germanium diodes were the first of the solid-state semiconductor rectifiers. They have an extremely low forward voltage drop but are relatively temperature sensitive, having high reverse leakage currents at higher temperatures. They can be easily destroyed by overheating during soldering as well. Germanium diodes are no longer used as power rectifiers.

Today, silicon diodes are the primary choice for virtually all power rectifier applications. They are characterized by extremely high reverse resistance (low reverse leakage), forward drops of a volt or less and operation at junction temperatures up to 125 °C. Some multi-junction HV diodes will have forward drops of several volts, but that is still low compared to the voltage at which they are being used.

Many different types of silicon diodes are available for different applications. Silicon rectifiers fall into to two general categories: PN-junction diodes and Schottky barrier diodes (see the **Circuits and Components** chapter). Schottky diodes are the usual choice for low output voltages (<20 V) where their low forward conduction drop is critical for efficiency. For higher voltages however, the high reverse leakage of Schottky diodes is not acceptable and PN-junction diodes are normally chosen.

For 50/60 Hz applications, diodes with reverse recovery times of a microsecond or even more are suitable and very economical. For switchmode converters and inverters that regularly operate at 25 kHz and higher frequencies, fast-recovery diodes are needed. These converters typically have waveform transitions of less than 1 µs within the circuit. MOSFET power transistors often have transitions of less than 100 ns.

During the switching transitions, previously conducting diodes see a reversal of current direction. This change tends to reverse-bias those diodes, and thereby put them into an open-circuit condition. Unfortunately, as explained in the **Circuits and Components** chapter, solid-state rectifiers cannot be made to cease conduction instantaneously. As a result, when the opposing diodes in a bridge rectifier or full-wave rectifier become conductive at the time the converter switches states, the diodes being turned off will actually conduct in the reverse direction for a brief time. That effectively short circuits the converter for a period of time depending on the reverse recovery characteristics of the rectifiers. This characteristic can create high current transients that stress the switching transistors and lead to increased loss and electromagnetic interference. As the switching frequency increases, more of these transitions happen each second, and more power is lost because of diode cross-conduction.

These current transients and associated losses are reduced by using *fast recovery* diodes, which are specially doped diodes designed to minimize storage time. Diodes with recovery times of 50 ns or less are available.

7.7.2 Rectifier Strings or Stacks

DIODES IN SERIES

When the PIV rating of a single diode is not sufficient for the application, similar diodes may be used in series. (Two 500 PIV diodes in series will withstand 1000 PIV and so on.) There used to be a general recommendation to place a resistor across each diode in the string to equalize the PIV drops. With modern diodes, this practice is no longer necessary.

Modern silicon rectifier diodes are constructed to have an avalanche characteristic. Simply put, this means that the diffusion process is controlled so the diode will exhibit a Zener characteristic in the reverse-biased direction before destructive breakdown of the junction can occur. This provides a measure of safety for diodes in series. A diode will go into Zener conduction before it self-destructs. If other diodes in the chain have not reached their avalanche voltages, the current through the avalanched diode will be limited to the leakage current in the other diodes. This should normally be very low. For this reason, shunting resistors are generally not needed across diodes in series rectifier strings. In fact, shunt resistors can actually create problems because they can produce a low-impedance source of damaging current to any diode that may have reached avalanche potential.

DIODES IN PARALLEL

Diodes can be placed in parallel to increase current-handling capability. Equalizing resistors should be added as shown in **Figure 7.15**. Without the resistors, one diode may take most of the current. The resistors should be selected to have a drop of several tenths of a volt at the expected peak current. A disadvantage of this form of forced current sharing will be the increase in power loss because of the added resistors.

7.7.3 Rectifier Ratings versus Operating Stress

Power supplies designed for amateur equipment use silicon rectifiers almost exclusively. These rectifiers are available in a wide range of voltage and current ratings: PIV ratings of 600 V or more and current ratings as high as 400 A are available. At 1000 PIV, the current ratings may be several amperes. It is possible to stack several units in series for higher voltages. Stacks are available commercially that will handle peak inverse voltages up to 10 kV at a load current of 1 A or more.

7.7.4 Rectifier Protection

The discussion of rectifier circuits included the peak reverse voltage seen by the rectifiers in each circuit. You will need this information to select the voltage rating of the diodes in given application. It is normal good practice to not expose the diodes to more than 75% of their rated voltage for the worst case reverse voltage. This will probably be when operating at the highest input voltage but should also take into account transients that may occur.

The important specifications of a silicon diode are:
1. PIV — the peak inverse voltage.
2. I_0 — the average dc current rating.
3. I_{REP} — the peak repetitive forward current.
4. I_{SURGE} — a non-repetitive peak half-sine wave of 8.3 ms duration (one-half cycle of 60-Hz line frequency).
5. Switching speed or reverse recovery time.
6. Power dissipation and thermal resistance.

The first two specifications appear in most catalogs. I_{REP} and I_{SURGE} are not often specified in catalogs, but they are very important. Except in some switching regulator and capacitive filter circuits, rectifier current typically flows half the time — when it does conduct, the rectifier has to pass at least twice the average direct current. With a capacitor-input filter, the rectifier conducts much less than half the time. In this case, when it does conduct, it may pass as much as 10 to 20 times the average dc current, under certain conditions.

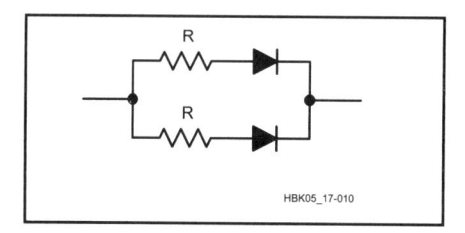

Figure 7.15 — Diodes can be connected in parallel to increase the current-handling capability of the circuit. Each diode should have a series current-equalizing resistor, with a value selected to have a drop of several tenths of a volt at the expected current.

CURRENT INRUSH

When the supply is first turned on, the filter capacitors are discharged and act like a dead short. The result can be a very heavy current surge through the diode for at least one half-cycle and sometimes more. This current transient is called I_{SURGE}. The maximum surge current rating for a diode is usually specified for a duration of one-half cycle (at 60 Hz), or about 8.3 ms. Some form of surge protection is usually necessary to protect the diodes until the filter capacitors are nearly charged, unless the diodes used have a very high surge-current rating (several hundred amperes). If a manufacturer's data sheet is not available, an educated guess about a diode's capability can be made by using these rules of thumb for silicon diodes commonly used in Amateur Radio power supplies:

Rule 1. The maximum I_{REP} rating can be assumed to be approximately four times the maximum I_0 rating, where I_0 is the average dc current rating.

Rule 2. The maximum I_{SURGE} rating can be assumed to be approximately 12 times the maximum I_0 rating. This figure should provide a reasonable safety factor. Silicon rectifiers with 750 mA dc ratings, for example, seldom have 1-cycle surge ratings of less than 15 A; some are rated up to 35 A or more. From this you can see that the rectifier should be selected on the basis of I_{SURGE} and not on I_0 ratings.

Although you can sometimes rely on the resistance of the transformer windings to provide surge-current limiting, this is seldom adequate in high-voltage power supplies. Series resistors are often installed between the secondary and the rectifier strings or in the transformer's primary circuit, but these can be a deterrent to good voltage regulation.

One way to have good surge current limiting at turn-on without affecting voltage regulation during normal operation is to have a resistor in series with the input, along with a relay across the resistor that shorts it out after 50 ms or so. This kind of arrangement is particularly important in HV supplies.

VOLTAGE TRANSIENTS

Vacuum-tube rectifiers had little problem with voltage transients on the incoming power lines. The possibility of an internal arc was of little consequence, since the heat produced was of very short duration and had little effect on the massive plate and cathode structures.

Unfortunately, such is not the case with silicon diodes. Because of their low forward voltage drop, silicon diodes create very little heat with high forward current and therefore have tiny junction areas. However, conduction in the reverse direction beyond the normal reverse recovery time (reverse avalanching) can cause junction temperatures to rise extremely rapidly with the resulting destruction of the semiconductor junction.

To protect semiconductor rectifiers from voltage transients, special surge-absorption devices are available for connection across the incoming ac bus or transformer secondary. These devices operate in a fashion similar to a Zener diode; they conduct heavily when a specific voltage level is reached. Unlike Zener diodes, however, they have the ability to absorb very high transient energy levels without damage. With the clamping level set well above the normal operating voltage range for the rectifiers, these devices normally appear as open circuits and have no effect on the power-supply circuits. When a voltage transient occurs, however, these protection devices clamp the transient and thereby prevent destruction of the rectifiers.

Transient protectors are available in three basic varieties:

1. *Silicon Zener diodes* — large junction Zeners specifically made for this purpose and available as single junction for dc (unipolar) and back-to-back junctions for ac (bipolar). These silicon protectors are available under the trade name of TransZorb from General Semiconductor Corporation and are also made by other manufacturers. They have the best transient-suppressing characteristics of the three varieties mentioned here, but are expensive and have the least energy absorbing capability per dollar of the group.

2. *Varistors* — made of a composition metal-oxide material that breaks down at a certain voltage. Metal-oxide varistors, also known as MOVs, are cheap and easily obtained, but have a higher internal resistance, which allows a greater increase in clamped voltage than the Zener variety. Varistors can also degrade with successive transients within their rated power handling limits (this is not usually a problem in the ham shack where transients are few and replacement of the varistor is easily accomplished).

Varistors usually become short-circuited when they fail. Large energy dissipation can result in device explosion. Therefore, it is a good idea to include a fuse that limits the short-circuit current through the varistor, and to protect people and circuitry from debris.

3. *Gas tube* — similar in construction to the familiar neon bulb, but designed to limit conducting voltage rise under high transient currents. Gas tubes can usually withstand the highest transient energy levels of the group. Gas tubes suffer from an ionization time problem, however. A high voltage across the tube will not immediately cause conduction. The time required for the gas to ionize and clamp the transient is inversely proportional to the level of applied voltage in excess of the device ionization voltage. As a result, the gas tube will let a little of the transient through to the equipment before it activates.

In installations where reliable equipment operation is critical, the local power is poor and transients are a major problem, the usual practice is to use a combination of protectors. Such systems consist of a varistor or Zener protector, combined with a gas-tube device. Often there is an indicator light to warn when a surge has blown out the varistor. Operationally, the solid-state device clamps the surge immediately, with the beefy gas tube firing shortly thereafter to take most of the surge from the solid-state device.

HEAT

The junction of a diode is quite small, so it must operate at a high current density. The heat-handling capability is, therefore, quite small. Normally, this is not a prime consideration in high-voltage, low-current supplies. Use of high-current rectifiers at or near their maximum ratings (usually 2 A or larger, stud-mount rectifiers) requires some form of heat sinking. Frequently, mounting the rectifier on the main chassis — directly or with thin thermal insulating washers — will suffice.

When a rectifier is directly mounted on the heatsink it is good practice to use a thin layer of thermal grease between the diode and the heat sink to assure good heat conduction. Most modern insulating thermal washers do not require the use of grease, but the older mica and other washers may benefit from a *very thin layer* of grease. Thermal grease and heat conducting insulating washers and pads are standard products available from mail-order component sellers.

Large, high-current rectifiers often require special heat sinks to maintain a safe operating temperature. Forced-air cooling from a fan is sometimes used as a further aid. Safe case temperatures are usually given in the manufacturer's data sheets and should be observed if the maximum capabilities of the diode are to be realized. See the thermal design section in the chapter on **Electrical Fundamentals** for more information.

7.8 Power Filtering

Most loads will not tolerate the ripple (an ac component) of the pulsating dc from the rectifiers. Filters are required between the rectifier and the load to reduce the ripple to a low level. As pointed out earlier, some capacitances or inductances may be inherent in the rectifier connection, reducing the ripple amplitude. In most cases, however, additional filtering is required. The design of the filter depends to a large extent on the dc voltage output, the desired voltage regulation of the power supply and the maximum load current. Power-supply filters are low-pass devices using series inductors and/or shunt capacitors.

7.8.1 Load Resistance

In discussing the performance of power-supply filters, it is sometimes convenient to characterize the load connected to the output as a resistance. This *load resistance* is equal to the output voltage divided by the total load current, including the current drawn by the bleeder resistor.

7.8.2 Voltage Regulation

In an unregulated supply, the output voltage usually decreases as more current is drawn. This happens not only because of increased voltage drops in the transformer and filter chokes, but also because the output voltage at light loads tends to soar to the peak value of the transformer voltage as a result of charging the first capacitor. Proper filter design can reduce this effect. The change in output voltage with load is called the *voltage regulation* and is expressed as a percentage.

$$\text{Percent Regulation} = \frac{(E1 - E2)}{E2} \times 100\% \quad (2)$$

where
E1 = the no-load voltage
E2 = the full-load voltage.

A steady load, such as that represented

by a receiver, speech amplifier or unkeyed stages of a transmitter, does not require good (low) regulation as long as the proper voltage is obtained under load conditions. The filter capacitors must have a voltage rating safe for the highest value to which the voltage will rise when the external load is removed.

Typically the output voltage will display a larger change with long-duration changes in load resistance than with short transient changes. The reason for this is that transient load currents are supplied from energy stored in the output capacitance. The regulation with long-term changes is often called the *static regulation*, to distinguish it from the *dynamic regulation* (transient load changes). A load that varies at a syllabic or keyed rate, as represented by some audio and RF amplifiers, usually requires good dynamic regulation (<15%) if distortion products are to be held to a low level. The dynamic regulation of a power supply can be improved by increasing the output capacitance.

When essentially constant voltage is required, regardless of current variation (for stabilizing an oscillator, for example), special voltage regulating circuits described later in this chapter are used.

7.8.3 Bleeder Resistors

A *bleeder resistor* is a resistance (R) connected across the output terminals of the power supply as shown in **Figure 7.16A**. Its functions are to discharge the filter capacitors as a safety measure when the power is turned off and to improve voltage regulation by providing a minimum load resistance. When voltage regulation is not of importance, the resistance may be as high as 100 Ω per volt of output voltage. The resistance value to be used for voltage-regulating purposes is discussed in later sections. From the consideration of safety, the power rating of bleeder resistors should be as conservative as possible — having a burned-out bleeder resistor is dangerous!

7.8.4 Ripple Frequency and Voltage

The ripple at the output of the rectifier is an alternating current superimposed on a steady direct current. From this viewpoint, the filter may be considered to consist of: 1) shunt capacitors that short circuit the ac component while not interfering with the flow of the dc component; and/or 2) series chokes that readily pass dc but will impede the ac component.

The effectiveness of the filter can be expressed in terms of percent ripple, which is the ratio of the RMS value of the ripple to the dc value in terms of percentage.

$$\text{Percent Ripple (RMS)} = \frac{E1}{E2} \times 100\% \quad (3)$$

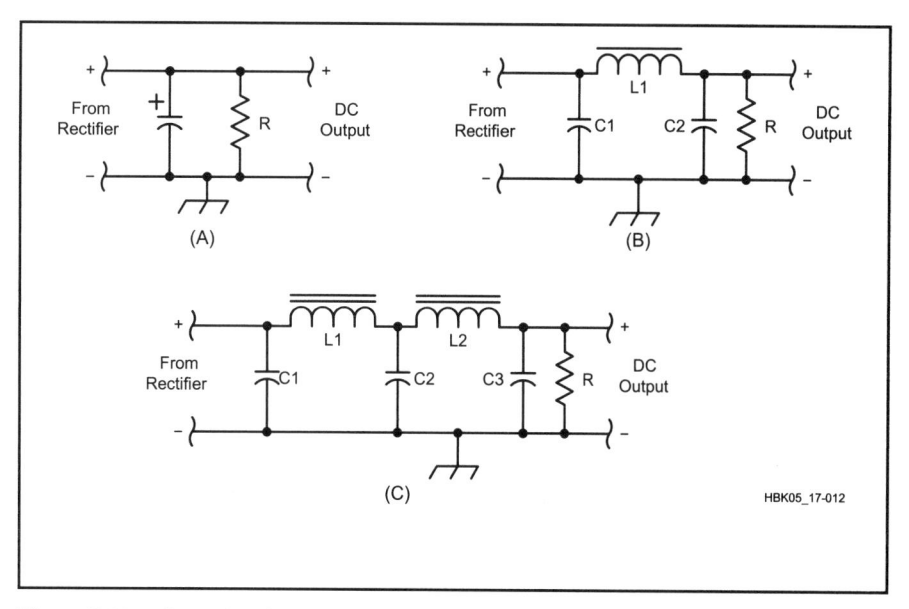

Figure 7.16 — Capacitor-input filter circuits. At A is a simple capacitor filter. B and C are single- and double-section filters, respectively.

where
E1 = the RMS value of ripple voltage
E2 = the steady dc voltage.

Any frequency multiplier or amplifier supply in a CW transmitter should have less than 5% ripple. A linear amplifier can tolerate about 3% ripple on the plate voltage. Bias supplies for linear amplifiers should have less than 1% ripple. VFOs, speech amplifiers and receivers may require no greater than 0.01% ripple.

Ripple frequency refers to the frequency of the pulsations in the rectifier output waveform — the number of pulsations per second. The ripple frequency of half-wave rectifiers is the same as the line-supply frequency — 60 Hz with a 60-Hz supply. Since the output pulses are doubled with a full-wave rectifier, the ripple frequency is doubled — to 120 Hz with a 60-Hz supply.

The amount of filtering (values of inductance and capacitance) required to give adequate smoothing depends on the ripple frequency. More filtering is required as the ripple frequency is reduced. This is why the filters used for line-frequency rectification are much larger than those used in switchmode converters where the ripple frequency is often in the hundreds of kHz.

7.8.5 Capacitor-Input Filters

Typical capacitor-input filter systems are shown in Figure 7.16. The ripple can be reduced by making C1 larger, but that can lead to very large capacitances and high inrush currents at turn-on. Better ripple reduction will be obtained when moderate values of C1 are employed and LC sections are added as shown in Figure 7.16B and C.

INPUT VERSUS OUTPUT VOLTAGE

The average output voltage of a capacitor-input filter is generally poorly regulated with load-current variations. As shown earlier (Figure 7.6) the rectifier diodes conduct for only a small portion of the ac cycle to charge the filter capacitor to the peak value of the ac waveform. When the instantaneous voltage of the ac passes its peak, the diode ceases to conduct. This forces the capacitor to support the load current until the ac voltage on the opposing diode in the bridge or full wave rectifier is high enough to pick up the load and recharge the capacitor. For this reason, the peak diode currents are usually quite high.

Since the cyclic peak voltage of the capacitor-filter output is determined by the peak of the input ac waveform, the minimum voltage and, therefore, the ripple amplitude, is determined by the amount of voltage discharge, or "droop," occurring in the capacitor while it is discharging and supporting the load. Obviously, the higher the load current, the proportionately greater the discharge, and therefore the lower the average output.

There is an easy way to approximate the peak-to-peak ripple for a certain capacitor and load by assuming a constant load current. We can calculate the droop in the capacitor by using the relationship:

$$C \times E = I \times t \quad (4)$$

where
C = the capacitance in microfarads

E = the voltage droop, or peak-to-peak ripple voltage
I = the load current in milliamperes
t = the length of time in ms per cycle during which the rectifiers are not conducting, during which the filter capacitor must support the load current. For 60-Hz, full-wave rectifiers, t is about 7.5 ms.

As an example, let's assume that we need to determine the peak-to-peak ripple voltage at the dc output of a full-wave rectifier/ filter combination that produces 13.8 V dc and supplies a transceiver drawing 2.0 A. The filter capacitor in the power supply is 5000 μF. Using the above relationship:

$$C \times E = I \times t \qquad (5)$$

5000 μF × E = 2000 mA × 7.5 ms

$$E = \frac{2000 \text{ mA} \times 7.5 \text{ ms}}{5000 \text{ μF}} = 3 \text{ V P-P}$$

Obviously, this is too much ripple. A capacitor value of about 20,000 μF would be better suited for this application. If a linear regulator is used after this rectifier/filter combination, then it is possible to trade off higher ripple voltage against high power dissipation in the regulator. A properly designed linear regulator can reduce the ripple amplitude to a very small value.

7.8.6 Choke-Input Filters

Choke-input filters provide the benefits of greatly improved output voltage stability over varying loads and low peak-current surges in the rectifiers. On the negative side, the output voltage will be lower than that for a capacitor-input filter.

In line-frequency power supplies, choke-input filters are less popular than they once were. This change came about in part because of the high surge current capability of silicon rectifiers, but more importantly because size, weight and cost are reduced when large filter chokes are eliminated. However, choke input filters are frequently used in high-frequency switchmode converters where the chokes will be much smaller.

As long as the inductance of the choke is large enough to maintain a continuous current over the complete cycle of the input ac waveform, the filter output voltage will be the average value of the rectified output. The average dc value of a full-wave rectified sine wave is 0.637 times its peak voltage. Since the RMS value is 0.707 times the peak, the output of the choke input filter will be (0.637 / 0.707), or 0.9 times the RMS ac voltage.

As shown in **Figure 7.17**, there is a minimum or "critical" load current below which the choke does not provide the necessary filtering. For light loads, there may not be enough energy stored in the choke during the input waveform crest to allow continuous current over the full cycle. When this happens, the filter output voltage will rise as the filter assumes more and more of the characteristics of a capacitor-input filter. One purpose of the bleeder resistor is to keep the minimum load current above the critical value.

The value for the critical (or minimum) inductance for a given maximum value of load resistance in a single phase, full-wave rectifier with a sine wave source voltage can be approximated from:

$$L_c = R/A \qquad (6)$$

where
R = the maximum load resistance
A = a constant obtained from Figure 7.18, derived from the frequency of the input current (see Reference 1).

Low values for minimum load current (high minimum load R) can lead to large values for L_C which may not be practical. Standard filter inductors typically have a relatively constant value for L as the dc current is varied but it is possible to use a swinging choke instead. This is an inductor which has a high inductance at low currents and much lower inductance at high currents. Using a swinging choke will usually result in a much smaller filter choke and/or better output regulation.

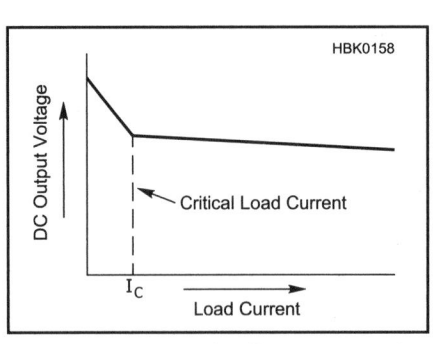

Figure 7.17 — Inductive filter output voltage regulation as a function of load current. The transition from capacitive peak charging to inductive averaging occurs at the critical load current, I_C.

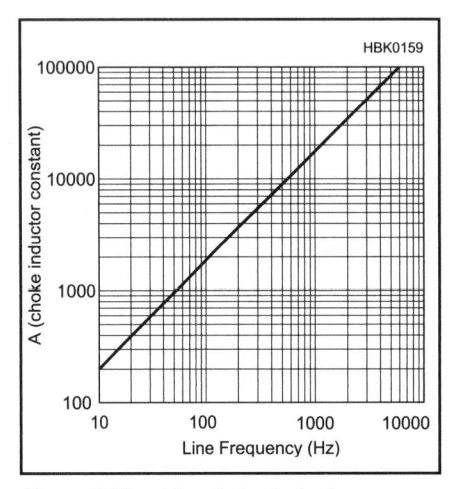

Figure 7.18 — The choke inductor constant, A, is used to solve equation 6.

7.9 Power Supply Regulation

The output of a rectifier/filter system may be usable for some electronic equipment, but for today's transceivers and accessories, further measures may be necessary to provide power sufficiently clean and stable for their needs. Voltage regulators are often used to provide this additional level of conditioning.

Rectifier/filter circuits by themselves are unable to protect the equipment from the problems associated with input-power-line fluctuations, load-current variations and residual ripple voltages. Regulators can eliminate these problems, but not without costs in circuit complexity and power-conversion efficiency.

7.9.1 Zener Diodes

A Zener diode (developed by Dr Clarence Zener) can be used to maintain the voltage applied to a circuit at a practically constant value, regardless of the voltage regulation of the power supply or variations in load current. The typical circuit is shown in **Figure 7.19**. Note that the cathode side of the diode is connected to the positive side of the supply.

Zener diodes are available in a wide variety of voltages and power ratings. The voltages range from less than 2 V to a few hundred volts, while the power ratings (power the diode can dissipate) run from less than 0.25 W to 50 W. The ability of the Zener diode to stabilize a voltage depends on the diode's conducting impedance. This can be as low as 1 Ω or less in a low-voltage, high-power diode or as high as 1000 Ω in a high-voltage, low-power diode.

The circuit in Figure 7.19 is a *shunt* regulator in that it "shunts" current through a controlling device (the Zener diode) to maintain a constant output voltage. To design a Zener shunt regulator, you must know the minimum and maximum input voltage (E_{DC}); the

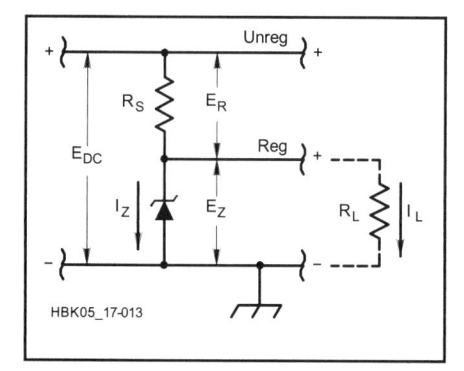

Figure 7.19 — Zener-diode voltage regulation. The voltage from a negative supply may be regulated by reversing the power-supply connections and the diode polarity.

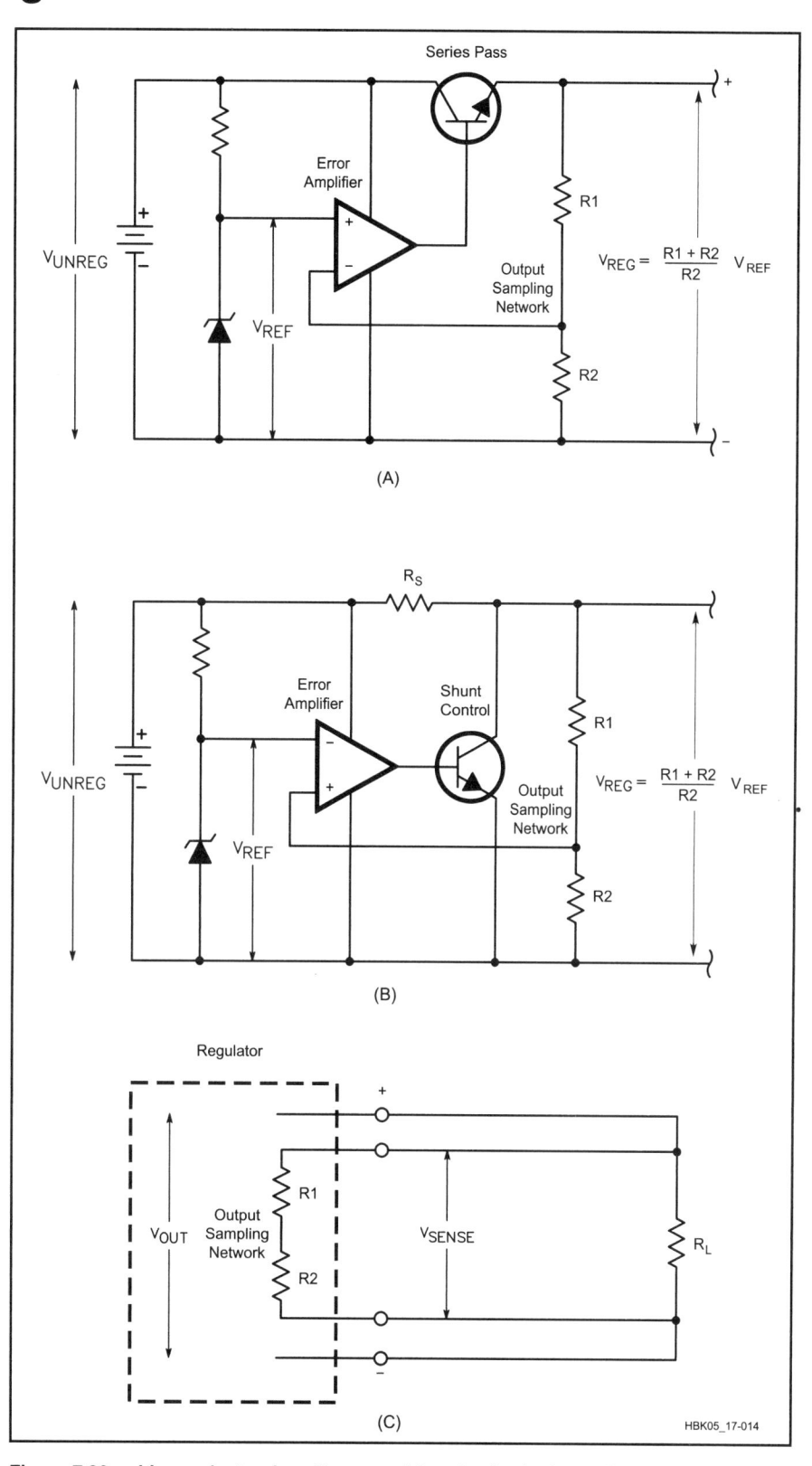

Figure 7.20 — Linear electronic voltage regulator circuits. In these diagrams, batteries represent the unregulated input-voltage source. A transformer, rectifier and filter would serve this function in most applications. Part A shows a series regulator and Part B shows a shunt regulator. Part C shows how remote sensing overcomes poor load regulation caused by the IR drop in the connecting wires by bringing them inside the feedback loop. The use of extra connections to sense voltage is called a "four wire Kelvin connection."

$$V_{REG} = \frac{R1 + R2}{R2} V_{REF}$$

output voltage, which is equal to the Zener diode voltage (E_Z); and the minimum and maximum load current (I_L) through R_L. If the input voltage is variable, you must specify the maximum and minimum values for E_{DC}. As a rule of thumb, the current through the Zener should be 10% of the maximum load current for good regulation and must be greater than the $I_{Z(min)}$ at which the Zener diode maintains its constant voltage drop. Once these quantities are known the series resistance, R_S, can be determined:

$$R_S = \frac{E_{DC(min)} - E_Z}{1.1\, I_{L(max)}} \quad (7)$$

The power dissipation of the Zener diode, P_D, is

$$P_{DZ} = \left[\frac{E_{DC(max)} - E_Z}{R_S} - I_{L(min)}\right] E_Z \quad (8)$$

and of the series resistor, R_S,

$$P_{DR} = \frac{\left(E_{DC(max)} - E_Z\right)^2}{R_S} \quad (9)$$

It is good practice to provide a five times rated power dissipation safety margin for both the series resistor and the Zener diode. This avoids heating in the Zener and the resulting drift in voltage. High-power Zener diodes (10 W dissipation or more) will require heat-sinking as discussed in the section on Managing Heat in the **Circuits and Components** chapter.

7.9.2 Linear Regulators

Linear regulators come in two varieties, *series* and *shunt*, as shown in **Figure 7.20**. The shunt regulator is simply an electronic (also called "active") version of the Zener diode. For the most part, the active shunt regulator (Figure 7.20B) is rarely used since the series regulator is a superior choice for most applications.

The series regulator (Figure 7.20A) consists of a stable voltage reference, which is usually established by a Zener diode, a transistor in series between the power source and the load (called a *series pass transistor*), and an error amplifier. In critical applications a temperature-compensated reference diode would be used instead of the Zener diode.

The output voltage is sampled by the error amplifier, which compares the output (usually scaled down by a voltage divider) to the reference. If the scaled-down output voltage becomes higher than the reference voltage, the error amplifier reduces the drive current to the pass transistor, thereby allowing the output voltage to drop slightly. Conversely, if the load pulls the output voltage below the desired value, the amplifier drives the pass transistor into increased conduction.

The "stiffness" or tightness of regulation of a linear regulator depends on the gain of the error amplifier and the ratio of the output scaling resistors. In any regulator, the output is cleanest and regulation stiffest at the point where the sampling network or error amplifier is connected. If heavy load current is drawn through long leads, the voltage drop can degrade the regulation at the load. To combat this effect, the feedback connection to the error amplifier can be made directly to the load. This technique, called *remote sensing*, or a *four wire Kelvin connection*, moves the point of best regulation to the load by bringing the connecting loads inside the feedback loop. This is shown in Figure 7.20C.

INPUT VERSUS OUTPUT VOLTAGE

In a series regulator, the pass-transistor power dissipation is directly proportional to the load current and input/output voltage differential. The series pass element can be located in either leg of the supply. Either NPN or PNP devices can be used, depending on the ground polarity of the unregulated input.

The differential between the input and output voltages is a design tradeoff. If the input voltage from the rectifiers and filter is only slightly higher than the required output voltage, there will be minimal voltage drop across the series pass transistor. A small drop results in minimal thermal dissipation and high power-supply efficiency. The supply will have less capability to provide regulated power in the event of power line brownout and other reduced line voltage conditions, however. Conversely, a higher input voltage will provide operation over a wider range of input voltage, but at the expense of increased heat dissipation.

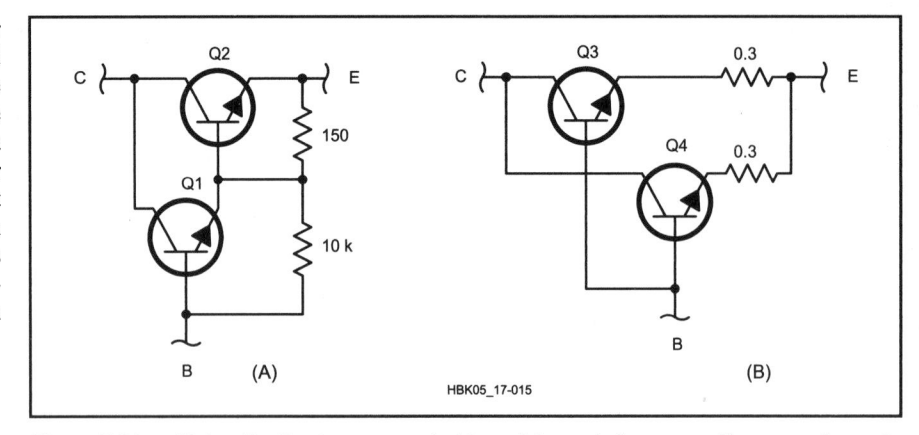

Figure 7.21 — At A, a Darlington-connected transistor pair for use as the pass element in a series-regulating circuit. At B, the method of connecting two or more transistors in parallel for high-current output. Resistances are in ohms. The circuit at A may be used for load currents from 100 mA to 5 A, and the one at B may be used for currents from 6 A to 10 A.

Q1 — NPN transistor, MJE340 or equivalent

Q2-Q4 — Power transistor such as 2N3055 or 2N3772

7.9.3 Linear Regulator Pass Transistors

DARLINGTON PAIRS

A simple Zener-diode reference or IC op-amp error amplifier may not be able to source enough current to a pass transistor that must conduct heavy load current. The Darlington configuration of **Figure 7.21A** multiplies the pass-transistor beta, thereby extending the control range of the error amplifier. If the Darlington arrangement is implemented with discrete transistors, resistors across the base-emitter junctions may be necessary to prevent collector-to-base leakage currents in Q1 from being amplified and turning on the transistor pair. These resistors are contained in the envelope of a monolithic Darlington device.

When a single pass transistor is not available to handle the current required from a regulator, the current-handling capability may be increased by connecting two or more pass transistors in parallel. The circuit of Figure 7.21B shows the method of connecting these pass transistors. The resistances in the emitter leads of each transistor are necessary to equalize the currents.

TRANSISTOR RATINGS

When bipolar (NPN, PNP) power transistors are used in applications in which they are called upon to handle power on a continuous basis, rather than switching, there are four parameters that must be examined to see if any maximum limits are being exceeded. Operation of the transistor outside these limits can easily result in device failure, and these parameters must be considered during the design process.

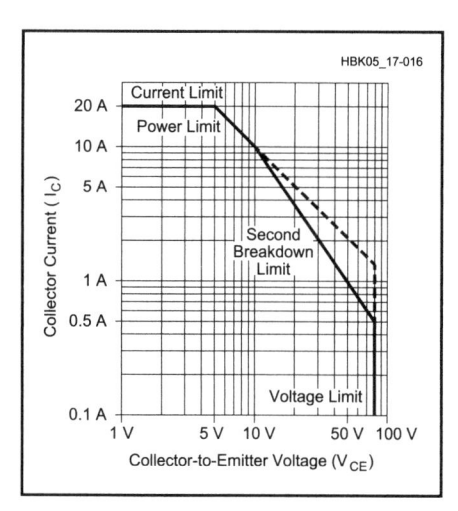

Figure 7.22 — Typical graph of the safe operating area (SOA) of a transistor. See text for details. Safe operating conditions for specific devices may be quite different from those shown here.

The four limits are maximum collector current (I_C), maximum collector-emitter voltage (V_{CEO}), maximum power and *second breakdown* (I_{SB}). All four of these parameters are graphically shown on the transistor's data sheet on what is known as a *safe operating area (SOA)* graph. (see **Figure 7.22**) The first three of these limits are usually also listed prominently with the other device information, but it is often the fourth parameter — secondary breakdown — that is responsible for the "sudden death" of the power transistor after an extended operating period.

The maximum current limit of the transistor ($I_{C\ MAX}$) is usually the current limit for fusing of the bond wire connected to the emitter, rather than anything pertaining to the transistor chip itself. When this limit is exceeded, the bond wire can melt and open circuit the emitter. On the operating curve, this limit is shown as a horizontal line extending out from the Y-axis and ending at the voltage point where the constant power limit begins.

The maximum collector-emitter voltage limit of the transistor ($V_{CE\ MAX}$) is the point at which the transistor junctions can no longer withstand the voltage between collector and emitter.

With increasing collector-emitter voltage drop at maximum collector current, a point is reached where the power in the transistor will cause the junction temperature to rise to a level where the device leakage current rapidly increases and begins to dominate. In this region, the product of the voltage drop and the current would be constant and represent the maximum power (P_t) rating for the transistor; that is, as the voltage drop continues to increase, the collector current must decrease to maintain the power dissipation at a constant value.

With most transistors rated for higher voltages, a point is reached on the constant power portion of the curve whereby, with further increased voltage drop, the maximum power rating is *not* constant, but decreases as the collector to emitter voltage increases. This decrease in power handling capability continues until the maximum voltage limit is reached.

This special region is known as the *forward bias second breakdown* (FBSB) area. Reduction in the transistor's power handling capability is caused by localized heating in certain small areas of the transistor junction ("hot spots"), rather than a uniform distribution of power dissipation over the entire surface of the device.

The region of operating conditions contained within these curves is called the safe operating area, or SOA. If the transistor is always operated within these limits, it should provide reliable and continuous service for a long time.

MOSFET TRANSISTORS

The bipolar junction transistor (BJT) is rapidly being replaced by the MOSFET in new power supply designs because MOSFETs are easier to drive. The N-channel MOSFET (equivalent to the NPN bipolar) is more popular than the P-channel for pass transistor applications.

There are some considerations that should be observed when using a MOSFET as a linear regulator series pass transistor. Several volts of gate drive are needed to start conduction of the device, as opposed to less than 1 V for the BJT. MOSFETs are inherently very-high-frequency devices and will readily oscillate with stray-circuit capacitances. To prevent oscillation in the transistor and surrounding circuits, it is common practice to insert a small resistor of about 100 Ω directly in series with the gate of the series-pass transistor to reduce the gate circuit Q.

OVERCURRENT PROTECTION

Damage to a pass transistor can occur when the load current exceeds the safe amount. **Figure 7.23A** illustrates a simple current-limiter circuit that will protect Q1. All of the load current is routed through R1. A voltage difference will exist across R1; the value will depend on the exact load current at a given time. When the load current exceeds a predetermined safe value, the voltage drop across R1 will forward-bias Q2 and cause it to conduct. Because Q2 is a silicon transistor, the voltage drop across R1 must exceed

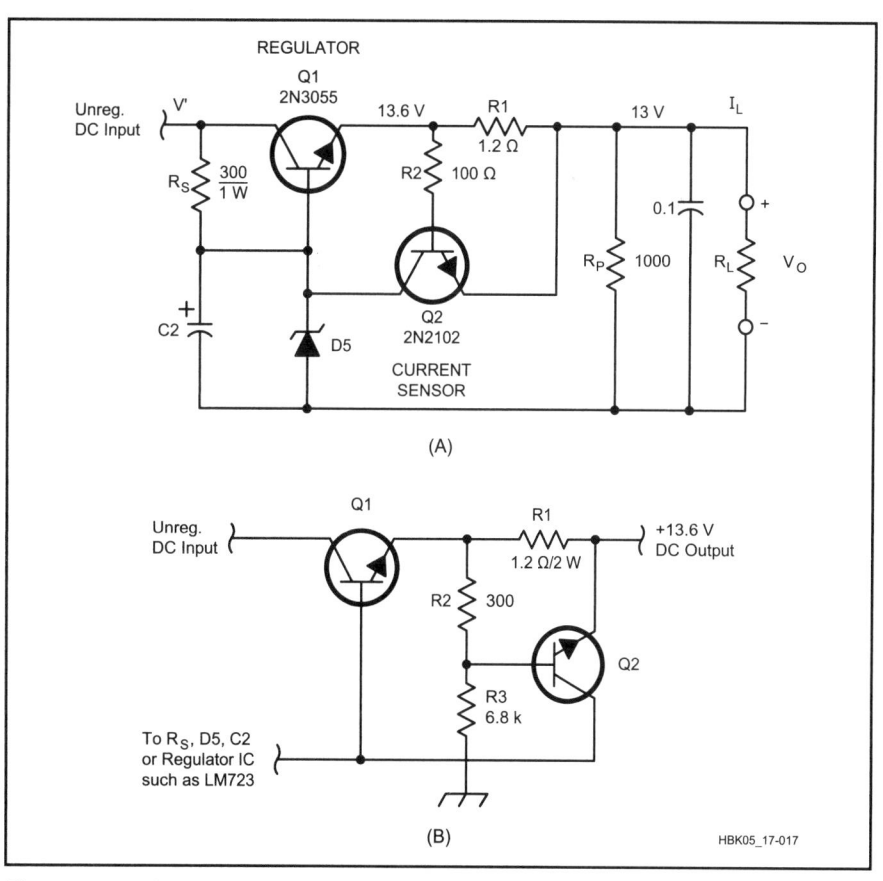

Figure 7.23 — Overload protection for a regulated supply can be implemented by addition of a current-overload-protective circuit, as shown at A. At B, the circuit has been modified to employ current-foldback limiting.

0.6 V to turn Q2 on. This being the case, R1 is chosen for a value that provides a drop of 0.6 V when the maximum safe load current is drawn. In this instance, the drop will be 0.6 V when I_L reaches 0.5 A. R2 protects the base-emitter junction of Q2 from current transients, or from destruction in the event Q1 fails under short-circuit conditions.

When Q2 turns on, some of the current through R_S flows through Q2, thereby depriving Q1 of some of its base current. This action, depending upon the amount of Q1 base current at a precise moment, cuts off Q1 conduction to some degree, thus limiting the current through it.

FOLDBACK CURRENT LIMITING

Under short-circuit conditions, a constant-current type current limiter must still withstand the full source voltage and limited short-circuit current simultaneously, which can impose a very high power dissipation or second breakdown stress on the series pass transistor. For example, a 12 V regulator with current limiting set for 10 A and having a source of 16 V will have a dissipation of 40 W [(16 V – 12 V) × 10 A] at the point of current limiting (knee). But its dissipation will rise to 160 W under short-circuit conditions (16 V × 10 A).

A modification of the limiter circuit can cause the regulated output current to decrease with decreasing load resistance beyond the over-current knee. With the output shorted, the output current is only a fraction of the knee current value, which protects the series-pass transistor from excessive dissipation and possible failure. Using the previous example of the 12 V, 10 A regulator, if the short-circuit current is designed to be 3 A (the knee is still 10 A), the transistor dissipation with a short circuit will be only 16 V × 3 A = 48 W.

Figure 7.23B shows how the current-limiter example given in the previous section would be modified to incorporate foldback limiting. The divider string formed by R2 and R3 provides a negative bias to the base of Q2, which prevents Q2 from turning on until this bias is overcome by the drop in R1 caused by load current. Since this hold-off bias decreases as the output voltage drops, Q2 becomes more sensitive to current through R1 with decreasing output voltage. See **Figure 7.24**.

The circuit is designed by first calculating the value of R1 for short-circuit current. For example, if 0.5 A is chosen, the value for R1 is simply 0.6 V / 0.5 A = 1.2 Ω (with the output shorted, the amount of hold-off bias supplied by R2 and R3 is very small and can be neglected). The knee current is then chosen. For this example, the selected value will be 1.0 A. The divider string is then proportioned to provide a base voltage at the knee that is just sufficient to turn on Q2 (a value of 13.6 V for 13.0 V output). With 1.0 A flowing through R1, the voltage across the divider will be 14.2 V. The voltage dropped by R2 must then be 14.2 V –13.6 V, or 0.6 V. Choosing a divider current of 2 mA, the value of R2 is then 0.6 V / 0.002 A = 300 Ω. R3 is calculated to be 13.6 V / 0.002 A = 6800 Ω.

7.9.4 Three-Terminal Voltage Regulators

The modern trend in regulators is toward the use of three-terminal devices commonly referred to as *three-terminal regulators*. Inside each regulator is a voltage reference, a high-gain error amplifier, temperature-compensated voltage sensing resistors and a pass element. Many currently available units have thermal shut-down, overvoltage protection and current foldback, making them virtually destruction-proof. It is easy to see why regulators of this sort are so popular when you consider the low price and the number of individual components they can replace.

Three-terminal regulators have connections for unregulated dc input, regulated dc output and ground, and they are available in a wide range of voltage and current ratings. Fixed-voltage regulators are available with output ratings in most common values between 5 and 28 V. Other families include devices that can be adjusted from 1.25 to 50 V.

The regulators are available in several different package styles, depending on current ratings. Low-current (100 mA) devices frequently use the plastic TO-92 and DIP-style cases. TO-220 packages are popular in the 1.5 A range, and TO-3 cases house the larger 3 A and 5 A devices. They are available in surface mount packages too.

Three-terminal regulators are available as positive or negative types. In most cases, a positive regulator is used to regulate a positive voltage and a negative regulator a negative voltage. Depending on the system ground requirements, however, each regulator type may be used to regulate the "opposite" voltage.

Figure 7.25A and B illustrate how the regulators are used in the conventional mode. Several regulators can be used with a common-input supply to deliver several voltages with a common ground. Negative regulators may be used in the same manner. If no other common supplies operate from the input supply to the regulator, the circuits of Figure 7.25C and D may be used to regulate positive voltages with a negative regulator and vice versa. In these configurations the input supply is floated; neither side of the input is tied to the system ground.

Manufacturers have adopted a system of

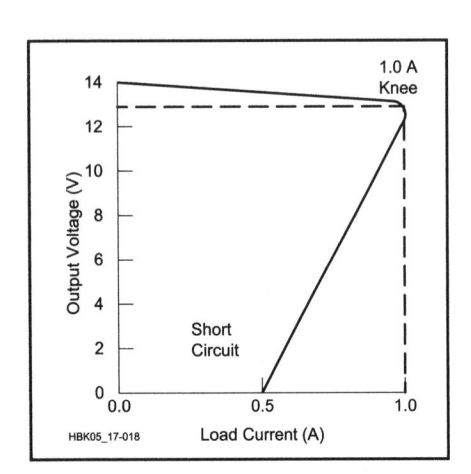

Figure 7.24 — The 1 A regulator shown in Figure 7.23B will fold back to 0.5 A under short-circuit conditions. See text.

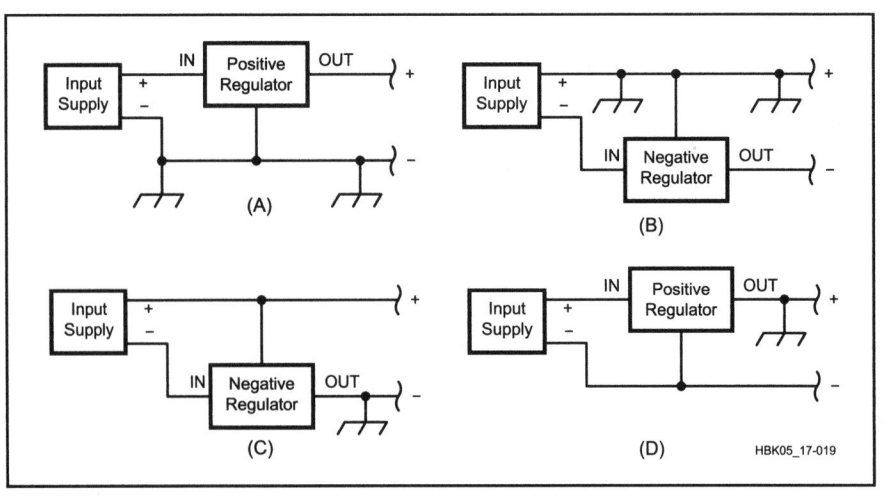

Figure 7.25 — Parts A and B illustrate the conventional manner in which three-terminal regulators are used. Parts C and D show how one polarity regulator can be used to regulate the opposite-polarity voltage.

family numbers to classify three-terminal regulators in terms of supply polarity, output current and regulated voltage. For example, 7805 describes a positive 5 V, 1.5 A regulator and 7905 a negative 5 V, 1.5 A unit. Depending on the manufacturer, the full part number might have a prefix such as LM, UA or MC, along with various suffixes (for example, LM7805CT or MC7805CTG). There are many such families with widely varied ratings available from manufacturers. More information may be found in the **Component Data and References** chapter.

SPECIFYING A REGULATOR

When choosing a three-terminal regulator for a given application, the most important specifications to consider are device output voltage, output current, minimum and maximum input-to-output differential voltages, line regulation, load regulation and power dissipation. Output voltage and current requirements are determined by the load with which the supply will ultimately be used.

Input-to-output differential voltage is one of the most important three-terminal regulator specifications to consider when designing a supply. The differential value (the difference between the voltage applied to the input terminal and the voltage on the output terminal) must be within a specified range. The minimum differential value, usually about 2.5 V, is called the *dropout voltage*. If the differential value is less than the dropout voltage, no regulation will take place. Special *low dropout regulators* with lower minimum differential values are available as well. At the other end of the scale, maximum input-output differential voltage is generally about 40 V. If this differential value is exceeded, device failure may occur.

Increases in either output current or differential voltage produce proportional increases in device power consumption. By employing current foldback, as described above, some manufacturers ensure that maximum dissipation will never be exceeded in normal operation. **Figure 7.26** shows the relationship between output current, input-output differential and current limiting for a three-terminal regulator nominally rated for 1.5 A output current. Maximum output current is available with differential voltages ranging from about 2.5 V (dropout voltage) to 12 V. Above 12 V, the output current decreases, limiting the device dissipation to a safe value. If the output terminals are accidentally short circuited, the input-output differential will rise, causing current foldback, and thus preventing the power-supply components from being over stressed. This protective feature makes three-terminal regulators particularly attractive in simple power supplies.

When designing a power supply around a particular three-terminal regulator, input-output voltage characteristics of the regulator should play a major role in selecting the transformer-secondary and filter-capacitor component values. The unregulated voltage applied to the input of the three-terminal device should be higher than the dropout voltage, yet low enough that the regulator does not go into current limiting caused by an excessive differential voltage. If, for example, the regulated output voltage of the device shown in Figure 7.26 were 12 V, then unregulated input voltages of between 14.5 and 24 V would be acceptable if maximum output current is desired.

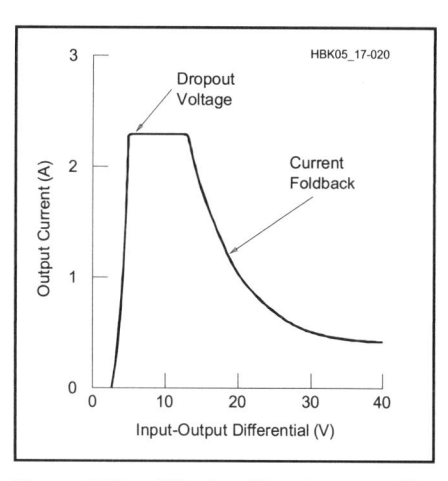

Figure 7.26 — Effects of input-output differential voltage on three-terminal regulator current.

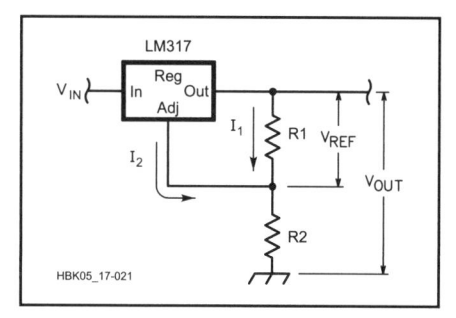

Figure 7.27 — By varying the ratio of R2 to R1 in this simple LM317 schematic diagram, a wide range of output voltages is possible. See text for details.

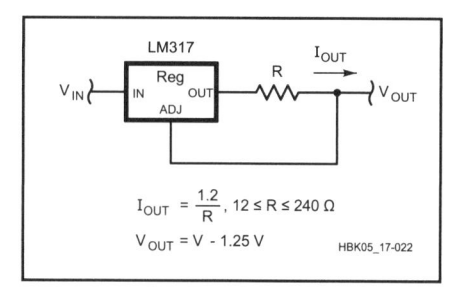

Figure 7.28 — The basic LM317 voltage regulator is converted into a constant-current source by adding only one resistor.

In use, all but the lowest-current regulators generally require an adequate external heat sink because they may be called on to dissipate a fair amount of power. Also, because the regulator chip contains a high-gain error amplifier, bypassing of the input and output leads is essential for stable operation.

Most manufacturers recommend bypassing the input and output directly at the leads where they protrude through the heat sink. Solid tantalum capacitors are usually recommended because of their good high-frequency capabilities.

External capacitors used with IC regulators may discharge through the IC junctions under certain circuit conditions, and high-current discharges can harm ICs. Look at the regulator data sheet to see whether protection diodes are needed, what diodes to use and how to place them in any particular application.

Adjustable Regulators

In addition to fixed-output-voltage ICs, high-current, adjustable voltage regulators are available. These ICs require little more than an external potentiometer for an adjustable output range from 5 to 24 V at up to 5 A. The unit price on these items is only a few dollars, making them ideal for test-bench power supplies. A very popular low current, adjustable output voltage three terminal regulator, the LM317, is shown in **Figure 7.27**. It develops a steady 1.25 V reference, V_{REF}, between the output and adjustment terminals. By installing R1 between these terminals, a constant current, I1, is developed, governed by the equation:

$$I1 = \frac{V_{REF}}{R1} \tag{10}$$

Both I1 and a 100 µA error current, I2, flow through R2, resulting in output voltage V_O. V_O can be calculated using the equation:

$$V_O = V_{REF}\left(1 + \frac{R2}{R1}\right) + I2 \times R2 \tag{11}$$

Any voltage between 1.2 and 37 V may be obtained with a 40 V input by changing the ratio of R2 to R1. At lower output voltages, however, the available current will be limited by the power dissipation of the regulator.

Figure 7.28 shows one of many flexible applications for the LM317. By adding only one resistor with the regulator, the voltage regulator can be changed into a constant-current source capable of charging NiCd batteries, for example. Design equations are given in the figure. The same precautions should be taken with adjustable regulators as with the fixed-voltage units. Proper heat sinking and lead bypassing are essential for proper circuit operation.

INCREASING REGULATOR OUTPUT CURRENT

When the maximum output current from an IC voltage regulator is insufficient to operate the load, discrete power transistors may be connected to increase the current capability. **Figure 7.29** shows two methods for boosting the output current of a positive regulator, although the same techniques can be applied to negative regulators.

In A, an NPN transistor is connected as an emitter follower, multiplying the output current capacity by the transistor beta. The shortcoming of this approach is that the base-emitter junction is not inside the feedback loop. The result is that the output voltage is reduced by the base-emitter drop, and the load regulation is degraded by variations in this drop.

The circuit at B has a PNP transistor "wrapped around" the regulator. The regulator draws current through the base-emitter junction, causing the transistor to conduct. R1 provides bias voltage for turning on Q1 so that U1 doesn't see the excess current. For example, a 6 Ω resistor will limit the current U1 sees to 100 mA. The IC output voltage is unchanged by the transistor because the collector is connected directly to the IC output (sense point). Any increase in output voltage is detected by the IC regulator, which shuts off its internal-pass transistor, and this stops the boost-transistor base current.

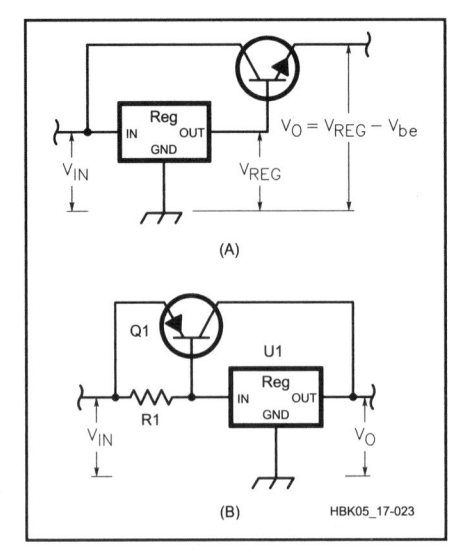

Figure 7.29 — Two methods for boosting the output-current capacity of an IC voltage regulator. Part A shows an NPN emitter follower and B shows a PNP "wraparound" configuration. Operation of these circuits is explained in the text.

7.10 "Crowbar" Protective Circuits

Electronic components *do* fail from time to time. In a regulated power supply, the only component standing between an elevated dc source voltage and your transceiver is one transistor, or a group of transistors wired in parallel. If the transistor, or one of the transistors in the group, happens to short internally, your equipment could suffer lots of damage.

To safeguard the load equipment against possible overvoltage, some power-supply manufacturers include a circuit known as a *crowbar*. This circuit usually consists of a silicon-controlled rectifier (SCR) or thyristor connected directly across the output of the power supply, with an over-voltage-sensing trigger circuit tied to its gate. The SCR is large enough to take the full short-circuit output current of the supply, as if a crowbar were placed across the output terminals, thus the name.

In the event the output voltage exceeds the trigger set point, the SCR will fire, and the output is short circuited. The resulting high current in the power supply (shorted output in series with a series pass transistor failed short) will blow the power supply's line fuses. This is a protection for the supply as well as an indicator that something has malfunctioned internally. For these reasons, never replace blown fuses with ones that have a higher current rating.

An example of a crowbar overvoltage protection circuit can be found as a project at the end of this chapter. It provides basic design equations that can be adapted to a wide range of power supply applications.

7.11 DC-DC Switchmode Power Conversion

Very often the power source is dc, such as a battery or solar cell, or the output of an unregulated rectifier connected to an ac source. In most applications high conversion efficiency is desired, both to conserve energy from the source and to reduce heat dissipation in the converter. When high efficiency is needed, some form of switching circuit will be employed for dc-dc power conversion. Besides being more efficient, switching circuits are usually much smaller and lighter than conventional 60 Hz, transformer-rectifier circuits because they operate at much higher frequencies — from 25 to 400 kHz or even higher. Switching circuits go by many names; *switching regulators* and *switchmode converters* are just two of the more common names.

The possibility of achieving high conversion efficiency stems directly from the use of switches for the power conversion process, along with low-loss inductive and capacitive elements. An active switch is a device that is either ON or OFF and the state of the switch (ON or OFF) can be controlled with an external signal. The loss in the switch is always the product of the voltage across the switch and the current flowing through it ($P = E \times I$).

In the ON (conducting) state the voltage drop across the switch is small, and in the OFF state the current through the switch is small. In both cases the losses can be small relative to the power level of the converter. During transitions between ON and OFF states, however, there will simultaneously be both substantial voltage across the switch and significant current flowing through it. This results in power dissipation in the switch, called *switching loss*. This loss is minimized by making the switching transitions as short as possible. In this way even though the instantaneous power dissipation may be high, the average loss is low because of the small duty cycle of the transitions. Of course the more frequently the switch operates (higher switching frequency), the higher the average loss will be and this eventually limits the maximum operating frequency. A limitation on the lower end of the switching frequency range is that it needs to be above audible frequencies (>25 kHz).

This is quite different from the linear regulators discussed earlier in which there is always some voltage drop across the pass transistor (which is acting as a controlled variable resistor) while current is flowing through it. As a result the efficiency of a linear regulator can be very low, often 65% or less. Switchmode converters on the other hand will typically have efficiencies in the range of 85 to 95%.

Switchmode circuits can also generate radio-frequency interference (RFI) through VHF because of switching frequency harmonics and ringing induced by the rapid rise and fall times of voltage and current. In attempting to minimize the ON-OFF transition time, significant amounts of RF energy can be generated. To prevent RFI to sensitive receivers, careful bypassing, shielding and filtering of both input and output circuits is required. (RFI from switchmode or "switching" supplies is also discussed in the chapter on **RF Interference**.)

There are literally hundreds of different switchmode circuits or "topologies" (see Reference 2) but we will only look at a few of those most commonly used by amateurs. Fortunately, the characteristics of the simpler circuits are to a large extent replicated in more complex circuits so that an understanding of the basic circuits provides an entry point to many other circuits.

The following discussion is only an introduction to the basics of switchmode converters. To really get a handle on designing these circuits the reader will have to do some additional reading. Fortunately a very large amount of useful information is freely available on-line. Many useful application notes are available from semiconductor manufacturers, and additional information can be found on the websites of filter capacitor and ferrite core manufacturers (see References 3 and 4). There are also numerous books on the subject, often available in libraries and used book stores.

Switchmode circuits can and have been implemented with many different kinds of switches, from mechanical vibrators to vacuum and gas tubes to semiconductors. Today however, semiconductors are the universal choice. For converters in the power range typical of amateur applications (a few watts through 2-3 kW) the most common choices of semiconductor switches would be either bipolar junction transistors (BJTs) or power MOSFETs. BJTs have a long history of use in switchmode applications, but to employ BJTs in a reliable and trouble-free circuit requires a relatively sophisticated understanding of them. While the MOSFET must also be used carefully, it is generally easier for a newcomer. The following circuit diagrams will show MOSFETs or generic switch symbols for the switches but keep in mind that all of the circuits can be implemented with other types of switches.

7.11.1 The Buck Converter

A schematic for a *buck converter* is shown in **Figure 7.30A**. This circuit is called a "buck" converter because the output voltage is always less than or equal to the input voltage. Power is supplied from the dc source (V_S)

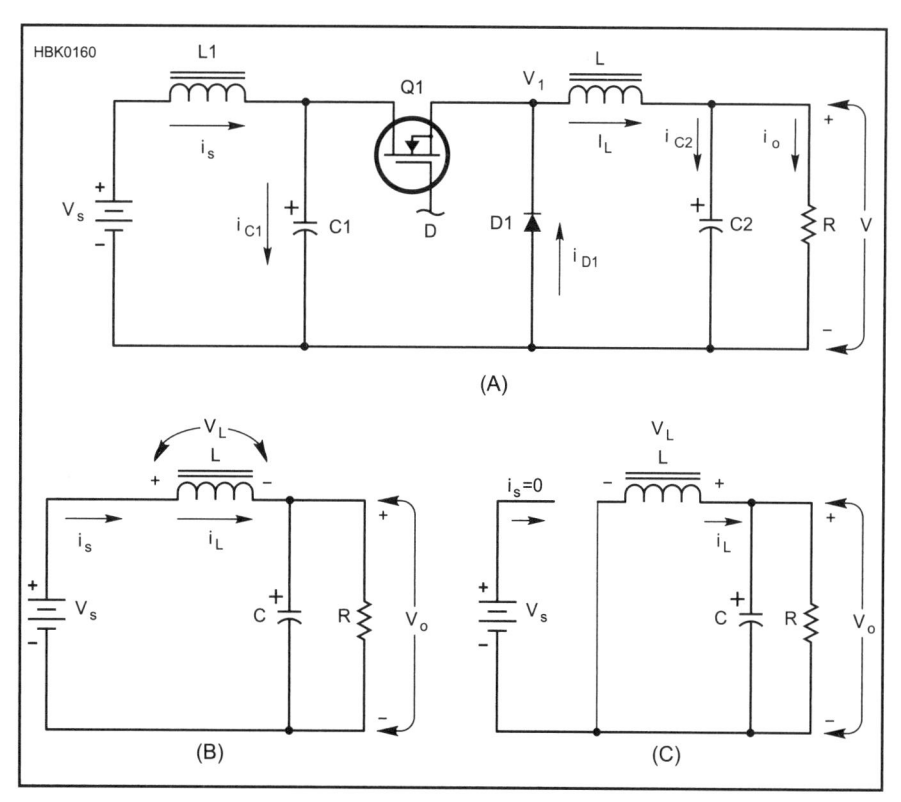

Figure 7.30 — Typical buck converter.

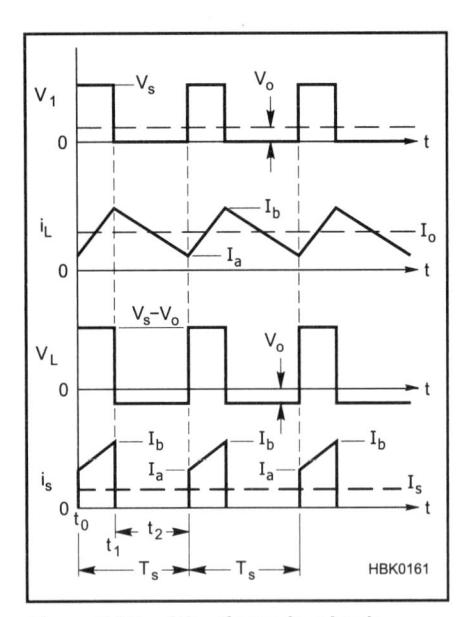

Figure 7.31 — Waveforms in a buck converter.

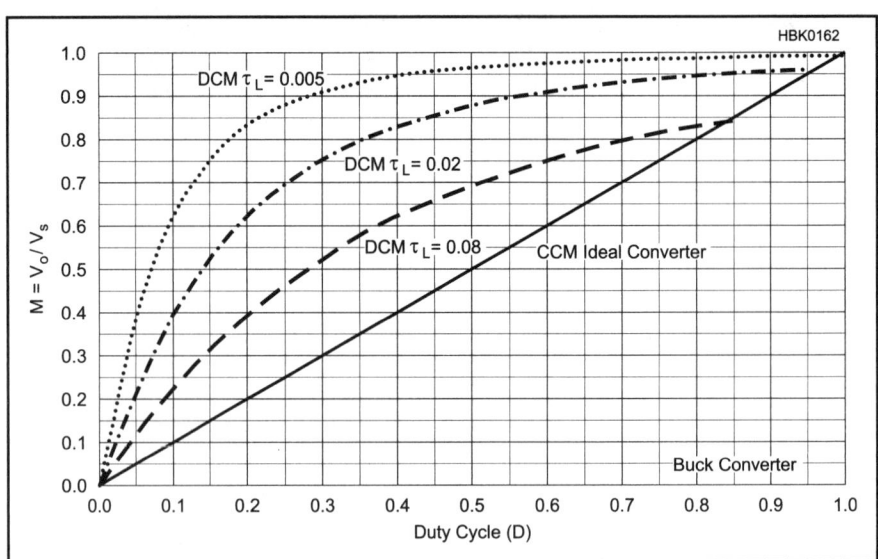

Figure 7.32 — Change in output voltage to input voltage ratio (M=VO/VS) as a function of switch duty cycle (D).

through the input filter (L1, C1) to the drain of the switch (Q1). The load (R) is connected across the output filter (L, C2).

The equivalent circuit when Q1 is ON is shown in Figure 7.30B (where the input filter components are assumed to be part of V_S). V_S is connected to one end of the output inductor (L) and, because $V_O < V_S$, current flows from the source to the output delivering energy from the source to the output and also storing energy in L. At some point Q1 is turned OFF and the current flowing in L commutates (switches) to D1, as shown in Figure 7.30C. (The current in an inductor cannot change instantaneously, so when Q1 turns OFF, the collapsing magnetic field in L pulls current through shunt diode D1, called a *free-wheeling diode*.) The energy in L is now being discharged into the output. This cycle is repeated at the switching frequency (f_s). The ratio of the switch ON-time to the total switching period ($T_s = t_{on} + t_{off} = 1/f_s$) is called the *duty cycle (D)*.

Typical voltage and current waveforms for a buck converter are shown in **Figure 7.31** where V_1 is the voltage at the junction of Q1, D1 and L (see Figure 7.30A).

The interval 0-t_1 corresponds to the ON time of Q1 and $T_s - t_1$ corresponds to the OFF time ($T_s = t_1 + t_2$). From the waveforms it can be seen that the current in the inductor rises while Q1 is ON and falls while Q1 is OFF. The energy in the inductor is proportional to $LI^2/2$.

The input current (I_s) is pulsating at the switching frequency. This pulsation in the input current is the reason for the input filter (L1 and C1). We need to keep this high frequency noise (the ac component of the pulsation) out of the source. All switchmode converters require some form of filter on the input to keep switching noise out of the source. Some form of filter is also required on the output to keep the switching noise out of the load. In Figure 7.30, L and C2 form the output filter. For applications requiring low ripple it would not be unusual to see an additional stage of L-C filtering added to the output.

The voltage waveform (V_1) at the input to the output filter (L and C2) is pulse-width modulated (PWM) and V_O (the dotted line in the waveform for V_1 in Figure 7.31A) is the time average of V_1. V_O is controlled or regulated by adjusting the duty cycle of Q1 in response to input voltage or output load changes. If we increase D we increase V_O up to the point where D = 1 (the switch is ON all the time) and $V_O \approx V_S$. If we never turn Q1 on (D = 0) then $V_O = 0$. Normal operation will be somewhere between these extremes.

The inductor current waveform in Figure 7.31 does not go to zero while Q1 is OFF. In other words, not all of the energy stored in L is discharged into the output by the end of each switching cycle. This is a common mode of operation for heavier loads. It is referred to as the *continuous conduction mode* or CCM, where the conduction referred to is the current in L. There is another possibility: during the time Q1 is off all of the energy in L may be discharged and for some period of time the inductor current is zero until Q1 is turned ON again. This is referred to as the *discontinuous conduction mode* or DCM. A typical converter will operate in CCM for heavy loads but as the load is reduced, at some point the circuit operation will change to DCM. CCM is often referred to as the "heavy load" condition and DCM as the "light load" condition.

This distinction turns out to be very important because the behavior of the circuit, for both small signal and large signal, is radically different between the two modes. **Figure 7.32** shows the relationship between the duty cycle (D) of Q1 and the ratio of the output voltage to the input voltage (M = V_O/V_S) as a function of τ_L in Figure 7.32:

$$\tau_L = \left(\frac{L}{R}\right) f_S \quad (12)$$

τ_L is just a convenient way to make Figure 7.32 more general by tying together the variables L, R and f_s. Smaller values for τ_L correspond to lighter loads (larger values for R). As can been seen in Figure 7.32, for very light loads the higher values for D have little effect on the output/input voltage ratio. This is basically charging of the output capacitor (C2) to the peak value of $V_1 \approx V_S$.

For CCM operation, M is a linear function of D. As we vary the load, V_O will remain relatively constant. But when we go into DCM, the relation between D and M is no longer linear and in addition is heavily dependent on the load: V_O will vary as the load is changed unless the duty cycle is varied to compensate. This kind of behavior is typical of all switching regulators, even those not directly related to the buck converter. In fact, we have seen this behavior already in the section on choke input filters in Figure 7.17 where the output voltage is close to the peak input voltage for light loads and decreases as the load increases until a point is reached (I_C) where V_O stabilizes.

In a buck converter the value for the critical inductance (L_C) can be found from:

$$L_c = R\left(\frac{1-M}{2f_S}\right) \quad (13)$$

This looks just like equation 6 (in the

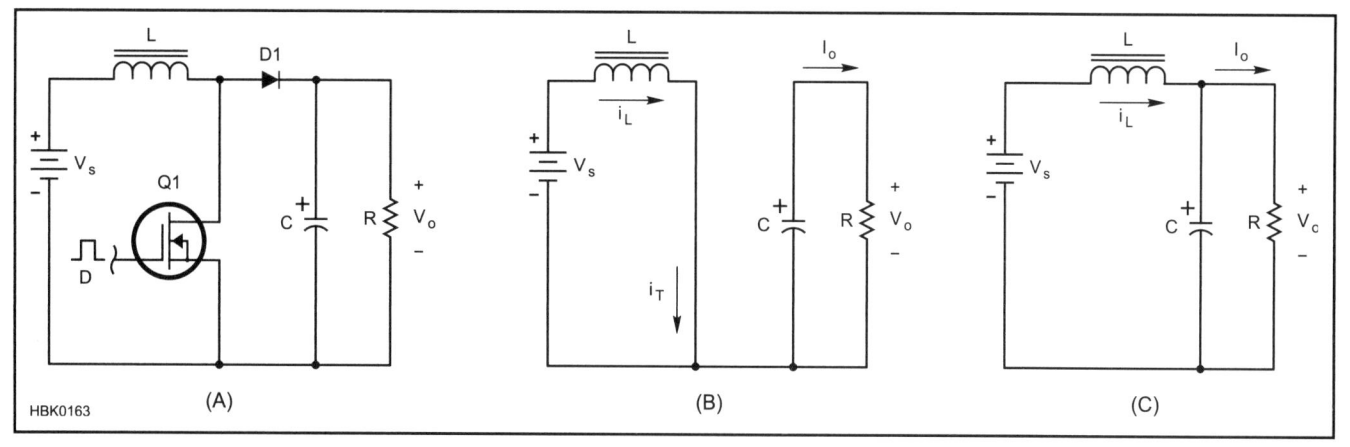

Figure 7.33 — Typical boost converter.

7.11.2 The Boost Converter

A *boost converter* circuit is shown in **Figure 7.33A**. This circuit is called a "boost" converter because the output voltage is always greater than or equal to the input voltage.

When Q1 is ON (Figure 7.33B), L is connected in parallel with the source (V_S) and energy is stored in it. During this time interval load energy is supplied from C. When Q1 turns OFF (Figure 7.33C), L is connected via D1 to the output and the energy in L, plus additional energy from the source, is discharged into the output. The value for L, V_S and length of time it is charged determines the energy stored in L. Again we have the possibilities that either some (CCM) or all (DCM) the energy in L is discharged during the OFF-time of Q1. The variation in the ratio of the output-to-input voltage (M) with duty cycle is shown in **Figure 7.34**.

As we saw in the buck converter, the conduction mode of L is important. In an ideal converter operating in CCM, the output voltage is substantially independent of load and $M \approx 1 / (1 - D)$. In realistic boost converters there is an important limit on the CCM value for M. In an ideal boost converter you could make the boost ratio (M) as large as you wish but in real converters the parasitic resistances associated with the components will limit the maximum value of M as indicated by the dashed line for CCM operation. The exact shape of this part of the control function will depend on the ratio of the parasitic resistance within the converter to the load resistance (see Reference 2).

There is also another very important practical effect of this limitation on the peak value for M. When the duty cycle is increased beyond the point of maximum M (this occurs at D = 0.9 in Figure 7.34), the sign of the slope of the control function changes so that

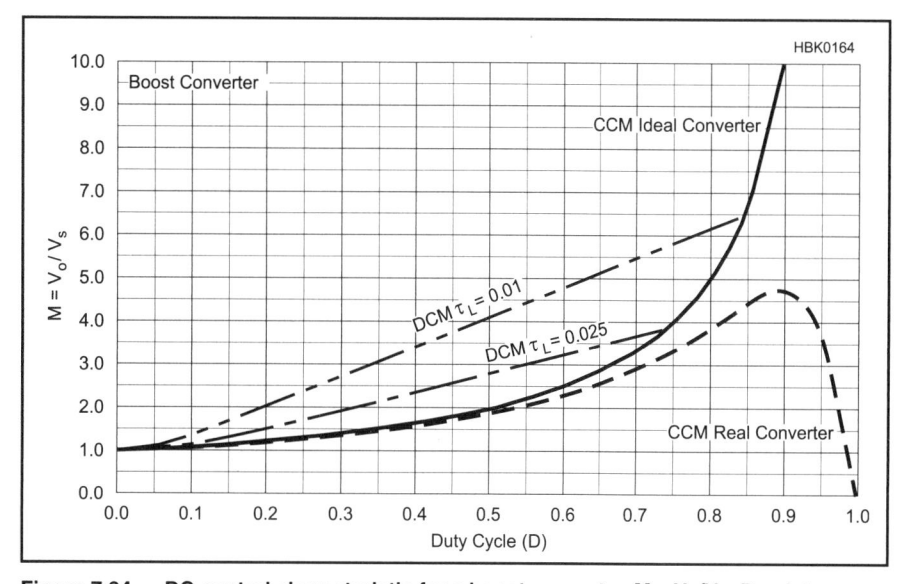

Figure 7.34 — DC control characteristic for a boost converter. $M = V_O/V_S$, D = duty cycle of Q1 and $\tau_L = f_s (L/R)$.

the control loop will change from negative feedback to positive feedback. This can cause the converter to latch up under some load conditions if the control circuit allows D to exceed the value at maximum M. In boost converters the design of the control circuit must limit the maximum value for D so that latch-up is not possible although this may be difficult for overload conditions.

As in the case of the buck converter, in DCM the control function for M is very different from what it is in CCM and is strongly dependent on the load R. One advantage of the DCM operation is that the limitation on the maximum value for M because of parasitic circuit resistances is not nearly so pronounced. By operating in DCM it is possible to have M > 5.

An important limitation of the boost converter is that with Q1 turned OFF, you have no control over V_O. V_O will simply equal V_S. In addition, when V_S is turned on there will be an inrush current through D1, into C which cannot be controlled by Q1. In the case of the buck converter, if Q1 is kept OFF when V_S is turned on, there will be no inrush current charging the output filter capacitor (C2). In the buck converter C2 can be charged slowly by ramping up the duty cycle of Q1 during turn-on but this is not possible in the boost converter.

7.11.3 Buck-Boost and Flyback Converters

Figure 7.35 shows an example of a *buck-boost converter*. The name "buck-boost" comes from the fact that the magnitude of the output voltage can be either greater or less than the input voltage.

When S1 is ON, V_S is applied across L and energy is stored in it. During the ON time of Q1, D1 is reverse-biased and non-conducting. The output voltage (V_O) across

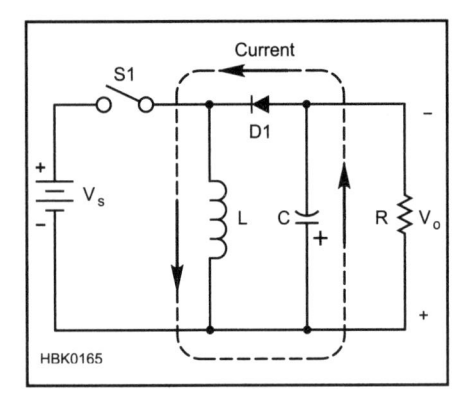

Figure 7.35 — An example of a buck-boost converter.

the load (R) is supported solely from the energy stored in C. When S1 is OFF, the energy in L is discharged into C through D1. Note that the polarity of V_O is inverted from V_S: *positive V_S means negative V_O*. The relationship between V_O and V_S as a function of duty cycle is shown in **Figure 7.36**.

This graph closely resembles that for the boost converter (Figure 7.34) with one important exception: |M| begins at zero. This allows the magnitude of the output voltage to be either below or above the source voltage, hence the name "buck-boost."

FLYBACK CONVERTERS

Simple buck-boost converters are occasionally used, but much more often it is the transformer-coupled version of this converter, referred to as a *flyback converter*, that is employed. The relationship between the flyback

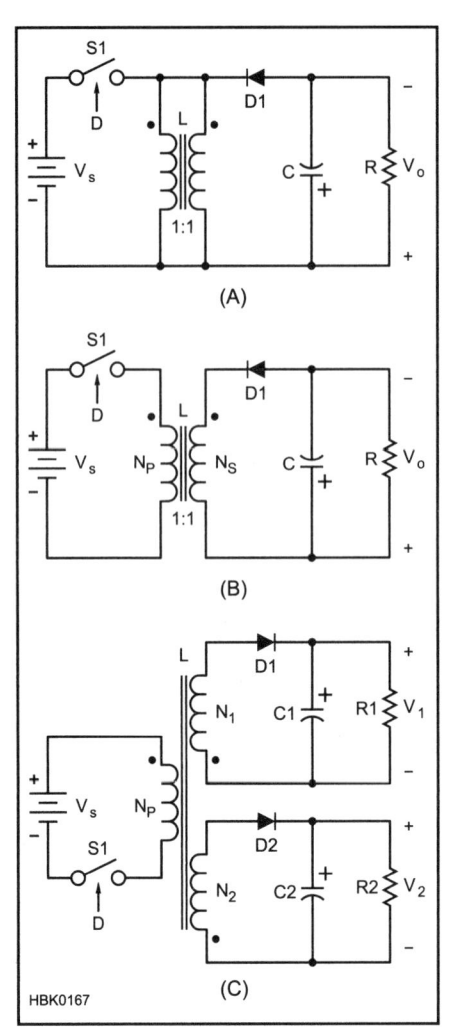

Figure 7.37 — The relationship between buck-boost and flyback converters.

and buck-boost converters is illustrated in **Figure 7.37**. In Figure 7.37A we have a standard buck-boost converter, the only change from Figure 7.35 being two parallel and equal windings on the inductor. In Figure 7.37B we remove the links at the top and bottom of the two parallel windings, converting the inductor into a transformer with primary and secondary windings. The only change is that when S1 is ON, current flows in the primary of the transformer and when S1 is OFF, the current flows in the secondary winding delivering the stored energy to the output. At this point the circuit operation is the same except that we have introduced primary-to-secondary galvanic isolation.

We are now free to change the turns ratio from 1:1 to anything we wish. We can also change the polarity of the output voltages and/or add more windings with other voltages and additional loads as shown in Figure 7.37C, a typical example of a flyback converter. These are most often used in the power range of a few watts to perhaps 200 W. For higher power levels other circuits are generally more useful.

The advantages of the flyback converter lie in its simplicity. It requires only one power switch and one diode on each of the output windings. The inductor is also the isolation transformer so you have only one magnetic component. The disadvantage of this circuit is that both in the input and output current waveforms are pulsating. The result is that more filtering is required and the filter capacitors are exposed to high RMS currents relative to the power level.

7.11.4 The Forward Converter

The buck converter has many useful properties but it lacks input-to-output galvanic isolation, the ability to produce output voltages higher than the input voltage, and/or multiple isolated output voltages for multiple loads. We can overcome these drawbacks by inserting a transformer between the switch (S1) and the shunt diode (D1). To make this simple idea work however, we also have to add a diode in series with the output of the transformer (D2), and a third winding (N_R) with another diode (D3) to the transformer. This is done to provide a means for resetting the core (returning the magnetic flux to zero) by the end of each switching cycle. The result is the *forward converter* shown in **Figure 7.38**.

The circuit in A is the one just described. The variation in B uses two switches (S1 and S2, which switch ON and OFF *simultaneously*) instead of one but eliminates the need for a reset winding on the transformer. For the circuit in A and a given input voltage, the voltage across the switch (in the OFF state) will be equal to V_S plus the reset voltage during the OFF-time. Typically the peak switch voltage

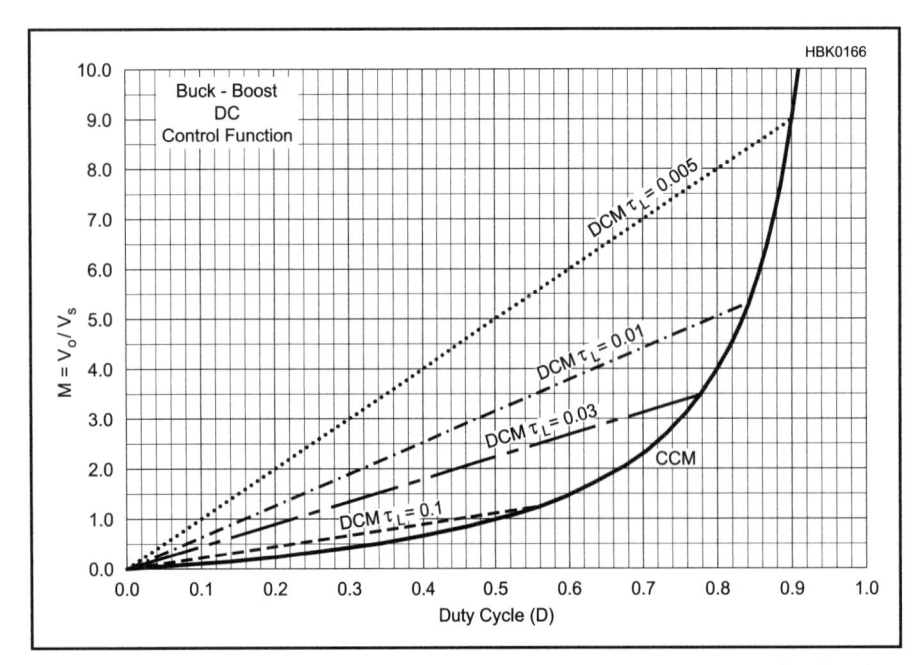

Figure 7.36 — DC control function for an ideal buck-boost converter. $M = V_O/V_S$, D = duty cycle of Q1 and $\tau_L = f_s (L/R)$.

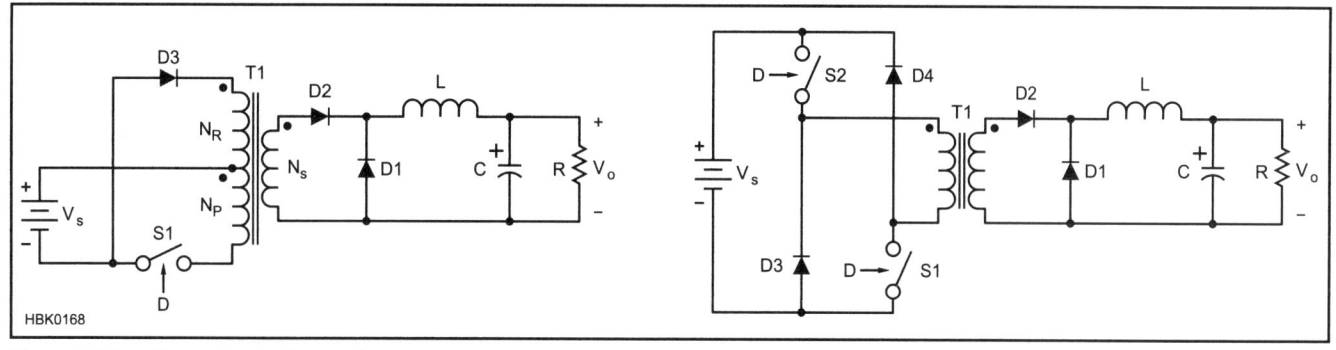

Figure 7.38 — Example of a forward converter.

Figure 7.39 — Example of a parallel quasi-square wave dc-dc

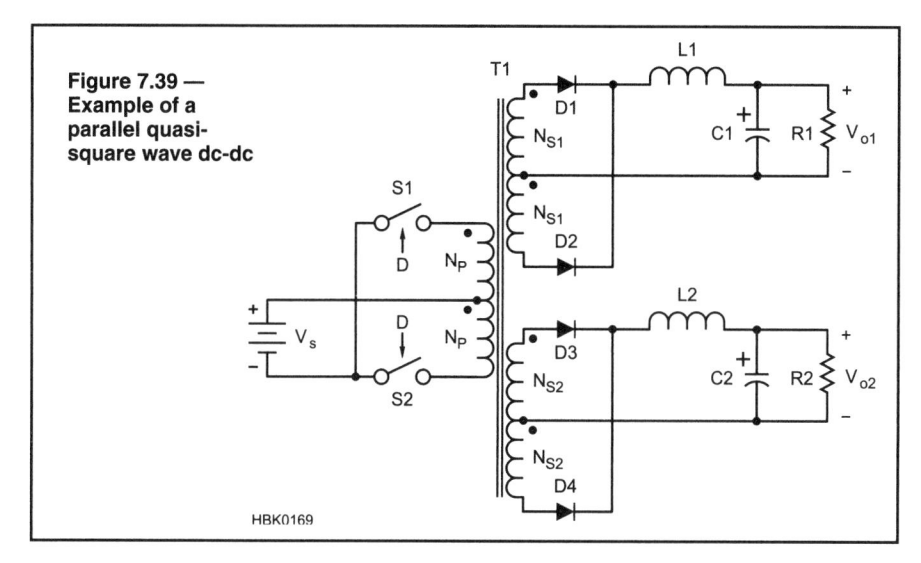

will be about $2V_S$. In the circuit shown in B the switch voltage is limited to V_S which is very helpful at higher line voltages. These circuits behave just like a buck converter except you can now have multiple isolated outputs with arbitrary voltages and polarities. These circuits are typically used in converters with power levels of 100 to 500 W.

7.11.5 Parallel, Half and Full-Bridge Converters

As the power level increases it becomes advantageous to use more switches in a somewhat more complex circuit. For applications where the input voltage is low (<100V) and the current high, the push-pull *quasi-square wave* circuit shown in **Figure 7.39** is often used.

S1 and S2 are switched on alternately with duty cycles <0.5. The output voltages are controlled by the duty cycle, D. The peak switch currents are equal to the input current but the peak switch voltages will be $2V_S$.

This circuit is still just a buck converter, but with an isolation transformer added that allows multiple outputs with different voltages above or below the input voltage. It would be very common to have a 5 V, high-current output and ±12 V, lower-current outputs, for example. This converter is typically used for operation from vehicular power with loads up to several hundred watts.

Operating directly from rectified ac utility power usually means that V_S will be 200 V or more. For these applications, **Figure 7.40** shows how the switches are configured in either a half- (Figure 7.40A) or full-bridge (Figure 7.40B) circuit.

In A, S1 and S2 switch alternately and are pulse-width modulated (PWM) to control the output. CA and CB are large capacitors that form a voltage divider with $V_S/2$ across each capacitor. The peak switch voltages will be equal to V_S but the switch currents will be $2I_S$. The peak voltage across the primary winding will be $V_S/2$. This circuit would typically be used for off-line applications with output powers of 500 W or so.

In B, S1 and S4 switch simultaneously alternating with S2 and S3 which also switch simultaneously. The output is controlled by PWM. The peak switch voltage will be equal to V_S and the peak switch current close to I_S (the peak value is a little higher due to ripple on the inductor current which is reflected back into the primary winding). The full-bridge circuit is typically used for power levels of 500 W to several kW. C_S is present in the full-bridge circuit to prevent core saturation due to any asymmetry in the primary PWM voltage waveforms. Cs should be a non-polarized capacitor since differences in duty cycle

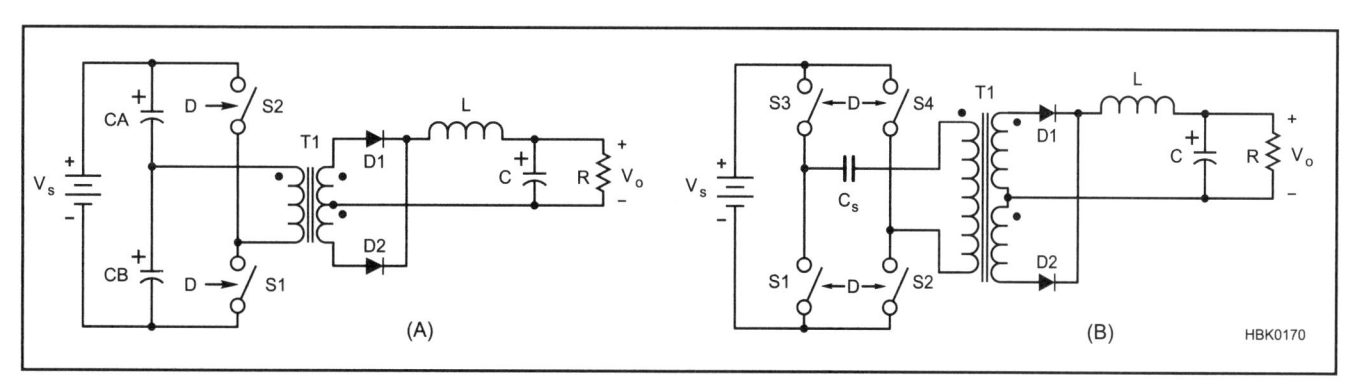

Figure 7.40 — Examples of half and full-bridge quasi-square wave dc-dc converters.

Power Sources 7.25

between S1-4 can create dc voltages of either polarity across it.

7.11.6 Building Switchmode Power Supplies

Selecting a switching circuit or topology is just the first step in building a practical switchmode power supply. In the actual circuit you will have to sample the output voltage, provide a voltage reference against which to compare the output, include a modulator that will convert the error voltages to a variable-duty cycle signal and finally provide correct drive to the power switches. Fortunately, all of these functions can be provided with readily available integrated

Figure 7.41 — Block representation of an LM20343 connected to external components.

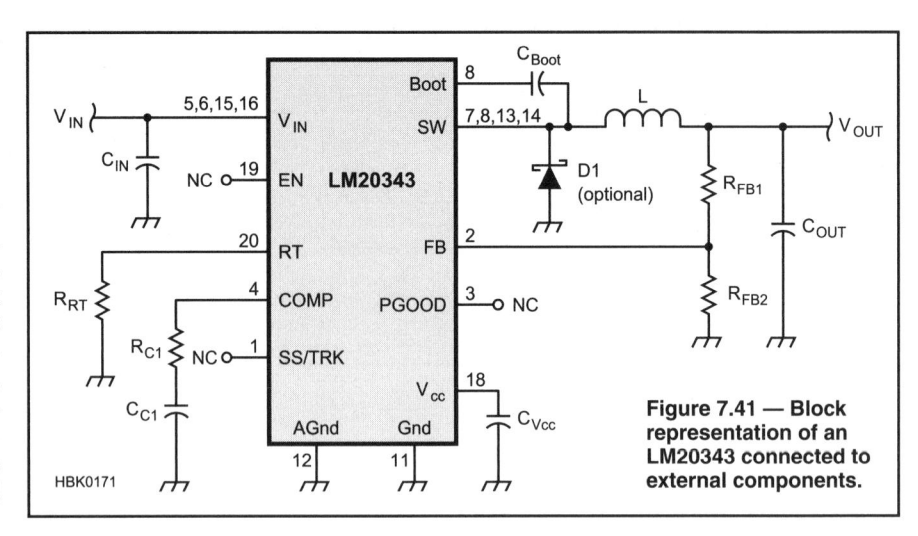

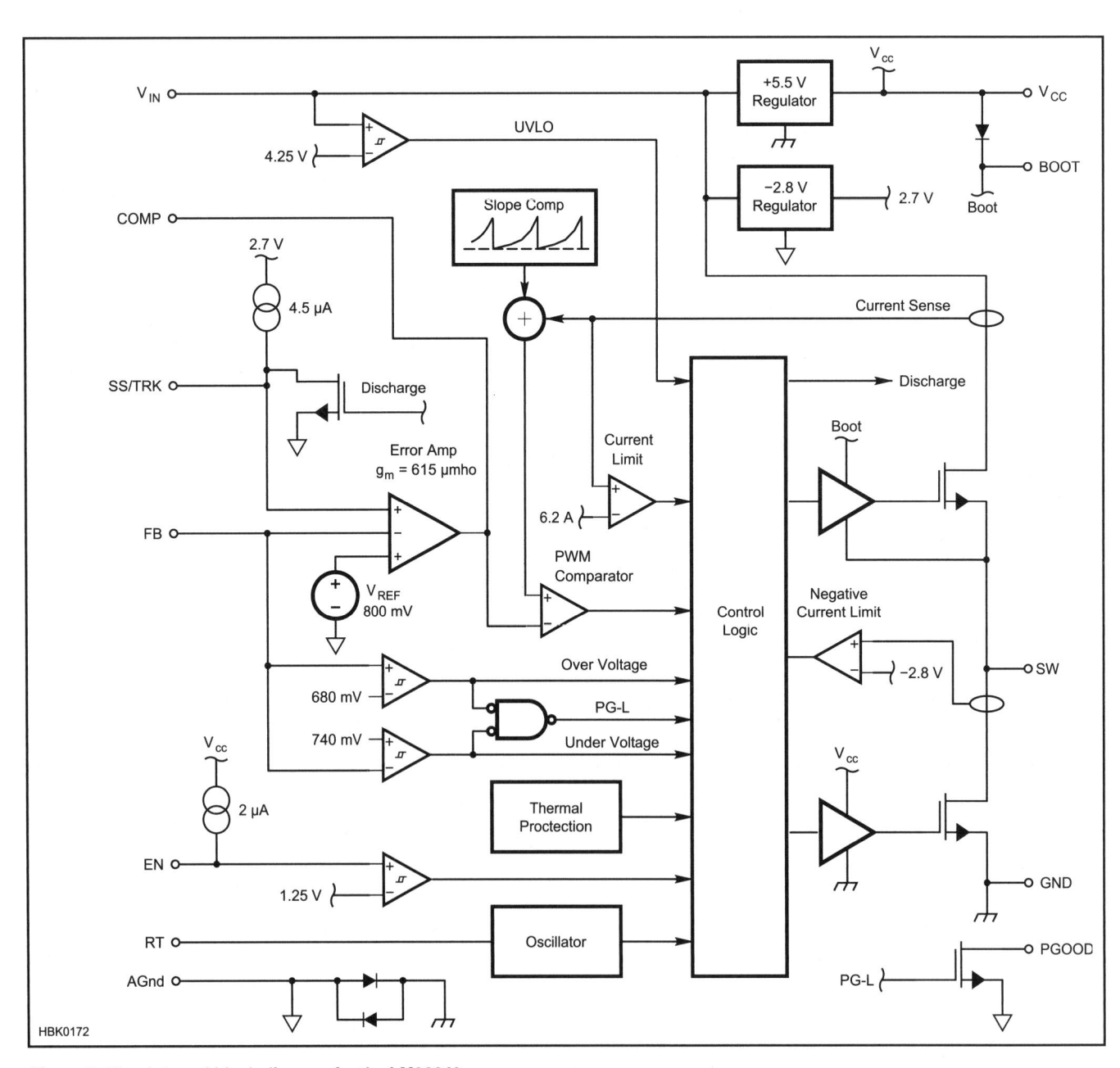

Figure 7.42 — Internal block diagram for the LM20343.

7.26   Chapter 7

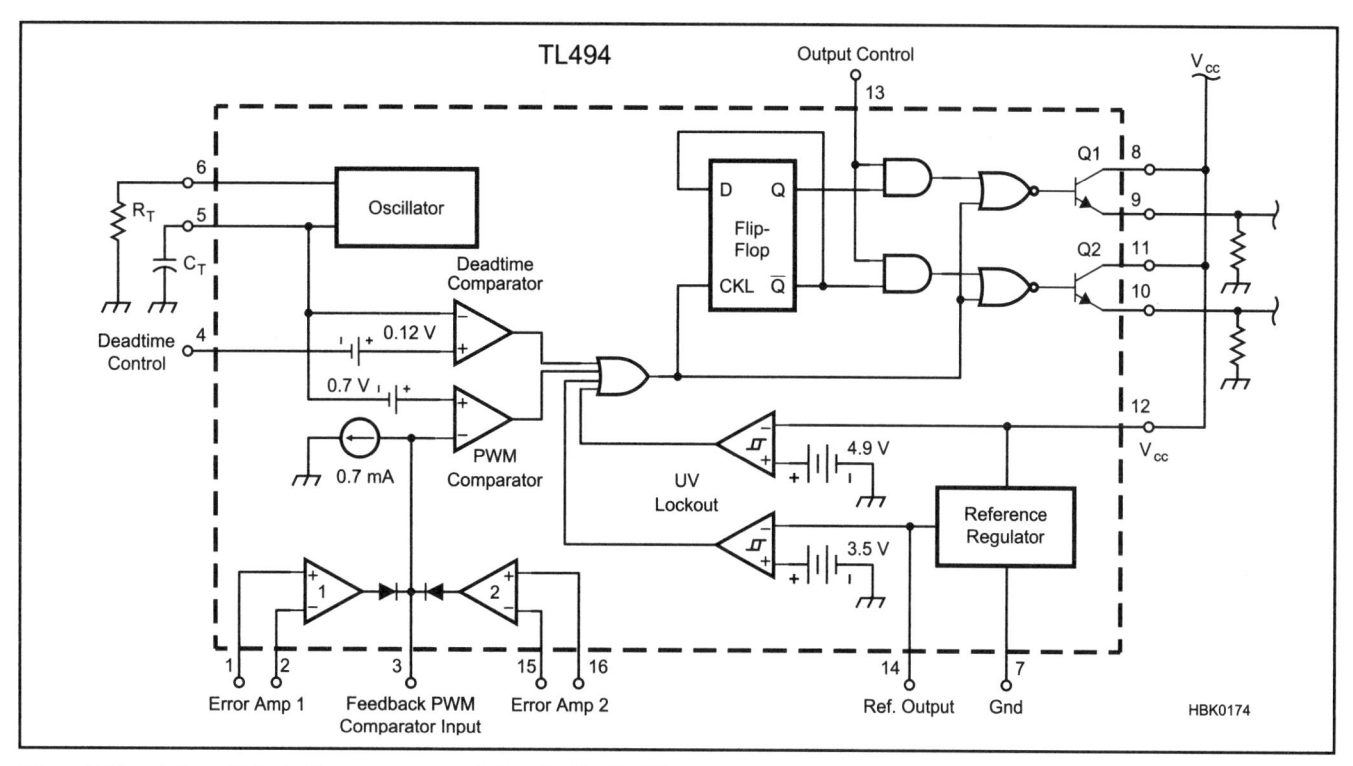

Figure 7.43 — Internal block diagram representation for the TL494.

circuits and a few external components. These ICs typically come with extensive applications information.

Particularly for low power applications (<100 W) there are ICs that provide all the control functions *and* the power switch. In some cases a power diode is also included. **Figure 7.41** gives an example of one of these ICs. Similar ICs are made by many different manufacturers.

The IC provides most of the components for a buck converter but some external components are still needed: filter capacitors (C_{IN}, C_{OUT}, C_{VCC}), the output inductor (L), output voltage sensing (R_{FB1} and R_{FB2}) and components to set the switching frequency (R_{C1} and C_{C1}). The shunt diode (D1) is marked as optional because there is an internal switch that can perform this function for lower powers.

Figure 7.42 and **Figure 7.43** show the internal block-diagram of typical voltage regulator control ICs. (See the manufacturer data sheets for application information and reference designs.) In addition to the control functions there are also some protective functions such as input under- and overvoltage protection, over-temperature (thermal) protection, over-current limiting and slow-starting

(slowly ramping up D) to limit inrush current at turn-on. ICs similar to this one are available for boost, buck-boost and flyback converters, as well as many other topologies. There are also ICs available that implement more complex control schemes such as current mode control and feed-forward compensation.

7.11.7 Switchmode Control Loop Issues

We do not have the space in this book to explain all the control issues associated with switchmode converters, but it is important to recognize that designing stable, high performance control loops for switchmode converters is a much more complex task than it would be for a series pass-regulator or an audio amplifier. All we can do here is to alert the reader to some of the issues and suggest consulting Reference 2 with detailed explanations and examples. In addition, there are numerous books and applications notes on switchmode converter design that go into the necessary detail.

The complexities arise from the inherent behavior of switchmode circuits. This behavior is often non-intuitive and sometimes even bizarre. As we've seen already, the dc behavior differs dramatically between CCM and DCM modes of operation. This difference is even more pronounced in the small-signal control-to-output characteristics. It is very common to see poles and zeros in the control system's response (see the **Circuits and Components** chapter) that move with input voltage, duty cycle and/or load. Fixed double-poles can change to moving single-poles. Moving right-half-plane zeros (this is a zero with decreasing phase-shift instead of increasing phase-shift with frequency) are inherent in CCM operation of boost and buck-boost circuits and their derivatives. There can also be large signal instabilities such as oscillations at sub-harmonics of the switching frequency and occasionally chaotic response to large load current or line voltage changes.

This is not intended to discourage readers from working with switchmode converters, but to simply alert them in advance to some of the difficulties. Once a basic understanding is achieved, the design of switchmode converters can be very interesting and rewarding.

Switchmode Converter Design Aids

Today, there are hundreds of ICs on the market, from dozens of manufacturers, aimed at controlling the power conversion process. These devices have grown from their simplest forms when introduced over 20 years ago to include a long list of ancillary functions aimed at reducing the supporting circuitry and enhancing the quality and efficiency of the power conversion process. As a result, the task of designing these ICs into the final power conversion circuit has actually become more complex. To the circuit designer who is below the expert level, the task can seem daunting, indeed.

In answer to this problem, many IC manufacturers provide computer-aided design tools that greatly simplify the task of using their products. These tools take several forms, from the most rudimentary cookbook-style guides, to full-fledged circuit simulation tools like *SPICE*. The purpose of these tools is to help the designer pick appropriate resistors, capacitors and magnetic components for the design, and also to estimate the stresses on the power-handling components.

These design tools fall generally into two types: equation-based design tools and iterative circuit simulators. The differences are that the equation-based tools simply automate the basic design equations of the circuit, providing recommended choices for the components and then solving equations to compute the voltage, current and power stresses on the components. In some cases, thermal analysis is also included.

The simulators, on the other hand, use detailed mathematical models for the components and provide both dc and ac simulation of the circuits. This allows the user to see the dynamic behavior of the circuit. The simulation includes details during the switching intervals and shows rise times, parasitic effects caused by component capacitance, internal resistance and other characteristics.

In modern power converter design, the magnetic components — transformers, power inductors and filter inductors — can be a challenge to the designer not versed in magnetic design. As a result, the vendors of these parts usually furnish design tools created specifically to the design of these components and/or the proper choice of off-the-shelf versions.

The reader is encouraged to explore design aids available from the websites of manufacturers (**Table 7.A1**). The following is far from complete, but should give the reader valuable insight into the vast array of available tools. Remember also that manufacturers of passive components such as capacitors, resistors, heat sinks and thermal hardware may also have helpful and informative design aids on their websites. — *Chuck Mullett, KR6R*

Table 7.A1
Switchmode Converter Design Aids

Vendor	Main Web Site	Design Tools
Fairchild Semiconductor	www.fairchildsemi.com	From the home page, select "Design Center"
Infineon	www.infineon.com	From the home page Search window, select "Website" and "Search Technical Documents", then select "Power Management IC's" from the pull-down menu. From the subsequent list, select "Application Notes"
International Rectifier	www.irf.com/indexsw.html	www.irf.com/design-center/mypower/
Intersil	www.intersil.com	www.intersil.com/design/
National Semiconductor	www.national.com/analog	www.national.com/analog/power/simple_switcher
ON Semiconductor	www.onsemi.com	onsemi.com/PowerSolutions/supportDoc.do?type=tools
Texas Instruments	www.power.ti.com	From the Power Management page, click "Tools and Software"
Linear Technology Corp	www.linear.com	Search for "LTSpice" in the home page window to access the simulation tools page.

7.12 High-Voltage Techniques

The construction of high-voltage supplies requires special considerations in addition to the normal design and construction practices used for lower-voltage supplies. In general, the builder needs to remember that physical spacing between leads, connections, parts and the chassis must be sufficient to prevent arcing. Also, the series connection of components such as capacitor and resistor strings needs to be done with consideration for the distribution of voltage stresses across the components. High-voltages can constitute a safety hazard and great care must be taken to limit physical access to components and wiring while high potentials are present.

7.12.1 High-Voltage Capacitors

For reasons of economy and availability, electrolytic capacitors are frequently used for output filter capacitors. Because these capacitors have relatively low voltage ratings (<600 V), in HV applications it will usually be necessary to connect them in series strings to form an equivalent capacitor with the capability to withstand the higher applied voltage. Electrolytic capacitors have relatively high leakage currents (low leakage resistance) especially at higher temperatures.

To keep the voltages across the capacitors in the series string relatively constant, equal-value bypassing resistors are connected across each capacitor. These *equalizing resistors* should have a value low enough to equalize differences in capacitor leakage resistance between the capacitors, while high enough not to dissipate excessive power. Also, capacitor bodies need to be insulated from the chassis and from each other by mounting them on insulating panels, thereby preventing arcing to the chassis or other capacitors in the string. The insulated mounting for the capacitors is often plastic or other insulating material in board form. A typical example from a commercial amplifier that implements some the guidelines given in this section is shown in **Figure 7.44**.

Equalizing resistors are needed because of differences in dc leakage current between different capacitors in the series string. The data sheet for an electrolytic capacitor will usually give the dc leakage current at 20 °C in the form of an equation. For example:

$$I_{leakage} = 3\sqrt{CV} \quad (14)$$

where
  C = the value in µF
  V = the working voltage
  $I_{leakage}$ = leakage current in µA.

Keep in mind that the leakage current will

High Voltage Safety Considerations

We are all so besieged these days with verbose safety warnings on mostly harmless consumer goods that it is easy to forget that some things really are dangerous. High voltage power supplies definitely fall into this category, especially since many amateurs are accustomed to solid-state circuits and seldom encounter any dc voltage higher than 12 V. ***This power supply produces voltages that are highly lethal.*** So please take to heart the following 10 precautions. Furthermore, don't expect to learn from your mistakes, because if you don't exercise proper precautions the first time, you're unlikely ever to have a second chance.

1. Don't let your reach exceed your grasp. High voltage power supplies are not a project for beginners. You should not attempt to build this type of power supply unless you're a seasoned builder who has experience with high voltage circuitry.

2. Young amateurs should not attempt this type of project alone. Working with high voltages requires the maturity and patience that comes with age and experience.

3. Never work around high voltage when you are tired, stressed, or in a hurry.

4. Never work around high voltage after drinking alcohol. Even one beer or glass of wine can impair your judgment and make you careless.

5. Before working on a high voltage power supply, always follow these three steps: Unplug (the ac power cord), discharge (the filter capacitors) and verify (that the output voltage is truly zero). Time-honored practice is to use a "chicken stick" (a wooden dowel or PVC tube, with one end attached to a grounded wire) to make sure filter capacitors are completely discharged. See Figure 7.46 for an example.

6. When working on a high voltage power supply, remember that a dangerous time is after the power supply has just been turned off, but before the filter capacitors have fully discharged. A 50 µF capacitor charged to 4000 V holds a potentially deadly 400 joules of energy. Even with bleeder resistors, it can take a minute or more to discharge fully.

7. When removing a recently discharged filter capacitor from a power supply, tie the two terminals together with wire. Large high voltage capacitors can self-charge to dangerous levels if the terminals are left floating.

8. Don't stake your life on the expectation that bleeder resistors, fuses, circuit breakers, relays, and switches are always going to do their job. Even though modern components are very reliable, it is safe practice always to assume the worst.

9. Don't build a high voltage power supply if you don't understand how the circuit works. High power amplifiers and power supplies are not "plug-and-play" projects with step-by-step instructions. Builders must be knowledgeable enough to improvise, make component substitutions, and implement design changes.

10. With high voltage projects, it doesn't pay to be "penny wise and pound foolish." Use high quality components throughout and save your forty-year-old junk box parts for projects where safety and reliability are not paramount requirements.

(The preceding guidelines are taken from the *QEX* article "A Deluxe High Voltage Supply" by Jim Garland, W8ZR, which is included with this book's downloadable supplemental content.)

Figure 7.44 — Example of the filter capacitor/bleeder resistor installation in a high voltage power supply.

increase as the capacitor temperature rises above 20 °C. A value of 3 to 4 times the 20 °C value would not be unusual because of normal heating.

We can use an approximation which includes allowance for heating to determine the maximum value of the divider resistors:

$$R \leq \frac{V_r - V_m}{I_{leakage}} \quad (15)$$

where
V_r = the voltage rating of the capacitor
V_m = the voltage across the capacitor during normal operation.

A typical 3000 V power supply might use eight 330 μF, 450 V capacitors in series. In that case, V_r = 450 V, V_m = 375 V and $I_{leakage}$ = 1.06 mA. This would make R = 68 kΩ (standard value) or a total of 544 kΩ for the resistor string. With 3000 V across the resistor string, the total power dissipation would be 16.5 W or about 2.06 W per resistor. To be conservative you should use resistors rated for at least 4 W each.

The equalizing resistors may dissipate significant power and become quite warm. It is important that these resistors do not heat the capacitors they are associated with, as this will increase the capacitor leakage current. You also have to be careful that the heat from the resistors is not trapped under the plastic support panels. The best practice is to place the resistors above the capacitors and their mounting structure allowing the heat to rise unobstructed as shown in Figure 7.44.

OIL-FILLED CAPACITORS

For high voltages, oil-filled paper-dielectric capacitors are superior to electrolytics because they have lower internal impedance at high frequencies, higher leakage resistance and are available with much higher working voltages. These capacitors are available with values of several microfarads and have working voltage ratings of thousands of volts. On the other hand, they can be expensive, heavy and bulky.

Oil-filled capacitors are frequently offered for sale at flea markets at attractive prices. One caution: It is best to avoid older oil-filled capacitors because they may contain polychlorinated biphenyls (PCBs), a known cancer-causing agent. Newer capacitors have eliminated PCBs and have a notice on the case to that effect. Older oil-filled capacitors should be examined carefully for any signs of leakage. Contact with leaking oil should be avoided, with careful washing of the hands after handling. Do not dispose of any oil-filled capacitors with household trash, particularly older units. Contact your local recycling agency for information about how to dispose of them properly.

7.12.2 High-Voltage Bleeder Resistors

Bleeder resistors across the output are used to discharge the stored energy in the filter capacitors when the power supply is turned off and should be given careful consideration. These resistors provide protection against shock when the power supply is turned off and dangerous wiring is exposed. A general rule is that the bleeder should be designed to reduce the output voltage to 30 V or less within 30 seconds of turning off the power supply.

Take care to ensure that the maximum voltage rating of the resistor is not exceeded. In a typical divider string, the resistor values are high enough that the voltage across the resistor is not dissipation limited. The voltage limit is typically related to the insulation intrinsic to the resistor. Resistor maximum voltage ratings are usually given in the manufacturer's data sheet and can be found online. Two major resistor manufacturers are Ohmite Electronics (**www.ohmite.com**) and Stackpole Electronics (**www.seielect.com**).

A 2 W carbon composition resistor will have a maximum voltage rating of 500 V. As a rough estimate, larger wire-wound power resistors are typically rated at 500 V_{RMS} per inch of length — but check with the manufacturer to be sure.

The bleeder will consist of several resistors in series. Typically wire-wound power resistors are used for this application. One additional recommendation is that two separate (redundant) bleeder strings be used, to provide safety in the event one of the strings fails. When electrolytic capacitors are used, the equalizing resistors can also serve as the bleeder resistor but they should be redundant. Again, give careful attention to keeping the heat from the resistors away from the capacitors as shown in Figure 7.44.

In the example given above for calculating the equalizing resistor value, eight 330 μF capacitors in series created the equivalent of a 41 μF capacitor with a 3000 V rating. The total resistance across the capacitors was 8 × 63 kΩ = 504 kΩ. This gives us a time constant (R × C) of about R × C ≈ 21 seconds. To discharge the capacitors to 30 V from 3000 V would take about four time constants (about 84 seconds) which is well over a minute. To get the discharge time down to 30 seconds would require reducing the equalizing resistors to 25 kΩ each. The bleeder power dissipation would then be:

$$P = \frac{V^2}{R} = \frac{3000^2}{200,000} = 45 \text{ W} \quad (16)$$

For a 2 or 3 kV power supply, this is a reasonable value but it is still a significant amount of power and you need to make sure the resulting heat is properly managed.

7.12.3 High-Voltage Metering Techniques

Special considerations should be observed for metering of high-voltage supplies, such as the plate supplies for linear amplifiers. This is to provide safety to both personnel and to the meters themselves.

To monitor the current, it is customary to place the ammeter in the supply return (ground) line. This ensures that both meter terminals are close to ground potential. Placing the meter in the positive output line creates a hazard because the voltage on each meter terminal would be near the full high-voltage potential. Also, there is the strong possibility that an arc could occur between the wiring and coils inside the meter and the chassis of the amplifier or power supply itself. This hazardous potential cannot exist with the meter in the negative leg.

Another good safety practice is to place a low-voltage Zener diode across the terminals of the ammeter. This will bypass the meter in the event of an internal open circuit in the meter. A 1 W Zener diode will suffice since the current in the metering circuit is low.

The chapter on **RF Power Amplifiers** contains examples of how to perform current and voltage metering in high voltage supplies and amplifiers. In the past, amplifier articles have shown the meters mounted on plastic boards with stand-off insulators behind a plastic window in the amplifier or power supply front panel. While this can work it is not considered good practice today. It is usually possible to arrange the metering so that the meters are close to ground potential and may be safely mounted on the front panel of either the amplifier or the power supply.

For metering of high voltage, the builder should remember that resistors to be used in multiplier strings will often have voltage-breakdown ratings well below the total voltage being sampled. Usually, several identical series resistors will be used to reduce voltage stress across individual resistors. A basic rule of thumb is that these resistors should be limited to a maximum of 200 V, unless rated otherwise. For example, in a 2000 V power supply, the voltmeter multiplier should have a string of 10 resistors connected in series to distribute the voltage equally. The comments on resistor voltage rating in the sections on capacitor equalization and bleeder resistors apply to this case, as well.

7.12.4 High-Voltage Transformers and Inductors

Usable transformers and filter inductors can often be found at amateur flea markets but frequently these are very old units, often dating from WWII. The hermetically-sealed military components are likely to still be

Figure 7.45 — Example of a high voltage board with a solder ball on a protruding lead and the use of a cap nut to terminate the end of a screw thread.

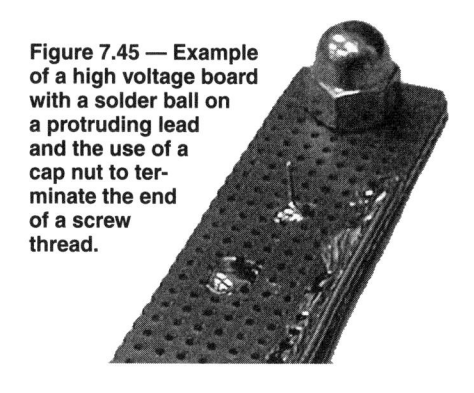

good, especially if they have not been used. Open-frame units, with insulation that has been directly exposed to the atmosphere and moisture for long periods of time, should be considered suspect. These units can be checked by running what is called a "hipot test" (high potential test). This involves a low current, variable output voltage power supply with a high-value resistor in series with the output. Unfortunately this equipment is seldom available to amateurs. Some motor repair shops will have an insulation tester called a "Megger" and may be willing to perform an insulation test on a transformer or inductor for you. This is not a completely definitive test but will certainly detect any gross problems with the insulation.

An alternative would be to perform the transformer tests discussed earlier with a variable autotransformer on the ac input. Slowly increase the input voltage until full line voltage is reached and let the transformer run for an hour or two while watching to see if there are any signs of failure. Doing this test in a dark room makes it easier to see any visible corona discharge, another sign of insulation problems. Because the transformer terminals will be at full voltage great care should be taken to avoid contact with the HV terminals. Some form of transparent insulating shield for the test setup is necessary.

7.12.5 Construction Techniques for High-Voltage Supplies

Layout and component arrangement in HV supplies requires some additional care beyond those for lower voltage projects. The photographs in the **RF Power Amplifiers** chapter are a good start, but there are some points which may not be obvious from the pictures.

SHARP EDGES

Sharp points, board edges and/or hardware with ragged edges can lead to localized intensification of the electric field's strength, resulting in a possible breakdown. One common offender is the component leads on the soldered side of a printed-circuit board. These are usually soldered and then cut off leaving a small but often very sharp point. The best way to handle this is to cut the lead as close to the board as practical and form a small solder ball or mound around the cutoff lead end. An example of these suggestions is given in **Figure 7.45**. The protruding component wire near the top would have a high field gradient. Below that we see a wire cut short with a rounded mound of solder covering the end of the wire.

The ends of bolts with sharp threads often protrude beyond the associated nut. One way to eliminate this is to use the dome-style nuts (cap nuts) that capture the end of the bolt or screw, forming a nicely rounded surface. An example of a cap nut is shown in Figure 7.45.

Sheet metal screws, with their needle-sharp ends, should be avoided if possible. Sheet metal screws used to close metal housings at high potential should have the screw tips inside the enclosure, which would be normal in most cases. You must also be careful of the tips of sheet metal screws that protrude on the inside of an outer enclosure. If these are in proximity to circuits at high potential, they can also lead to arcing. Keeping sheet metal screw tips well away from high voltage circuitry is the best defense.

Small pieces of sheet metal that may be part of a structure at high potential should have their edges rounded off with a file. Copper traces near the edges of circuit boards do not benefit from rounding, however. In fact, filing may make the edge sharper, ragged and more prone to breakdown. In critical areas, a small solid round wire can be soldered to the edges of a copper trace to form a rounded edge as illustrated at the right side of Figure 7.45.

INSULATORS

Some portions of the circuit may be mounted on insulators or plastic sheets. A new, clean insulator should easily withstand 10 kV per inch without creepage or breakdown across the insulating surface, but over time that surface will accumulate dirt and dust. Reducing the high-voltage stress across insulators to 5 kV per inch would be more conservative.

In theory the spacing between two smooth surfaces across an air gap can be much smaller, perhaps 20 to 30 kV per inch or even higher. But given the uncertainties of layout and voltage gradients around hardware, wiring, components and board edges, sticking with 5 kV per inch is good idea even for air gaps. This separation will seldom cause construction layout problems unless you are trying to build a very compact unit.

WIRE

Be sure to use wire that is rated for high voltage and for high temperatures. Pomona Electronics type 6733 test lead wire is stranded #18 AWG, rated for 10 kV and 150°C with silicone insulation, available in both red and black. Flexible and durable, it is easy to route around a chassis or to fit inside sleeving with other wires. The outer diameter (0.144 inch) is thinner and more flexible than spark plug wire or most HV cable.

FUSES

Sometimes a fuse will be placed in series with a high voltage output to provide protection in case of load arcing. These fuses pose special problems. When a fuse blows, the fuse element will at least melt and perhaps even vaporize. There may be an interval when most, if not all, the output voltage appears across the fuse but the fuse has not stopped conducting. That is, there can be a sustained arc in the fuse.

Fuses have voltage ratings that are the maximum voltages across the fuse for which the arc can be expected to quench quickly. The standard 0.25 × 1.25 inch fuses used in the input ac line are typically rated for 250 V. While no doubt these ratings are conservative, this type of fuse cannot be expected to reliably clear an arc with 2 to 3 kV across the fuse and should not be used in series with a high-voltage output.

Your first choice for HV fuses should be the recommended part specified by the power supply manufacturer. If those are unavailable or you are building the supply yourself, fuses for microwave oven transformer secondary use are often suitable. Do not substitute lower-voltage fuses or fuse holders not rated for HV service. When working on a HV power supply with the fuse visible and uncovered, be sure to wear safety glasses as the fuse may explode during a high-current overload, scattering shards of glass or ceramic at high speed.

7.12.6 Construction Practices for High-Voltage Safety

The voltages present in HV power supplies are potentially lethal. Every effort must be made to restrict physical access to any high potentials. A number of steps can be taken:

1) Build the power supply within a closed box, preferably a metal one.

2) Install interlocks on removable panels used for access to the interior. An interlock is usually a normally-open microswitch in series with the input power line. The microswitch is positioned so that it can be closed only when the overlying panel has been secured in place. When the panel is removed the switch moves to the open position, removing power from the supply.

3) As noted previously, the use of a bleeder resistor to rapidly discharge the capacitors is mandatory.

4) To further protect the operator when accessing the inside of a high-voltage power

supply, a grounding hook like that shown in **Figure 7.46A** should be used to positively discharge each capacitor by touching the hook to each capacitor terminal. The hook is connected to the chassis via the wire shown and held by the insulated handle. It is normal practice to leave the hook in place across the capacitors while the supply is being worked on, just in case primary power is inadvertently applied. When the work is finished, remove the hook and replace the covers on the power supply.

Figure 7.46B shows how to construct a grounding stick of your own. A large screw eye or hook is substituted for the hook. It is important that the grounding wire be left *outside* the handle so that any hazardous voltages or currents will not be present near your hand or body.

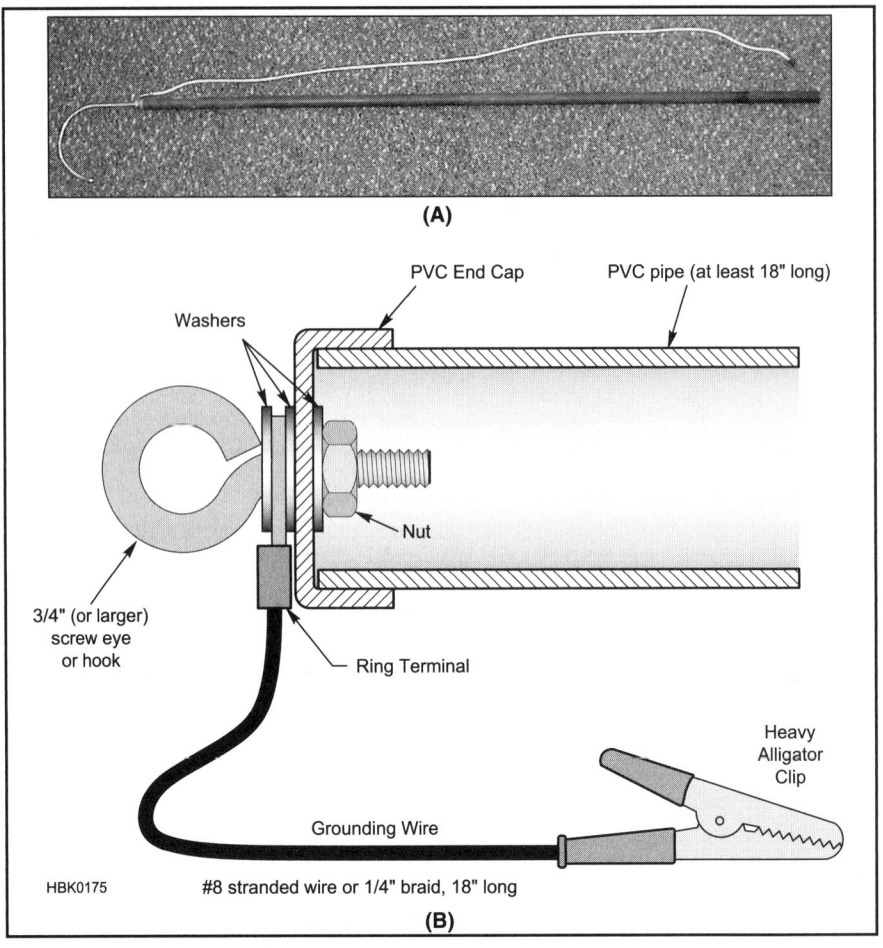

Figure 7.46 — Example of a grounding stick or hook to discharge capacitor energy safely. The end of the wire is connected to ground and the hook is touched to the capacitor terminals to discharge them. A diagram showing how to construct a grounding stick is shown at B.

7.13 Batteries

A battery is a group of individual *cells*, usually series-connected to give some desired multiple of the *cell voltage*. The cell voltage is usually in the range of 1 to 4 V. Each chemical system used in the cell gives a particular nominal voltage that will vary with temperature and state of charge. This must be taken into account to make up a particular battery voltage. For example, four 1.5 V carbon-zinc cells make a 6 V battery and six 2 V lead-acid cells make a 12 V battery. **Table 7.1** lists the dimensions of commonly used batteries.

The following sections on battery types and usage consist primarily of excerpts from *Batteries in a Portable World* by Isidor Buchmann, CEO of Cadex Electronics (**www.cadex.com**), a leading manufacturer of battery charging and related equipment. The ARRL appreciates having been given permission to use this material. The book discusses the issues summarized here (and many others) in detail. The reader is directed to the original text for more complete information. This summary is intended to present and compare the various options commonly used by amateurs. Additional information and an extensive battery glossary is provided online at **www.batteryuniversity.com**.

Batteries are divided into two categories: *primary* (non-rechargeable) and *secondary* (rechargeable). Secondary batteries are expected to account for more than 80% of global battery use by 2015. The most common types of battery chemistry are lithium, lead and nickel-based systems.

Batteries store energy well and for a considerable length of time. Primary batteries hold more energy than secondary, and their *self-discharge* is lower. Alkaline cells are good for 10 years with minimal losses. Lead, nickel and lithium-based batteries need periodic recharges to compensate for lost power. **Figure 7.47** illustrates the energy and power densities of lead acid, nickel-cadmium (NiCd), nickel-metal-hydride (NiMH), and the lithium-ion family (Li-ion).

Rather than giving batteries unique names by type, they are broadly distinguished by the following characteristics:

Chemistry — the families of chemicals used to make the battery. The most common chemistries are lead, nickel and lithium.

Voltage — the nominal open circuit voltage (OCV), which varies with chemistry and the number of cells connected in series.

Size — standard sizes of batteries or cells, such as AAA, AA, C and D.

Capacity (C) — the specific energy in ampere-hours (Ah).

Cold Cranking Amps (CCA) — a starter battery's ability to supply high load current at –18° C (0° F) as specified by the vehicle standard SAE J357.

Specific energy — battery capacity in watt-hours per kilogram (Wh/kg)

Specific power — indicates the loading capability or the amount of current the battery can provide in watts/kilogram (W/kg)

C-rate — charge and discharge rate specified in units of C (capacity). At 1 C, the battery charges or discharges at a current numeri-cally equal to its Ah rating. For example, a 2000 mAh battery discharging at 1 C is supplying a current of 2 A. At 0.5 C, the current would be 1 A, and so forth.

Load — whatever draws energy from the battery. Internal battery resistance and

---

Battery Safety

In addition to the precautions given for each type of battery, the following precautions apply to all battery types. Always follow the manufacturer's advice! Extensive application information can found on manufacturer's websites.

Hydrogen gas escaping from storage batteries can be explosive. Keep flames or any kind of burning material away, including cigarettes, cigars, pipes and so on. Use and charge batteries in well-ventilated areas to prevent hydrogen gas from building up.

No battery should be subjected to unnecessary heat, vibration or physical shock. The battery should be kept clean. Frequent inspection for leaks is a good idea. Electrolyte that has leaked or sprayed from the battery should be cleaned from all surfaces. The electrolyte is chemically active and electrically conductive, and may ruin electrical equipment. Acid may be neutralized with sodium bicarbonate (baking soda), and alkalis (found in NiCd batteries) may be neutralized with a weak acid such as vinegar. Both neutralizers will dissolve in water and should be quickly washed off. Do not let any of the neutralizer enter the battery.

Keep a record of the battery use, and include the last output voltage and, for lead-acid storage batteries, the hydrometer reading. This allows prediction of useful charge remaining, and the recharging or procuring of extra batteries, thus minimizing failure of battery power during an excursion or emergency.

Batteries can contain a number of hazardous materials such as lead, cadmium, mercury or acid, and some thought is needed for their disposal at the end of useful life. Municipal and county waste disposal sites and recycling centers will usually accept lead acid batteries because they can readily be recycled. Other types of batteries are typically not recycled and should be treated as hazardous waste. Most disposal sites and recycling centers will have occasional special programs for accepting household hazardous waste. Hardware and electronic stores may have battery recycling programs, as well. Take advantage of them.

Table 7.1
Dimensions of Common Standard Cells

Size	Dimensions	Notes
D	34 × 61 mm	
C	25.5 × 50 mm	
A	17 × 50 mm	Only available for NiCd; also available in half-length size
AA	14.5 × 50 mm	
AAA	10.5 × 44.5 mm	
AAAA	8.3 × 42.5 mm	Typical size of cell making up 9 V batteries
N	12 × 32 mm	
9 V	48.5 × 26.5 × 17.5 mm	Contains six AAAA cells in series, snap terminals
18650	18 × 65 mm	Commonly used in lithium-ion battery packs
Lantern	115 × 68.2 × 68.2	Spring terminals
CR2016	20 × 1.6 mm	Coin cell
CR2025	20 × 2.5 mm	Coin cell
CR2032	20 × 3.2 mm	Coin cell

Information courtesy of Cadex and from **http://en.wikipedia.org/wiki/List_of_battery_sizes**

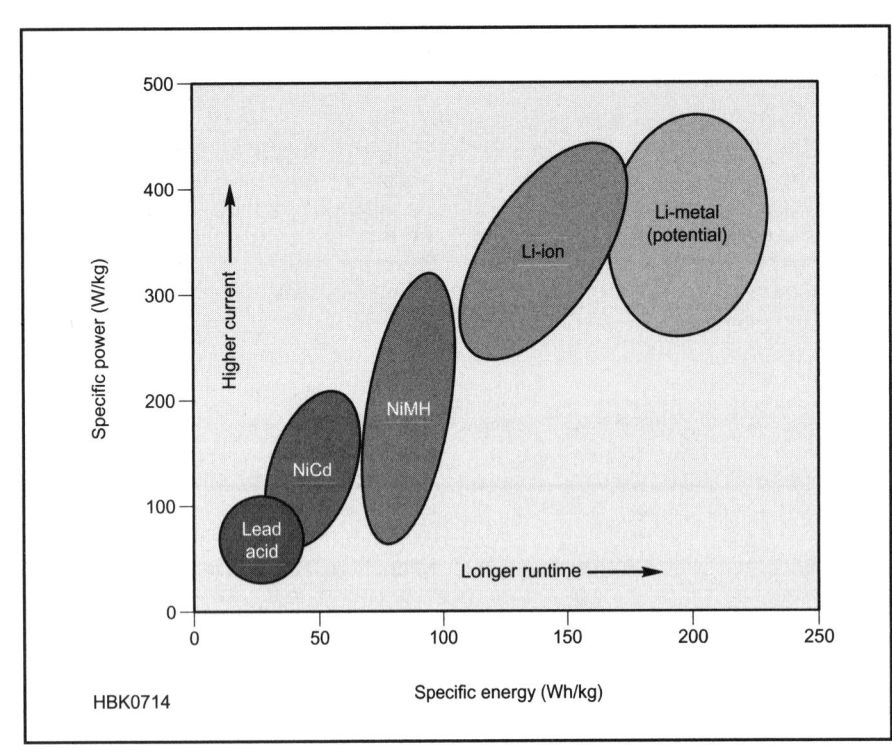

Figure 7.47 — Specific energy and specific power of rechargeable batteries. (Courtesy of Cadex)

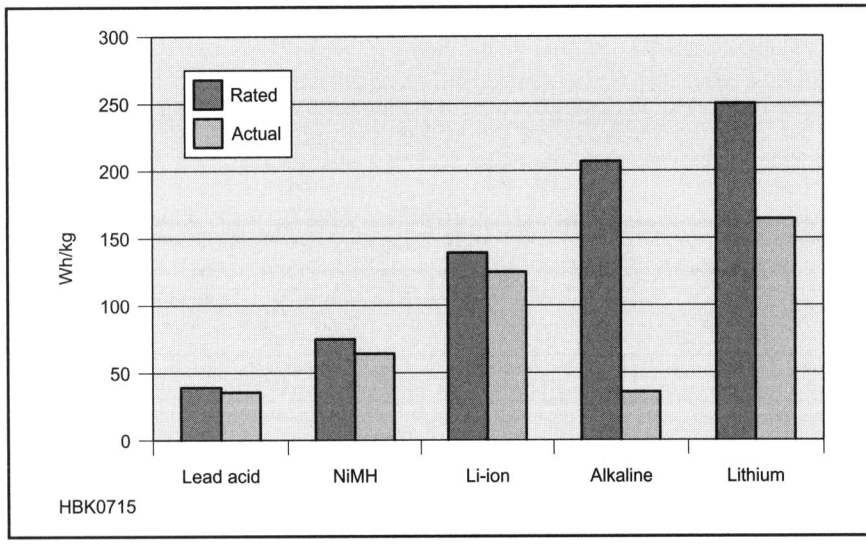

Figure 7.48 — Energy comparison of different battery types at a load of 1 C. (Courtesy of Cadex)

Table 7.2
Alkaline Specifications of Standard Batteries at Low Load

Battery Type	Nominal Voltage (V)	Rated Capacity (mAh)	Voltage Cutoff (V)	Rated Load (Ω)	Discharge C-rate
9 V	9	570	4.8	620	0.025
AAA	1.5	1150	0.8	75	0.017
AA	1.5	2870	0.8	75	0.007
C	1.5	7800	0.8	39	0.005
D	1.5	17,000	0.8	39	0.0022

(Table courtesy of Cadex)

depleting the battery's state of charge cause the voltage to drop.

Primary batteries have one of the highest energy densities. One of the most common primary batteries is the *alkaline-manganese*, or alkaline battery. The *carbon-zinc* or *Leclanché battery* is less expensive but holds less energy than the alkaline battery. Although secondary batteries have improved, a regular household alkaline cell provides 50% more energy than lithium-ion.

Primary batteries tend to have high internal resistance, which limits the discharge to light loads. This reduces the battery's specific power, even though its specific energy may be quite high. Non-rechargeable lithium metal and alkaline batteries are commonly used in low power applications such as clocks, meter LCDs, keyers and so forth.

Manufacturers of primary batteries specify specific energy at a small fraction of C and the batteries are allowed to discharge to a very low voltage of 0.8 volts per cell. **Figure 7.48** compares primary and secondary batteries discharged at a rate of 1 C. The primary (alkaline and lithium) batteries are unable to deliver their rated specific energy at heavy loads. **Table 7.2** gives typical specifications for alkaline batteries at light loads, such as operating a handheld radio during receive.

If recharging is available, using primary batteries can be expensive — about thirty-fold higher than for secondary batteries. Amateurs using batteries in the field, particularly for emergency communications, may want to maintain the ability to use primary batteries for times when recharging for secondary batteries is not available.

7.13.1 Choices of Secondary Batteries

The following discussion examines today's most popular secondary battery systems according to specific energy, years of service life, load characteristics, safety, price, self-discharge, environmental issues, maintenance and disposal. **Table 7.3** compares the characteristics of four commonly used rechargeable battery systems showing average performance rating at the time of publication in 2013.

The lithium-ion family is divided into three major battery types, so named by their cathode oxides, which are cobalt, manganese and phosphate. The characteristics of these Li-ion systems are as follows:

Lithium-ion-cobalt or **lithium-cobalt** ($LiCoO_2$) — Has high specific energy with moderate load capabilities and modest service life.

Lithium-ion-manganese or **lithium-manganese** ($LiMn_2O_4$) — Is capable of high charge and discharge currents but has low specific energy and modest service life.

Lithium-ion-phosphate or **lithium-**

phosphate (LiFePO$_4$) — often abbreviated LiPo. Is similar to lithium-manganese; nominal voltage is 3.3 V/cell; offers long cycle life, has a good safety record but exhibits higher self-discharge than other Li-ion systems.

Another type of lithium-ion cell is the popular *lithium-ion-polymer* or *Li-polymer*. While Li-ion systems get their name from their unique cathode materials, Li-polymer differs by having a distinct architecture in which a gelled electrolyte replaces the usual porous separator between the anode and cathode. The gelled electrolyte acts as a catalyst to enhance the electrical activity of the other battery materials.

7.13.2 Lead Acid Batteries

Most lead acid batteries used today are *maintenance-free* types in which the liquid electrolyte is sealed inside the battery in liquid or gel form. Two similar types are used: the *sealed lead acid* (SLA) and the *valve-regulated lead acid* (VRLA). SLA batteries have capacities up to about 30 Ah. VRLA batteries are larger and have capacities from 30 Ah to several thousand Ah. Table 7.4 summarizes the advantages and limitations of lead acid battery systems.

Applying the right voltage limit when

Table 7.3
Characteristics of Commonly Used Rechargeable Batteries

Specification	Lead Acid	NiCd	NiMH	Li-ion Cobalt	Li-ion Manganese	Li-ion Phosphate
Specific energy (Wh/kg)	30-50	45-80	60-120	150-190	100-135	90-120
Internal resistance[1] (mΩ)	<100 12 V pack	100-200 6 V pack	200-300 6 V pack	150-300 7.2 V	25-75[2] per cell	25-50[2] per cell
Cycle life[4] (80% DoD)	200-300	1000[3]	300-500[3]	500-1000	500-1000	1000-2000
Fast-charge time	8-16 h	1 h typical	2-4 h	2-4 h	1 h or less	1 h or less
Overcharge tolerance	High	Moderate	Low	Low. Cannot tolerate trickle charge	Low. Cannot tolerate trickle charge.	Low. Cannot tolerate trickle charge.
Self-discharge/month (room temp)	5%	20%[5]	30%[5]	<10%[6]	<10%[6]	<10%[6]
Cell voltage (nominal)	2 V	1.2 V[7]	1.2 V[7]	3.6 V[8]	3.8 V[8]	3.3 V
Peak load current (best result)	5C[9] (0.2 C)	20 C (1 C)	5 C (0.5 C)	>3 C (<1 C)	>30 C (<10 C)	>30 C (<10 C)
Operating temp.[10] (discharge only)	−20 to 60° C	−40 to 60° C	−20 to 60° C	−20 to 60° C	−20 to 60° C	−20 to 60° C
Maintenance requirement	3-6 months[11]	30-60 days	60-90 days	Not required	Not required	Not required
Safety requirements	Thermally stable	Thermally stable, fuse protection common	Thermally stable, fuse protection common	Protection circuit mandatory	Protection circuit mandatory	Protection circuit mandatory
In use since	Late 1800s	1950	1990	1991	1996	2006
Toxicity	Very high	Very high	Low	Low	Low	Low

Table Notes:
[1] Internal resistance of a battery pack varies with milliampere-hour (mAh) rating, wiring and number of cells. Protection circuit of lithium-ion adds about 100 mΩ.
[2] Based on 18650 cell size. Cell size and design determines internal resistance.
[3] Cycle life is based on battery receiving regular maintenance.
[4] Cycle life is based on the depth of discharge (DoD). Shallow DoD improves cycle life.
[5] Self-discharge is highest immediately after charge. NiCd loses 10% in the first 24 hours, then declines to 10% every 30 days. High temperature increases self-discharge.
[6] Internal protection circuits typically consume 3% of the stored energy per month
[7] The traditional voltage is 1.25 V; 1.2 V is more commonly used.
[8] Low internal resistance reduces the voltage drop under load and Li-ion is often rated higher than 3.6 V/cell. Cells marked 3.7 V and 3.8 V are fully compatible with 3.6 V.
[9] Capable of high current pulses; needs time to recuperate.
[10] Applies to discharge only; charge temperature is more confined.
[11] Maintenance may be in the form of equalizing or topping charge to prevent sulfation
(Table courtesy of Cadex)

charging lead acid systems is critical and will be a compromise between capacity when recharged and maintaining the battery's internal materials. A low charge limit voltage may shelter the battery but this causes poor performance and a buildup of *sulfation* on the negative plate. A high voltage limit improves performance but it promotes irreversible grid corrosion on the positive plate. Temperature also changes the voltage threshold.

Lead acid does not lend itself to fast charging and a fully saturated charge requires 14 to 16 hours. The battery must always be stored at full state-of-charge to avoid sulfation. Lead acid is not subject to memory, but correct charge and float voltages are important to get a long life (see the section on charging below). While NiCd loses approximately 40% of its stored energy in three months, lead acid self-discharges the same amount in one year.

Lead acid batteries are inexpensive on cost-per-watt basis but are less suitable for repeated deep cycling. A full discharge causes strain and each discharge/charge cycle permanently robs the battery of a small amount of capacity. The fading becomes more acute as the battery falls below 80% of its nominal capacity. Depending on the depth of discharge and operating temperature, lead acid for deep-cycle applications provides 200 to 300 discharge/charge cycles.

High temperature reduces the number of available cycles. As a guideline, every 8° C (13° F) rise above the optimum temperature of 25° C (77° F) cuts battery life in half.

Lead acid batteries are rated at a 5-hour (0.2 C) and 20-hour (0.05 C) discharge, and the battery performs best when discharged slowly. Lead acid can deliver high pulse currents of several C if done for only a few seconds, making lead acid well suited as a *starter battery*.

STARTER AND DEEP-CYCLE BATTERIES

The *starter* battery is designed to crank an engine with a momentary high power burst; the *deep-cycle* battery, on the other hand, is built to provide continuous power. The starter battery is made for high peak power and does not tolerate deep cycling well. The deep-cycle battery has a moderate power output but permits cycling.

Starter batteries have a CCA rating in amperes and a very low internal resistance. Deep-cycle batteries are rated in Ah or minutes of runtime. A starter battery cannot be swapped with a deep-cycle battery and vice versa because of their different internal construction. **Table 7.5** compares the typical life of starter and deep-cycle batteries when deep-cycled.

ABSORBENT GLASS MAT (AGM)

AGM is an improved lead acid battery in which the electrolyte is absorbed in a mat of fine glass fibers. This makes the battery spill-proof. AGM has very low internal resistance, is capable of delivering high currents and offers long service even if *occasionally* deep-cycled. It also stands up well to high and low temperatures and has a low self-discharge. AGM has a higher specific power rating for high load currents and allows faster charge times (up to five times faster) than conventional lead acid. AGM has a slightly lower specific energy and higher manufacturing cost.

AGM batteries are sensitive to overcharging. They can be charged to 2.40 V/cell without problems but the float charge should be reduced to 2.25 to 2.30 V/cell and summer temperatures may require lower voltages. Automotive charging systems designed for flooded lead acid often have a fixed float voltage setting of 14.40 V (2.40 V/cell) and a direct replacement with an AGM battery could result in overcharge on a long drive.

Heat can be a problem for AGM and other gelled electrolyte batteries. Manufacturers recommend halting charge if the battery core reaches 49° C (120° F). However, AGM batteries can sit in storage for long periods before a recharge to prevent sulfation becomes necessary.

7.13.3 Nickel-based Batteries
NICKEL-CADMIUM (NiCd)

The standard NiCd remains one of the most rugged and forgiving batteries but needs proper care to attain longevity. Nickel-based batteries also have a flat discharge curve that ranges from 1.25 to 1.0 V/cell. **Table 7.6** summarizes the advantages and limitations of NiCd battery systems.

NICKEL-METAL-HYDRIDE (NiMH)

NiMH provides 40% higher specific energy than standard NiCd, but the decisive advantage is the absence of toxic metals. NiMH also has two major advantages over Li-ion: price and safety. NiMH is offered in AA and AAA sizes.

NiMH is not without drawbacks. It has a lower specific energy than Li-ion and also has high self-discharge, losing about 20% of its capacity within the first 24 hours, and 10% per month thereafter. New types of NiMH such as the Eneloop from Sanyo, ReCyko by GP and others have reduced the self-discharge by a factor of six, increasing storage life by the same amount at the sacrifice of some capacity. **Table 7.7** summarizes the advantages and limitations of NiMH battery systems.

7.13.4 Lithium-based Batteries

The specific energy of Li-ion is twice that of NiCd and the high nominal cell voltage of 3.60 V as compared to 1.20 V for nickel systems contributes to this gain. The load characteristics are good, and the flat discharge curve offers effective utilization of the stored energy in a desirable voltage spectrum of 3.70 to 2.80 V/cell. Li-ion batteries vary in performance

---

Table 7.4
Advantages and Limitations of Lead Acid Batteries

Advantages Inexpensive and simple to manufacture; lowest cost per watt-hour
Mature and well-understood technology; provides dependable service
Low self-discharge; lowest among rechargeable batteries
High specific power, capable of high discharge currents
Limitations Low specific energy; poor weight-to-energy ratio
Slow charge; fully saturated charge takes 14 hours
Must always be stored in charged condition
Limited cycle life; repeated deep-cycling reduces battery life
Flooded version requires watering
Not environmentally friendly
Transportation restrictions on the flooded type
(Table courtesy of Cadex)

Table 7.5
Cycle Performance of Starter and Deep-Cycle Batteries

Depth of Discharge	Starter Battery	Deep-cycle Battery
100%	12-15 cycles	150-200 cycles
50%	100-120 cycles	400-500 cycles
30%	130-150 cycles	1000 and more cycles

(Table courtesy of Cadex)

Table 7.6
Advantages and Limitations of NiCd Batteries

Advantages	Fast and simple charging even after prolonged storage
	High number of charge/discharge cycles; provides over 1000 charge/discharge cycles with proper maintenance
	Good load performance; rugged and forgiving if abused
	Long shelf life; can be stored in a discharged state
	Simple storage and transportation; not subject to regulatory control
	Good low-temperature performance
	Economically priced; NiCd is the lowest in terms of cost per cycle
	Available in a wide range of sizes and performance options
Limitations	Relatively low specific energy compared with newer systems
	Memory effect; needs periodic full discharges
	Environmentally unfriendly; cadmium is a toxic metal and cannot be disposed of in landfills
	High self-discharge; needs recharging after storage

(Table courtesy of Cadex)

Table 7.7
Advantages and Limitation of NiMH Batteries

Advantages	30-40% higher capacity than a standard NiCd
	Less prone to memory than NiCd
	Simple storage and transportation; not subject to regulatory control
	Environmentally friendly; contains only mild toxins
	Nickel content makes recycling profitable
Limitations	Limited service life; deep discharge reduces service life
	Requires complex charge algorithm
	Does no absorb overcharge well; trickle charge must be kept low
	Generates heat during fast-charge and high-load discharge
	High self-discharge; chemical additives reduce self-discharge at the expense of capacity
	Performance degrades if stored at elevated temperatures; should be stored in a cool place at about 40% state-of-charge

(Table courtesy of Cadex)

according to the choice of cathode materials. **Table 7.8** presents the characteristics of common Li-ion battery chemistries and **Table 7.9** summarizes the advantages and limitations of lithium-ion battery systems.

Lithium-polymer employs a gelled electrolyte in a micro-porous separator between the anode and cathode. Li-polymer is a construction technique and not a type of battery chemistry, so it can be applied to any of the lithium battery chemistries. Most Li-polymer battery packs are based on Li-cobalt. Charge and discharge characteristics of Li-polymer are identical to other Li-ion systems and this chemistry does not require a special charger.

Figure 7.49 compares the specific energy of lead, nickel and lithium-based systems. While Li-cobalt is the clear winner in terms of higher capacity than other systems, this only applies to specific energy. In terms of specific power and thermal stability, Li-manganese and Li-phosphate are superior.

7.13.5 Charging Methods

The performance and longevity of rechargeable batteries are to a large extent governed by the quality of the charger. Choosing a quality charger is important considering the costs of battery replacement and poor performance.

CHARGERS

This discussion focuses on third-party chargers designed to charge and maintain individual cells or batteries. *Fleet chargers* designed for maintaining many batteries of a common type in a company or agency environment are often provided by the equipment OEM and usually have special features for battery conditioning.

Table 7.8
Characteristics of the Four Most Commonly Used Lithium-ion Batteries

Specifications	Li-cobalt LiCoO$_2$ (LCO)	Li-manganese LiMn$_2$O$_4$ (LMO)	Li-phosphate LiFePO$_4$ (LFP)	NMC[1] LiNiMnCoO$_2$
Voltage (V)	3.60	3.80	3.30	3.60/3.70
Charge limit (V)	4.20	4.20	3.60	4.20
Cycle life[2]	500-1000	500-1000	1000-2000	1000-2000
Operating temperature	Average	Average	Good	Good
Specific energy (Wh/kg)	150-190	100-135	90-120	140-180
Specific Power (C)	1	10, 40 pulse	35 continuous	10
Safety	Average[3]	Average[3]	Very safe[4]	Safer than Li-cobalt[4]
Thermal runaway[5] (°C/°F)	150/302	250/482	270/518	210/410
Cost	Raw material high	30% less than cobalt	High	High
In use since	1994	1996	1999	2003

Table Notes
[1] NMC (nickel-manganese-cobalt), NCM, CMN, CNM, MNC and MCN are basically the same. The order of Ni, Mn and Co does not matter much
[2] Application and environment govern cycle life; the numbers do not always apply correctly
[3] Requires protection circuit and cell balancing of multi cell pack. Requirements for small formats with 1 or 2 cells can be relaxed
[4] Needs cell balancing and voltage protection
[5] A fully charged battery raises the thermal runaway temperature, a partial charge lowers it

(Table courtesy of Cadex)

Table 7.9
Advantages and Limitations of Li-ion Batteries

Advantages	High specific energy
	Relatively low self-discharge; less than half that of NiCd and NiMH
	Low maintenance. No periodic discharge is needed; no memory
Limitations	Requires protection circuit to limit voltage and current
	Subject to aging, even if not in use (life span is similar to other chemistries)
	Transportation regulations apply when shipping in larger quantities

(Table courtesy of Cadex)

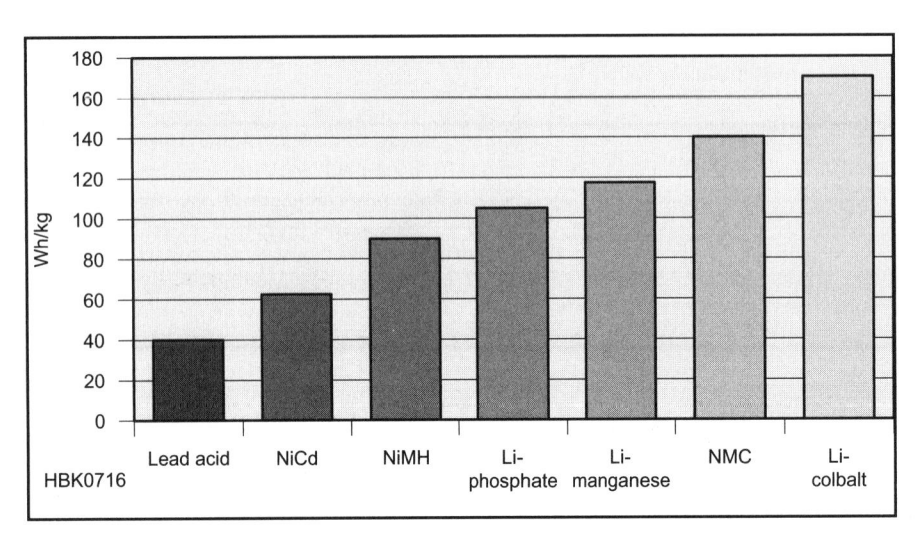

Figure 7.49 — Typical energy densities of lead, nickel- and lithium-based batteries

"Smart" chargers include valuable additional features beyond simply applying current to a battery. Temperature protection is particularly important to slow or prevent charging below freezing or above recommended thresholds when the battery is hot. Advanced lead acid chargers adjust the float and trickle charge thresholds based on temperature and battery age. **Table 7.10** summarizes the types of third-party chargers.

There are two common charge methods: voltage limiting (VL) and current limited (CL). Lead and lithium-based chargers cap the voltage at a fixed threshold. When reaching the cutoff voltage, the battery begins to saturate and the current drops while receiving the remaining charge on its own timetable. Full charge detection occurs when the current drops to a designated level.

Nickel-based batteries charge with a controlled current and the voltage is allowed to fluctuate freely. A slight voltage drop after a steady rise indicates a fully charged battery. The voltage drop method works well in terminating a fast charge, but the charger should detect and protect against shorted or mismatched cells. Most chargers include temperature sensors to end the charge if the temperature exceeds a safe level. (Some batteries also have internal temperature sensors.)

A temperature rise is normal as nickel-based batteries approach full charge. When in "ready" mode, the battery must cool down to room temperature. Heat causes stress and prolonged exposure to elevated temperature shortens battery life. Extended trickle charge also inflicts damage on nickel-based batteries, which should not be left in the charger continuously or beyond a few days.

A lithium-based battery should not get warm in a charger, and if this happens either the battery or charger may be faulty. Li-ion chargers do not apply a trickle charge and disconnect the battery electrically when fully charged. If the battery is left in the charger, a recharge may occur when its open circuit voltage drops below a set threshold. It is not necessary to remove Li-ion batteries from a charger.

SIMPLE GUIDELINES WHEN BUYING A CHARGER

• Use the correct charger for battery chemistry. Most chargers service one chemistry only.
• The battery voltage must agree with the charger. Do not charge if different.
• The Ah rating of a battery can be somewhat higher or lower than specified on the charger. A larger battery will take longer to charge than a smaller one and vice versa.
• The higher the amperage of the charger, the shorter the charge time will be, subject to limits on how fast the battery can be charged.
• Accurate charge termination and correct trickle charge prolong battery life.
• When fully saturated, a lead acid charger should switch to a lower voltage; a nickel-based charger should have a trickle charge; a Li-ion charger provides no trickle charge.
• Chargers should have a temperature override to end charge on a malfunctioning battery.
• Observe the temperature of the charger and battery. Lead acid batteries stay cool during charge; nickel-based batteries elevate the temperature toward the end of charge and should cool down after charge; Li-ion batteries should stay cool throughout charge.

SLOW CHARGERS

This type of charger applies a fixed current of about 0.1 C (one-tenth of the rated capacity) as long as the battery is connected. Slow chargers have no full-charge detection, charge current is always applied, and the charge time for a fully discharged battery is 14 to 16 hours.

Table 7.10
Charger Characteristics

Type	Chemistry	C-rate (C)	Time	Charge Termination
Slow	NiCd, Lead acid	0.1	14 h	Continuous low charge or fixed timer. Subject to overcharge. Remove battery when charged.
Rapid	NiCd, NiMH, Li-ion	0.3-0.5	3-6 h	Senses battery by voltage, current, temperature, and time-out timer
Fast	NiCd, NiMH, Li-ion	1	1+ h	Same as rapid charger with faster service
Ultra-Fast	Li-ion, NiCd, NiMH	1-10	10-60 min	Applies ultra-fast charge to 70% SoC; limited to specialty batteries

All values specified over 0°C to 45°F (32°F to 113°F) range
(Table courtesy of Cadex)

Most slow chargers have no "ready" indicator.

When fully charged, a slow charger keeps NiCd batteries lukewarm to the touch. Some overcharge is acceptable and the battery does not need to be removed immediately when ready. Leaving the battery in the charger can cause internal crystal growth that leads to "memory effects" in NiCd batteries.

Charging a battery with a lower Ah rating than specified for the charger will cause the battery to heat up as it approaches full charge due to the higher charging rate. Because slow chargers have no provision to lower the current or terminate the charge, the excessive heat will shorten the life of the battery.

The opposite can occur when a slow charger is charging a larger battery than it is rated for. In this case, the battery may never reach full charge and remains cold. Battery performance will be poor because of insufficient charge. Repeated partial charging can also cause crystal growth and memory effects.

RAPID CHARGERS

Falling between a slow and fast charger, the rapid charger is designed for nickel and lithium-based batteries. Unless specially designed, the rapid charger cannot service both types of batteries.

Rapid chargers are designed to charge fully discharged batteries and battery packs in 3 to 6 hours. When full charge is reached, the charger switches to a "ready" state. Most rapid chargers include temperature protection.

FAST CHARGERS

The fast charger typically applies charge at a 1 C rate so that a fully discharged battery is recharged in a little over 1 hour. As the battery approaches full charge, the charger may reduce the charge current (particularly for NiCd), and when the battery is fully charged, the charger switches to a trickle or maintenance charge mode.

Most nickel-based fast chargers accommodate NiCd and NiMH batteries and apply the same charging algorithm, but cannot charge Li-ion batteries. To service a Li-ion pack, specialty dual-mode chargers can read a security code on the battery to switch to the right charger setting.

Lead acid batteries cannot be fast-charged and the term "fast charge" is a misnomer for lead acid chargers. Most lead acid chargers charge the battery in 14 hours; anything slower may be a compromise. Lead acid can be charged relatively quickly to 70% of full charge with the important saturation charge consuming the remaining time. A partial charge at high rate is acceptable provided the battery receives a fully saturated charge once every few weeks to prevent sulfation.

ULTRA-FAST CHARGERS

Large NiCd and Li-ion batteries can be charged at a very high rate (10 C is typical) up to 70% of full charge. Ultra-fast charging stresses batteries. If possible, charge the battery at a more moderate current. An ultra-fast charger should offer user-selectable rates to optimize the charging requirements.

At a rate of 10 C, a battery can be charged in a few minutes but several conditions must be observed:

• The battery must be designed to accept an ultra-fast charge.

• Ultra-fast charging only applies during the first charge phase and charge current must be lowered once the 70% state-of-charge (SoC) threshold is reached.

• All cells in a pack must be balanced and in good condition. Older batteries with high internal resistance will heat up and are no longer suitable for ultra-fast charging.

• Ultra-fast charging can only be done at moderate temperatures. Low temperatures slow the chemical reaction and the unabsorbed energy results in gassing and heat buildup.

• The charge must include temperature compensation and other safety provisions to end the charge if the battery is overly stressed.

CHARGING FROM A USB PORT

The universal serial bus (USB) interface has become ubiquitous on computers and consumer electronics. It is increasingly used on radio equipment. A drawing and pin connections for the USB interface are available in the **Component Data and References** chapter.

USB hubs are specified to provide 5 V and 500 mA of current. (Current can only flow out of a USB interface.) While this would be enough to charge a small Li-ion battery, it could overload the hub if other devices are attached. Many hubs limit the current and will shut down if overloaded, so charging capacity is quite limited.

The most common USB chargers are designed for single-cell Li-ion batteries. The charge begins with a constant current charge to 4.20 V/cell, at which point the voltage levels off and current begins to decrease. Due to voltage drops in the USB cable and charger circuit, the hub may not be able to fully charge the battery. This will not damage a Li-ion battery but it will deliver shorter than expected runtimes.

CHARGING LEAD ACID

Lead acid batteries should be charged in three stages as shown in **Figure 7.50**:
1 — constant-current charge
2 — topping charge
3 — float charge

The constant-current charge applies the bulk of the charge and takes up roughly half of the required charge time. The topping charge continues at a lower charge current and provides saturation. The float charge compensates for the loss caused by self-discharge.

During the constant-current charge the battery charges to 70% SoC in 5 to 8 hours and the remaining 30% is supplied by the slower topping charge that lasts another 7 to 10 hours. The topping charge is essential for the well-being of the battery. If topping charge is not performed, the battery will eventually lose the ability to accept a full charge and performance will decrease because of sulfation. The float charge maintains the battery at full charge.

The switch to topping charge happens when the battery reaches the set voltage limit. Current begins to drop as the battery starts to saturate and full charge is reached when the current decreases to 3% of the rated current. A battery with high leakage may never reach this level and a timer is required to start charging termination.

The correct setting of the charge voltage is critical, ranging from 2.3 to 2.45 V per cell. The threshold is selected as a compromise between charging to maximum capacity and creating internal corrosion and gassing. The battery voltage also shifts with temperature, with warmer temperatures requiring slightly lower voltage thresholds. If variable voltage thresholds are not available in the charger, it is better to use a lower voltage threshold for safety.

Once fully charged through saturation, the battery should not dwell at the *topping voltage* for more than 48 hours and must be reduced to the *float voltage* level. This is especially critical for sealed systems because they are less able to tolerate overcharge than the flooded type due to heating and gas (hydrogen) generation. The recommended float voltage of most lead acid batteries is 2.25 to 2.27 V/cell. Manufacturers recommend lowering the float charge at ambient temperatures above 29° C (85° F). Not all chargers feature float charge. If the charger remains at the topping voltage and does not drop below 2.30 V/cell, remove the charger after a maximum of 48 hours of charge.

Aging batteries develop imbalances between cells that can result in overcharge and gassing from weak cells. This can also cause a strong cell to be undercharged and develop sulfation. Some battery manufacturers have developed cell-balancing devices that compensate for cell imbalance.

Lead acid batteries must always be stored in a charged state. A topping charge should be applied every six months to prevent the voltage from dropping below 2.10 V/cell. With AGM, these requirements can be somewhat relaxed.

Measuring the open circuit voltage (OCV) while in storage provides a reliable indication of the battery's state-of-charge (SoC). A voltage of 2.10 V at room temperature indicates a charge of about 90%. (That is equivalent to

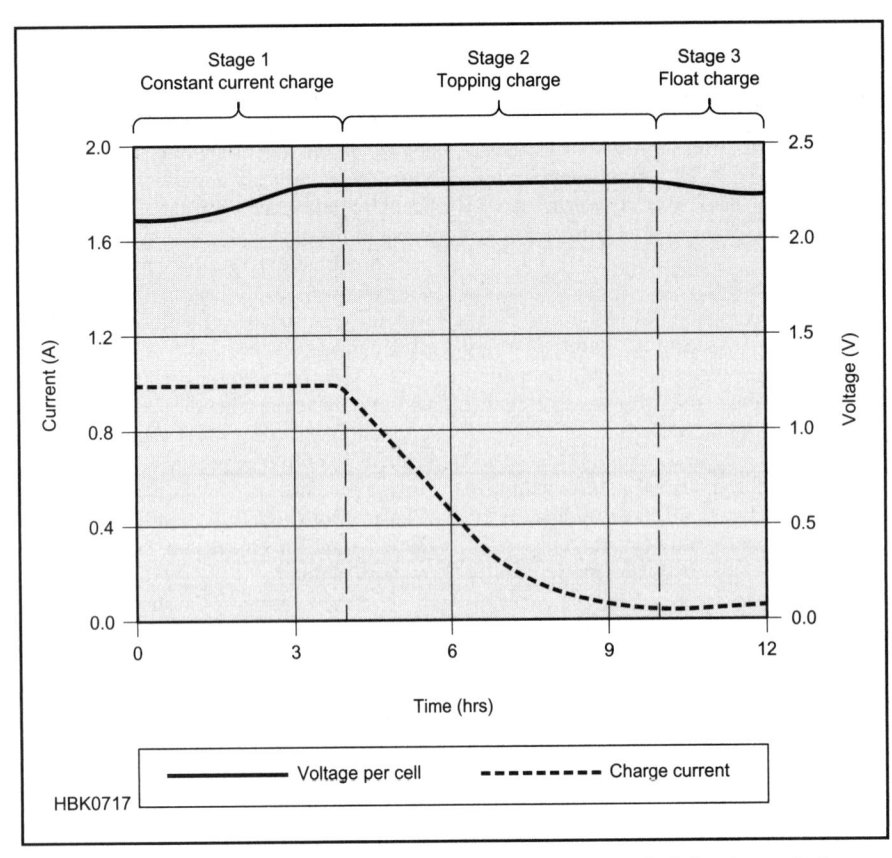

Figure 7.50 — Charge stages of a lead acid battery. The battery is fully charged when the current drops to a pre-determined level or levels out in stage 2. The float voltage must be reduced at full charge. (Courtesy of Cadex)

12.6 V for a typical six-cell "12 V" lead acid battery.) Such a battery is in good condition and needs only a brief full charge prior to use. If the OCV is lower, the battery must be charged to prevent sulfation. Cool temperatures increase OCV slightly and warm temperatures lower it. Use OCV as an SoC indicator after the battery has rested for a few hours to allow the effects of charging to dissipate.

SIMPLE GUIDELINES FOR CHARGING LEAD ACID BATTERIES

• Charge in a well-ventilated area. Hydrogen gas generated during charging is explosive.

• Choose the appropriate charge program for flooded, gel and AGM batteries. Follow the manufacturer's specifications of voltage thresholds.

• Charge lead acid batteries after each use to prevent sulfation. Do not store on low charge.

• The plates of flooded batteries must always be fully submerged in electrolyte. Fill battery with distilled or de-ionized water to cover the plates if low. Never add electrolyte.

• Fill water level to designed level *after* charging. Overfilling a discharged battery can result in overflow and acid spillage.

• Formation of gas bubbles in a flooded lead acid battery is an indication of approaching full charge.

• Reduce float charge if the ambient temperature is higher than 29° C (85° F).

• Do not allow a lead acid battery to freeze and never charge a frozen battery.

• Do not charge at temperatures above 49° C (120° F).

CHARGING NICKEL-CADMIUM

Battery manufacturers recommend that new NiCd batteries be slow-charged for 16 to 24 hours before use. A slow charge brings all cells in a battery pack to an equal charge level. This is important because each cell within the NiCd battery may have self-discharged at its own rate. Furthermore, during long storage the electrolyte tends to gravitate to the bottom of the cell and the initial trickle charge helps redistribute the electrolyte to eliminate dry spots on the separator. The cells will reach optimal performance after several charge/discharge cycles.

Full-charge Detection by Temperature

Full-charge detection of sealed nickel-based batteries is more complex than for lead acid and lithium-ion systems. Low-cost chargers often use temperature sensing to end the fast-charge, but this can be inaccurate due to internal and external temperature differences. Charger manufacturers use 50° C (122° F) as the temperature cutoff. Although any prolonged temperature above 45° C (113° F) is harmful, brief overshoot is acceptable if temperature will drop quickly when the charger changes to the "ready" state.

Some microprocessor-controlled chargers sense the rate of temperature increase with time, using the rapid temperature rise toward the end of charge to trigger the "ready" state. This is referred to as *delta temperature over delta time* or dV/dt. A rate of 1° C (1.8° F) per minute terminates charging. This keeps the battery cooler, but the cells need to charge reasonably fast for temperature to rise at the required rate. An absolute temperature of 60° C (140° F) terminates charging under any circumstances.

Chargers relying on temperature inflict harmful overcharges when fully charged batteries are inserted into the charger, such as if a hand-held radio is left in the charger between each use. This is not the case with Li-ion batteries where the charger uses voltage as the SoC indicator.

Full-charge Detection by Voltage Signature

Advanced chargers terminate charging when a defined voltage signature or profile with time occurs, referred to as *negative delta V* or NDV. This provides more precise full-charge detection for nickel-based batteries than temperature-based methods. Charging is terminated when the battery voltage drops as full charge is reached. NDV is the recommended method for NiCd cells that do not include an internal thermistor for temperature control and avoids overcharging of fully-charged batteries. NDV requires a charge rate of at least 0.5 C to generate a reliably measurable change in voltage and works best with fast charging. At a charge rate of 1 C, a fully discharged battery is recharged in about an hour.

Figure 7.51 illustrates the relationship of cell voltage, pressure, and temperature of a charging NiCd battery. Up to about 70% SoC, the battery accepts almost all of the energy supplied (called *charge efficiency*). Above 70%, the battery loses ability to accept charge, begins to generate gases so that pressure rises, and temperature increases rapidly.

Ultra-high-capacity NiCd batteries tend to heat up more than standard batteries when charging at 1 C and higher rates due to their higher internal resistance. Applying a high current during initial charge and tapering to a lower rate achieves good results with all nickel-based batteries and moderates temperature rise.

Some chargers can "burp" a charging battery by applying a load to generate a discharge pulse to cause gases to recombine and lower

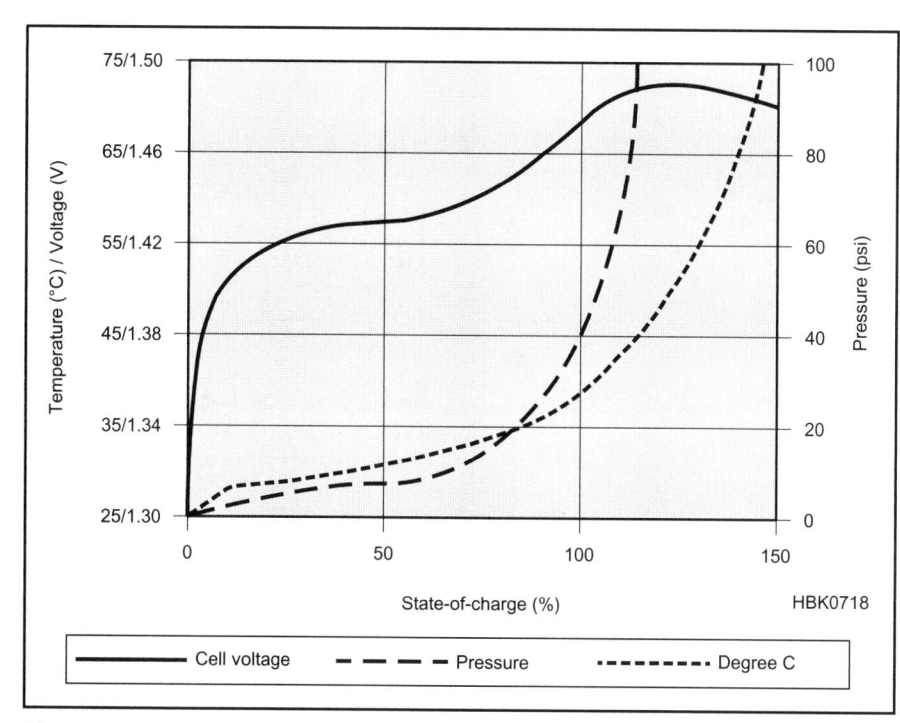

Figure 7.51 — Charge characteristics of a NiCd cell. Above 70% state-of-charge, temperature and cell pressure rise quickly. NiMH has similar charge characteristics. (Courtesy of Cadex)

internal pressure. The result is a cooler and more effective charge than with conventional dc charging. Pulse charging does not apply to lead and lithium-based systems.

After full charge, the NiCd battery receives a trickle charge of between 0.05 C and 0.1 C to compensate for self-discharge. To avoid possible overcharge, trickle charging should be done at the lowest possible rate and the batteries should be removed from the charger after more than a few days.

CHARGING NICKEL-METAL-HYDRIDE

The charging algorithm for NiMH is similar to NiCd with the exception that NiMH is more complex. The NDV method of measuring full charge has difficulty because the voltage drop at full charge is very small — about 5 mV/cell. As a result, modern chargers combine the various methods of measuring voltage and temperature into a composite algorithm that reacts depending on battery condition.

Some advanced chargers apply an initial fast charge at 1 C. After reaching a certain voltage threshold, a few minutes rest is taken to allow the battery to cool. Charging then resumes at lower currents as the charge progresses to full charge. This is known as the "step-differential charge" and works well for all nickel-based batteries, achieving an extra capacity of about 6% above basic chargers. A drawback of this method is that the fast-charge stress on the battery will shorten overall battery life by 10 to 20%.

NiMH cannot absorb overcharge well and the trickle charge current must be limited to around 0.05 C. In comparison, a basic NiCd charger trickle charges at 0.1 C. This higher trickle charge and the need for sensitive full-charge detection render the basic NiCd chargers unsuitable for NiMH batteries. On the other hand, NiCd cells can be charged in a NiMH charger at the lower trickle charge rate.

Slow charging should not be used for NiMH batteries. At the charging rate of 0.1 to 0.3 C, the voltage and temperature profiles make it very difficult to measure full charge accurately so the charger must depend on a timer. Harmful overcharge will occur if a fixed timer is used, particularly when charging partially or fully charged batteries. The same is true for charging old batteries with reduced capacity.

Inexpensive chargers are prone to incorrect charging because of the difficulty in correctly sensing full charge. Remove the batteries from the charger when you think they are fully charged. For high charge rates, remove the batteries when they are warm to the touch. It is better to remove the batteries and recharge them before use than to leave them in the charger where they might be overcharged and damaged.

SIMPLE GUIDELINES ON CHARGING NICKEL-BASED BATTERIES

• Do not charge at high or freezing temperatures; room temperature is best.

• Do not use chargers that allow the batteries to heat; remove the batteries when warm to the touch.

• Nickel-based batteries are best fast charged.

• NiMH chargers can charge NiCd batteries but not vice versa.

• High charge current or overcharging on an aging battery may cause heat build-up.

• Do not leave a nickel-based battery in the charger for long periods, even with correct trickle charge. Remove and apply a brief charge before use.

• Nickel- and lithium-based batteries require different charge algorithms and cannot share the same charger unless it can switch between the different chemistries.

CHARGING LITHIUM-ION

The Li-ion charger is a voltage-limiting device that is similar to the lead acid system. The difference lies in a higher voltage per cell, tighter voltage tolerance and the absence of trickle or float charge at full charge. Li-ion cannot accept overcharge — any extra charging causes stress.

Most Li-ion cells charge to 4.20 V/cell with a tolerance of ±50 mV/cell. **Figure 7.52** shows the voltage and current signature as lithium-ion passes through the stages for constant current and topping charge. The charge rate of a typical consumer Li-ion battery is between 0.5 and 1 C in Stage 1 and the charge time is about three hours. Manufacturers recommend charging the 18650 cell at 0.8 C or less. The cell should remain cool during the charging process although there may be a slight temperature rise of a few degrees when reaching full charge. Full charge occurs when the battery reaches the voltage threshold and the current drops to 3% of the rated current, or if the charging current reaches a constant value and does not decrease further. The latter may be due to elevated self-discharge.

Li-ion does not need to be fully charged, as is the case with lead acid, nor is it desirable to do so. In fact, it is better not to fully charge so as not to stress the battery. Choosing a lower voltage threshold or eliminating saturation charge prolongs battery life at the cost of reduced runtime. Without a saturation stage, the battery is usually charged to around 85% of capacity.

Once charging is terminated, the battery voltage begins to drop and this eases the voltage stress. Over time, the open circuit voltage (OCV) will settle to between 3.60 and 3.90 V/cell. A battery receiving a fully saturated charge will keep the higher voltage longer than a battery that was fast charged and terminated without a saturation charge.

If a lithium-ion battery must be left in the charger for operational readiness, some chargers apply a brief topping charge to

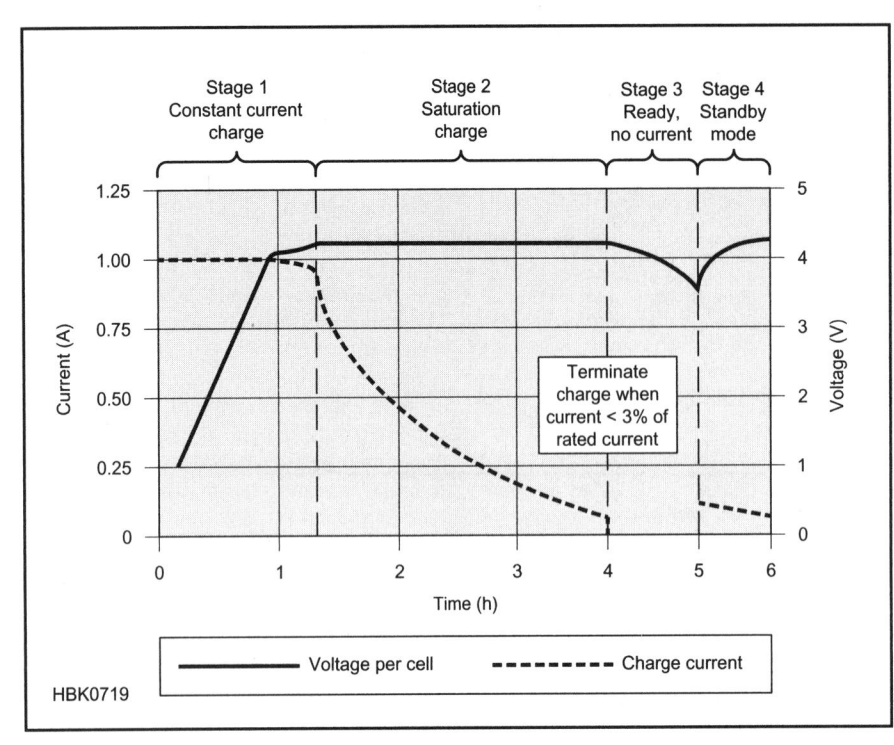

Figure 7.52 — Charge stages of lithium ion. Li-ion is fully charged when the current drops to a predetermined level or levels out at the end of Stage 2. In lieu of trickle charge, some chargers apply a topping charge when the voltage drops to 4.05 V/cell (Stage 4). (Courtesy of Cadex)

compensate for the small self-discharge of the battery and its protective circuit. It is common to let the battery voltage drop to 4.00 V/cell and then recharge to 4.05 V/cell to reduce voltage-related stress and prolong battery life. Battery-powered devices should be turned off when charging their battery. Otherwise, the *parasitic load* of the device can confuse the charger, distorting the charge cycle and stressing the battery.

Overcharging Lithium-ion

Lithium-ion systems operate safely within the designated operating voltages; however, the battery becomes unstable if inadvertently charged to a voltage higher than specified. Prolonged charging above 4.30 V/cell forms plating of metallic lithium on the anode, while the cathode material becomes an oxidizing agent, loses stability and produces CO_2. Cell pressure rises until the internal *current interrupt device* (CID) disconnects the current at 1380 kPa (200 psi).

Should the pressure rise further, a safety membrane bursts open at 3450 kPa (500 psi) and the cell might eventually vent with flame. The thermal runaway moves lower when the battery is fully charged; for Li-cobalt this threshold is between 130-150° C (266-302° F), for nickel-manganese-cobalt (NMC) between 170-180° C (338-356° F), and manganese is 250° C (482° F). Li-phosphate enjoys similar and better temperature stabilities than manganese.

Lithium-ion is not the only battery that is a safety hazard if overcharged. Lead and nickel-based batteries are also known to melt down and cause fires if improperly handled. Properly designed charging equipment is paramount for all battery systems.

SIMPLE GUIDELINES FOR CHARGING LITHIUM-BASED BATTERIES

• A battery-powered device should be turned off while charging.
• Charge at a moderate temperature. Do not charge below freezing.
• Lithium-ion does not need to be fully charged; a partial charge is better.
• Chargers use different methods for "ready" indication and may not always indicate a full charge.
• Discontinue using a charger and/or battery if the battery gets excessively warm.
• Before prolonger storage, apply some charge to bring a pack to about half charge.

SUMMARY OF CHARGING

Batteries have unique needs and **Table 7.11** explains how to satisfy these needs with correct handling. Because of similarities within the battery families, only lead, nickel and lithium systems are covered. Along with these guidelines, you can prolong battery life by following three simple rules: keep the battery at moderate temperatures, control the level and rate of discharge, and avoid abusing the battery.

7.13.6 Discharge Methods
C-RATE

According to the definition of *coulomb*, a current of 1 ampere is a flow of 1 coulomb (C) of charge per second. Today, the battery industry uses *C-rate* to scale the charge and discharge current of a battery.

Most portable batteries are rated at 1 C, meaning that a 1000 mAh battery that is discharged at 1 C should under ideal conditions provide a current of 1000 mA for 1 hr. The same battery discharging at 0.5 C would provide 500 mA for 2 hours, and at 2 C, the 1000 mAh battery would deliver 2000 mA for 30 minutes. 1 C is also known as a one-hour discharge; a 0.5 C is a two-hour discharge, a 2 C is a half-hour discharge, and so on.

A battery's capacity — the amount of energy a battery can hold — can be measured with a *battery analyzer*. The analyzer discharges the battery at a calibrated current while measuring the time it takes to reach its specified end-of-discharge voltage. If a 1000 mAh battery could provide 1000 mA for 1 hour, 100% of the battery's nominal energy rating would be reached. If the discharge only lasted 30 minutes before reaching the specified voltage, the battery has a capacity of 50% of its nominal rating.

When discharging a battery at different rates a higher C-rate will produce a lower capacity reading due to the internal resistance turning some of the energy into heat instead of delivering it as current to a load. Lower C-rate discharges will produce a higher capacity.

For example, to obtain a reasonably good capacity rating, manufacturers commonly rate lead acid batteries at 0.05 C, or a 20-hour discharge. **Figure 7.53** illustrates the discharge times of a lead acid battery at various loads expressed in C-rate.

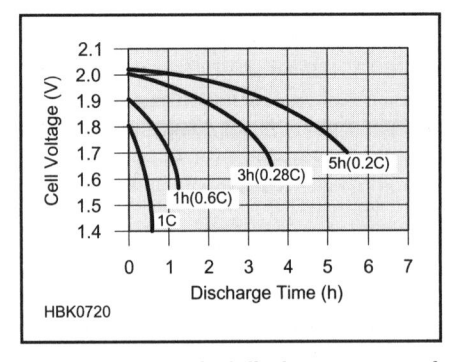

Figure 7.53 — Typical discharge curves of lead acid as a function of C-rate. Smaller batteries are rated at a 1 C discharge rate. Due to sluggish behavior, lead acid is rated at 0.2 C (5 hours) and 0.05 C (20 hours). (Courtesy of Cadex)

Table 7.11
Best Charging Methods

Frequently Asked Question	Lead Acid (Sealed, flooded)	Nickel-Based (NiCd and NiMH)	Lithium-ion (Li-ion, Polymer)
How should I prepare a new battery?	Battery comes fully charged. Apply topping charge	Charge 14-16 h. Priming may be needed.	Apply a topping charge before use. No priming needed
Can I damage a battery with incorrect use?	Yes, do not store partially charged, keep fully charged	Battery is robust and the performance will improve with use.	Keep some charge. Low charge can turn off protection circuit.
Do I need to apply a full charge?	Yes, partial charge causes sulfation.	Partial charge is fine.	Partial charge better than a full charge.
Can I disrupt a charge cycle?	Yes, partial charge causes no harm.	Interruptions can cause heat buildup.	Yes, partial charge causes no harm.
Should I use up all battery energy before charging?	No, deep discharge wears the battery down. Charge more often.	Apply scheduled discharges only to prevent memory.	No, deep discharge wears the battery down.
Do I have to worry about "memory"?	No memory	Discharge NiCd every 1-3 months.	No memory
How do I calibrate a "smart" battery?	Not applicable	Apply discharge/charge when the fuel gauge gets inaccurate. Repeat every 1-3 months.	Apply discharge/charge when the fuel gauge gets inaccurate. Repeat every 1-3 months.
Must I remove the battery when fully charged?	Depends on charger; needs correct float voltage	Remove after a few days in charger.	Not necessary; charger turns off
How do I store my battery?	Keep cells above 2.10 V, charge every 6 months	Store in cool place; a total discharge causes no harm.	Store in cool place partially charged, do not fully drain
Is the battery allowed to heat up during charge?	Battery may get lukewarm toward the end of charge.	Battery gets warm but must cool down on ready.	Battery may get lukewarm toward the end of charge.
How do I charge when cold?	Slow charge (0.1C): 0°-45°C (32°-113° F) Fast charge (0.5-1C): 5°-45° C (41°-113° F)	Slow charge (0.1C): 0°-45° C (32°-113° F) Fast charge (0.5-1C): 5°-45° C (41°-113° F)	Do not charge above 50° C (122° F) Do not charge above 50° C (122° F)
Can I charge at hot temperatures?	Above 25° C, lower threshold by 3 mV/°C.	Battery will not fully charge when hot	Do not charge above 50° C (122° F)
What should I know about chargers?	Charger should float at 2.25-2.30 V/cell when ready.	Battery should not get too hot; should include temp sensor.	Battery must stay cool; no trickle charge when ready.

(Table courtesy of Cadex)

DEPTH OF DISCHARGE

The end-of-discharge voltage for lead acid is 1.75 V/cell; for nickel-based systems it is 1.00 V/cell; and for most Li-ion it is 3.00 V/cell. At this level, roughly 95% of the battery's stored energy has been spent and voltage would drop rapidly if discharge were to continue. Most devices prevent operation beyond the specified end-of-discharge voltage. When removing the load after discharge, the voltage of a healthy battery gradually recovers toward the nominal voltage.

Because of internal resistance, wiring, protection circuits and contact resistance, a high load current lowers the battery voltage and the end-of-discharge voltage threshold should be lowered accordingly. The cutoff voltage should also be lowered when discharging at very cold temperatures. **Table 7.12** shows typical end-of-discharge voltages of various battery chemistries. The lower end-of-discharge voltage for higher loads compensates for the losses from internal battery resistance.

Since the cells in a battery pack can never be perfectly matched, a negative voltage potential can occur across a weaker cell on a multi-cell pack if the discharge is allowed to continue beyond a safe cutoff point. Known as *cell reversal*, the weak cell suffers damage to the point of developing a permanent electrical short circuit. The larger the number of cells in the pack, the greater the likelihood that a cell might reverse under heavy load. Over-discharge, particularly at low temperatures, is

Table 7.12
Recommended End-of-Discharge Voltages in V/Cell

End-of-discharge	Li-manganese	Li-phosphate	Lead-acid	NiCd/NiMH
Normal load	3.00	2.70	1.75	1.00
Heavy load	2.70	2.45	1.40	0.90

(Table courtesy of Cadex)

a large contributor to battery failure of cordless power tools, especially for nickel-based packs. Li-ion packs have protection circuits and the failure rate is lower.

DISCHARGING AT HIGH AND LOW TEMPERATURES

Batteries achieve optimum service life if used at 20° C (68° F) or slightly below, and nickel-based chemistries degrade rapidly when cycled at high ambient temperatures. Higher temperature operation lowers internal resistance and speeds up the chemical reactions but shortens service life if prolonged.

The performance of all battery chemistries drops drastically at low temperatures. At –20° C (–4° F) most nickel, lead, and lithium-based batteries stop functioning. Although NiCd can be used down to –40° C (–40° F), the permissible discharge is only 0.2 C (5-hour rate). Lead acid also has the problem of the electrolyte freezing which can crack the enclosure. Lead acid electrolyte also freezes more easily at a low charge.

SIMPLE GUIDELINES FOR DISCHARGING BATTERIES

• Battery performance decreases with cold temperature and increases with heat.
• Heat increases battery performance but shortens cycle life by a factor of two for every 10° C (18° F) above 25-30° C (18° F above 77-86° F).
• Only charge at moderate temperatures. Check the manufacturer's specifications for charging below freezing.
• Use heating blankets if batteries need rapid charging at cold temperatures.
• Prevent over-discharging. Cell reversal can cause an electrical short circuit.
• Use a larger battery if repetitive deep discharge cycles cause stress.
• A moderate dc discharge is better for a battery than pulsed loads.
• Lead acid systems are sluggish and require a few seconds of recovery between heavy loads.

7.13.7 Battery Handling

This section touches on the most important aspects of handling batteries when they are new, during their service life, and how to store and dispose of them.

FORMATTING AND PRIMING BATTERIES

Rechargeable batteries may not deliver their full rated capacity when new and will require *formatting* — a process that essentially completes the manufacturing process. Li-ion systems require less care in this regard, but cycling these batteries after long storage has been reported to improve performance. *Priming* is a conditioning cycle that is applied to improve battery performance during usage or after prolonged storage. Priming applies mainly to nickel-based batteries.

Formatting of lead acid batteries occurs by applying a charge, followed by a discharge and recharge as part of regular use. Gradually increase the load on a new battery, allowing it to reach full capacity after 50 to 100 cycles.

Manufacturers advise to trickle charge a nickel-based battery pack for 16 to 24 hours when new and after a long storage. This allows the individual cells to reach an equal charge level. A slow charge also helps to redistribute the electrolyte to eliminate dry spots on the separator that may have formed due to gravity. Applying several charge/discharge cycles through normal use or with a battery analyzer completes the formatting process. This can require from five to seven cycles or as many as 50 cycles depending on battery quality.

Cycling also restores lost capacity when a nickel-based battery has been stored for six months or longer. Storage time, state-of-charge, and storage temperature all affect battery recovery. The longer the storage and the higher the temperature, the more cycles are required to regain full capacity.

Lithium-ion does not need formatting when new, nor does it require the level of maintenance that nickel-based batteries do. Maximum capacity is available immediately. A discharge/charge cycle may be beneficial for calibrating a "smart" battery but this does not improve the internal chemistry.

STORING BATTERIES

The recommended storage temperature for most batteries is 15° C (59° F) and the extreme allowable temperature is –40° C to 50° C (–40° F to 122° F) for most chemistries. While lead acid must be kept at full charge during storage, nickel and lithium-based chemistries should be stored at around 40% state-of-charge.

Storage will always cause batteries to age. **Table 7.13** illustrates the *recoverable capacity* of lithium and nickel-based batteries at various temperatures and charge levels over one year. Recoverable capacity is the available battery capacity after storage with a full charge.

A sealed lead acid battery can be stored up to two years. It is important to apply a charge when the battery falls to 70% SoC, typically 2.07 V/cell or 12.42 V for a 12 V pack.

Nickel-metal-hydride can be stored for about three years. The capacity drop that occurs during storage can partially be reversed with priming.

Primary alkaline and lithium batteries can be stored for up to 10 years with minimum capacity loss.

SIMPLE GUIDELINES FOR STORING BATTERIES

• Remove batteries from equipment and store in a dry and cool place.
• Avoid freezing. Batteries freeze more easily if in a discharged state.
• Charge lead acid before storing and monitor the voltage frequently; apply a charge if below 2.10 V/cell.
• Nickel-based batteries can be stored for five years and longer, prime before use.
• Lithium-ion must be stored in a charged state, ideally 40%.
• Discard Li-ion if the voltage has stayed below 2.00 V/cell for more than a week.

RECYCLING BATTERIES

The main objective for recycling batteries is to prevent hazardous materials from entering landfills. Lead acid and NiCd batteries are of special concern.

Under no circumstances should batteries be incinerated, as fire can cause an explosion. Wear approved gloves when touching electrolyte. On exposure to skin, flush with water immediately. If eye exposure occurs,

---

Testing and Monitoring Batteries

Several sections of the "Testing and Monitoring" chapter from *Batteries in a Portable World* are provided with this book's downloadable supplemental content. The information covers measuring internal resistance and state-of-charge, measuring capacity, and special techniques for measuring nickel- and lithium-based batteries.

Table 7.13
Estimated Recoverable Capacity After Storage For 1 Year

Temp (°C)	Lead acid at full charge	Nickel-based at any charge	Lithium-ion (Li-cobalt) 40% charge	100% charge
0	97%	99%	98%	94%
25	90%	97%	96%	80%
40	62%	95%	85%	65%
60	38% (after 6 months)	70%	75%	60% (after 3 months)

(Table courtesy of Cadex)

flush with water for 15 minutes and consult a physician immediately.

Automotive and larger lead acid batteries can be recycled through auto parts stores and battery dealers. A recycling fee is usually charged when the battery is purchased.

Smaller batteries, including smaller SLA, can be recycled at many electronics and hardware stores, or your local municipal recycling center. Perform an Internet search for battery recyclers in your area.

It is helpful to create a specific location or designate a container for spent batteries at your home, office or workbench. This makes it easy to recycle the batteries by keeping them together in one spot.

7.13.8 DC-AC Inverters

For battery-powered operation of ac-powered equipment, dc-ac inverters are used. An inverter is a dc-to-ac converter that provides 120 V ac. Inverters come with varying degrees of sophistication. The simplest type of inverter switches directly at 60 Hz to produce a square-wave output. This is no problem for lighting and other loads that don't care about the input waveform. However, some equipment will work poorly or not at all when supplied with square wave power because of the high harmonic content of the waveform.

The harmonic content of the inverter output waveform can be reduced by the simple expedient of reducing the waveform duty cycle from 50% (for the square wave) to about 40%. For many loads, such as computers and other electronic devices, this may still not be adequate, and so many inverters use waveform shaping to approximate a sine-wave output. The simplest of these methods is a resonant inductor-capacitor filter. This adds significant weight and size to the inverter. Most modern inverters use high-frequency pulse-width modulation (PWM) techniques to synthesize the 60 Hz sinusoidal output waveform, much like a switching power supply. See **Figure 7.54**.

Inverters are usually rated in terms of their VA or "volt-ampere product" capability although sometimes they will be rated in watts. Care is required in interpreting inverter ratings. A purely resistive load operating from a sinusoidal voltage source will have a sinusoidal current flowing in phase with the voltage. In this case, VA, the product of the voltage (V) and the current (A), will equal the actual power in watts delivered to the load so that the VA and the watt ratings are the same. Some loads, such as motors and many rectifier power supplies, will shift the phase of load current away from the source voltage; or the load current will flow in short pulses as shown earlier for capacitor input filters. In these cases (which are very common), the VA product for that type of load can be much larger than the delivered power in watts. In the absence of detailed knowledge of the load characteristics it is prudent to select an inverter with a VA or wattage capability of 25% or more above the expected load.

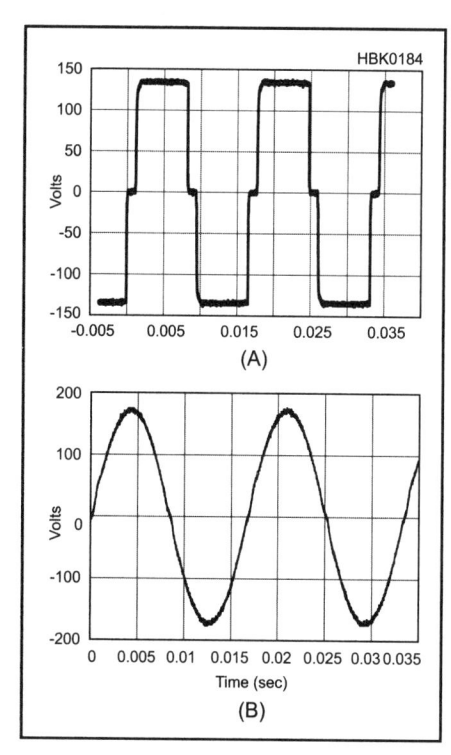

Figure 7.54 — Output waveforms of typical dc-ac inverters. At A, the output of a modified sine wave inverter. Note the stepped square waves. At B, the output of a "pure sine wave" inverter. Note the close approximation of a commercial ac sine wave.

7.13.9 Selecting a Battery for Mobile Operation

There are two basic modes of mobile operation: *in-motion*, and *stationary*. Each mode has unique power requirements and thus different battery requirements. To satisfy these needs, there are three basic battery types. It is important to understand the differences between the types and to apply them properly.

Standard vehicle batteries are referred to as *SLI* (starting, lights, ignition) or just *starter* batteries. Their primary function is to start the engine and then act as a power filter for the alternator which is the actual long-term power source. The most important rating of an SLI battery is the *cold cranking amps* (CCA) rating — the number of amps that the battery can produce at 32 °F (0 °C) for 30 seconds.

Batteries designed for repeated cycles of charging and discharging use are often called *deep-cycle* although the term is widely overused. A true deep-cycle battery is designed to be repeatedly discharged to 20% remaining capacity. The term "deep cycle" is a misnomer, as all lead-acid batteries are considered discharged when their output voltage drops below 10.5 V at some specified current draw as outlined by the Battery Council Institute (BCI — **www.batterycouncil.org**). At 10.5 V, a six-cell lead-acid battery is considered discharged.

Marine batteries are designed to be stored without charging for up to two years, yet still maintain enough power to start a marine engine. Contrary to common practice, they're not really designed for extended low-current power delivery. Marine batteries often have hybrid characteristics between SLI and deep-cycle batteries.

To differentiate true deep-cycle batteries from SLI and marine batteries, examine a battery's *reserve capacity* (RC). A battery's RC rating is the number of minutes that the battery can deliver 25 A while maintaining an output voltage above 10.5 V. Deep cycle batteries typically have RC ratings 20% or more higher than SLI batteries and perhaps 50% higher under ICAS (intermittent, commercial, and amateur service) conditions. A deep-cycle battery has a lower CCA rating than an SLI battery due to its internal construction that favors long-term power delivery over high-current starting loads.

With these facts in mind, we can now select the correct battery for our style of mobile operating. For in-motion operation with power outputs up to 200 W, a second trunk-mounted battery is seldom needed if the power cabling wire size is chosen correctly. (See the **Assembling a Station** chapter for information on wire sizes in mobile applications.)

When an amplifier is added for higher output power levels, it is often less expensive to add a second trunk-mounted battery than to install larger cables to the main battery. In these cases, the second battery can be of almost any type, as long as it is lead-acid. The second battery should be connected in parallel to the vehicle's main SLI battery. The battery's ampere-hour rating should be close to that of the vehicle's main SLI battery.

All secondary wiring should be properly fused, as outlined in the **Assembling a Station** chapter's section on mobile installations. The use of relays and circuit breakers should be avoided. Remember, should a short circuit occur, good-quality lead-acid batteries can deliver upwards of 3000 A which exceeds the break circuit ratings of most relays and circuit breakers. A better solution is a FET switch such as those made by Perfect Switch (**www.perfectswitch.com**).

Assuming the second battery is mounted inside the vehicle's passenger compartment or in the trunk, it should be an AGM type. AGM (Absorption Glass Mat) batteries do not outgas explosive hydrogen gas under normal

Power Sources   7.45

operating conditions. Flooded (liquid electrolyte) batteries should *never* be used in an enclosed environment.

For stationary operation, select a battery with a large RC rating because it will not be continuously charged. There are two main considerations; the ampere-hour rating (Ah) and the reserve capacity rating, typically listed as C/8, C/10, or C/20, with units of hours. (C is the battery's capacity in Ah.) Dividing the Ah rating by the load amperage (8, 10 or 20 A) will give you the reserve capacity in hours, but the actual ampere-hours any given battery can deliver before the voltage reaches 10.5 V (nominal discharge level) will vary with the load, both average and peak. Heavier loads will reduce the actual ampere-hours available.

Automotive batteries are arranged in BCI group sizes (**www.batterystuff.com/kb/tools/bci-battery-group-sizes.html**), from 21 through 98. Generally speaking, the larger the group size the larger the battery and the higher the Ah rating. For example, size 24 (small car) has an average rating of 40 Ah, and size 34 (large car) has an average rating of 55 Ah. Exact ratings, including their reserve capacity, are available from the manufacturers' websites listed below. A good rule of thumb is to select a battery as physically large as you have room for, consistent with the highest RC rating for any given Ah rating.

Batteries are heavy, and need to be properly secured inside a battery box or by using factory-supplied brackets. For example, a BIC group 34 (average SLI size) battery weighs about 55 pounds. Some battery models (such as the Optima) come supplied with mounting brackets and terminal protection covers. Even though battery boxes aren't always needed, they should be used as a safety precaution to prevent accidental contact with the terminals and can protect the battery from external items. Battery restraints should be adequate to provide 6 Gs of lateral and 4 Gs of vertical retention, ruling out sheet metal screws and most webbing material. Use the proper brackets!

There are three other considerations: isolating the battery electrically, recharging the battery, and output voltage regulation. Diode-based battery isolators are not all equal. Models with FET bypass switches are the preferred type because of the low voltage-drop across the FET.

If you have wired the battery in parallel with the vehicle's main SLI battery, recharging is taken care of whenever the vehicle is running. If you plan on operating in stationary mode, you'll need a separate recharging system. Most vehicle factory-installed trailer wiring systems also include a circuit for charging RV or boat "house" batteries. Check with your dealer's service personnel about these options.

Voltage regulators, commonly called "battery boosters," are almost a necessity for stationary operation. A model with a low-voltage cutoff should be used to avoid discharging the battery below 10.5 V, as discharging a lead-acid battery beyond this point drastically reduces its charge-cycle life — the number of full-charge/full-discharge cycles. (See the November 2008 *QST* Product Review column.)

For additional information on battery ratings, sizes, and configuration, visit these websites:
optimabatteries.com, www.exide.com
www.interstatebatteries.com
www.lifelinebatteries.com

7.14 Glossary of Power Source Terms

Bleeder — A resistive load across the output or filter of a power supply, intended to quickly discharge stored energy once the supply is turned off.

Boost converter — A switchmode converter in which the output voltage is always greater than or equal to the input voltage.

Buck converter — A switchmode converter in which the output voltage is always less than or equal to the input voltage.

Buck-boost converter — A switchmode converter in which the magnitude of the output voltage can be either greater or less than the input voltage.

C-rate — The charging rate for a battery, expressed as a ratio of the battery's ampere-hour rating.

CCA (cold cranking amps) — A measure of a battery's ability to deliver high current to a starter motor.

Circular mils — A convenient way of expressing the cross-sectional area of a round conductor. The area of the conductor in circular mils is found by squaring its diameter in mils (thousandths of an inch), rather than squaring its radius and multiplying by pi. For example, the diameter of 10-gauge wire is 101.9 mils (0.1019 inch). Its cross-sectional area is 10380 CM, or 0.008155 square inches.

Core saturation (magnetic) — That condition whereby the magnetic flux in a transformer or inductor core is more than the core can handle. If the flux is forced beyond this point, the permeability of the core will decrease, and it will approach the permeability of air.

Crowbar — A last-ditch protection circuit included in many power supplies to protect the load equipment against failure of the regulator in the supply. The crowbar senses an overvoltage condition on the supply's output and fires a shorting device (usually an SCR) to directly short-circuit the supply's output and protect the load. This causes very high currents in the power supply, which blow the supply's input-line fuse.

Darlington transistor — A package of two transistors in one case, with the collectors tied together, and the emitter of one transistor connected to the base of the other. The effective current gain of the pair is approximately the product of the individual gains of the two devices.

DC-DC converter — A circuit for changing the voltage of a dc source to ac, transforming it to another level, and then rectifying the output to produce direct current.

Deep-cycle — A battery designed for repeated charge-discharge cycles to 20% of remaining capacity.

Equalizing resistors — Equal-value bypassing resistors placed across capacitors connected in series for use in a high-voltage power supply to keep the voltages across the capacitors in the string relatively constant.

Fast recovery rectifier — A specially doped rectifier diode designed to minimize the time necessary to halt conduction when the diode is switched from a forward-biased state to a reverse-biased state.

Flyback converter — A transformer-coupled version of the **buck-boost converter**.

Forward converter — A **buck converter** with multiple isolated outputs at different voltage levels and polarities.

Foldback current limiting — A special type of current limiting used in linear power supplies, which reduces the current through the supply's regulator to a low value under short circuited load conditions in order to protect the series pass transistor from excessive power dissipation and possible destruction.

Ground fault (circuit) interrupter (GFI or GFCI) — A safety device installed between the household power mains and equipment where there is a danger of personnel touching an earth ground while operating the equipment. The GFI senses any current flowing directly to ground and immediately switches off all power to the equipment to minimize electrical shock. GFCIs are now standard equipment in bathroom and outdoor receptacles.

Input-output differential — The voltage drop appearing across the series pass transistor in a linear voltage regulator. This term is usually stated as a minimum value, which is that voltage necessary to allow the regulator to function and conduct current. A typical figure for this drop in most three-terminal regulator ICs is about 2.5 V. In other words, a regulator that is to provide 12.5 V dc will need a source voltage of at least 15.0 V at all times to maintain regulation.

Inverter — A circuit for producing ac power from a dc source.

Li-ion — Lithium-ion, a type of rechargeable battery that is about ⅓ the weight and ½ the volume of a **NiCd** battery of the same capacity.

Low dropout regulator — A three-terminal regulator designed to work with a low minimum input-output differential value.

Marine — A battery designed to retain significant energy over long periods of time without being continuously charged.

NiCd — Nickel cadmium, a type of rechargeable battery.

NiMH — Nickel metal hydride, a type of rechargeable battery that does not contain toxic substances.

Peak inverse voltage (PIV) — The maximum reverse-biased voltage that a semiconductor is rated to handle safely. Exceeding the peak inverse rating can result in junction breakdown and device destruction.

Power converter — Another term for a power supply.

Power processor — Another term for a power supply.

Primary battery — A battery intended for one-time use and then discarded.

RC (reserve capacity) — A measure of a battery's ability to deliver current over long periods.

Regulator — A device (such as a Zener diode) or circuitry in a power supply for maintaining a constant output voltage over a range of load currents and input voltages.

Resonant converter — A form of dc-dc converter characterized by the series pass switch turning on into an effective series-resonant load. This allows a zero current condition at turn-on and turn-off. The resonant converter normally operates at frequencies between 100 kHz and 500 kHz and is very compact in size for its power handling ability.

Ripple — The residual ac left after rectification, filtration and regulation of the input power.

RMS — Root Mean Square. Refers to the effective value of an alternating voltage or current, corresponding to the dc voltage or current that would cause the same heating effect.

Secondary battery — A battery that may be recharged many times. Also called a *storage battery*.

Secondary breakdown — A runaway failure condition in a transistor, occurring at higher collector-emitter voltages, where hot spots occur due to (and promoting) localization of the collector current at that region of the chip.

Series pass transistor, or pass transistor — The transistor(s) that control(s) the passage of power between the unregulated dc source and the load in a regulator. In a linear regulator, the series pass transistor acts as a controlled resistor to drop the voltage to that needed by the load. In a switch-mode regulator, the series pass transistor switches between its ON and OFF states.

SLI (starter, lights, ignition) — An automotive battery designed to start the vehicle and provide power to the lighting and ignition systems.

SOA (Safe Operating Area) — The range of permissible collector current and collector-emitter voltage combinations where a transistor may be safely operated without danger of device failure.

Surge — A moderate-duration perturbation on a power line, usually lasting for hundreds of milliseconds to several seconds.

Switching regulator — Another name for a switchmode converter.

Switchmode converter — A high-efficiency switching circuit used for dc-dc power conversion. Switching circuits are usually much smaller and lighter than conventional 60 Hz, transformer-rectifier circuits because they operate at much higher frequencies — from 25 to 400 kHz or even higher.

Three-terminal regulator — A device used for voltage regulation that has three leads (terminals) and includes a voltage reference, a high-gain error amplifier, temperature-compensated voltage sensing resistors and a pass element.

Transient — A short perturbation or "spike" on a power line, usually lasting for microseconds to tens of milliseconds.

Varistor — A surge suppression device used to absorb transients and spikes occurring on the power lines, thereby protecting electronic equipment plugged into that line. Frequently, the term MOV (Metal Oxide Varistor) is used instead.

Volt-Amperes (VA) — The product obtained by multiplying the current times the voltage in an ac circuit without regard for the phase angle between the two. This is also known as the apparent power delivered to the load as opposed to the actual or real power absorbed by the load, expressed in watts.

Voltage multiplier — A type of rectifier circuit that is arranged so as to charge a capacitor or capacitors on one half-cycle of the ac input voltage waveform, and then to connect these capacitors in series with the rectified line or other charged capacitors on the alternate half-cycle. The voltage doubler and tripler are commonly used forms of the voltage multiplier.

Voltage regulation — The change in power supply output voltage with load, expressed as a percentage.

7.15 References and Bibliography

REFERENCES

1) Landee, Davis and Albrecht, *Electronic Designer Handbook*, 2nd edition, (McGraw-Hill, 1977), page 12-9. This book can frequently be found in technical libraries and used book stores. The power supply section is well worth reading.
2) Severns and Bloom, *Modern DC-to-DC Switchmode Power Converter Circuits*, (Van Nostrand Reinhold, 1984, ISBN: 0-442-21396-4). A reprint of this book is currently available at the Power Sources Manufacturers Association website, **www.psma.com**.
3) Fair-Rite website, **www.fair-rite.com**
4) Magnetics website, **www.mag-inc.com**

OTHER RESOURCES

M. Brown, *Power Supply Cookbook*, (Butterworth-Heinemann, 2001).
I. Buchmann, *Batteries In a Portable World*, (Cadex Electronics, 2011).
J. Fielding, ZS5JF, *Power Supply Handbook*, (RSGB, 2006).
K. Jeffrey, *Independent Energy Guide*, (Orwell Cove Press, 1995). Includes information on batteries and inverters.
O. Schade, "Analysis of Rectifier Operation," Proceedings of the I.R.E., July 1943.
W. Silver, *Grounding and Bonding for the Radio Amateur* (ARRL 2017).

7.16 Power Source Projects

Construction of a power supply or accessory — basic to all of the radio equipment we operate and enjoy — can be one of the most rewarding projects undertaken by a radio amateur. Final testing and adjustment of most power-supply projects requires only a voltmeter, and perhaps an oscilloscope — tools commonly available to most amateurs.

General construction techniques that may be helpful in building the projects in this chapter are outlined in the **Construction Techniques** chapter. Other chapters in the *Handbook* contain basic information about the components that make up power supplies.

Safety must always be carefully considered during design and construction of any power supply. Power supplies contain potentially lethal voltages, and care must be taken to guard against accidental exposure. For example, electrical tape, insulated tubing ("spaghetti") or heat-shrink tubing is recommended for covering exposed wires, components leads, component solder terminals and tie-down points. Whenever possible, connectors used to mate the power supply to the outside world should be of an insulated type designed to prevent accidental contact.

Connectors and wire should be checked for voltage and current ratings. Always use wire with an insulation rating higher than the working voltages in the power supply. For supply voltages above 300 V, use wire with insulation rated accordingly. The **Component Data and References** chapter contains a table showing the current-carrying capability of various wire sizes. Scrimping on wire and connectors to save money could result in flashover, meltdown or fire.

All fuses and switches should be placed in the hot circuit(s) only. The neutral circuit should not be interrupted. Use of a three-wire (grounded) power connection will greatly reduce the chance of accidental shock. The proper wiring color code for 120 V circuits is: black — hot; white — neutral; and green — ground. For 240 V circuits, the second hot circuit generally uses a red wire.

POWER SUPPLY PRIMARY-CIRCUIT CONNECTOR STANDARD

The International Commission on Rules for the Approval of Electrical Equipment (CEE) standard for power-supply primary-circuit connectors for use with detachable cable assemblies is the CEE-22. The CEE-22 has been recognized by the ARRL and standards agencies of many countries. Rated for up to 250 V, 6 A at 65 °C, the CEE-22 is the most commonly used three-wire (grounded), chassis-mount primary circuit connector for electronic equipment in North America and Europe. It is often used in Japan and Australia as well.

When building a power supply requiring 6 A or less for the primary supply, a builder would do well to consider using a CEE-22 connector and an appropriate cable assembly, rather than a permanently installed line cord. Use of a detachable line cord makes replacement easy in case of damage. CEE-22 compatible cable assemblies are available with a wide variety of power plugs including most types used overseas.

Some manufacturers even supply the CEE-22 connector with a built-in line filter. These connector/filter combinations are especially useful in supplies that are operated in RF fields. They are also useful in digital equipment to minimize conducted interference to the power lines.

CEE-22 connectors are available in many styles for chassis or PC-board mounting. Some have screw terminals; others have solder terminals. Some styles even contain built-in fuse holders.

7.16.1 Four-Output Switching Bench Supply

This project by Larry Cicchinelli, K3PTO, describes the four-output bench power supply shown in **Figure 7.55** with three positive outputs and one negative output. The three positive outputs use identical switching regulator circuits that can be set independently to any voltage between 3.3 V and 20 V at up to 1 A. The fourth output is a negative regulator capable of about 250 mA. As built, the supply has two fixed outputs and two variable outputs, but any module can be built with variable output. (Construction diagrams and instructions, a complete parts list, and additional design details are included with this book's downloadable supplemental content.)

The only dependency among the outputs is that they are all driven by a single transformer. The transformer used is rated at 25 V and 2 A — good for 50 W. Assuming that the regulator IC being used has a 75% efficiency, a total of about 37 W is available from the power supply outputs.

One of the features of a switching regulator is that you can draw more current from the outputs than what the transformer is supplying — at a lower voltage, of course — as long as you stay within the 37 W limit and maximum current for the regulator. Most of the discussion in this article will be about the positive regulators as the negative regulator was an add-on after the original system was built.

Figure 7.55 — The front panel of the four-output switching supply.

POSITIVE REGULATOR

Figure 7.56 is the circuit for the positive regulator modules — a buck-type regulator. There are several variations of the circuit, any of which you can implement.

• L2 and C4 are optional. These two components implement a low-pass filter that will decrease high frequency noise that might otherwise appear at the output.

• The pads for R1 will accommodate a small, multi-turn potentiometer. You can insert one here or you can use the pads to connect a panel-mounted potentiometer.

• If you want a fixed output you can simply short out R1 and use R2 by itself.

• You can also insert a fixed resistor in the R1 position in the case where the calculated value is non-standard and you want to use two fixed resistors.

The formula for setting output voltage using the 3.3 V version of the regulator is based on knowing the current (in mA) through the regulator's internal voltage divider = 3.3 V / 2.7 kΩ = 1.22 mA. The sum of R1 and R2 must cause the voltage at the regulator FB pin to equal 3.3 V. Thus, R1 + R2 in kΩ = (V_{out} − 3.3) / 1.22 and V_{out} = 1.22 (R1 + R2) + 3.3. If R1 = R2 = 0, a direct connection from the output voltage to the FB pin, the calculation results in an output of 3.3 V. The leakage current of the Error Amplifier in the regulator is somewhat less than 25 nA so it can be ignored. The values for R1 and R2 are shown in the caption for Figure 7.56.

The only critical parts are R1 and R2 which form the voltage dividers for the regulator module. Even their values can be changed, within reason, as long as the ratios are maintained. If you want to have an accurate, fixed output voltage, select a value for R2 that is lower than the calculated value and use a potentiometer for R1 to set the voltage exactly. The value of C3 is not especially critical; however, it should be a low-ESR (equivalent series resistance) type that is intended for use in switchmode circuits.

NEGATIVE REGULATOR

The negative regulator is a buck-boost configuration — it converts a positive voltage into a negative one — see **Figure 7.57**. This

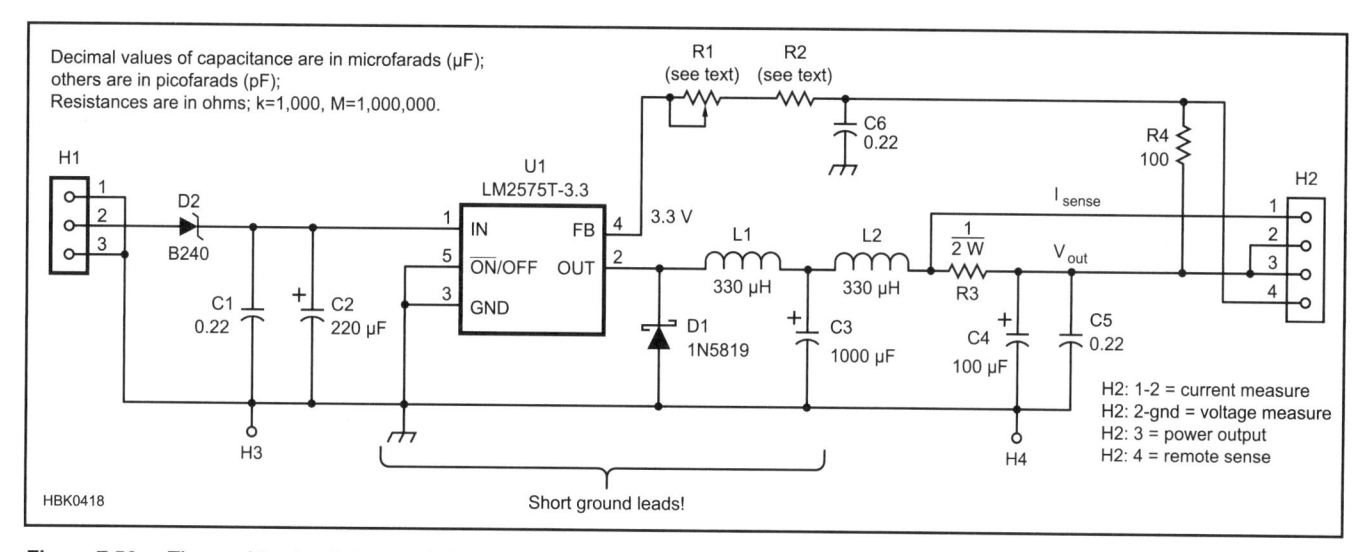

Figure 7.56 — The positive buck-type switchmode regulator uses the LM2575-3.3, a fixed-voltage regulator, with an external voltage-set resistor (R1 + R2). See text for details of the calculations needed to determine the value of R1 and R2. As noted in the text, these values are the total resistance for both parts, and can be made from one fixed resistor, one variable resistor or a combination. Some common values (R1 + R2 total) are: For a 12 V fixed supply, 7.1 kΩ; for 5 V, 1.4 kΩ; for a 3.3 to 20 V variable supply, 0-13.7 kΩ (use a 15 kΩ pot); for 5 to 15 V, 1.4-9.6 kΩ (use 1 kΩ fixed-value resistor and a 1 kΩ pot). A full parts list is included with this book's downloadable supplemental content.

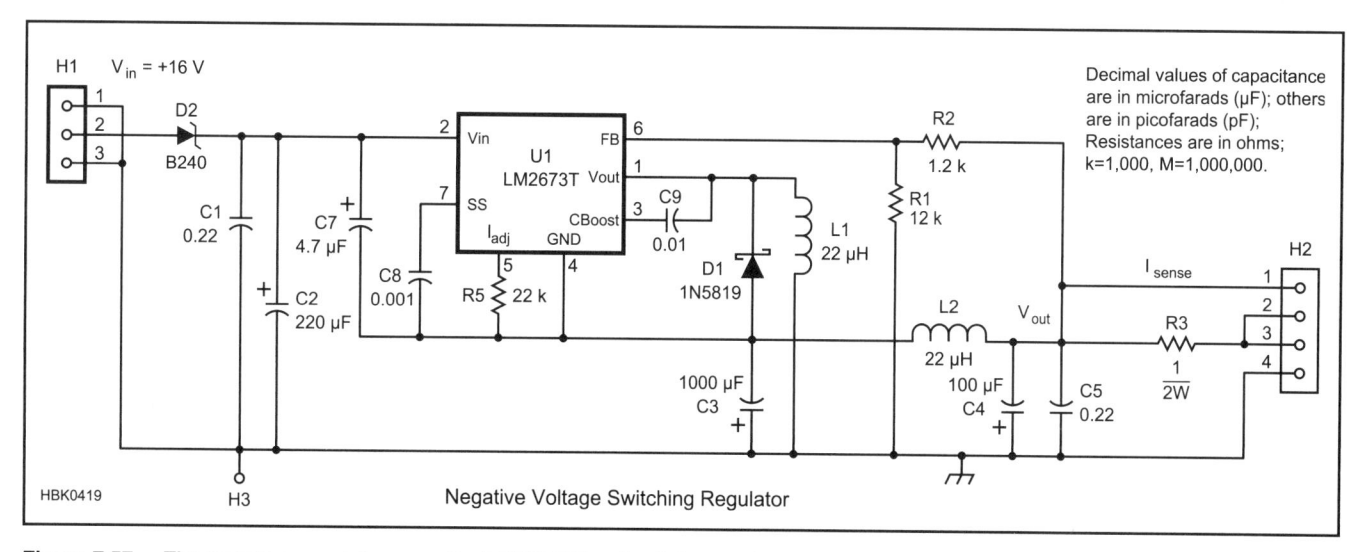

Figure 7.57 — The negative regulator uses the LM2673T in a buck-boost circuit. This circuit inverts the output voltage from the input voltage. A full parts list is included with this book's downloadable supplemental content.

Power Sources   7.49

design uses many of the same component values as the positive regulators except the regulator IC is an LM2673 to improve circuit stability. The author was unable to implement the current measuring circuit within a feedback loop. Several configurations introduced a significant low frequency noise component to the output voltage. There was also some 50 kHz noise present on the output, but an additional low-pass filter on the output reduced it considerably.

REMOTE SENSING

Many power supplies use remote sensing to compensate electronically for the voltage drop in the wires carrying current to the load. Even with relatively short wires, there can be significant voltage drop between the regulator and its load. There is provision for remote sensing in this circuit described in the support information for this project included with this book's downloadable supplemental content.

If you are not going to use remote sensing then you should insert a jumper in place of R4 in Figure 7.56. R4 (100 Ω) is there for protection just in case the remote sense connection is missing. If you do not want to use remote sensing you can simplify the digital panel meter (DPM) switch wiring to use a two-pole switch instead of the three-pole model listed. In this case, do not use S2.2 and connect S1.2 to the common of S2.3 instead of S2.2.

SUB-CIRCUIT INTERCONNECTION

Figure 7.58 shows the connections among the parts of the system: regulator boards, the digital panel meter (DPM), and rectifier circuit. The components used for the main rectifier circuit can be mounted on a terminal strip and do not need to be on a printed-circuit board.

THE DIGITAL PANEL METER

Another feature of the unit is the DPM which can be switched to measure the output voltage (H2 pin 1 to ground) as well as the current draw (voltage between H2 pins 1 and 2) for each of the positive supplies. Figure 7.58 shows the 3-pole, 4-position rotary switch (S2) that selects which power supply to monitor and a 3PDT toggle switch (S1) that selects between measuring voltage and current.

In order to measure the voltage drop across the 1 Ω current sense resistors, the DPM needs either an isolated power supply or some more circuitry. This system uses an isolated power supply. A series regulator is used simply because they are somewhat easier to implement and the DPM has a very low current requirement. All components except the transformer are mounted on a piece of perforated board. Since the 1.2 mA current for the feedback circuit flows through the current sense resistor it will be included in the value displayed by the DPM when current is selected.

The DPM also has a set of jumpers that allow you to set the decimal point location. As can be seen in Figure 7.58, one pole of the toggle switch selects its location.

CONSTRUCTION DETAILS

Both the DPM and the regulators use pin headers for all of the connections that come off the boards (see the parts list for details). This allows assembly of the subsystems without having to consider any attached wires. Wire lengths can be determined later, then install the mating connectors on the wires and simply push them onto the pins.

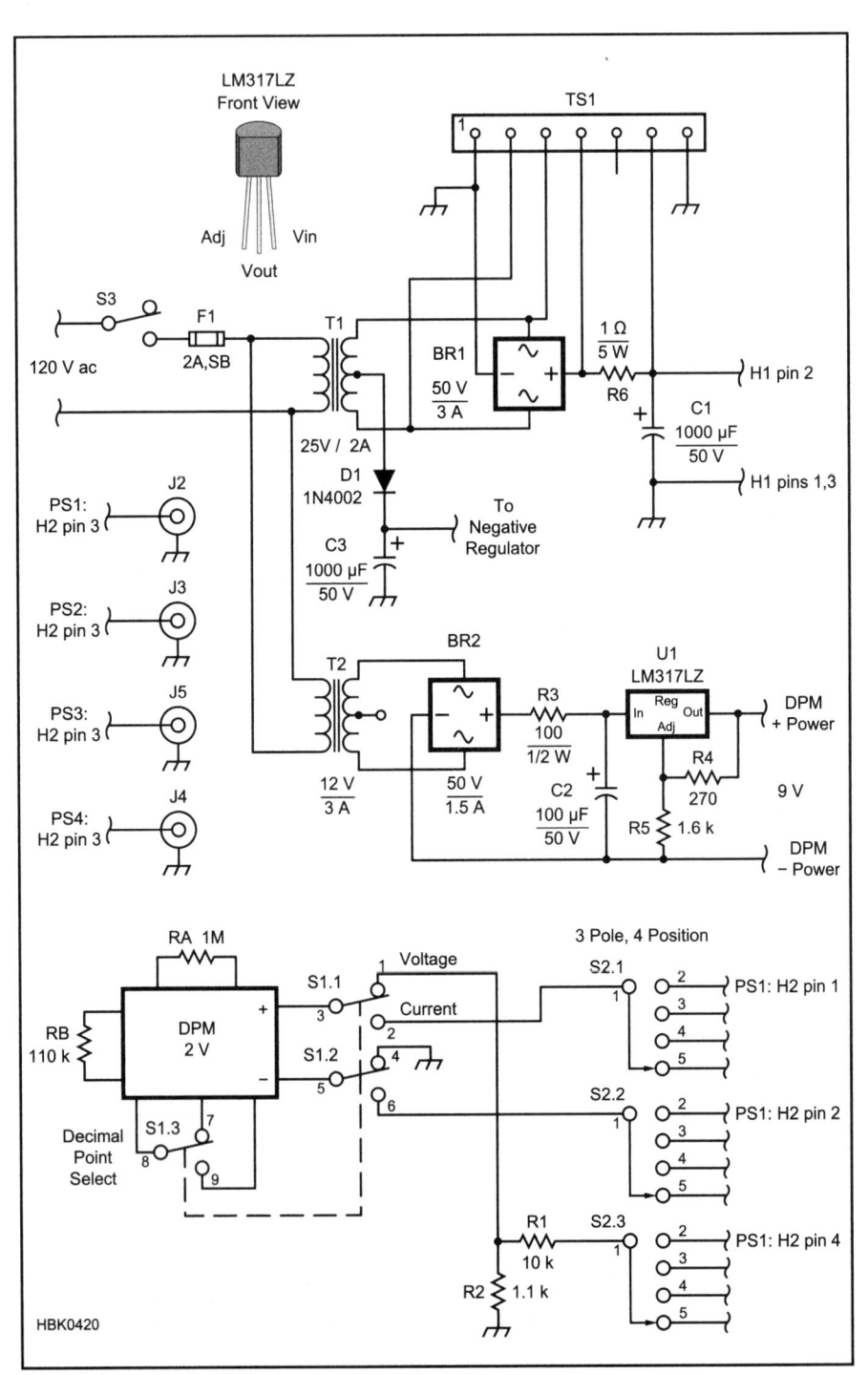

Figure 7.58 — Rectifier and metering schematic. The panel meter is switched between the four modules with a rotary switch (S2) and between voltage and current with a 3PDT toggle (S1). A separate rectifier provides power for the negative supply and a separate three-terminal regulator circuit provides power to the DPM. A full parts list is included with this book's downloadable supplemental content.

PC boards are available from FAR Circuits (www.farcircuits.net), a company that provides a lot of boards for ham-related projects. A caution regarding the circuit boards is in order — the boards do not have plated through holes so you will have to be sure that you solder the through-hole components on *both* sides of the board.

Artwork for the PC board layout, Gerber files, and a drill file are available with this book's downloadable supplemental content. The schematic capture software *DipTrace* was used in the development of this project. Source files for the schematic and PCB files are also included with this book's downloadable supplemental content.

7.16.2 12 V, 15 A Linear Power Supply

This power supply is a linear 12 V, 15 A design by Ed Oscarson, WA1TWX. It is suitable for typical mobile radios and offers adjustable output voltage and current limiting. Supply regulation is excellent, typically exhibiting a change of less than 20 mV from no load to 15 A. This basic design, with heftier components and additional pass transistors, can deliver over 30 A — enough to supply a 100 W class transceiver. (All numbered notes, additional circuit design information, a discussion of how to change the supply voltage and/or current ratings, construction and testing notes, a PCB template and a complete parts list are included with this book's downloadable supplemental content.)

CIRCUIT DESCRIPTION

Figure 7.59 is the supply's schematic. The ac line input is fused by F1, switched on and off by S1 and filtered by FL1. F1 and S1 are rated at about ¼ of the output current requirement (for 15 A output, use a 4 or 5 A slow-blow fuse or a similarly rated circuit breaker). FL1 prevents any RF from the secondary or load from coupling into the power line and prevents RF on the power line from disturbing supply operation. If your ac power line is clean, and you experience no RF problems, you can eliminate FL1, but it's inexpensive insurance.

When discharged, filter capacitor C1 looks like a short circuit across the output of rectifier U2 when ac power is applied. That usually subjects the rectifier and capacitor to a large inrush current, which can damage them. Fortunately a simple and inexpensive means of inrush-current limiting is available. Keystone Carbon Company (and others) produce a line of inrush-current limiters (thermistors) for this purpose. The device (RT1) is placed in series with one of the transformer primary leads. RT1 has a current rating of 6 A[1], and a cold resistance of 5 Ω. When it's hot, RT1's resistance drops to 0.11 Ω. Such a low resistance has a negligible effect on supply operation. Thermistors run *hot* so they must be mounted in free air, and away from anything that can be damaged by heat.[2,3]

The largest and most important part in the power supply is the transformer (T1). If purchased new, it can also be the most costly. Fortunately, a number of surplus dealers offer power transformers that can be used in this supply.

T1 produces 17 V ac RMS at 20 A; the center tap is not used. Bridge rectifier U2 provides full-wave rectification. Full-wave rectification reduces the ripple component of current that flows in the filter capacitor, resulting in less power dissipation in the capacitor's internal resistance. U2's voltage rating should be at least 50 V, and its current rating about 25% higher than the normal load requirement; a 2 A bridge rectifier will do. U2 is secured to the chassis or a heat sink because it dissipates heat.

C1 is a computer-grade electrolytic. Any capacitor value from 15,000 to 30,000 μF will suffice. This version uses a 19,000 μF, 40 V capacitor. The capacitor's voltage rating should be at least 50% higher than the expected no-load rectified dc voltage. In this supply, that voltage is 25 V, and a 40 V capacitor provides enough margin,

R5, a 75 Ω, 20 W bleeder resistor, is connected across C1's terminals to discharge the supply when no load is attached or one is removed, Any resistance value from 50 Ω to 200 Ω is fine; adjust the resistor's wattage rating appropriately.

At the terminals of C1, we have a dc voltage, but it varies widely with the load applied. When keying a CW transmitter or switching a rig from receive to full output, 5 V swings can result. The dc voltage also has an ac ripple component of up to 1.5 V under full load. Adding a solid-state regulator (U1) provides a stable output voltage even with a varying input and load.

VOLTAGE REGULATOR IC AND PASS TRANSISTORS

The LM723 used at U1 has a built-in voltage reference and sense amplifier, and a 150 mA drive output for a pass-transistor array. U1's voltage reference provides a stable point of comparison for the internal regulator circuitry. In this supply, it's connected to the non-inverting input of the voltage-sense op amp. The reference is set internally to 7.15 V, but the absolute value is not critical because an output-voltage adjustment (R12) is provided. What is important is that the voltage is stable, with a specified variation of 0.05% per 1000 hours of operation. This is more than adequate for the supply.

[1] See the full article included with this book's downloadable supplemental content for a list of numbered notes.

For the regulator to work properly, its ground reference must be at the same point as the output ground terminal. The best way to ensure this is to use the output GROUND terminal (J4) as a single-point ground for all of the supply grounds. Run wires to J4 from each component requiring a ground connection. Figure 7.59 attempts to show this graphically through the use of parallel connections to a single circuit node.

The output pass transistor array consists of a TIP112 Darlington-pair transistor (Q5) driving three 2N3055 power transistors (Q1-Q3). This two-stage design is less efficient than connecting the power transistors directly to the LM723, but Q5 can provide considerably more base current to the 2N3055s than the 150 mA maximum rating of the LM723. You can place additional 2N3055s in parallel to increase the output current capacity of the supply.

This design is not fussy about the pass transistors or the Darlington transistor used. Just ensure all of these devices have voltage ratings of at least 40 V. Q5 must have a 5 A (or greater) collector-current rating and a beta of over 100. The pass transistors should be rated for collector currents of 10 A or more, and have a beta of at least 10.[5]

Resistors R17, R18 and R19 prevent leakage current through the collector-base junction from turning on the transistor by diverting it around the base-emitter junction. When the pass transistors are hot, at the V_{CE} encountered in this design, the leakage current can be as high as 3 mA. The resulting drop across the 33 Ω resistors is 0.1 V — safely below the turn-on value for V_{BE}.

When unmatched transistors are simply connected in parallel they usually don't equally share the current.[6] By placing a low-value resistor in each transistor's emitter lead (emitter-ballasting resistors, R1-R3), equal current sharing is ensured. When a transistor with a lower voltage drop tries to pass more current, the emitter resistor's voltage drop increases, allowing the other transistors to provide more current. Because the voltage-sense point is on the load side of the resistors, the transistors are forced to dynamically share the load current.

With a 5 A emitter current, 0.25 V develops across each 0.05 Ω resistor, producing 1.25 W of heat. Ideally, a resistor's power rating should be at least twice the power it's called upon to dissipate. To help the resistors dissipate the heat, mount them on a heat sink, or secure them to a metal chassis. You can use any resistor with a value between 0.065 and 0.1 Ω, but remember that the power dissipated is higher with higher-value resistors (10 W resistors are used here).

At the high output currents provided by this supply, the pass transistors dissipate considerable power. With a current of 5 A through each

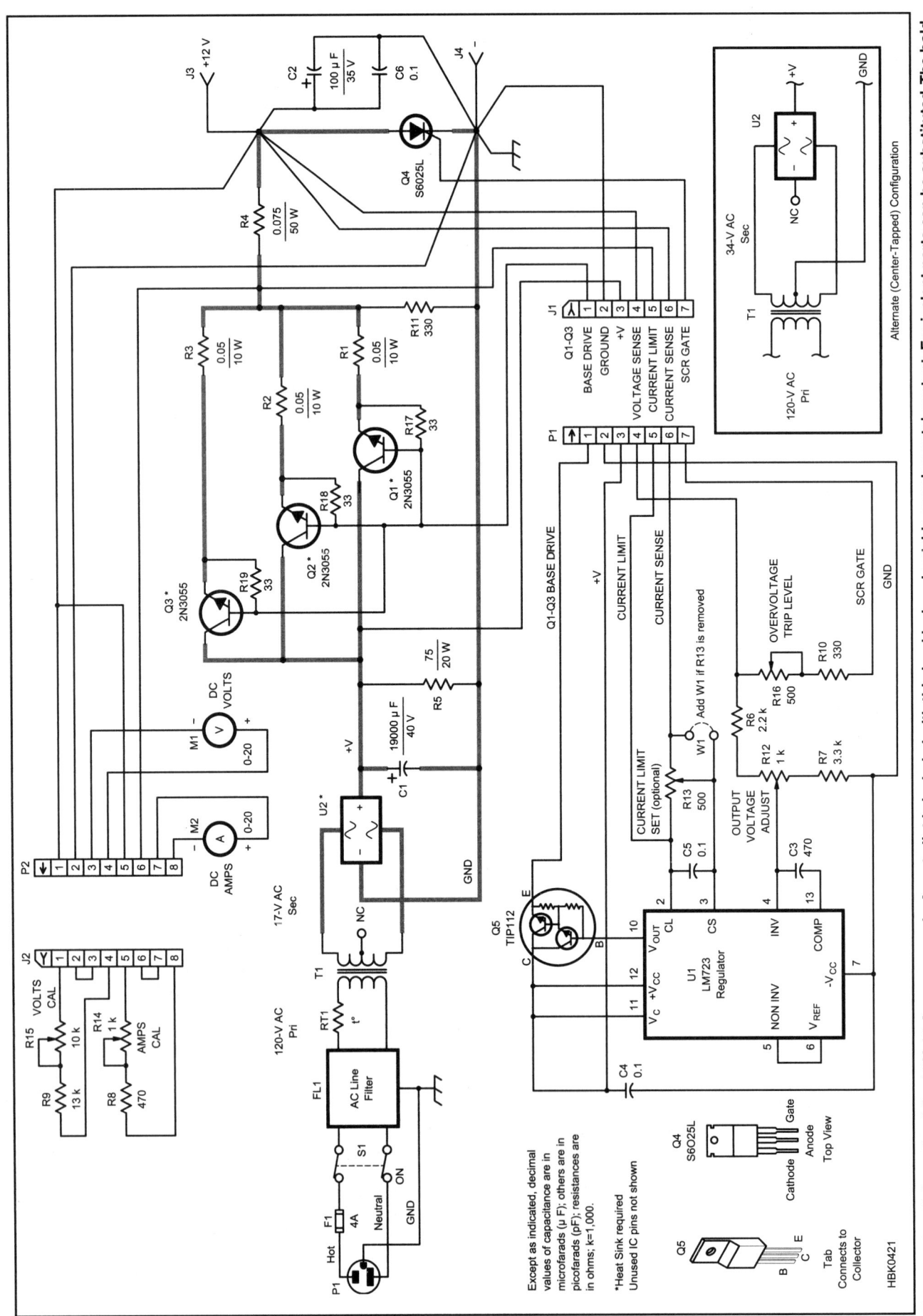

Figure 7.59 — Schematic of the 12 V, 15 A power supply. A parts list is included with this book's downloadable supplemental content. Equivalent parts can be substituted. The bold lines indicate high-current paths that should use heavy-gauge (#10 or #12 AWG) wire. This schematic graphically shows wiring to a single-point ground; see text. The majority of the parts used in this supply are available as surplus components.

7.52   Chapter 7

transistor-and assuming a 9 V drop across the transistor — each device dissipates 45 W. Because the 2N3055's rating is 115 W when used with a properly sized heat sink, this dissipation level shouldn't present a problem. If the supply is to be used for continuous-duty operation, increase the size of the heat sink and mount it with the fins oriented vertically to assist in air circulation.

The output-voltage sense is connected through a resistive divider to the negative input of U1. U1 uses the difference between its negative and positive inputs to control the pass transistors that in turn provide the output current. C3, a compensation capacitor, is connected between this input and a dedicated compensation pin to prevent oscillation. The output voltage is adjusted by potentiometer R12 and two fixed-value resistors, R6 and R7.[7] The voltage-sense input is connected to the supply's positive output terminal, J3.

Current sensing is done through R4, a 0.075 Ω, 50 W resistor connected between the emitter-ballasting resistors and J3. R4's power dissipation is much higher than that of R1, R2 or R3 because it sees the total output current. At 15 A, R4 dissipates 17 W. At 20 A, the dissipated power increases to 30 W.

U1 provides current limiting via two sense inputs connected across R4. Limiting takes place when the voltage across the sense inputs is greater than 0.65 V.[8] For a 15 A maximum output-current limit, this requires a 0.043 Ω resistor. By using a larger-value sense resistor and a potentiometer, you can vary the current limit. Connecting potentiometer R13 across R4 provides a current-limiting range from full limit voltage (8.7 A limit) to no limit voltage. This allows the current limit to be fine-tuned, if needed, and also permits readily available resistor values (such as the author's 0.075 Ω resistors) to be used. A current limit of 20 A is at the top end of the ammeter scale.

R20 maintains a small load of 35-40 mA depending on power supply output voltage. This reduces the effect of leakage current in the pass transistors and keeps the regulator's feedback action active, even if no external load is connected.

METERING

Voltmeter M1 is a surplus meter. R8 and potentiometer R15 provide for voltmeter calibration. If the correct fixed-value resistor is available, R15 can be omitted. The combined value of the resistor and potentiometer is determined by the full-scale current requirement of the meter used.[9]

Ammeter M2 is actually a voltmeter (also surplus) that measures the potential across R4. The positive side of M2 connects to the high side of R4. R8 and potentiometer R14 connect between the positive output terminal (J3) and the negative side of M2 to provide calibration adjustment. The values of R8 and R14 are determined by the coil-current requirements of the meter used. (Digital panel meters or a dedicated DMM can be used instead of separate analog meters.)

OUTPUT WIRING AND CROWBAR CIRCUIT

The supply output is connected to the outside world by two heavy-duty banana jacks, J3 and J4. C2, a 100 µF capacitor, is soldered directly across the terminals to prevent low-frequency oscillation. C6, a 0.1 µF capacitor, is included to shunt RF energy to ground. Heavy-gauge wire must be used for the connections between the pass transistors and J3 and between chassis ground and J4. The voltage-sense wire must connect directly to J3 and U2's ground pin must connect directly to J4 (see Figure 7.59). This provides the best output voltage regulation.

An over-voltage crowbar circuit prevents the output voltage from exceeding a preset limit. If that limit is exceeded, the output is shunted to ground until power is removed. If the current-limiting circuitry in the supply is working properly, the supply current-limits to the preset value. If the current limiting is not functioning, the crowbar causes the ac-line fuse to blow. Therefore, it's important to use the correct fuse size: 4 to 5 A for a 15 A supply.

The crowbar circuit is a simple design based on an SCR's ability to latch and conduct until the voltage source is removed. The SCR (Q4) is connected across output terminals J3 and J4. (The SCR can also be connected directly across the filter capacitor, C1, for additional protection.) R10 and potentiometer R16 in series with the Q4's gate provide a means of adjusting the trip voltage. The prototype crowbar is set to conduct at 15 V. The S6025L SCR is rated at 25 A and should be mounted on a metal chassis or heat sink. (Note: Some SCRs are isolated from their mounting tabs, others are not. The S6025L and the 65-ampere S4065J are isolated types. If the SCR you use is not isolated, use a mica washer or thermal pad to insulate it from the chassis or heat sink.)

The bold lines in Figure 7.59 indicate high-current paths that should use heavy-gauge (#10 or #12 AWG) wire. Traces that are connected to the output terminals in the schematic by individual lines should be connected directly to the terminals by individual wires. This establishes a 4-wire measurement, where the heavy wires carry the current (and have voltage drops) and the sense wires carry almost no current and therefore voltage errors are not caused by voltage drops in the wiring. If desired, the sense wire can be carried out to the load, but that may introduce noise into the sense feedback circuit, so use caution if that is done.

7.16.3 13.8 V, 5 A Linear Power Supply

This power supply was designed by Ben Spencer, G4YNM, provides 13.8 V dc at 5 A, suitable for many low-power transceivers and accessories. It features time-dependent current limiting and short-circuit protection, thermal overload protection within the safe operating area of the regulator IC, and overvoltage protection for the equipment it powers. The prototype supply powers a 25 W transmitter that continually draws 4.5 A.

Construction, testing and calibration are straightforward, requiring no special skills or equipment. Many of the components can be found in junk boxes, or purchased at hamfests or from mail-order suppliers.

CIRCUIT DESCRIPTION

Figure 7.60 is the power supply schematic. Incoming ac line current is filtered by a chassis-mounted line filter (FL1) and, after passing through the fuse (F1), is routed S1 to T1.

U1 rectifies, and C1 filters, the ac output of T1. U2 is an LM338K voltage regulator. This IC features a current-limited continuous output of 5 A, with a guaranteed peak output of 7 A. It also has on-chip thermal and safe-operating-area protection for itself. U2's output voltage is set by two resistors (R2 and R3) and a trimmer potentiometer (R8), which allows for adjustment over a small range. U2's input and output are bypassed by C2, C3, and C4. D1 and D2 protect U2 against these capacitors discharging through it.

Overvoltage protection is provided by an SCR, Q1, across the regulator input. Normally, Q1 presents an open circuit, but under fault conditions, it's triggered and short-circuits the unregulated dc input to ground. This discharges C1 through F2 which is rated at 10 A in order for C1 to quickly discharge below 12 V, avoiding damage to connected equipment.

U3, an overvoltage-protection IC, continuously monitors the output voltage. When the output voltage rises above a predetermined level, U3 starts charging C5. If the overvoltage duration is sufficiently long, U3 triggers Q1. This built-in delay (about 1 ms) allows short transient noise spikes on the output voltage to be safely ignored while still triggering the SCR if a true fault occurs. The monitored voltage is set by R5 and R6 and trimmer potentiometer R9, which allows for adjustment over a limited range.

D3 protects the supply from reverse-polarity discharge from connected equipment. The presence of output voltage is indicated by an LED, DS1. R7 is a current limiting resistor for DS1.

CONSTRUCTION

How you construct your supply depends

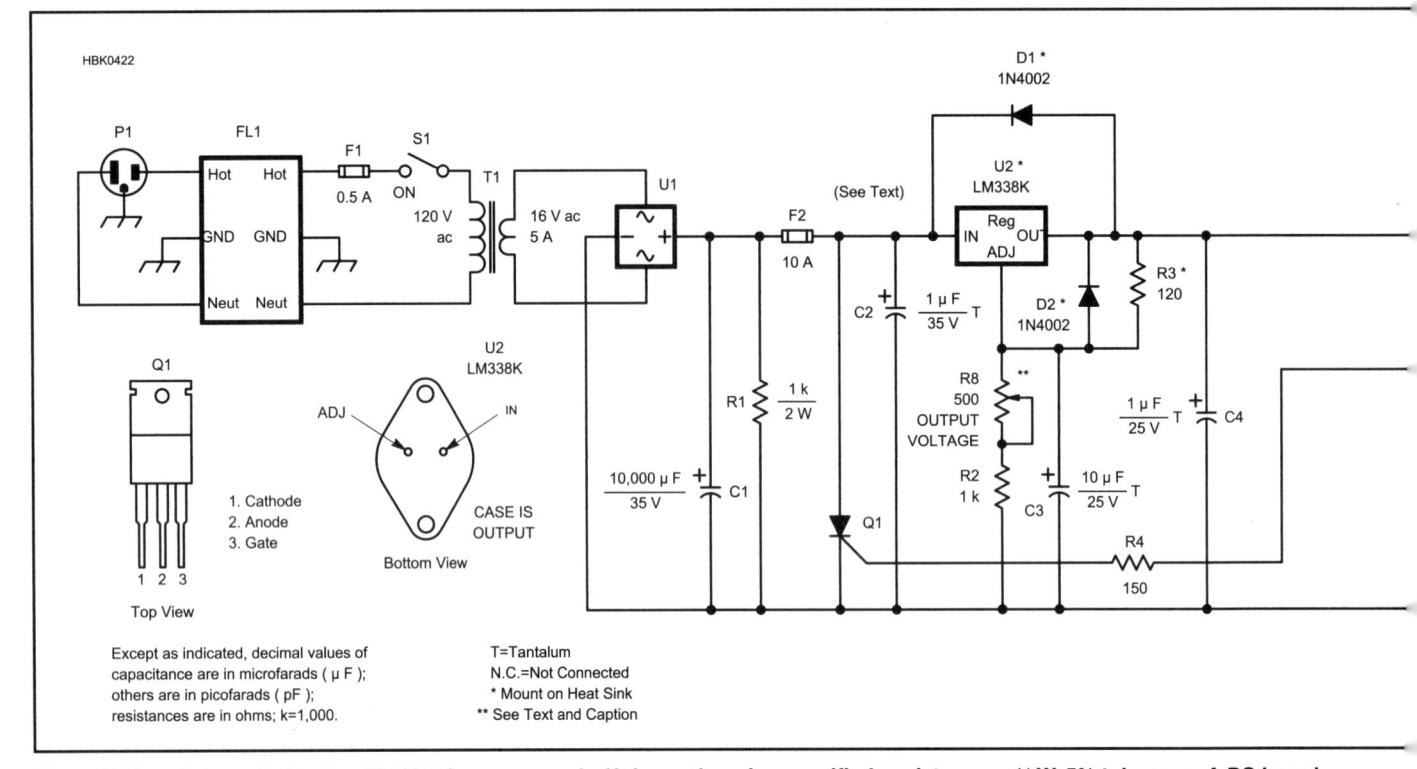

Figure 7.60 — Schematic for the 13.8 V, 5 A power supply. Unless otherwise specified, resistors are ¼ W, 5% tolerance. A PC board and U3 are available from FAR Circuits (www.farcircuits.net). Early versions of the circuit board from FAR mislabel U1 vs Q1. Check the board traces to be sure the parts are installed correctly. The PC board has mounting holes and pads to allow for handling different trimmer-potentiometer footprints. A PC board template is included with this book's downloadable supplemental content. The author may be contacted at scskits@charter.net for assistance in obtaining parts and printed-circuit boards.

C1 — 10,000 µF, 35 V electrolytic.
C2, C4 — 1 µF, 35 V tantalum.
C3 — 10 µF, 35 V tantalum.
C5 — 0.1 µF, 25 V ceramic disc.
D1-D3 — 1N4002.
DS1 — Red LED.
F1 — Slow-blow 0.5 A fuse.
F2 — Fast-acting 10 A fuses; three required (see text).
FL1— Ac-line filter.

Q1 — BT152 400 V, 25 A SCR in TO-220A package (NTE5554)
R8 — 500 Ω, single-turn trimmer potentiometer.
R9 — 500 Ω or 1 kΩ, single-turn trimmer potentiometer.
S1 — SPST panel-mount switch.
T1 — 120 V primary, 16- to 20 V, 5 A secondary.
U1 — 100-PIV, 6 A bridge rectifier.

U2 — LM338K 5 A adjustable power regulator in a TO-3 package.
U3 — MC3423P1 overvoltage protection IC.
Misc: two panel-mount fuse holders; line cord; heat sinks for TO-3 case transistors; TO-3 mounting kit and heat-sink grease; black and red binding posts; chassis or cabinet; PC board; hardware, rubber hoods, heat-shrink tubing or electrical tape for F1 and FL1, hook-up wire.

on the size of the components and enclosure you use. General physical layout is not important, although there are a couple of areas that require some attention. In the unit shown in **Figure 7.61**, FL1, the fuse holders, S1, the heat sink, DS1 and the binding posts are mounted on the front and rear enclosure panels. T1 and the PC board are secured to the enclosure's bottom plate. C1's mounting clamp is attached to the rear panel. Bleeder resistor R1 is connected directly across C1's terminals. D3 is soldered directly across the output binding posts.

U2, D1, D2 and R3 are all mounted directly on the heat sink with the transistor pins and solder lugs acting as a terminal strip. It's important to keep R3 attached as closely as possible to U2's terminals to prevent instability. Use a TO-3 mounting kit and heat-conductive grease or thermal pad to electrically isolate U2 from the heat sink.

Mount U2, C1, and the PC board close to each other and keep the wire runs between these components as short as possible. Excessively long wire runs may lead to unpredictable behavior.

Cover all ac-input wiring (use insulated wire and heat-shrink tubing) to prevent electrical shock and route the ac wiring away from the dc wiring. Mount the heat sink on the enclosure with fins oriented vertically. Louvers or ventilation holes in the cabinet will help cool internal components.

TEST AND CALIBRATION

An accurate multimeter covering ranges of 30 V dc and 10 A dc is required. A variable resistive load with a power rating of 100 W is also needed; this can he made using a heat-sink-mounted 2N3055 power transistor and a couple of components as shown in the next project.

First, set R8 (OUTPUT VOLTAGE) fully clockwise and R9 (OVERVOLTAGE) fully counterclockwise. Insert a fuse in the dc line at F2. Connect the ac line, turn on S1 and check that DS1 lights. Measure the output voltage: it should be about 12 V. Adjust R8 counterclockwise until you obtain 14.2 V output; this sets the trip voltage. (Note that CCW adjustment *increases* voltage.)

While monitoring the output voltage, gradually adjust R9 clockwise until the voltage suddenly falls to zero. This indicates that the SCR has triggered and blown F2. Disconnect the ac line cord from the wall socket. *Don't make any adjustment to R9!* Instead, adjust R8 fully clockwise.

With the ac line cord removed, check that F2 is open. Replace F2 with a new fuse (now you know why two of the three fuses are called for). Reconnect the ac line cord, and while continually monitoring the output voltage, gradually adjust R8 until Q1 again triggers at 14.2 V, blowing F2. If you find the adjustment of R9 to be too sensitive, use a 500 Ω potentiometer in its place and reduce the value of R5 (if necessary) to provide the required adjustment range.

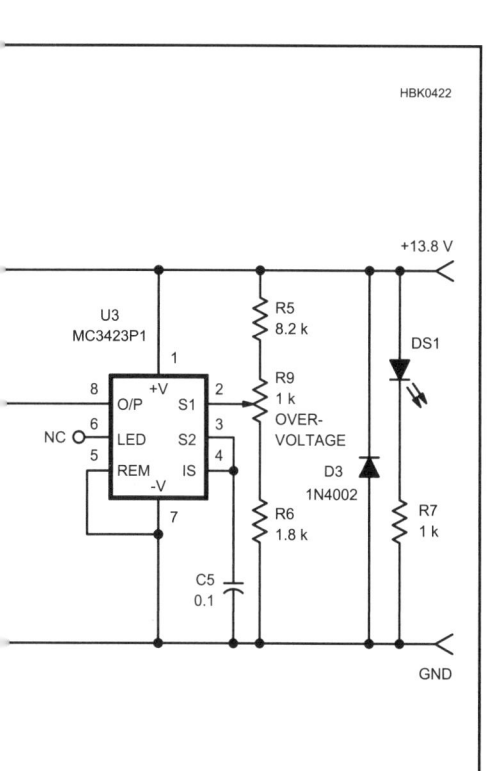

Again disconnect the line cord from the wall socket, set R8 fully clockwise, replace F2 (there's the third fuse!) and reset R8 for 13.8 V. This completes the voltage calibration and overvoltage protection tests. The power supply is now set to 13.8 V output, with the overvoltage protection set for 14.2 V.

Adjust R2 of the variable resistive load in Figure 7.62 to maximum resistance (minimum load current) and connect it to the power supply output in series with the ammeter. Turn on the power supply and gradually adjust R2 until a current of 5 A flows. Decrease the resistance further and check that the current limits between 5.5 A and 0.5 A.

Finally, be thoroughly unpleasant and apply a short circuit via the ammeter. Check that the current-limiting feature operates correctly. The prototype limited at approximately 3.5 A. Disconnect the ac line cord and test equipment, close up the case and your power supply is ready for service.

7.16.4 Adjustable Resistive Load

Figure 7.62 shows the schematic of an adjustable resistive load that can be used to test and adjust power supplies at currents up to 10 A if the 2N3055 transistor is mounted on an adequate heat sink. R1 and R2 vary the base bias to control the collector current of Q1. For extended use, be sure to use a large heat sink with adequate ventilation. Use heavy wire through the current meter to the collector and from the emitter of Q1.

7.16.5 Inverting DC-DC Converter

It's often the case that you need +V and –V when all you have is +V. For example, you need +12 V and –12 V, but all that's available is +12 V. It would be really handy to have a "black box" that would give you –V out when you put +V in, and work over a range of voltages without adjustment. This project by Jim Stewart, which originally appeared in the January 2013 issue of *Nuts and Volts Magazine* (**www.nutsvolts.com**), fills that need by using a switchmode voltage mirror to supply more than 100 mA without a significant drop in voltage.

The following text summarizes how the circuit works. A PDF version of the complete article is included with this book's downloadable supplemental content. It contains more details about the circuit's design, plus construction and testing information. A PCB and parts kit is available from the *Nuts and*

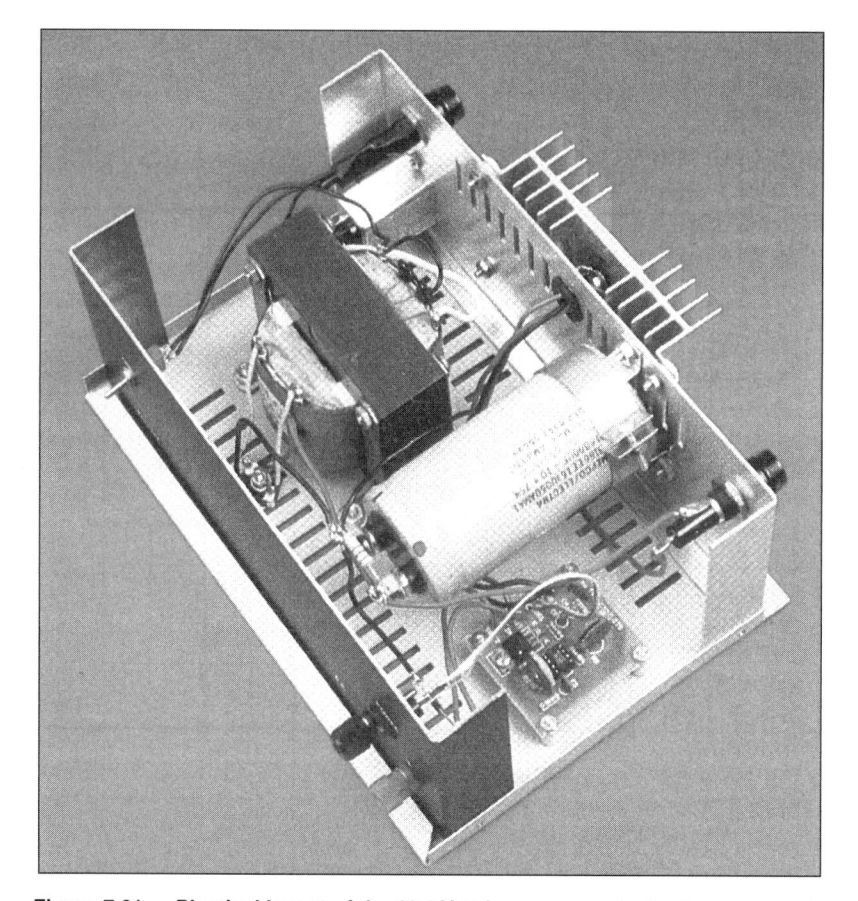

Figure 7.61 — Physical layout of the 13.8 V, 5 A power supply. On the rear panel, left, are the ac-line filter and F1. The regulator's heat sink is at the middle of the panel and F2 is to the right. At the bottom of the enclosure, in front of T1, is the diode bridge rectifier. Because C1 is too tall to mount vertically within the Hammond #1426O cabinet, its mounting clamp is secured to the inside rear panel. Immediately to the right of C1 is the PC board. On the front panel are the on/off switch, LED power-on indicator and output-voltage binding posts.

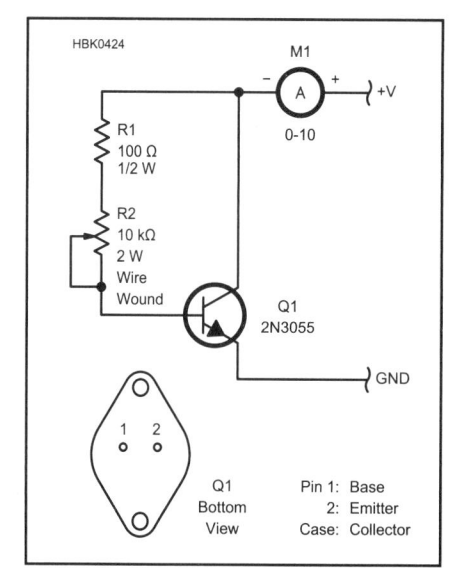

Figure 7.62 — An active resistive load to use in testing power supplies up to 10 A with adequate heat sinking. Adjustment of R2 is sensitive.
M1 — Multimeter or ammeter capable of measuring 10 A.
Q1 — 2N3055; mount on heat sink.

Power Sources 7.55

Volts online store, as well. An ExpressPCB file (PV2NV.PCB) is available for download at **www.nutsvolts.com/index.php?/magazine/article/january2013_Stewart**.

CIRCUIT DESIGN

The circuit in **Figure 7.63** is a buck-boost dc-dc converter as described earlier in this chapter. This particular design has five important parameters:
- Input voltage: V_{IN}
- Output voltage: V_{OUT}
- Load resistance: R_{LOAD}
- Oscillation frequency: f
- Inductance value: L

The parameters are related to each other by $f \times L < (V_{IN} / V_{OUT})^2 \times (R_{LOAD} / 8)$. For $V_{IN} = V_{OUT}$, the equation simplifies to $f \times L < (R_{LOAD} / 8)$. (See the complete article included with this book's downloadable supplemental content for the derivation of these equations.)

Figure 7.63 shows the schematic of the circuit. A square wave oscillator (U2) drives a MOSFET (Q2) that, in turn, drives a PNP switching transistor (Q3). The oscillator is enabled/disabled by the output of the comparator (U1) with inputs that are a set point voltage (V_S on the comparator's + input) and a feedback voltage (V_F at the comparator's – input). (Comparators are described in the **Analog Fundamentals** chapter.) The frequency of the oscillator is $f = 1 / 2.2 (R7 \times C3)$.

When the output voltage, V_{OUT}, is the correct value, V_S exceeds V_F by a few µV and the oscillator is disabled by Q1 so that the PNP switch is off. When V_S is less than V_F, the oscillator is enabled and the PNP transistor switches on and off. V_S is half the input voltage $V_S = V_{IN}/2$ as set by the R3-R4 voltage divider.

V_F is set by the R1-R2 divider to equal $V_{IN}/2$ when the output voltage $V_{OUT} = -V_{IN}$. D2 is a commutating diode that blocks +V from the output while charging the inductor. It then provides a current path for the discharging inductor to transfer charge to the output capacitor.

The switching action continues until the voltage on the capacitor equals $-V_{IN}$. At that point, the comparator disables the oscillator and Q3 stays OFF. When voltage across the capacitor drops, the comparator enables the oscillator and the inductor is pumped up again.

Since there is a single input voltage, each op-amp uses a resistor divider to "split the rail" to create a signal ground. That allows the negative input to sense positive and negative voltages with respect to the positive input. C2 and C4 bypass the signal grounds to the supply voltage ground.

C1 and C5 are low-ESR (equivalent series resistance — see the **Electrical Fundamentals** chapter) aluminum electrolytic capacitors. Tantalum capacitors might be a bit better, but are more expensive. ESR determines how much power the capacitor can safely dissipate. $P_{DISS} = I^2_{RC} \times ESR$, where I_{RC} is the ac ripple current in the capacitor. The capacitors chosen are rated for a maximum ripple current of 840 mA.

D1 and D2 are Schottky diodes that can go from conducting to non-conducting very quickly, allowing a high switching frequency. They also have a low voltage drop when conducting to reduce power loss. D1 limits the output voltage in case the feedback fails.

Q3 is a ZTX550 PNP transistor, chosen because its specifications suit this application well:
- Maximum power dissipation, P_{MAX} = 1 W @ 25 °C
- Maximum continuous collector current, I_C = 1 A
- Maximum collector-base voltage, V_{CBO} = 60 V
- Maximum saturation voltage, V_{CE} = 0.25 V @ I_C = 150 mA
- Transition frequency, f_T = 150 MHz minimum
- Package: E-Line (slightly smaller than TO-92)

For this design, the chosen values are L = 220 µH, f = 45 kHz, and R_{LOAD} = 100 Ω. Verifying that $f \times L$ is less than $R_{LOAD} / 8$, $f \times L = (45 \times 10^3) \times (220 \times 10^{-6}) = 9900 \times 10^{-3} = 9.9$ Ω and $R_{LOAD} / 8 = 100/8 = 12.5$ Ω which is less than $R_{LOAD} / 8 = 12.5$. Higher

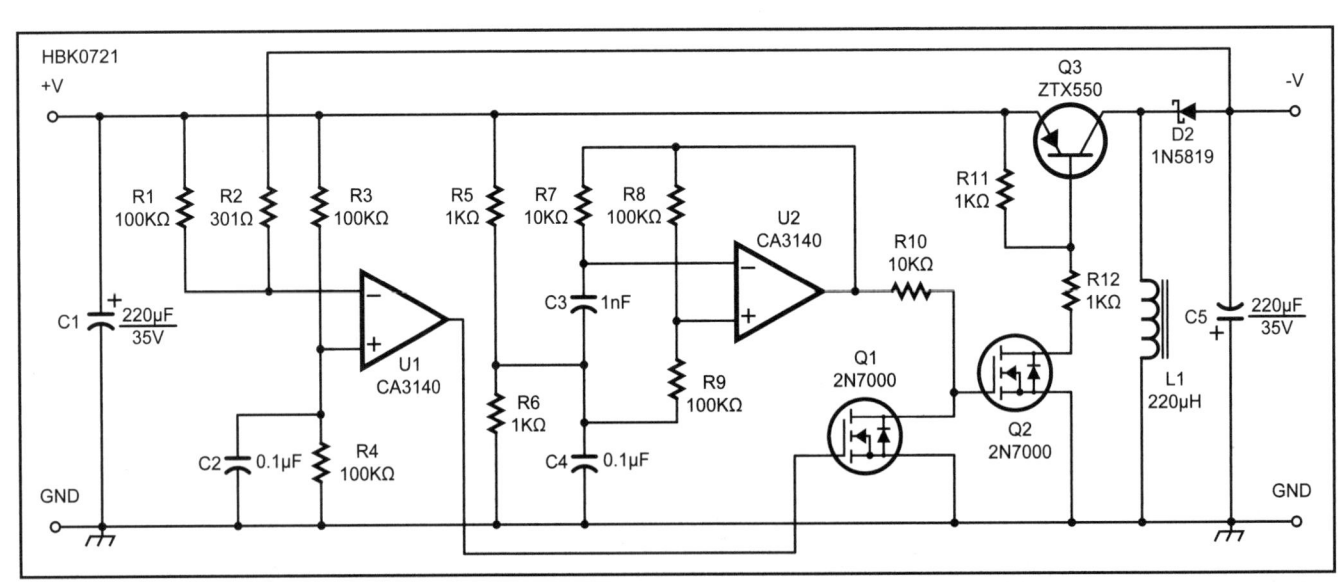

Figure 7.63 — A voltage mirror dc-dc power converter based on a buck-boost converter. The negative output —V is equal in magnitude to the positive input voltage +V at an output current up to approximately 100 mA

C1 — 220 µF, 35 V (Digi-Key part #493-1578-ND or equiv).
C2 — 0.1 µF, 50 V, ceramic.
C3 — 1 nF film, 5% (Digi-Key part #399-5871-ND or equiv).
C4 — 0.1 µF, 50 V, ceramic.
C5 — 220 µF, 35 V (Digi-Key part #493-1578-ND or equiv).
D1 — Not required, do not install.
D2 — Schottky, 1 A, 1N5819 or equiv.
L1 — 220 µH (Digi-Key part #811-1316-ND or equiv).
Q1, Q2 — 2N7000.
Q3 — ZTX550 PNP.
R1, R3, R4, R8, R9 — 100 kΩ, ¼ W, 1%.
R2 — 301 kΩ, ¼ W, 1%.
R5, R6, R11, R12 — 1 kΩ, ¼ W, 1%.
R7, R10 — 10 kΩ, ¼ W, 1%.
U1, U2 — CA3140.
Terminal Blocks (optional) — Two-position, 5 mm spacing (Jameco part #2094485 or equiv).

values of R_{LOAD} (lower output current) also satisfy the equation. Increasing the value of L or f will require that the circuit be tested to verify that it works.

7.16.6 High-Voltage Power Supply

The downloadable supplemental content includes "A Deluxe High Voltage Supply" by Jim Garland, W8ZR, which is discussed here, and "A Small, Lightweight High-Voltage Switch-Mode Power Supply" by Ralph Crumrine, NØKC.

This two-level, high-voltage power supply was designed and built by Dana G. Reed, W1LC. It was designed primarily for use with an RF power amplifier. The supply is rated at a continuous output current of 1.5 A, and will easily handle intermittent peak currents of 2 A. The 12 V control circuitry and the low-tap setting of the plate transformer secondary make it straightforward to adapt the design to homemade tube amplifiers.

The step-start circuit is straightforward and ensures that the rectifier diodes are current-limited when the power supply is first turned on. A 6 kV meter is used to monitor high-voltage output.

Figure 7.64 is a schematic diagram of the bi-level supply. An ideal power supply for a high-power linear amplifier should operate from a 240 V circuit, for best line regulation. A special, hydraulic/magnetic circuit breaker also serves as a disconnect for the plate transformer primary. Don't substitute a standard circuit breaker, switch or fuses for this breaker; fuses won't operate quickly enough to protect the amplifier or power supply in case of an operating abnormality. The 100 kΩ, 3 W bleeder resistors are of stable metal-oxide film design. These resistors are wired across each of the 14 capacitors to equalize voltage drops in the series-connected bank. This choice of bleeder resistor value provides a lighter load (less than 25 W total under high-tap output) and benefits mainly the capacitor-bank filter by yielding much less heat as a result. A reasonable, but longer bleed-down time to fully discharge the capacitors results — about nine minutes after power is removed. A small fan is included to remove any excess heat from the power supply cabinet during operation.

POWER SUPPLY CONSTRUCTION

The power supply can be built in a 23½ × 10¾ × 16-inch cabinet. The plate transformer is quite heavy, so use ⅛-inch aluminum for the cabinet bottom and reinforce it with aluminum angle for extra strength and stability. The capacitor bank will be sized for the specific capacitors used. This project employed ⅜-inch thick polycarbonate for reasonable mechanical stability and excellent high-voltage isolation. The full-wave bridge consists of four commercial diode block assemblies.

POWER SUPPLY OPERATION

When the front-panel breaker is turned on, a single 50 Ω, 100 W power resistor limits primary inrush current to a conservative value as the capacitor bank charges. After approximately two seconds, step-start relay K1 actuates, shorting the 50 Ω resistor and allowing

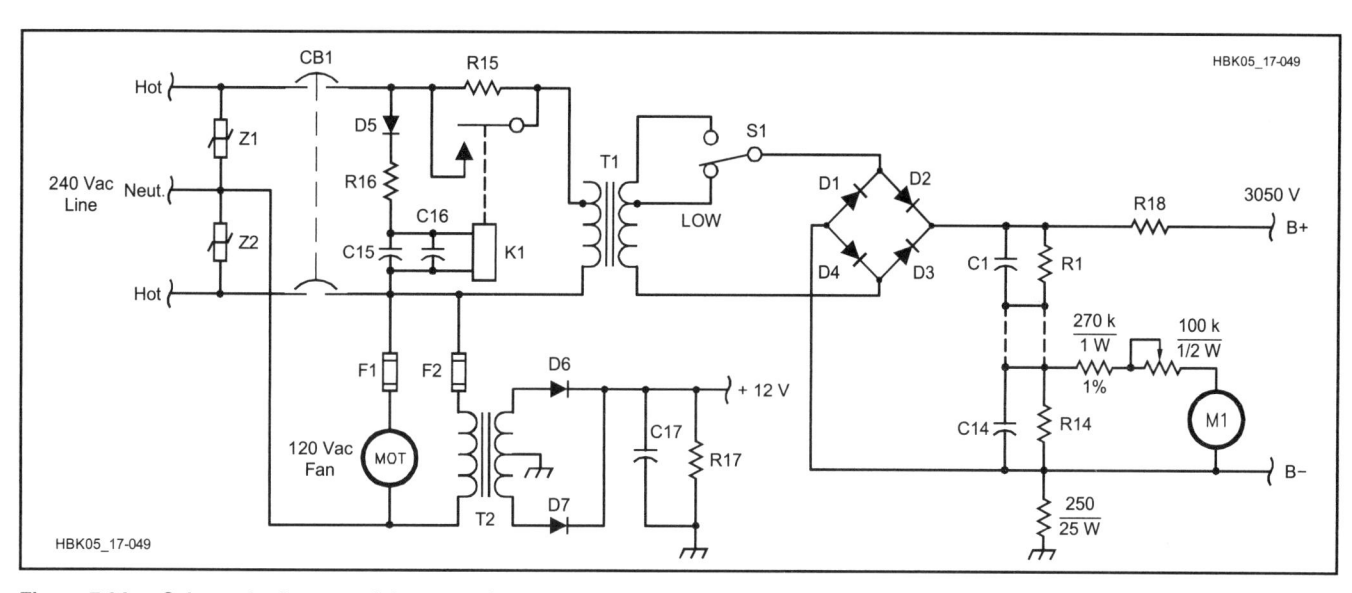

Figure 7.64 — Schematic diagram of the 3050 V/5400 V high-voltage power supply.

C1-C14 — 800 μF, 450 V electrolytic.
C15, C16 — 4700 μF, 50 V electrolytic.
C17 — 1000 μF, 50 V electrolytic.
CB1 — 20 A hydraulic/magnetic circuit breaker (TE Connectivity/Potter & Brumfield W68-X2Q12-20 or equiv). 40 A version required for commercial applications/ service (TE Connectivity/Potter & Brumfield W92-X112-40).
D1-D4 — String of 1000 PIV, 6 A diodes (6A10 or equiv).
D5 — 1000 PIV, 3 A, 1N5408 or equiv.
D6, D7 — 200 PIV, 3 A, 1N5402 or equiv.
F1, F2 — 0.5 A, 250 V (Littelfuse 313 Series, 3AG glass body or equiv).
K1 — DPDT power relay, 24 V dc coil; both poles of 240 V ac/25 A contacts in parallel (TE Connectivity/Potter & Brumfield PRD-11DYO-24 or equiv).

M1 — High-voltage meter, 6 kV dc full scale. (Important: Use a 1 mA or smaller meter movement to minimize parallel-resistive loading at R14. Also, select series meter-resistor and adjustment-potentiometer values to calibrate your specific meter. Values shown are for a 1 mA meter movement.)
MOT1 — Cooling fan, 119 mm, 120 V ac, 30-60 CFM, (EBM Pabst 4800Z or equiv).
R1-R14 — Bleeder resistor, 100 kΩ, 3 W, metal oxide film.
R15 — 50 Ω, 100 W.
R16 — 3.9 kΩ, 25 W.
R17 — 30 Ω, 25 W.
R18 — 20 Ω, 50 W.
S1 — Ceramic rotary, 2 position tap-select switch (optional). Voltage rating between tap positions should be at least 2.5 kV. Mount switch on insulated or ungrounded material such as a metal plate on standoff insulators, or an insulating plate, and use only a *nonconductive* or otherwise *electrically-isolated* shaft through the front panel for safety.
T1 — High-voltage plate transformer, 220/240 V primary, 2000/3500 V, 1.5 A CCS JK secondary, Hypersil C-core (Hammond Engineering, www.hammfg.com). Primary 220 V tap fed with nominal 240 V ac line voltage to obtain modest increase in specified secondary voltage levels.
T2 — 120 V primary, 18 V CT, 2 A secondary (Mouser 41FJ020).
Z1-Z2 — 130 V MOV.

full line voltage to be applied to the plate transformer. No-load output voltages under low- and high-tap settings as configured and shown in Figure 7.64 are 3050 V and 5400 V, respectively. Full-load levels are somewhat lower, approximately 2800 V and 4900 V. If a tap-select switch is used as described in the schematic parts list, it should only be switched when the supply is off.

7.16.7 Reverse-Polarity Protection Circuits

The following material was collected from various public-domain sources by Terry Fletcher, WAØITP(www.wa0itp.com/revpro. html) and published in the QRP Quarterly, Spring 2012 issue. (www.qrparci.org)

DC power is the standard for most amateur radios and accessories, usually a nominal 12 V (10.5 to 13.8 V). There are many different types of connectors used for dc power — from screw terminals to custom-molded multi-pin designs. This makes it easy to accidentally apply power with reversed polarity and damage equipment. Even a few milliseconds of reversed power can be sufficient to destroy a semiconductor or burn out a narrow PCB trace. This can be a particular problem when using 9 V batteries as it is easy to reverse the snap-on connector when changing or installing a battery.

The following collection of circuits illustrates ways to protect equipment from reverse-polarity dc power. The suitability of the circuits depends on the equipment and power source. All dc power sources, particularly batteries, should be fused or current-limited to mitigate fire hazards and other damage from overheating wires and other conductors.

Figure 7.65 shows several passive circuits that dissipate some power due to the series forward voltage drop of the diodes. At currents above 1 A, the power dissipated can easily exceed 1 W and the maximum junction temperature of the diode can be exceeded without some sort of thermal protection or heat sinking. (The shunt diode circuit in Figure 7.65D does not dissipate power.) **Figure 7.66** shows two methods of using an electromechanical relay that avoid the forward voltage drop of diode-based protection circuits. Which circuit you choose depends on the type of equipment and constraints on power dissipation and voltage drop.

PASSIVE CIRCUITS

Blocking diode (Figure 7.65A) — A series diode is very simple and inexpensive. Its PIV rating should be at least twice the expected applied voltage — 50 V PIV is a good minimum value for automotive and 12 V dc use. Its maximum average forward current rating should be several times the expected

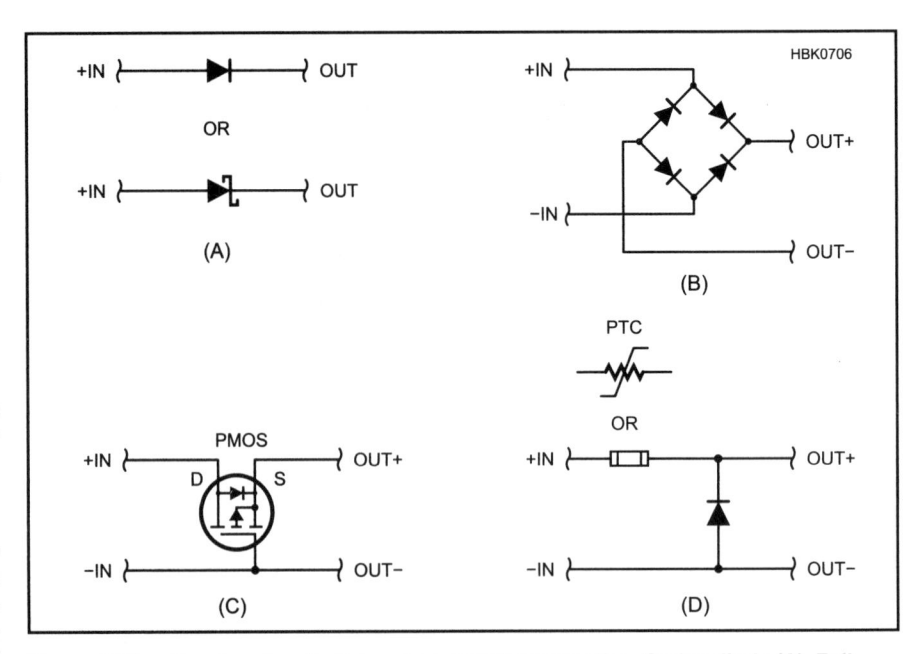

Figure 7.65 — Passive circuits for reverse-polarity protection. Series diode (A). Full-wave rectifier (B). PMOS MOSFET with integral body diode shown as separate component (C). Shunt diode (D). Schottky barrier diodes may be used in all circuits as a substitute for silicon junction rectifiers. See text for circuit comparison.

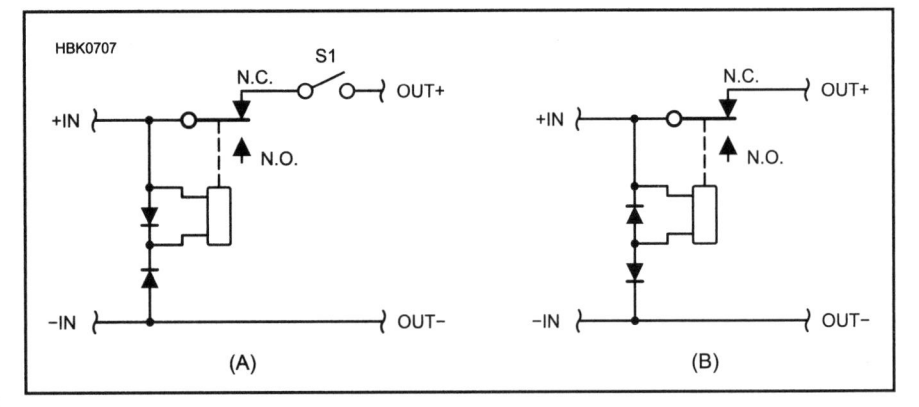

Figure 7.66 — Relay-based circuits for reverse-polarity protection. Normally-closed contacts (A) and normally-open contacts (B). See text for circuit comparison.

maximum steady-state current draw.

Remember that a silicon junction diode's forward voltage drop, V_f, is at least 0.6 V and can approach 1.0 V at high forward current. This can result in significant power dissipation ($P = V_f \times I_f$) and cause the diode's maximum rated junction temperature to be exceeded unless some means of cooling the diode is provided.

The forward voltage drop of the diode will also reduce the voltage available to the equipment being powered. This will raise the minimum allowable power supply voltage for the equipment to operate properly. For example, if a piece of equipment is rated to operate properly at or above 11 V, a series diode with V_f = 0.6 V raises the minimum allowable power supply voltage to 11 + 0.6 = 11.6 V. This may be significant in battery-powered installations.

The Schottky barrier diode shown as an alternate may be a better choice due to its forward voltage drop being lower by several tenths of a volt, reducing power dissipation. A Schottky diode may be used in place of any of the diodes in Figures 7.65 and 7.66. Be sure the reverse current leakage of the Schottky diode is acceptable.

Full-wave bridge rectifier (Figure 7.65B) — The full-wave circuit has the advantage of always supplying voltage with the proper polarity to the equipment being powered. Full-wave rectifiers are also available as integrated packages, making them easy to install. Remember that the forward voltage drop and power dissipation of this circuit will be twice that of the single series diode because two diodes are always in series with supply current.

PMOS P-channel MOSFET (Figure

7.65C) — This circuit uses a P-channel enhancement-mode (PMOS) MOSFET that conducts current with the gate connected as shown. PMOS devices have low on-resistance ($R_{ds(on)}$) and high maximum current ratings. Devices with on-resistance of 0.050 Ω and lower are commonly available. For more information about using PMOS and NMOS devices for polarity protection see Maxim Electronics Application Note 636, "Reverse-Current Circuitry Protection" (**www.maxim-ic.com/app-notes/index.mvp/id/636**). N-channel devices may also be used in the current return or ground lead, but opening the return connection can create other problems inside the equipment and with other devices on the same power circuits.

Shunt diode with fuse (Figure 7.65D) — These configurations use a single diode that acts to blow a fuse (either a fusible-link or positive temperature coefficient PTC resettable device) if reverse polarity voltage is applied. The advantage of this circuit is that no power is dissipated by the diode during normal operation. The diode must be sufficiently rated to handle the high surge current from shorting the power source and have current ratings significantly higher than the fuse current rating.

If the diode fails shorted or in a low-resistance state, it will continue to blow the fuse until replaced. If the diode fails open or high-resistance, it will no longer protect the circuit. If shunt diode protection is used and the fuse opens, check the diode to be sure it has not failed as well.

RELAY-BASED CIRCUITS

Relay-based circuits have the advantage of little to no voltage drop, even at high currents as long as the contact ratings are sufficient. The circuits are more complex than the diode-based circuits in the preceding section but can generally handle more current and are not damaged by reverse polarity voltages. The circuits reset themselves automatically.

Relay with normally-closed contacts (Figure 7.66A) — There is no current drain through the relay coil until reverse-polarity is applied. However, there will be a few milliseconds during which reverse polarity volt-age is applied if no power switch (S1) is used or the power switch is closed. This is generally enough time for damage to occur so this circuit is only recommended if a power switch is used to turn the equipment ON and OFF.

Relay with normally-open contacts (Figure 7.66B) — The relay contacts close and supply power to the equipment only when applied voltage has the proper polarity. The relay coil draws current continuously during normal operation. This may be unacceptable for low-power and battery-powered equipment.

7.16.8 Simple Sealed Lead-Acid Battery Float Charger and Switch

This charger was designed by John Boal, K9JEB, to keep a sealed lead-acid (SLA) battery charged from an external power source such as a vehicle, solar panel, or ac power supply. The battery will remain connected to the load if external power is removed or the power source voltage drops to below the battery voltage. The circuit float-charges the battery from the external power source and includes an overvoltage detection circuit to prevent overcharging the battery. (A charger with a controlled charging profile is described in the project "Automatic Sealed Lead-Acid Battery Charger" that is included in the downloadable supplemental information for this book.)

The circuit has a low-profile (½-inch height) battery-top size that matches 7 to 12 Ah SLA form factor batteries with F1 or F2 connectors. The assembled unit is shown mounted on such a battery in **Figure 7.67**. The schematic and parts list for the circuit are provided by **Figure 7.68**. The circuit is intended for use with batteries from 1 to 35 Ah. Wet-cell lead-acid batteries may be used if the cells are kept topped off with electrolyte. Do not use this charger with lithium, nickel, or other battery chemistries.

POWER CONTROL

The input power source and the battery share the output load. The input source recharges the battery directly, as well. If the input source is disconnected, the battery takes over supplying the load. Low-power input sources can be used to charge the battery as long as their terminal voltage remains higher than the battery voltage.

D3 is an optional diode to prevent power from back-feeding current into the power source when the source voltage is lower than the battery voltage. D3 should be installed if the external power voltage can fall below the battery voltage, such as for automotive or solar power applications.

Q3 acts as the master battery ON/OFF switch. It is an ultra-low R_{ds}-ON 40B207 MOSFET rated to carry dozens of amps continuously. It is connected as a *low-side switch* from the battery negative terminal to the circuit common and input negative or return terminal (ground).

Q1, a PNP transistor, is biased on by R4 and R6. It supplies enough current through R3 and D2 to raise the gate voltage of Q3 so that it is fully on. This lowers the resistance between the drain and source of Q3 to about 4 mΩ. R2 limits the total current through Q1 to about 13 mA. D2 is the Battery ON indicator.

Q3 dissipates heat while conducting according to $P = I_{ds}^2 R_{ds}$. The design of the PC board includes bare heat-sinking traces on top and bottom of the board, as well as the FET mounting screw and nut. Installed directly on the board, Q3 can dissipate up to 2 W without damaging the device: if P = 2 W and R = 4 mΩ, then I_{dsMAX} = 22 A. The 15 A battery fuse in the parts list should open at about 18 A continuous or 20 A surge. Even a 20 A fuse can probably be used safely if required.

S2 is a Battery OFF switch that physically disconnects the battery's negative terminal. Since S2 carries the full battery current, be sure it is rated adequately for your battery and peak load current. (An alternative is to use a switch to ground the gate of Q3, turning it off along with D2. The battery remains connected to Q3 in this case.) The specified mini-toggle switch is rated at 5 A which is adequate for most 7 to 9 Ah battery applications. To carry higher currents, replace S2 with a heavier switch. If the Battery OFF function is not required, S2 can be replaced with a heavy jumper.

Figure 7.67 — The charging circuit shown mounted directly on a 9 Ah SLA battery. Note the USB charging module mounted next to J1 at the left-hand side of the board.

Power Sources 7.59

POWER DISTRIBUTION

Anderson Powerpole connectors are used for both input and output power. Up to six output power connections are available. Any of the connectors can be used as the input power source connection. All of the power connectors are connected in parallel on a large-trace bus on the bottom of the board which should carry 25 to 30 A safely. If higher currents are required, #14 AWG wire can be soldered to the traces which are kept bare for this purpose. Power output cables may be hard-wired to the traces if required. It is recommended that the pairs of connectors be secured with wire-ties as shown in Figure 7.67.

While the circuit board and transistor can handle a higher load, the battery's terminals and internal plate construction should limit input or output current to 15 to 20 A maximum continuous load. Even loads of 25 A or more are okay for a few seconds but should not be continuous. Radios in the 100 W class can be used at full power on SSB or CW. Digital modes should be used at reduced power to prevent battery or circuit overload. (S2 will have to be replaced by a heavier switch, however. Battery voltage below 12 V may cause erratic or improper operation of transceivers designed for 13.8 V supply voltages.)

CHARGING CIRCUIT

The chemistry of the SLA battery allows it to be kept charged at a constant voltage between 13 and 13.8 V, with 13.8 V being the optimum voltage. The circuit keeps the battery connected to the input power source through Q3, so it can be kept fully charged. For a 7 to 12 Ah SLA battery discharged to about 11 V, inrush current to the battery through Q3 is about 4 A, decreasing to just a few mA within a few seconds as the battery voltage comes up to the input voltage. The battery is then float-charged by the external source. (A trickle-charger supplies a small amount of current to the battery at all times.)

OVER-VOLTAGE CUTOFF CIRCUIT

The battery is disconnected by turning off Q3 if the input charging voltage is too high, which can damage the battery by overcharging it. Voltages above 13.8 V are common in automotive electrical systems and solar panels. Zener diode D1 drops the input voltage across trimpot R1 to V_{in} – 8.2 V. As input voltage rises, the voltage on the wiper of R1 eventually turns on Q2, shorting the gate of Q3 to ground and turning it OFF. This also turns off the Battery ON indicator, D2.

The user should set the desired threshold voltage for the overvoltage protection circuit at about 13.7 or 13.8 V. Set the threshold by applying 13.8 V dc to the input, adjusting R1 until D2 goes out, then reverse the adjustment

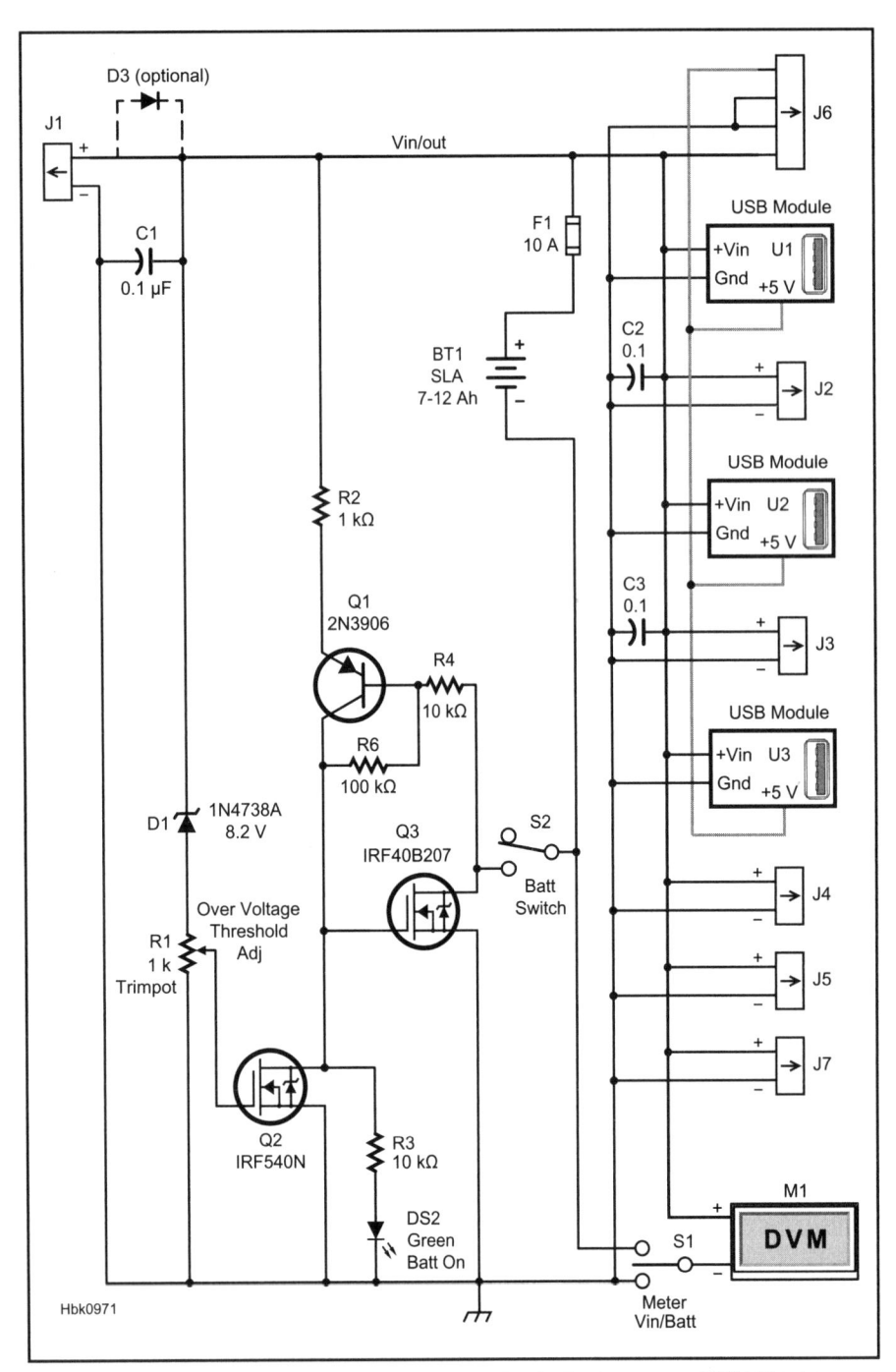

Figure 7.68 — Schematic of the battery charger circuit. Resistors are ⅛ W, 5% tolerance. Equivalent parts may be substituted. A complete kit of parts with PC board as well as separate PC boards are available from the author at his website, k9jeb.com. Enclosure design is the responsibility of the builder.

BT1 — SLA battery: 7-12 Ah (not supplied with parts kit)
C1, C2, C3 — 0.1 µF, 50 V ceramic
D1 — 1N4738A, 8.2 V Zener diode
D2 — LED, green
D3 — 10A10 10A Schottky diode (optional, install in series with J1)
F1 — 15A automotive blade fuse, standard
J1, J2, J3, J4, J5, J7 — Anderson Powerpole connector pair, including housing and contact
J6 — 0.1-inch DIP header, 2×2 (optional)
M1 — DVM module

Q1 — 2N3906 transistor
Q2 — RF540N MOSFET
Q3 — IRF40B207 MOSFET
R1 — 1 kΩ trimpot
R2 — 1 kΩ resistor
R3, R4 — 10 kΩ resistor
R6 — 100 kΩ resistor
S1 — Sub-micro toggle switch, On-Off-On (center off)
S2 — Mini toggle switch, On-On
U1, U2, U3 — USB charging module
Wire ties for securing the Powerpole connectors
PC board (available from K9JEB at k9jeb.com)

until D2 just turns back on. At this setting, the circuit will allow 13.8 V to charge the battery but disconnect the battery at any higher voltage. If the input voltage drops below 13.8 V, the battery will be reconnected and D2 will turn on again.

USB CHARGING MODULES

Up to three +5 V, 2.5 A USB charger modules can be added in three places on the board, each replacing an Anderson Powerpole connector pair. One can be seen at the left-hand side of the PC board in Figure 7.67. These modules are widely available as commodity-type parts from a variety of sources.

Modules can be added along any of three edges of the board for flexibility in possible mounting configurations. All of the module +5 V outputs are connected in parallel and to J6 for external use if needed. As with all dc-dc converters, these modules are switched (at about 250 kHz) and may occasionally cause RF interference (RFI). If RFI from the USB charging modules is objectionable, a linear regulator such as the 2 A, +5V L78S05CV (with heatsink) can be used as a noise-free 5 V power supply, but it will generate about 9 W of heat for every 5 W delivered to the load. It also requires filter capacitors of 0.01 µF and 100 µF.

MISCELLANEOUS

C1, C2, and C3 are 0.1 µF capacitors to reduce HF and VHF noise on the dc power busses. Different values may be substituted if noise at higher or lower frequencies is encountered.

The DVM is a typical miniature 3-digit meter/display module available from many vendors. S1 switches the DVM to either display input voltage, turns it off, or to display the actual battery voltage.

J6 is an optional 2×2 pin header that provides a connection to both input and output voltages, +5 V dc from the USB charging modules if installed, and common (ground). Note that the input source connection to J6 is not fused.

7.16.9 Simple Adjustable Tracking Power Supply

This project by Bryant Julstrom, KC0ZNG, was originally published in the Spring 2014 issue of the QRP ARCI *QRP Quarterly*. A PDF version of the original article, including all figures, is available with this book's downloadable supplemental content.

The typical experimenter's bench power supply provides an adjustable positive voltage of up to 25 V at up to 1 A of current. This suffices for many circuits and projects, but others require positive and negative voltages of equal magnitude. Op-amp circuits, for example, often require ±15 V.

THE CIRCUIT

The circuit is implemented using two garden-variety ICs, an LM317 positive regulator and an LM337 negative regulator, both in TO-220 packages. (Note that the orientation of the input-common-output connections are different between the two regulators!) The input voltages of the circuit are limited only by the maximum inputs of the two regulators, ±40 V. (An alternate implementation based on the LT1033 tracking regulator is shown in an article included with this book's downloadable supplemental content.) A voltmeter is switched between either of the supply's outputs and common.

Input power to the tracking regulator is supplied by a power transformer with a center-tapped secondary. The peak secondary output voltage on each side of the center-tap should be several volts higher than the maximum supply output at full load. See this chapter's section on power supply ripple to determine the minimum required filter capacitance.

In the author's case, the heaviest transformer available provided only 26 V CT (center-tapped) and the input to the regulator of ±13 V was too low. One possible solution would be to use two identical transformers with their primary windings in parallel and their secondaries in series with the connection between secondaries serving as the center-tap.

Since 24 to 28 V CT is a common secondary voltage range, however, the author chose to use the available transformer and back-to-back half-wave voltage doublers, one on either side of the secondary winding's center tap, to provide about ±26 V to the tracking regulator. This halves the current that can be drawn from the transformer, but if the

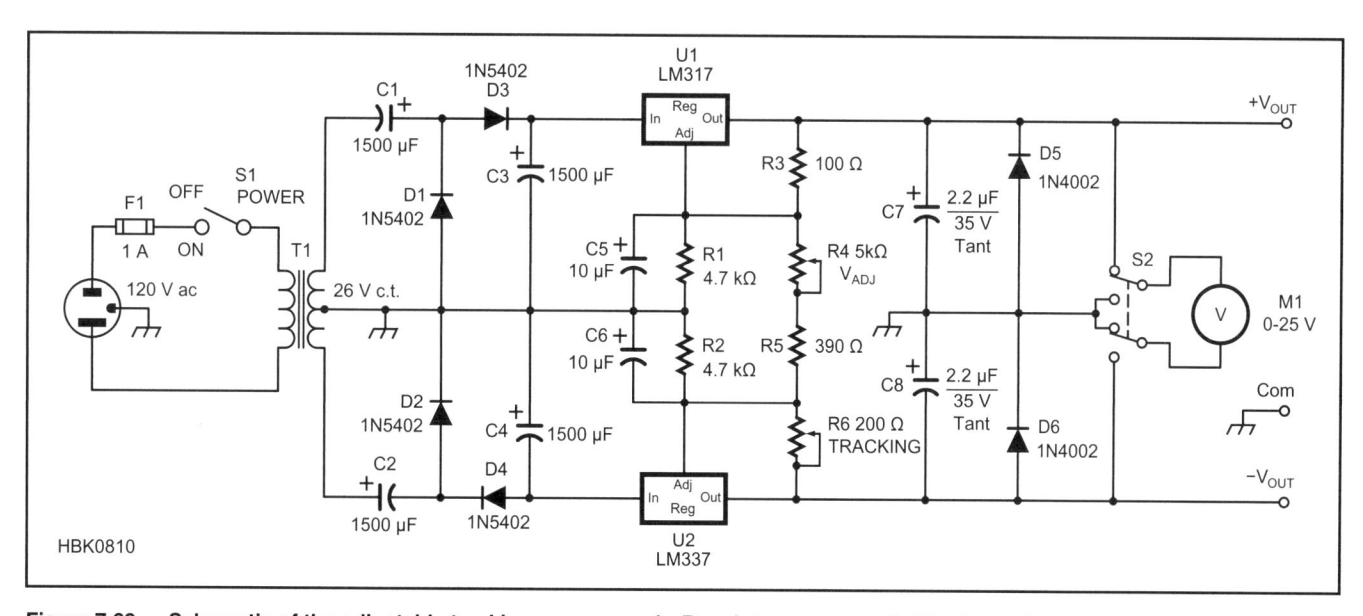

Figure 7.69 — Schematic of the adjustable tracking power supply. Regulators are mounted to the enclosure, which serves as a heat sink. Resistors are ¼ W film, 5% tolerance unless noted otherwise.

C1-C4 — 1500 µF, 50 V electrolytic
C5, C6 — 10 µF, 50 V electrolytic
C7, C8 — 2.2 µF, 35 V, solid tantalum
D1-D4 — 1N5402 or equivalent
D5, D6 — 1N4002 or equivalent
F1 — 250 V, 1 A ac fuse and fuse holder

M1 — 0-25 V voltmeter or equivalent
R1, R2 — 4.7 kΩ
R3 — 100 Ω
R4 — 5 kΩ, panel-mount potentiometer
R5 — 390 Ω
R6 — 200 Ω trimmer potentiometer
S1 — SPST toggle switch

S2 — DPDT miniature toggle switch
T1 — 26 V CT at 2 A secondary or equivalent (see text)
U1 — LM317 adjustable positive voltage regulator
U2 — LM337 adjustable negative voltage regulator

transformer secondary is rated at 2 A, the resulting maximum output current of 1 A in each leg of the supply is sufficient for a wide range of projects.

Figure 7.69 shows the circuit of the tracking power supply. The author used 1N5402 rectifiers in the voltage doublers because they were available, but any 100 V diode rated at 3 A or more of average forward current will work. The two 2.2 µF capacitors should be solid tantalum types.

R4, a front-panel potentiometer, is used for voltage adjustment. R6, a 200 Ω trimmer potentiometer, provides for fine tracking adjustment. The 390 Ω resistor (R5) sets the regulator's minimum outputs at about ±3.6 V for reasons described below.

CONSTRUCTION

As constructed, the front panel holds three binding posts (positive output, negative output, and common), two miniature toggle switches (on/off and voltmeter switching), the voltage-adjustment potentiometer and its knob, and a voltmeter. Note that the common connection of the power supply is usually left floating from the enclosure ground which must be connected to the "third-wire" ac safety ground. If desired, a binding post connected to the enclosure can be added so that a jumper can be used to connect the power supply common to the ac safety ground.

The voltmeter used by the author is a three-digit LED unit from Marlin P. Jones (**www.mpja.com**; part number 30217 ME with blue digits, also available in green and red). The meter is powered by the voltage it measures, as long as the voltage is at least 3.6 V as determined by R5 as explained previously. An analog meter or a digital meter with a separate power supply would allow lower minimum output voltages. One could augment the supply's measurements with current metering or with simultaneous measurements of both outputs.

The enclosure holds the power transformer and two circuit boards. The two voltage doublers occupy one circuit board and the tracking regulator the other. The circuit is simple enough that perforated board ("Perfboard") was used with point-to-point wiring.

The LM317 and LM337 are mounted at the edge of the regulator board and attached to the back panel, which serves as a heat sink, using mica insulators, nylon bolts, and a thin coating of heat sink compound. The rear panel also holds a snap-in IEC three-wire ac line connector. (Photographs of the finished power supply are provided in an article included with this book's downloadable supplemental content.)

ADJUSTMENT AND PERFORMANCE

The only internal adjustment in the supply is the tracking potentiometer (R6), which must be set so that the two voltages track each other accurately. This is touchy, but the two voltages can be made to match within 0.1 V throughout the supply's range. The completed supply provides closely matched positive and negative voltages from ±3.6 V to about ±23 V, and a maximum current of 1 A in each leg.

The tracking adjustment and the front-panel voltage adjustment (R4) are delicate. In both cases, multi-turn potentiometers would be much easier to set. The tracking control could also be replaced with a series resistor and a smaller-value potentiometer to make adjustment less sensitive.

7.16.10 Overvoltage Protection for AC Generators

When using portable generators, there is always a possibility of damage to expensive equipment as a result of generator failure, especially from overvoltage. If the generator supplying power to this equipment puts out too much voltage, you run the risk of burning up power supplies or other electronic components. This project, by Jerry Paquette, WB8IOW, addresses the problem of increased voltage (not lower voltage) or surges and spikes lasting for a few microseconds.

Using a portable generator overvoltage protection circuit and ground-fault circuit interrupter (GFCI) as shown in **Figure 7.70** is good insurance. This overvoltage protection device must be used in conjunction with a GFCI at each station! (More information on GFCIs may be found in the **Safety** chapter.)

CIRCUIT DESCRIPTION

Refer to Figure 7.70 for this description. R1 places an intentional fault on the load side of the GFCI. With the value resistor used, the fault is limited to 10 mA. (The normal tripping threshold of a GFCI is 5 mA. This current forces the GFCI to trip in just a few

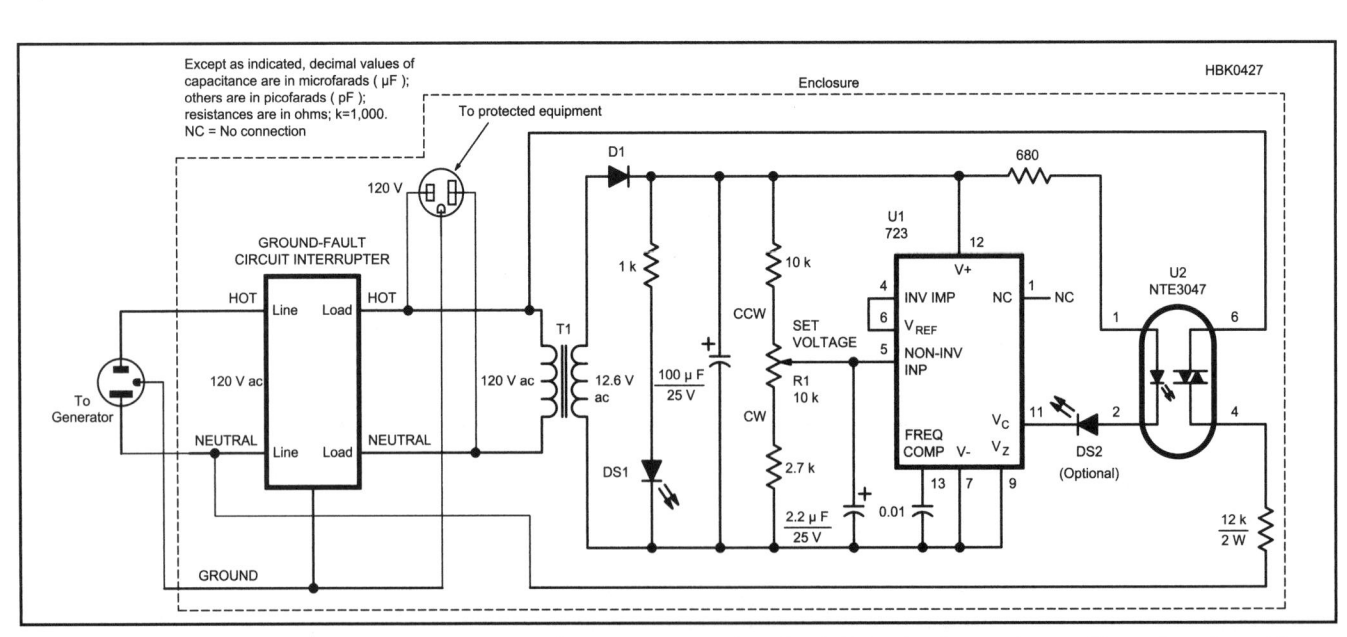

Figure 7.70 — Schematic of the Field Day equipment overvoltage-protection circuit. This circuit must be used in conjunction with a ground fault circuit interrupter (GFCI). A separate GFCI must be installed at each station. Unless otherwise specified, resistors are ¼ W, 5% tolerance. A PC board is available from FAR Circuits (www.farcircuits.net).

D1 — 200 PIV, 1 A diode; 1N4003 or equiv.
DS1, DS2 — Small LEDs
R1 — 10 kΩ board-mounted, multi-turn potentiometer

T1 — 12.6 V ac transformer (see text)
U1 — 723 adjustable voltage regulator IC

U2 — Optoisolator with TRIAC output; NTE3047 or equiv

milliseconds. This circuit will not function at all without the use of a GFCI. A GFCI must be used at each station. If a single GFCI were used at the generator, rather than one at each location, premature tripping could occur. Several hundred feet of extension cords could have enough leakage to trip the GFCI.

You can see that the GFCI has separate lines (inputs) and loads (outputs). GFCI input terminals must be connected to the generator output. The GFCI ground must be tied to the ground of the generator. The load (computers, radios, etc) will plug into the GFCI or are wired to the load side of the GFCI. The primary of T1 is wired to the load side of the GFCI. The 12 kΩ/2 W resistor, however, must be wired to neutral on the *line* side of the GFCI in order for it to trip when used with generators that have windings isolated from ground. For safety, construct the entire unit in a single enclosure including the GFCI and its wiring. The generator connection can be made through a wired plug or using a male receptacle mounted on the enclosure.

T1 can be any 120 V to 12.6 V transformer capable of delivering 100 mA or more. Mounting of this transformer varies depending on the type used. All remaining components mount on a circuit board. D1 rectifies the ac from T1 and the 100 µF capacitor filters the dc. This voltage provides the power to the 723 voltage regulator.

Two fixed resistors and a potentiometer form the voltage-divider network supplying voltage to the LM723 input, pin 5. R1, the board-mounted potentiometer, has only three leads, but there are four pads on the circuit board, to accommodate different styles of pots. The 2.2 µF capacitor provides a slight delay, to prevent false tripping when the circuit is powered up. The 0.01 µF capacitor from pin 13 of the 723 to the negative supply bus should always be used. When the voltage at pin 5 goes higher than the reference voltage at pins 4 and 6, pin 11 goes low, turning on the trip indicator LED DS2 and the optical coupler LED. LED current is limited by the 1 kΩ resistor. The optical coupler turns on the TRIAC, which creates a 10 mA fault current between the hot wire and ground of the GFCI. DS2 will remain lit as an indicator until the 100 µF capacitor is discharged.

ADJUSTMENT

Adjustment is simple. You'll need a variable ac transformer (Powerstat or Variac). Turn R1 fully clockwise and use the variable transformer to adjust input to 130 V ac. Turn the pot counterclockwise until the GFCI trips.

7.16.11 Overvoltage Crowbar Circuit

If the regulator circuitry of a power supply should fail — for example, if a pass transistor should short — the unregulated supply voltage could appear at the output terminals. This could cause a failure in the equipment connected to the supply. The overvoltage "crowbar" circuit shown here has been shown to be effective as a last line of defense against power supply overvoltage failures. When an overvoltage condition is detected, the heavy-duty SCR is fired, becoming a short circuit — as if a crowbar (representing any over-sized conductor capable of handling the supply's short-circuit output current) had been connected across the supply, thus the name.

This circuit shown in **Figure 7.71** was originally designed for a 28 V power supply. The use of the MC3423 overvoltage protection IC provides quicker triggering and more reliable gate drive to the SCR than comparable Zener-based circuits. Power supply builders can incorporate the overvoltage protection circuit into any dc power supply with the required component value adjustments.

The crowbar circuit is usually connected with the power input and the sense input connected together at the supply positive output and COMMON to the supply negative output. Another option is to connect power input and common across the rectifier filter capacitor and the sense input to the power supply output.

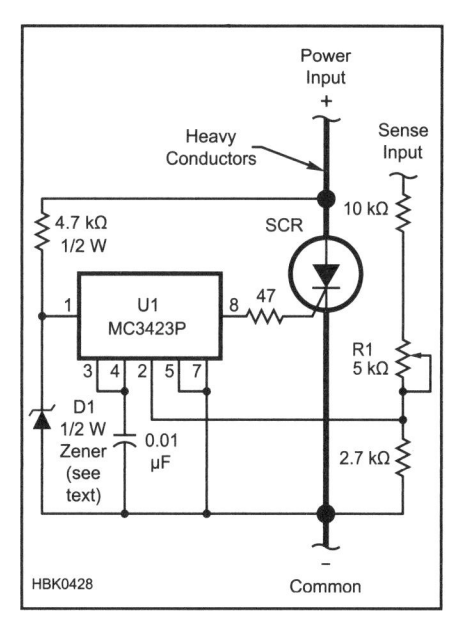

Figure 7.71 — Schematic of the overvoltage crowbar circuit. Unless otherwise specified, resistors are ¼ W, 5% tolerance. A PC board is available from FAR Circuits (www.farcircuits.net).
SCR — C38M stud-mount (TO-65 package)
U1 — MC3423P or NTE7172 voltage protection circuit, 8-pin DIP
D1 — Zener diode, ½ W (see text)
R1 — 5 kΩ, PC board mount trimmer potentiometer

In either case, the power input and common wires should be adequately sized to handle the full short-circuit current and are shown as heavy lines on the schematic.

The crowbar circuit functions as follows: the 4.7 kΩ resistor and Zener diode D1 create a supply voltage for the MC3423. U1 will function properly with a supply voltage of 4.5-40 V. Use a Zener diode with a voltage rating a few volts below that of the crowbar circuit positive-to-negative power input voltage. For example, if the crowbar is connected to a 12 V supply output, D1 voltage should be 6 to 9 V. The exact value is not critical.

U1 contains a 2.5 V reference and two comparators. When the voltage at pin 2 (sense terminal) reaches 2.5 V, the output voltage (pin 8) changes from the negative input voltage to the positive input voltage. This drives the gate of the SCR through the 47 Ω resistor. The trip voltage is set by the resistive divider across the + and − inputs:

$$V_{trip} = 2.5 \left(1 + \frac{10 \text{ k}\Omega + R}{2.7 \text{ k}\Omega} \right)$$

The application notes for the MC3423 recommend that the resistance from the sense input to the negative input be less than 10 kΩ for minimum drift, suggesting the value of 2.7 kΩ. The value of 10 kΩ for the fixed portion of the adjustable resistance is selected for V_{trip} = 15 V at the midpoint of the 5 kΩ potentiometer (R1) travel. For other trip voltages, the fixed resistor value should be the closest standard value to

$$R_{fixed} = 2.7 \text{ k}\Omega \left(\frac{V_{trip}}{2.5} - 1 \right) - 2.5 \text{ k}\Omega$$

assuming the potentiometer value remains at 5 kΩ.

When the SCR turns on, it short-circuits the inputs, causing any protective fuses or circuit breakers to open. The SCR will stay on until the current through drops below the "keep alive" threshold, at which point the SCR turns off. The SCR will stay on even if the input voltage to U1 drops below 4.5 V.

If the crowbar circuit fires due to RFI, an additional 0.01 µF capacitor should be connected from pin 2 of U1 to common and another across the D1.

More information may be found in the MC3423 datasheet and "Semiconductor Consideration for DC Power Supply Voltage Protector Circuits," ON Semi AN004E/D, both available from ON Semiconductor.

Additional Projects and Information

Additional power source projects and supporting files are included with this book's downloadable supplemental content.

Contents

8.1 Introduction to DSP
8.2 Introduction to SDR
   8.2.1 SDR Architecture Options
   8.2.2 Advantages and Limitations of DSP and SDR
8.3 Analog-Digital Conversion
   8.3.1 Basic Conversion Metrics
   8.3.2 Analog-to-Digital Converters
   8.3.3 Analog-to-Digital Converter Subsystems
   8.3.4 Digital-to-Analog Converters (DAC)
   8.3.5 Choosing a Converter
8.4 Data Converters for SDR and DSP
   8.4.1 Using Audio ADC for SDR
   8.4.2 High-Speed ADC for SDR
8.5 Digital Signal Processors
   8.5.1 Microprocessor-type DSP ICs
   8.5.2 Fixed-Point versus Floating-Point
   8.5.3 DSP in Embedded Systems
   8.5.4 Typical DSP Processors
   8.5.5 DSP Without a Dedicated Processor
   8.5.6 Using Graphics Processors for DSP
8.6 Digital (Discrete-time) Signals
   8.6.1 Sampling — Digitization in Time
   8.6.2 Decimation and Interpolation
   8.6.3 Quantization — Digitization in Amplitude
8.7 The Fourier Transform
   8.7.1 The Fast Fourier Transform (FFT)
   8.7.2 Non-periodic Signals
   8.7.3 The Inverse Fourier Transform (IFT)
8.8 Glossary
8.9 References and Bibliography

Chapter 8 — Downloadable Supplemental Content

Supplemental Files
- Selected SDR: Simplified columns by Ray Mack, W5IFS, from *QEX* magazine

Chapter 8

DSP and SDR Fundamentals

This chapter was updated and edited by Doug Grant, K1DG, based on material originally created by Alan Bloom, N1AL. It explores the fundamentals of digital signal processing (DSP) and software defined radio (SDR). Material is also taken from *QEX* "SDR: Simplified" articles by Ray Mack, W5IFS. Key to DSP and SDR, analog-digital conversion and types of converters are covered, as well.

In recent years, DSP technology has progressed to the point where it is an integral part of our radio equipment. DSP is rapidly replacing traditional analog hardware circuits with digital processors and software, offering amateurs flexibility and features only dreamed of in the past.

Software defined radio is the biggest advance in radio technology since the superheterodyne was introduced nearly a century ago. SDR is only possible through DSP techniques implemented on the advanced platforms that have become available at amateur-friendly prices in the past few years.

This chapter begins with the fundamentals of DSP and extends them to SDR design. Subsequent chapters will cover DSP methods in more detail for implementing oscillators, modulation, filters, and the functions associated with receiving and transmitting.

For the fullest understanding of this chapter the reader should have a basic familiarity of the topics covered in the **Radio Fundamentals** chapter as well as some high-school trigonometry. (Various math tutorials are provided or referenced in the **Radio Mathematics** downloadable supplemental content provided with this book's online information.)

Additional background and support materials may be found online in the downloadable supplemental content material provided with this book.

8.1 Introduction to DSP

Digital signal processing (DSP) has been around a long time. The essential theory was developed by mathematicians such as Newton, Gauss, and Fourier in the 17th, 18th, and 19th centuries. It was not until the latter half of the 20th century, however, that digital computers became available that could do the calculations fast enough to process signals in real time. Today DSP is important in many fields, such as seismology, acoustics, radar, medical imaging, nuclear engineering, audio and video processing, as well as voice and data communications.

In all those systems, the idea is to process a digitized signal so as to extract information from it or to control its characteristics in some way. For example, an EKG monitor in a hospital extracts the essential characteristics of the signal from the patient's heart for display on a screen. A digital communications receiver uses DSP to filter and demodulate the received RF signal before sending it to the speaker, headphones, or waterfall/band-scope display. In some systems, the signal to be processed may have more than one dimension. An example is image data, which requires two-dimensional processing. Similarly, the controller for an electrically-steerable antenna array uses multi-dimensional DSP techniques to determine the amplitude and phase of the RF signal in each of the antenna elements. A CT scanner analyzes X-ray data in three dimensions to determine the internal structures of a human body.

A typical DSP system is conceptually very simple. It consists of only three sections, as illustrated in **Figure 8.1**. An ADC at the input converts an analog signal into a series of digital numbers that represent snapshots of the signal at a series of equally spaced sample times. The digital signal processor itself does some kind of calculations on that digital signal to generate a new stream of numbers at its output. A DAC then converts those numbers back into analog form.

Some DSP systems may not have all three components. For example, a DSP-based audio-frequency generator does not need an ADC. Similarly, there is no need for a DAC in a measurement system that monitors some sensor output, processes the signal, and stores the result in a computer file or displays it on a digital readout.

The term "DSP" is normally understood to imply processing that occurs in real time, at least in some sense. For example, an RF or microwave signal analyzer might include a DSP coprocessor that processes chunks of sampled data in batch mode for display a fraction of a second later.

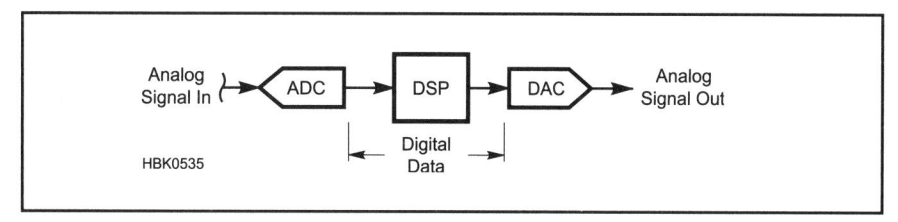

Figure 8.1 — A generic DSP system.

8.2 Introduction to SDR

The concept of a *software-defined radio* (SDR) has been around for a long time, but became popular in the 1990s. By then, DSP and data converter technology had developed to the point that it was possible to implement almost all the signal-processing functions of a transceiver using inexpensive programmable digital hardware. The frequency, bandwidth, modulation, filtering, and other characteristics can be changed under software control, rather than being fixed by the hardware design as in a conventional analog radio. Adding a new modulation type or a new improved filter design is a simple matter of downloading new software.

Compared to analog radios, SDR has some major advantages. In analog radios, passive components such as capacitors, resistors, and even inductors are subject to changes in value due to temperature drift and aging. They also have loose initial value tolerances and often require adjustments or calibration. Likewise, active components such as amplifiers and mixers also are subject to variations in performance. If the function of these components can be replaced with software, most of these problems disappear.

SDR is appealing to regulatory bodies such as the FCC because it makes possible a communications system called *cognitive radio* in which multiple radio services can share the same frequency spectrum.[1] Each node in a wireless network is programmed to dynamically change its transmission or reception characteristics to avoid interference to or from other users. In this way, services that in the past enjoyed fixed frequency allocations but that only use their channels a small percentage of the time can share their spectrum with other wireless users with minimal interference.

There has been much, sometimes heated, discussion about the precise definition of a *software-defined radio* (SDR). Most feel that, at minimum, an SDR must implement in software at least some of the functions that have traditionally been done in hardware. Others feel that a radio doesn't count as an SDR unless nearly all the signal-processing functions, from the RF input to the audio output (for the receiver) and from the microphone ADC (analog-to-digital converter, or A/D) to the power amplifier input (for the transmitter), are done in software. Others add the requirement that the software must be reconfigurable by downloading new code, preferably open-source. For our purposes we will use a rather loose definition and consider any signal-processing function done in software to fall under the general category of SDR.

Some SDRs use a personal computer to do the computational work and external hardware to convert the transmitted and received RF signals to lower-frequency signals that the computer's audio interface can handle. Some SDRs avoid the use of the PC's sound card by including their own audio *codec* (short for "coder-decoder," a chip that includes both A/D and D/A converter functions) and using analog audio for the user interface. Some SDRs transfer the downconverted (and possibly filtered) data to the PC via a USB port. Modern PCs provide a lot of computational power for the money and are getting cheaper and more powerful all the time. They also come with a large color display, a keyboard and mouse for easy data entry and navigation, a large memory and hard disk, which allows running logging programs and other software while simultaneously doing the signal processing required by the SDR.

Smaller, even less expensive, computing platforms such as Arduino, Raspberry Pi, Beaglebone, Red Pitaya and many others have become available. While they often lack the peripherals and user interfaces of a complete PC, some of them have sufficient computational power to be useful for SDR experimentation.

Some SDRs have almost no knobs or buttons on the box and none of the traditional features such as frequency display, meters, and so on. In such radios, all control functions are done on an external PC with control software provided by the manufacturer. The user interface is the PC keyboard, monitor, and mouse. Other SDRs look more like conventional analog radios and don't need an external PC for control. While the signal processing is done with one or more embedded DSPs, the user interface consists of knobs and pushbuttons which many users prefer to a mouse and keyboard and pull-down menus. Some newer SDRs use a touchscreen for the user interface to emulate the buttons.

Either method offers all the important advantages of applying DSP techniques to signal processing. The channel filter can have a much better *shape factor* (the ratio between the width of the passband and the frequency difference of the stopband edges). FIR filters are linear phase and have less ringing than analog filters of the same bandwidth and shape factor. Once the signal is in the digital domain all the fancy digital signal processing algorithms can be applied such as automatic notch filters, adaptive channel equalization, noise reduction, noise blanking, and feed-forward automatic gain control. Correcting bugs, improving performance or adding new features is as simple as downloading new software.

Following an overview of SDR systems, the details of the various blocks used in such systems, including analog-digital conversion, are then explored. The chapter concludes with a discussion of the basic theory of discrete-time and digital signals, with emphasis on topics relevant to radio communications.

8.2.1 SDR Architecture Options

The transition between analog and digital signals can occur at any of several places in the signal chain between the antenna and the user interface. This choice is an important factor in determining the overall architecture of the SDR. This section presents several block-diagram-level concepts for software-defined radio and compared architecture options.

DSP AT AUDIO FREQUENCIES

The initial use of DSP by amateur operators was to implement audio-frequency filtering. By the early 1990s, converter costs were reasonable and the processing power required was available in relatively inexpensive microprocessors with enhanced math function capability. The flexibility of digital filters (see the **Analog and Digital Filtering** chapter) and the ability to alter bandwidth and perform noise reduction resulted in quick adoption of DSP techniques in amateur equipment.

In 1992, Dave Hershberger, W9GR, designed an audio-frequency DSP filter based on the TMS320C10, one of the earliest practical DSP chips available.[2] This filter was an external standalone unit that plugged into the headphone jack of a receiver and included filters with various bandwidths, an automatic multi-frequency notch filter, and an adaptive noise filter.

The advantage of DSP at audio frequencies is that it can be easily added to an unmodified analog radio as in **Figure 8.2**. Many amateurs use a similar approach to implement digital modulation modes, using a PC and software as the outboard DSP processor. The software produces the required waveforms (and demodulates the received signal), using the PC's audio input and output connected to

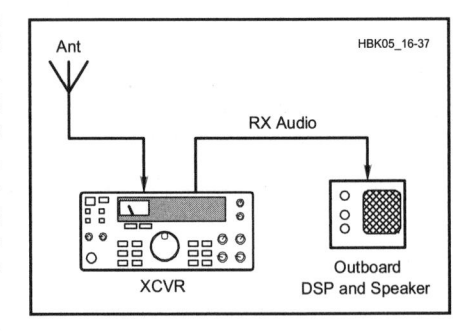

Figure 8.2 — An outboard DSP processor.

the audio input and output of a conventional SSB transceiver.

DOWNCONVERSION TO ANALOG BASEBAND

A related technique is to *downconvert* a slice of the radio spectrum to baseband audio using a technique similar to the direct-conversion receivers popular with simple low-power CW transceivers. (See the **Receiving** chapter.) This idea was pioneered by Gerald Youngblood, AC5OG (now K5SDR), with the SDR-1000 transceiver, which he described in a series of *QEX* articles in 2002 and 2003.[3] The receiver block diagram is shown in **Figure 8.3**. It uses a unique I/Q demodulator designed by Dan Tayloe, N7VE, to convert the RF frequency directly to baseband I ("In-phase") and Q ("Quadrature") signals.[4] (I/Q modulation and quadrature signals are discussed in the **Modulation** chapter.)

The baseband signals are fed to the stereo input of a PC's sound card, represented by the low-pass filters and analog-to-digital converters (A/D, or ADC) in the figure. Software in the PC does all the signal processing and demodulation, ultimately producing audio for the operator to hear or a display of decoded bits in the form of text on the screen. The transmitter is the same block diagram in reverse, with an I/Q modulator converting the I/Q signal from the sound card up to the RF frequency where it is filtered and amplified to the final power level.

The sound card method manages to achieve reasonable performance with simple, inexpensive hardware. Once the A/D converters in the sound card have digitized the signal, the DSP capability of the PC can do amazing things with it. In addition to implementing conventional transceiver functions such as several types of detector, variable-bandwidth filters, software AGC, an S-meter and speech compression, the software can include some extra features such as an automatic notch filter, noise reduction, a panadapter spectrum display and decoding of signals such as RTTY, PSK, and WSJT modes.

The simple hardware of the SDR-1000 does impose some performance limitations. Because of imperfections in the analog downconverter, unwanted-sideband rejection is not perfect. This is called "image rejection" in the SDR-1000 literature. On the panadapter display, strong signals show up weakly on the opposite side of the display, equally-spaced from the center. DC offset in the analog circuitry causes a spurious signal to appear at the center of the bandwidth. To prevent an unwanted tone from appearing in the audio output, the software demodulator is tuned slightly off frequency, but that means interference at the image frequency can cause problems because of the imperfect image rejection. The dynamic range depends on the sound card performance as well as the RF hardware. Some newer SDRs include an integrated audio codec optimized for the application so that the PC's sound card is not needed.

DIGITIZING AT IF

Another option for implementing software-defined radios involves performing the analog-digital conversion at an intermediate frequency. **Figure 8.4** shows such a design. In the receiver, placing the A/D converter after a crystal IF filter improves the *blocking dynamic range* (BDR) for interfering signals that fall outside the crystal filter bandwidth. BDR is the ratio, expressed in dB, between the noise level (normally assuming a 500 Hz bandwidth) and an interfering signal strong enough to cause 1 dB gain reduction of the desired signal. (See the **Receiving** chapter.) As shown, the downconversion to I/Q format still uses lower-speed A/D converters, but often the signal is actually at a low IF, say, 15 kHz or so. This allows an SSB-bandwidth signal to be contained within the 20 kHz band-

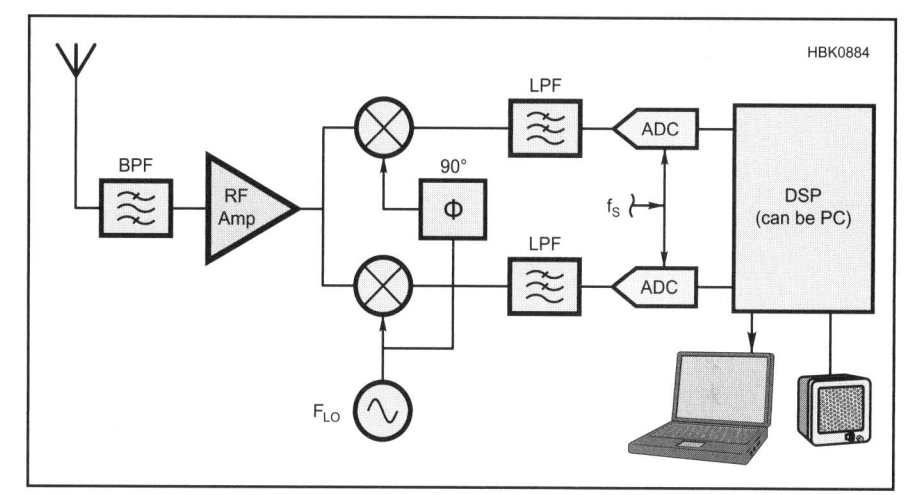

Figure 8.3 — Direct-to-baseband SDR receiver architecture.

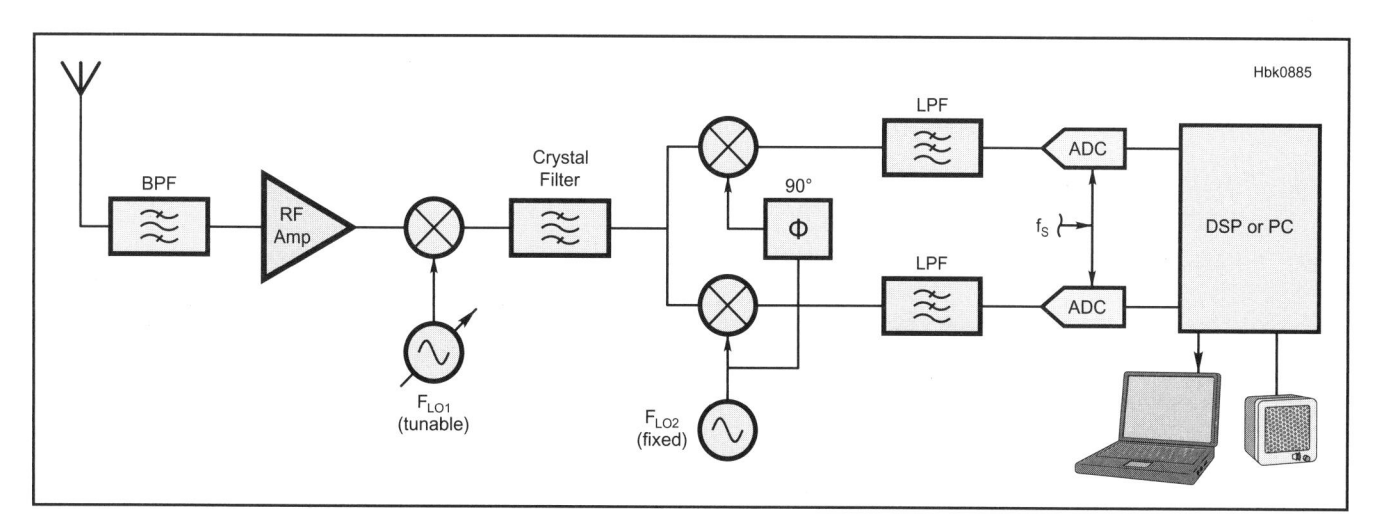

Figure 8.4 — Hybrid superhet/DSP SDR receiver architecture.

width of a typical audio codec and avoids errors due to dc offsets in the signal path. With careful design, a receiver with such an architecture can achieve 140 dB or more of BDR (if there are no other limiting factors such as LO phase noise). The third-order dynamic range is similar to that achieved with a conventional analog architecture since the circuitry up to the crystal filter, including amplifiers and mixer(s) is the same.

Another advantage of the IF-based approach compared to directly sampling the RF frequency is that the ADC does not have to run at such a high sample rate. In fact, because the crystal filter acts as a high-performance, narrow-bandwidth anti-aliasing filter, *under-sampling* is possible if the A/D converter has sufficient sampling bandwidth (ADCs intended for audio applications generally do not). With bandwidths of a few kHz or less, sample rates in the tens of kHz can be used even though the center frequency of the IF signal is much higher, so long as the ADC's sample-and-hold circuit has sufficient bandwidth.

Some systems, especially in VHF/UHF applications such as cellular base stations which deal with signals that are tens of MHz wide, often use the approach shown in **Figure 8.5**. Here, a high-speed, high-bandwidth ADC digitizes an IF typically in the hundreds of MHz. The output data rate of such a converter is too high to be handled by a PC or even a low-cost programmable DSP microprocessor. The conversion from the original signal to I/Q components is done in a dedicated digital hardware block.

DIRECT RF DIGITIZING

The ultimate SDR architecture is to convert between the analog and digital domains right at the frequency to be transmitted or received, or convert a wide range of frequencies and do all filtering in the digital domain. The receive path of such a design is shown in **Figure 8.6**. In this receiver, the only remaining analog components in the signal chain are a wideband anti-aliasing filter similar to a preselector and an amplifier to improve the noise figure of the ADC if necessary. The local oscillator, mixer, IF filters, AGC, demodulators and other circuitry are all replaced by digital hardware and software. The digital/software implementations of these functions are perfectly stable with time and temperature, and need no adjustments.

It has only been recently that low-cost high-speed ADCs have become available with specifications good enough to allow reasonable performance in an RF-sampling communications receiver. Today it is possible to achieve blocking dynamic range of 130 dB. That is not quite as good as the best analog or hybrid radios, but with every new generation of A/D converter that becomes available for use in SDR, the performance gap becomes narrower.

It is worth noting here that while huge BDR numbers can be measured in the laboratory, the performance achieved in a real-world environment with a receiver connected to an antenna is quite different. Often local noise sources raise the noise floor such that the receiver's full BDR cannot be utilized and other specifications become more important. In many of these specifications (dynamic range for close-spaced signals, and so on), RF-sampling SDRs can provide performance comparable or superior to conventional all-analog and IF-sampling receivers.

Third-order dynamic range (3IMD DR or IP$_3$) is not a meaningful specification for this type of radio because it is based on the behavior of analog circuits. Calculation of 3IMD DR assumes that distortion products increase 3 dB for each 1 dB increase in signal level, which is not always true for an ADC. The level of the distortion products in an ADC tends to be more-or-less independent of signal level until the signal peak exceeds the ADC's full scale input, at which point the distortion increases dramatically. It is important to read the data sheet carefully and note the test conditions for the distortion measurements.

There are definite advantages to sampling at RF. For one thing, it saves a lot of analog circuitry. Even though a high-speed ADC is more expensive than an audio converter, the radio may be end up being cheaper to build because of the reduced component count and fewer adjustments. Performance is improved in some areas. For example, image rejection is no longer a worry, as long as the anti-aliasing filter is doing its job. (See the **Receiving** chapter.) The dynamic range of an SDR theoretically does not depend on signal spacing — close-in dynamic range is often better than with a conventional architecture that uses a wide IF filter. With no crystal filters in the signal chain, the entire system has a completely linear phase response, which can improve the quality of both analog and digital signals after demodulation.

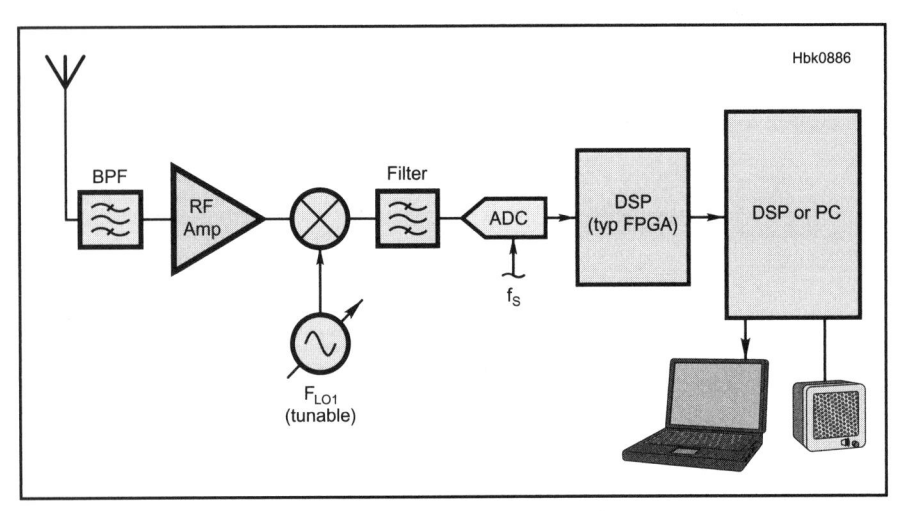

Figure 8.5 — High-IF sampling SDR receiver architecture.

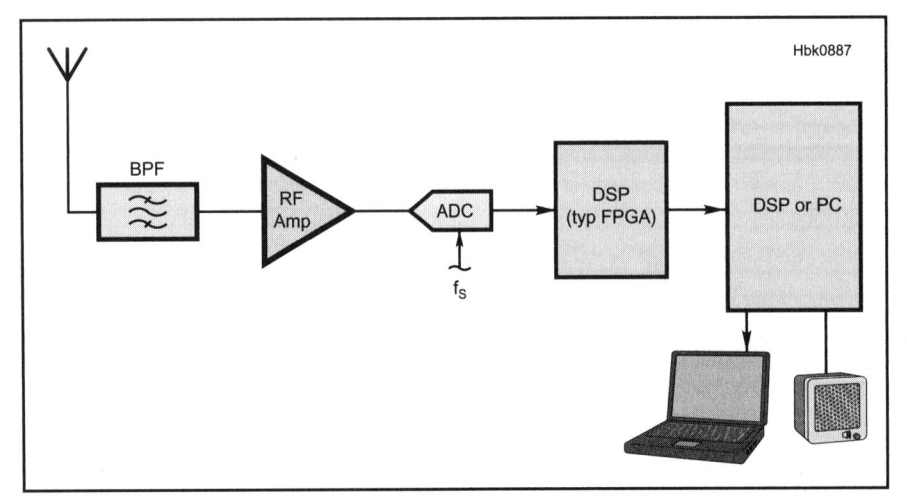

Figure 8.6 — Direct RF-sampling DSP SDR receiver architecture.

The biggest challenge with RF sampling is what to do with the torrent of high-speed data coming out of the receiver's ADC and how to generate transmit data fast enough to keep up with the DAC sample rate. To cover 0-54 MHz without aliasing requires a sample rate of at least 120 or 130 MHz, and commercial products typically operate the ADC at sample rates well over 200 MHz. That is much faster than a typical microprocessor or programmable DSP can handle. The local oscillator, mixer, and decimator or interpolator must be implemented in digital hardware so that the DSP can send and receive data at a more-reasonable sample rate. *Digital downconverters* (DDC) perform those functions and output a lower-sample-rate digital I/Q signal to the DSP. Stand-alone DDC ICs were available in the past, but the function is now usually integrated with the A/D converter. It is also possible to implement a DDC in an *field-programmable gate array* or FPGA. (See the **Transceiver Design Topics** chapter.) *Digital upconverters* (DUC) do the same conversion in reverse for the transmitter and are available integrated with the D/A converter or can be implemented in an FPGA. Some commercial integrated DDC/DAC products even include the capability to encode several digital modulation formats such as GMSK, QPSK and π/4 DQPSK. In an attempt to simplify the interface to the digital domain, many high-speed converters now use a standardized serial interface specification called JESD204B, capable of handling up to 12Gb/s. Code to implement this interface on the digital FPGA is readily available.

Some designers have been successful in repurposing a graphics processor (GPU) for this purpose, and some GPU manufacturers now offer FFT libraries to assist in the design process.

8.2.2 Advantages and Limitations of DSP and SDR

Digital signal processing has the reputation of being more complicated than the analog circuitry that it replaces. In reality, once the analog signal has been converted into the digital domain, complicated functions can be implemented in software much more simply than would be possible with analog components. For example, the traditional "phasing" method of generating an SSB signal without an expensive crystal filter requires various mixers, oscillators, filters and a wide-band audio-frequency phase-shift network built with a network of high-precision resistors and capacitors. To implement the same function in a DSP system requires adding one additional subroutine to the software program — and no additional hardware.

Many features that are straightforward with DSP techniques are difficult or impractical to implement with analog circuitry. A few examples drawn just from the communications field are imageless mixing, noise reduction, OFDM (orthogonal frequency division multiplexing) modulation and adaptive channel equalization. Digital signals can have much more dynamic range than analog signals, limited only by the number of bits used to represent the signal. For example, it is easy to add an extra 20 or 30 dB of headroom to the intermediate signal processing stages to ensure that there is no measurable degradation of the signal in a filter, for example. It would be difficult or impossible to add that much dynamic range with analog circuitry. Replacing analog circuitry with software algorithms eliminates the problems of non-linearity and drift of component values with time and temperature. The programmable nature of most DSP systems means you can make the equivalent of circuit modifications without having to unsolder any components.

Despite its many advantages, we don't mean to imply that DSP is best in all situations. High-power and very high-frequency signals are still the domain of analog circuitry. Where simplicity and low power consumption are primary goals, a DSP solution may not be the best choice. For example, a simple CW receiver that draws a few milliamps from the power supply can be built with two or three analog ICs and a handful of discrete components. We are still a long way from that kind of low power radio using SDR.

In many high-performance systems, the performance of the analog-to-digital converter and digital-to-analog converter are the limiting factors. That is why, even with the latest generation of affordable ADC technology, it is still possible to obtain better blocking dynamic range in an HF receiver using a hybrid analog-digital system rather than going all-digital by routing the RF input directly to an ADC. This may change as A/D converter technology continues to evolve and performance rises.

8.3 Analog-Digital Conversion

Analog-digital conversion consists of taking data in one form, such as digital binary data or an analog ac RF waveform, and creating an equivalent representation of it in the opposite domain. Converters that create a digital representation of analog voltages or currents are called *analog-to-digital converters* (ADC), *analog/digital converters*, *A/D converters* or *A-to-D converters*. Similarly, converters that create analog voltages or currents from digital quantities are called *digital-to-analog converters* (DAC), *digital/analog converters*, *D/A converters* or *D-to-A converters*. The word "conversion" in this first section on the properties of converting information between the analog and digital domains will apply equally to analog-to-digital or digital-to-analog conversion.

Converters are typically implemented as

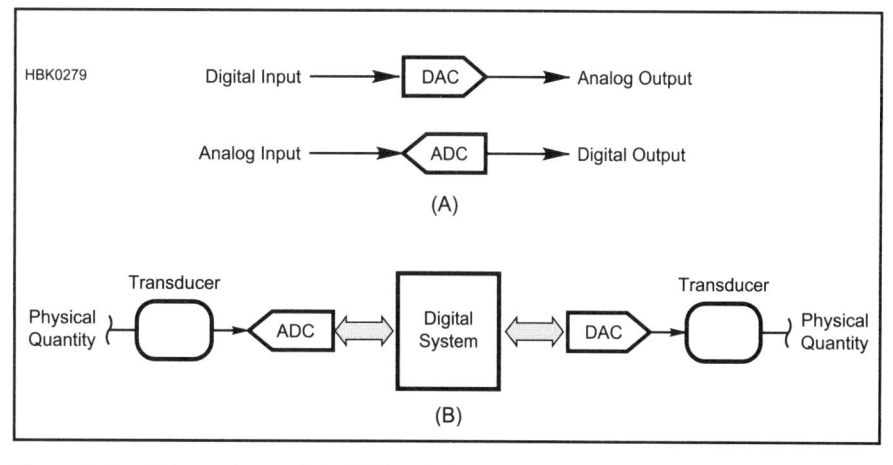

Figure 8.7 — Schematic symbols (A) for digital-to-analog converters (DAC) and analog-to-digital converters (ADC). The general block diagram of a system (B) that digitizes an analog signal, operates on it as digital data, then converts it back to analog form.

integrated circuits that include all of the necessary interfaces and sub-systems to perform the entire conversion process. Schematic symbols for ADCs and DACs are shown in **Figure 8.7**.

This section defines the basic elements of analog-digital conversion along with an overview of different types of converters and their key specifications and behaviors. The following section discusses the use of converters for DSP and SDR functions which are the most demanding application in radio.

8.3.1 Basic Conversion Metrics

Figure 8.8 shows two different representations of the same physical phenomenon; an analog voltage changing from 0 to 1 V. In the analog world, the voltage is continuous and can be represented by any real number between 0 and 1. In the digital world, the number of possible values that can represent any phenomenon is limited by the number of bits contained in each value.

In Figure 8.8, there are only four two-bit digital values 00, 01, 10, and 11, each corresponding to the analog voltage being within a specific range of voltages. If the analog voltage is anywhere in the range 0 to 0.25 V, the digital value representing the analog voltage will be 00, no matter whether the voltage is 0.0001 or 0.24999 V. The range 0.25 to 0.5 V is represented by the digital value 01, and so forth.

The process of converting a continuous range of possible values to a limited number of discrete values is called *digitization* and each discrete value is called a *code* or a *quantization code*. If the code is a binary number, the number of possible codes that can represent an analog quantity is 2^N, where N is the number of bits in the code. A two-bit number can have four codes as shown in Figure 8.8, a four-bit number can have sixteen codes, an eight-bit number 256 codes, and so forth. Assuming that the smallest change in code values is one bit, that value is called the *least significant bit* (LSB) regardless of its position in the format used to represent digital numbers.

Binary-coded-decimal (BCD) is a code in which groups of four bits represent individual decimal values of 0-9. In the *hexadecimal* code, groups of four bits represent decimal values of 0-15. Other types of codes that may be encountered include *Gray code* and *octal*.

RESOLUTION AND RANGE

The *resolution* or *step size* of the conversion is the smallest change in the analog value that the conversion can represent. The *range* of the conversion is the total span of analog values that the conversion can process.

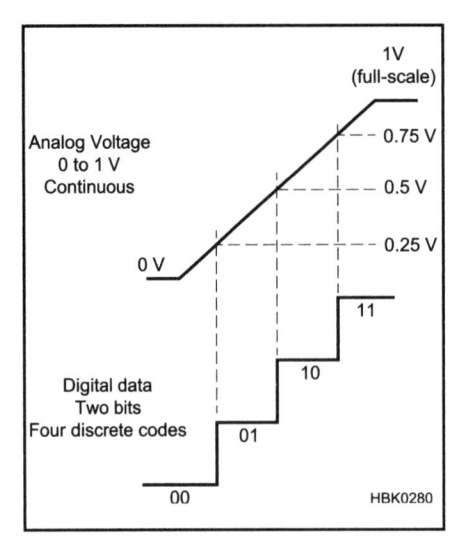

Figure 8.8 — The analog voltage varies continuously between 0 and 1 V, but the two-bit digital system only has four values to represent the analog voltage, so representation of the analog voltage is coarse.

The maximum value in the range is called the *full-scale* (F.S.) value. In Figure 8.8, the conversion range is 1 V. The resolution of the conversion is

$$\text{resolution} = \frac{\text{range}}{2^N}$$

In Figure 8.8, the conversion resolution is $1/4 \times 1$ V = 0.25 V in the figure. If each code had four bits instead, it would have a resolution of $1/2^4 \times 1$ V = 0.083 V. Conversion range does not necessarily have zero as one end point. For example, a conversion range of 5 V may span 0 to 5 V, –5 to 0 V, –2.5 to +2.5 V, and so on.

Analog-digital conversion can have a range that is *unipolar* or *bipolar*. Unipolar means a conversion range that is entirely positive (or negative), usually referring to voltage. Bipolar means the range can take on both positive and negative values.

Because each code represents a range of possible analog values, the limited number of available codes creates *quantization error*. This is the maximum variation in analog values that can be represented by the same code. In Figure 8.8, any value from 0.25 through 0.50 V could be represented by the same code: 01. The quantization error in this case is 0.25 V.

Resolution can also be defined by the number of bits in the conversion. The higher the number of bits, the smaller the resolution as demonstrated above. Since many converters have variable ranges set by external components or voltages, referring to percent resolution or as a number of bits is preferred. The conversions between percent resolution and number of bits are as follows:

$$\% \text{resolution} = \frac{1}{2^N} \times 100\%$$

and

$$N = \frac{\log\left(\frac{100\%}{\% \text{resolution}}\right)}{\log 2}$$

Quantization error can also be specified as a number of least significant bits (LSB) where each bit is equivalent to the conversion's resolution.

ACCURACY

The number of bits of an A/D converter's resolution does not equate to the accuracy of the converter. A companion to resolution, *accuracy* refers to the ability of the converter to either assign the correct code to an analog value or create the true analog value from a specific code. As with resolution, it is most convenient to refer to accuracy as either a percentage of full scale or in bits. *Full-scale error* is the maximum deviation of the code's value or the analog quantity's value as a percentage of the full scale value. If a converter's accuracy is given as 0.02% F.S. and the conversion range is 5 V, the conversion can be in error by as much as 0.02% × 5 V = 1 mV from the correct or expected value. Most A/D converters include provision for user adjustment to calibrate the converter's full-scale range. Some A/D converters include a reference voltage source internal to the device, while others require an external reference. External references can often provide higher accuracy and stability over temperature than internal references. *Offset* has the same meaning in conversion as it does in analog electronics — a consistent shift in the value of the conversion from the ideal value. It can also be adjusted if necessary by the user.

Linearity error represents the maximum deviation of the code transition points from the ideal code transition points after adjusting for the full scale and errors. This is also called *integral nonlinearity* (INL). In the converter of Figure 8.8, ideal step transitions occur at 0.25 V intervals. If the linearity error for the conversion was given as 0.05% F.S., any actual step size could be in error by as much as 0.05% × 5 V = 2.5 mV due to the transition to the next step being at the wrong point. *Differential nonlinearity* is a measure of how much any two adjacent step sizes deviate from the ideal step size. Errors can be represented as a number of bits, usually assumed to be least significant bits, or LSB, with one bit representing the same range as the conversion resolution. A typical A/D converter may specify its INL or DNL error as +/- 0.5 LSB (least-significant bits).

CONVERSION RATE AND BANDWIDTH

Another important parameter of the conversion is the *conversion rate* or its reciprocal, *conversion speed*. A digital code that represents an analog value at a specific time is called a *sample*, so conversion rate, f_S, is specified in *samples per second* (sps) and conversion speed as some period of time per sample, such as 1 msec. Because of the mechanics by which conversion is performed, conversion speed can also be specified as a number of cycles of clock signal used by the digital system performing the conversion. Conversion rate then depends on the frequency of the clock.

According to the *Nyquist Sampling Theorem*, in order to accurately represent the input signal, a conversion must occur at a rate twice the highest frequency present in the analog signal. This minimum rate is the *Nyquist rate* and the maximum frequency allowed in the analog signal is the *Nyquist frequency*. In this way, the converter *bandwidth* is limited to one-half the conversion rate.

Referring to the process of converting analog signals to digital samples, if a lower rate is used, called *undersampling*, false signals called *aliases* will be created in the digital representation of the input signal at frequencies related to the difference between the Nyquist sampling rate and f_S. This is called *aliasing*. Sampling faster than the Nyquist rate is called *oversampling*.

Because conversions occur at some maximum rate, there is always the possibility of signals greater than the Nyquist frequency being present in an analog signal undergoing conversion or that is being created from digital values. These signals would result in aliases and must be removed by *band-limiting filters* that remove them prior to conversion. The mechanics of the sampling process are discussed later in this and following chapters as they apply to specific functions.

8.3.2 Analog-to-Digital Converters

There are a number of methods by which the conversion from an analog quantity to a set of digital samples can be performed. Each has its strong points — simplicity, speed, resolution, accuracy — all affect the decision of which method to use for a particular application. In order to pick the right type of ADC, it is important to decide which of these criteria most strongly affect the performance of your application.

FLASH CONVERTER

The simplest type of ADC is the *flash converter*, shown in **Figure 8.9**. It continually generates a digital representation of the analog signal at its input. The flash converter uses an array of comparators that compare the amplitude of the input signal to a set of reference voltages. There is one reference voltage for each step.

The outputs of the comparator array represent a digital value in which each bit indicates whether the input signal is greater (1) or less than (0) the reference voltage for that comparator. A digital logic *priority encoder* then converts the array of bits into a digital output code. Each successive conversion is available as quickly as the comparators can respond and the priority encoder can create the output code. Flash converters are generally used for applications in which high speed is more important than bits of resolution.

Flash converters are the fastest of all ADCs (conversion speeds can be in the ns range, equivalent to sampling rates in the gigasamples/second range) but do not have high resolution because of the number of com-

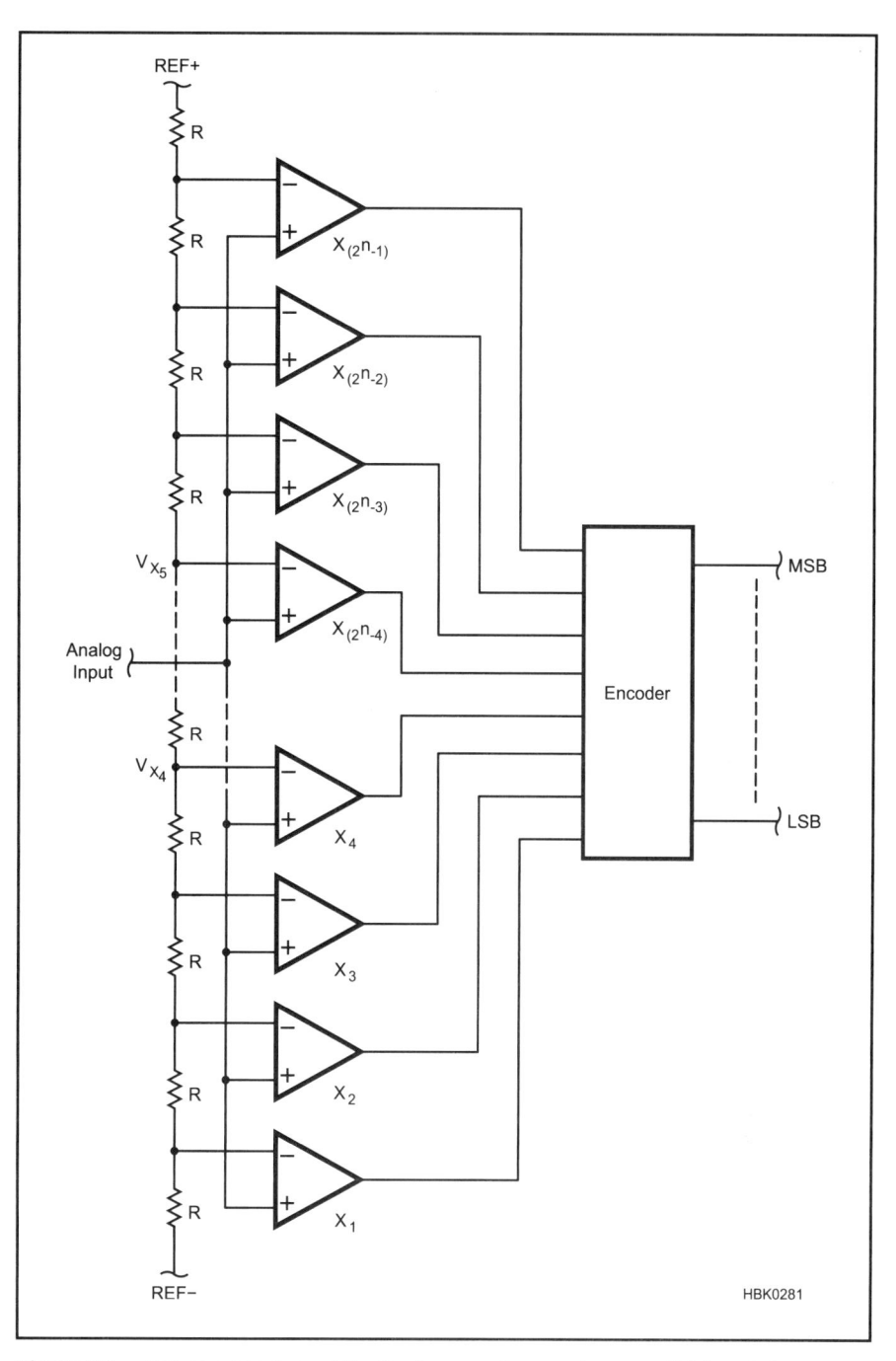

Figure 8.9 — The comparators of the flash converter are always switching state depending on the input signal's voltage. The decoder section converts the array of converter output to a single digital word.

parators and reference voltages required. For example, an 8-bit flash converter requires 255 comparators, while a 12-bit version would require 4095 comparators.

One specialized variant of the flash converter is the *bar-graph display driver*. Such devices accept an analog input and deliver output signals capable of directly driving an LED display rather than a binary digital output word. These devices are commonly used to replace meters as front panel displays for signals that represent relatively slow-varying parameters such as transmitter output power. The LM3914 from Texas Instruments is one such device.

SUCCESSIVE-APPROXIMATION CONVERTER

The *successive-approximation* A/D converter is one of the most widely-used types of converters. As shown in **Figure 8.10**, it uses a single comparator and DAC (digital-to-analog converter) to arrive at the value of the input voltage by comparing it to successive analog values generated by the DAC. This type of converter offers a good compromise of conversion speed and resolution.

The DAC control logic begins a conversion by setting the output of the DAC to 1/2 of the conversion range. If the DAC output is greater than the analog input value, the output of the comparator is 0 and the most significant bit of the digital value is set to 0. The DAC output then either increases or decreases by 1/4 of the range, depending on whether the value of the first comparison was 1 or 0. One test is made for each bit in digital output code and the result accumulated in a storage register, called the Successive-Approximation Register, which is why such converters are often called "SAR" converters. The process is then repeated, forming a series of approximations, until a test has been made for all bits in the code.

While the digital circuitry to implement the SAR is more complex, it is less expensive to build and calibrate than the array of comparators and precision resistors of the flash converter, especially for higher resolutions. Each conversion also takes a known and fixed number of clock cycles. SAR A/D converters are used for speeds up to a few Msps. They are often used with an analog multiplexer in front so that multiple signals in a system can be measured relatively quickly, rather than using a separate converter for every signal.

DUAL-SLOPE INTEGRATING CONVERTERS

The *dual-slope integrating ADC* is shown in **Figure 8.11**. It makes a conversion by integrating the input signal by charging a capacitor for a fixed period of time then measuring the time it takes for the capacitor to discharge back to its starting value. The integration period is often set to reject an interfering signal by integrating it over an exact number of cycles. For example, setting the integration period to 100 ms results in 6 full cycles of a 60 Hz sinusoidal interferer and 5 full cycles of a 50 Hz interferer.

Dual-slope ADCs are low-cost and relatively immune to temperature variations. Due to the slow speed of the conversion these converters are generally only used in test instruments, such as multimeters, or measurement of slowly-varying dc signals.

DELTA-ENCODED CONVERTERS

Instead of charging and discharging a capacitor from 0 V to the level of the input signal, and then back to 0 V, the *delta-encoded ADC* in **Figure 8.12** continually compares the output of a DAC to the input signal using a comparator. Whenever the signal changes, the DAC is adjusted until its output is equal to the input signal. Digital counter circuits keep track of the DAC value and generate the digital output code.

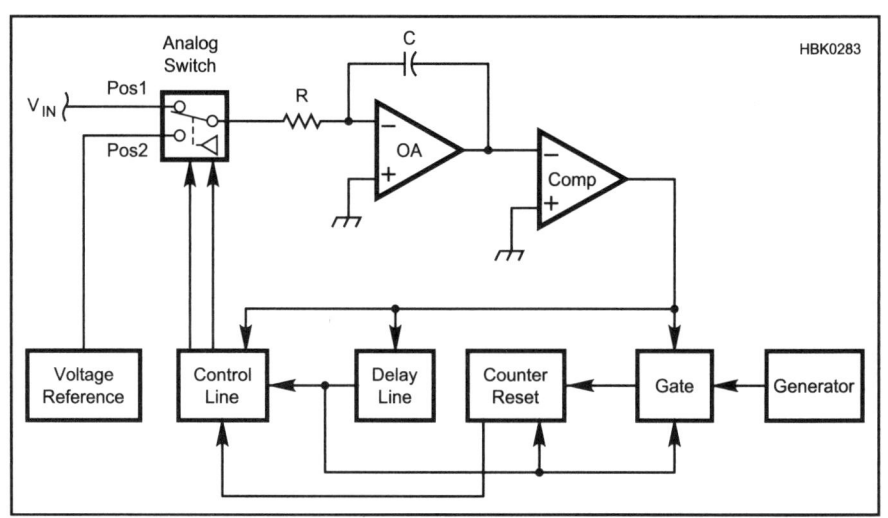

Figure 8.11 — Dual-slope integrating converter. By using a constant-current source to continually charge a capacitor to a known reference voltage then discharge it, the resulting frequency is directly proportional to the resistor value.

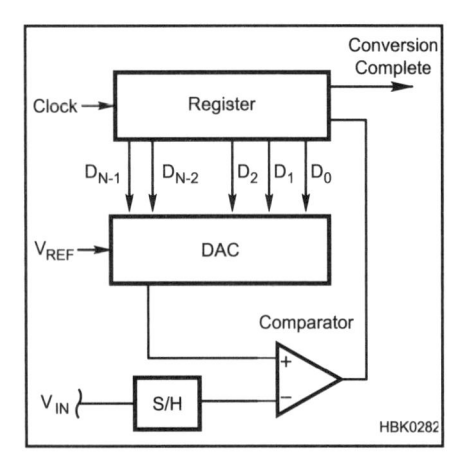

Figure 8.10 — The successive-approximation converter creates a digital word as it varies the DAC signal in order to keep the comparator's noninverting terminal close to the input voltage. A sample-and-hold circuit (S/H) holds the input signal steady while the measurement is being made.

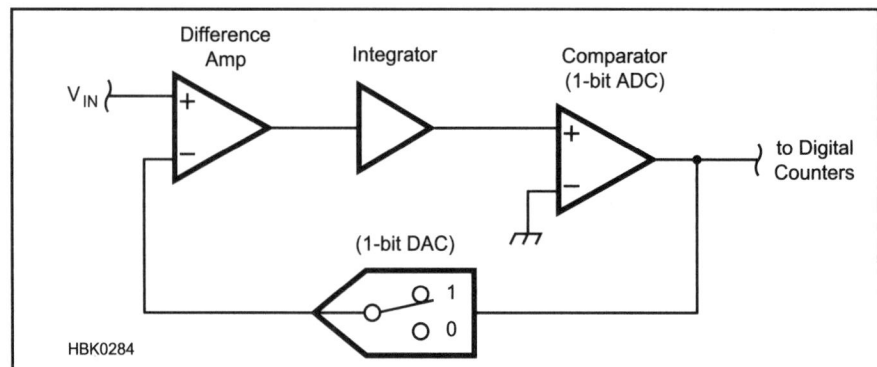

Figure 8.12 — Delta-encoded converter. The 1-bit DAC is operated in such a way that the bit stream out of the comparator represents the value of the input voltage.

SIGMA-DELTA CONVERTERS

The *sigma-delta converter* also uses a DAC and a comparator in a feedback loop to generate a digital signal as shown in **Figure 8.13**. An integrator stores the sum of the input signal and the DAC output. (This is "sigma" or sum in the converter's name.) The comparator output indicates whether the integrator output is above or below the reference voltage and that signal is used to adjust the DAC's output so that the integrator output stays close to the reference voltage. (This is the "delta" in the name.) The stream of 0s and 1s from the comparator forms a high-speed digital bit stream that is digitally-filtered to form the output code. Sigma-delta converters are used where high resolution (16 to 24 bits) is required at sampling rates in the ksps range, including very slowly-varying signals and even audio signals.

OTHER A/D CONVERTER TYPES

There are many more A/D converter architectures but a detailed treatment is beyond the scope of this chapter. Some interesting variations combine multiple stages of converters. For example, multi-stage flash A/D converters apply the output code of a first-stage flash A/D to a D/A converter, and subtract the D/A's output from the original analog input signal sample. The resulting error signal is amplified and applied to another stage of flash A/D conversion. This process may be repeated several times. The multiple stage digital outputs are combined digitally to yield more bits than a single-stage flash converter would produce. In addition, once the error signal has been sampled, the first stage is free to digitize the next sample. The result is a pipeline of output samples flowing continuously, without having to wait for all stages to complete.

A/D and D/A converters are produced using either resistors or capacitors as the bit-weighting elements, and may also include on-chip calibration capability to improve the full-scale, offset, and linearity.

8.3.3 Analog-to-Digital Converter Subsystems

SAMPLE-AND-HOLD

ADCs that use a sequence of operations to create the digital output code must have a means of holding the input signal steady while the measurements are being made. This function is performed by the circuit of **Figure 8.14**. A high input-impedance buffer drives the external storage capacitor, C_{HOLD}, so that its voltage is the same as the input signal. Another high input-impedance buffer is used to provide a replica of the voltage on C_{HOLD} to the conversion circuitry.

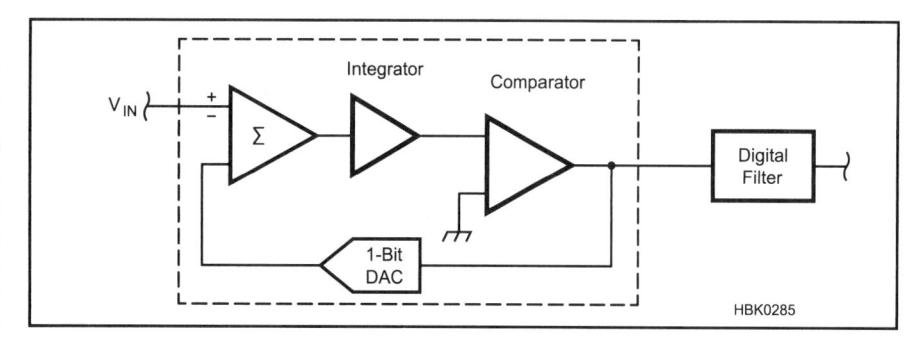

Figure 8.13 — Sigma-delta converter. Similar to the delta-encoded converter (Figure 8.12), the converter runs much faster than the output samples and uses a digital filter to derive the actual output value.

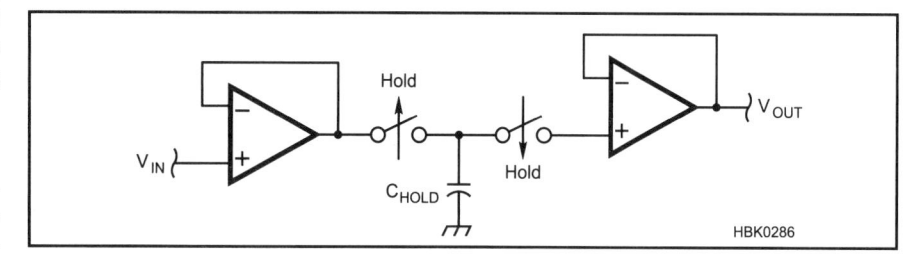

Figure 8.14 — Sample-and-hold (S/H). An input buffer isolates the sampled voltage from the input signal by charging the capacitor C_{HOLD} to that voltage with the input switch closed and the output switch open. When a measurement is being taken, the input switch is open to prevent the input signal from changing the capacitor voltage, and the output switch is closed so that the output buffer can generate a steady voltage at its output.

When a conversion is started, a digital control signal opens the input switch, closes the output switch, and the capacitor's voltage is measured by the converter. It is important that the capacitor used for C_{HOLD} have low *leakage* so that while the measurement is being made, the voltage stays constant for the few ms required. This is of particular important in high-precision conversion.

SINGLE-ENDED AND DIFFERENTIAL INPUTS

The input of most ADCs is *single-ended*, in which the input signal is measured between the input pin and a common ground. Shown in **Figure 8.15A**, this is acceptable for most applications, but if the voltage to be measured is small or is the difference between two nonzero voltages, an ADC with *differential inputs* should be used as in Figure 8.15B. Differential inputs are also useful when measuring current as the voltage across a small resistor in series with the current. In that case, neither side of the resistor is likely to be at ground, so a differential input is very useful. Differential inputs also help avoid the issue of noise contamination as discussed below.

INPUT BUFFERING AND FILTERING

The input impedance of most ADCs is high enough that the source of the input signal is unaffected. However, to protect the ADC input and reduce loading on the input source, an external buffer stage can be used. **Figure 8.16** shows a typical buffer arrangement with clamping diodes to protect against electro-

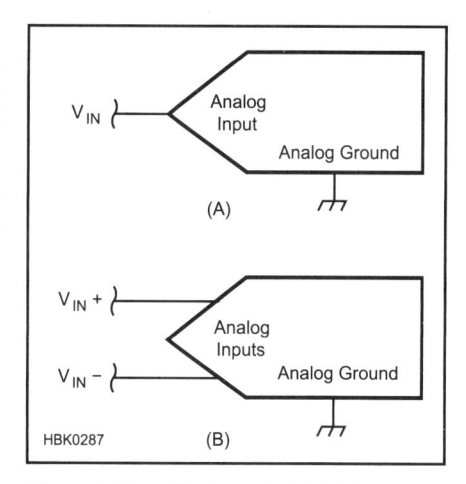

Figure 8.15 — Single-ended ADC inputs have a single active line and a ground or return line (A). Single-ended ADC input are often susceptible to noise and common mode signals or any kind of disturbance on their ground rails. In (B), the differential inputs used help the circuit "ignore" offsets and shifts in the input signal.

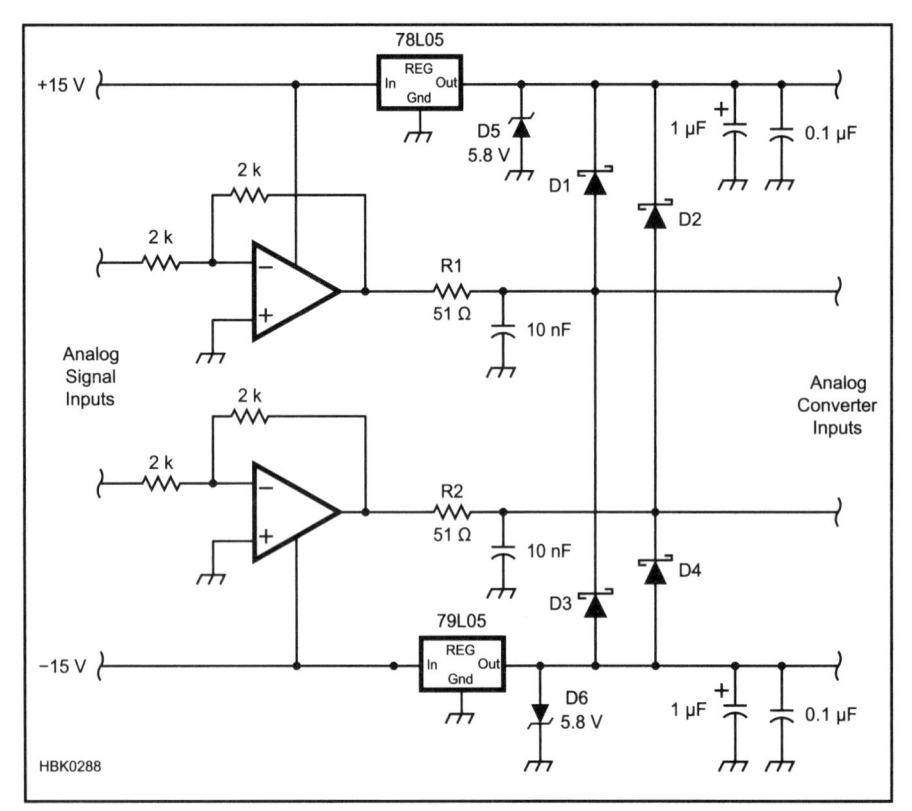

Figure 8.16 — Typical ADC input buffer-filter circuit. Unity-gain voltage followers help isolate the ADC from the input source. RC filters following the buffers act as band-limiting filters to prevent aliasing. Zener diodes are used to clamp the transient voltage and route the energy of transient into the power supply system.

As each new digital value is converted to analog, the output of the DAC makes an abrupt *step change*. Even if very small, the response of the DAC output does not respond perfectly or instantaneously. *Settling time* is the amount of time required for the DAC's output to stabilize within a certain amount of the final value. It is specified by the manufacturer and can be degraded if the load connected to the DAC is too heavy or if it is highly reactive. Settling time is critical in control applications and is also sets the limit on update sampling rate.

Monotonicity is another aspect of characterizing the DAC's accuracy. A DAC is monotonic if in increasing the digital input value linearly across the conversion range, the output of the DAC increases with every step. Because of errors in the internal conversion circuitry, it is possible for there to be some steps that are too small or too large, leading to output values that seem "out of order." These are usually quite small, but if used in a precision control application where the DAC is part of a feedback loop, monotonicity is important because the control system can go unstable.

SUMMING DAC

A *summing DAC*, shown in **Figure 8.17**, is a summing amplifier with all of the inputs connected to a single reference voltage through switches. The digital value to be converted controls which switches are closed. The larger the digital value, the more switches are closed. Higher current causes the summing amplifier's output voltage to be higher, as well.

The input resistors are *binary weighted* so that the summing network resistors representing the more significant bit values inject more current into the op amp's summing junction. Each resistor differs from its neighboring resistors in the amount of current it injects into the summing node by a factor of

static discharge (ESD) and an RC-filter to prevent RF signals or noise from affecting the input signal. In addition, to attenuate higher-frequency signals that might cause aliases, the input filters can also act as band-limiting filters.

ANALOG AND DIGITAL "GROUND"

By definition, ADCs straddle the analog and digital domain. In principle, the signals remain separate and isolated from each other. In practice, however, voltages and currents from the analog and digital circuitry can be mixed together. This can result in the contamination of an analog signal with components of digital signals, and rarely, vice versa. Mostly, this is a problem when trying to measure small voltages in the presence of large power or RF signals.

The usual problem is that currents from high-speed digital circuitry find their way into analog signal paths and create transients and other artifacts that affect the measurement of the analog signal. Thus, it is important to have separate current paths for the two types of signals. The manufacturer of the converter will provide guidance for the proper use of the converter either in the device's data sheet or as application notes. Look for separate pins on the converter, such as "AGND" or "DGND" that indicate how the two types of signal return paths should be connected.

8.3.4 Digital-to-Analog Converters (DAC)

Converting a digital value to an analog quantity is considerably simpler than the reverse, but there are several issues primarily associated with DACs that affect the selection of a particular converter.

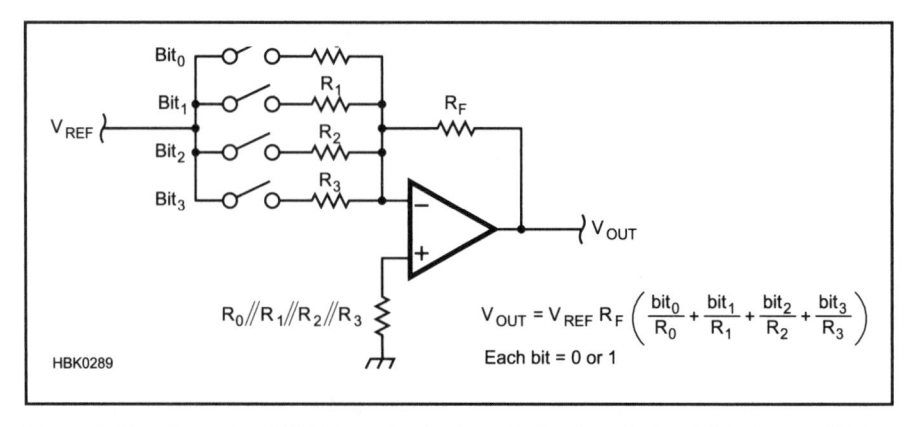

$$V_{OUT} = V_{REF} R_F \left(\frac{bit_0}{R_0} + \frac{bit_1}{R_1} + \frac{bit_2}{R_2} + \frac{bit_3}{R_3} \right)$$

Each bit = 0 or 1

Figure 8.17 — Summing DAC. The output voltage is the inverted, weighted sum of the inputs to each summing resistor at the input. Digital data at the input controls the current into the summing resistors and thus, the output voltage.

two, recreating the effect of each digital bit in the output voltage. At high resolutions, this becomes a problem because of the wide spread in resistor values — a 12-bit DAC would require a spread of 2048 between the largest and smallest resistor values. Summing DACs are generally only available with low resolution for that reason.

The *current output DAC* functions identically to the summing DAC, but does not have an op amp to convert current in the digitally-controlled resistor network to voltage. It consists only of the resistor network, so an external current-to-voltage circuit (discussed in the previous section on op amps) is required to change the current to a voltage. In some applications, the conversion to voltage is not required or it is already provided by some other circuit.

R-2R LADDER DAC

The summing and current output DACs both used binary weighted resistors to convert the binary digital value into the analog output. The practical limitation of this design is the large difference in value between the smallest and largest resistor. For example, in a 12-bit DAC, the smallest and largest resistors differ by a factor of 2048 (which is 2^{12-1}). This can be difficult to fabricate in an IC since it is difficult to match a wide range of resistors values closely enough to maintain the desired binary-weighted relationship with sufficient accuracy. For DACs with high-resolutions of 8 bits or more, the R-2R ladder DAC of **Figure 8.18** is a better design. R-2R DACs can operate in either voltage mode or current mode.

The problems of manufacturing are greatly reduced when resistances are fairly close in value. By using the *R-2R ladder* shown in the figure, the same method of varying current injected into an op amp circuit's summing junction can be accomplished with resistors of only two values, R and 2R. In fact, since the op amp feedback resistor is also one of the IC resistors, the absolute value of the resistance R is unimportant, as long as the ratio of R:2R is maintained. This simplifies manufacturing greatly and is an example of IC design being based on ratios instead of absolute values. For this reason, most DACs use the R-2R ladder design and the performance differences lie mostly in their speed and accuracy.

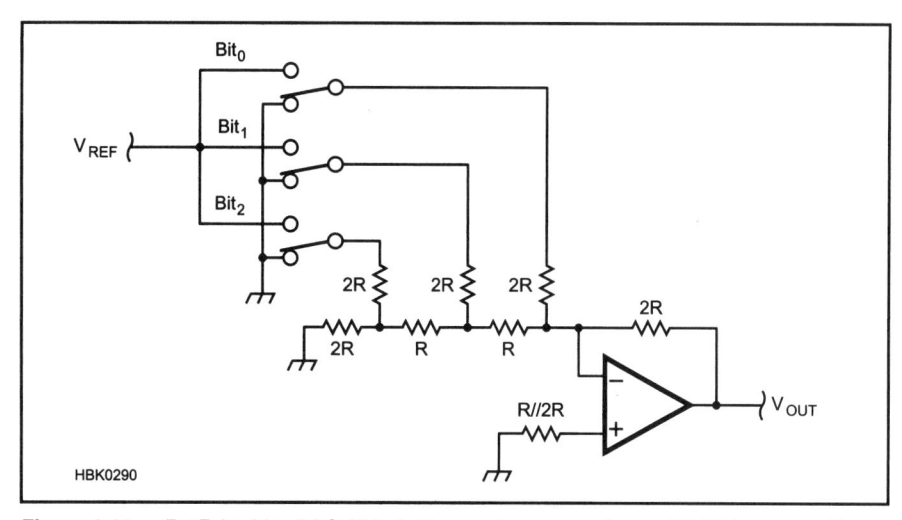

Figure 8.18 — R-2R Ladder DAC. This is the most common form of DAC because all of the resistor values are similar, making it easier to manufacture. The similarity in resistor values also means that there will be less variation of the comparator with temperature and other effects that affect all resistors similarly.

DIGITAL POTENTIOMETERS

Since D/A converters are commonly used to provide digitally-controlled adjustments, a special class of D/A converters has evolved, specifically intended for use as calibration/adjustment devices. These are known as "digital potentiometers". They differ from traditional D/A converters in that they appear as three-terminal variable resistors of known value, and often include non-volatile control registers. They are specified in terms of resistance value, number of steps, and number of devices per package.

8.3.5 Choosing a Converter

From the point of view of performance, choosing a converter, either an ADC or a DAC, comes down to resolution, accuracy and speed. Begin by determining the percent resolution or the dynamic range of the converter. Use the equations in the preceding section to determine the number of bits the converter must have. Select from converters with the next highest number of bits. For example, if you determine that you need 7 bits of resolution, use an 8-bit converter.

Next, consider accuracy. If the converter is needed for test instrumentation, you'll need to perform an *error budget* on the instrument's conversion processes, include errors in the analog circuitry. Once you have calculated percent errors, you can determine the requirements for FS error, offset error, and nonlinearities. If an ADC is going to be used for receiving applications, the spur-free dynamic range may be more important than high precision.

The remaining performance criterion is the speed and rate at which the converter can operate. Conversions should be able to be made at a minimum of twice the bandwidth of the signal you wish to reproduce. If the converter will be running near its maximum rate, be sure that the associated digital interface, supporting circuitry, and software can support the required data rates, too!

Having established the conversion performance requirements, the next step is to consider cost, amount of associated circuitry, power requirements, and so forth. For example, a self-contained ADC is easier to use and takes up less PC board space, but may not be as accurate as one that allows the designer to use an external voltage reference to set the conversion range. Other considerations, such as the nature of the required digital interface, as discussed in the next section, can also affect the selection of the converter.

DSP and SDR Fundamentals 8.11

8.4 Data Converters for SDR and DSP

In this section we will focus more closely on converters for use with DSP and SDR. The first requirement when selecting a DAC or ADC is that it be able to handle the required *sample rate*. For communications-quality voice (300-3000 Hz), a sample rate on the order of 8000 samples per second (8 ksps) is adequate and has been used in the public switched telephone network for decades. For CD-quality music (20-20,000 Hz), the standard sample rate is 44.1 ksps, while 48 ksps and even 96 or 192 ksps are used for newer audio formats and applications such as professional studio equipment.

In an SDR system intended to use microphone inputs and speaker or headphone outputs, there is a need to convert between analog and digital at audio rates. Fortunately, combination A/D and D/A chips and software packages called *codecs* (short for coder-decoder) are readily available to do this job. Both "audio codecs", with sample rates consistent with high-fidelity audio up to 20 kHz or so, and "voice codecs", intended for voice-quality audio up to 4 or 8 kHz) are available. The switched telephone network originally used 8-bit logarithmic codecs to digitize and reconstruct voiceband audio signals. Logarithmic coding was used to compress the dynamic range of a voice signal to reduce the number of bits to be transported.

Today, linear-coded devices have become preferable since DSP algorithms work on linear-coded data and often perform more efficient compression algorithms to reduce the number of bits needed to transport digitized voice. Since audio codecs are used in PC and other consumer systems they are very low cost (or are free if the PC is part of the SDR system). They have more than adequate performance for SDR applications dealing with relatively narrowband signals, such as CW, SSB, AM, and digital signals such as RTTY, PACTOR, and JT65 that use bandwidths comparable to SSB.

Processing wideband RF signals requires data converters with sample rates in the megasamples per second (Msps) range. Fortunately, manufacturers of digital communications infrastructure equipment for the cellular industry have similar needs, and manufacturers of data converter ICs have developed products that are produced in reasonable volume (which lowers the cost) and can be repurposed for amateur SDRs.

The resolution of a data converter expressed as the number of bits in the data words gives an approximation of the converter's signal-to-noise ratio. For example, an 8-bit ADC can only represent the sampled analog signal as one of $2^8 = 256$ possible numbers. The smallest signal that it can resolve is therefore 1/256 of full scale. In terms of signal-to-noise ratio, the rule of thumb is 6 dB per bit, so an ideal 8-bit converter should have a dynamic range of about 48 dB.

The actual formula is slightly different. In an ideal, error-free ADC, the *quantization error* is up to ±1/2 of one least-significant bit (LSB) of the digital word, or ±1/512 of full scale with 8-bit resolution. Similarly, a DAC can only generate the analog signal to within ±1/2 LSB of the desired value. These unavoidable errors are indistinguishable from noise in a signal-processing system.

It can be shown mathematically that a series of uniformly-distributed random numbers between +0.5 LSB and –0.5 LSB has an RMS value of

$$\frac{LSB}{\sqrt{12}}$$

This represents the quantization noise of an A/D.

The **Radio Fundamentals** chapter shows that a sinusoidal signal of 2 volts peak-to-peak (1 V peak) has an RMS voltage equal to 0.707 volts, or $\sqrt{2}/2$ volts. In the case of a full-scale sinusoidal signal applied to an ADC of N bits (2^N LSBs), the RMS signal voltage can be written as $(2^{N-1} LSB)/\sqrt{2}$.

Combining that information results in the following equation for the signal-to-noise ratio in decibels for an ideal data converter word of width N bits:

$$SNR = 20 \log \left(\frac{\frac{2^{N-1} LSB}{\sqrt{2}}}{\frac{LSB}{\sqrt{12}}} \right)$$

which simplifies to

$$SNR = (6.02N + 1.76) \text{ dB}$$

The extra 1.76 dB arises from the fact that noise has a lower RMS value than a sine wave for the same peak-to-peak amplitude. Therefore, with an ideal 8-bit converter, SNR = 49.9 dB. A perfect 16-bit ADC would achieve a 98.1 dB signal-to-noise ratio. Of course, real-world devices are never perfect so actual performance is always somewhat less. Internally-generated noise degrades the SNR, and errors in the linearity of the converter's transfer function give rise to distortion in the form of spurious spectral components and harmonics. (See also "Clocking the RF ADC: Should you worry about jitter or phase noise?" a Texas Instruments application note available for download at **www.ti.com/lit/an/slyt705/slyt705.pdf**.)

Distortion and Noise

Distortion and noise in a conversion are characterized by several parameters all related to linearity and accuracy. THD+N (Total Harmonic Distortion + Noise) is a measure of how much distortion and noise is introduced by the conversion. THD+N can be specified in percent or in dB. Smaller values are better. SINAD (Signal to Noise and Distortion Ratio) is related to THD+N, generally specified along with a desired signal level to show what signal level is required to achieve a certain level of SINAD or the highest signal level at which a certain level of SINAD can be maintained. (See the Analog Devices application note MT-003 by Kester in the Bibliography for further information about SINAD and other noise metrics.)

8.4.1 Using Audio ADC for SDR

A/D and D/A converters used in audio systems and PC "sound cards" are often re-purposed for use in hybrid SDRs. While they may offer as many as 24 bits of resolution, in reality audio A/D converters only provide 110-120 dB of SNR and "dynamic range", and the best "24-bit" audio D/A converters deliver 128 dB. According to the formula above, a 24-bit converter should have 1.76 + (6.02 x 24), or 146.2 dB. What happened to the remaining 20-40 dB?

Part of the reason that audio converters use 24-bit data words is that the recording and playback formats for many systems (such as Blu-Ray Disc and studio equipment) are designed to accommodate 24-bit data words, even if the lower-order bits are essentially meaningless. For reference, a least-significant bit for a typical 24-bit audio converter with a 5 V p-p signal range is about 100 nanovolts (0.1 microvolts) and it is difficult to keep noise that low in the real world.

Furthermore, the testing of A/D converters intended for use in audio systems is different from how we might specify them for radio applications. For example, the "dynamic range" specification in digital audio systems is tested by measuring the THD+N (Total Harmonic Distortion plus Noise) for a 1 kHz input signal at a level 60 dB below full-scale, converting the number to a positive value, then adding 60. For example, an audio D/A converter that delivers THD+N of –51 dB under this test condition can be specified as having a dynamic range of 111 dB. While this is not the same way that communications systems define dynamic range, the goal of both audio and radio systems is to evolve towards higher dynamic range, so the performance generally heads in the right direction in both fields.

SIGMA-DELTA CONVERTERS

The noise spectrum of an A/D converter occupies the bandwidth from dc to one-half the sampling frequency, and is more-or-less uniformly spread out over that range. Thus, in any smaller slice of the output spectrum, the noise is much lower compared to the full-scale output of the converter. Thus, if we have an A/D converter sampling at a very high rate relative to the bandwidth of interest, and then add a digital filter after the A/D converter that eliminates the noise components outside the spectrum of interest, we can in principle increase the SNR in the desired bandwidth. An A/D conversion system that operates this way is said to be *oversampling*.

Oversampling by a factor of N improves the SNR in a given bandwidth by the square root of N since the number of samples of the desired signal is multiplied by N, and the noise, which is uncorrelated, increases as the square root of N. This can be simplified to 3 dB SNR improvement for every doubling of the sample rate. Thus, a 4x oversampling rate is equal to adding another bit of resolution to a converter.

Audio converters are an example of oversampled converters, and usually use a technique known as *sigma-delta modulation*. The sigma-delta converter introduced earlier uses a DAC and a comparator in a feedback loop to generate a digital signal. An integrator stores the sum of the input signal and the DAC output. This is "sigma" or sum in the converter's name. The comparator is in essence a one-bit A/D converter, and its output indicates whether the integrator output is above or below the reference voltage. That signal is used to adjust the DAC's output so that the integrator output stays close to the reference voltage. This is the "delta" in the name. The stream of 0s and 1s from the comparator forms a high-speed digital bit stream that is digitally-filtered to form the output code, at a much lower output sample rate.

Most ADCs and DACs used in audio systems use an extreme form of oversampling, where the internal converter may oversample by a rate of 128 or 256 times the desired output rate. For example, the comparator of an audio A/D intended for a 48 ksps output rate may be clocked at 256 × 48 ksps, or 12.288 MHz. In addition, sigma-delta audio converters use a technique called noise shaping to push most of the quantization noise to frequencies above the audio band, thereby reducing it in the audio spectrum. Noise shaping is accomplished by adding more integrators in the feedback loop of the simple sigma-delta modulator to form a "higher-order loop"

with a low-pass response for the signal, but a high-pass response for the noise. The digital low-pass filter then removes the noise and produces output data words of higher width at the desired sample rate. The high input sampling rate of the converter also relaxes the requirements for external band-limiting (anti-aliasing) filters on the input signal. **Figure 8.19** illustrates the relationship between loop order, sample rate, and improvements in signal-to-noise ratio.

Since audio A/D converters are the audio input device on many PC-based systems, they are quite inexpensive. The Left- and Right-channel stereo inputs can be repurposed and renamed "I" and "Q" for use in SDR applications. Even if the converter specifications are not exactly ideal they provide adequate performance for a hybrid SDR.

8.4.2 High-Speed ADC for SDR

Commercial applications such as cellular base stations have driven the need for high-speed converters capable of sampling RF or high-IF signals directly. These have enabled the development of amateur radio HF transceivers using direct RF sampling. In addition to the usual specifications of linearity, etc., most manufacturers of high-speed data converters intended for use in wideband SDR systems now include a specification for *spurious-free dynamic range* (SFDR). This is the ratio, normally expressed in dB, between a (usually) full-scale sine wave and the worst-case spurious signal. It is a useful figure of merit for comparing such converters. (High-speed SDR hardware from several manufacturers and vendors is addressed in the column "SDR: Simplified" by Ray Mack, W5IFS, in the Jan/Feb 2013 issue of *QEX*.)

PIPELINED ADC ARCHITECTURE

Most high-speed converters intended for SDR applications use a *pipelined* architecture. This type of A/D converter consists of multiple stages, each of which includes a sample-and-hold function, low-resolution A/D and D/A converter, and a gain stage. The first stage performs a coarse quantization

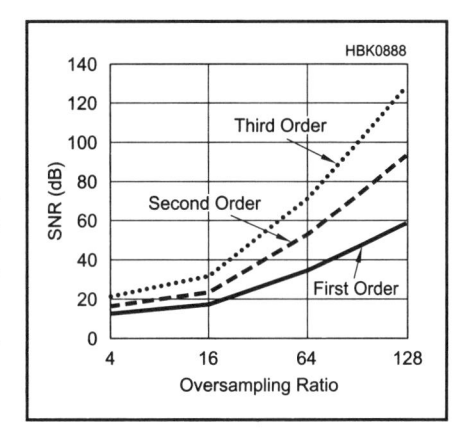

Figure 8.19 — The benefits of noise-shaping as the order of the sigma-delta converter feedback loop is increased.

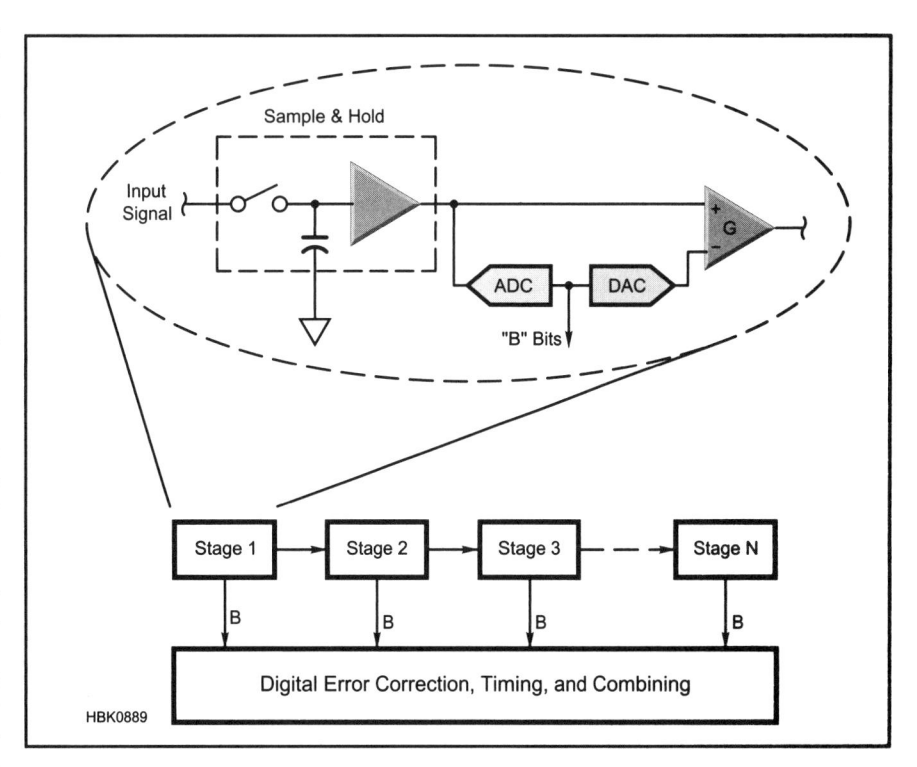

Figure 8.20 — Block diagram of pipelined high-speed A/D converter.

of the input signal, of say, "B" bits, where B is typically 1 to 4 in commercial products. The resultant data word is applied to a D/A converter, and the output analog voltage is subtracted from the original input signal, producing an error signal. That error signal is amplified and passed to another, usually identical, converter stage with enough overlap to compensate for any errors in the previous conversion. Many stages can be connected together, with the last stage only including an A/D converter. The digital outputs from each stage are combined and corrected, as well as time-aligned, to produce a higher-resolution output. **Figure 8.20** illustrates the basic pipelined structure.

Since each stage is typically a low resolution flash converter, pipelined converters are capable of quite high resolution – up to 16 bits – and sample rates in the hundreds of Msps, even into the Gsps (Gigasamples per second) range. There is a delay before the first sample emerges, of course, since an N-stage pipeline converter must perform N conversions before the first valid output is available. However, each successive sample is produced at the full sample rate.

Some pipelined converters also include some basic digital down conversion on chip, with some degree of programmability.

The cost of an A/D or D/A converter is generally proportional to both speed and resolution, so it is important to avoid over specifying these components. Later in this chapter we will discuss how to determine the required sample rate and resolution for a given application.

While sample rate, resolution, and SFDR are the principal selection criteria for data converters in a DSP system, other parameters such as signal-to-noise ratio, harmonic and intermodulation distortion, full-power bandwidth, and aperture delay jitter can also affect system performance. Of course, basic specifications such as power requirements, interface type (serial or parallel), and cost also determine a device's suitability for a particular application. As with any electronic component, it is very important to read and fully understand the data sheet.

Most manufacturers of high-performance converters also include recommendations on support circuitry to be used with their devices to extract the best possible performance. For example, some ADCs require buffer amplifiers to drive the input, or external voltage references to set the full scale range. Many converters, especially high-speed and high-resolution devices are very sensitive to circuit layout, power supply decoupling and grounding. Most manufacturers provide evaluation boards to allow testing the converter IC on the bench, and the layout files can be copied into the final system design.

CLOCKING HIGH-SPEED CONVERTERS

ADCs generally require some kind of clock function to set the sample rate. Any cycle-to-cycle variation in the sample timing ("jitter") causes an error. It can be shown that in RF-sampling converters, sample-clock jitter is analogous to phase noise in the local oscillators of analog radios, and can degrade the performance of the converter substantially. **Figure 8.21** shows how this comes about.

As A/D and D/A converters achieve higher and higher sample rates and signal bandwidths, the clocking becomes critical. Most logic families produce output waveforms that have more timing jitter than can be tolerated.

The degradation of a high-frequency sampled signal due to sample jitter can be calculated and plotted. In **Figure 8.22** you can see that a 100 MHz signal sampled with a 1ps jitter sample clock (typical of ACT-series logic gates) will have just over 60 dB of signal-to-noise ratio, about equal to 10 bit performance, even if the A/D converter is capable of 16 bits! Improving the sample clock jitter to 0.125 ps using a specialized clock-distribution IC, improves the system performance to nearly 14 bits.

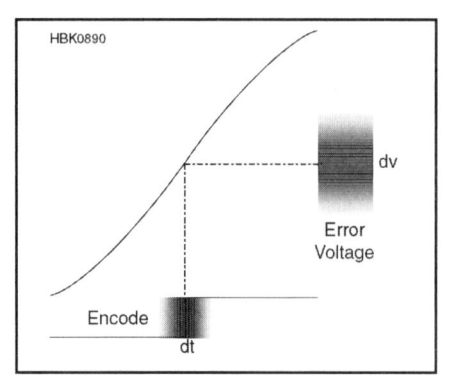

Figure 8.21 — RMS jitter vs. rms noise effect of sampling uncertainty on signal-to-noise. [from Figure 1 of Analog Devices Application Note AN-501, available at www.analog.com, used with permission]

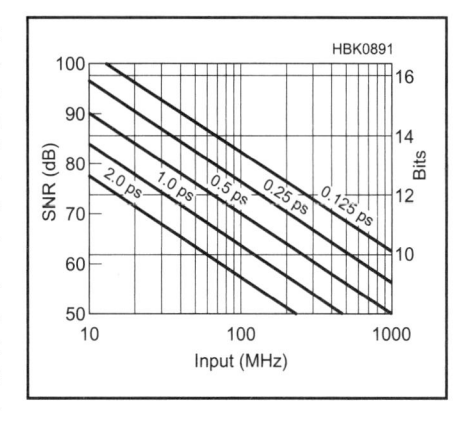

Figure 8.22 — Signal-to-noise ratio due to aperture jitter. [from Figure 1 of Analog Devices Application Note AN-501, available at www.analog.com, used with permission]

8.5 Digital Signal Processors

The term *digital signal processor* (DSP) is commonly understood to mean a special-purpose microprocessor with an architecture that has been optimized for signal processing rather than data processing. And indeed, in many systems the box labeled "DSP" in Figure 8.1 is such a device. A microprocessor has the advantage of flexibility because it can easily be re-programmed. Even with a single program, it can perform many completely different tasks at different points in the code. On-chip hardware resources such as multipliers and other computational units are used efficiently because they are shared among various processes.

That is also the Achilles' heel of programmable DSPs. Any hardware resource that is shared among various processes can be used by only one process at a time. That can create bottlenecks that limit the maximum computation speed. Some DSP chips include multiple computational units or multiple *cores* (basically multiple copies of the entire processor) that can be used in parallel to speed up processing.

8.5.1 Microprocessor-type DSP ICs

Programming a DSP IC is relatively easy. C compilers are available for most devices, so you don't have to learn assembly language. Typically you include a connector on your circuit board into which is plugged an *in-circuit programmer* (ICP), which is connected to a PC via a serial or USB cable. The software is written and compiled on the PC and then downloaded to the DSP. The same hardware often also includes an *in-circuit debugger* (ICD) so that the program can be debugged on the actual circuitry used in the design. The combination of the editor, compiler, programmer, debugger, simulator and related software is called an *integrated development environment* (IDE).

Until recently, you had to use an *in-circuit emulator* (ICE), which is a device that plugs into the circuit board in place of the microprocessor. The ICE provides sophisticated debugging tools that function while the emulator runs the user's software on the target device at full speed. Nowadays, however, it is more common to use the ICD function that is built into many DSP chips and which provides most of the functions of a full-fledged ICE. It is much cheaper and does not require using a socket for the microprocessor chip.

The architecture of a digital signal processor shares some similarities to that of a general-purpose microprocessor but also differs in important respects. For example, DSPs generally don't spend much of their lives handling large computer files, so they tend to have a smaller memory address space than processors intended to be used in computers. On the other hand, the memory they do have is often built into the DSP chip itself to improve speed and to reduce pin count by eliminating the external address and data bus.

Most microprocessors use the traditional *Von Neumann architecture* in which the program and data are stored in the same memory space. However, most DSPs use a *Harvard architecture*, which means that data and program are stored in separate memories. That speeds up the processor because it can be reading the next program instruction at the same time as it is reading or writing data in response to the previous instruction. Some DSPs have two data memories so they can read and/or write two data words at the same time. Most devices actually use a modified Harvard architecture by providing some (typically slower and less convenient) method for the processor to read and write data to program memory.

Probably the key difference between general-purpose and digital-signal processors is

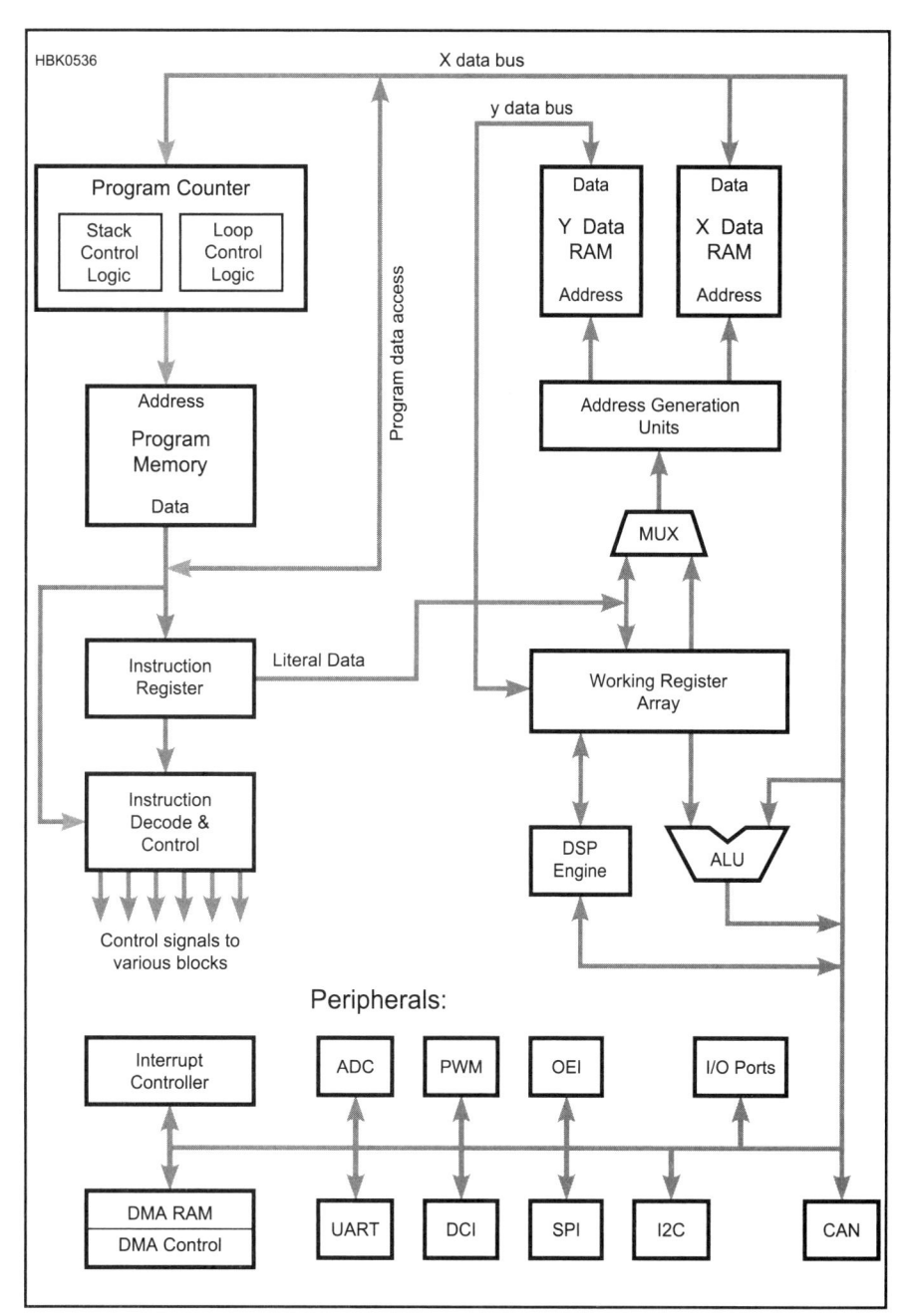

Figure 8.23 — Simplified block diagram of a dsPIC processor.

in the computational core, often called the *arithmetic logic unit* (ALU). The ALU in a traditional microprocessor only performs integer addition, subtraction and bitwise logic operations such as AND, OR, one-bit shifting and so on. More-complicated calculations, such as multiplication, division and operations with floating-point numbers, are done in software routines that exercise the simple resources of the ALU multiple times to generate the more-complicated results.

In contrast, a DSP has special hardware to perform many of these operations much faster. For example, the *multiplier-accumulator* (MAC) multiplies two numbers and adds (accumulates) the product with the previous results in a single step. Many common DSP algorithms involve the sum of a large number of products, so nearly all DSPs include this function. **Figure 8.23** is a simplified block diagram of the dsPIC series from Microchip. Its architecture is basically that of a general-purpose microcontroller to which has been added a DSP engine, which includes a MAC, a barrel shifter and other DSP features. It uses a modified Harvard architecture with two data memories that can be simultaneously accessed.

8.5.2 Fixed-Point versus Floating-Point

DSP microprocessors are sometimes differentiated on their ability to handle fixed-point (integer) or *floating-point* numbers.

A floating-point number is the binary equivalent of scientific notation. Recall that the decimal integer 123000 is expressed as 1.23×10^5 in scientific notation. It is common practice to place the decimal point after the first non-zero digit and indicate how many digits the decimal point must be moved by the *exponent* of ten, 5 in this case. The 1.23 part is called the *mantissa*. In a computer, base-2 binary numbers are used in place of the base-10 decimal numbers used in scientific notation. The *binary point* (equivalent to the decimal point in a decimal number) is assumed to be to the left of the first non-zero bit. For example the binary number 00110100 when converted to a 16-bit floating point number would have an 11-bit mantissa of 11010000000 (with the binary point assumed to be to the left of the first "1") and a 5-bit exponent of 00110 (decimal +6).

A floating point number can represent a signal with much more dynamic range than an integer number with the same number of bits. For example, a 16-bit fixed-point signed integer can vary from –32768 to +32767. The difference between the smallest (1) and largest signal that can be represented is $20 \log(65535) = 96$ dB. If the 16 bits are divided into an 11-bit mantissa and 5-bit exponent, the available range is $20 \log(2048) = 66$ dB from the mantissa and $20 \log(2^{32}) = 193$ dB from the exponent for a total of 259 dB. The disadvantage is that the mantissa has less resolution, potentially increasing noise and distortion. Normally floating-point numbers are at least 32 bits wide to mitigate that effect.

Some DSPs can process floating-point numbers directly in hardware. Fixed-point DSPs can also handle floating-point numbers, but it must be done in software and that slows the computations down. The additional dynamic range afforded by floating-point processing is normally not needed for radio communications signals. The dynamic range of radio signals can usually be handled by the 16-bit data words used by most fixed-point DSPs. Using integer arithmetic and a fixed-point processor saves the additional cost of a floating-point processor or the additional computational overhead of floating-point calculations on a fixed-point device. However, it requires careful attention to detail on the part of the programmer to make sure the signal can never exceed the maximum integer value or get so weak that the signal-to-noise ratio is degraded. If cost or computation time is not an issue, it is much easier to program in floating point since dynamic range issues can be ignored for most computations.

The term *pipeline* refers to the ability of a microprocessor to perform portions of several instructions at the same time. The sequence of operations required to perform an instruction is broken down into steps. Since each step is performed by a different chunk of hardware, different chunks can be working on different instructions at the same time. Most DSPs have at least a simple form of pipelining in which the next instruction is being fetched while the previous instruction is being executed. Some DSPs can do a multiply-accumulate while the next two multiplicands are being read from memory and the previous accumulated result is being stored so that the entire operation can occur in a single clock cycle. MACs per second is a common figure of merit for measuring DSP speed. For conventional microprocessors, a more common figure of merit is millions of instructions per second (MIPS) or floating-point operations per second (FLOPS).

Many DSPs have a sophisticated address generation unit that can automatically increment one or more data memory pointers so that repetitive calculations can step through memory without the processor having to calculate the addresses. *Zero-overhead looping* is the ability to automatically jump the address pointer back to the beginning of the array when it reaches the end. That saves several microprocessor instructions per loop that normally would be required to check the current address and jump when it reaches a predetermined value.

While most DSPs do not include a full hardware divider, some do include special instructions and hardware to speed up division calculations. A *barrel shifter* is another common DSP feature. It allows shifting a data word a specified number of bits in a single clock cycle. *Direct memory access* (DMA) refers to special hardware that can automatically transfer data between memory and various peripheral devices or ports without processor overhead.

8.5.3 DSP in Embedded Systems

An *embedded system* is a device that is not a "computer" but nevertheless has a microprocessor or DSP chip embedded somewhere in its circuitry. Examples are microwave ovens, automobiles, mobile telephones and software-defined radios. DSPs intended for embedded systems often include a wide array of on-chip peripherals such as various kinds of timers, multiple hardware interrupts, serial ports of various types, a real-time clock, pulse-width modulators, optical encoder interfaces, A/D and D/A converters and lots of general-purpose digital I/O pins. Some DSPs have architectures that are well-suited for general-purpose control applications as well as digital signal processing.

Table 8.1 lists some manufacturers of DSP chips targeted to embedded systems. It should be mentioned that microprocessors made by Intel and AMD and intended for use as CPUs in personal computers also include extensive DSP capability. However, they are optimized for data-processing applications under an operating system such as Windows or Linux, and are not very efficient at signal-processing applications.

8.5.4 Typical DSP Processors

When selecting a DSP device for a new design, often the available development environment is more important than the characteristics of the device itself. Microchip's dsPIC family of DSPs was chosen for the examples in this chapter because their integrated development environment is extensive and easy to use and the IDE software is available for free download from their website.[5] The processor instruction set is a superset of the PIC24 family of general-purpose microcontrollers, with which many hams are already familiar. The company offers a line of low-cost evaluation boards and starter kits as well as an inexpensive in-circuit debugger, the ICD 3. The free IDE software includes a simulator that can run dsPIC software on a PC (at a much slower rate, of course), so that you can experiment with DSP algorithms before buying any hardware.

The Microchip DSP family is limited to 70 million instructions per second. In a sys-

Table 8.1
Manufacturers of DSP Microprocessors

Company	Family	Data Bits	Speed MMACs	Nr. of Cores	ROM (bytes)	RAM (bytes)	Notes
Analog Devices www.analog.com	ADSP-21xx	16	25-160	1	12k-144k	8k-112k	Easy assembly language
	SHARC	32/40 fp	300-900	1	2-4M	0.5-5M	Runs fixed or floating point
	Blackfin	16/32	400-2400	1-2	External	53k-328k	Many on-chip peripherals
Cirrus Logic www.cirrus.com	CS48xxxx	32	150	1		96k	Audio applications
	CS49xxxx	32	300	2	512k	296k-328k	Audio applications
NXP www.nxp.com	StarCore	16	1000-48,000	1-6	External	0-1436k	former Freescale products
Microchip www.microchip.com	dsPIC	16	30-70	1	6k-256k	256-32k	Also a microcontroller Free IDE software
Texas Instruments www.ti.com	C5000	16	50-600	1	8k-256k	0-1280k	
	C6000	16/64 fp	300-24,000	1-3	0-384k	32k-3072	Fixed or floating point versions
Zilog www.zilog.com	Z89xxx	16	20	1	4k-8k	512	

tem with, say, a 70 kHz sample rate, 1000 instructions per sample are available which should be plenty if the calculations are not too complex. However if the sample rate is 1 MHz, then you get only 70 instructions per sample, which likely would be insufficient.

If more horsepower is required, you'll need to select a processor from a different manufacturer. Look for one with a well-integrated suite of development software that is powerful and easy to use. Also check out the cost and availability of development hardware such as evaluation kits, programmers and debuggers. Once those requirements are met, then you can move on to selecting a specific device with the performance and features required for your application. It can be helpful at the beginning of a project to first write some of the key software routines and test them on a simulator to estimate execution times, in order to determine how powerful a processor is needed.

When estimating execution time, don't forget to include the effect of interrupts. Most DSP systems require real-time response and make extensive use of interrupts to ensure that certain events happen at the correct times. Although this is hidden from the programmer's view when programming in C, the interrupt service routines contain quite a bit of overhead each time they are called (to save the processor state when responding and to recall the state just before returning from the interrupt). Sometimes an interrupt may be called more often than you expect, which can eat up processor cycles and so increase the execution time of other unrelated routines.

In the past, may embedded systems were written in assembly language so save memory and increase processing speed. Many early microprocessors and DSPs did not have enough memory to support a high-level language. Today, most processors have sufficient memory and processing speed to support a C kernel and library without difficulty. For anything but the simplest of programs, it is not only faster and easier to develop software in C but it is easier to support and maintain as well, especially if people other than the original programmer might become involved. Far more people know the C programming language than any particular processor's assembly language. It is true that the version of C used on a DSP chip is usually modified from standard ANSI C to support specific hardware features, but it would still be far easier to learn for a programmer familiar with writing C code on a PC or on a different DSP.

A common technique is first to write the entire application in C. Then, if execution time is not acceptable, analyze the system to determine in which software routines the bottlenecks are occurring. You can then rewrite those routines in assembly language. Having an already-working version written in C (even if too slow) can be helpful in testing and troubleshooting the equivalent assembly language.

8.5.5 DSP Without a Dedicated Processor

One way to speed up processing is to move all or part of the computations from the programmable DSP to an *application-specific integrated circuit* (ASIC), which has an architecture that has been optimized to perform some specific DSP function.

You could also design your own application-specific circuitry using a PC board full of discrete logic devices. Nowadays, however, it is more common to do that with a *programmable-logic device* (PLD). This is an IC that includes many general-purpose logic elements, but the connections between the elements are undefined when the device is manufactured. The user defines those connections by programming the device to perform whatever function is required. PLDs come in a wide variety of types, described by an alphabet soup of acronyms.

Programmable-array logic (PAL), *programmable logic array* (PLA), and *generic array logic* (GAL) devices are relatively simple arrays of AND gates, OR gates, inverters and latches. They are often used as "glue logic" to replace the miscellaneous discrete logic ICs that would otherwise be used to interface various larger digital devices on a circuit board. They are sometimes grouped under the general category of *small PLD* (SPLD). A *complex PLD* (CPLD) is similar but bigger, often consisting of an array of PALs with programmable interconnections between them.

A *field-programmable gate array* (FPGA) is bigger yet, with up to millions of gates per device. An FPGA includes an array of *complex logic blocks* (CLB), each of which includes some programmable logic, often

Table 8.2
PLD Manufacturers

Company	Devices	URL	Notes
Achronix	FPGA	www.achronix.com	High-speed FPGAs
Atmel	SPLD, CPLD, PGA, ASIC	www.atmel.com	Fine-grain-reprogrammable FPGAs with AVR microprocessors on chip
Intel	CPLD, FPGA, ASIC	www.intel.com/FPGA	Formerly Altera
Lattice Semiconductor	SPLD, CPLD, FPGA	www.latticesemi.com	Flash-based nonvolatile FPGAs
Microsemi	FPGA	www.microsemi.com	Mixed-signal flash-based FPGAs
Xilinx	CPLD, FPGA	www.xilinx.com	One of the top FPGA vendors

implemented with a RAM *look-up table* (LUT), and output registers. *Input/output blocks* (IOB) also contain registers and can be configured as input, output, or bi-directional interfaces to the IC pins. The interconnections between blocks are much more flexible and complicated than in CPLDs. Some FPGAs also include higher-level circuit blocks such as general-purpose RAM, dozens or hundreds of hardware multipliers, and even entire on-chip microprocessors.

Some of the more inexpensive PLDs are *one-time programmable* (OTP), meaning you have to throw the old device away if you want to change the programming. Other devices are re-programmable or even *in-circuit programmable* (ICP) which allows changing the internal circuit configuration after the device has been soldered onto the PC board, typically under the control of an on-board microprocessor. That offers the best of both worlds, with speed nearly as fast as an ASIC but retaining many of the benefits of the reprogrammability of a microprocessor-type DSP. Most large FPGAs store their programming in *volatile memory*, which is RAM that must be re-loaded every time power is applied, typically by a ROM located on the same circuit board. Some FPGAs have programmable ROM on-chip.

Programming a PLD is quite different from programming a microprocessor. A microprocessor performs its operations sequentially — only one operation can be performed at a time. Writing a PLD program is more like designing a circuit. Different parts of the circuit can be doing different things at the same time. Special *hardware-description languages* (HDL) have been devised for programming the more complicated parts such as ASICs and FPGAs. The two most common industry-standard HDLs are Verilog and VHDL. (The arguments about which is "best" approach the fervor of the *Windows* vs *Linux* wars!) There is also a version of the C++ programming language called SystemC that includes a series of libraries that extend the language to include HDL functions. It is popular with some designers because it allows simulation and hardware description using the same software tool.

Despite the speed advantage of FPGAs, most amateurs use microprocessor-type devices for their DSP designs, supplemented with off-the-shelf ASICs where necessary. The primary reason is that the design process for an FPGA is quite complicated, involving obtaining and learning to use several sophisticated software tools. The steps involved in programming an FPGA are:

1. Simulate the design at a high abstraction level to prove the algorithms.
2. Generate the HDL code, either manually or using some tool.
3. Simulate and test the HDL program.
4. Synthesize the gate-level netlist.
5. Verify the netlist.
6. Perform a timing analysis.
7. Modify the design if necessary to meet timing constraints.
8. "Place and route" the chip design.
9. Program and test the part.

Many of the software tools needed to perform those steps are quite expensive, although some manufacturers do offer free proprietary software for their own devices. Some principal manufacturers are listed in **Table 8.2**.

8.5.6 Using Graphics Processors for DSP

As PCs have become used for graphics-intensive applications such as games, developers quickly found out that the microprocessor chip in the PC was unable to provide enough computing horsepower to do complex graphics functions like 3D rendering, shading, etc. This gave rise to a new breed of specialized processors called Graphics Processing Units (GPU). These processors consist of simple computational blocks that are capable of only a few functions like multiplication and addition. However, unlike a typical PC CPU with a handful of cores to speed up processing, GPUs have hundreds or even thousands of cores! In addition, they are optimized for handling large arrays of data. This makes them well suited for DSP functions such as Fast Fourier Transforms.

Fortunately, some manufacturers of GPUs have recognized that their products are useful for applications other than graphics, and are now providing libraries and programming support for using their products in communications systems such as SDR. GPU manufacturer Nvidia, for example, offers the CUDA parallel computing platform and programming model with the cuFFT library.

The inexpensive Linux-based Raspberry Pi computer board has become very popular among amateurs and experimenters. The BCM283x main processor is a system-on-chip device manufactured by Broadcom (now owned by Avago) that contains both a CPU and a GPU. At 700MHz to 1.2 GHz, the CPU is too underpowered for many of the DSP algorithms used in SDR. However, the graphics processor included in the processor can be programmed to do some of the FFT algorithms, and offers a 10x speed improvement.[6]

8.6 Digital (Discrete-time) Signals

Digital signals differ from analog signals in two ways. One is that they are digitized in time, a process called *sampling*. The other is that they are digitized in amplitude, a process called *quantization*. Sampling and quantization affect the digitized signal in different ways so the following sections will consider their effects separately.

8.6.1 Sampling — Digitization in Time

Sampling is the process of measuring a signal at discrete points in time and recording the measured values. An example from history is recording the number of sunspots. If an observer goes out at noon every day and writes down the number of observed sunspots, then that data can be used to plot sunspot number versus time. In this case, we say the *sample rate* is one sample per day. The data can then be analyzed in various ways to determine short and long-term trends. After recording only a few months of data it will quickly become apparent that sunspot number has a marked periodicity — the numbers tend to repeat every 27 days (which happens to be the rotation rate of the sun as seen from earth).

What if, instead of taking a reading once a day, the readings were taken only once per month? With a 30-day sample period, the 27-day periodicity would likely be impossible to see. Clearly, the sample rate must be at least some minimum value to accurately represent the measured signal. Based on earlier work by Harry Nyquist, Claude Shannon proved in 1948 that in order to sample a signal without loss of information, the sample rate must be greater than the *Nyquist rate*, which is two times the bandwidth of the signal. In other words, the bandwidth must be less than the *Nyquist frequency*, which is one-half the sample rate. This is known as the *Nyquist sampling criterion*.

That simple rule has some profound implications. If all the frequency components of a signal are contained within a bandwidth of B Hz, then sampling at a rate greater than 2B samples per second is sufficient to represent the signal with 100% accuracy and with no loss of information. It is theoretically possible to convert the samples back to an analog signal that is exactly identical to the original.

Of course, a real-world digital system measures those samples with only a finite number of bits of resolution, with consequences that we will investigate in the section on quantization that follows. In addition, sampling theory assumes that there is absolutely no signal energy outside the specified bandwidth; in other words the stopband attenuation is infinity dB. Any residual signal in the stop-band shows up as distortion or noise in the sampled signal.

To simplify the discussion, let's think about sampling a signal of a single frequency (a sine wave). **Figure 8.24** illustrates what happens if the sample rate is too low. As shown, the sample rate is approximately 7/8 the sine-wave frequency. You can see that the sampled signal has a period about 8 times greater than the period of the sine wave, or 1/8 the frequency. The samples are the same as if the analog signal had been a sine wave of 1/8 the actual frequency.

That is an example of a general principle. Sampling a signal produces an output with components at frequencies equal to the difference between the actual frequency of the analog signal and the sample rate. If the sampling rate is too low (or the input signal too high in frequency) the signal at $(f_s - f_{sig})$ is indistinguishable from an in-band signal, which is why the new signal is called an *alias*. In the above example, the alias frequency f_o is

$$f_o = f_{sig} - f_s = (1 - 7/8)f_{sig} = (1/8)f_{sig}$$

where f_{sig} is the frequency of the signal before sampling and f_s is the sample rate.

The sampling process also creates aliases from any input signals around harmonics of the sampling frequency. **Figure 8.25** shows the frequency-domain representation of the signal relationships in a sampled-data system. Figure 8.25A shows the spectrum of a single sine wave input signal, and Figure 8.25B shows the spectrum of the sampling clock and its harmonics. You can look at Figure 8.25C two ways. First, you can consider all the individual frequencies as the output signals generated by sampling the input signal at f_o. On the other hand, those are also the input signal frequencies that alias to f_o, calculated from the equation

$$f_{sig} = |f_o - Nf_s|$$

where N is the harmonic number. Experienced RF engineers will recognize this phenomenon as being very similar to image-generation in the mixing process of a heterodyne receiver. The sampled signal (equivalent to the mixer output) contains the sum and difference frequencies of the input signal and all the harmonics of the sample frequency. Figure 8.25D shows the more general case of sampling a band of signals between f_L and f_H. Note the inversion of the aliased spectrum that extends below fs. If f_H is higher than $f_S/2$, the higher frequencies in the band will overlap

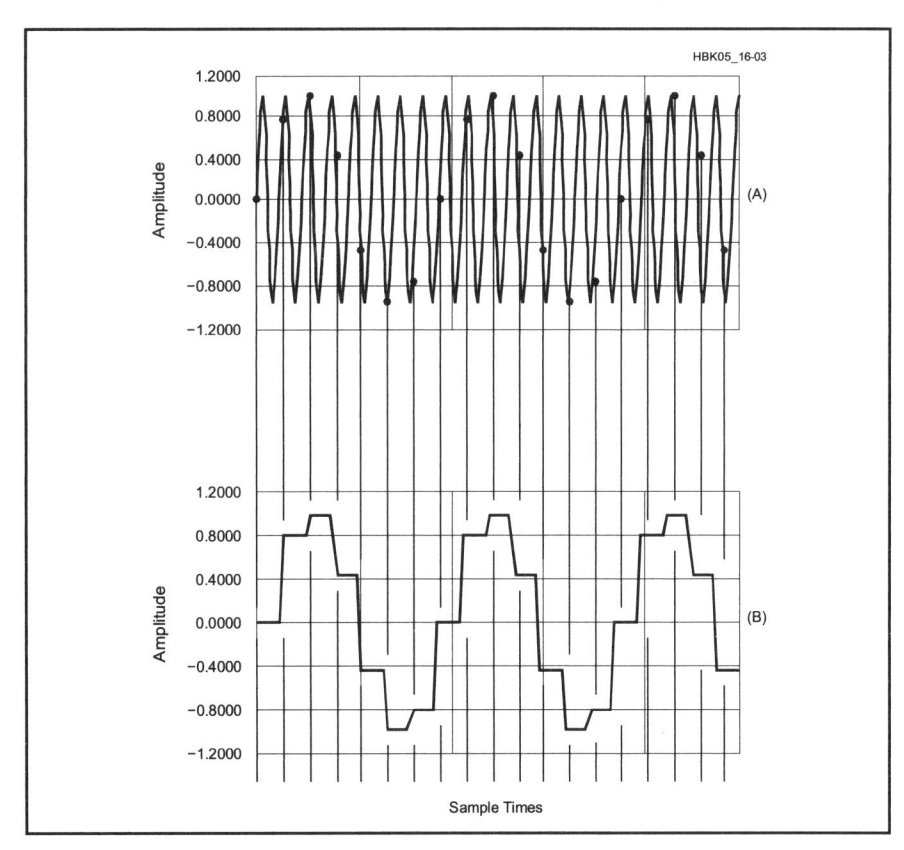

Figure 8.24 — Undersampled sine wave (A). Samples aliased to a lower frequency (B).

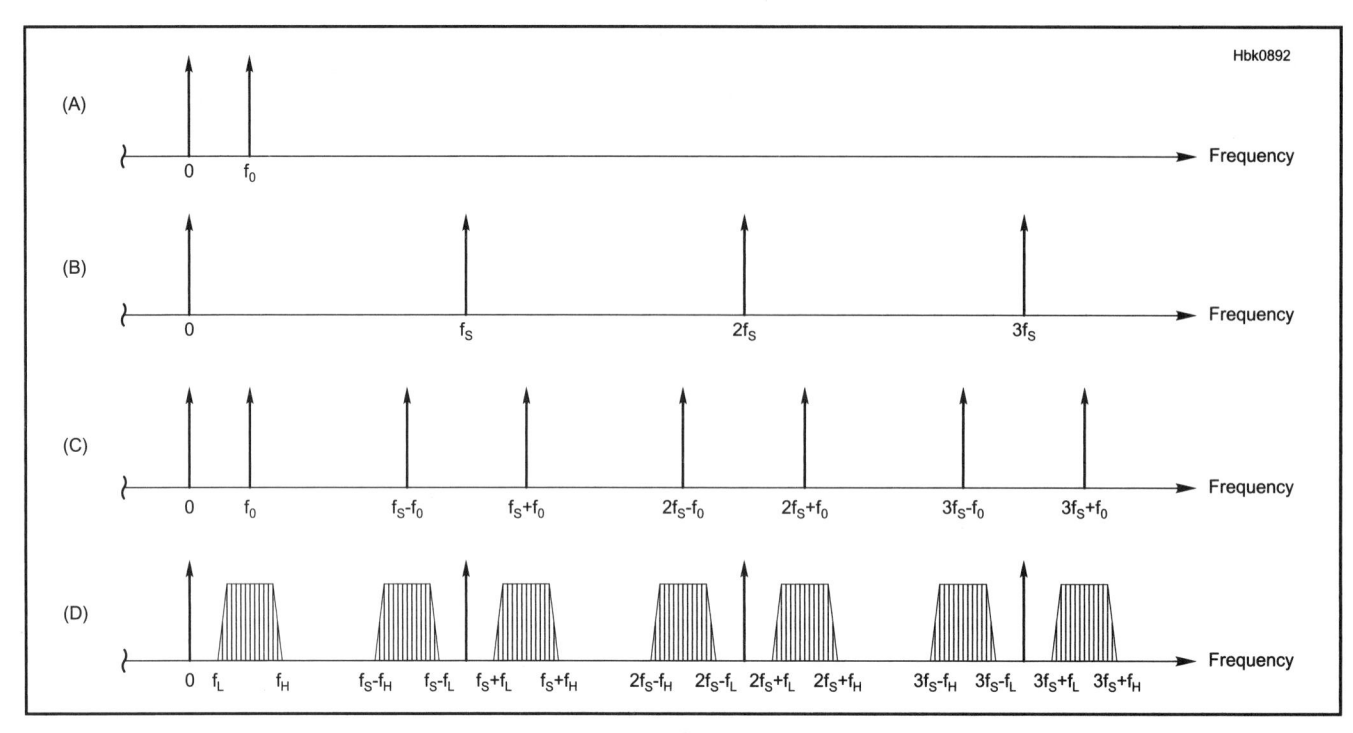

Figure 8.25 — Frequency relationships in a sampled-data system; Spectrum of an analog sine wave (A). The spectrum of the sampling function, including all harmonics (B). The spectrum of the sampled sine wave (C). The spectrum of a sampled band of frequencies between f_L and f_H (D).

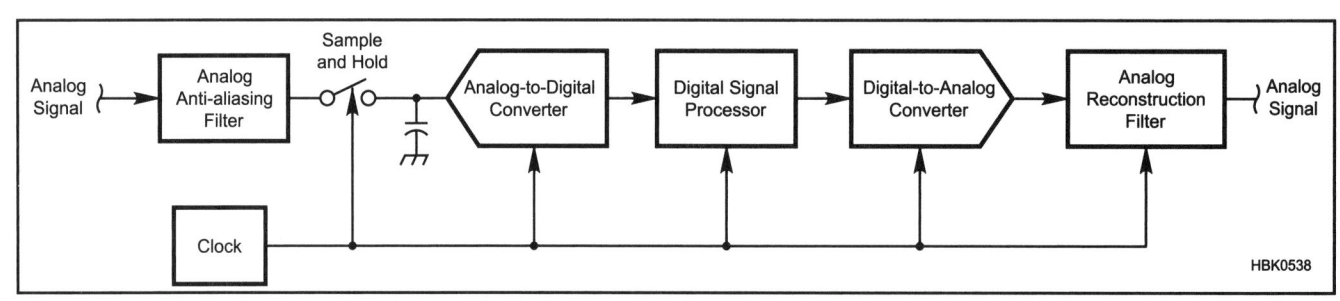

Figure 8.26 — A more complete block diagram of a DSP system.

the original band in the output spectrum and create artifacts.

An *anti-aliasing filter* before the sampler prevents unwanted signals from creating artifacts in the sampled data output, as shown in **Figure 8.26**. For a baseband signal (one that extends to zero Hz), the anti-aliasing filter is a low-pass filter whose stopband extends from the Nyquist frequency to infinity. Of course, practical filters do not transition instantaneously from the passband to the stopband, so the bandwidth of the passband must be somewhat less than half the sample rate.

Figure 8.24 showed each sample being held at a constant value for the duration of one sample period. However, sampling theory actually assumes that the sample is only valid at the instant the signal is sampled; it is zero or undefined at all other times. A series of such infinitely-narrow impulses has harmonics all the way to infinite frequency. Each harmonic has the same amplitude and is modulated by the signal being sampled. See Figure 8.25D. When a digitized signal is converted back to analog form, unwanted harmonics must be filtered out by a *reconstruction filter* as shown in Figure 8.26. This is similar to the anti-aliasing filter used at the input in that its bandwidth should be no greater than one-half the sample rate. It is a low-pass filter for a baseband signal and a band-pass filter for an undersampled signal.

Most DACs actually do hold each sample value for the entire sample period. This is called *zero-order hold* and results in a frequency response in the shape of a sinc function

$$\text{sinc}(f) = \frac{\sin(\pi f)}{\pi f}$$

where f is normalized to the sample rate, f = frequency / sample rate.

The graph of the sinc function in **Figure 8.27** shows both positive and negative fre-

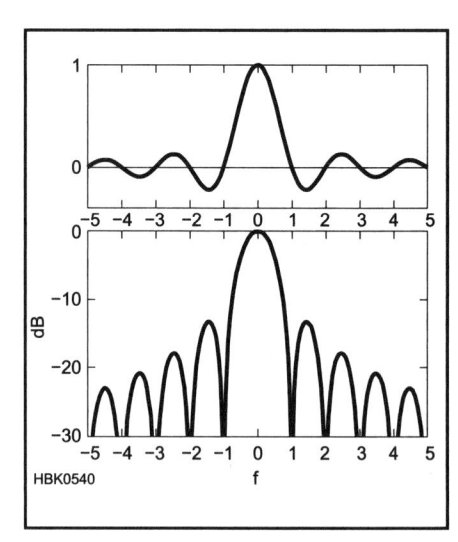

Figure 8.27 — The sinc function, where the horizontal axis is frequency normalized to the sample rate. At the bottom is the same function in decibels.

8.20   Chapter 8

quencies for reasons explained in the Analytic Signals section. Note that the logarithmic frequency response has notches at the sample rate and all of its harmonics. If the signal bandwidth is much less than the Nyquist frequency, then most of the signal at the harmonics falls near the notch frequencies, easing the task of the reconstruction filter. If the signal bandwidth is small enough (sample rate is high enough), the harmonics are almost completely notched out and a reconstruction filter may not even be required.

The $\sin(\pi f)/\pi f$ frequency response also affects the passband. For example if the passband extends to $f_S / 4$ (f = 0.25), then the response is

$$20 \log \frac{\sin(\pi \cdot 0.25)}{\pi \cdot 0.25} = -0.9 \text{ dB}$$

at the top edge of the passband. At the Nyquist frequency, (f = 0.5), the error is 3.9 dB. If the signal bandwidth is a large proportion of the Nyquist frequency, then some kind of digital or analog compensation filter may be required to correct for the high-frequency rolloff. The interpolation filters used in digital audio systems have this correction included in the frequency response.

8.6.2 Decimation and Interpolation

The term *decimation* simply means reducing the sample rate. For example to decimate by two, simply eliminate every second sample. That works fine as long as the signal bandwidth satisfies the Nyquist criterion at the lower, output sample rate. If the analog anti-aliasing filter is not narrow enough, then a digital anti-aliasing filter in the DSP can be used to reduce the bandwidth to the necessary value. This must be done *before* decimation to satisfy the Nyquist criterion.

If you need to decimate by a large amount, then the digital anti-aliasing filter must have a very small bandwidth compared to the sample rate. As we will see later, a digital filter with a small bandwidth is computationally intensive. For this reason, large decimation factors are normally accomplished in multiple steps, as shown in **Figure 8.28A**. The first decimation is by a small factor, typically 2, so that the first anti-alias filter can be as simple as possible. The second decimation stage then does not have to decimate by such a large factor, simplifying its task. In addition, since it is running at only half the input sample rate it has more time to do its calculations. Generally it is most efficient to decimate by the smallest factor in the first stage, a larger factor in the second, and the largest factors in the third and any subsequent stages. The larger the total decimation factor, the greater the number of stages is appropriate but more than three stages is uncommon.

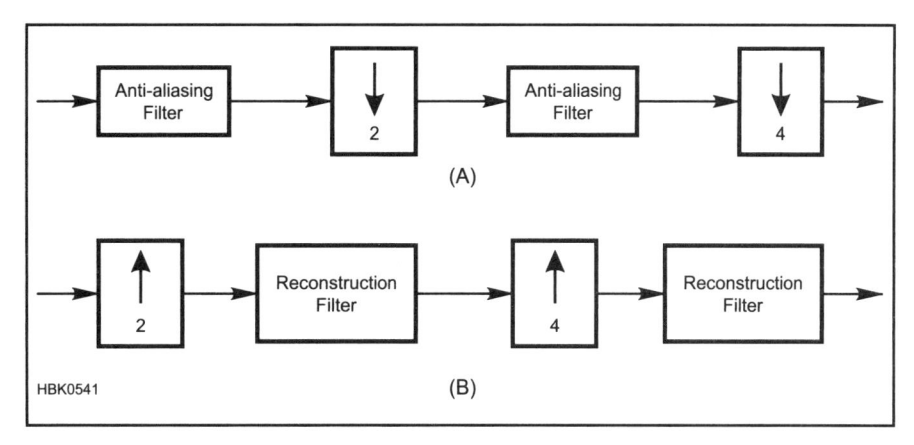

Figure 8.28 — Decimation (A) and interpolation (B). The arrow's direction indicates decimation (down) or interpolation (up) and the number is the factor.

Interpolation means increasing the sample rate. One way to do that is simply to insert additional zero-value samples, a process called *zero-stuffing*. For example, to interpolate by a factor of three, insert two zero-value samples after each input sample. That works, but may not give the results you expect. Recall that a sampled signal has additional copies of the baseband signal at all harmonics of the sample rate. All of those harmonics remain in the resampled signal, even though the sample rate is now higher. To eliminate them, the signal must be filtered after interpolation. After filtering, there is signal only at baseband and around the harmonics of the interpolated (higher-frequency) sample rate. It's as if the analog signal had been sampled at the higher rate to begin with, which relaxes the requirements on the reconstruction filter.

Just as with decimation, interpolation by a large factor is best done in stages, as shown in Figure 8.28B. In this case, the stage running at the lowest sample rate (again the first stage) is the one with the lowest interpolation factor.

Zero-stuffing followed by filtering is not the only way to interpolate. Really what you are trying to do is to fill in between the lower-rate samples with additional samples that "connect the dots" in as smooth a manner as possible. It can be shown that that is mathematically equivalent to zero-stuffing and filtering. For example, if instead of inserting zero-value samples you instead simply repeat the last input sample, you have a situation similar to the zero-order hold of a DAC output. It is equivalent to zero-stuffing followed by a low-pass filter with a frequency response of $\sin(\pi f)/\pi f$. If you do a straight-line interpolation between input samples (a "first-order" interpolation), it turns out that it is equivalent to a low pass filter with a frequency response of $[\sin(\pi f)/\pi f]^2$, which has a sharper cutoff and better stop-band rejection than a zero-order interpolation. Higher-order interpolations have smoother responses in the time domain which translate to better filter responses in the frequency domain.

So far we have only covered decimation and interpolation by integer factors. It is also possible to change the sample rate by a non-integer factor, which is called *resampling* or *multi-rate* conversion. For example, if you want to increase the sample rate by a factor of 4/3, simply interpolate by 4 and then decimate by 3. That method can become impractical for some resample ratios. For example, to convert an audio file recorded from a computer sound card at 48 kHz to the 44.1 kHz required by a compact disc, the resample ratio is 44,100 / 48,000 = 147 / 160. After interpolation by 147, the 44.1 kHz input file is sampled at 6.4827 MHz, which would result in excessive processing overhead.

In addition, the interpolation/decimation method only works for resample ratios that are rational numbers (the ratio of two integers). To resample by an irrational number, a different method is required. The technique is as follows. For each output sample, first determine the two nearest input samples. Calculate the coefficients of the Nth-order equation that describes the trajectory between the two input samples. Knowing the trajectory between the input samples and the output sample's relative position between them, the value of the output sample can be calculated from the equation.

8.6.3 Quantization — Digitization in Amplitude

While sampling (digitization in time) theoretically causes no loss of signal information, quantization (digitization in amplitude) always does. For example, an 8-bit signed number can represent a signal as a value from –128 to +127. For each sample, the A/D converter assigns whichever number in that range is closest to the analog signal at that instant. If a particular sample has a value of 10, there is no way to tell if the original signal was 9.5,

10.5 or somewhere in between. That information has been lost forever.

QUANTIZATION NOISE

When quantizing a complex signal such as speech, this error shows up as noise, called *quantization noise* as discussed in section 8.2.2. The error is random — it is equally likely to be anywhere in the range of –½ to +½ of a single step of the ADC. In **Figure 8.29** the smooth waveform is a band-limited analog noise signal plotted over a 4 ms period. The vertical axis of Figure 8.29A indicates the quantization error for each sample in LSB, represented by the staircase-like waveform. The spectrum of the signal is shown in Figure 8.29B, both before quantization and after quantization. While the original signal has the frequency components above 1 kHz reduced by analog filtering, the digitized version has considerable noise in the 1-5 kHz band.

One critical point that is sometimes overlooked is that quantization noise is spread over the entire bandwidth from zero Hz to the sample rate. If you are digitizing a 3 kHz audio channel with a 48 ksps sampler, only a fraction of the noise power is within the channel. For that reason, the effective signal-to-noise ratio depends not only on the number of bits but also the sample rate, f_s, and the signal bandwidth, B:

$$\text{SNR}_{\text{eff}} = \text{SNR} + 10\log\left(\frac{f_s}{2B}\right) \text{ dB}$$

The reason for the factor of two in the denominator is that the bandwidth of a positive-frequency scalar signal should be compared to the Nyquist bandwidth, $f_s/2$. When filtering a complex signal (one that contains I and Q parts), the 2B in the denominator should be replaced by B.

When choosing an A/D converter don't forget that the effective SNR depends on the sample rate. As an example, let's compare an Analog Devices AD9235 12-bit, 65 Msps ADC to an AD7653, which is a 16-bit 100 ksps ADC from the same manufacturer. Assume a 10 kHz signal bandwidth.

An ideal 12-bit ADC has a SNR of 1.76 + 6.02 × 12 = 74.0 dB. The AD9235's performance is not far from the ideal; its SNR is specified at 70.5 dB at its 65 Msps maximum sample rate. In a 10 kHz bandwidth, the effective SNR is 70.5 + 10 log (65,000/20) = 105.6 dB.

An ideal 16-bit ADC has an SNR of 98.1 dB. The AD7653 is specified at 86 dB. The effective SNR is 86 + 10log(100/20) = 93 dB.

So the 12-bit ADC with 70.5 dB SNR is actually 12.6 dB better than the 16-bit device with 86 dB SNR in this application! Even an ideal 16-bit, 100 ksps ADC would only have an effective SNR of 98.1 + 10log(100/20) = 105.1 dB, still worse than the actual performance of the AD9235 when measured with the same bandwidth. Note that to actually realize 105.6 dB of dynamic range the signal from the ADC would need to be filtered to a 10 kHz bandwidth while increasing the bits of data resolution.

Oversampling is the name given to the technique of using a higher-than-necessary sample rate in order to achieve an improved S/N ratio. Don't forget that when the high-sample-rate signal is decimated the data words must have enough bits to support the higher dynamic range at the lower sample rate. As a rule of thumb, the quantization noise should be at least 10 dB less than the signal noise in order not to significantly degrade the SNR. In the AD9235 example, assuming a 100 kHz output sample rate, about 18 bits would be required: 1.76 + 6.02 × 18 + 10log(100/20) = 117.1 dB, which is 11.5 dB better than the 105.6 dB dynamic range of the ADC in a 10 kHz bandwidth.

Most ADCs and DACs used in high-fidelity audio systems use an extreme form of oversampling, where the internal converter may oversample by a rate of 128 or 256 times, but with very low resolution (in some cases just a 1-bit ADC!). In addition, such converters use a technique called noise shaping to push most of the quantization noise to frequencies near the sample rate, and reduce it in the audio spectrum. The noise is then removed in the decimation filter.

Although quantization error manifests itself as noise when digitizing a complex non-periodic signal, it can show up as discrete spurious frequencies when digitizing

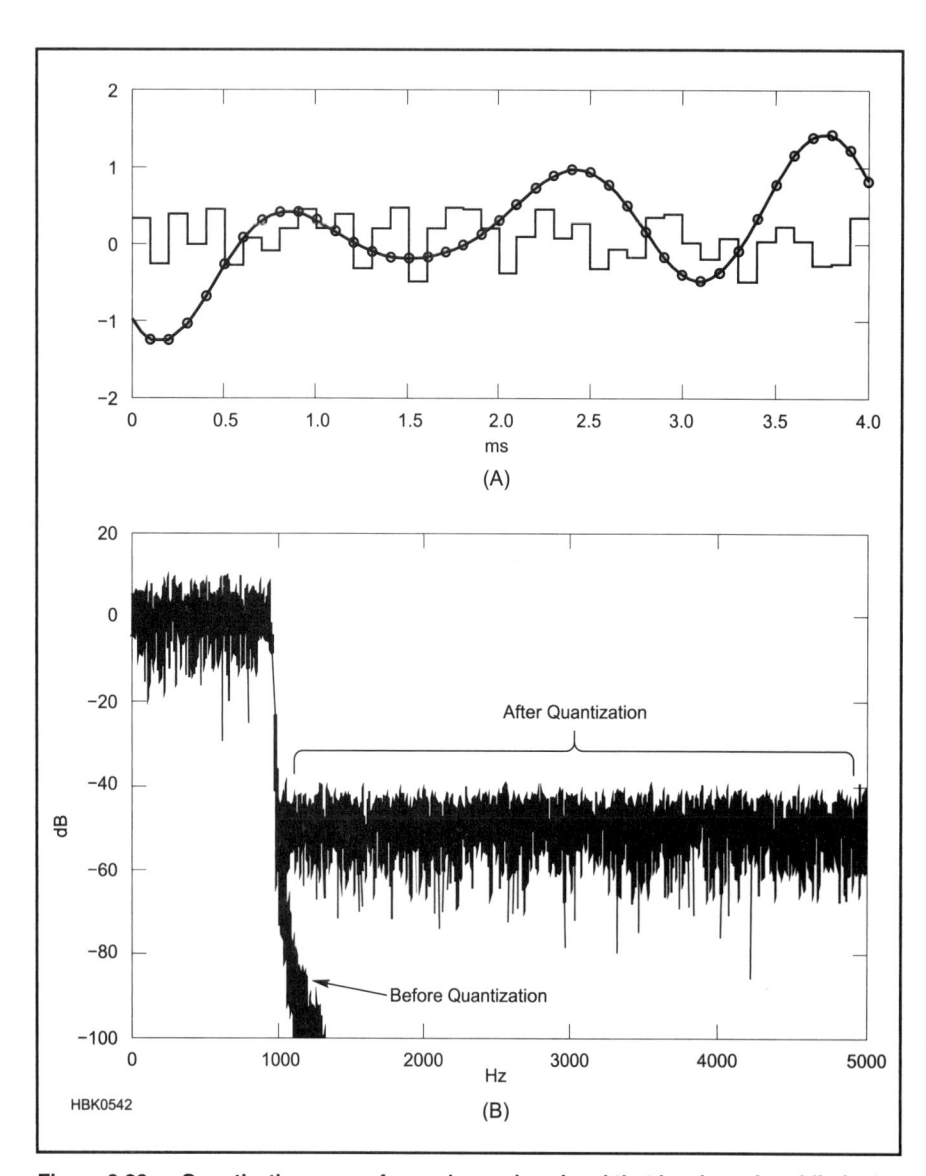

Figure 8.29 — Quantization error of a random noise signal that has been band-limited to 1 kHz to simulate an audio signal. (A) The sampler resolution is 8 bits and the sample rate is 10 kHz. Sample values are indicated by circles. Also shown is the quantization error, in units of LSB. Below is the frequency spectrum of the signal before and after quantization. (B).

a periodic signal. **Figure 8.30** illustrates a 1 kHz sine wave sampled with 8-bit resolution at a 9.5 kHz rate. On average there are 9.5 samples per cycle of the sine wave so that the sampling error repeats every second cycle. That 500-Hz periodicity in the error signal causes a spurious signal at 500 Hz and harmonics. As the signal frequency is changed, the spurs move around in a complicated manner that depends on the ratio of sample rate to signal frequency. In real-world ADCs, nonlinearities in the transfer function can also create spurious signals that vary unpredictably as a function of the signal amplitude, especially at low signal levels.

In many applications, broadband noise is preferable to spurious signals on discrete frequencies. The solution is to add *dithering*. Essentially this involves adding a small amount of noise, typically on the order of an LSB or two, in order to randomize the quantization error. Some DACs have dithering capability built in to improve the SFDR, even though it does degrade the SNR slightly. Dithering is also useful in cases where the input signal to an ADC is smaller than one LSB. Even though the signal would be well above the noise level after narrow-band filtering, it cannot be detected if the ADC input is always below one LSB. In many systems there is already sufficient noise from input amplifiers, other signals in the passband, as well as from the ADC itself, to cause natural dithering.

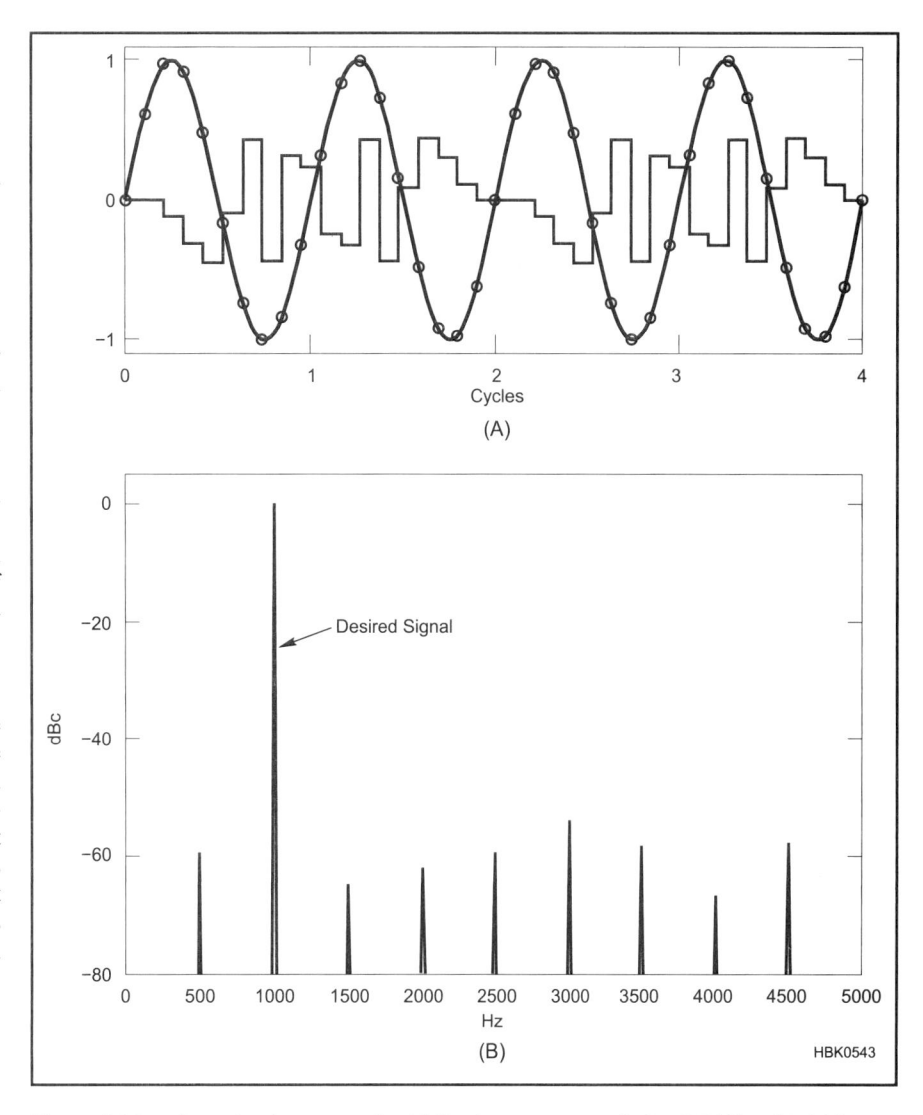

Figure 8.30 — Quantization error of a 1 kHz sine wave sampled at 9.5 kHz with 8-bit resolution (A). Sample values are indicated by circles. Also shown is the quantization error, in units of LSB. Below is the frequency spectrum, showing the spurious frequencies caused by the quantization (B).

8.7 The Fourier Transform

The *Fourier transform* is the software equivalent of a hardware spectrum analyzer. It takes in a signal in the time domain and outputs a set of data (that can also be thought of as a signal) in the frequency domain that shows the spectral content of the input signal. The Fourier transform works on both periodic and non-periodic signals, but since the periodic case is easier to explain we will start with that. (Joseph Fourier was a French mathematician and physicist who introduced the transformation technique bearing his name in 1822. His contributions to physics, mathematics, and engineering were wide-ranging and at the heart of many technologies used today.)

A *periodic* signal is one that repeats every τ seconds, where τ is the period. That means that the signal can consist only of frequencies whose sinusoidal waveforms have an integer number of cycles in τ seconds. In other words, the signal is made up of sinusoids that are at the frequency $1/\tau$ and its harmonics. Fourier's insight was that you can determine if a frequency is present by multiplying the waveform by a sinusoid of that frequency and integrating the result. The result of the integration yields the amplitude of that harmonic. If the integration yields zero, then that frequency is not present.

To see how that works, look at **Figure 8.31**. For the purpose of discussion, assume the signal to be tested consists of a single tone at the second harmonic as shown at (A). The first test frequency is the fundamental, shown at (B). When you multiply the two together you get the waveform at (C). Integrating that signal gives its average value, which is zero. However if you multiply the test signal by a sine wave at the second harmonic (D), the resulting waveform (E) has a large dc offset so the integration yields a large non-zero value. It turns out that all harmonics other than the second yield a zero result. That is, the second harmonic is *orthogonal* to all the others.

If the test waveform included more than one frequency, each of those frequencies would yield a non-zero result when tested with the equivalent-frequency sine wave. The presence of additional frequencies does not disturb the tests for other frequencies since they are all orthogonal with each other.

You may have noticed that this method only works if the test sine wave is in phase with the one in the signal. If they are 90° out of phase, the integration yields zero. The Fourier transform therefore multiplies the signal by both a sine wave and a cosine wave at each frequency. The results of the two tests then yield both the amplitude and phase of that frequency component of the signal using the equations

$$A = \sqrt{a^2 + b^2}$$

and

$$\varphi = \arctan\left(\frac{b}{a}\right)$$

where A is the amplitude, φ is the phase, a is the cosine amplitude and b is the sine amplitude.

If one period of the signal contains, say, 256 samples, then testing a single frequency requires multiplying the signal by the sine wave and by the cosine wave 256 times and adding the results 256 times as well, for a total of 512 multiplications and additions. (This is referred to as a *multiply-accumulate* for the processing instructions that are required.) There are 128 frequencies that must be tested, since the 128th harmonic is at the Nyquist frequency. The total number of calculations is therefore 512 x 128 = 256^2 multiplications and additions. That is a general result. For any sample size, n, calculating the digital Fourier transform requires n^2 multiply-accumulates.

An excellent visual representation of Fourier's discovery is available online at **blog.matthen.com/post/42112703604/the-smooth-motion-of-rotating-circles-can-be-used**. The fundamental and harmonics are shown as a series of rotating vectors. Each vector traces out a circle, rotating at its assigned frequency and phase. When vectors are added together and the result is the desired waveform!

8.7.1 The Fast Fourier Transform (FFT)

The number of calculations grows rapidly with sample size. Calculating the Fourier transform on 1024 samples requires over a million multiply-accumulate cycles. However, you may notice that there is some redundancy in the calculations. When testing the second harmonic, for example, each of the two cycles of the test sine wave is identical. It would be possible to pre-add signal data from the first and second halves of the sequence and then just multiply once by a single cycle of the test sine wave. Also, the first quarter cycle of a sine wave is just a mirror-image of the second quarter cycle and the first half is just the negative of the second half.

In 1965, J. W. Cooley and John W. Tukey published an algorithm that takes advantage of all the symmetries inherent in the Fourier transform to speed up the calculations. The *Cooley-Tukey algorithm*, usually just called the *fast Fourier transform* (FFT), makes the number of calculations proportional to $n\log_2(n)$ instead of n^2. For a 1024-point FFT, the calculation time is proportional to $1024\log_2(1024) = 10,240$ instead of $1024^2 = 1,048,576$, more than a 100-times improvement.

You'll notice that sample sizes are usually a power of two, such as $2^7 = 128$, $2^8 = 256$ and $2^9 = 512$. That is because the FFT algorithm is most efficient with sequences of such sizes. The algorithm uses a process called *radix-2 decimation in time*, that is, it first breaks the data into two chunks of equal size, then breaks each of those chunks into two still-smaller chunks of equal size, and so on. It is possible to squeeze even a little more efficiency out of the algorithm with a *radix-4* FFT which is based on decimation by four instead of by two. That is why you often see sample sizes that are powers of four, such as $4^3 = 64$, $4^4 = 256$ and $4^5 = 1024$. Other variations on the algorithm include decimation in frequency rather than time, mixed-radix FFTs that use different decimation factors at different stages in the calculation, and in-place calculation that puts the results into the same storage buffer as the input data, saving memory. The latter method causes the order of the output data to be scrambled by bit-reversing the address words. For example, address 01010000 becomes 00001010.

The heart of most FFT algorithms is a data flow pattern called a *butterfly*. **Figure 8.32** shows a two element butterfly. The input contains two elements x(0) and x(1), and the

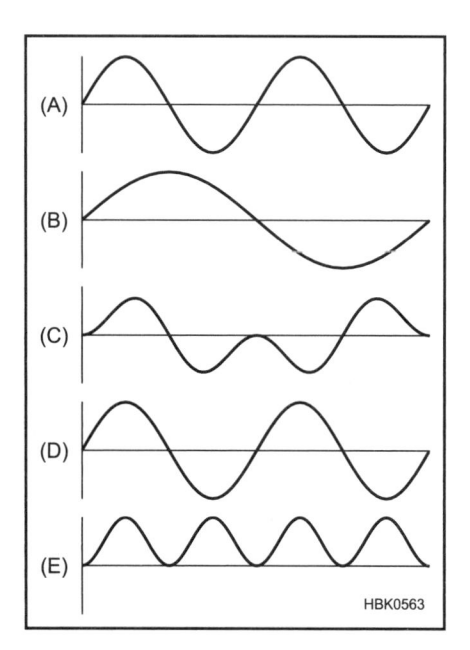

Figure 8.31 — Signal to be tested for frequency content (A). Fundamental test frequency (B). Product of signal and fundamental (C). Second harmonic test frequency (D). Product of signal and second harmonic (E).

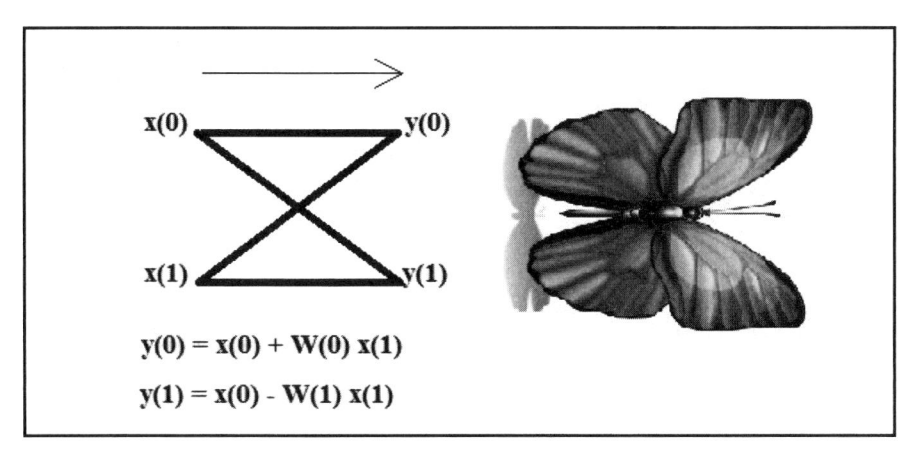

Figure 8.32 — A two-element "butterfly" signal flow diagram. The crossing of the lines makes the diagram look like stylized butterfly wings

output has two elements y(0) and y(1). The equations for the butterfly are:

$$y(0) = x(0) + x(1) W^k$$

$$y(1) = x(1) - x(1) W^k$$

where W^k is the sum of the sine and cosine harmonics $\cos(2k) + j\sin(2k)$.

Figure 8.33 shows the data flow diagram of the scrambled in/natural out (the output is ordered from lowest to highest element). The number in the circle at each stage indicates the value of k for W^k. Notice that the first stage of calculation performs four 2×2 butterfly operations, the second is two 4×4 butterfly operations, and the final is one 8×8 butterfly. Each stage has fewer butterfly operations so it is called a *decimation in time* algorithm.

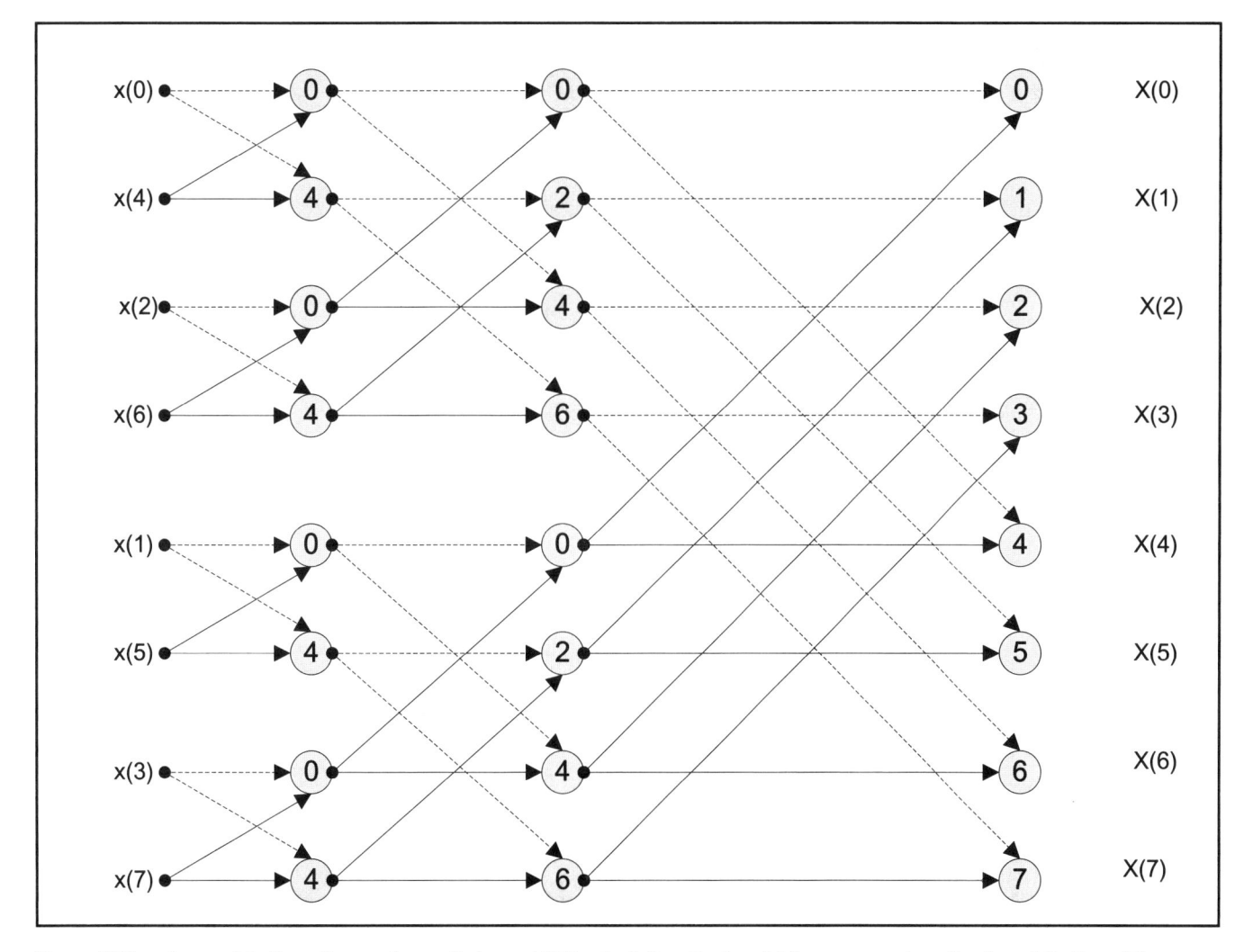

Figure 8.33 — A complete flow diagram for an 8-element FFT calculation. Each solid line represents a direct contribution of the element to the left. Each dashed line represents a contribution that is multiplied by the complex operator W^k. Each number in a circle represents the k value used for the multiplication. This example requires just 24 complex multiplication operations instead of a full 256 calculations.

8.7.2 Non-periodic Signals

So far we have assumed that the signal to be transformed is periodic, so that there is an integer number of cycles of each sine wave harmonic in the sequence. With a non-periodic signal, that is not necessarily so. The various frequencies in the signal are not exact harmonics of $1/\tau$ and are no longer orthogonal to the test frequencies. The result is *spectral leakage*; a single frequency in the signal may give a non-zero result when tested at a number of different harmonic frequencies. In **Figure 8.34**, (B) illustrates the FFT of a single sine wave at a non-harmonic frequency. You can see that the spurious response extends quite far from the actual frequency.

Those far-out spurious responses are primarily caused by the abrupt termination of the signal at the edges of the sequence. The spectrum can be cleaned up considerably by tapering the edges with a window, in the manner of digital filter coefficients as described in the **Analog and Digital Filtering** chapter. In fact, the same window functions are used for both. Figure 8.34 part C illustrates the result of applying a Hamming window to the signal in (A) and the resulting improved spectrum is shown at (D). Just as with FIR filters, different windows excel in different areas. Windows with a gradual transition to zero at the edges do a better job of suppressing spurious responses but smear adjacent spectral lines, analogous to using a wider resolution bandwidth in an analog spectrum analyzer. Windows with a wider center section and a more abrupt transition to zero at the edges have less smearing but more spurious responses.

8.7.3 The Inverse Fourier Transform (IFT)

It is also possible to run the Fourier transform "in reverse," changing frequency-domain data back into time-domain data. The IFT takes a collection of sine wave amplitude and phases and adds them together to create a waveform just as the "forward" Fourier transform changes the waveform into the collection of sine waves.

Just as clever ways of performing the Fourier transform led to the FFT, similarities in the calculations for the FFT and IFT allow the same calculations that perform the :"forward" FFT to be used to perform the IFT. **Figure 8.35** shows two methods of implementing an IFT using the FFT algorithm on the I and Q channel data. Both methods have as their input the frequency-domain data, I(m) and Q(m), which represent the amplitude and phase of sinusoidal components (harmonics). The output is a series of time-domain samples, I(n) and Q(n), which represent the waveform. The divide-by-N functions are scaling factors required by the calculations. Advanced methods are even able to perform the FFT and IFT simultaneously on different streams of data, allowing one specialized set of hardware to do double duty.

Transceivers don't generate transmittable signals using the IFT which is included in this discussion for completeness. Transmit chains usually perform I/Q modulation with digital data on the I and Q channel carriers, filter the output (either with analog or digital filters), and amplify it conventionally to useful levels. Nevertheless, the elegance of using the very same algorithm to convert between the time and frequency domains illustrate the deep mathematical connection between time and frequency.

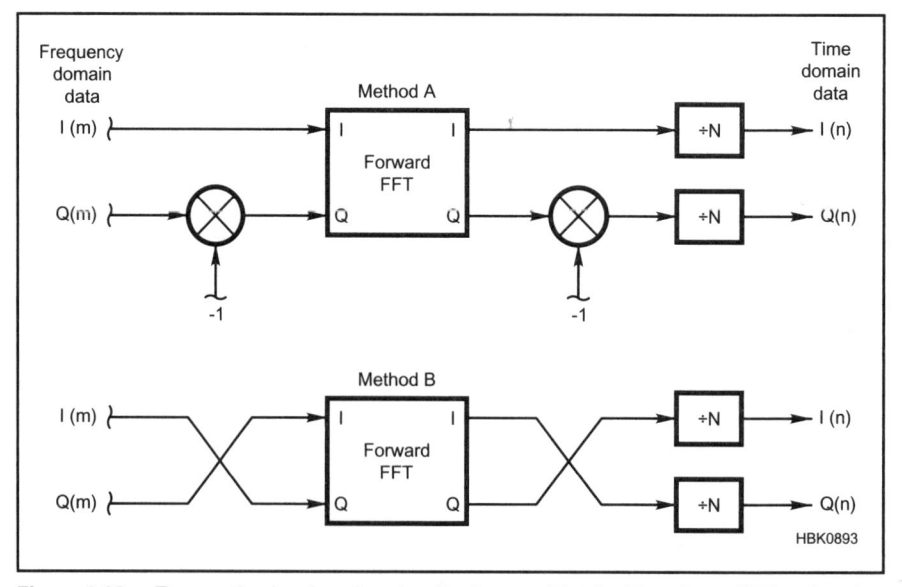

Figure 8.35 — Two methods of performing the Inverse Fourier Transform (IFT) using the "forward" FFT algorithm.

←Figure 8.34 — Illustrating the use of windowing to minimize spectral leakage, the figures show (A) a cosine waveform not at a harmonic frequency, (B) the resulting unwindowed power spectrum, (C) the same cosine waveform with a Hamming window, and (D) the much narrower power spectrum of the windowed waveform.

8.26   Chapter 8

8.8 Glossary

Analog-to-digital converter (ADC) — A device that samples an analog signal and outputs a digital number representing the amplitude of the signal.

Anti-aliasing filter — A band-limiting filter placed before a sampler to make sure the incoming signal satisfies the Nyquist criterion.

Application-specific integrated circuit (ASIC) — A non-programmable IC that is designed for a particular application.

Arithmetic logic unit (ALU) — The portion of a microprocessor that performs basic arithmetic and logical operations.

Barrel shifter — A circuit in a microprocessor that can bit-shift a number by multiple bits at one time.

Baseband — The low-frequency portion of a signal. This is typically the modulation.

Binary point — The symbol that separates the integer part from the fractional part of a binary number.

Blocking dynamic range (BDR) — The difference between the noise level (usually in a 500-Hz bandwidth) and the signal level that causes a 1 dB reduction in the level of a weaker signal.

Circular buffers — A buffer in which the final entry is considered to be adjacent to the first.

Cognitive radio — A radio system in which a wireless node automatically changes its transmission or reception parameters to avoid interference with other nodes.

Complex number — A number that contains real and imaginary parts.

Complex PLD (CPLD) — A programmable logic device that is more complex than a small PLD, such as a PAL, but with a similar architecture.

Convolution — A mathematical operation that modifies a sequence of numbers with another sequence of numbers so as to produce a third sequence with a different frequency spectrum or other desired characteristic. An FIR filter is a convolution engine.

Cooley-Tukey algorithm — Another name for the fast Fourier transform.

Decimation — Reduction of sample rate by an integer factor.

Decimation in time — The division of a sequence of numbers into successively smaller sub-sequences in order to facilitate calculations such as the Fourier transform.

Digital downconverter (DDC) — A device that translates a band of frequencies to baseband, typically at a lower sample rate.

Digital signal processing — The processing of sequences of digital numbers that represent signals.

Digital signal processor (DSP) — A device to do digital signal processing. The term normally is understood to refer to a microprocessor-type device with special capabilities for signal processing.

Digital-to-analog converter (DAC) — A device that converts digital numbers to an analog signal with an amplitude proportional to the digital numbers.

Digital upconverter (DUC) — A device that frequency-translates a baseband signal to a higher frequency, typically at a higher sample rate.

Dithering — Randomly varying the amplitude or phase of a signal in order to overcome quantization effects.

Embedded system — A system that includes a microprocessor for purposes other than general-purpose computing.

Exponent — The number of digits that the radix point must be moved to represent a number.

Fast Fourier transform (FFT) — An algorithm that can calculate the discrete Fourier transform with an execution time proportional to nlog(n), instead of n^2 as is required by the straight-forward application of the Fourier transform equation.

Field-programmable gate array (FPGA) — An IC that contains a large array of complex logic blocks whose function and connections can be re-programmed in the field.

Floating-point — Refers to a number whose value is represented by a mantissa and an exponent.

Fourier transform — A mathematical operation that derives the frequency spectrum of a time-domain signal.

Hardware-description languages (HDL) — A computer language to specify the circuitry of a digital device or system.

Harmonic sampling — The use of a sample rate that is less than twice the highest frequency of the signal to be sampled. The sample rate must be greater than two times the bandwidth of the signal.

Harvard architecture — A computer architecture in which the program and data are stored in separate memories.

Imaginary number — A real number multiplied by the square root of minus one.

Impulse — A pulse of finite energy with a width that approaches zero.

In-circuit emulator (ICE) — A device that emulates the operation of a microprocessor while providing debugging tools to the operator. The ICE normally plugs into an IC socket that normally holds the microprocessor.

In-circuit debugger (ICD) — A device that uses debugging features built into the microprocessor so that it can be tested while in the circuit.

In-circuit programmable (ICP) — A programmable IC that can be programmed while it is connected to the application circuit.

In-circuit programmer (ICP) — A device to facilitate programming of programmable ICs while they are connected to the application circuit.

In-phase (I) — The portion of a radio signal that is in phase with a reference carrier.

Integrated development environment (IDE) — An integrated collection of software and hardware tools for developing a microprocessor project.

Interrupt service routine (ISR) — A software subroutine that is called automatically when the main routine is interrupted by some event.

Least-significant bit (LSB) — When used as a measurement unit, the size of the smallest step of a digital number.

Linear phase — Refers to a system in which the delay is constant at all frequencies, which means that the phase is linear with frequency.

Mantissa — The decimal or binary part of a logarithm or floating-point number.

Multiplier-accumulator (MAC) — A device that can multiply two numbers and add the result to a previous result all in one operation.

Multi-rate — Refers to a system with more than one sample rate.

Nyquist criterion — The requirement that the sample rate must be at least twice the bandwidth of the signal.

Nyquist frequency — One half the sample rate.

Nyquist rate — Twice the signal bandwidth.

One-time programmable (OTP) — A programmable device that may not be re-programmed.

Orthogonal — Perpendicular. In analogy with the mathematics of perpendicular geometrical vectors, the term is used in communications to refer to two signals that produce zero when convolved.

Oversampling — Use of a sample rate higher than required by the Nyquist criterion in order to improve the signal-to-noise ratio.

Phasor diagram — A polar plot of the magnitude of the in-phase and quadrature components of a signal.

Pipeline — An arrangement of computational units in a microprocessor or other digital device so that different units can be working on different instructions or signal samples at the same time; also, and architecture commonly used for high-speed ADCs

Programmable-array logic (PAL) — A type of small PLD that consists of an array of AND gates, OR gates, inverters and latches.

Programmable gate array (PGA) — see *Field-progammable gate array*

Programmable-logic device (PLD) — A device with many logic elements whose connections are not defined at manufacturer but must be programmed.

Quadrature (Q) — The portion of a radio signal that is 90° out of phase with a reference carrier.

Quantization — The representation of a continuous analog signal by a number with a finite number of bits.

Quantization error — The difference in amplitude between an analog signal and its digital samples.

Quantization noise — Noise caused by random quantization error.

Radix – The base of a number system. Binary is radix 2 and decimal is radix 10.

Radix point — The symbol that separates the integer part from the fractional part of a number.

Reconstruction filter — A filter located after a digital-to-analog conversion or interpolation to filter out sampling spurs.

Resampling — Changing the sample rate by a non-integer ratio.

Resolution — The number of bits required to represent a digital number from its smallest to its largest value.

Sample rate — The rate at which samples are generated, processed or output from a system.

Sampling — The process of measuring and recording a signal at discrete points of time.

Software-defined radio (SDR) — A transmitter and/or receiver whose principal signal processing functions are defined by software.

Spectral leakage — In a Fourier transform, the indication of frequencies that are not actually present in the signal due to inadequate windowing.

Undersampling — Harmonic sampling.

Von Neumann architecture — A computer architecture that includes a processing unit and a single separate read/write memory to hold both program and data.

Windowing — Tapering the edges of a data sequence so that the samples do not transition abruptly to zero. This avoids passband and stopband ripple in an FIR filter and spectral leakage in a Fourier transform.

Zero-order hold — Holding of a data value for the entire sample period.

Zero-overhead looping — The ability of a microprocessor to automatically jump from the end of a memory block back to the beginning without additional instructions.

8.9 References and Bibliography

References

1. The FCC report and order authorizing software-defined radios in the commercial service is available at **www.fcc.gov/Bureaus/Engineering_Technology/Orders/2001/fcc01264.pdf**
2. Hershberger, D., W9GR, "Low-Cost Digital Signal Processing for the Radio Amateur," QST, Sep 1992, pp 43-51.
3. Youngblood, G., "A Software-Defined Radio for the Masses," *QEX*; Part 1, Jul/Aug 2002; Part 2, Sep/Oct 2002; Part 3, Nov/Dec 2002; Part 4, Mar/Apr 2003.
4. Tayloe, D., N7VE, "Notes on 'Ideal' Commutating Mixers (Nov/Dec 1999)" Letters to the Editor, QEX, Mar 2001, p 61.
5. The Microchip IDE software can be downloaded free at **www.microchip.com**.
6. For more details on using the Raspberry Pi GPU for SDR applications, see: **www.raspberrypi.org/blog/accelerating-fourier-transforms-using-the-gpu**
7. Blanchard, R., W6UYG, "Sugar-Coated Single Sideband," QST, Oct 1952, p 38ff.
8. Weaver, D.K., Jr, "A Third Method of Generation and Detection of Single-Sideband Signals" *Proc. IRE*, Dec. 1956.
9. Wright, Jr., H., W1PNB, "The Third Method of S.S.B.," QST, Sep 1957, pp 11-15.

BIBLIOGRAPHY

DSP Software Tools

The following books are referenced in the DSP files in the downloadable supplemental content.

Alkin, O., *PC-DSP*, Prentice Hall, Englewood Cliffs, NJ, 1990 (DF).

Kamas, A. and Lee, E., *Digital Signal Processing Experiments*, Prentice Hall, Englewood Cliffs, NJ, 1989 (DF).

Momentum Data Systems, Inc., *QEDesign*, Costa Mesa, CA, 1990 (DF).

Stearns, S. D. and David, R. A., *Signal Processing Algorithms in FORTRAN and C*, Prentice Hall, Englewood Cliffs, NJ, 1993 (DF).

Textbooks

Hayward, Wes, et al, *Experimental Methods in RF Design*, chapter 10 "DSP Components" and chapter 11 "DSP Applications in Communications," ARRL, 2009 (D).

Lathi, B.P., *Signal Processing and Linear Systems*, Oxford University Press, 1998.

Lyons, R., *Understanding Digital Signal Processing*, Third Edition, Pearson, 2012.

Madisetti, V. K. and Williams, D. B., Editors, *The Digital Signal Processing Handbook*, CRC Press, Boca Raton, FL, 1998 (D).

Mar, Amy (Editor), *Digital Signal Processing Applications Using the ADSP-2100 Family, Volume I*, Prentice Hall 1990. While oriented to the ADSP-2100, there is much good general information on DSP algorithms. Both volume I and II are available for free download on the Analog Devices Web site, **www.analog.com**.

Parks, T. W. and Burrus, C.S., *Digital Filter Design*, John Wiley and Sons, New York, NY, 1987.

Sabin, W. E. and Schoenike, E. O., Eds., *HF Radio Systems and Circuits*, rev. 2nd ed., Noble Publishing Corp, Norcross, GA, 1998.

Widrow, B. and Stearns, S. D., *Adaptive Signal Processing*, Prentice Hall, Englewood Cliffs, NJ, 1985.

Zverev, A. I., *Handbook of Filter Synthesis*, John Wiley and Sons, New York, NY, 1967.

Articles and Papers

Ahlstrom, J., "An All-Digital SSB Exciter for HF," *QEX*, May/Jun 2008, pp 3-10.

Ahlstrom, J., "An All-Digital Transceiver for HF," *QEX*, Jan/Feb 2011, pp 3-8.

Åsbrink, L., "Linrad: New Possibilities for the Communications Experimenter," *QEX*, Part 1, Nov/Dec 2002; Part 2, Jan/Feb 2003; Part 3 May/Jun 2003.

Bloom, J., "Measuring SINAD Using DSP," *QEX*, Jun 1993, pp 9-18.

Bloom, J., "Negative Frequencies and Complex Signals," *QEX*, Sep 1994.

Bloom, J., "Correlation of Sampled Signals," *QEX*, Feb 1996.

Brannon, B., "Basics of Digital Receiver Design," *QEX*, Sep/Oct 1999, pp 36-44.

Cahn, H., "Direct Digital Synthesis — An Intuitive Introduction," *QST*, Aug 1994, pp 30-32.

Cowling, S., "Hands-On SDR," *QEX*, columns beginning Sep 2014.

Danzer, P., "A Practical Demonstration of Fourier Series," *QST*, Apr 2007, p 37.

Dobranski, L., "The Need for Applications Programming Interfaces (APIs) in Amateur Radio," *QEX*, Jan/Feb 1999, pp 19-21.

Gradijan, S., "Build a Super Transceiver — Software for Software Controllable Radios," *QEX*, Sept/Oct 2004, pp 30-34.

Hightower, M., "Simple SDR Receiver," *QEX*, Mar/Apr 2012, pp 3-8.

Hill, C., "SDR2GO: A DSP Odyssey," *QEX*, Mar/Apr 2011, pp 36-43.

Kester, W., "SINAD, ENOB, SNR, THD, THD + N, and SFDR so You Don't Get Lost in the Noise Floor," Analog Devices, MT-003, **www.analog.com/media/en/training-seminars/tutorials/MT-003.pdf.**

Mack, Ray, "SDR: Simplified," *QEX*, columns beginning Nov 2009.

Martin, K., "Complex Signal Processing is NOT — Complex," **www.mikrocontroller.net/attachment/151612/complex_signals.pdf.**

Nickels, R., "Cheap and Easy SDR," *QST*, Jan 2013, pp 30-35.

Scarlett, J., "A High-Performance Digital Transceiver Design," *QEX*, Part 1, Jul/Aug 2002; Part 2, Mar/Apr 2003.

Smith, D., "Signals, Samples and Stuff: A DSP Tutorial, Parts 1-4," *QEX*, Mar/Apr-Sep/Oct, 1998.

Stephensen, J., Software Defined Radios for Digital Communications," *QEX*, Nov/Dec 2004, pp 23-35. [Open-source platform]

Veatch, J., "The DSP-610 Transceiver," *QST*, Aug 2012, pp 30-32.

Ward, R., "Basic Digital Filters," *QEX*, Aug 1993, pp 7-8.

Youngblood, G., "A Software-Defined Radio for the Masses," *QEX*; Part 1, Jul/Aug 2002; Part 2, Sep/Oct 2002; Part 3, Nov/Dec 2002; Part 4, Mar/Apr 2003.

SDR and DSP Receiver Testing

Hakanson, E., "Understanding SDRs and their RF Test Requirements," Anritsu Application Note.

MacLeod, J.R.; Beach, M.A.; Warr, P.A.; Nesimoglu, T., "Software Defined Radio Receiver Test-Bed," IEEE Vehicular Tech Conf, Fall 2001, VTS 54th, Vol 3, pp 565-1569.

R. Sierra, Rhode & Schwarz, "Challenges In Testing Software Defined Radios," SDR Forum Sandiego Workshop, 2007.

Sirmans, D. and Urell, B., "Digital Receiver Test Results," Next Generation Weather Radar Program.

"Testing and Troubleshooting Digital RF Communications Receiver Designs," Agilent Technologies Application Note 1314. **literature.cdn.keysight.com/litweb/pdf/5968-3579E.pdf?id=1000000479:epsg:apn**

Contents

9.1 How Oscillators Work
   9.1.1 Resonance
   9.1.2 Maintained Resonance (CW: Continuous Waves)
   9.1.3 Oscillator Start-Up

9.2 LC Variable Frequency Oscillator (VFO) Circuits
   9.2.1 Basic Oscillator Circuits
   9.2.2 Two Low-Noise VHF Oscillators
   9.2.3 Three High-Performance HF VFOs

9.3 Building an Oscillator
   9.3.1 VFO Components and Construction
   9.3.2 Temperature Compensation
   9.3.3 Shielding and Isolation

9.4 Crystal Oscillators
   9.4.1 Quartz and the Piezoelectric Effect
   9.4.2 Frequency Accuracy
   9.4.3 The Equivalent Circuit of a Crystal
   9.4.4 Crystal Oscillator Circuits
   9.4.5 Variable-frequency Crystal Oscillators (VXOs)
   9.4.6 Logic-Gate Crystal Oscillators

9.5 Oscillators at UHF and Above
   9.5.1 UHF Oscillators: Intentional and Accidental
   9.5.2 Microwave Oscillators
   9.5.3 Klystrons, Magnetrons, and Traveling Wave Tubes

9.6 Frequency Synthesizers
   9.6.1 Digital Frequency Synthesis
   9.6.2 Phase-Locked Loops (PLL)
   9.6.3 PLL Loop Filter Design
   9.6.4 Fractional-N Synthesizers
   9.6.5 A PLL Design Example
   9.6.6 PLL Measurements and Troubleshooting
   9.6.7 Commercial Synthesizer ICs
   9.6.8 Analog Frequency Synthesis

9.7 Phase Noise
   9.7.1 Effects of Phase Noise
   9.7.2 Reciprocal Mixing
   9.7.3 A Phase Noise Demonstration
   9.7.4 Transmitted Phase Noise
   9.7.5 PLL Synthesizer Phase Noise
   9.7.6 Improving VCO Noise Performance
   9.7.7 ARRL Lab Transmitter Phase Noise Measurement

9.8 Glossary of Oscillator and Synthesizer Terms

9.9 References and Bibliography

Chapter 9 — Downloadable Supplemental Content

Supplemental Files
- "Frequency Synthesis: Current and Future Projections" by Alexander Chenakin, *Microwave Journal*, April 2017
- "Simulation of the Low Noise Oscillator for Solid State Design for the Radio Amateur" by Linley Gumm, K7HFD
- "Crystal Test Oscillators" by Fred Brown, W6HPH
- Measuring Receiver Phase Noise
- "Oscillator Design Using *LTSpice*" by David Stockton, GM4ZNX (includes *LTSpice* simulation files in SwissRoll folder)
- Using the MC1648 in Oscillators
- "Novel Grounded Base Oscillator Design for VHF-UHF" by Ulrich Rohde, N1UL
- "Optimized Oscillator Design" by Ulrich Rohde, N1UL
- "Oscillator Phase Noise" by Ulrich Rohde, N1UL
- "Some Thoughts On Crystal Oscillator Design" by Ulrich Rohde, N1UL
- "Calculation of FM and AM Noise Signals of Colpitts Oscillators in the Time Domain" by Ulrich Rohde, N1UL
- "Some Thoughts on Designing Very High Performance VHF Oscillators" by Ulrich Rohde, N1UL
- "What You Always Wanted to Know About Colpitts Oscillators" by Ulrich Rohde, N1UL, and Anisha M. Apte
- "An Optimized Grounded Base Oscillator Design for VHF/UHF," by Ulrich Rohde, N1UL, and Ajay Poddar, AC2KG
- RC VFO Circuits

Chapter 9

Oscillators and Synthesizers

RF signals all begin with oscillators — circuits that generate a periodic output signal without any input signal. In general, we use sinusoidal waveforms for communication signals, and square-wave or pulse outputs for digital signals (clocks). Amateurs care greatly about oscillator design. In a crowded band, a stable and clean oscillator is necessary for the receiver to resolve each of the signals present. The same is required of oscillators in transmitters so that our signals use only the amount of spectrum necessary for communication. While this chapter includes a section on phase noise, the **RF Techniques** chapter discusses noise and noise metrics more generally.

This chapter includes material from Earl McCune, WA6SUH; Ulrich Rohde, N1UL; David Stockton, GM4ZNX; Fred Telewski, WA7TZY; and Jerry DeHaven, WAØACF. These authors and others have contributed articles on phase noise and oscillator design that are included in the downloadable supplemental content for the *Handbook*.

The sheer number of different oscillator circuits seen in the literature can be intimidating, but their great diversity is an illusion that evaporates once their underlying pattern is seen. Despite the number of combinations that are possible, a manageably small number of oscillator types will cover all but very special requirements. Look at an oscillator circuit and "read" it: What form of filter — resonator — does it use? What form of amplifier? How have the amplifier's input and output been coupled into the filter? How is the filter tuned? These are simple, easily answered questions that put oscillator types into appropriate categories and make them understandable. The questions themselves make more sense when we understand the mechanics of oscillation, in which resonance plays a major role.

Any oscillator is a fundamentally nonlinear device. Among other reasons, this circuit has an RF output even without any RF input. Any linear circuit can change the magnitude and phase shift on the signal only at its input.

9.1 How Oscillators Work

9.1.1 Resonance

We are all familiar with pendulums. A weight (a mass in a gravitational field) hanging from some kind of string will swing back and forth with a very regular period. It has been known for millennia that this period does not change as long as the length of the string does not change, regardless of the amount of weight or how far it swings. Only a few centuries ago did Isaac Newton invent enough calculus to show why this is true. Yet even before Newton's seminal work, people were comfortable enough with this very predictable swinging period that pendulums were adopted as the basis of clocks and timekeeping.

Newton showed that the pendulum works by continuously exchanging its energy between potential (height) and kinetic (moving) forms. The mass moves fastest when it has minimum height (all energy is kinetic), and stops moving (all energy is potential) when it has maximum height. Further, when the energy is all in one form, the ingredients are in place to assure that conversion to the other form will happen. At the bottom, when the mass is moving fastest, its momentum assures that it will keep moving. The string constrains that movement and forces it to rise. When the mass stops rising, the string pulls on it in a different direction from gravity, which is pulling it down. This assures that the mass will fall and pick up speed — and the cycle repeats.

An electrical equivalent is created by the combination of an inductor and a capacitance. The inductor stores energy in a magnetic field when there is a current (motion of charge) flowing through it. The capacitor stores energy in an electric field when there is a voltage (presence of charge) in it. Connect the two together and the charge in the capacitor (electric potential energy) forces a current to begin flowing through the inductor. When the charge in the capacitor is zero, the current in the inductor is maximum (magnetic energy) and the magnetic field forces the current to continue, which recharges the capacitor with the opposite polarity. Just like the pendulum, the combination of inductor and capacitor trade energy back and forth between two types. Because energy is being stored in this circuit, we call this a *tank circuit*.

The common features between a pendulum and an electrical tank circuit are shown in **Figure 9.1**. For the pendulum, the speed of the mass and the displacement (height) are both

Figure 9.1 — A resonator lies at the heart of every oscillatory mechanical and electrical system. A mechanical resonator (here, a pendulum) and an electrical resonator (here, a tuned circuit consisting of L and C in parallel) share the same mechanism: the regular movement of energy between two forms — potential and kinetic in the pendulum, electric and magnetic in the tuned circuit. Both of these resonators share another trait: Any oscillations induced in them eventually die out because of losses — in the pendulum, due to drag and friction; in the tuned circuit, due to the resistance, coupling to other circuits, and radiation. Note that the curves corresponding to the pendulum's displacement vs velocity and the tuned circuit's voltage vs current differ by one-quarter of a cycle, or 90°.

sinusoidal with time and offset in phase by 90 degrees. Similarly, the voltage and current in the LC tank circuit are sinusoidal and offset by 90 degrees.

Unfortunately, these oscillations do not continue forever. When you pull a pendulum aside and let it go, it will swing for a while and eventually stop. This is due to losses that take a little bit of energy away from the pendulum each time it swings. For a pendulum, one major loss mechanism is air drag: As the mass moves through the air, some energy is spent to move the air out of its way. There are losses from the string as well: Every time the string is bent, it warms up just a little bit. This also takes energy away from the pendulum. With these losses, the energy conversion is not complete between kinetic and potential forms, and each cycle of the oscillation is slightly smaller than the one before. We say that the oscillation is *damped*.

The electrical tank circuit works similarly. When an oscillation is started, say with a spark charging the capacitance as shown in **Figure 9.2**, we see that this oscillation is also damped. The primary losses include resistance in the inductor and interactions of the electric and magnetic fields with other conductors. There is also direct radiation of electromagnetic fields — exactly what we want to happen for radio communication, but counts as an energy loss from the resonator.

It was not hard to figure out that a damped oscillation is not very useful for radio communication. We need our signals to last for a longer time so they can carry useful information. The first attempt to solve this problem was to repeatedly apply sparks to the tank circuit in a manner like that of Figure 9.2B. This still is not a continuous sine wave and it is very noisy because, among other things, the timing of the sparks is extremely difficult to hold in exact synchronization with the tank oscillation. There has to be a better way…

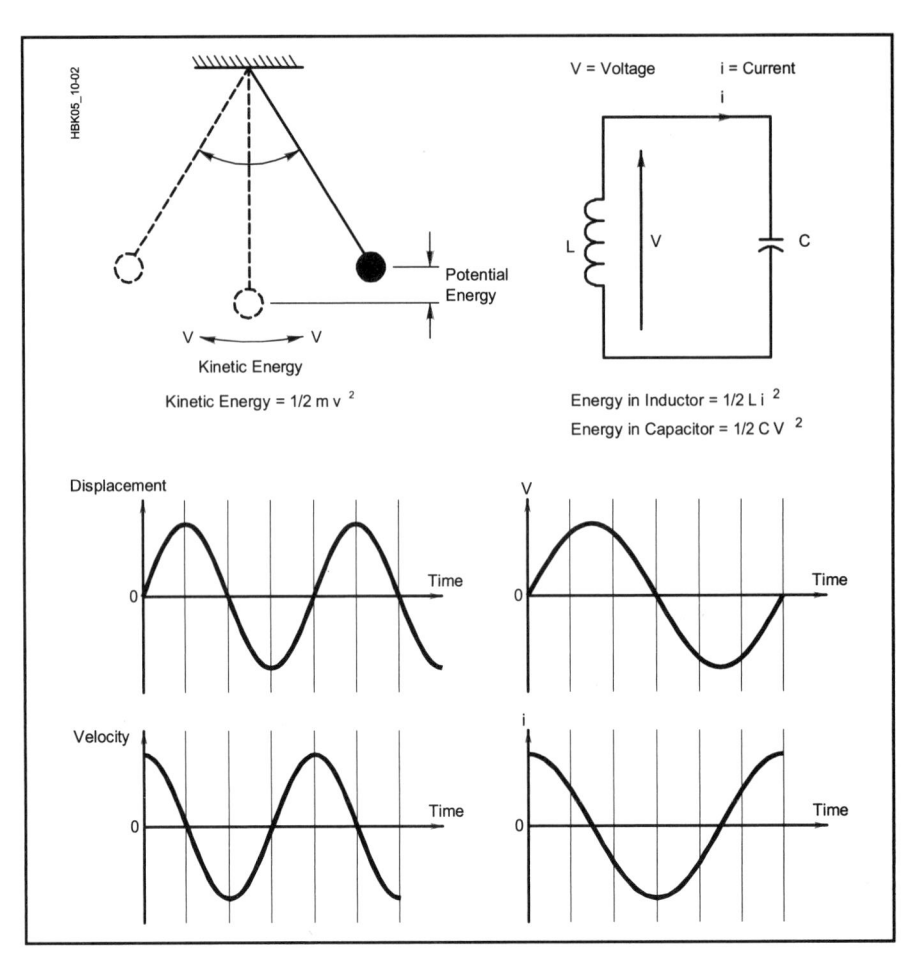

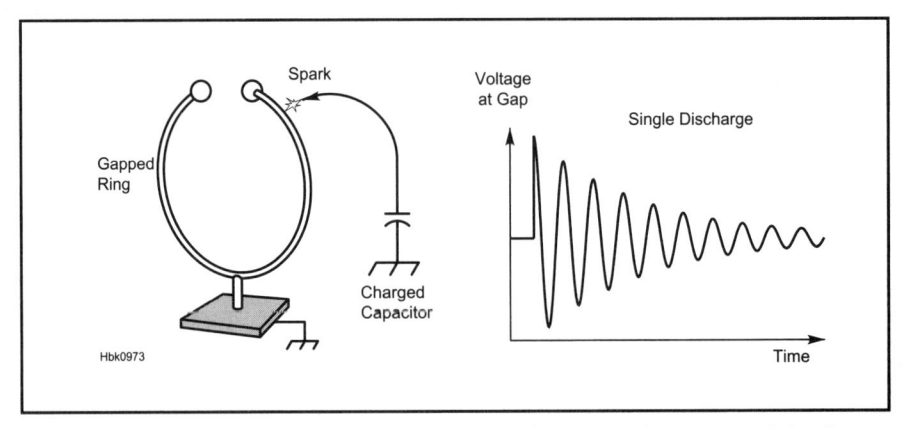

Kinetic Energy = $1/2\, m\, v^2$

Energy in Inductor = $1/2\, L\, i^2$
Energy in Capacitor = $1/2\, C\, V^2$

Figure 9.2 — Stimulating a resonance, 1880s style. Shock-exciting a gapped ring by a charged capacitor causes the ring to oscillate at its resonant frequency. The result is a damped wave, each successive alternation of which is weaker than its predecessor because of resonator losses. Repetitively stimulating the ring, such as with repeated discharges (i.e. – a spark transmitter), produces trains of damped waves, but oscillation is not continuous.

9.1.2 Maintained Resonance (CW: Continuous Waves)

What we need is a way to make up for the resonator losses, but only just enough to maintain the oscillation indefinitely. Invention of the escapement achieved this for the pendulum, and that's what provides the distinctive "tick-tock" of a pendulum clock. Electrically we use an amplifier to do the same thing.

By adding an amplifier to the tank circuit or *resonator*, we can take a small amount of the energy from the resonator, amplify it, and inject a part of the amplified tank signal back into the resonator. This process is shown in **Figure 9.3A**. Unlike in general amplifier design, here we are not interested in maximizing power transfer. Instead, we want to couple just enough energy into the resonator to overcome its losses, and to take only the mini- mum amount of energy out of the resonator needed to generate the restoring energy. Thus Figure 9.3A shows coupling networks instead of matching networks. We end up with a loop: The amplifier input comes from the output of the resonator, and the amplifier output goes to the input of the resonator.

The trick to oscillator design is to get the coupling networks and the amplifier gain working together just right. What this means is shown in Figure 9.3B. If we want to get a sine wave output, we need to get the loop gain — gain computed as the signal passes through the combination of amplifier, resonator, and both coupling networks — exactly equal to one, also called *unity*. If the loop gain is even slightly less than one, then not enough energy is supplied to overcome resonator losses and the damping still happens. If the loop gain is greater than one, then the magnitude of the sine wave will grow until the waveform is no longer sinusoidal.

There is more to making an oscillator work than getting the loop gain right. We also need to be sure that the energy from the amplifier output is applied to the resonator having the correct phase alignment with the oscillating signal in the resonator. Taken together these requirements are known as the *Barkhausen criteria*: to achieve oscillation the loop must 1) have a net zero phase shift (or some integer multiple of 360°) and 2) have a loop gain equal to one. Both of these are critically important. If either of these criteria is not met, the circuit will not oscillate.

How do we find out if we are meeting the Barkhausen criteria? We need to break the loop, usually at the input of the amplifier as shown in Figure 9.3C. We apply a signal slightly below the desired oscillation frequency, then sweep the frequency through and slightly past the desired oscillation frequency. During the sweep we monitor both the magnitude and phase response at the output of the resonator output coupling network. If everything is right, then at the desired frequency of oscillation the input and output signals will look exactly the same on an oscilloscope. If that doesn't happen, we have work to do.

Getting the phase response of the loop correct is usually the harder problem. Much of this difficulty comes from the many types of resonators that can be used, including:

• LC tank

• Quartz crystal (and other piezoelectric materials)

• Transmission line (stripline, microstrip, open-wire, coax, and so on)

• Microwave cavities, YIG spheres, dielectric resonators

• Surface-acoustic-wave (SAW) devices

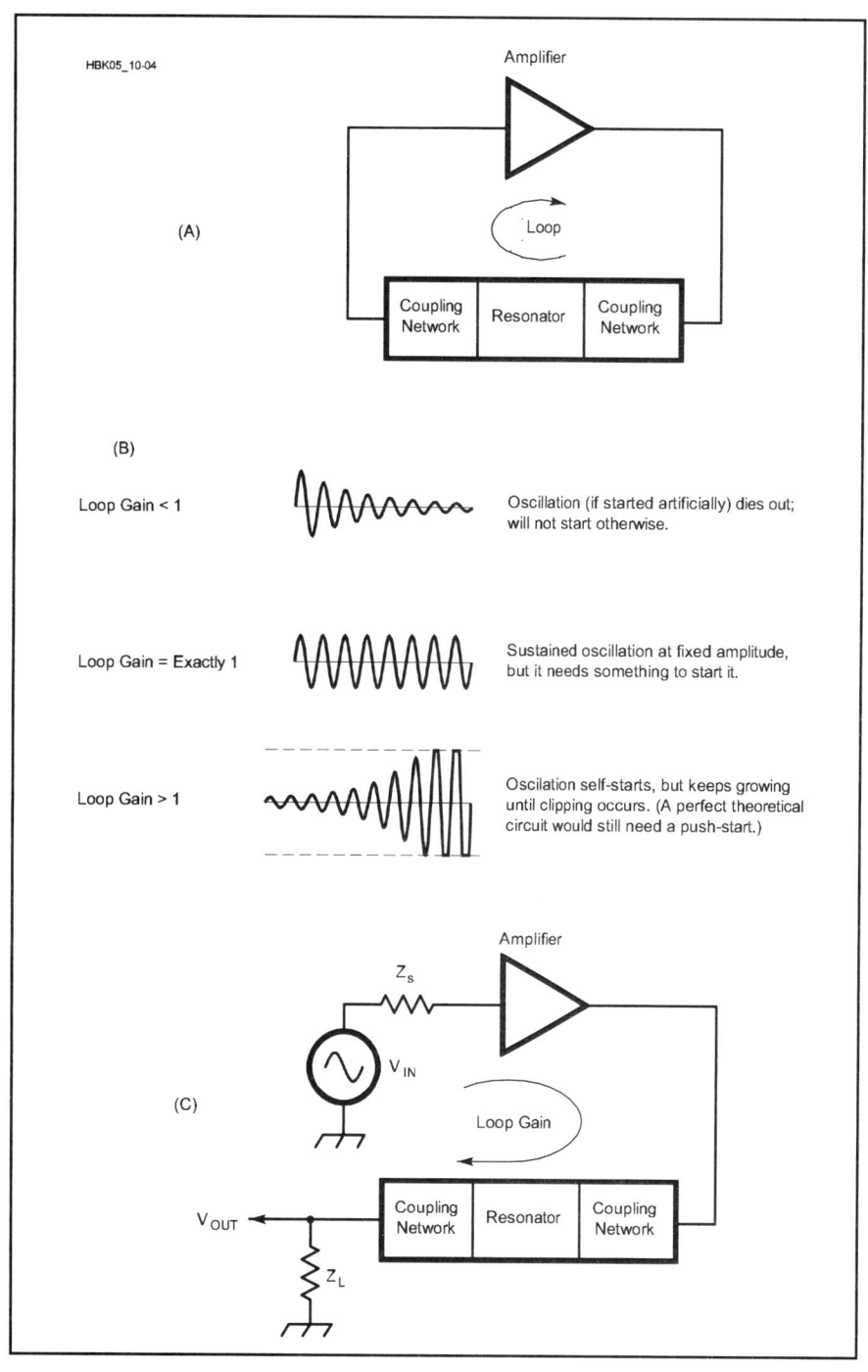

Figure 9.3 — A practical oscillator requires networks to couple power in and out of the resonator (A). At (B), we see the amount of loop gain determines whether the oscillations will die out (loop gain < 1), grow until the waveform is no longer a sine wave (>1), or sustain at a steady amplitude (=1). Breaking the loop, inserting a test signal and measuring the loop's overall gain allows us to determine whether the system can oscillate, sustain oscillation or clip (C).

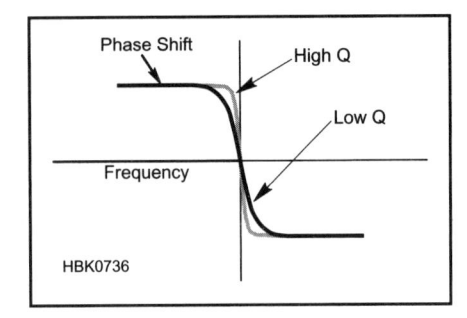

Figure 9.4 — Phase shift through the resonator depends on resonator Q. The higher resonator Q, the more abruptly phase changes through the resonator as frequency changes.

trical Fundamentals chapter). If we have a parallel LC tank, then at frequencies well below resonance the tank looks inductive ($X_L \ll X_C$) and the current lags the voltage. At frequencies well above resonance the tank looks capacitive ($X_C \ll X_L$) so the current leads the voltage. In between, the phase shift of the current relative to the voltage depends on the actual frequency. The rapidity of the phase shift with changing frequency is governed by resonator Q: the phase shift happens very rapidly when Q is high. This is shown in **Figure 9.4**. When the resonator Q is low then the phase changes much more slowly at different frequencies.

If we have a series resonator then the phase change profile is reversed (capacitive to inductive) but otherwise the shape is the same. There are an infinite number of combinations of L and C values that provide the same resonant frequency. If we are interested in high Q, for a series tank we want to select large inductor values and small capacitor values. For a high-Q parallel tank we want the opposite — large capacitor values and small inductor values. **Figure 9.5**, a modified version of the reactance vs frequency chart in the **Electrical Fundamentals** chapter, shows these regions for a resonant frequency of 10 MHz.

9.1.3 Oscillator Start-Up

Looking at Figure 9.3B we see that the oscillation will build up in magnitude only when the loop gain is greater than unity. Thus this is an important additional criterion for oscillator design. The loop gain must be slightly greater than unity for it to start oscillating. Otherwise we have the undesired condition in which there is no signal in the resonator, so we sample nothing from it and put nothing back into it.

Still we need one more thing — noise. Some kind of signal needs to be injected into the resonator for the oscillation to start building up. We are fortunate that all amplifiers have output noise when power is applied, even if there is no input signal. It is this noise that allows any oscillator to start. Amplifier noise initiates a resonant signal in the tank, and if loop gain is slightly greater than unity, more signal is fed back into the resonator than the resonator loses. The output signal builds up until something stops it.

Here we take advantage of an amplifier characteristic where gain is reduced as the output reaches some predefined value. This is referred to as *compression*: when the output signal gets large enough, the amplifier gain is reduced a little bit. When compression balances steady output amplitude with a loop gain of exactly unity, the oscillator has reached steady state operation and we are ready to go!

Why don't we have noise at the oscillator output instead of a sine wave? Because of the filtering action of the resonator, the filtered noise waveform appears mostly sinusoidal. The narrower the bandwidth of the resonator (the higher its Q), the more sinusoidal the waveform, but it actually consists of very well-filtered noise. It is impossible to get only a pure sine wave. Noise is inevitable, and tremendous efforts are spent in reducing this noise. This is discussed in this chapter's section on Phase Noise. A demonstration by David Stockton, GM4ZNX, of oscillator design based on a simulation of how oscillators start up by the free *LTSpice* simulation program is available in the book's downloadable supplemental material.

Each of these also can be called a filter. It is true that any filter can also be used as a resonator in an oscillator. The more complicated phase responses of filters makes meeting both of the Barkhausen criteria more challenging, but certainly possible.

The phase response of the resonator is related to its Q (quality factor — see the Elec-

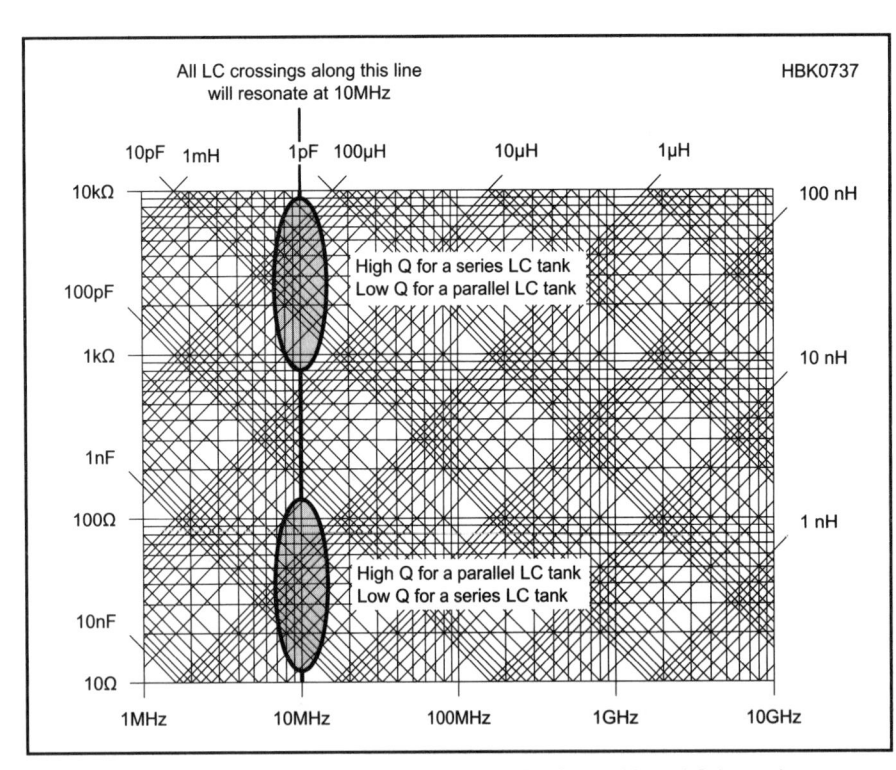

Figure 9.5 — There are an infinite number of combinations of L and C for a given resonant frequency. For a series-LC tank circuit, larger ratios of L to C result in higher values of Q and vice versa for parallel-LC tank circuits.

9.2 LC Variable Frequency Oscillator (VFO) Circuits

In this section we introduce some important oscillator circuits and provide well-tested guidelines on how to successfully build one. The following section presents a design example.

There are thousands of oscillator circuits, but just a few principal designs. One of the principal oscillator circuits is shown in **Figure 9.6**. An LC tank circuit is shown in Figure 9.6A. The usual single capacitance is replaced with two series capacitors having the same equivalent capacitance, C_{EQUIV}. The two capacitors act as an ac voltage divider, so that the voltage V1 at the midpoint is less than the total ac voltage of the tank, V_{TANK}.

What happens when we try to force V1 to be the same as V_{TANK} by adding an amplifier with unity voltage gain as shown in Figure 9.6B? The voltage division action of the capacitive divider does not change. If V1 is forced to be equal to V_{TANK} by the amplifier, then V_{TANK} will become greater than before. But then V1 will take on the new value of V_{TANK} and so forth. This is positive feedback and we have created an oscillator. Connecting an amplifier with low voltage gain to a split tank capacitance leads to the *Colpitts* group of oscillator designs.

It is certainly possible to "split" the inductor instead of the capacitor in a tank circuit and apply the same amplifier trick as before. This is shown in Figure 9.6C and describes the *Hartley* group of oscillators.

9.2.1 Basic Oscillator Circuits

(See also the papers "What You Always Wanted to Know About Colpitts Oscillators" by Ulrich Rohde, N1UL, and Anisha M. Apte, and "Calculation of FM and AM Noise Signals of Colpitts Oscillators in the Time Domain" by Ulrich Rohde, N1UL, included with the downloadable supplemental material accompanying this book.)

The LC oscillators used in radio equipment are usually designed to be variable frequency oscillators (VFOs). Tuning is achieved by either varying part of the capacitance of the resonator or, less commonly, by using a movable magnetic core to vary the inductance. Since the early days of radio, there has been a huge quest for the ideal, low-drift VFO. Amateurs and professionals have made immense efforts in this pursuit. A brief search of the literature reveals a large number of VFO designs, many accompanied by claims of high stability. The quest for stability has been solved by the development of low-cost frequency synthesizers, which give crystal-controlled stability. Synthesizers are generally noisier than a good VFO, so the VFO still has much to offer in terms of signal cleanliness, cost, and power consumption, making it attractive for homebrew construction. No single VFO circuit has any overwhelming advantage over any other — component quality, mechanical design and the care taken in assembly are much more important.

Let's take a look at three popular oscillator circuits stripped of any non-essential components so they can be more easily compared. The original Colpitts circuit (**Figure 9.7**) is now often referred to as the parallel-tuned Colpitts because its series-tuned derivative (**Figure 9.8**) has become the most common. The Hartley version of the oscillator is shown

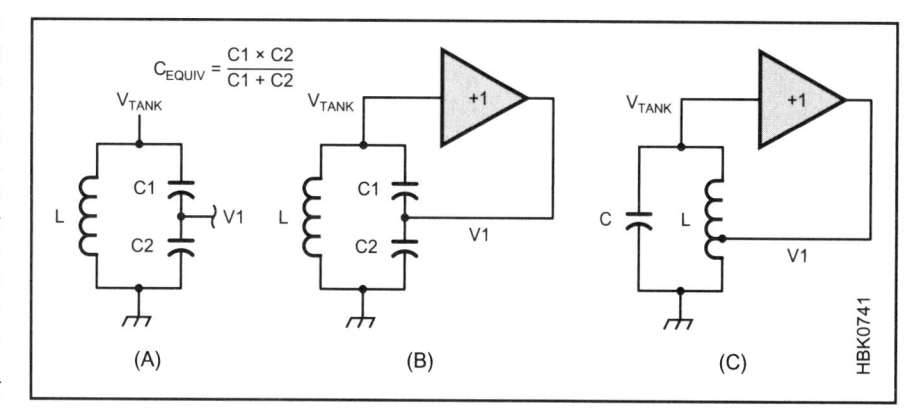

Figure 9.6 — The capacitor in an LC tank circuit (A) can be split into two capacitors with the same equivalent capacitance, C_{EQUIV}, so that the resonant frequency of the tank circuit is unchanged. (B) shows a unity-gain amplifier connected so that it forces V1 = V_{TANK}, creating positive feedback and a Colpitts oscillator results. (C) shows the same technique applied to the tank circuit inductor, creating a Hartley oscillator.

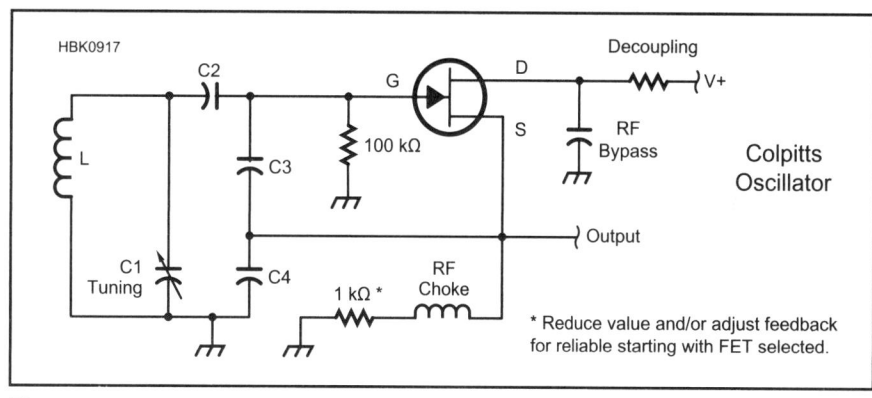

Figure 9.7 — The Colpitts oscillator circuit.

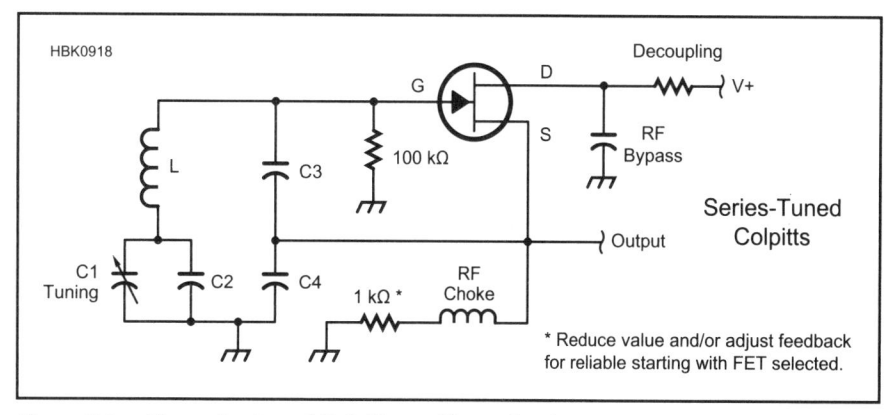

Figure 9.8 — The series-tuned Colpitts oscillator circuit.

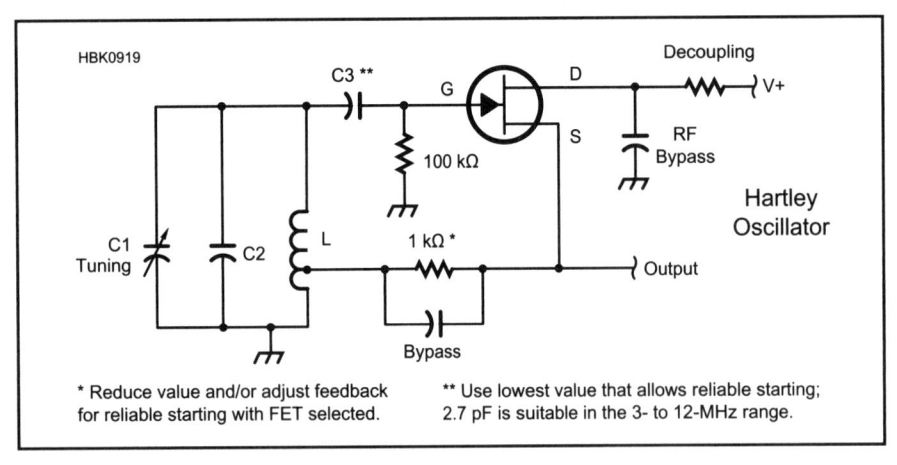

Figure 9.9 — The Hartley oscillator circuit.

* Reduce value and/or adjust feedback for reliable starting with FET selected.

** Use lowest value that allows reliable starting; 2.7 pF is suitable in the 3- to 12-MHz range.

in **Figure 9.9**. All three of these circuits use an amplifier with a voltage gain less than unity, but large current gain. The N-channel JFET source follower shown is the most popular current choice for the transistor amplifier circuit.

Rules of thumb for C3 and C4 in Figures 9.7 and 9.8 should be equal and valued such that their $X_C = 45\ \Omega$ at the operating frequency; for C2 in Figure 9.7, $X_C = 100\ \Omega$. For best stability, use C0G or NP0 units for all capacitors associated with the FET gates and sources. Depending on the FET chosen, the 1-kΩ source-bias-resistor value shown may require adjustment for reliable starting.

PARALLEL-TUNED COLPITTS VFO

In the parallel-tuned Colpitts, C3 and C4 are large values, perhaps 10 times larger than typical values chosen for C1 and C2 to resonate L at the desired frequency. This means only a small fraction of the total tank voltage is applied to the FET gate, and the FET can be considered to be only lightly coupled into the tank. Equally important, the values of C3 and C4 must be much larger than the FET device internal capacitances to provide good stability for the output frequency. This keeps small variations in the FET capacitances from having a significant effect on oscillator operation.

The FET is driven by the sum of the voltages across C3 and C4, while it drives the voltage across C4 alone. This means that the tank operates as a resonant, voltage-step-up transformer compensating for the less-than-unity-voltage-gain amplifier. The resonant circuit consists of L, C1, C2, C3 and C4. The resonant frequency can be calculated by using the standard formulas for capacitors in series and parallel to find the resultant capacitance effectively connected across the inductor, L, and then use the standard formula for LC resonance:

$$f = \frac{1}{2\pi\sqrt{LC}}$$

where
f = frequency in hertz
L = total inductance in henries
C = total capacitance in farads.

This equation holds for all cases. Its accuracy is dependent on the designer's ability to account for all of the contributions to tank inductance and capacitance. There are several rules of thumb that help a VFO designer identify the various "stray" contributions to tank inductance and capacitance:

1. Wherever there is voltage, stray capacitance must be considered.
2. Wherever there is current, stray mutual inductance must be considered.
3. All currents form loops, creating inductance.

These "rules" will help point out where to look for contributions to inductance and capacitance. At frequencies below 10 MHz the actual components you see and touch tend to be all you need to consider. As the oscillator frequency increases, consideration of stray capacitance and stray inductance — reactance effects that are not associated directly with a visible component — becomes increasingly important. If the oscillator frequency is noticeably lower than what you predict, it is almost certain that there are important stray reactances that you need to account for.

Getting back to the circuit of Figure 9.7, for a wide tuning range C2 must be kept small to reduce the swamping effect of C3 and C4 on the variable capacitor C1. (For more information on component selection, the chapters on oscillators in *Experimental Methods for RF Design* and *Introduction to Radio Frequency Design* listed in the References provide excellent material.) "Swamping" refers to a much larger value component reducing the effect of a small component connected to it.

A parallel-tuned Colpitts oscillator is the subject of the detailed paper "A Design Example for an Oscillator for Best Phase Noise and Good Output Power" by Ulrich Rohde, N1UL, available in the downloadable supplemental information for this book. The paper shows the design process by which both noise and power can be optimized in a simple oscillator.

SERIES-TUNED COLPITTS VFO

The series-tuned Colpitts circuit (Figure 9.8) works in much the same way. The difference is that the variable capacitor, C1, is positioned so that it is well-protected from being swamped by the large values of C3 and C4. In fact, small values of C3, C4 would act to limit the tuning range. Fixed capacitance, C2, is often added across C1 to allow the tuning range to be reduced to that required without interfering with C3 and C4, which set the amplifier coupling. The series-tuned Colpitts has a reputation for better stability than the parallel-tuned original. Note how C3 and C4 swamp the capacitances of the amplifier in both versions.

HARTLEY VFO

The Hartley oscillator of Figure 9.9 is similar to the parallel-tuned Colpitts, but the JFET amplifier source is connected to a tap on the tank inductance instead of the tank capacitance. A typical tap placement is 10% to 20% of the total turns up from the cold end of the inductor. (It's common to refer to the lowest-signal-voltage end of an inductor as "cold" and the other, with the highest signal voltage as "hot".) C2 limits the tuning range as required.

C3 is reduced to the minimum value that allows reliable starting. This is necessary because the Hartley's lack of the Colpitts' capacitive divider would otherwise couple the FET's internal capacitances to the tank more strongly than in the Colpitts, potentially affecting the circuit's frequency stability.

VFO DESIGN NOTES

Generally, VFOs can be adapted to work at other frequencies (within the limits of the active device). To do so, compute an adjustment factor: f_{old} / f_{new}. Multiply the value of each frequency determining or feedback L or C by that factor. As frequency increases and amplifier gain drops, it may be required to increase feedback more than indicated by the factor.

In all three circuits, there is a 1 kΩ resistor in series with the source bias circuit. This resistor does a number of desirable things. It spoils (lowers) the Q of the inevitable low-frequency resonance of the choke with the tank tap circuit. It reduces tuning drift due to choke impedance and winding capacitance variations. It also protects against spurious oscillation at undesired frequencies due to internal choke resonances. Less obviously, it acts to stabilize the loop gain of the built-in AGC action of this oscillator. Stable operating conditions act to reduce frequency drift.

Some variations of these circuits may be found with added resistors providing a dc bias to stabilize the system quiescent current. More elaborate still are variations characterized by a constant-current source providing bias. This can be driven from a separate AGC detector system to give very tight level control. The gate-to-ground clamping diode (1N914 or similar) long used by radio amateurs as a means of avoiding gate-source conduction has been shown by Ulrich Rohde, N1UL, to degrade oscillator phase-noise performance, and its use is virtually unknown in professional circles.

Figure 9.10 shows two more VFOs to illustrate the use of different devices. The vacuum-tube triode Hartley shown features permeability tuning, which has no sliding contact like that of a capacitor's rotor and can be made reasonably linear by artfully spacing the coil turns. The slow-motion drive can be done with a screw thread. The disadvantage is that special care is needed to avoid backlash and eccentric rotation of the core. If a non-rotating core is used, the slides have to be carefully designed to prevent motion in unwanted directions. The Collins Radio Company made extensive use of tube-based permeability tuners, and a semiconductor version can still be found in a number of Ten-Tec radios.

Vacuum tubes cannot run as cool as competitive semiconductor circuits, so care is needed to keep the tank circuit away from the tube heat. In many amateur and commercial vacuum-tube oscillators, oscillation drives the tube into grid current at the positive peaks, causing rectification and producing a negative grid bias. The oscillator thus runs in Class C, in which the conduction angle reduces as the signal amplitude increases until the amplitude stabilizes. As in the FET circuits of Figures 9.7 through 9.9, better stability and phase-noise performance can be achieved in a vacuum-tube oscillator by moving its operating point out of true Class C — that is, by including a bypassed cathode-bias resistor (the resistance appropriate for Class A operation is a good starting value). Vacuum-tube radios are still maintained in operation and occasionally constructed for enjoyment but the semiconductor long ago achieved dominance in VFOs.

Compared to the more frequently used JFET, bipolar transistors like the one used in Figure 9.10B are relatively uncommon in oscillators because their relatively low input and output impedances are more difficult to couple into a high-Q tank without loading it excessively. Bipolar devices do tend to give better sample-to-sample amplitude uniformity for a given oscillator circuit, because many of the bipolar transistor characteristics are due less to manufacturing than physics. This is not true for JFETs of any given type; JFETs tend to vary more in their characteristics because manufacturing variations directly affect their threshold or pinch-off voltage.

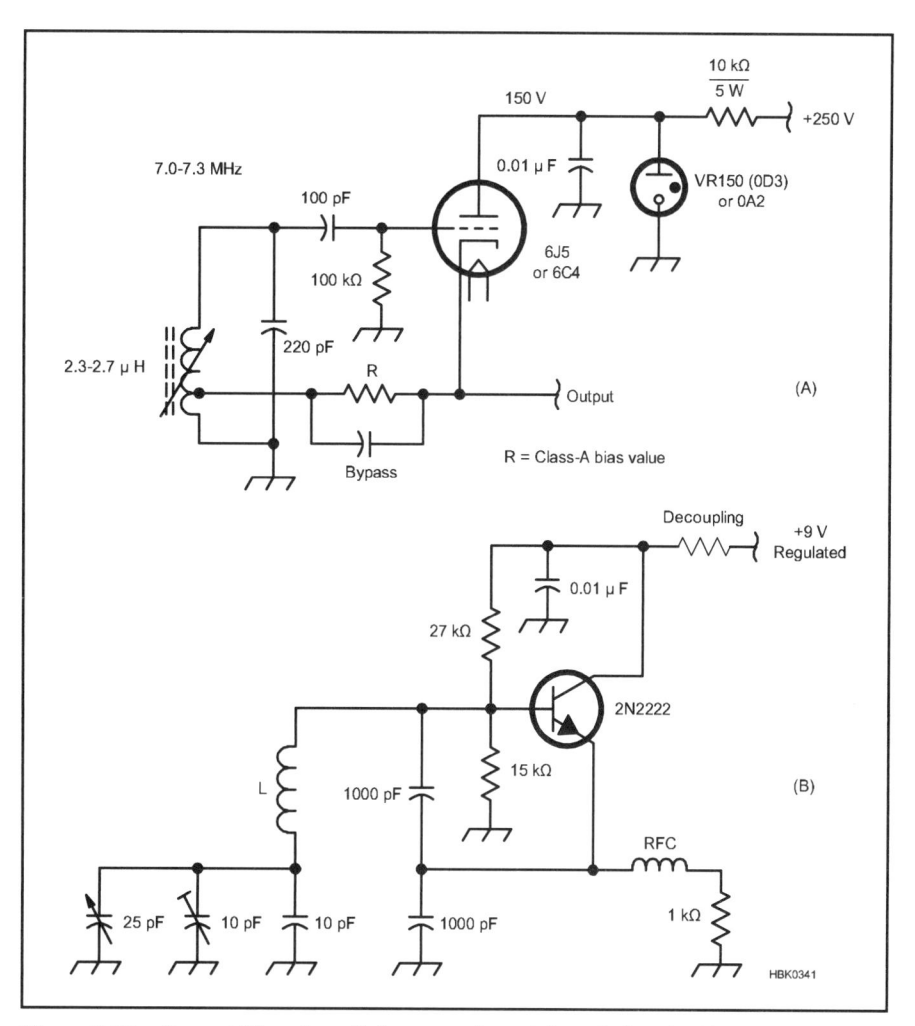

Figure 9.10 — Two additional oscillator examples: at A, a triode-tube Hartley; at B, a bipolar junction transistor in a series-tuned Colpitts.

SQUEGGING

The effect called *squegging* (or *squeeging*) can be loosely defined as oscillation on more than one frequency at a time, but may also manifest itself as RF oscillation interrupted at an audio frequency rate, as in a super-regenerative detector. One form of squegging occurs when an oscillator is fed from a power supply with high source impedance. The power supply charges up the decoupling capacitor until oscillation starts. The oscillator draws current and pulls down the capacitor voltage until it has starved itself of power and oscillation stops. The oscillator stops drawing current and the decoupling capacitor then recharges until oscillation restarts. The process, the low-frequency cycling of which is a form of relaxation oscillation, repeats indefinitely. The oscillator output can clearly be seen to be pulse modulated with an oscilloscope.

Squegging can be a consequence of poor design in battery-powered radios. As the cells become exhausted, their internal resistance often rises and circuits that they power can begin to misbehave. In audio stages, such misbehavior may manifest itself in the "putt-putt" sound of the slow relaxation oscillation called "motorboating."

9.2.2 Two Low-Noise VHF Oscillators

The following section is excerpted from the May/June 2018 QEX article "An Optimized Grounded Base Oscillator Design for VHF/UHF," by Ulrich Rohde, N1UL, and Ajay Poddar, AC2KG. The full article is available as a PDF file in this book's downloadable supplemental information. Interested readers are encouraged to read the original article which includes a comprehensive set of references and all design details.

The design of VHF/UHF oscillators has been described in many books and journals with most of the emphasis on frequency stability and to some smaller part on output/efficiency. Since the introduction of reliable phase noise measurements and the ability to predict/simulate the phase noise, the improvement of this important parameter with the help of CAD and analytic equations has gained more attention. The novel design concept described in the article with the downloadable supplemental content uses a time domain approach to provide both the best output power and the best phase noise performance. This very simple but powerfully scalable set of formulas for the oscillator synthesis provides extremely good results. In addition, the design principle for fixed or narrowband oscillators discussed here also applies to the broadband VCO design. This design methodology works over a multi-octave tuning range.

CIRCUIT DESIGN GUIDELINES

The results we have obtained so far were based on mathematical calculations. Some of these calculations are difficult to obtain (see the original *QEX* article). However, there are certain relationships between the values of the capacitance of the tuned circuit and the two feedback capacitors, the collector-emitter capacitor and the emitter-to-ground capacitor. The following shows the set of recommended steps for easy design of such oscillators.

A very popular circuit for VHF/UHF oscillators is the grounded-base configuration, which is shown in **Figure 9.11**. Its phase noise can be made very good, since the RF voltage swing at the collector can be close to the supply voltage. The circuit is simple and has been used for decades. This oscillator type works well from RF frequencies such as 10 MHz to above 1000 MHz.

The oscillator function is based on the principle that power from the output is taken and fed to the emitter. This feedback arrangement generates a negative resistance at the output, compensating the losses of the output-tuned circuit, and starts oscillating and then stabilizing the oscillation amplitude. The circuit has simple design rules where C_E and C_F are the feedback capacitors that generate the negative resistance to compensate for the loss resistance in the resonator network comprised of L_E and C^*_L.

Theoretically, the grounded-base configuration can be rotated to be the Colpitts circuit. If we look at the performance, in the case of the Colpitts oscillator the RF voltage swing is limited by the base-emitter and emitter-to-ground voltage and as a result there is less energy stored in the circuit and because of loading the operational Q can be less than in the grounded-base configuration. The Colpitts oscillator is popular because of its simplicity, and its perceived high isolation as the output power is taken at the collector. However, due to the strong Miller effect at very high frequencies, this is not a true statement.

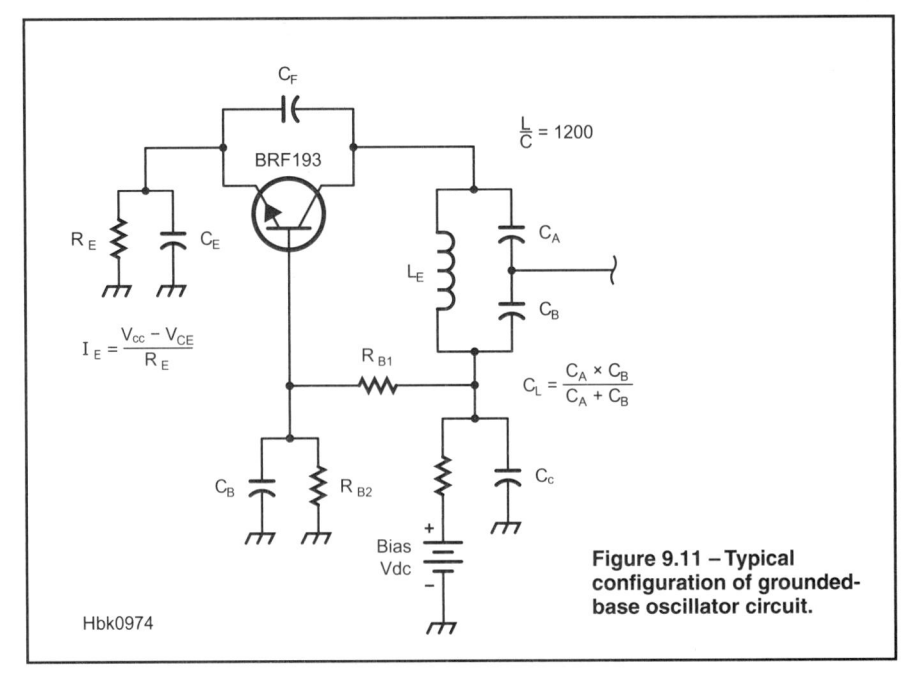

Figure 9.11 – Typical configuration of grounded-base oscillator circuit.

SIMPLE DESIGN RULES

By setting the L/C ratio to a fixed value of 1200 (for optimum energy storage, group delay and energy transfer for a given cycle in the resonator network), the following should be used.

$$\frac{L}{C} = \left[\frac{L_E}{C^*_L}\right]_{Grounded-Base} = 1200$$

$$\Rightarrow Z_0 = \sqrt{1200} \cong 34.6\ \Omega$$

$$L = 1200 \times C$$

$$\Rightarrow L_E = 1200 \times C^*_L$$

$$f = \frac{1}{2\pi\sqrt{LC}} = \frac{1}{2\pi C\sqrt{1200}}$$

$$C^*_L = C_L + \frac{C_E C_F}{C_E + C_F}$$

where C_E and C_F are feedback capacitors.

$$C_L = \frac{C_A C_B}{C_A + C_B}$$

where C_A and C_F are feedback capacitors.

$$C_B = 10\ C_A$$

The reader is reminded that this "recipe" was developed based on the Y-parameters, transconductance, and package parasitics for the BRF193 transistor. Using a transistor greatly different than the BRF193 requires the full design process to be performed as described in the original article.

144 MHz GROUNDED-BASE OSCILLATOR

The oscillator circuit in **Figure 9.12** is designed using the procedure of the preceding section.

$$C^*_L = \frac{1}{2\pi f \sqrt{1200}} \Rightarrow C \cong 31\ \text{pF}$$

$$L_L = \frac{1}{(2\pi f)^2 C} \Rightarrow L \cong 39\ \text{nH}$$

$$C_F = 0.3 \times C^*_L \cong 11\ \text{pF}$$

$$C_L = 2 \times C_F \cong 22\ \text{pF}$$

$$C_E = 4 \times C_F \cong 44\ \text{pF}$$

$$C_A = 22\ \text{pF}$$

$$C_B = 220\ \text{pF}$$

These results are frequency scalable with minor corrections possibly necessary.

Figure 9.12A shows the schematic of the 144 MHz oscillator at $I_C = 10$ mA. The oscillator uses a lumped inductor of 39 nH and an unloaded Q of 200 at the operating frequency. Even at these frequencies the layout is quite critical. The example layout in Figure 9.12B shows an assembly of components where the lead inductances have been kept small. The inductor is a standard off the shelf component. (Note that the sample layout is given only as a guideline and not as a template.)

Figure 9.12C shows the CAD simulated phase noise plot. The output power is 11.5 dBm and the second and third harmon-

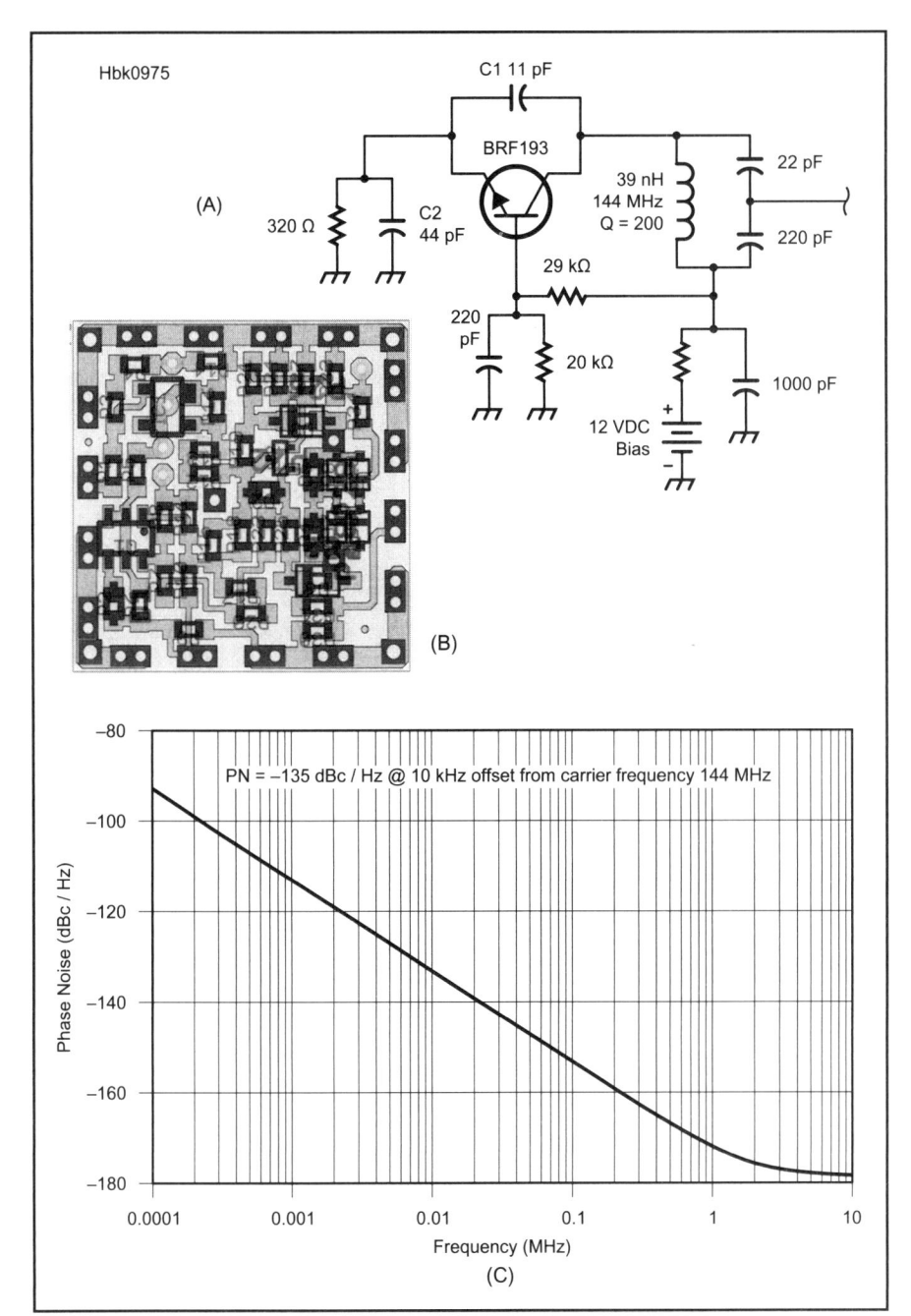

Figure 9.12 — 144 MHz oscillator circuit for I_E = 10 mA ((A), an example of the circuit layout using LC lumped inductor-capacitor resonator network (B), and simulated phase noise plot (C).

The Vackar Oscillator

The original Vackar oscillator is named for Jirí Vackár, who invented the circuit in the late 1940s. The circuit's description — a refinement of the Clapp oscillator — can be found in older editions of the Radio Society of Great Britain's Radio Communication Handbook, with some further comments on the oscillator in RSGB's Amateur Radio Techniques. The circuit is also described in the Nov 1955 QST "Technical Correspondence" column by W9IK. The Vackar circuit optimized the Clapp oscillator for frequency stability: the oscillator transistor is isolated from the resonator, tuning does not affect the feedback coupling, and the transistor's collector output impedance is kept low so that gain is the minimum necessary to sustain oscillation.

a different output coupling scheme because in this configuration, the loading would vary with frequency. This can easily be achieved by adding some inductive coupling to the circuit. In case of a printed resonator this can be accomplished quite simply.

Figure 9.13B shows a sample guideline layout of the 432 MHz oscillator circuit using a buried printed coupled line resonator network (stripline resonator in the middle layer). The actual resonator would not be visible if the oscillator is visually inspected.

Figure 9.13C shows the simulated phase noise plot with the expected noise degradation of 9 dB, as the frequency is approximately three times higher. The resulting simulated output power at 432 MHz is 16 dBm, compared to 18 dBm at 144 MHz. This is due to internal package parasitics, which could not be compensated externally. The second harmonic is suppressed by 38 dB; this is due to the higher operating Q.

ics are about –28 dBm and –34 dBm. Using phase noise simulation, the result is –134 dBc/Hz and –94 dBc/Hz at 10 kHz and 100 Hz offset. Calculated, simulated, and measured results closely agree within 1 dB.

If the same transistor is operated at 30 mA, the phase noise at 10 kHz offset will improve to be –144 dBc/Hz and the output power is increased to 20 dBm. This shows that for low phase noise design a more powerful transistor is a good choice. It is important to keep the dc dissipation of the device in mind, as the CAD process will probably not flag a misuse of the device.

MODIFIED CIRCUIT FOR UHF (432 MHz) AND HIGHER CURRENT

At 432 MHz and at I_E = 30 mA, the loading of the tank circuit decreases the operating Q significantly. The way around this to use a center-tapped inductor. As the coupling at these frequencies from winding to winding is not extremely high, two separate identical inductors can be used successfully.

Figure 9.13A shows the schematic of 432 MHz grounded base oscillator using the tapped inductor. This is a modification of the circuit we have used previously. In the case of a VCO, it would be advantageous to use

9.2.3 Three High-Performance HF VFOs

THE N1UL MODIFIED VACKAR VFO

The oscillator circuit of **Figure 9.14A** is contributed by Ulrich Rohde, N1UL. It is a modified Vackar design (see the sidebar) in which a small coupling capacitor (8 pF) and voltage divider capacitor (18 pF) isolate the resonator circuit (10 µH and 50 pF tuning capacitor) from the oscillator transistor.

The oscillator transistor is followed by a buffer stage to isolate the oscillator from the load. Because the coupling between the transistor base and the resonator is fixed and light, stability of the oscillator is high across a wide tuning range from 5.5 to 6.6 MHz. Either the inductor or capacitor may be varied to tune the oscillator, but a variable capacitor is rec-

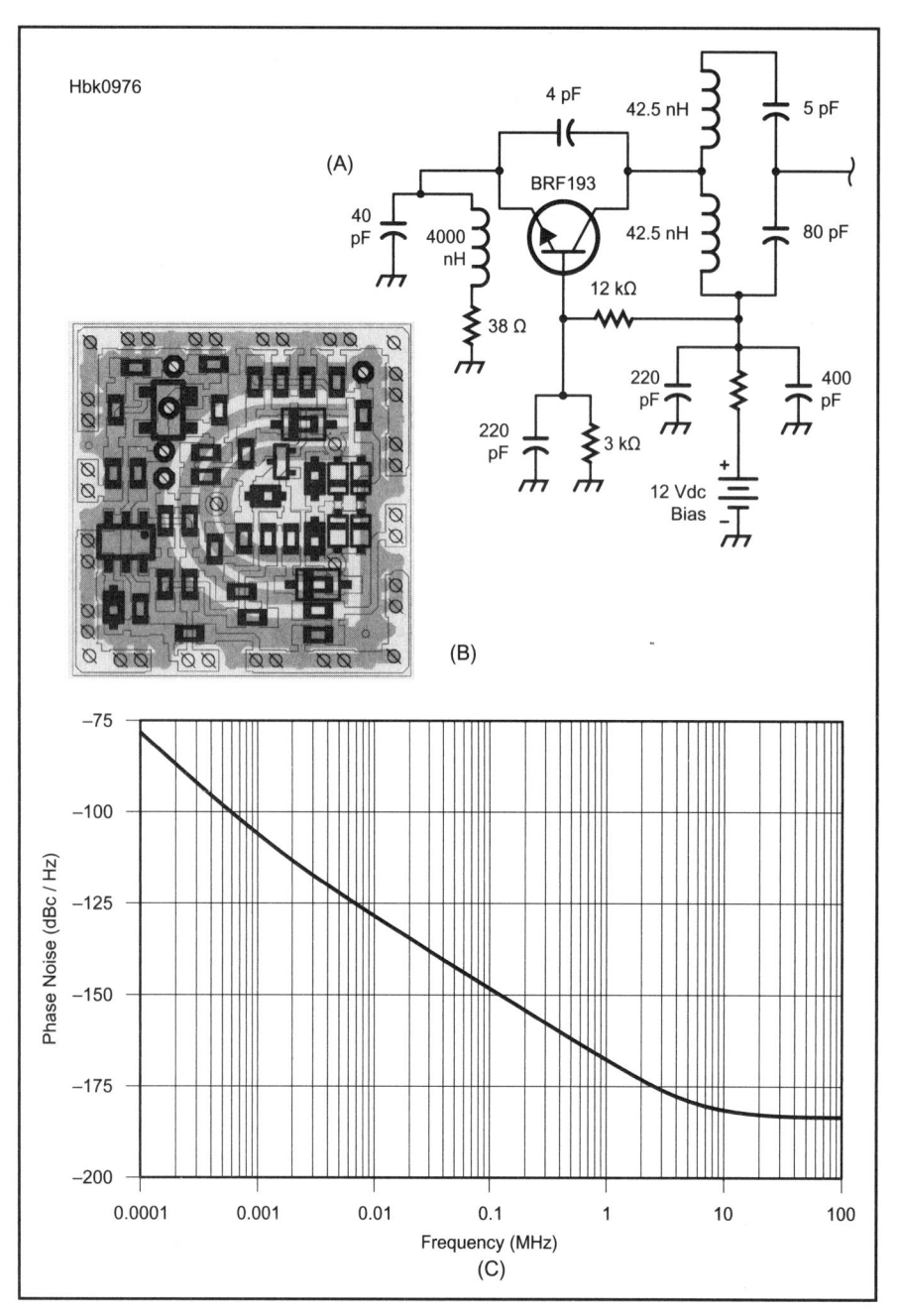

Figure 9.13 — 432 MHz oscillator circuit using tapped inductor and I_E = 30 mA (A), an example of the circuit layout using buried printed coupled line resonator (stripline resonator) in the middle layer of the board (B), and simulated phase noise plot (C).

ommended as more practical and gives better performance.

Because of the oscillator transistor's large capacitors from base to ground (220 pF) and collector to ground (680 pF), the various parameters of the oscillator transistor have little practical influence on circuit performance. The widely available 2N3904 performs well for both the oscillator and buffer transistors.

Practical resonator coil and the tuning capacitors will have a positive temperature coefficient. The 8 pF and the 18 pF capacitors should have an N150 temperature coefficient to partially compensate for their drift. After 1 hour, the observed frequency drift for this circuit was less than 10 Hz / hour.

THE K7HFD LOW-NOISE DIFFERENTIAL OSCILLATOR

The other high performance oscillator example, shown in **Figure 9.15**, is designed for low-noise performance by Linley Gumm, K7HFD, and appears on page 126 of the ARRL's *Solid State Design for the Radio Amateur* (out of print, but available used and through libraries). This circuit uses no unusual components and looks simple, yet it is a subtle and sophisticated circuit. (An analysis and simulation of this circuit by its designer is included in the downloadable supplemental material for this book.)

The effects of limiting in reducing AM oscillator noise were covered previously. However, because AM noise sidebands can get translated into PM noise sidebands by imperfect limiting, there is an advantage to stripping off the AM as early as possible, in the oscillator itself. An ALC system in the oscillator will counteract and cancel only the AM components within its bandwidth, but an oscillator based on a limiter will do this over a broad bandwidth. K7HFD's oscillator uses a differential pair of bipolar transistors as a limiting amplifier. The dc bias voltage at the bases and the resistor in the common emitter path to ground establishes a controlled dc bias current, here 25 to 27 mA. The ac voltage between the bases switches this current between the two collectors. This applies a rectangular pulse of current into link winding L2, which drives the series-resonant tank L1-C1. The output impedance of the collector is high in both the current-on and current-off states. Along with the small number of turns of the link winding, this presents very high impedance to the tank circuit, which minimizes degradation of the tank Q. The input impedance of this limiter is also quite high and is applied across only a one-turn tap of L1, which similarly minimizes any impact on the tank Q. The input transistor base is driven into conduction only on one peak of the tank waveform. The output transformer has the inverse of the current pulse applied to it, so the output is not a low distortion sine wave, although the output harmonics will not be as extensive as simple theory would suggest because the circuit's high output impedance allows stray capacitances to attenuate high-frequency components. The low-frequency transistors used here also act to reduce the harmonic power.

With an output of +17 dBm, this is a power oscillator, running with nearly 300 mW of dc input power, so appreciable heating is present that can cause temperature-induced drift. The circuit's high-power operation is a deliberate ploy to create a high signal-to-noise ratio by having as high a signal power as possible. This also reduces the problem of the oscillator's broadband noise output. The limitation on the signal level in the tank is the transistors' base-emitter-junction breakdown voltage. The circuit runs with a few volts peak-to-peak across the one-turn tap, so the full tank is running at over 50 V_{P-P}.

Excessive voltage levels for the transistors can easily be generated by this circuit. The single easiest way to damage a bipolar transistor is to reverse bias the base-emitter junction until it avalanches. Most devices are rated

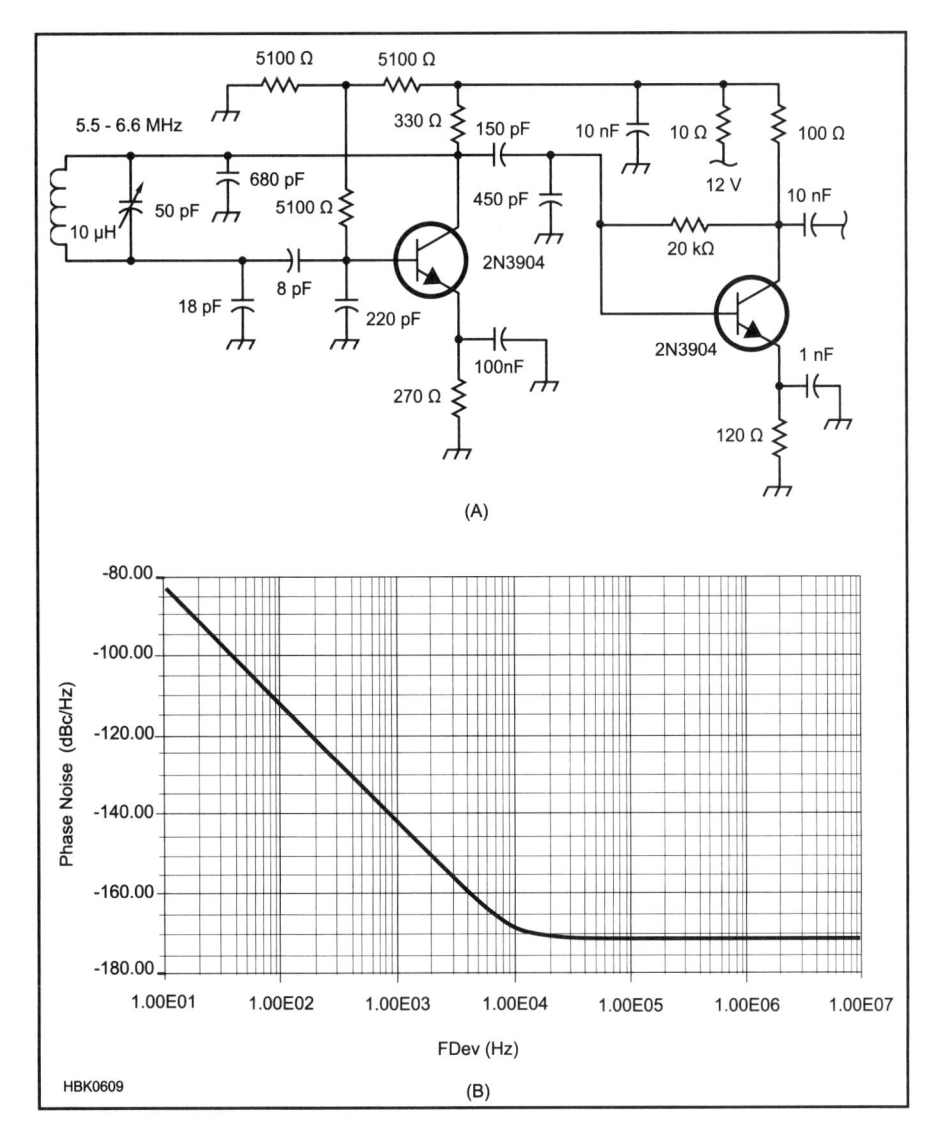

Figure 9.14 — At A, N1UL's Modified Vackar VFO is tuned from 5.5 to 6.6 MHz using the 50 pF capacitor. Tuning may be restricted to narrower ranges by placing a fixed capacitor in parallel with a smaller variable capacitor. The resonant frequency of the oscillator is determined by the 10 µH inductor and 50 pF tuning capacitor. B shows the excellent phase noise performance of the modified Vackar VFO in this *Harmonica* simulation. At 1 kHz from the carrier, noise is –144 dBc.

to withstand only 5 V applied this way, the current needed to do damage is small, and very little power is needed. If the avalanche current is limited to less than that needed to perform immediate destruction of the transistor, it is likely that there will be some degradation of the device, a reduction in its bandwidth and gain along with an increase in its noise. These changes are irreversible and cumulative. Small, fast signal diodes have breakdown voltages of over 30 V and less capacitance than the transistor bases, so one possible experiment would be to try the effect of adding a fast signal diode in series with the base of each transistor and running the circuit at even higher levels.

The oscillation amplitude is controlled by the drive current limit. The voltage on L2 must never allow the collector of the transistor driving it to go into saturation, for if this happens the transistor presents very low impedance to L2 and badly loads the tank, wrecking the Q and the noise performance. The circuit can be checked to verify the margin from saturation by probing the hot end of L2 and the emitter with an oscilloscope. Another, less obvious, test is to vary the power-supply voltage and monitor the output power. While the circuit is under current control, there is very little change in output power, but if the supply is low enough to allow saturation, the output power will change significantly with varying supply voltage.

The use of the 2N3904 is interesting, as it is not normally associated with RF oscillators. It is a cheap, plain, general-purpose type more often used at dc or audio frequencies. There is evidence that suggests some transistors that have good noise performance at RF have worse noise performance at low frequencies, and that the low-frequency noise they create can modulate an oscillator, creating noise sidebands. Experiments with low-noise audio transistors may be worthwhile, but many such devices have high junction capacitances.

In the description of this circuit in *Solid State Design for the Radio Amateur*, the results of a phase-noise test made using a spectrum analyzer with a crystal filter as a preselector are given. Ten kilohertz away from the carrier, in a 3 kHz measurement bandwidth, the noise was more than 120 dB below the carrier level. This translates into better than –120 – 10 log (3000), which equals –154.8 dBc/Hz, SSB, consistent with the modeled phase noise performance shown in Figure 9.15B. At this offset, –140 dBc is usually considered to be excellent. This VFO provides state-of-the art performance by today's standards — in a 1977 publication.

A JFET HARTLEY VFO

Figure 9.16 shows an 11.1 MHz version of a VFO and buffer closely patterned after that used in 7 MHz transceiver designs published by Roger Hayward, KA7EXM, and Wes Hayward, W7ZOI ("The Ugly Weekender") and Roy Lewallen, W7EL ("The Optimized QRP Transceiver"). In it, a Hartley oscillator using a 2N5486 JFET drives the two-2N3904 buffer attributed to Lewallen. This version diverges from the originals in that its JFET uses source bias (the bypassed 910 Ω resistor) instead of a gate-clamping diode and is powered from a low-current 7 V regulator IC instead of a Zener diode and dropping resistor. The 5 dB pad sets the buffer's output to a level appropriate for "Level 7" (+7 dBm LO) diode ring mixers.

The circuit shown was originally built with a gate-clamping diode, no source bias and a 3 dB output pad. Adjusting the oscillator bias as shown increased its output by 2 dB without degrading its frequency stability (200 to 300 Hz drift at power up, stability within ±20 Hz thereafter at a constant room temperature).

In recognition that precision mechanical tuning components are hard to obtain, the resonator uses "Bandset" and "Bandspread" variable capacitors. These terms are from the early days of radio: bandset is for coarse-tuning and bandspread is for fine-tuning.

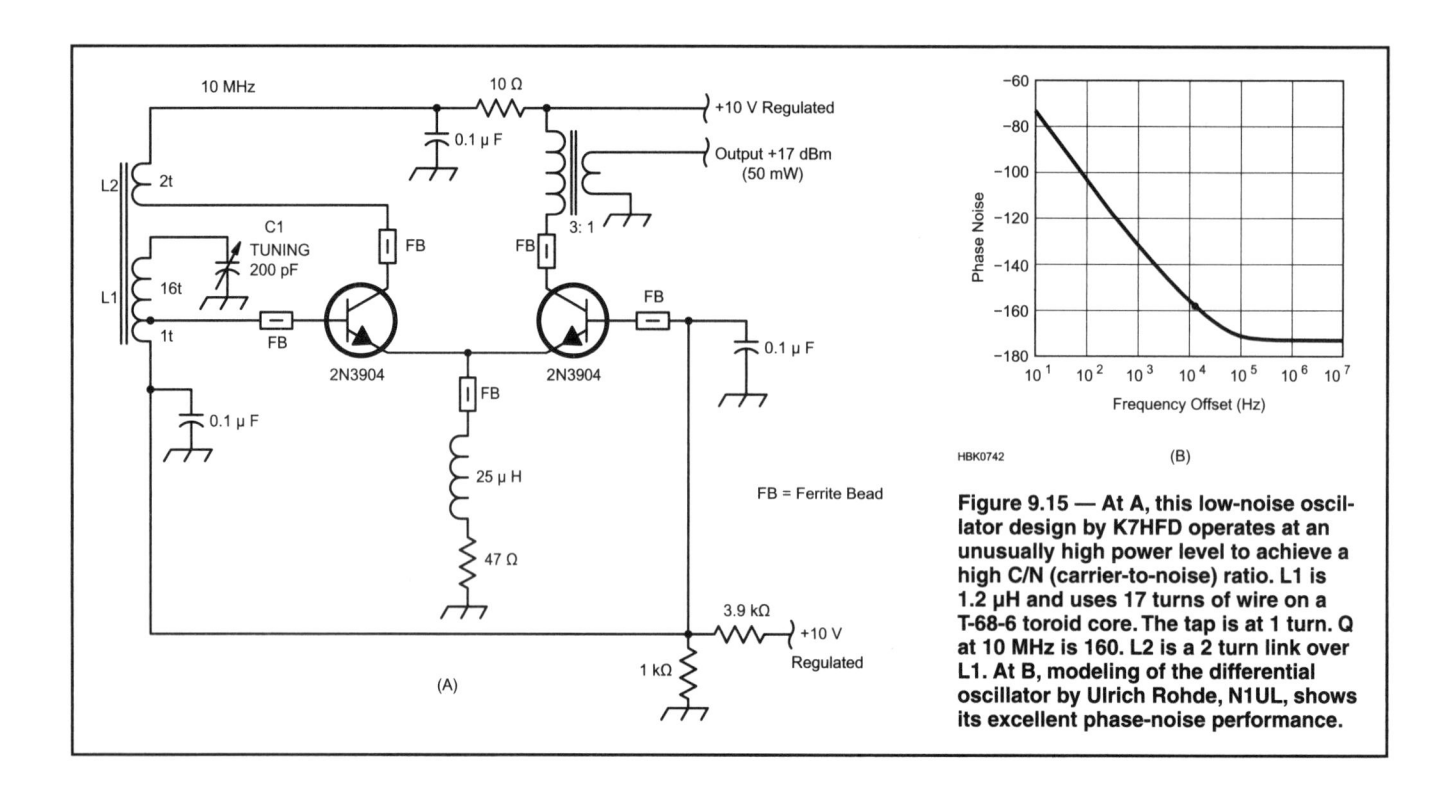

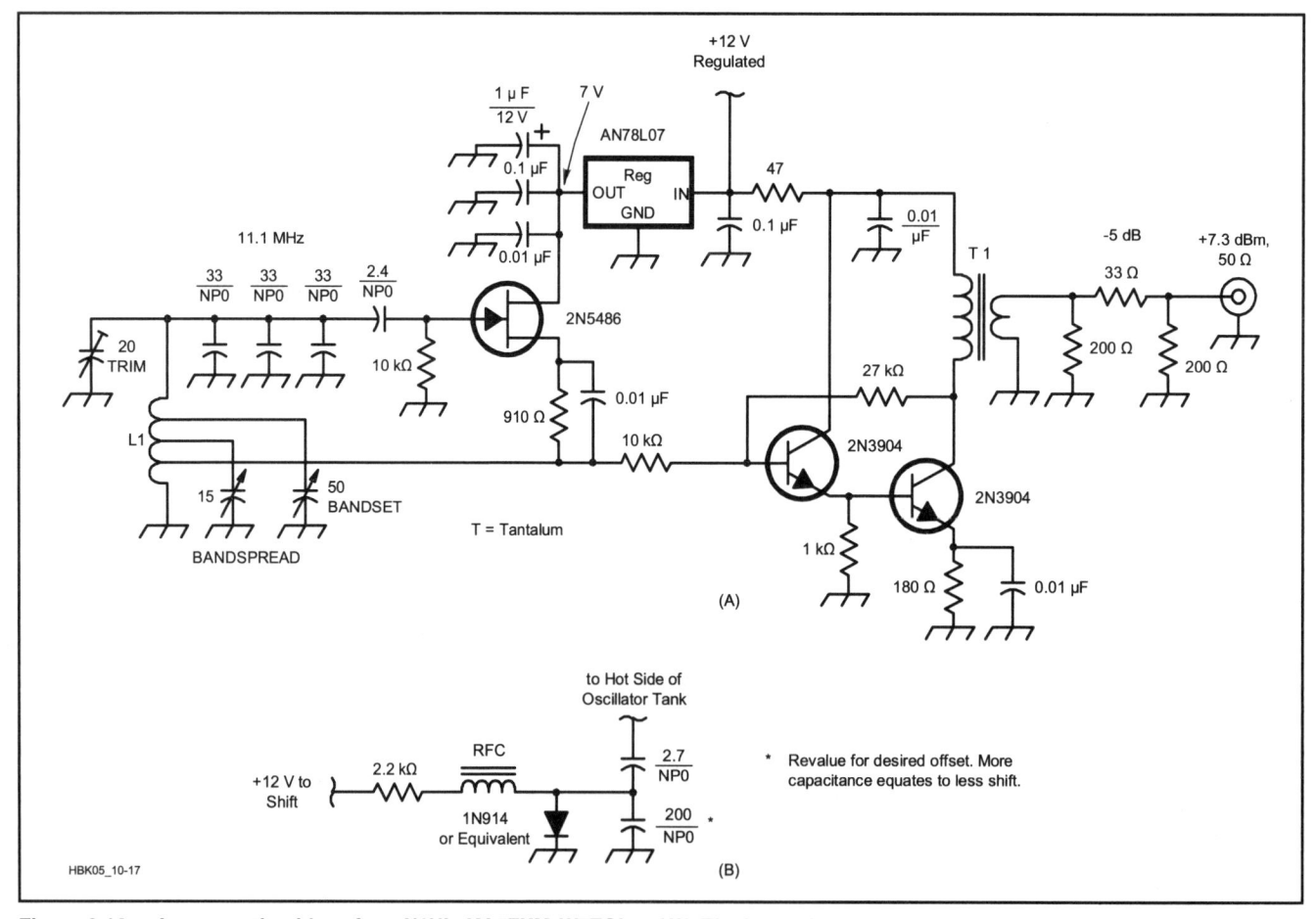

Figure 9.15 — At A, this low-noise oscillator design by K7HFD operates at an unusually high power level to achieve a high C/N (carrier-to-noise) ratio. L1 is 1.2 μH and uses 17 turns of wire on a T-68-6 toroid core. The tap is at 1 turn. Q at 10 MHz is 160. L2 is a 2 turn link over L1. At B, modeling of the differential oscillator by Ulrich Rohde, N1UL, shows its excellent phase-noise performance.

Figure 9.16 — Incorporating ideas from N1UL, KA7EXM, W7ZOI and W7EL, the oscillator at A achieves excellent stability and output at 11.1 MHz without the use of a gate-clamping diode, as well as end-running the shrinking availability of reduction drives through the use of bandset and bandspread capacitors. L1 consists of 10 turns of B & W #3041 Miniductor (#22 tinned wire, 5/8 inch in diameter, 24 turns per inch). The source tap is 2½ turns above ground; the tuning-capacitor taps are positioned as necessary for bandset and bandspread ranges required. T1's primary consists of 15 turns of #28 enameled wire on an FT-37-72 ferrite core; its secondary, 3 turns over the primary. B shows a system for adding fixed TR offset that can be applied to any LC oscillator. The RF choke consists of 20 turns of #26 enameled wire on an FT-37-43 core.

9.12   Chapter 9

9.3 Building an Oscillator

We've covered a lot of ground about how oscillators work, their limitations and a number of interesting circuits, so the inevitable question arises of how to design one. Let's make an embarrassing confession right here: Very few oscillators you see in published circuits or commercial equipment were designed by the equipment's designer. Almost all have been adopted from other sources. While recycling in general is important for the environment, it means in this case that very few professional or amateur designers have ever designed an oscillator from scratch. We all have collections of circuits we've "harvested," and we adjust a few values or change a device type to produce something to suit a new project.

Oscillators aren't designed, they evolve. They seem to have a life of their own. The Clarke & Hess book listed in the references contains one of the few published classical design processes. The ARRL book *Experimental Methods in RF Design* contains extensive material on oscillator circuits that is well worth reading.

9.3.1 VFO Components and Construction

TUNING CAPACITORS AND REDUCTION DRIVES

As most commercially made radios now use frequency synthesizers, it has become increasingly difficult to find certain key components needed to construct a good VFO. Slow-motion drives and variable capacitors are available from *QST* advertiser National RF (**www.nationalrf.com**), Dan's Small Parts and Kits (**www.danssmallpartsandkits.net**), and Antique Electronic Supply (**www.tubesandmore.com**). Variable capacitors should be a high-quality component with double ball-bearings and silver-plated surfaces and contacts.

An alternate approach is also available: Scavenge suitable parts from old equipment; use tuning diodes instead of variable capacitors — an approach that, if uncorrected through phase locking, generally degrades stability and phase-noise performance; or use two tuning capacitors, one with a capacitance range ⅕ to ⅒ that of the other, in a bandset/bandspread approach.

Assembling a variable capacitor to a chassis and its reduction drive to a front panel can result in *backlash* — an annoying tuning effect in which rotating the capacitor shaft deforms the chassis and/or panel rather than tuning the capacitor. One way of minimizing this is to use the reduction drive to support the capacitor, and use the capacitor to support the oscillator circuit board, which is then attached to the chassis.

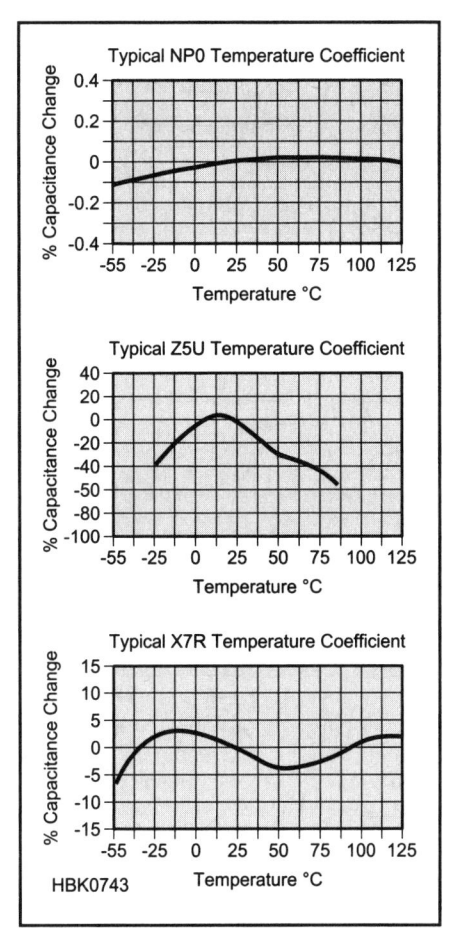

Figure 9.17 — EIA capacitor temperature coefficients specify change in capacitance with temperature. See the Component Data and References chapter for a complete table of temperature coefficient identifiers and characteristics.

FIXED CAPACITORS

Use silvered-mica or other highly-stable capacitors for all fixed-value capacitors in the oscillator circuit. Power-supply decoupling capacitors may be any convenient type, such as ceramic or film.

Traditionally, silver-mica fixed capacitors have been used extensively in oscillators, but their temperature coefficient is not as low as can be achieved with other types, and some silver micas have been known to behave erratically. Polystyrene film has become a proven alternative. One warning is worth noting: polystyrene capacitors exhibit a permanent change in value should they ever be exposed to temperatures much above 70 °C; they do not return to their old value on cooling.

Particularly suitable for oscillator construction are the low-temperature-coefficient ceramic capacitors, often described as NP0 or C0G types. (NP0 and C0G are equivalent) These abbreviations are actually temperature-coefficient codes. **Figure 9.17** contains graphs showing the behavior of three common temperature coefficients. Some ceramic capacitors are available with deliberate, controlled temperature coefficients so that they can be used to compensate for other causes of frequency drift with temperature. For example, the code N750 denotes a part with a temperature coefficient of −750 parts per million per degree Celsius. These parts are now somewhat difficult to obtain, so other methods are needed. (Values for temperature coefficients and other attributes of capacitors are presented in the **Component Data and References** chapter.)

In a Colpitts circuit, the two large-value capacitors that form the voltage divider for the active device still need careful selection. It is tempting to use any available capacitor of the right value, because the effect of these components on the tank frequency is reduced by the proportions of the capacitance values in the circuit. This reduction is not as great as the difference between the temperature stability of an NP0 ceramic part and some of the low-cost, decoupling-quality X7R-dielectric ceramic capacitors. It's worth using low-temperature coefficient parts even in the seemingly less-critical parts of a VFO circuit — even for the bypass capacitors. Chasing the cause of temperature drift is more challenging than fun. Buy critical components like high-stability capacitors from trustworthy sources.

TUNING CAPACITOR NETWORKS

Often an available variable capacitor has greater capacitance than required for a desired frequency range. While plates can sometimes be removed, a better solution embeds the variable capacitor in a network of fixed capacitors. The evolution of this network is shown in the middle section of **Figure 9.18**. The variable capacitor, C_V, and C_2 are paralleled to form the equivalent C_{2V}. This is then placed in series with C_1 for the equivalent C_{12V}. This is, in turn, paralleled by C_3 to form the total capacitor, C_{NET}. The overall frequency is calculated from the usual resonance relationship. The equations are shown, with capacitance in farads, inductance in henries, and frequency in Hz.

There is considerable flexibility available to the designer, afforded by picking C_1 and C_2 values. Some combinations with C_1 much smaller than the variable capacitor can produce highly nonlinear tuning.

INDUCTORS

Ceramic coil forms can give excellent results, as can self-supporting air-wound coils (Miniductor). If the required inductance is small enough, wind the coil on a ceramic

Oscillators and Synthesizers 9.13

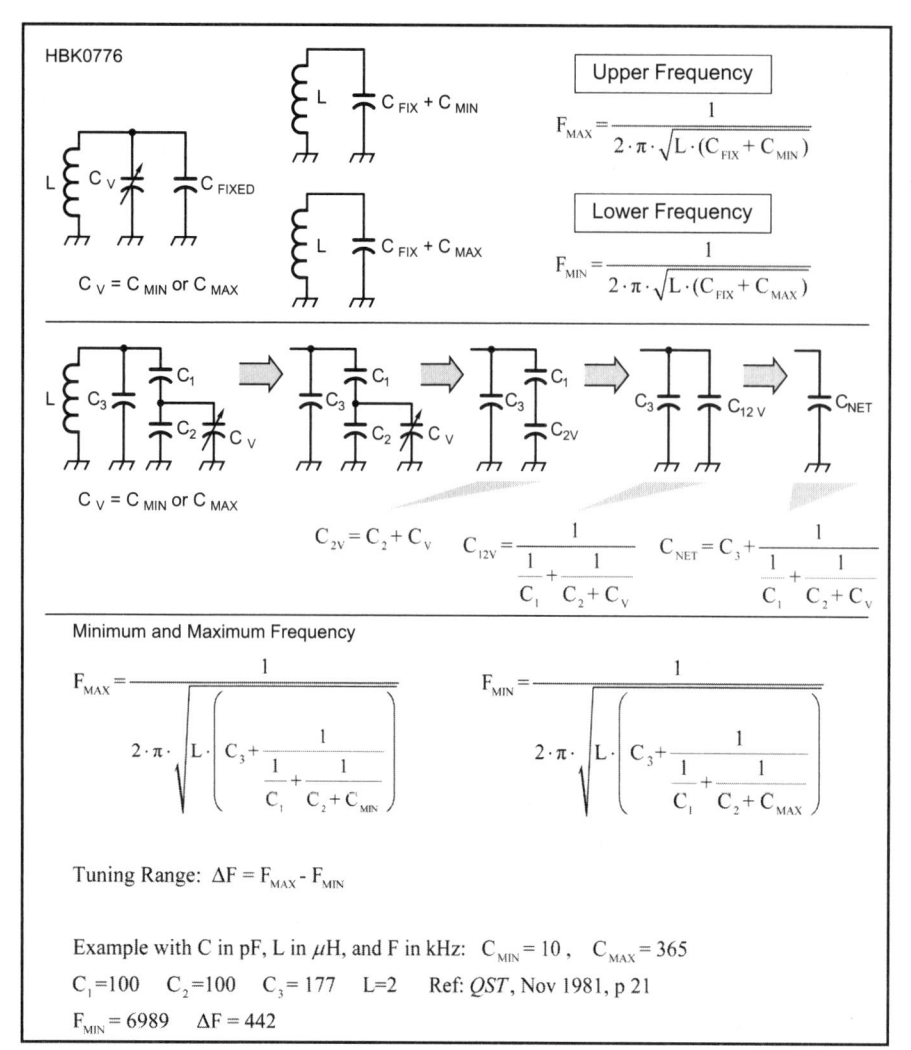

Figure 9.18 — A simple resonant circuit is tuned with parallel capacitors as shown in the top section. The tuning range is controlled by the ratio of the variable capacitance to the fixed capacitance.

Upper Frequency
$$F_{MAX} = \frac{1}{2\cdot\pi\cdot\sqrt{L\cdot(C_{FIX}+C_{MIN})}}$$

Lower Frequency
$$F_{MIN} = \frac{1}{2\cdot\pi\cdot\sqrt{L\cdot(C_{FIX}+C_{MAX})}}$$

$C_V = C_{MIN}$ or C_{MAX}

$$C_{2V} = C_2 + C_V \qquad C_{12V} = \frac{1}{\frac{1}{C_1}+\frac{1}{C_2+C_V}} \qquad C_{NET} = C_3 + \frac{1}{\frac{1}{C_1}+\frac{1}{C_2+C_V}}$$

Minimum and Maximum Frequency

$$F_{MAX} = \frac{1}{2\cdot\pi\cdot\sqrt{L\cdot\left(C_3 + \frac{1}{\frac{1}{C_1}+\frac{1}{C_2+C_{MIN}}}\right)}}$$

$$F_{MIN} = \frac{1}{2\cdot\pi\cdot\sqrt{L\cdot\left(C_3 + \frac{1}{\frac{1}{C_1}+\frac{1}{C_2+C_{MAX}}}\right)}}$$

Tuning Range: $\Delta F = F_{MAX} - F_{MIN}$

Example with C in pF, L in μH, and F in kHz: $C_{MIN} = 10$, $C_{MAX} = 365$
$C_1 = 100 \quad C_2 = 100 \quad C_3 = 177 \quad L = 2 \quad$ Ref: *QST*, Nov 1981, p 21
$F_{MIN} = 6989 \quad \Delta F = 442$

---

form that is securely mounted.

If you use a magnetic core, use powdered iron and support it securely. Do not use ferrite because of its temperature instability. Stable VFOs have been made using toroidal cores. Micrometals mix #6 has a low temperature coefficient and works well in conjunction with NP0 ceramic capacitors. Other materials have to be assessed on an individual basis.

A material's temperature stability will not be apparent until you try it in an oscillator, but you can apply a quick test to identify those nonmetallic materials that are lossy enough to spoil a coil's Q. Put a sample of the coil-form material into a microwave oven along with a glass of water and cook it about 10 seconds on low power. Do not include any metal fittings or ferromagnetic cores. Good materials will be completely unaffected; poor ones will heat and may even melt, smoke, or burst into flame. (This operation is a fire hazard if you try more than a tiny sample of an unknown material. Observe your experiment continuously and do not leave it unattended!)

W7ZOI suggests annealing toroidal VFO coils after winding. W7EL reports achieving success with this method by boiling his coils in water and letting them cool in air.

VOLTAGE REGULATORS

VFO circuits must be powered by well-regulated, low-noise supplies. Three-terminal regulators are inexpensive and have low output noise. It is easy to include them locally with the oscillator circuit. If the regulator is not part of the oscillator circuit, include a decoupling R-C combination to act as a noise filter.

Many oscillator circuits include Zener diode regulators. Zeners have some idiosyncrasies that could spoil the oscillator. They are noisy, so decoupling is needed down to audio frequencies to filter this out. Zener diodes are often run at much less than their specified optimum bias current. Although this saves power, it results in a lower output voltage than intended and the diode's impedance is much greater, increasing its sensitivity to variations in input voltage, output current and temperature. Some common Zener types may be designed to run at as much as 20 mA; check the data sheet for your diode family to find the optimum current.

True Zener diodes are low-voltage devices; above a couple of volts, so-called Zener diodes are actually avalanche types. The temperature coefficient of these diodes depends on their breakdown voltage and crosses through zero for diodes rated at about 5 V. If you intend to use nothing fancier than a common-variety Zener, designing the oscillator to run from 5 V and using a 5.1 V Zener will give you a free advantage in voltage-versus-temperature stability.

There are some diodes available with especially low temperature coefficients, usually referred to as reference or temperature-compensated diodes. These usually consist of a series pair of diodes designed to cancel each other's temperature drift. The 1N821A diode has a temperature coefficient of ±100 ppm/°C. Running at 7.5 mA, the 1N829A provides 6.2 V ±5% and a temperature coefficient of just ±5 parts per million (ppm) maximum per degree Celsius. A change in bias current of 10% will shift the voltage less than 7.5 mV, but this increases rapidly for greater current variation. The curves in **Figure 9.19** show how the temperature coefficients of these diodes are dependent on bias current.

The LM399 is a complex IC that behaves like a superb Zener at 6.95 V, ±0.3 ppm/°C. Precision, low-power, three-terminal regulators are also available that are designed to be used as voltage references, some of which can provide enough current to run a VFO. There are comprehensive tables of all these devices between pages 334 and 337 of Horowitz and Hill, *The Art of Electronics, 2nd ed.*

OSCILLATOR DEVICES

The 2N3819 FET, a classic from the 1960s, has proven to work well in VFOs but, like the MPF102 which is also long-popular with ham builders, it is manufactured to wide tolerances. Considering an oscillator's importance in receiver stability, you should not hesitate to spend a bit more on a better device. The 2N5484, 2N5485 and 2N5486 are worth considering; together, their transconductance ranges span that of the MPF102, but each is a better-controlled subset of that range. The 2N5245 is a more recent device with better-than-average noise performance that runs at low currents like the 2N3819. The 2N4416/A, also available as the plastic-cased PN4416, is a low-noise device, designed for VHF/UHF amplifier use, which has been featured in a number of good oscillators up to the VHF region. Its low internal capacitance contributes to low frequency drift. The J310 (plastic;

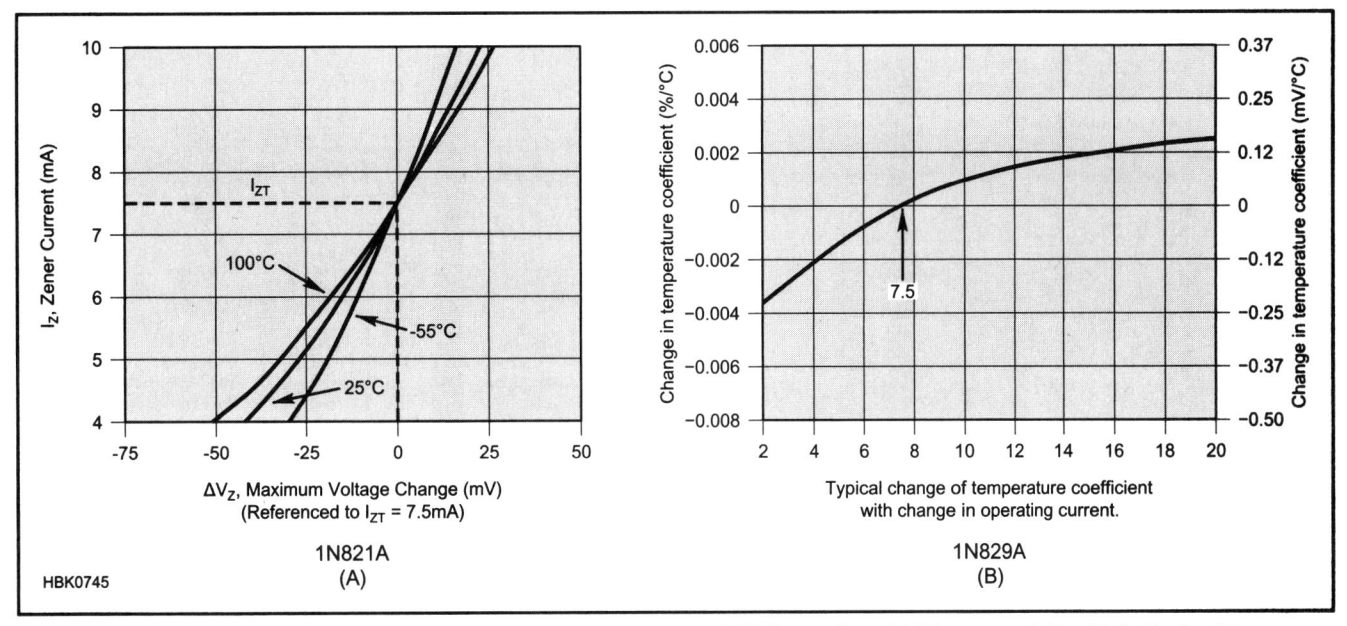

Figure 9.19 — The temperature coefficient of temperature-compensated diodes varies with bias current. To obtain the best temperature performance, use the specific bias current for the diode.

the metal-cased U310 is similar) is another popular JFET for use in oscillators.

The 2N5179 (plastic, PN5179 or MPS5179) is a bipolar transistor capable of good performance in oscillators up to the top of the VHF region. Care is needed because its absolute-maximum collector-emitter voltage is only 12 V, and its collector current must not exceed 50 mA. Although these characteristics may seem to convey fragility, the 2N5179 is sufficient for circuits powered by stabilized 6 V power supplies.

VHF-UHF capable transistors are not really necessary in LC VFOs because such circuits are rarely used above 10 MHz. (High-bandwidth transistors also increase high-frequency harmonic content in the output signal.) Absolute frequency stability is progressively harder to achieve with increasing frequency, so free-running oscillators are used only rarely to generate VHF-UHF signals for radio communication. Instead, VHF-UHF radios usually use voltage-tuned, phase-locked oscillators in some form of synthesizer. Bipolar devices like the BFR90 and MRF901, with f_T in the 5 GHz region and mounted in stripline packages, are needed for successful oscillator design at UHF.

The popular SA/NE602 mixer IC has a built-in oscillator and can be found in many published circuits. This device has separate input and output pins to the tank and has proved to be quite tame. It may not have been "improved" yet (so far, it has progressed from the SA/NE602 to the SA/NE602A, the A version affording somewhat higher dynamic range than the original SA/NE602). It might be a good idea for anyone laying out a board using one to take a little extra care to keep PCB traces short in the oscillator section to build in some safety margin so that the board can be used reliably in the future. Professional designers know that their designs are going to be built for possibly more than 10 years and have learned to make allowances for the progressive improvement of semiconductor manufacture.

MECHANICAL CONSTRUCTION

• All oscillator components should be clean and attached to a solid support to minimize thermal changes and mechanical vibration.

• The enclosure should be solid and isolated from mechanical vibration.

• Keep component leads short and if point-to-point wiring is employed, use heavy wire (#16 to #18 AWG).

• Single-point grounding of the oscillator components is recommended to avoid stray inductance and to minimize noise introduced from other sources. If a PCB is used, include a ground plane.

It is often instructive to look at commercial or military equipment to see what techniques and materials are used for those demanding applications. The mechanical assemblies and parts can be removed from surplus equipment for home-built VFOs, as well.

9.3.2 Temperature Compensation

The general principle for creating a high-stability VFO is to use components with minimal temperature coefficients in circuits that are as insensitive as possible to changes in components' secondary characteristics. Even after careful minimization of the causes of temperature sensitivity, further improvement can still be desirable. The traditional method was to split one of the capacitors in the tank so that it could be apportioned between low-temperature-coefficient parts and parts with deliberate temperature dependency. Only a limited number of different, controlled temperature coefficients are available, so the proportioning between low coefficient and controlled coefficient parts was varied to "dilute" the temperature sensitivity of a part more sensitive than desired. This is a tedious process, involving much trial and error, an undertaking made more complicated by the difficulty of arranging means of heating and cooling the unit being compensated. (Hayward described such a means in December 1993 *QST*.) As commercial and military equipment have been based on frequency synthesizers for some time, supplies of capacitors with controlled temperature sensitivity are drying up. An alternative approach is needed.

A temperature-compensated crystal oscillator (TCXO) is an improved-stability version of a crystal oscillator that is used widely in industry. Instead of using controlled-temperature coefficient capacitors, most TCXOs use a network of thermistors and normal resistors to control the bias of a tuning diode. Manufacturers measure the temperature vs. frequency characteristic of sample oscillators, and then use a computer program to calculate the optimum normal resistor values for production. This can reliably achieve at least a tenfold improvement in stability. We here are not interested in mass manufacture, but the idea of a thermistor tuning a varactor is worth adopting. The parts involved are likely to be available for a long time.

Browsing through component suppliers'

Oscillators and Synthesizers 9.15

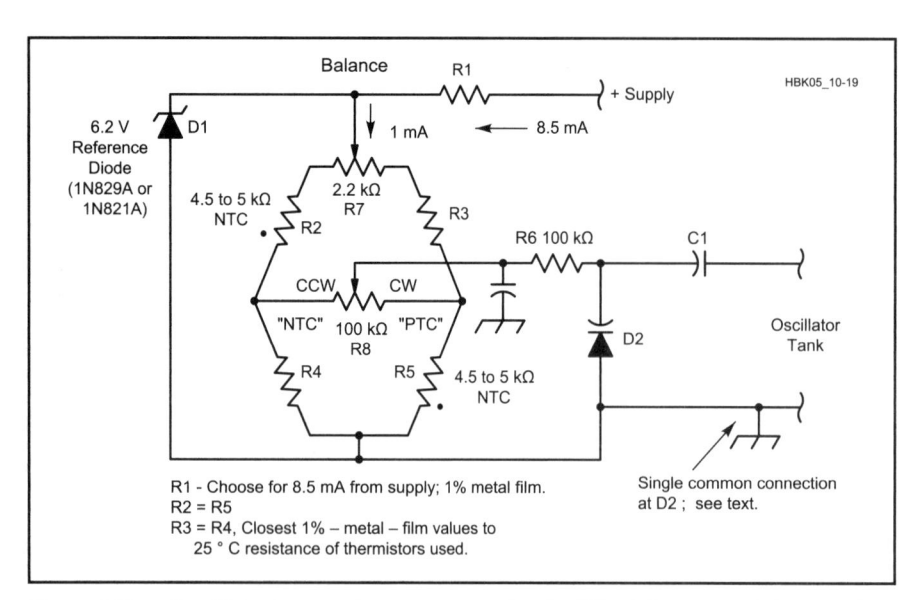

Figure 9.20 — Oscillator temperature compensation is difficult because of the scarcity of negative-temperature-coefficient capacitors. This circuit by GM4ZNX uses a bridge containing two identical thermistors to steer a tuning diode for drift correction. The 6.2 V Zener diode used (a 1N821A or 1N829A) must be a temperature-compensated part; just any 6.2 V Zener will not do.

catalogs shows ready availability of 4.5 to 5 kΩ bead thermistors intended for temperature-compensation purposes, at less than a dollar each. **Figure 9.20** shows a circuit based on this form of temperature compensation. Commonly available thermistors have negative temperature coefficients, so as temperature rises, the voltage at the counterclockwise (CCW) end of R8 increases, while that at the clockwise (CW) end drops. Somewhere near the center there is no change. Increasing the voltage on the tuning diode decreases its capacitance, so settings toward R8's CCW end simulate a negative-temperature-coefficient capacitor; toward its clockwise end, a positive-temperature-coefficient part. Choose R1 to pass 8.5 mA from whatever supply voltage is available to the 6.2 V reference diode, D1. The 1N821A/1N829A-family diode used has a very low temperature coefficient and needs 7.5 mA bias for best performance; the bridge takes the other 1 mA. R7 and R8 should be good-quality multi-turn trimmers. D2 and C1 need to be chosen to suit the oscillator circuit. Choose the least capacitance that provides enough compensation range. This reduces the noise added to the oscillator. (It is possible, though tedious, to solve for the differential varactor voltage with respect to R2 and R5, via differential calculus and circuit theory. The equations in Hayward's 1993 article can then be modified to accommodate the additional capacitors formed by D2 and C1.) Use a single ground point near D2 to reduce the influence of ground currents from other circuits. Use good-quality metal-film components for the circuit's fixed resistors.

The novelty of this circuit is that it is designed to have an easy and direct adjustment process. The circuit requires two adjustments, one at each of two different temperatures, and achieving them requires a stable frequency counter that can be kept far enough from the radio so that the radio, not the counter, is subjected to the temperature extremes. (Using a receiver to listen to the oscillator under test can speed the adjustments.) After connecting the counter to the oscillator to be corrected, run the radio containing the oscillator and compensator in a room-temperature, draft-free environment until the oscillator's frequency reaches its stable operating temperature (rise over the ambient temperature). Lock its tuning, if possible. Adjust R7 to balance the bridge. This causes a drop of 0 V across R8, a condition you can reach by winding R8 back and forth across its range while slowly adjusting R7. When the bridge is balanced and 0 V appears across R8, adjusting R8 causes no frequency shift. When you've found this R7 setting, leave it there, set R8 to the exact center of its range and record the oscillator frequency.

Run the radio in a hot environment and allow its frequency to stabilize. Adjust R8 to restore the frequency to the recorded value. The sensitivity of the oscillator to temperature should now be significantly reduced between the temperatures at which you performed the adjustments. You will also have somewhat improved the oscillator's stability outside this range.

For best results with any temperature-compensation scheme, it's important to group all the oscillator and compensator components in the same enclosure, avoiding differences in airflow over components. A good oscillator should not dissipate much power, so it's feasible, even advisable, to mount all of the oscillator components in an unventilated box. In the real world, temperatures change and if the components being compensated and the components doing the compensating have different thermal time constants, a change in temperature can cause a temporary change in frequency until the slower components have caught up. One cure for this is to build the oscillator in a thick-walled metal box that's slow to heat or cool, and so dominates and reduces the possible rate of change of temperature of the circuits inside. This is sometimes called a *cold oven*.

9.3.3 Shielding and Isolation

It is important to remember that any inductor acts as half of a transformer. Oscillators contain inductors running at moderate power levels and so can radiate strong enough signals to cause interference with other parts of a radio or with other radios. This is the tank (or other) inductor behaving as a transformer primary. Oscillators are also sensitive to radiated signals or other nearby varying magnetic fields. This is the tank (or other) inductor also behaving as a transformer secondary. Effective shielding is therefore vital.

Any oscillator is particularly sensitive to interference on the same or very nearby frequency. If this interference is strong enough an undesirable effect called *injection locking* will occur. The oscillator effectively stops oscillating and instead directly follows the interfering signal. For example, a VFO used to directly drive a power amplifier and antenna (to form a simple CW transmitter) can prove surprisingly difficult to shield well enough because of injection locking from any leakage of the power amplifier's high-level signal back into the oscillator. Even if injection locking does not fully kick in, the wrestling inside the VFO between its own oscillation and the interference can affect its frequency, resulting in an unstable transmitted signal. If the radio gear is in the station antenna's near field, there are also strong fields that are coherent with the VFO oscillation, making sufficient shielding even more difficult.

The following rules of thumb continue to serve ham builders well:

• Use a complete metal box, with as few holes drilled in it as possible, with good contact around surface(s) where its lid(s) fit(s) on.

• Use feedthrough capacitors on power and control lines that pass in and out of the VFO enclosure and on the transmitter or transceiver enclosure as well.

• Use buffer amplifier circuitry that amplifies the signal by the desired amount and provides sufficient attenuation of signal energy flowing in the reverse direction. This is known as *reverse isolation* and is a frequently overlooked loophole in shielding. Figures 9.14 and 9.16 include buffer circuitry of proven performance. Another (and higher-cost) option is to consider using a high-speed buffer-amplifier IC (such as the LM6321N by National Semiconductor, a part that combines the high input impedance of an op amp with the ability to drive 50-Ω loads directly up into the VHF range).

• Use a mixing-based frequency-generation scheme instead of one that operates straight through or by means of multiplication. Such a system's oscillator stages can operate on frequencies with no direct frequency relationship to its output frequency. This essentially eliminates the possibility of injection locking the VFO.

• Use the time-tested technique of running your VFO at a sub-harmonic of the output signal desired — say, 3.5 MHz in a 7 MHz transmitter — and multiply its output frequency in a suitably nonlinear stage for further amplification at the desired frequency. This does reduce the tendency to injection lock.

9.4 Crystal Oscillators

Because crystals afford Q values and frequency stabilities that are orders of magnitude better than those achievable with LC circuits, fixed-frequency oscillators usually use quartz crystal resonators. Master references for frequency counters and synthesizers are always based on crystal oscillators.

So glowing is the crystal's reputation for stability that newcomers to radio experimentation naturally believe that the presence of a crystal in an oscillator will force oscillation at the frequency stamped on the can. This impression is usually revised after the first few experiences to the contrary! There is no sure-fire crystal oscillator circuit (although some are better than others); reading and experience soon provide a learner with plenty of anecdotes to the effect that:

• Some circuits have a reputation of being temperamental, even to the point of not always starting.

• Crystals sometimes mysteriously oscillate on unexpected frequencies.

Even crystal manufacturers have these problems, so don't be discouraged from building crystal oscillators. The occasional uncooperative oscillator is a nuisance, not a disaster, and it just needs a little individual attention. Knowing how a crystal behaves is the key to a cure.

Ulrich Rohde, N1UL, has generously contributed a pair of detailed papers that discuss the crystal oscillator along with several HF and VHF designs. Both papers, "Quartz Crystal Oscillator Design" and "A Novel Grounded Base Oscillator Design for VHF/UHF Frequencies" are included with the downloadable supplemental material accompanying this book.

9.4.1 Quartz and the Piezoelectric Effect

Quartz is a crystalline material with a regular atomic structure that can be distorted by the simple application of force. Remove the force, and the distorted structure springs back to its original form with very little energy loss. This property allows *acoustic waves* — sound — to propagate rapidly through quartz with very little attenuation, because the velocity of an acoustic wave depends on the elasticity and density (mass/volume) of the medium through which the wave travels.

If you heat a material, it expands. Heating may cause other characteristics of a material to change — such as elasticity, which affects the speed of sound in the material. In quartz, however, expansion and change in the speed of sound are very small and tend to cancel, which means that the transit time for sound to pass through a piece of quartz is very stable.

The third property of this wonder material is that it is *piezoelectric*. Apply an electric field to a piece of quartz and the crystal lattice distorts just as if a force had been applied. The electric field applies a force to electrical charges locked in the lattice structure. These charges are captive and cannot move around in the lattice as they can in a semiconductor, for quartz is an insulator. A capacitor's dielectric stores energy by creating physical distortion on an atomic or molecular scale. In a piezoelectric crystal's lattice, the distortion affects the entire structure. In some piezoelectric materials, this effect is sufficiently pronounced that special shapes can be made that bend *visibly* when a field is applied.

Consider a rod made of quartz. Any sound wave propagating along it eventually hits an end, where there is a large and abrupt change in acoustic impedance. Just as when an RF wave hits the end of an unterminated transmission line, a strong reflection occurs. The rod's other end similarly reflects the wave. At some frequency, the phase shift of a round trip will be such that waves from successive round trips exactly coincide in phase and reinforce each other, dramatically increasing the wave's amplitude. This is *resonance*.

The passage of waves in opposite directions forms a standing wave with antinodes at the rod ends. Here we encounter a seeming ambiguity: not just one, but a family of different frequencies, causes standing waves — a family fitting the pattern of ½, ⅔, ⅖, ⅐ and so on, wavelengths into the length of the rod. And this is the case: A quartz rod can resonate at any and all of these frequencies.

The lowest of these frequencies, where the crystal is ½ wavelength long, is called the *fundamental* mode. The others are named the third, fifth, seventh and so on, *overtones*. There is a small phase-shift error during reflection at the ends, which causes the frequencies of the overtone modes to differ slightly from odd integer multiplies of the fundamental. Thus, a crystal's third overtone is very close to, but not exactly, three times its fundamental frequency. Many people are confused by overtones and harmonics. Harmonics are additional signals at exact integer multiples of the fundamental frequency. Overtones are not signals at all; they are additional resonances that can be exploited if a circuit is configured to excite them.

The crystals we use most often resonate in the 1 to 30 MHz region and are of the *AT-cut, thickness shear* type, although these last two characteristics are rarely mentioned. A 15 MHz fundamental crystal of this type is about 0.15 mm thick. Because of the widespread use of pressure-mounted FT-243 crystals, you may think of crystals as small rectangles on the order of a half-inch in size. The crystals we commonly use today are discs, etched and/or doped to their final dimensions, with metal electrodes deposited directly on the quartz. A crystal's diameter does not directly affect its frequency; diameters of 8 to 15 mm are typical. (Quartz crystals are also discussed in the **Analog and Digital Filtering** chapter.)

AT-cut is one of a number of possible standard designations for the orientation at which a crystal disc is sawed from the original quartz crystal. The crystal lattice atomic structure is asymmetric, and the orientation of this with respect to the faces of the disc influences the crystal's performance. *Thickness shear* is one of a number of possible orientations of the crystal's mechanical vibration with respect to the disc. In this case, the crystal vibrates perpendicularly to its thickness. This is not easy to visualize, and diagrams don't help much, but **Figure 9.21** is an attempt at illustrating this. Place a moist bathroom sponge between the palms of your hands, move one hand up and down, and you'll see thickness shear in action.

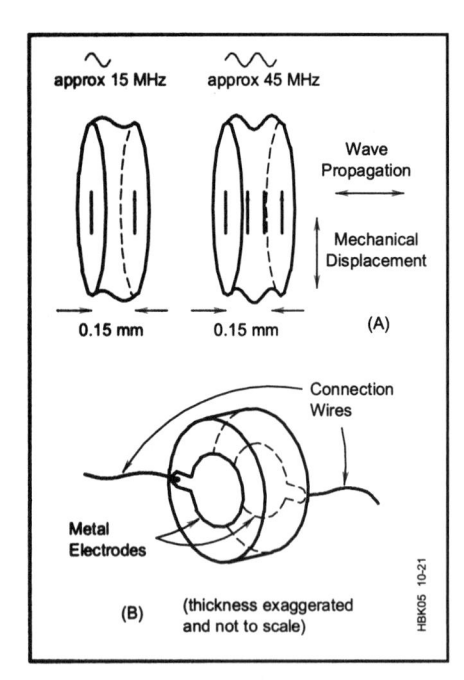

Figure 9.21 — Thickness-shear vibration at a crystal's fundamental and third overtone (A); B shows how the modern crystals commonly used by radio amateurs consist of etched quartz discs with electrodes deposited directly on the crystal surface.

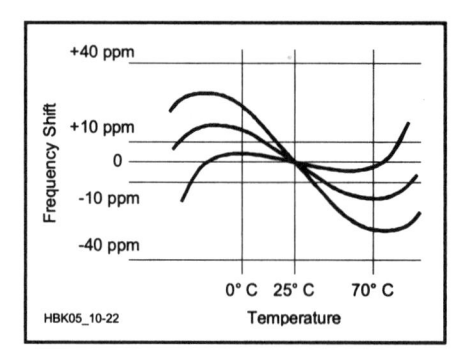

Figure 9.22 — Slight changes in a crystal cut's orientation shift its frequency-versus-temperature curve.

There is a limit to how thin a disc can be made, given requirements of accuracy and price. Traditionally, fundamental-mode crystals have been made up to 20 MHz, although 30 MHz is now common at a moderately raised price. Using techniques pioneered in the semiconductor industry, crystals have been made with a central region etched down to a thin membrane, surrounded by a thick ring for robustness. This approach can push fundamental resonances to over 100 MHz, but these are more lab curiosities than parts for everyday use. The easy solution for higher frequencies is to use a manufacturably-thick crystal on an overtone mode. All crystals have multiple modes, so if you order a 28.060 MHz, third-overtone unit for a little QRP transmitter, you'll get a crystal with a fundamental resonance somewhere near 9.353333 MHz, but its manufacturer will have adjusted the thickness to plant the third overtone exactly on the ordered frequency. An accomplished manufacturer can do tricks with the flatness of the disc faces to make the wanted overtone mode a little more active and the other modes a little less active. (As some builders discover, however, this does not *guarantee* that the wanted mode is the most active!)

Quartz's piezoelectric property provides a simple way of driving the crystal electrically. Early crystals were placed between a pair of electrodes in a case. This gave amateurs the opportunity to buy surplus crystals, open them and grind them a little to reduce their thickness, thus moving them to higher frequencies. The frequency could be reduced very slightly by loading the face with extra mass, such as by blackening it with a soft pencil. Modern crystals have metal electrodes deposited directly onto their surfaces (Figure 9.21B), and such tricks no longer work.

The piezoelectric effect works both ways. Deformation of the crystal produces voltage across its electrodes, so the mechanical energy in the resonating crystal can also be extracted electrically by the same electrodes. Seen electrically, at the electrodes, the mechanical resonances look like electrical resonances. Their Q is very high. A Q of 10,000 would characterize a *poor* crystal today; 100,000 is often reached by high-quality parts. For comparison, a Q of over 200 for an LC tank is considered good.

9.4.2 Frequency Accuracy

A crystal's frequency accuracy is as outstanding as its Q. Several factors determine a crystal's frequency accuracy. First, the manufacturer makes parts with certain tolerances: ±200 ppm for a low-quality crystal for use as in a microprocessor clock oscillator, ±10 ppm for a good-quality part for professional radio use. Anything much better than this starts to get expensive! A crystal's resonant frequency is influenced by the impedance presented to its terminals, and manufacturers assume that once a crystal is brought within several parts per million of the nominal frequency, its user will perform fine adjustments electrically.

Second, a crystal ages after manufacture. Aging could give increasing or decreasing frequency; whichever, a given crystal usually keeps aging in the same direction. Aging is rapid at first and then slows down. Aging is influenced by the care in polishing the surface of the crystal (time and money) and by its holder style. The cheapest holder is a soldered-together, two-part metal can with glass bead insulation for the connection pins. Soldering debris lands on the crystal and affects its frequency. Alternatively, a two-part metal case can be made with flanges that are pressed together until they fuse, a process called *cold-welding*. This is much cleaner and improves aging rates roughly fivefold compared to soldered cans. An all-glass case can be made in two parts and fused together by heating in a vacuum. The vacuum raises the Q, and the cleanliness results in aging that's roughly 10 times slower than that achievable with a soldered can. The best crystal holders borrow from vacuum-tube assembly processes and have a *getter*, a highly reactive chemical substance that traps remaining gas molecules, but such crystals are used only for special purposes.

Third, temperature influences a crystal. A reasonable, professional quality part might be specified to shift not more than ±10 ppm over 0 to 70 °C. An AT-cut crystal has an *S*-shaped frequency-versus-temperature characteristic, which can be varied by slightly changing the crystal cut's orientation. **Figure 9.22** shows the general shape and the effect of changing the cut angle by only a few seconds of arc. Notice how all the curves converge at 25 °C. This is because this temperature is normally chosen as the reference for specifying a crystal. The temperature stability specification sets how accurate the manufacturer must make the cut. Better stability may be needed for a crystal used as a receiver frequency standard, frequency counter clock and so on. A crystal's temperature characteristic shows a little hysteresis. In other words, there's a bit of offset to the curve depending on whether temperature is increasing or decreasing. This is usually of no consequence except in the highest-precision circuits.

It is the temperature of the quartz that is important, and as the usual holders for crystals all give effective thermal insulation, only a couple of milliwatts dissipation by the crystal itself can be tolerated before self-heating becomes troublesome. Because such heating occurs in the quartz itself and does not come from the surrounding environment, it defeats the effects of temperature compensators and ovens.

The techniques shown earlier for VFO temperature compensation can also be applied to crystal oscillators. An after-compensation drift of 1 ppm is routine and 0.5 ppm is good. The result is a *temperature-compensated crystal oscillator* (*TCXO*). Recently, oscillators have appeared with built-in digital thermometers, microprocessors and ROM look-up tables customized on a unit-by-unit basis to control a tuning diode via a digital-to-analog converter (DAC) for temperature compensation. These *digitally temperature-compensated oscillators* (*DTCXOs*) can reach 0.1 ppm over the temperature range. With automated production and adjustment, they promise to become the cheapest way to achieve this level of stability.

Oscillators have long been placed in temperature-controlled *ovens*, which are typically held at 80 °C. Stability of several parts per billion can be achieved over temperature, but this is a limited benefit as aging can easily dominate the accuracy. These are usually called *oven-controlled crystal oscillators* (*OCXOs*).

Fourth, the crystal is influenced by the impedance presented to it by the circuit in which it is used. This means that care is needed to make the rest of an oscillator circuit stable, in terms of impedance and phase shift.

Gravity can slightly affect crystal resonance. Turning an oscillator upside down usually produces a small frequency shift, usually much less than 1 ppm; turning the oscillator back over reverses this. This effect is quantified for the highest-quality reference oscillators.

9.4.3 The Equivalent Circuit of a Crystal

Because a crystal is a passive, two-terminal device, its electrical appearance is that of an impedance that varies with frequency. **Figure 9.23A** shows a very simplified sketch of the magnitude (phase is ignored) of the impedance of a quartz crystal. The general trend of dropping impedance with increasing frequency implies capacitance across the crystal. The sharp fall to a low value resembles a series-tuned tank, and the sharp peak resembles a parallel-tuned tank. These are referred to as series and parallel resonances. Figure 9.23B shows a simple circuit that will produce this impedance characteristic. The impedance looks purely resistive at the exact centers of both resonances, and the region between them has impedance increasing with frequency, which looks inductive.

C1 (sometimes called *motional capacitance*, C_m, to distinguish it from the lumped capacitance it approximates) and L1 (*motional inductance*, L_m) create the series resonance, and as C0 and R1 are both fairly small, the impedance at the bottom of the dip is very close to R1. At parallel resonance, L1 is resonating with C1 and C0 in series, hence the higher frequency. The impedance of the parallel tank is extremely high; the terminals are connected to a capacitive tap, which causes them to see only a small fraction of what is still a very large impedance. The overtones should not be neglected, so Figures 9.23C and 9.23D include them. Each overtone has series and parallel resonances and so appears as a series tank in the equivalent circuit. C0 again provides the shifted parallel resonance.

This is still simplified, because real-life crystals have a number of spurious, unwanted modes that add yet more resonances, as shown in Figure 9.23E. These are not well controlled and may vary a lot even between crystals made to the same specification. Crystal manufacturers work hard to suppress these spurs and have evolved a number of recipes for shaping crystals to minimize them. Just where they switch from one design to another varies from manufacturer to manufacturer.

Always remember that the equivalent circuit is just a representation of crystal behavior and does not represent circuit components actually present. Its only use is as an aid in designing and analyzing circuits using crystals. **Table 9.1** lists typical equivalent-circuit values for a variety of crystals. It is impossible to build a circuit with 0.026 to 0.0006 pF capacitors; such values would simply be swamped by strays. Similarly, the inductor must have a Q that is orders of magnitude better than is practically achievable, and impossibly low stray C in its winding.

The values given in Table 9.1 are nothing more than rough guides. A crystal's frequency is tightly specified, but this still allows inductance to be traded for capacitance. A good manufacturer could hold these characteristics within a ±25% band or could vary them over a 5:1 range by special design. Similarly marked parts from different sources vary widely in motional inductance and capacitance.

Quartz is not the only material that behaves in this way, but it is the best. Resonators can be made out of lithium tantalate and a group of similar materials that have lower Q, allowing them to be *pulled* over a larger frequency range in VXOs. Much more common, however, are ceramic resonators based on the technology of the well-known ceramic IF filters. These have much lower Q than quartz and much poorer frequency precision. They serve mainly as clock resonators for cheap microprocessor systems in which every last cent must be saved. A ceramic resonator

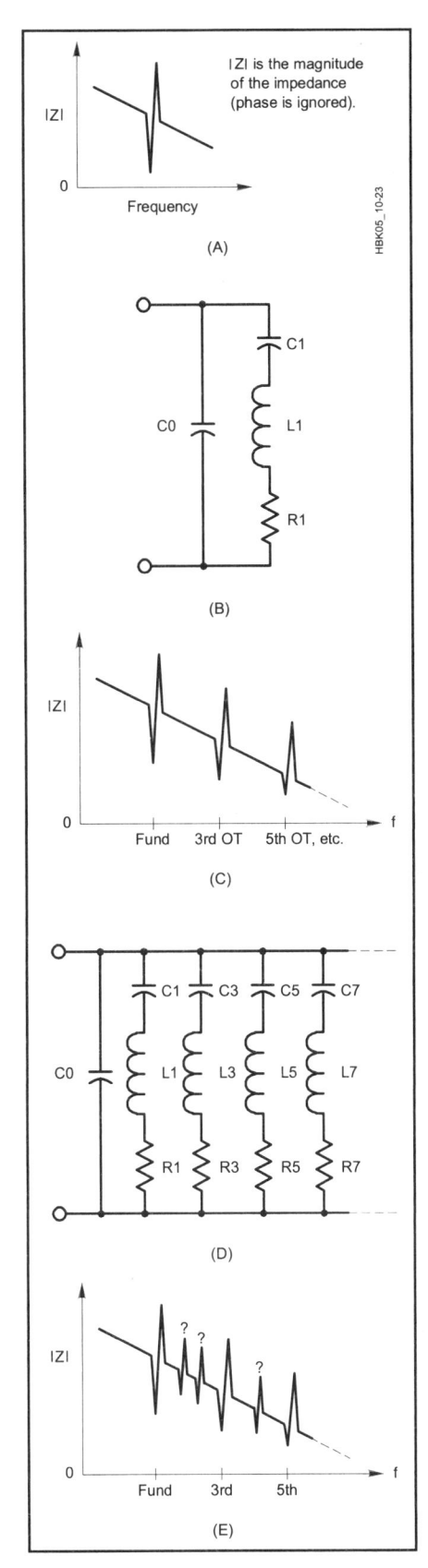

Figure 9.23 — Exploring a crystal's impedance (A) and equivalent circuit (B) through simplified diagrams. C and D extend the investigation to include overtones; E, to spurious responses not easily predictable by theory or controllable through manufacture. A crystal may oscillate on any of its resonances under the right conditions.

Table 9.1
Typical Equivalent Circuit Values for a Variety of Crystals

Crystal Type	Series L	Series C (pF)	Series R (Ω)	Shunt C (pF)
1 MHz fundamental	3.5 H	0.007	340	3.0
10 MHz fundamental	9.8 mH	0.026	7	6.3
30 MHz third overtone	14.9 mH	0.0018	27	6.2
100 MHz fifth overtone	4.28 mH	0.0006	45	7.0

could be used as the basis of a wide range, cheap VXO, but its frequency stability would not be as good as a good LC VFO.

9.4.4 Crystal Oscillator Circuits

(See also the papers "What You Always Wanted to Know About Colpitts Oscillators," "Quartz Crystal Oscillator Design," "A Novel Grounded Base Oscillator Design for VHF/UHF Frequencies," and "Some Thoughts on Designing Very High Performance VHF Oscillators" by Ulrich Rohde, N1UL, included with the downloadable supplemental material accompanying this book.)

Crystal oscillator circuits are usually categorized as series- or parallel-mode types, depending on whether the crystal's low- or high-impedance resonance comes into play at the operating frequency. The series mode is now the most common; parallel-mode operation was more often used with vacuum tubes. **Figure 9.24** shows a basic series-mode oscillator. Some people would say that it is an overtone circuit, used to run a crystal on one of its overtones, but this is not necessarily true. The tank (L-C1-C2) tunes the collector of the common-base amplifier. C1 is larger than C2, so the tank is tapped in a way that transforms to lower impedance, decreasing signal voltage, but increasing current. The current is fed back into the emitter via the crystal. The common-base stage provides a current gain of less than unity, so the transformer in the form of the tapped tank is essential to give loop gain. There are *two* tuned circuits, the obvious collector tank and the series-mode one "in" the crystal. The tank kills the amplifier's gain away from its tuned frequency, and the crystal will only pass current at the series resonant frequencies of its many modes. The tank resonance is much broader than any of the crystal's modes, so it can be thought of as the crystal setting the frequency, but the tank selecting which of the crystal's modes is active. The tank could be tuned to the crystal's fundamental, or one of its overtones.

Fundamental oscillators can be built without a tank quite successfully, but there is always the occasional one that starts up on an overtone or spurious mode. Some simple oscillators have been known to change modes while running (an effect triggered by changes in temperature or loading) or to not always start in the same mode! A series-mode oscillator should present low impedance to the crystal at the operating frequency. In Figure 9.24, the tapped collector tank presents a transformed fraction of the 1-kΩ collector load resistor to one end of the crystal, and the emitter presents a low impedance to the other. To build a practical oscillator from this circuit, choose an inductor with a reactance of about 300 Ω at the wanted frequency and

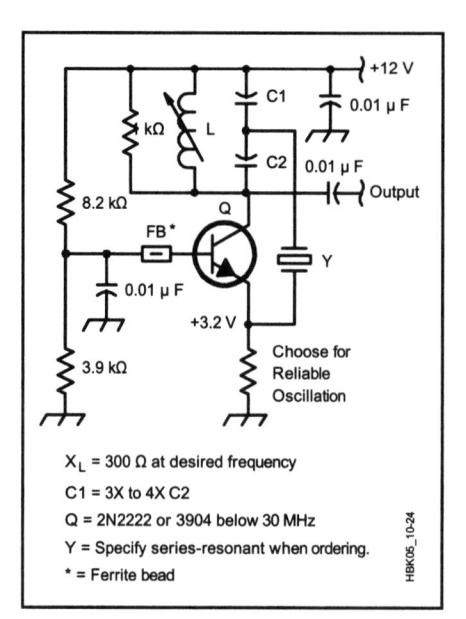

Figure 9.24 — A basic series-mode crystal oscillator. A 2N5179 can be used in this circuit if a lower supply voltage is used; see text.

calculate C1 in series with C2 to resonate with it. Choose C1 to be 3 to 4 times larger than C2. The amplifier's quiescent ("idling") current sets the gain and hence the operating level. This is not easily calculable, but can be found by experiment. Too little quiescent current and the oscillator will not start reliably; too much and the transistor can drive itself into saturation. If an oscilloscope is available, it can be used to check the collector waveform; otherwise, some form of RF voltmeter can be used to allow the collector voltage to be set to 2 to 3 V RMS. 3.3 kΩ would be a suitable starting point for the emitter bias resistor. The transistor type is not critical; 2N2222A or 2N3904 would be fine up to 30 MHz; a 2N5179 would allow operation as an overtone oscillator to over 100 MHz (because of the low collector voltage rating of the 2N5179, a supply voltage lower than 12 V is required). The ferrite bead on the base gives some protection against parasitic oscillation at UHF.

If the crystal is shorted, this circuit should still oscillate. This gives an easy way of adjust-

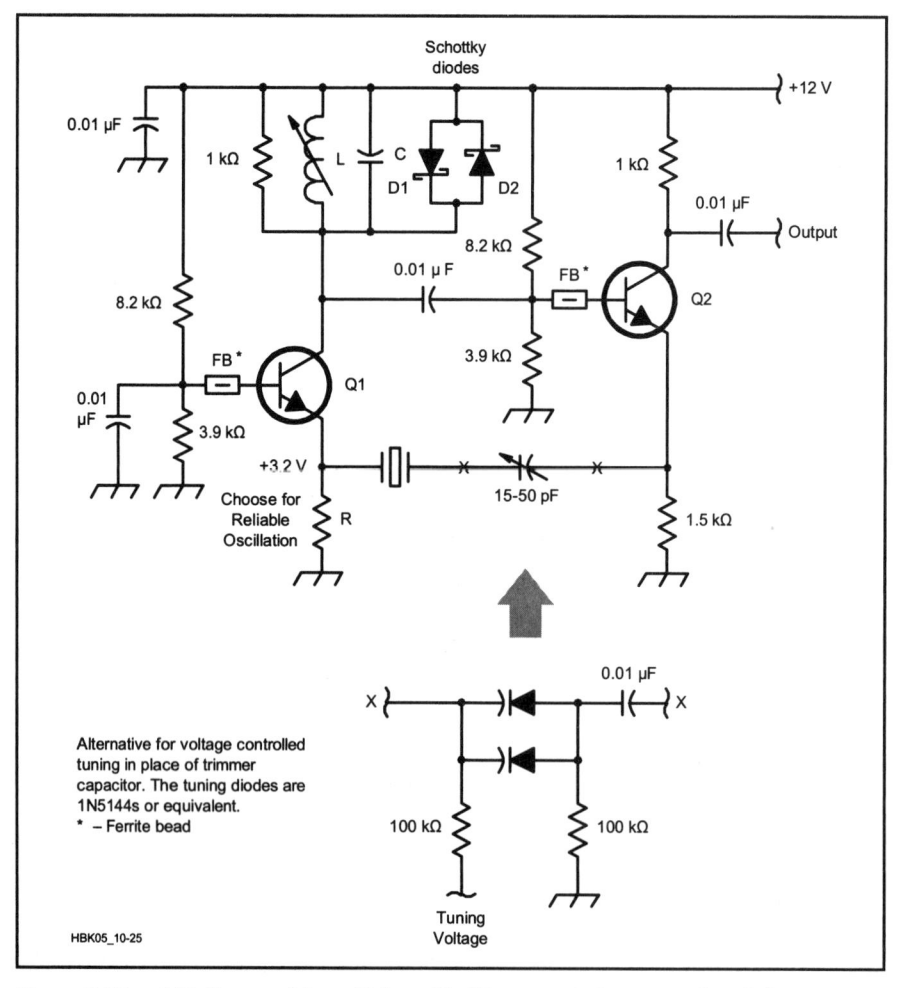

Figure 9.25 — A Butler crystal oscillator with Q2 connected as an emitter follower to drive the crystal's low series-resonant impedance.

ing the tank; it is even better to temporarily replace the crystal with a small-value (tens of ohms) resistor to simulate its *equivalent series resistance* (ESR), and adjust L until the circuit oscillates close to the wanted frequency. Then restore the crystal and set the quiescent current. If a lot of these oscillators were built, it would sometimes be necessary to adjust the current individually due to the different equivalent series resistance of individual crystals. One variant of this circuit has the emitter connected directly to the C1/C2 junction, while the crystal is a decoupler for the transistor base (the existing capacitor and ferrite bead not being used). This works, but with a greater risk of parasitic oscillation.

We commonly want to trim a crystal oscillator's frequency. While off-tuning the tank a little will pull the frequency slightly, too much detuning spoils the mode control and can stop oscillation (or worse, make the circuit unreliable). The answer to this is to add a trimmer capacitor, which will act as part of the equivalent series tuned circuit, in series with the crystal. This will shift the frequency in one way only, so the crystal frequency must be re-specified to allow the frequency to be varying around the required value. It is common to specify a crystal's frequency with a standard load (30 pF is commonly specified), so that the manufacturer grinds the crystal such that the series resonance of the specified mode is accurate when measured with a capacitor of this value in series. A 15 to 50 pF trimmer can be used in series with the crystal to give fine frequency adjustment. Too

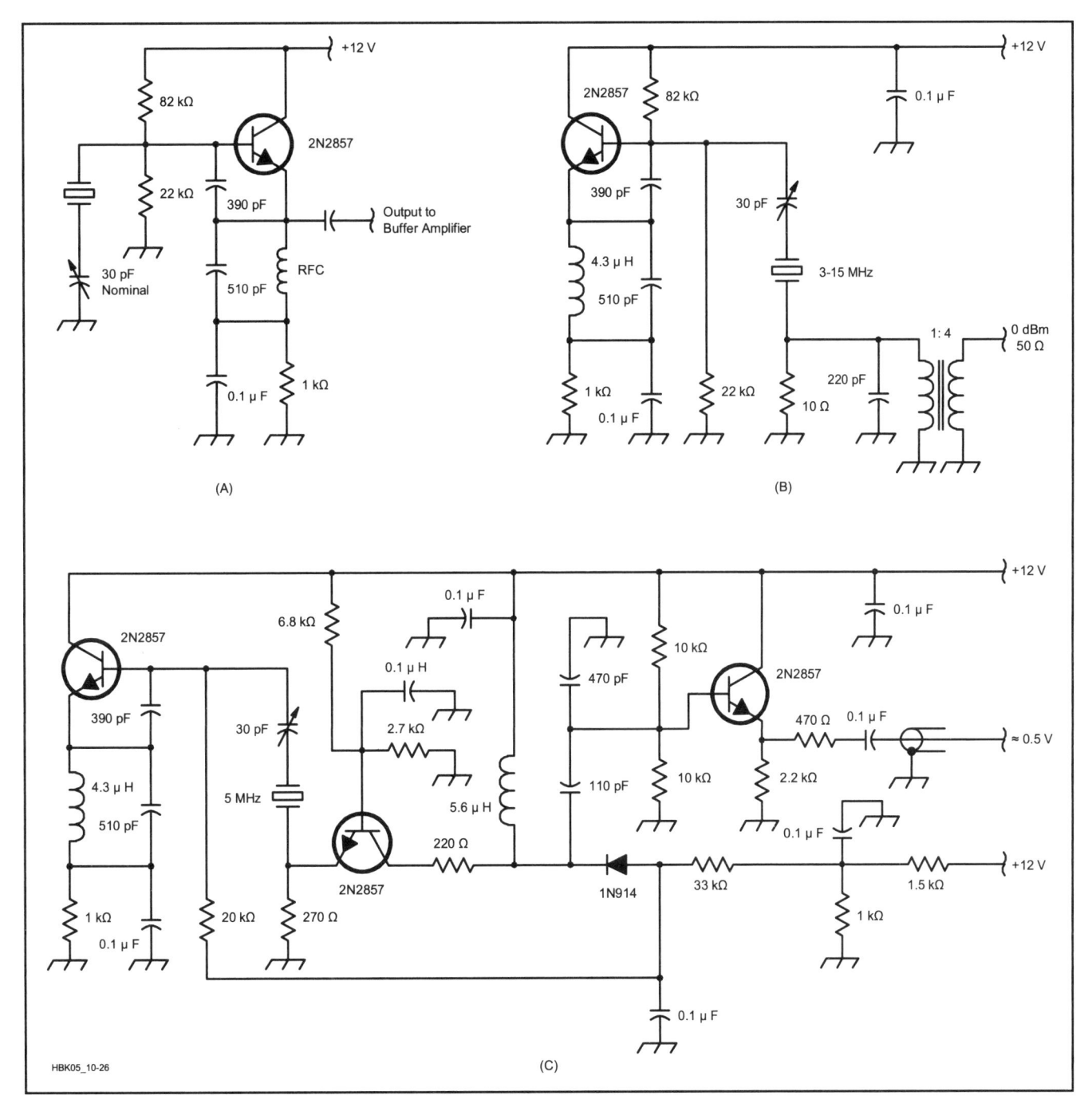

Figure 9.26 — The crystal in the series-tuned Colpitts oscillator at A operates in its series-resonant mode. B shows N1UL's low-noise version, which uses the crystal as a filter and features high harmonic suppression (from Rohde, *Microwave and Wireless Synthesizers Theory and Design*; see references). The circuit at C builds on the B version by adding a common-base output amplifier and ALC loop.

Oscillators and Synthesizers 9.21

little capacitance can stop oscillation or prevent reliable starting. The Q of crystals is so high that marginal oscillators can take several seconds to start!

This circuit can be improved by driving the crystal's lower series-resonant impedance with an emitter follower as in **Figure 9.25**. This is the *Butler* oscillator. Again the tank controls the mode to either force the wanted overtone or protect the fundamental mode. The tank need not be tapped because Q2 provides current gain, although the circuit is sometimes seen with C split, driving Q2 from a tap. The position between the emitters offers a good, low-impedance environment to keep the crystal's in-circuit Q high. R, in the emitter of Q1, is again selected to give reliable oscillation. The circuit has been shown with a capacitive load for the crystal, to suit a unit specified for a 30 pF load. An alternative circuit to give electrical fine tuning is also shown. The diodes across the tank act as limiters to stabilize the operating amplitude and limit the power dissipated in the crystal by clipping the drive voltage to Q2. The tank should be adjusted to peak at the operating frequency, not used to trim the frequency. The capacitance in series with the crystal is the proper frequency trimmer.

The Butler circuit works well, and has been used in critical applications to 140 MHz (seventh-overtone crystal, 2N5179 transistor). Although the component count is high, the extra parts are cheap ones. Increasing the capacitance in series with the crystal reduces the oscillation frequency but has a progressively diminishing effect. Decreasing the capacitance pulls the frequency higher, to a point at which oscillation stops; before this point is reached, start-up will become unreliable. The possible amount of adjustment, called *pulling range*, depends on the crystal; it can range from less than 10 to several hundred parts per million. Overtone crystals have much less pulling range than fundamental crystals on the same frequency; the reduction in pulling is roughly proportional to the square of the overtone number.

LOW-NOISE CRYSTAL OSCILLATORS

Figure 9.26A shows a crystal operating in its series mode in a series-tuned Colpitts circuit. Because it does not include an LC tank to prevent operation on unwanted modes, this circuit is intended for fundamental mode operation only and relies on that mode being the most active. If the crystal is ordered for 30 pF loading, the frequency trimming capacitor can be adjusted to compensate for the loading of the capacitive divider of the Colpitts circuit. An unloaded crystal without a trimmer would operate slightly off the exact series resonant frequency in order to create an inductive impedance to resonate with the divider capacitors. Ulrich Rohde, N1UL, in Figure 4-47 of his book *Digital PLL Frequency Synthesizers — Theory and Design*, published an elegant alternative method of extracting an output signal from this type of circuit, shown in Figure 9.26B. This taps off a signal from the current in the crystal itself. This can be thought of as using the crystal as a band-pass filter for the oscillator output. The RF choke in the emitter keeps the emitter bias resistor from loading the tank and degrading the Q. In this case (3 MHz operation), it has been chosen to resonate close to 3 MHz with the parallel capacitor (510 pF) as a means of forcing operation on the wanted mode. The 10-Ω resistor and the transformed load impedance will reduce the in-circuit Q of the crystal, so a further development substituted a common base amplifier for the resistor and transformer. This is shown in Figure 9.26C. The common-base amplifier is run at a large quiescent current to give a very low input impedance. Its collector is tuned to give an output with low harmonic content and an emitter follower is used to buffer this from the load. This oscillator sports a simple ALC system, in which the amplified and rectified signal is used to reduce the bias voltage on the oscillator transistor's base. This circuit is described as achieving a phase noise level of −168 dBc/Hz a few kilohertz out from the carrier. This may seem far beyond what may ever be needed, but frequency multiplication to high frequencies, whether by classic multipliers or by frequency synthesizers, multiplies the deviation of any FM/PM sidebands as well as the carrier frequency. This means that phase noise worsens by 20 dB for each tenfold multiplication of frequency. A clean crystal oscillator and a multiplier chain is still the best way of generating clean microwave signals for use with narrow-band modulation schemes.

It has already been mentioned that overtone crystals are much harder to pull than fundamental ones. This is another way of saying that overtone crystals are less influenced by their surrounding circuit, which is helpful in a frequency-standard oscillator like this one. Even though 5 MHz is in the main range of fundamental-mode crystals and this circuit will work well with them, an overtone crystal has been used. To further help stability, the power dissipated in the crystal is kept to about 50 μW. The common-base stage is effectively driven from a higher impedance than its own input impedance, under which conditions it gives a very low noise figure.

9.4.5 Variable-frequency Crystal Oscillators (VXOs)

Some crystal oscillators have frequency trimmers. If the trimmer is replaced by a variable capacitor as a front-panel control, we have a *variable crystal oscillator* (*VXO*): a crystal-based VFO with a narrow tuning range, but good stability and noise performance. VXOs are often used in small, simple QRP transmitters to tune a few kilohertz around common calling frequencies. Artful constructors, using optimized circuits and components, have achieved 1000-ppm tuning ranges. Poor-quality "soft" crystals are more pull-able than high-Q ones. Overtone crystals are not suited to VXOs. For frequencies beyond the usual limit for fundamental mode crystals, use a fundamental unit and frequency multipliers.

ICOM and Mizuho made some 2 meter SSB transceivers based on multiplied VXO local oscillators. This system is simple and

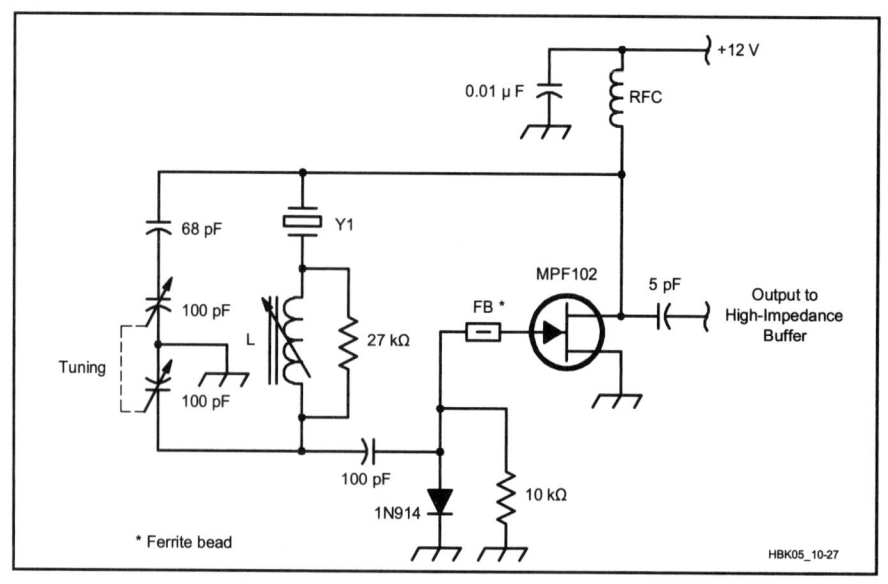

Figure 9.27 — A wide-range variable-crystal oscillator (VXO) by W7ZOI and W1FB. It was originally designed for use in low-power radios without the usual wide-range VFO.

can yield better performance than many expensive synthesized radios. SSB filters are available at 9 or 10.7 MHz, to yield sufficient image rejection with a single conversion. Choice of VXO frequency depends on whether the LO is to be above or below signal frequency and how much multiplication can be tolerated. Below 8 MHz, multiplier filtering is difficult. Above 15 MHz, the tuning range per crystal narrows. A 50-200 kHz range per crystal should work with a modern front-end design feeding a good 9 MHz IF, for a contest quality 2 meter SSB receiver.

The circuit in **Figure 9.27** is a JFET VXO from Wes Hayward, W7ZOI, and Doug DeMaw, W1FB, optimized for wide-range pulling. Published in *Solid State Design for the Radio Amateur*, many have been built and its ability to pull crystals as far as possible has been proven. Ulrich Rohde, N1UL, has shown that the diode arrangement as used here to make signal-dependent negative bias for the gate confers a phase-noise disadvantage, but oscillators like this that pull crystals as far as possible need any available means to stabilize their amplitude and aid start-up. In this case, the noise penalty is worth paying. This circuit can achieve a 2000-ppm tuning range with amenable crystals. If you have some overtone crystals in your junk box whose fundamental frequency is close to the wanted value, they are worth trying.

This sort of circuit doesn't necessarily stop pulling at the extremes of the possible tuning range; sometimes the range is set by the onset of undesirable behavior such as jumping mode or simply stopping oscillating. L was a 16 µH slug-tuned inductor for 10 MHz operation. It is important to minimize the stray and inter-winding capacitance of L since this dilutes the range of impedance presented to the crystal.

One trick that can be used to aid the pulling range of oscillators is to tune out the C0 of the equivalent circuit with an added inductor. **Figure 9.28** shows how. L is chosen to resonate with C0 for the individual crystal, turning it into a high-impedance parallel-tuned circuit. The Q of this circuit is orders of magnitude less than the Q of the true series resonance of the crystal, so its tuning is much broader. The value of C0 is usually just a few picofarads, so L has to be a fairly large value considering the frequency at which it is resonated. This means that L has to have low stray capacitance or else it will self-resonate at a lower frequency. The tolerance on C0 and the variations of the stray C of the inductor means that individual adjustment is needed. This technique can also work wonders in crystal ladder filters.

9.4.6 Logic-Gate Crystal Oscillators

The frequency-determining network of an RC oscillator has a Q of less than one, which means that phase shift changes very slowly with different frequencies (see the prior section on RC Oscillators). The Pierce crystal oscillator discussed previously is a converted phase-shift oscillator, with the crystal taking the place of one series resistor. The crystal provides a much higher phase shift than an RC stage, so the crystal "controls" the frequency of oscillation.

The actual frequency of oscillation is the frequency at which the Barkhausen criteria are met. The crystal must operate near its series resonance in order for the loop gain to be unity. Oscillation then settles at the frequency where the crystal phase shift, added to the RC phase shifts, equals 180 degrees. The crystal usually provides between 45 and 60 degrees of phase shift, so the oscillation frequency is above the series resonance and below the parallel resonance of the crystal where the crystal behaves as a large inductor. (See the figure showing crystal response in the section Quartz Crystal Filters in the **Analog and Digital Filtering** chapter.)

The Pierce circuit is rarely seen in this full form. Instead, a cut-down version is the most common circuit in many microprocessors and other digital ICs that need a crystal-controlled clock. **Figure 9.29** shows this minimalist Pierce, using a CMOS logic inverter as the amplifier. R_{bias} provides dc negative feedback to bias the gate into its linear region. This value is not critical, anything between 100 kΩ and 10 MΩ works fine. The RC phase shifts needed to make this work come from R_{out}-C1 and $R_{crystal}$-C2. This circuit has a reputation of being temperamental, mainly because neither R_{out} nor $R_{crystal}$ are well documented or controlled in manufacturing. There is also a general belief that this circuit requires C1 = C2, which is not true.

A great improvement in performance is achieved by adding one resistor, R1, as shown in Figure 9.29. R_{bias} remains connected directly across the CMOS inverter. R1 is inserted in series from the gate output to the feedback network. The benefits are multiple:

• The edge speed of modern CMOS gates is extremely fast, so R1C1 eliminates the possibility of this fast edge exciting overtone operation.

• Phase shift into the crystal can be intentionally designed by R1 and C1 value selection.

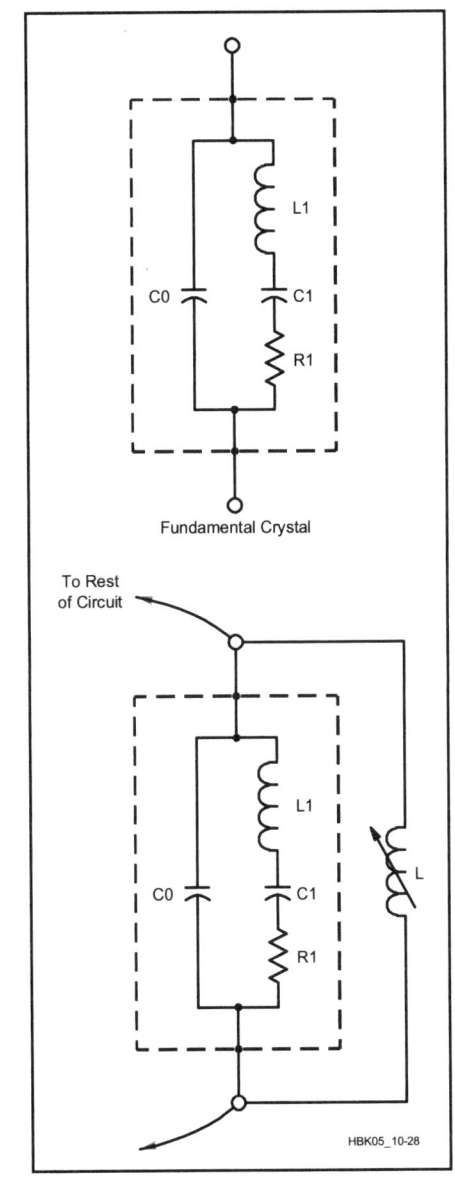

Figure 9.28 — Using an inductor to "tune out" C0 can increase a crystal oscillator's pulling range.

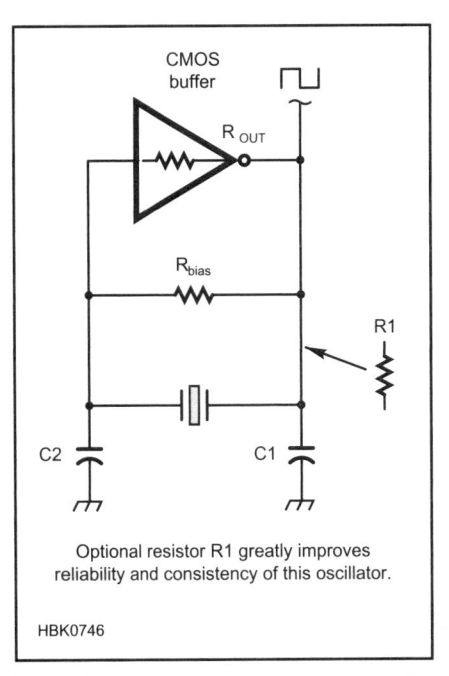

Figure 9.29 — The simplified Pierce oscillator using a logic-gate for the inverting amplifier. Adding R1 improves oscillator design and reliability.

Oscillators and Synthesizers 9.23

- Drive from the inverter output is reduced into the crystal, possibly saving it from being damaged.
- Loop gain can now be controlled for best waveform and startup characteristics.

Design values are strongly dependent on the actual crystal frequency needed. C2 is selected first, to provide around 60 degrees of phase shift working against the crystal equivalent series resistance (usually a few tens of ohms, but the value needs to be verified!). The time constant R1 C1 is usefully chosen to be the reciprocal of the crystal radian frequency ($1/2\pi f_{XTAL}$). Higher values of R1 reduce the loop gain and provide better protection for the crystal, until the loop gain gets too small and oscillation stops.

9.5 Oscillators at UHF and Above

The traditional way to make signals at higher frequencies is to make a signal at a lower frequency (where oscillators are easier) and multiply it up to the wanted range. Frequency multiplication is still one of the easiest and best ways of making a clean UHF/microwave signal. The design of a multiplier depends on whether the multiplication factor is an odd or even number. For odd multiplication, a Class-C biased amplifier can be used to create a series of harmonics; a filter selects the one wanted. For even multiplication factors, a full-wave-rectifier arrangement of distorting devices can be used to create a series of harmonics with strong even-order components, with a filter selecting the wanted component. At higher frequencies, diode-based passive circuits are commonly used. Oscillators using some of the LC circuits already described can, with care in construction, be used in the VHF range. At UHF, different approaches become necessary.

9.5.1 UHF Oscillators: Intentional and Accidental

The biggest change when working at UHF and microwave frequencies is that stray reactances and resistance dominates everything, making lumped circuit elements impractical. Success at these high frequencies requires making peace with the situation and developing a very good sense of where stray circuit elements reside in your layout and their approximate magnitude.

Figure 9.30 shows a pair of oscillators based on a resonant length of line, which is a distributed circuit element. The first one is a return to basics: a resonator, an amplifier and a pair of coupling loops. The amplifier can be a single bipolar or FET device or one of the monolithic microwave integrated circuit (MMIC) amplifiers. The second circuit is really a Hartley oscillator, and one is made as a test oscillator for the 70 cm band from a 10 cm length of wire suspended 10 mm over an unetched PC board as a ground plane, bent down and soldered at one end, with a trimmer at the other end. The FET is a BF981 dual-gate device used as a source follower.

No free-running oscillator is really stable enough on these bands. Oscillators in this range are almost invariably tuned with tuning diodes controlled by phase-locked-loop synthesizers, which are themselves controlled by a crystal oscillator. This transfers the same stability of the crystal oscillator to the UHF oscillator.

There is one extremely common UHF oscillator that is almost always an undesired accident, being a very common form of spurious VHF/UHF oscillation in circuitry intended to process lower-frequency signals. **Figure 9.31A** shows the circuit in its simplest form. Analyzing this circuit using a comprehensive model of the UHF transistor reveals that the emitter presents an impedance that is small, resistive, and negative to the outside world. If this negative resistance is large enough to more than cancel the effective series resistance of a tank placed on the emitter, oscillation will occur.

At UHF your schematic diagram probably will not show a tank circuit is present. But the high frequency transistor will know it is there, since it "sees" all of the stray reactances present in the layout. Figure 9.31B shows a very basic emitter-follower circuit with some capacitance to ground on both the input and output. If the capacitor shunting the input is a distance away from the transistor, the trace to the transistor's base looks like an inductor. The trace at the emitter of the transistor also looks like an inductor, and any nearby conductor will look like a capacitor to that trace (two conductors separated by a dielectric, which here is air and the PC board material). Any intentional capacitors add to this. If the transistor has gain at any frequency where the phasing from all of these stray reactances is right for oscillation (see Barkhausen criteria in previous sections) then oscillation will happen. This circuit is effectively the same

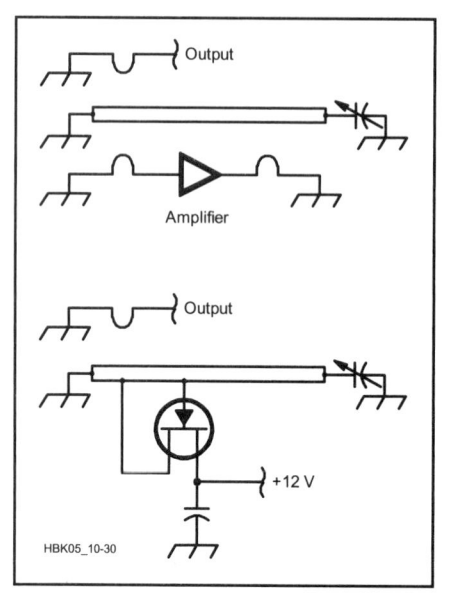

Figure 9.30 — Oscillators that use transmission-line segments as resonators. Such oscillators are more common than many of us may think, as Figure 9.31 reveals.

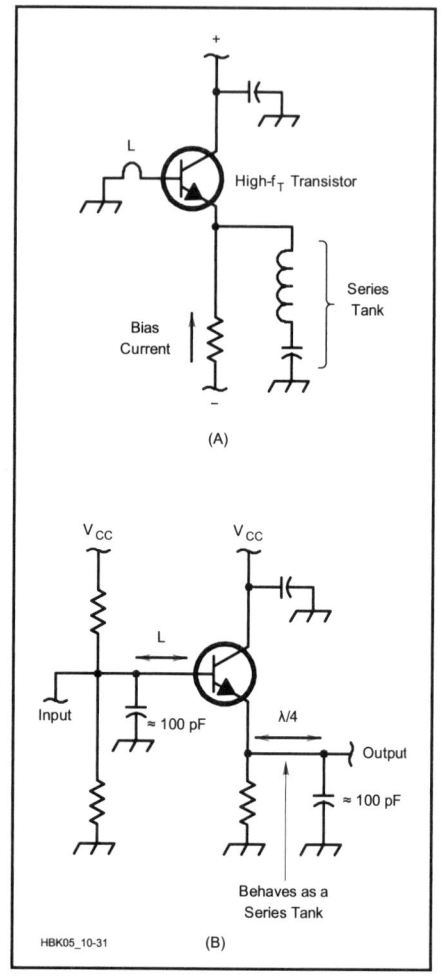

Figure 9.31 — High device gain at UHF and resonances in circuit board traces can result in spurious oscillations even in non-RF equipment.

as that in Figure 9.31A. This is a good reason to use the lowest-frequency transistor that you can for any application.

Stray reactances do not always have to cause headaches. Indeed you can use them, knowing that they are there. The circuit of Figure 9.31A can be deliberately built as a useful wide-tuning oscillator covering say, 500 MHz to 1 GHz! This circuit is well-suited to construction with printed-circuit inductors. Common FR4 glass-epoxy board is lossy at these frequencies; better performance is achieved by using (the much more expensive) glass-Teflon board. If you can get surplus pieces of this type of material, it has many uses at UHF and microwave, but it is difficult to use as the adhesion between the copper and the substrate can be weak. A high-UHF transistor with a 5 GHz f_T such as the BFR90 is suitable; the base inductor can be 30 mm of 1 mm trace folded into a hairpin shape (inductance, less than 10 nH).

The upshot of this is that there is no longer any branch of electronics where RF design and layout techniques can be ignored safely. A circuit must not just be designed to do what it should do; it must also be designed so that it cannot do what it should not do.

If you have an accidental oscillator, there are three ways of taming such a circuit: adding a small resistor of perhaps 50 to 100 Ω in the collector lead close to the transistor, or adding a similar resistor in the base lead, or by fitting a ferrite bead over the base lead under the transistor. Extra resistors can disturb dc conditions, depending on the circuit and its operating currents. Ferrite beads have the advantage that they can be easily added to existing equipment and have no effect at dc and low frequencies. Beware of some electrically conductive ferrite materials that can short transistor leads! If an HF oscillator uses beads to prevent any risk of spurs (such as shown in Figure 9.15), the beads should be anchored with a spot of adhesive to prevent movement which can cause small frequency shifts. Ferrite beads of Fair-Rite #43 material are especially suitable for this purpose; they are specified in terms of impedance, not inductance. Ferrites at frequencies above their inductive range become very lossy and can make a lead present a few tens of ohms of resistance.

9.5.2 Microwave Oscillators

Using conventional PC-board techniques with surface-mount components and extraordinarily careful layout allows the construction of circuits up to 4 GHz or so. Above this, commercial techniques and fancier materials become necessary unless we take the step to the ultimate distributed circuit — the cavity resonator.

Older than stripline techniques and far more amenable to home construction, cavity-based oscillators can give the highest possible

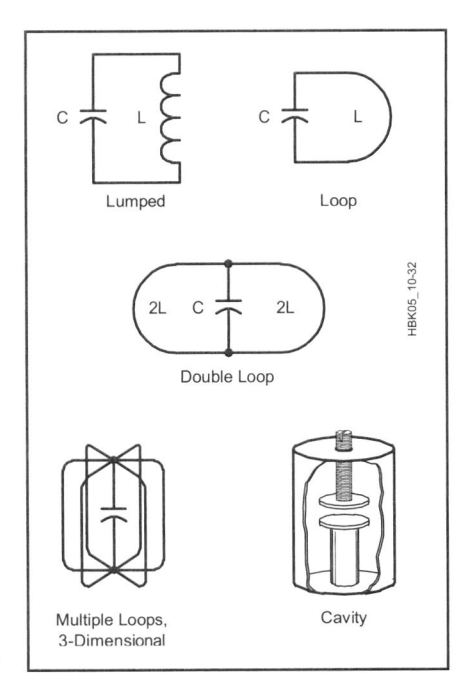

Figure 9.32 — Evolution of the cavity resonator.

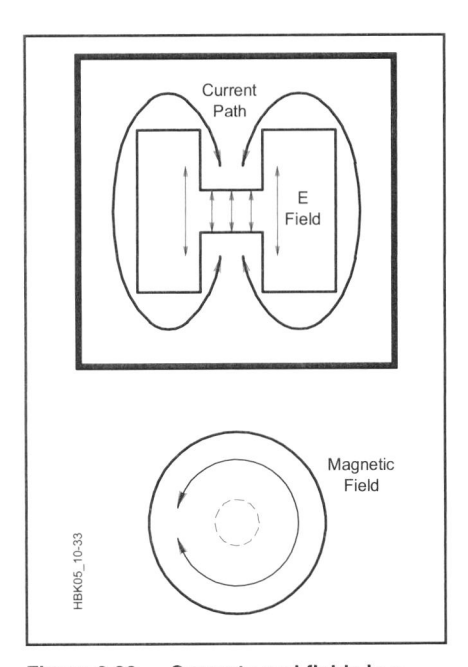

Figure 9.33 — Currents and fields in a cavity.

performance at microwave frequencies. Air is a very low-loss dielectric with a dielectric constant of 1, so it gives high Q and does not force excessive miniaturization. **Figure 9.32** shows a series of structures used by G. R. Jessop, G6JP, to illustrate the evolution of a cavity from a tank made of lumped components. All cavities have a number of different modes of resonance, the orientation of the currents and fields are shown in **Figure 9.33**. The cavity can take different shapes, but the one shown here has proven to suppress unwanted modes well. The gap need not be central and is often right at the top. A screw can be fitted through the top, protruding into the gap, to adjust the frequency.

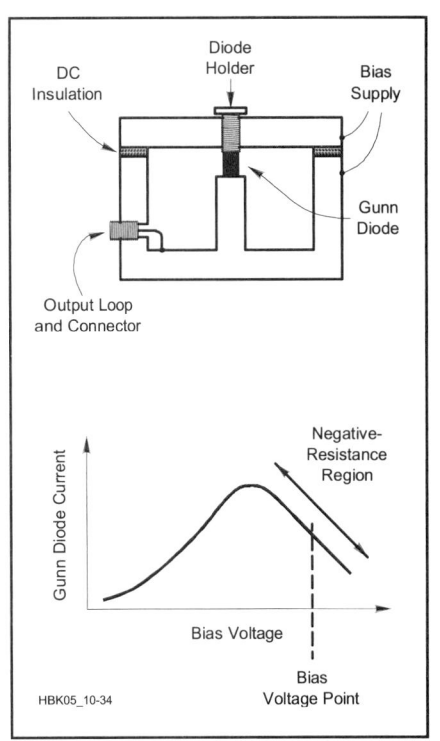

Figure 9.34 — A Gunn diode oscillator uses negative resistance and a cavity resonator to produce radio energy.

SEMICONDUCTOR CAVITY OSCILLATORS

To make an oscillator using a cavity, an amplifier is needed. Gunn and tunnel diodes have regions in their characteristics where their current falls with increasing bias voltage. This is negative resistance. If such a device is mounted in a loop in a cavity and bias is applied, the negative resistance can more than cancel the effective loss resistance of the cavity, causing oscillation. These diodes are capable of operating at extremely high frequencies and were discovered long before transistors were developed that had any gain at microwave frequencies.

A Gunn-diode cavity oscillator is the basis of many of the Doppler radar modules used to detect traffic or intruders and of the Gunnplexer 10 GHz transceiver modules used by amateurs. **Figure 9.34** shows a common configuration. The coupling loop and coax output connector could be replaced with a simple aperture to couple into waveguide or a mixer cavity. **Figure 9.35** shows a transistor cavity oscillator version using a modern microwave transistor, which can be either a FET or bipolar device. The two coupling loops are electrically completed by the capacitance of the feedthrough capacitors.

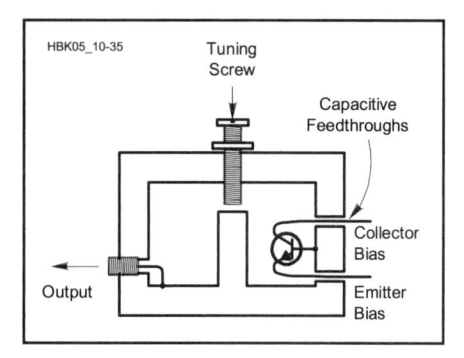

Figure 9.35 — A transistor can also directly excite a cavity resonator.

DIELECTRIC-RESONATOR OSCILLATORS (DRO)

The dielectric-resonator oscillator (DRO) is a very common microwave oscillator, as it is used in the downconverter of satellite TV receivers. The dielectric resonator itself is a ceramic cylinder, like a miniature hockey puck, several millimeters in diameter. The ceramic has a very high dielectric constant, so the surface (where ceramic meets air in an abrupt dielectric mismatch) reflects electromagnetic waves and makes the ceramic body act as a resonant cavity. It is mounted on a substrate and coupled to the active device of the oscillator by a stripline that runs past it. At 10 GHz, a FET made of gallium arsenide (GaAsFET), rather than silicon, is normally used. The dielectric resonator elements are made at frequencies appropriate to mass applications like satellite TV. The setup charge to manufacture small quantities at special frequencies is likely to be prohibitive for the foreseeable future.

The challenge with these devices is to devise new ways of using oscillators on industry standard frequencies. Their chief attraction is their low cost in large quantities and compatibility with microwave stripline (microstrip) techniques. Frequency stability and Q are competitive with good cavities, but are inferior to that achievable with a crystal oscillator and chain of frequency multipliers.

YIG TUNED OSCILLATORS (YTO)

The yttrium-iron garnet (YIG) oscillator is a fundamental microwave source with a very wide tuning range and a linear tuning characteristic. Many YIG oscillators can be tuned over more than an octave and some tune more than five octaves! They are complete units that appear as heavy blocks of metal with low-frequency connections for power supplies and tuning, and an SMA connector for the RF output. The manufacturer's label usually states the tuning range and often the power supply voltages. This is very helpful because, with new units being very expensive, it is important to be able to identify the characteristics of surplus units. The majority of YTOs operate within the 2 to 18 GHz region, although units down to 500 MHz and up to 40 GHz are occasionally found. At microwave frequencies there is no octave-tunable device that can equal their signal cleanliness and stability. A typical stability for a 3 GHz YTO is less than 1 kHz per second drift. This may seem poor — until we realize that this is 0.33 ppm per second. Still, any YIG application involving narrow-band modulation will require some form of frequency stabilizer.

Nearly all surplus RF spectrum analyzers use YTOs as their first LO. For example, a 0 to 1500 MHz analyzer usually uses a 2 to 3.5 GHz YTO with a 2.0 GHz first IF. To understand the YTO tuning circuits, should there be need for troubleshooting and repair, a basic understanding of YIG oscillators definitely helps.

Figure 9.36 shows the construction of a YIG oscillator. A YTO is based on a YIG sphere that is carefully oriented within a coupling loop. This resonator is connected to a negative-resistance device and the whole assembly is placed between the poles of an electromagnet. Negative-resistance (Gunn) diodes were originally used in these oscillators, but transistor circuits are now essentially universal and use much less power. The support for the YIG sphere often contains a controlled heater to reduce temperature variation. YIG spheres are resonant at a frequency controlled not only by their physical dimensions, but also by any magnetic field around them. Hence the electromagnet: by varying the current through the electromagnet's windings, a controlled variable magnetic field is applied across the YIG sphere. This tunes the oscillator across a very wide range. The frequency/current relationship can have excellent linearity, typically around 20 MHz/mA.

Magnetically-tuned oscillators bring some unique problems with them. The first problem is that magnetic fields, especially at low frequencies, are extremely difficult to shield. Therefore YTO tuning is influenced by any local magnetic fields, causing frequency

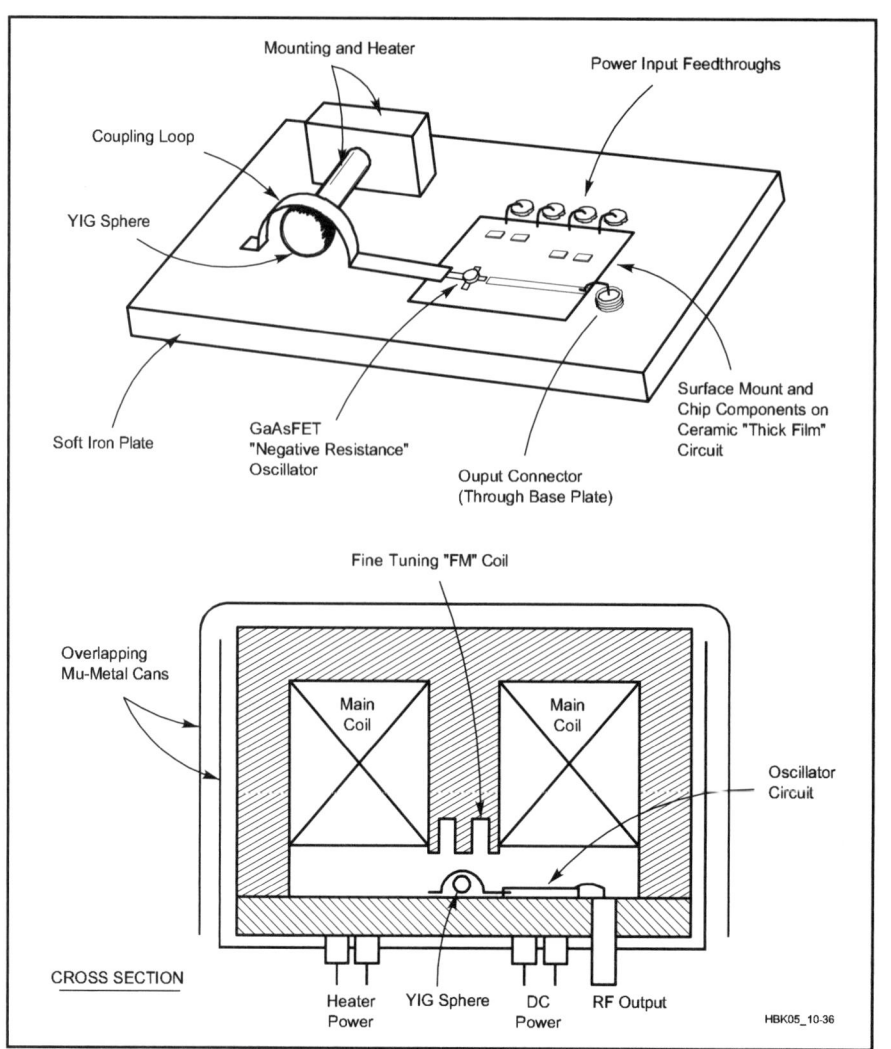

Figure 9.36 — A yttrium-iron-garnet (YIG) sphere serves as the resonator in the sweep oscillators used in many spectrum analyzers.

modulation. The YTO's magnetic core must be carefully designed to be all-enclosing in an attempt at self-shielding, and then one or more nested mu-metal cans are fitted around everything. It is still important to place the YTO away from obvious sources of magnetic fields, like power transformers. Cooling fans are also sources of fluctuating magnetic fields, with some fans generating fields 20 dB higher than from a well-designed 200 W 50/60-Hz transformer.

The second new problem is that the YTO's internal tuning coil needs significant current from the power supply to create the strong tuning field. This can be eased by adding a permanent magnet as a fixed "bias" field, but the bias shifts as the magnet ages. The main tuning coil still has many turns, and therefore high inductance (often more than 0.1 henrys). Large inductances require a high supply voltage for rapid tuning, with correspondingly high power consumption. The usual compromise is to have dual coils: One with many turns for slow tuning over a wide range, and a second coil with far fewer turns for fast tuning or FM over a limited range. This "FM coil" has a sensitivity around 1% to 2% of the main coil, perhaps 500 kHz/mA.

9.5.3 Klystrons, Magnetrons, and Traveling Wave Tubes

There are a number of thermionic (vacuum-tube) devices that are widely used as amplifiers or fundamental oscillators at microwave frequencies. Standard vacuum tubes (see the **RF Amplifiers** chapter for an introduction to vacuum tubes) work well for frequencies up to hundreds of megahertz. At frequencies higher than this, the amount of time that the electrons take to move between the cathode and the plate becomes a limiting factor. There are several special tubes designed to work at microwave frequencies, usually providing more power than can be obtained from solid-state devices.

Two of the following tubes (klystrons and traveling wave tubes) use the principle of *velocity-modulation* to extract RF energy from an electron beam. The general principles of velocity modulation and basic properties of devices using it are presented in the online tutorial **www.radartutorial.eu/druck/Book5.pdf**. Additional resources are described below.

THE KLYSTRON

The klystron tube uses the principle of velocity modulation of the electrons to avoid transit time limitations. The beam of electrons travels down a metal drift tube that has interaction gaps along its sides. RF voltages are applied to the gaps and the electric fields that they generate accelerate or decelerate the passing electrons. The relative positions of the electrons shift due to their changing velocities, causing the electron density of the beam to vary. This variation of electron beam density is used to perform amplification or oscillation.

Klystron tubes can be relatively large, and they can easily provide hundreds of watts to hundreds of kilowatts of microwave power. These power levels are useful for UHF broadcasting and particle accelerators, for example. Unfortunately klystrons have relatively narrow bandwidths, and may not be re-tunable for operation on amateur frequencies. A video titled "How a Klystron Tube Works" can be found online on YouTube.com and a detailed history and tutorial is available at **www.slac.stanford.edu/cgi-wrap/getdoc/slac-pub-7731.pdf**.

THE MAGNETRON

The magnetron tube is an efficient oscillator for microwave frequencies. Magnetrons are most commonly found in microwave ovens and high-powered radar equipment. The anode of a magnetron is made up of a number of coupled resonant cavities that surround the cathode. The applied magnetic field causes the electrons to rotate around the cathode and the energy that they give off as they approach the anode adds to the RF electric field. The RF power is obtained from the anode through a vacuum window.

Magnetrons are self-oscillating with the frequency determined by the construction of their anodes; however, they can be tuned by coupling either inductance or capacitance to the resonant anode. The range of frequencies depends on how fast the tuning must be accomplished. The tube may be tuned slowly over a range of approximately 10% of the center frequency. If faster tuning is necessary, such as is required for frequency modulation, the range decreases to about 5%.

Excellent drawings showing how magnetrons work are available at **hyperphysics.phy-astr.gsu.edu/hbase/waves/magnetron.html** and a thorough introduction for the interested reader is can be downloaded from **www.cpii.com/docs/related/2/Mag%20tech%20art.pdf**.

THE TRAVELING WAVE TUBE

A third type of tube operating in the microwave range is the traveling wave tube (TWT). For wide-band amplifiers in the microwave range this is the tube of choice. Either permanent magnets or electromagnets are used to focus the beam of electrons that travels through the TWT. This electron beam passes through a helical slow-wave structure, in which electrons are accelerated or decelerated, providing density modulation due to the applied RF signal, similar to that in the klystron. The modulated electron beam induces voltages in the helix that provides an amplified output signal whose gain is proportional to the length of the slow-wave structure. After the RF energy is extracted from the electron beam by the helix, the electrons are collected and recycled to the cathode. Traveling wave tubes can often be operated outside their designed frequencies by carefully optimizing the beam voltage.

9.6 Frequency Synthesizers

Like many of our modern technologies, the origins of frequency synthesis can be traced back to WW II. The driving force was the desire for stable, rapidly switchable and accurate frequency control technology to meet the demands of narrow-band, frequency-agile HF communications systems without resorting to large banks of switched crystals. Early synthesizers were cumbersome and expensive, and therefore their use was limited to only the most sophisticated communications systems. With the help of the same technologies that have taken computers from room-sized to now fitting into the palms of our hands, frequency synthesis techniques have become one of the most enabling technologies in modern communications equipment.

Every communications device manufactured today, be it a handheld transceiver, cell phone, pager, AM/FM entertainment radio, scanner, television, HF communications equipment, or test equipment, contains a frequency synthesizer. Synthesis is the technology that allows an easy interface with both computers and microprocessor controllers. It provides amateurs with many desirable features, such as the feel of an analog knob with precision 10-Hz frequency increments, wide-band accuracy and stability determined by a single precision crystal oscillator, frequency memories, and continuously variable precision frequency splits. Now reduced in size to small integrated circuits, frequency synthesizers have long replaced the cumbersome chains of frequency multipliers and filters in VHF, UHF and microwave equipment, giving rise to the highly portable communications devices we use today. Frequency synthesis has also had a major impact in lowering the cost of modern equipment, particularly by reducing manufacturing complexity.

Frequency synthesizers are categorized in two general types: *direct synthesizers*, where the output signal is the result of operations directly performed on the input signal; and *indirect synthesizers*, where selected characteristics of the input signal are transferred onto a separately generated output signal. One defining feature of any direct synthesizer is that no feedback is used, so there is never any dynamic stability problem. Indirect synthesizers always include feedback control loops, so dynamic stability is a major design concern.

Direct synthesizers include the major techniques of *direct analog synthesis* (DAS) and *direct digital synthesis* (DDS). Direct analog synthesizers consist primarily of frequency multipliers, frequency dividers, mixers, and filters. DAS is very useful for generating small numbers of signals, with widely spaced frequencies, from a reference oscillator. DAS is particularly useful when more than one output signal is required at the same time. Direct digital synthesizers are essentially dedicated microprocessors that have one program, to create an output signal waveform given a desired frequency (in digital form) using the applied reference signal. Unlike DAS, the output frequencies from a DDS can easily be separated by millihertz (0.001 Hz) while keeping all of the stability of the reference oscillator. Both being direct techniques, neither DAS nor DDS use feedback control loops, so switching from one frequency to another happens in nanoseconds.

Indirect synthesizers include the major techniques of frequency-locked loops (FLL) and phase-locked loops (PLL). The whole idea behind any indirect synthesizer is to transfer characteristics of one signal onto another separate signal. An FLL transfers only frequency characteristics of the input signal onto the output signal. Major FLL applications used by radio amateurs include *automatic frequency control* (AFC) loops and tone decoders. PLLs are more precise because not only frequency characteristics of the reference oscillator, but also its phase characteristics, are transferred to the oscillator generating the output signal. There are two main application classes in which PLLs find wide use. The first is as a *frequency generator*, where we call it a *frequency synthesizer*. In transmitters this synthesizer may also include modulation, particularly for FM and FSK signals. The second PLL application class is as an angle (frequency or phase) demodulator, where we call it a *tracking demodulator* or *synchronizer*. Tracking demodulators used in deep space communication and clock recovery used in digital communication are major applications today.

It is curious to note that using modern digital circuitry, it actually is easier to make a PLL than an FLL. This turns out to be fortuitous! This section will focus on the PLL used as a frequency synthesizer. For readers interested in PLL use as a demodulator or as a synchronizer, there are many textbooks available that discuss these applications in great detail.

9.6.1 Digital Frequency Synthesis

A digital process is defined to be quantized in both value and time. (See the **DSP and SDR Fundamentals** chapter for background on digital signals and systems.) This is important to remember because there are sampled signal processes that are not digital. One is the sample-and-hold, which is discrete in time but analog in value. The opposite is the phase-frequency detector used in phase-locked loops, which is discrete in value but analog in time. Digital frequency synthesis is a true digital process.

The origins of digital frequency synthesis go back to 1972, even before the widespread use of microprocessors. In essence, these techniques directly calculate the desired output waveform, including any modulations. When no feedback used these are called Direct Digital Synthesis (DDS), and sometimes you also see the name Direct Digital Frequency Synthesis (DDFS) used. The DDS name is older, though DDFS is more specific. Both names survive but here we will use the original DDS.

DDS has many attractive properties and two major drawbacks. Its attractions include very fine frequency resolution (microhertz is practical), essentially instant switching speed, no frequency drift, and absolute frequency set-ability. If modulation is included, this also happens with digital precision. Direct control of frequency, phase shift, and amplitude are available and independent of each other. For frequency and phase shift, this is new. Any analog oscillator does not have the ability to independently address frequency and phase.

DDS drawbacks are also significant. Being a digital process, DDS is a sampled data system and so must adhere to the Nyquist criterion for waveform reconstruction as explained in the **DSP and SDR Fundamentals** chapter. This effectively means that the output frequency from a DDS is restricted to being less than half of the DDS clock frequency. The practical upper limit is around 35-40% of the clock frequency. Interestingly, there is no effective lower limit. Any DDS can tune all the way down to zero hertz (dc) since 0 is a legitimate tuning command.

The second drawback is more operationally serious. We demand a high quality sine wave from our oscillators and DDS is no exception. But as a sampled data system, the DDS output is a sampled sine wave. Sampling a sine wave without error requires infinite resolution due to the properties of the sinusoid. We do not have infinite resolution available to our designs, so some errors creep in as the signal is constructed. These errors

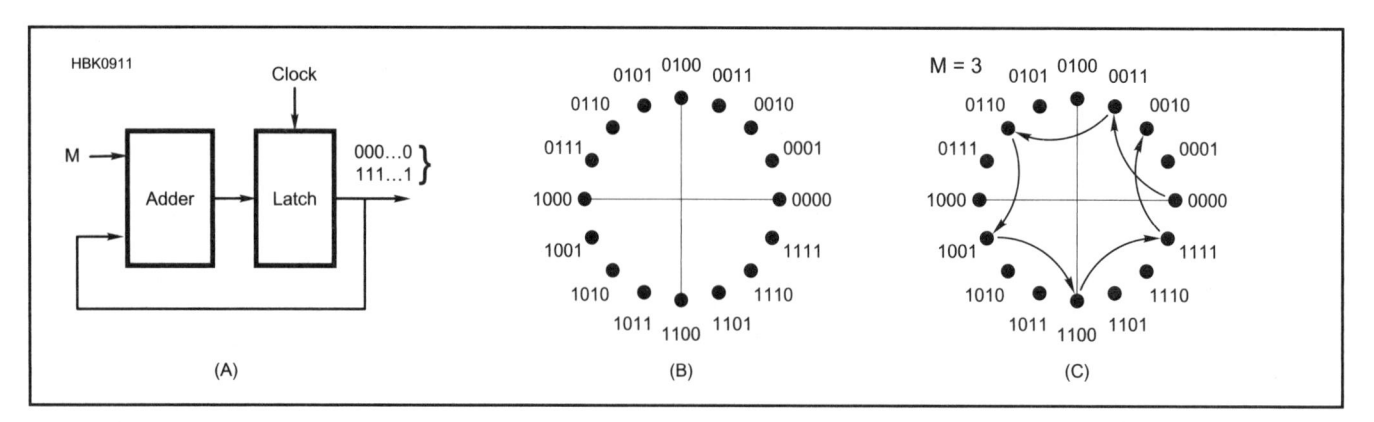

Figure 9.37 — Direct digital synthesis is based on the accumulator circuit (A). For our purposes, we assign all of the possible states that the accumulator can have around a circle and call them "phase" (B). The accumulator continuously adds its input number, once each clock cycle, to the present count. When the adder overflows, the overflow is dropped and counting continues around the circle as in (C).

manifest themselves as non-harmonic spurious output signals, a.k.a. "spurs," which can be a huge problem. Much DDS design spends a lot of time dealing with spurs.

DDS PRINCIPLES

DDS is based on the simple counter structure of an accumulator, as shown in **Figure 9.37**. We choose to interpret the digital outputs from this counter as signal phase, and commonly represent the states as points around a circle, which means that one cycle through the accumulator states represents one output cycle from this synthesizer. The figure shows an example of the 16 digital states from a 4-bit accumulator. Action of this accumulator when its input number M is set to 3 is shown in (c), showing how the "wraparound" from one cycle to the next continues when the adder overflows. It is common to have the state progression from one output cycle to the next be a different state sequence. What is vitally important is that the jump size from one state to the next be exactly the same. This sets the phase change to be

$$\frac{\Delta \theta}{\Delta t} = \frac{\Delta \text{ PHASE}}{1 \text{ CLOCK CYCLE}} = M$$

Frequency is simply how fast phase changes with time, so this accumulator input M is our direct tuning control. For an N-bit accumulator then the DDS frequency control is given by

$$f_{DDS} = \frac{f_{CLOCK}}{2^N} \times M$$

Note that this relationship is perfectly linear. Also note that f_{DDS} is quantized, because the tuning number M must be an integer. There are some frequencies that a DDS cannot generate. But 0 Hz at M = 0 is legitimate!

One of the really important properties of DDS, which makes it particularly useful, is that N can be a reasonably large number. As examples, for N=24 the denominator 2^N = 16,777,216. N = 32 is common, and then 2^N = 4,294,967,296. This means that the DDS frequency resolution, if a 100 MHz clock frequency is used, is 5.96 Hz when N = 24, and 0.023 Hz when N = 32. This is extremely fine frequency resolution and it is as accurate as the clock frequency. The only way that the DDS output frequency can drift is if the clock frequency drifts. Because everything else is digital, that cannot drift.

However, we need to have a sine wave output from our synthesizer. The full DDS block diagram is shown in **Figure 9.38**, where a new block called the waveform map is included. This is a digital process, usually implemented as a non-volatile memory, that converts the phase information from the accumulator into sinusoid waveform values which are then converted to a sampled waveform in a DAC. The output low-pass filter is critical to getting the desired sine wave.

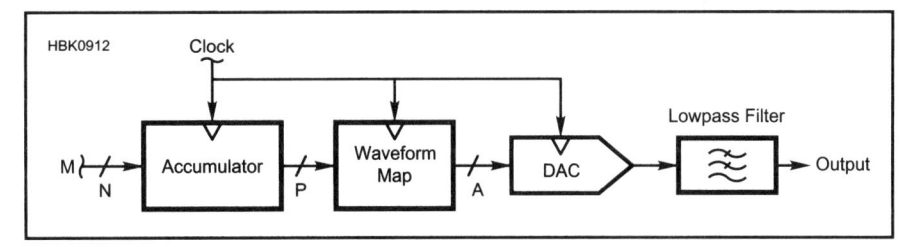

Figure 9.38 — Complete block diagram of a DDS.

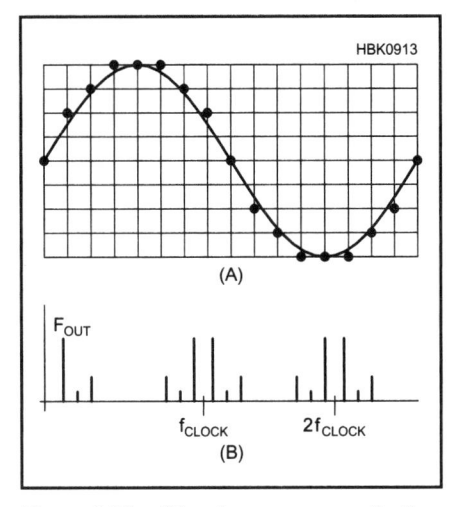

Figure 9.39 — Waveform map quantization forces output waveform errors because the output signal values must remain at the intersection of the grid lines (A). This results in output non-harmonic spurious signals from the DDS (B).

DDS NOISE

DDS is a frequency divider and by the rules of frequency division the output phase noise is lower than the input phase noise, which in any DDS comes from the clock. There is no VCO to add noise to the output signal, like we have in PLLs.

ADDITIONAL DDS PRINCIPLES

In addition to very fine frequency resolution, extremely good tuning linearity, very low output phase noise, and tuning bandwidth that goes all the way down to dc, an additional important benefit of DDS is that it tunes very quickly. Indeed, as soon as the tuning number M is changed, the DDS immediately shifts to calculating the new output waveform. The tuning dynamics of PLLs are not present here. Likewise, the stability issues of a PLL do not happen in DDS designs.

The presence of non-harmonic spurious signals remains the biggest issue in successful application of DDS to amateur equipment. In principle, a 32-bit DDS can cover all HF amateur bands with 0.23 Hz resolution when clocked at 100 MHz. No VCOs, no bandswitching, no tuning — it sounds like a dream! — but we need to apply our RF design skills to get rid of those pesky spurs. The quantization level of modern waveform maps is sufficient to keep the sinusoid quantization noise spurs below -100 dBc. The largest remaining problem is the DAC.

The signal sampling theorem does not predict spurs other than those generated by quantization. That means any additional spurs are a result of the actual output wave form not being exactly what the signal digital quantization requires. Normal DAC specifications of integral nonlinearity (INL) and differential nonlinearity (DNL) turn out to not be very important in the DDS application. More important are the symmetry of output transition times for up and down steps, and having no overshoot on either transition direction. DACs with the latter two properties generally work very well for precision DDS use.

9.6.2 Phase-Locked Loops (PLL)

As mentioned in the introduction, the PLL is a key component of any indirect synthesizer. The sidebar "An Introduction to Phase-Locked Loops" provides an overview of this technology. This section presents a detailed discussion of design and performance topics of PLL synthesizers and the circuits used to construct them.

ARCHITECTURE

The principle of the PLL synthesizer is straightforward. A tunable oscillator is first built to cover the required output frequency range; then the PLL system is constructed around this oscillator to keep it tuned to the desired frequency. This is done by continuously comparing the phase of the oscillator to a stable reference, such as a crystal oscillator, and using the result to steer tuning of the oscillator. If the oscillator frequency is too high, the phase of its output will start to lead that of the reference by an increasing amount. This is detected and is used to decrease the frequency of the oscillator. Too low a frequency causes an increasing phase lag, which is detected and used to increase the frequency of the oscillator. In this way, the oscillator is locked into a fixed-phase relationship with the reference, which means that their frequencies are held exactly equal.

A representative block diagram of a PLL is shown in **Figure 9.40**. Measurement of any error in the output signal phase is made by the *phase detector* (PD). The measured error is supplied to the *loop filter* and *loop amplifier* which work together to tune the *voltage controlled oscillator* (VCO) just enough to make the error go to zero. The phase detector determines the actual frequency and phase of the VCO through the *feedback divider* (N). The phase detector operates at a lower frequency which is a sub-multiple of both the crystal oscillator frequency reference (f_{XO}) and the output frequency (f_{OUT}). This lower frequency is correctly called the PLL *reference frequency* (f_{REF}) because it sets the operating conditions of the PLL.

There is unfortunate history about the term reference frequency. It is often used to refer to both the operating frequency of the phase detector and to the frequency reference applied to the PLL. If the *reference divider* (R) is not present then of course these two frequencies are the same. But in general, the reference divider is present and these frequencies are different. Ambiguity here is widespread and a big problem, even today many decades into the widespread use of PLLs. We must be very careful in the words we choose to use!

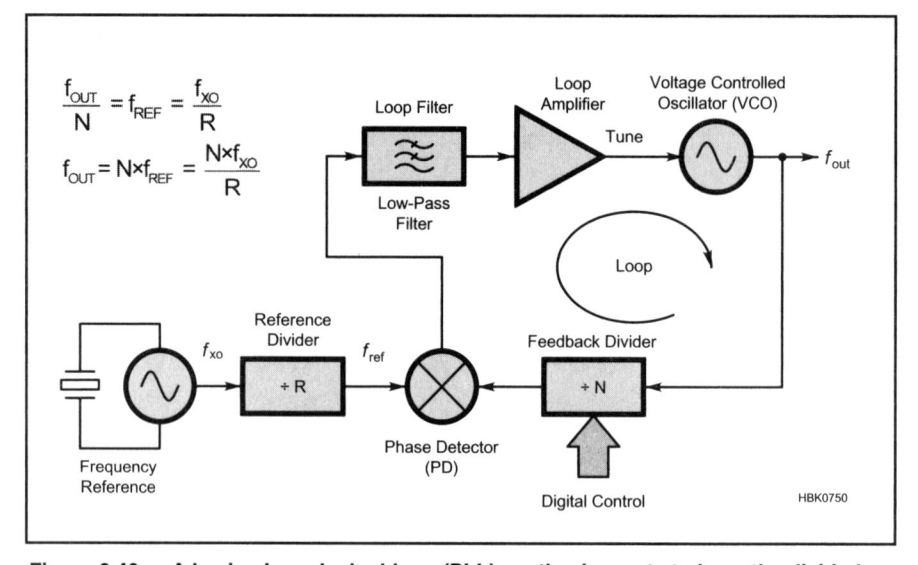

$$\frac{f_{OUT}}{N} = f_{REF} = \frac{f_{XO}}{R}$$

$$f_{OUT} = N \times f_{REF} = \frac{N \times f_{XO}}{R}$$

Figure 9.40 — A basic phase-locked-loop (PLL) synthesizer acts to keep the divided-down signal from its voltage-controlled oscillator (VCO) phase-locked to the divided-down signal from its reference oscillator. Fine tuning steps are therefore possible without the complication of direct synthesis.

FREQUENCY RESOLUTION (STEP SIZE)

Frequency of the output signal can be easily changed by changing the divide ratio of the feedback divider. For example if the reference frequency (at the phase detector!) is 100 kHz and the output frequency is 147.5 MHz, the feedback divider number must be N = 1475. If we changed the value of N to 1474, the frequency at the output of the feedback divider becomes 100.068 kHz. The phase detector notices that the frequency of the VCO is too high, and "tells" the loop filter to reduce the frequency of the VCO until the frequency out of the feedback divider becomes exactly 100.000 kHz. This will happen when the VCO is retuned to a frequency of 147.4 MHz.

By changing the value of N by 1, we have just tuned the frequency synthesizer by its smallest available step. This is called the *frequency resolution* of the synthesizer, or equivalently the synthesizer *step size*. Here we note that this step size is (147.5 − 147.4) = 0.1 MHz. It is no accident that this frequency is exactly equal to the PLL reference frequency f_{REF}. This result is an important reason to avoid all ambiguity in the term "reference frequency." f_{REF} is equal to the synthesizer output frequency step size.

There certainly are applications where we want the step size to be a small number, say 10 Hz. You might guess — correctly — that there are problems in building a PLL synthesizer for a very low f_{REF}. The usual solution is to combine multiple PLLs with some DAS techniques to get around these problems.

DYNAMIC STABILITY AND LOOP BANDWIDTH

Because feedback control is required to transfer the frequency and phase characteristics from the crystal oscillator onto the VCO, all of the stability problems inherent in feedback control apply to PLL design. If the gain and phase responses are not well designed the PLL can oscillate. In this case instead of getting the stability transfer we want, the output is essentially a frequency modulated signal spread across the entire tuning bandwidth of the synthesizer — clearly a very bad thing. How to perform this design is discussed below.

For the moment let us assume that our PLL dynamics are properly designed. One other characteristic of feedback control is now important: how fast can the output frequency be changed from one value to another? This is controlled by the *loop bandwidth* of the PLL. For practical reasons the loop bandwidth should be less than 5% of f_{REF}. Using the example above in which f_{REF} = 100 kHz, the loop bandwidth we design for cannot exceed 5 kHz. To answer our question, we can use the rule of thumb that in a well-designed loop, the settling time should be between 1 and 2 times the reciprocal of the loop bandwidth. For a 5 kHz loop bandwidth the settling time should not exceed 2/5000 = 400 μs. We can begin to see one problem with PLL design if f_{REF} is very small: To get a 1 kHz step size from a PLL synthesizer the maximum loop bandwidth available is 50 Hz. This is impractically small.

This loop bandwidth also influences how we can modulate our PLL synthesizer in an FM transmitter. Imagine now that we apply a very small amount of FM to the reference oscillator f_{XO}. The amount of deviation will be amplified by N/R — but this is true only for low modulating frequencies. If the modulating frequency is increased, the VCO has to change frequency at a higher rate. As the modulating frequency continues to increase, eventually the VCO has to move faster than the available *settling time*. The PLL now acts as a low-pass filter, reducing the available deviation from higher modulating frequencies. The cut-off frequency of this PLL low-pass action is equal to this same loop bandwidth.

PLL COMPONENTS

Let us continue our discussion of phase-locked loop synthesizers by examining the role of each of the component pieces of the system. They are the phase detector, the VCO, the dividers (with possible prescalers), the loop filter, and of course the reference oscillator.

Phase Detectors

Phase detection is the key operation in any PLL. Remembering that we are making a phase locked loop, what we really need is not *absolute* phase measurement but a *relative* phase measurement. We need to know only how the phase of the VCO output signal f_{OUT} is changing with respect to the phase of the crystal reference f_{XO}.

9.30   Chapter 9

An Introduction to Phase-Locked Loops
By Jerry DeHaven, WAØACF

Phase locked loops (PLLs) are used in many applications from tone decoders, to stabilizing the pictures in your television set, to demodulating your local FM station or 2 meter repeater. They are used for recovering weak signals from deep space satellites and digging out noisy instrumentation signals. Perhaps the most common usage for PLLs in Amateur Radio is to combine the variability of an LC oscillator with the long term stability and accuracy of a crystal oscillator in PLL frequency synthesizers. Strictly speaking a PLL is not necessarily a frequency synthesizer and a frequency synthesizer is not necessarily a PLL, although the terms are used interchangeably.

PLL Block Diagram

The block diagram in **Figure 9.41** shows a basic control loop. An example of a control loop is the furnace or air conditioning system in your house or the cruise control in your car. You input a desired output and the control loop causes the system output to change to and remain at that desired output (called a *setpoint*) until you change the setpoint. Control loops are characterized by an input, an output and a feedback mechanism as shown in the simple control loop diagram. The setpoint in this general feedback loop is called the reference.

In the case of a heating system in your house, the reference would be the temperature that you set at the thermostat. The feedback element would be the temperature sensor inside the thermostat. The thermostat performs the comparison function as well. The generator would be the furnace which is turned on or off depending on the output of the comparison stage. In general terms, you can see that the reference input is controlling the output of the generator.

Like other control loops, the design of a PLL is based on feedback, comparison and correction as shown in Figure 9.41. In this section we will focus on the concepts of using a phase locked loop to generate (synthesize) one or more frequencies based on a single reference frequency.

In a typical PLL frequency synthesizer there are six basic functional blocks as shown in **Figure 9.42**. The PLL frequency synthesizer block diagram is only slightly more complicated than the simple control loop diagram, so the similarity should be evident. After a brief description of the function of each block we will describe the operational behavior of a PLL frequency synthesizer.

In Figure 9.42, the general control loop is implemented with a bit more

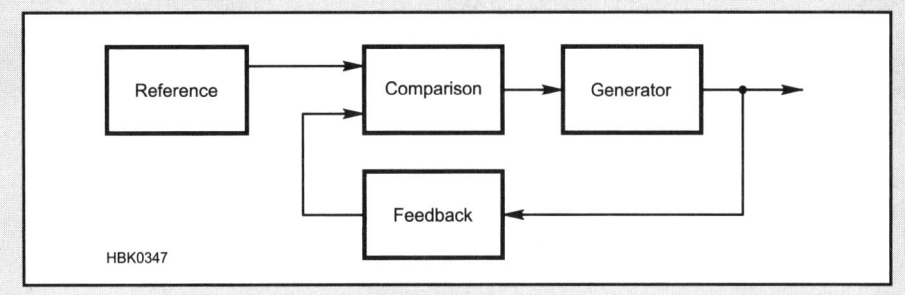

Figure 9.41 — Simple control loop. The Comparison block creates a control signal for the Generator by comparing the output of the Reference and Feedback blocks.

detail. The Reference block is composed of the Reference Oscillator and the Reference Divider. The Comparison block consists of the Phase Detector and Loop Filter. The Generator is replaced by the Voltage-Controlled Oscillator (or VCO) and the Feedback block is replaced by the Frequency Divider. The two signals being compared are both frequencies; the reference frequency and variable frequency signals. The output of the Loop Filter is made up of dc and low frequency ac components that act to change the VCO frequency. The output of the PLL is an integer multiple of the reference frequency (the output of the Reference Divider). It is probably not obvious why, but read on to find out!

The Reference Oscillator — The reference oscillator is usually a crystal oscillator with special attention paid to thermal stability and low mechanical and electronic noise. The main function of the reference oscillator is to generate a stable frequency for the PLL. Let us make a distinction between the reference oscillator frequency and the reference frequency. The output of the reference oscillator is at the crystal frequency, say 5.000 MHz. The choice of the actual crystal frequency depends on the PLL design, the availability of another oscillator in the radio, the avoidance of spurious responses in the receiver, and so on.

The reference frequency is the output of the reference (crystal) oscillator divided by the integer M to a relatively low frequency, say 10 kHz. In this case, 10 kHz is the reference frequency. The reference frequency equals the step size between the PLL output frequencies. In this simple example the crystal frequency can be any frequency that is an integer multiple of 10 kHz and within the operating range of the Reference Divider.

The Phase Detector — There are many types of phase detectors, but for now let us consider just a basic mixer, or a multiplier. The phase detector has two inputs and one output. In its simplest form, the output of the phase detector is a dc voltage proportional to the phase difference between the two inputs. In practice, a phase detector can be built using a diode double-balanced mixer or an active multiplier.

The output of the mixer consists of products at many frequencies both from multiplication and from nonlinearities. In this application, the desired output is the low frequency and dc terms so all of the RF products are terminated in a load and the low frequency and dc output is passed to the PLL loop filter.

When the PLL is locked — meaning that the output frequency is the desired multiple of the reference frequency — the phase detector output is a steady dc voltage somewhere between ground and the PLL power supply voltage. When the PLL is commanded to change to another frequency, the phase detector output will be a complex, time-varying signal that gradually settles in on its final value.

The Loop Filter — The loop filter is a low-pass filter that filters the output of the phase detector. The loop filter can be a simple resistor-capacitor (RC) low-pass filter or an active circuit built with bipolar transistors or operational amplifiers. The cutoff frequency of the low pass filter is on the order of 100 Hz to 10 kHz. Although the frequencies involved are dc and low audio frequencies the design of the loop filter is critical for good reference suppression and low noise performance of the PLL frequency synthesizer.

The output of the loop filter is a dc voltage that "steers" the following stage, the Voltage Controlled Oscillator. The dc value can vary over a substantial portion of the PLL power supply. For example, if the loop filter runs off a 9 V power supply you may expect to see the output voltage range from about 2 V to 7 V depending on the VCO frequency range.

Voltage Controlled Oscillator (VCO) —The VCO is probably the most critical stage in the PLL frequency synthesizer. This stage is the subject of many con-

(continued on page next page)

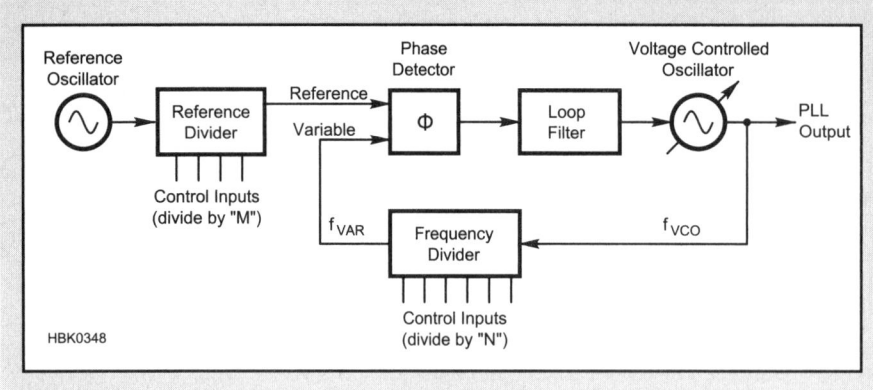

Figure 9.42 — PLL frequency synthesizer block diagram. The PLL is locked when the frequency PLL Output / N is the same as that of the Reference Oscillator / M.

flicting design goals. The VCO must be electrically tunable over the desired frequency range with low noise and very good mechanical stability. Ideally, the output frequency of the VCO will be directly proportional to the input control voltage. A key characteristic is the VCO constant or tuning gain, usually expressed in MHz per volt (MHz/V). The VCO has one input, the dc voltage from the loop filter, and usually two outputs; one for the PLL output, the other driving the feedback stage — the frequency divider.

The Frequency Divider — The VCO frequency divider that acts as the feedback block is a programmable frequency divider or counter. The division ratio N is set either by thumbwheel switches, diode arrays or a microprocessor. The input to the divider is the VCO output frequency. The output of the divider is the VCO output frequency divided by N.

When the PLL is unlocked, such as when the PLL is first turned on, or commanded to change to another frequency, the frequency divider's output frequency will vary in a nonlinear manner until the PLL locks. Under locked conditions, the divider's output frequency (VCO Output / N) is the same as the reference frequency (Reference Oscillator / M).

The function of the frequency divider as the feedback element is easier to understand with an example. Let's assume that the desired PLL output frequency is 14.000 MHz to 14.300 MHz and it should change in steps of 10 kHz (0.010 MHz). A step size of 10 kHz means that the reference frequency must be 10 kHz. There are 31 output frequencies available — one at a time, not simultaneously. (Don't forget to count 14.000 MHz.) Let us arbitrarily choose the reference oscillator as a 5.000 MHz crystal oscillator. To generate the 10 kHz reference frequency, the reference divider must divide by M = 500 = 5.000 MHz / 0.010 MHz. (Use the same units, don't divide MHz by kHz.)

To generate a matching 10 kHz signal from the VCO output frequency, the Frequency Divider (the feedback stage) must be programmable to divide by N = 1400 to 1430 = 14.000 to 14.300 MHz / 0.010 MHz. The reference divisor (M = 500) is fixed, but the Frequency Divider stage needs to be programmable to divide by N = 1400 to 1430 in steps of 1. In this way, the output frequency of the PLL is compared and locked to the stable, crystal-generated value of the reference frequency.

PLL Start-up Operation

Let's visualize the PLL start-up from power on to steady state, visualizing in sequence what each part of the PLL is doing. Some portions of the loop will act quickly, in microseconds; other parts will react more slowly, in tens or hundreds of milliseconds.

The reference oscillator and its dividers will probably start oscillating and stabilize within tens of microseconds. The reference oscillator divider provides the reference frequency to one input of the phase detector.

The VCO will take a bit longer to come up to operation because of extensive power supply filtering with high-value capacitors. The VCO and the programmable dividers will probably reach full output within a few hundred microseconds, although the VCO will not yet be oscillating at the correct frequency.

At this point the phase detector has two inputs but they are at different frequencies. The mixer action of the phase detector produces a beat note at its output. The beat note, which could be tens or hundreds of kHz, is low-pass filtered by the PLL loop filter. That low-pass filter action averages the beat note and applies a complicated time-varying ac/dc voltage to the VCO input.

Now the VCO can begin responding to the control voltage applied to its input. An important design consideration is that the filtered VCO control signal must steer the VCO in the correct direction. If the polarity of the control signal is incorrect, it will steer the VCO away from the right frequency and the loop will never lock. Assuming correct design, the control voltage will begin steering the VCO in such a direction that the VCO divider frequency will now get closer to the reference frequency.

With the phase detector inputs a little bit closer in frequency, the beat note will be lower in frequency and the low pass filtered average of the phase detector output will change to a new level. That new control voltage will continue to steer the VCO in the right direction even closer to the "right" frequency. With each successive imaginary trip around the loop you can visualize that eventually a certain value of VCO control voltage will be reached at which the VCO output frequency, when divided by the frequency divider, will produce zero frequency difference at the inputs to the phase detector. In this state, the loop is locked. Once running, the range over which a PLL can detect and lock on to a signal is its *capture range*.

PLL Steady-state Operation

When the divided-down VCO frequency matches the reference frequency, the PLL will be in its steady-state condition. Since the comparison stage is a phase detector, not just a frequency mixer, the control signal from the loop filter to the VCO will act in such a way that maintains a constant relationship between the phase of the reference frequency and the frequency divider output. For example, the loop might stabilize with a 90° difference between the inputs to the phase detector. As long as the phase difference is constant, the reference frequency and the output of the frequency divider (and by extension, the VCO output) must also be the same.

As the divisor of the frequency divider is changed, the loop's control action will keep the divided-down VCO output phase locked to the reference frequency, but with a phase difference that gets closer to 0 or 180°, depending on which direction the input frequency changes. The range over which the phase difference at the phase detector's input varies between 0° and 180° is the widest range over which the PLL can keep the input and VCO signals locked together. This is called the loop's *lock range*.

If the divisor of the frequency divider is changed even further, the output of the loop filter will actually start to move in the opposite direction and the loop will no longer be able to keep the VCO output locked to the reference frequency and the loop is said to be *out of lock* or *lost lock*.

Loop Bandwidth

Whether you picture a control loop such as the thermostat in your house, the speed control in your car or a PLL frequency synthesizer, they all have "bandwidth," that is, they can only respond at a certain speed. Your house will take several minutes to heat up or cool down, your car will need a few seconds to respond to a hill if you are using the speed control. Likewise, the PLL will need a finite time to stabilize, several milliseconds or more depending on the design.

This brings up the concept of loop bandwidth. The basic idea is that disturbances outside the loop have a low-pass characteristic up to the loop bandwidth, and that disturbances inside the loop have a high-pass characteristic up to the loop bandwidth. The loop bandwidth is determined by the phase detector gain, the loop filter gain and cutoff frequency, the VCO gain and the divider ratio. Loop bandwidth and the phase response of the PLL determine the stability and transient response of the PLL.

PLLs and Noise

Whether the PLL frequency synthesizer output is being used to control a receiver or a transmitter frequency, the spectral cleanliness of the output is important. Since the loop filter output voltage goes directly to the VCO, any noise or spurious frequencies on the loop filter output will modulate the VCO causing FM sidebands. On your transmitted signal, the sidebands are heard as noise by adjacent stations. On receive, they can mix with other signals, resulting in a higher noise floor in the receiver.

A common path for noise to contaminate the loop filter output is via the power supply. This type of noise tends to be audible in your receiver or transmitter audio. Use a well-regulated supply to minimize 120-Hz power supply ripple. Use a dedicated low-power regulator separate from the receiver audio stages so you do not couple audio variations from the speaker amplifier into the loop filter output. If you have a computer / sound card interface, be careful not to share power supplies or route digital signals near the loop filter or VCO.

A more complicated spectral concern is the amount of reference frequency feed-through to the VCO. This type of spurious output is above the audio range (typically a few kHz) so it may not be heard but it will be noticed, for example, in degraded receiver adjacent channel rejection. In the example above, Figure 9.42, the reference frequency is 10 kHz. High amounts of reference feed-through on the VCO control input will result in FM sidebands on the VCO output.

Loop filter design and optimization is a complicated subject with many trade-offs. This subject is covered in detail in the PLL references, but the basic tradeoff is between loop bandwidth (which affects the speed at which a PLL can change frequency and lock) and reference rejection. Improved phase detectors can be used which will minimize the amount of reference feed-through for the loop filter to deal with. Another cause of high reference sidebands is inadequate buffering between the VCO output and the frequency divider stage.

One indication of PLL design difficulty is the spread of the VCO range expressed either in percent or in octaves. It is fairly difficult to make a VCO that can tune over one octave, a two-to-one frequency spread. Typically, the greater the spread of the VCO tuning range, the worse the noise performance gets. The conflicting design requirements can sometimes be conquered by trading off complexity, cost, size, and power consumption.

A common source of noise in the VCO is microphonics. Very small variations in capacitance can frequency modulate the VCO and impose audible modulation on the VCO output. Those microphonic products will be heard on your transmit audio or they will be superimposed on your receiver audio output. Under vibration, an air-wound inductor used in a VCO can move slightly relative to a metal shield for example. A common technique to minimize microphonics is to cover the sensitive parts with wax, epoxy, or a silicone sealer. As with the loop filter use a well-filtered, dedicated regulator for the VCO to minimize modulation by conducted electrical noise.

Types of PLLs

One of the disadvantages of a single loop PLL frequency synthesizer is that the reference frequency determines the step size of the output frequency. For two-way radio and other systems with fixed channel spacing that is generally not a problem. For applications like amateur radio CW and SSB operation, tuning steps smaller than 10 Hz is almost a necessity. Like so many design requirements, there are trade-offs with making the reference frequency smaller and smaller. Most evident is that the loop filter bandwidth would have to keep getting lower and lower to preserve spectral cleanliness and loop stability. Because low frequency filters take longer to settle, a single-loop PLL with a 10 Hz loop bandwidth would take an unacceptably long time to settle to the next frequency.

Creative circuit architectures involving two or more PLLs operating together achieve finer tuning increments with only moderate complexity. Once you understand the basics of a single loop PLL you will be able to learn and understand the operation of a multi-loop PLL.

As usual, there are both analog and digital circuit techniques available to perform phase detection. For frequency synthesizer design the analog techniques are seldom used. Analog phase detectors are used only in receiver and demodulator applications. There are two that sometimes still appear in ham equipment, the multiplier/mixer of **Figure 9.43A** and the sampling phase detector shown in Figure 9.43B.

The mixer is a very low noise device when used as a phase detector, which explains why it is not yet completely gone from synthesizer design. It remains only in PLL designs where f_{REF} is very high, greater than 10-100 MHz. The main reason for this is that a PLL using a mixer for the PD is subject to a phenomenon called *false lock*, where the PLL may act like it is locked even though it really isn't. Detecting and eliminating a false lock condition is much easier to do at higher frequencies. The sampling phase detector is now used only in synthesizers with output frequencies in the high microwave region, typically well above 10 GHz. The gain of this sampling circuit is very low, so it is used only if there is no viable alternative.

The most widely used digital phase detector is the exclusive-OR (XOR) gate shown in Figure 9.43C. If inputs A and B are almost in phase, the output will be low most of the time, and its average filtered value will be close to the logic 0 level. If inputs A and B are almost in phase opposition, the output will be high most of the time, and its average voltage will be close to logic 1. The average voltage is near its mid-value when the inputs are shifted in phase by 90 degrees. In this respect the XOR gate is much like the analog mixer. To achieve this circuit's full output-voltage range, it's important that the reference and VCO signals at its input have a 50% duty cycle.

Phase-Frequency Detector

One problem common to *all* phase detectors is the possibility of false lock. This happens because the output of any phase detector can have an average value of zero even when the frequencies at its inputs are not equal. This is a very serious problem that

---

Oscillators and Synthesizers 9.33

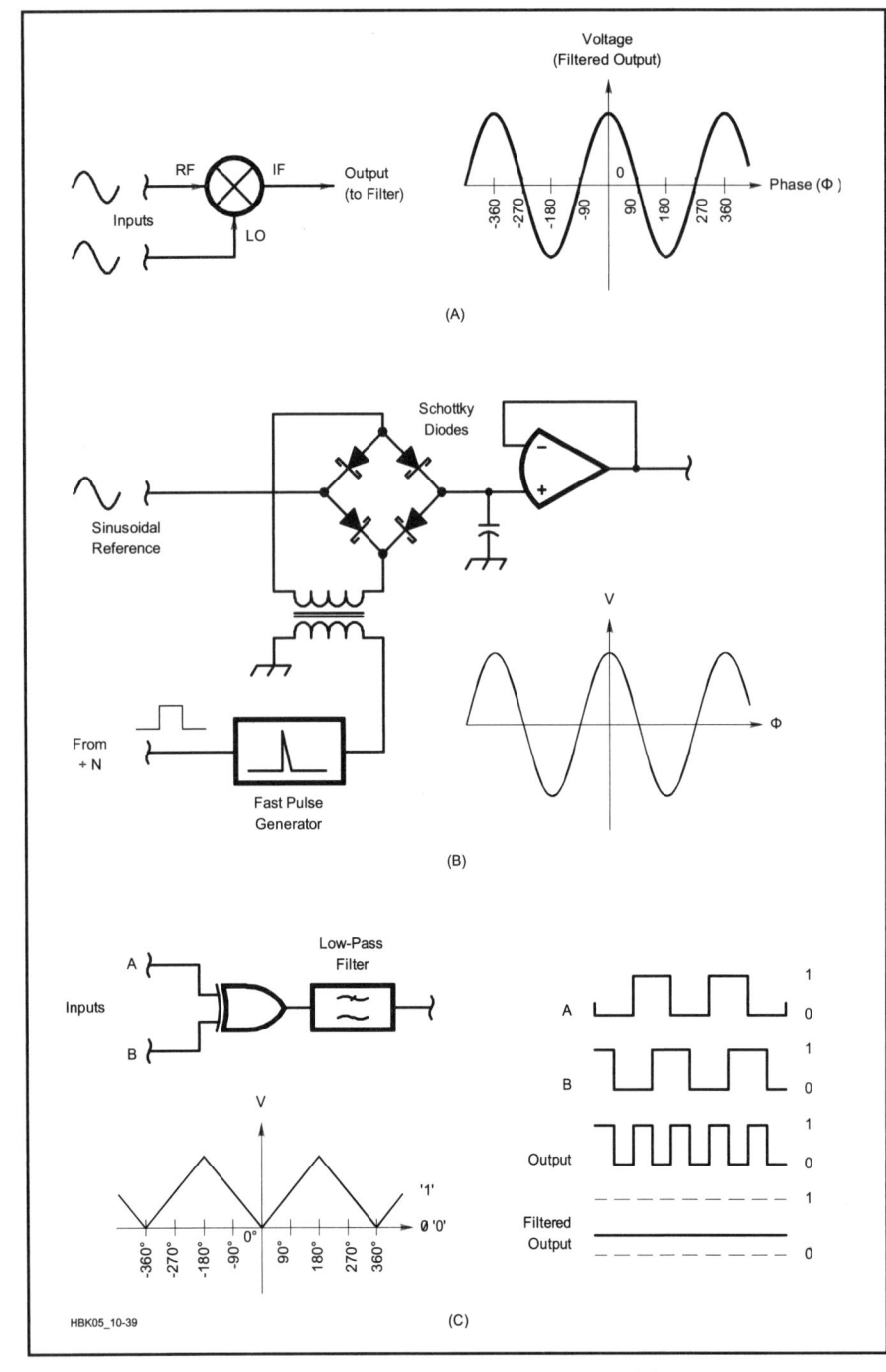

Figure 9.43 — Simple phase detectors: a mixer (A), a sampler (B) and an exclusive-OR gate (C).

requires any PLL using them to have additional circuitry to serve as an acquisition aid. If the PLL tries to settle when the PD inputs are not at the same frequency, this acquisition aid must prod the PLL to keep moving toward the true lock frequency. Such acquisition aids are not needed when a *phase-frequency detector* (PFD) is used.

The benefit of the PFD is that if the input signals are at different frequencies, even if they are at very different frequencies, the output is never zero. The PFD output always produces a dc shift in the direction the PLL needs to move until the lock condition is achieved. No acquisition aids are ever needed. This alone is enough to explain its nearly universal adoption today.

As seen in **Figure 9.44A**, the PFD is a simple digital circuit. This also helps make it attractive to use in this era of CMOS integrated circuits. Other designs for the PFD exist, but they all follow the logic shown in Figure 9.44A. Of particular importance is that the PFD has two outputs.

The PFD operates by measuring the time difference between the rising edges of the reference signal and the divided VCO. The first signal to arrive sets its flip-flop. The second edge to arrive also sets its flip-flop, which immediately causes both flip-flops to be reset, ready for the next set of signal edges. By operating at high speed, the PFD is very sensitive to phase differences between the input signals. The PFD does require an equal number of edges for each signal, so it is not useful when the signals have varying numbers of edges, such in a receiver's demodulator or a synchronizer.

If the VCO frequency is too low only the /U output is active, causing the loop filter to raise the VCO frequency. On the other hand, when the VCO frequency is high only the /D output is active, causing the loop filter to lower the VCO frequency. It is interesting to note that unlike the mixer and XOR phase detectors, which require the inputs to be in phase quadrature, the PFD locks when the input signals are in exact phase alignment.

Being an edge triggered circuit, PFD operation is essentially independent of input signal duty cycle. This eliminates the need for input waveform processing. If the input frequencies are different, the time differences measured by the PFD will be either constantly increasing or decreasing. As a result only one of the PFD output signals will be active, informing the PLL unambiguously which way to correct the controlled source to achieve phase lock.

Charge Pumps

Because the PFD has two outputs and most loop filters have only one input, something is needed to bridge the PFD and the loop filter. The usual technique is the *charge pump*, shown in Figure 9.44B. The charge pump gets its name by allowing current to flow only for the brief interval, here when the /D or /U outputs are active. Current flow in short bursts is equivalent to a finite charge transfer.

Charge pumps come in two configurations, voltage mode and current mode, as shown in **Figure 9.45**. Voltage mode (Figure 9.45A) was the original version, though now current mode (Figure 9.45B) is most widely used with integrated circuit PLLs.

The voltage mode charge pump directly connects voltage sources to the loop filter when the PFD output signals are active. When the PFD output signals are at rest (both high) both voltage sources are disconnected from the loop filter. These voltage spikes transfer charge to the integrator in accordance with the PLL loop filter time constant. One voltage source inputs current to the loop filter and the other removes it.

The current mode charge pump is architecturally similar to the voltage mode charge pump, with voltage sources replaced by cur-

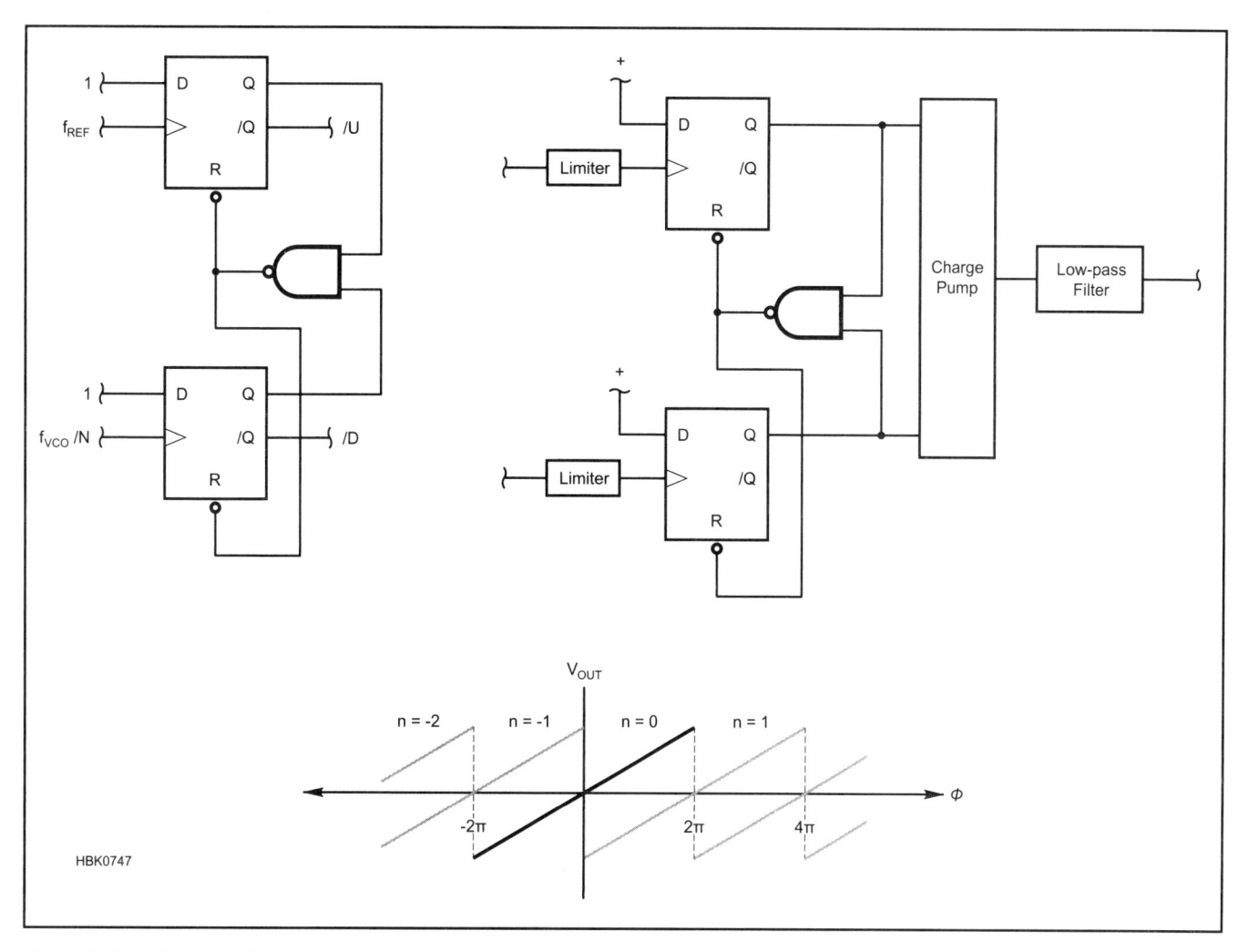

Figure 9.44 — The phase frequency detector (PFD) makes a measurement of the time difference between two rising edges of the input signals.

rent sources. Like the voltage mode charge pump, this circuit disconnects both sources when the PFD output signals are at rest. In this case, current spikes transfer charge to and from the loop filter integrator. This transfer is independent of the loop filter series resistances.

The current mode charge pump has some advantages to the frequency synthesizer designer. Three are particularly significant:

• Pump current flows at a constant value independent of the loop filter voltage. Unless V_H and V_L are both very large compared with any possible loop filter voltage, the amount of charge transfer will vary with different loop filter voltage values.

• During the PFD reset time, both output sources are active. The voltage mode charge pump will attempt to connect both voltage sources to the loop filter during this brief period, which can generate some undesirably large power supply current spikes. During PFD reset, the current mode charge pump loads the power supply with a single current value of I_{QP}. If both current sources are well matched, their currents completely cancel at the loop filter input, effectively disconnecting them that much earlier.

• At low offset frequencies, the loop gain flattens out with a voltage mode charge pump. Loop gain continues to increase with a current mode charge pump, effectively matching active filter performance.

VCO

The design and characteristics of oscillators, including tunable oscillators, is the major topic of this chapter so it will not be repeated here. Of particular importance to PLL design are the tuning characteristic of the VCO and the VCO tuning bandwidth.

The tuning characteristic of an oscillator shows the output frequency versus the tuning voltage, such as the example of **Figure 9.46A**. The slope of this curve is called the VCO's *modulation gain* (K_0) and it is this modulation gain that is most important to PLL design. For wideband VCOs the variation of K_0 can exceed 5:1 from minimum to maximum frequency. The design method below shows how a wide gain variation such as this is handled with a single loop filter design.

It is important to realize that the VCO has no idea that it is controlled by a PLL. While it is oscillating it continues to drift and jitter with time and temperature like any other oscillator. You must characterize these variations to be assured that the tuning capability has sufficient range for the PLL to "find" a tuning voltage value that will retune the VCO to the required frequency, under all circumstances.

The primary VCO characteristic of interest to the synthesizer designer is the tuning gain "constant," K_0. Almost never a constant, K_0 is a local measure of how much the VCO output frequency changes with a change in tuning voltage.

VCO designers go to great lengths to make K_0 an actual constant. This additional effort often increases the VCO design complexity and usually results in a more expensive design. If no linearization effort is undertaken, K_0 can easily vary from 3:1 to 10:1 over the tuning band. This also complicates

Oscillators and Synthesizers 9.35

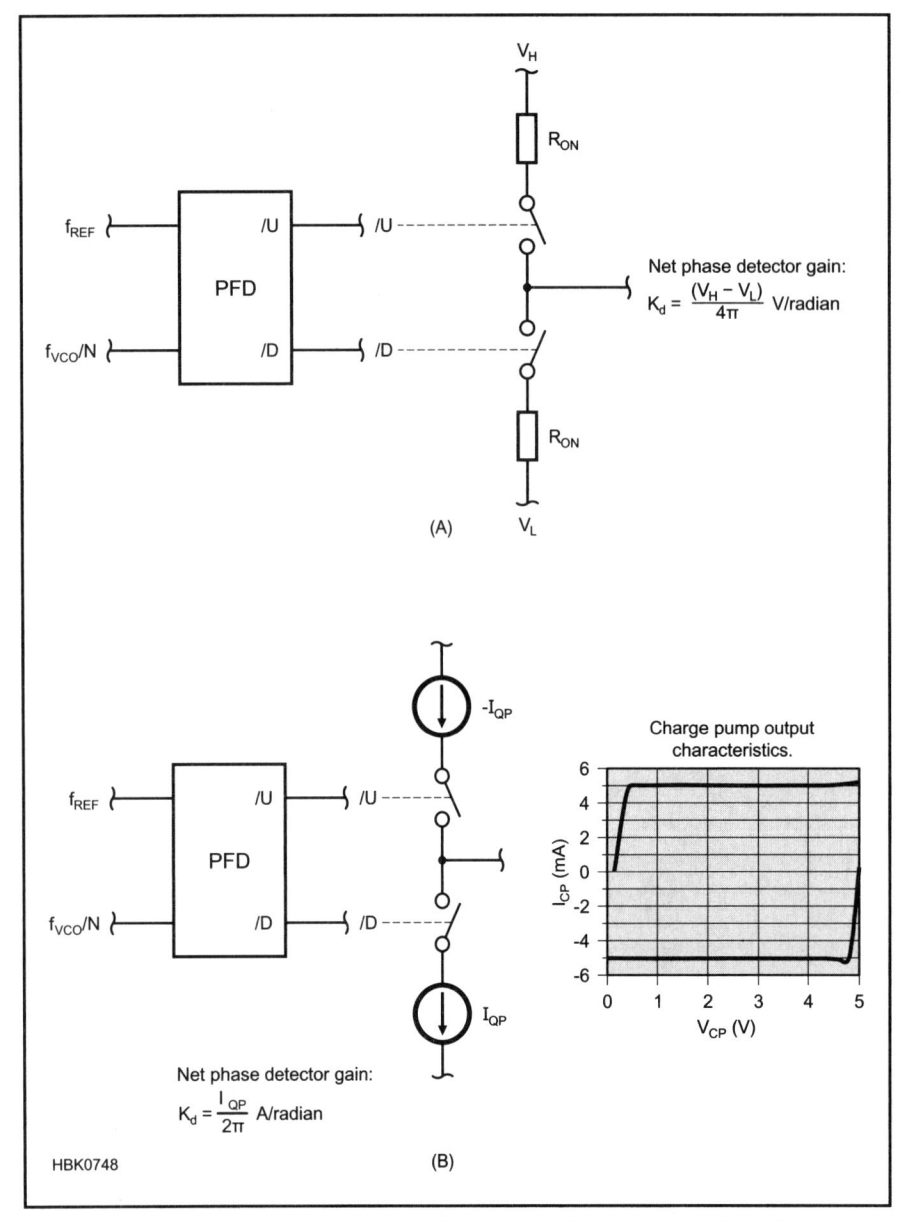

Figure 9.45 — The charge pump delivers short bursts of current to the loop filter under the control of the phase frequency detector (PFD) outputs. A voltage mode charge pump is shown at A and a current mode charge pump at B.

the frequency synthesizer design. Specific applications will dictate where effort needs to be expended: in the VCO design or the PLL design.

All PLL design algorithms assume that there is no delay between when the loop filter presents a tuning change command to the VCO and when the VCO frequency actually changes. This situation is true when the VCO tuning bandwidth is much greater than the PLL loop bandwidth. If the VCO tuning bandwidth is not much greater than the PLL loop bandwidth, there are additional phase shifts that will cause problems with PLL stability. It is usually much easier to narrow the loop bandwidth than to redesign the VCO. If redesigning the VCO is a possibility, reduce the capacitance seen at the tuning input to increase the tuning bandwidth.

The VCO tuning bandwidth is important mainly for PLL designs that have wide loop bandwidths. Measuring the frequency deviation as the modulating frequency varies is best done by looking at the FM sidebands on a spectrum analyzer, as shown in Figure 9.46B. For constant deviation, FM sidebands follow the top profile. When the modulating frequency doubles, the sidebands drop below the profile by 6 dB, and if it triples, by 10 dB. The first FM sideband must exceed all other sidebands by 10 dB for proper VCO *characterization* — the process of determining the VCO's characteristic parameters such as the tuning sensitivity, noise spectrum, dynamic response to changes in the tuning input signal, and so on. (See the Agilent application note "Boosting PLL Design Efficiency" in the References section.) VCO tuning bandwidth is determined by the point at which increasing the modulating frequency deviates from (drops below) the profile shown in Figure 9.46B.

Reference Divider

The reference divider is one of the easiest parts of a PLL to design, though technically is it outside the PLL. The input frequency is well known — it is the crystal reference. The output frequency is also well known, being the phase detector frequency f_{REF}. The ratio of these two frequencies is the required counter divide-by ratio or *modulus*.

When designing PLL synthesizers, f_{REF} is usually specified but f_{XO} is not. This provides some flexibility in design to use easy counter implementations if the resulting f_{XO} is also easy to get. The easiest digital counters to use for any divider are those operating with binary numbers (divide by 2, 4, 8, 16, …, 128, …). For example, if $f_{REF} = 20$ kHz and you choose R = 512 then $f_{XO} = 10.24$ MHz, which is a readily available crystal frequency.

Feedback Divider and Prescalers

The feedback divider is more of a challenge. First and foremost, this divider must work properly with whatever possible frequency it may ever see at its input. Whatever the highest and lowest frequencies the VCO may be, the divider must handle them all.

The feedback divider is almost always programmable so that the output frequency can be changed. Programmable counters are always slower than non-programmable designs, so some speed limitation occurs. Fortunately in this era of tiny CMOS integrated circuits the problems of past years in getting programmable counters to operate at hundreds of MHz are nearly over. Older equipment still has feedback divider designs that are carefully crafted to handle the frequencies at which they must operate.

Fixed Prescaler

When the programmable counter does not have sufficient speed to handle the frequencies required, then the VCO frequency must be divided down ahead of the programmable counter to assure that everything works reliably. This additional divider usually has a fixed binary value so it will go fast enough without using too much power. Called a *prescaler*, as long as the output frequency from the prescaler is always within the operating range of the programmable divider the PLL will be reliable.

Of course, there are consequences: when a prescaler is used, the PLL step size is multiplied by the prescaler divider value. For our $f_{REF} = 100$ kHz, if we adopt a divide-by-16 prescaler then the step size increases by a

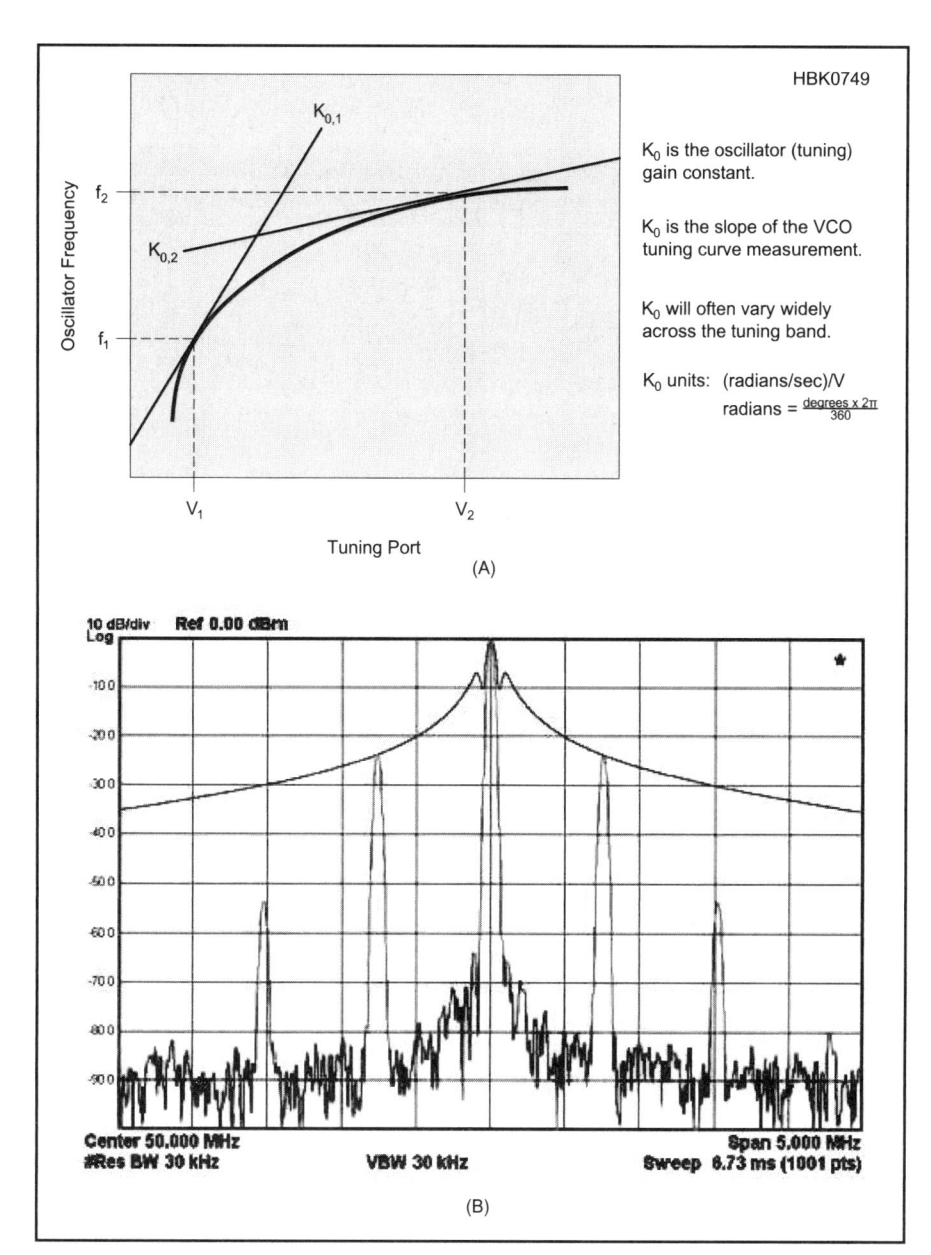

Figure 9.46 — (A) Measurement of the VCO tuning characteristic provides a curve describing frequency versus tuning voltage. The VCO tuning gain at a particular frequency (or tuning voltage) is the slope of this curve at that point. (B) A spectrum analyzer is used to measure frequency deviation of the VCO and the modulating frequency varies. FM sideband peak amplitudes follow the top profile when deviation is constant.

factor of 16 to 1.6 MHz. The direct way to correct for this is to reduce f_{REF} by the same factor of 16, which unfortunately means that the PLL loop bandwidth is also reduced by a factor of 16. Is there a solution with fewer compromises?

Dual-Modulus Prescaling

Yes, there is such a solution. If the prescaler is designed to divide by two values separated by 1, say 16 and 17, or 8 and 9, then we call this a *dual-modulus P/P+1 prescaler*. Using dual-modulus prescaling we can leave f_{REF} unchanged, keeping our step size and loop bandwidth while gaining much higher operating frequency for the feedback divider.

Dual modulus prescaling is a cooperative effort between a high speed prescaler and a much lower speed programmable counter. The result of this cooperation is a programmable counter that operates at a very high input frequency while maintaining unit division resolution. Dual-modulus prescaling works by allocating quotient and remainder values from the division N/P as shown in **Figure 9.47A**.

The improvement comes from viewing the operation of division in a slightly different way. The division ratio (N) of any two integers will always provide a quotient (Q) and a remainder (R). If Q counts of prescaled f_{in}/P are followed by R counts of f_{in} directly, then N = QP + R. One way to build this counter would be to first count a quotient's worth of prescaled input, and then count a remainder's amount of the input frequency directly. This last step is hard because of the high frequency.

A second approach is to add the remainder counts to the prescaled output as follows: If Q – R counts of prescaled f_{in}/P are followed by R counts of prescaled $f_{in}/(P + 1)$, then N = (Q – R) P + R (P + 1). This is the same as N = QP – RP + RP + R = QP + R.

If the remainder counts are distributed among the quotient counts by increasing the prescaler modulus by one from P to P + 1 for the remainder's amount of cycles, then returning the prescaler to its nominal division ratio while the rest of the quotient counts are made, the same result is achieved. This design always operates the programmable counter at a much lower frequency than the input frequency, which is a much more robust design.

The catch, however, is that there have to be enough quotient counts over which to distribute any amount of remainder counts. If you run out of quotient counts before remainder counts the technique falls apart and that particular loop divisor will not be *realizable*. For real dividers, all of the terms — Q, P, and R — must be positive integers, so Q – R must be greater than zero for N = QP+R to be realizable.

The maximum remainder, R_{max} = P – 1. The minimum quotient is equal to R_{max}. So the minimum remainder, R_{min} = 0. That means:

$$N_{min} = Q_{min} P + R_{min} = (P - 1) P + 0 = P^2 - P$$

If the PLL design always requires N to be greater than P2 – P then there are no problems. If N does need to go below P2 – P, then the only solution is to choose a dual modulus prescaler with a smaller value of P. Various values of P and N_{min} are:

P	N_{min}
8	56
16	240
64	4032
128	16256

Dual-modulus prescaling therefore implies a minimum divisor value before continuous divider value coverage is realized. The value of this minimum divisor depends on the base modulus of the prescaler, P, and increases quadratically. Proper choice of prescaler modulus is one of the important decisions the frequency synthesizer designer has to make.

Figure 9.47B shows how a typical dual-modulus prescaler is implemented. Each cycle of the system begins with the last output pulse having loaded the frequency control

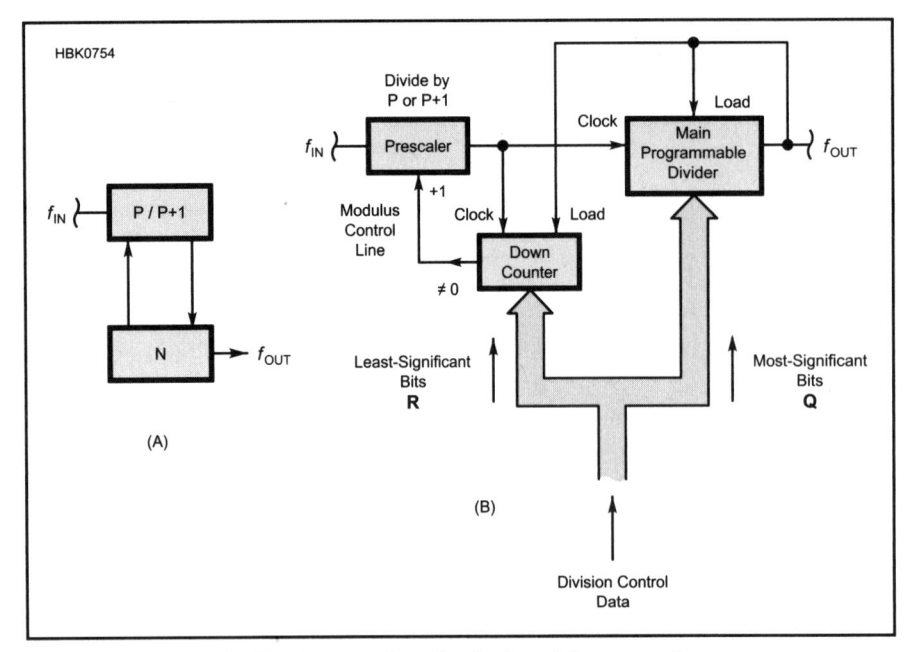

Figure 9.47 — A typical implementation of a dual-modulus prescaler.

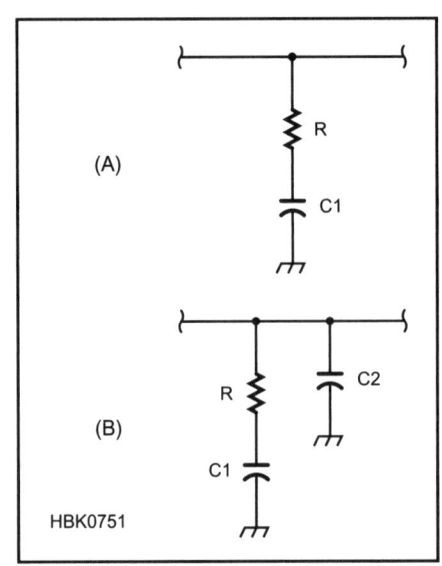

Figure 9.48 — Passive loop filters for current mode charge pump PFD outputs.

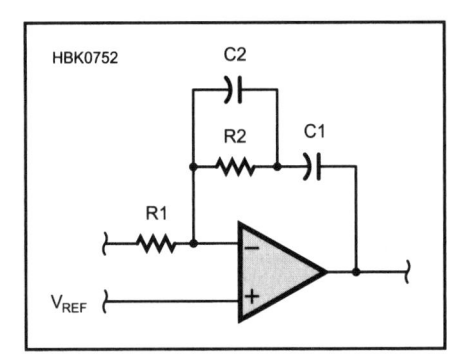

Figure 9.49 — Third-order active loop filter isolates the loop filter output voltage from the charge pump outputs.

word, shown as "Division Control Data," into both the main divider and the prescaler controller. If the division control data's least significant bits (which make up R) loaded into the prescaler controller are not zero, the prescaler is set to divide by P + 1, 1 greater than its normal ratio, P. The main divider counts Q pulses from the prescaler.

Each cycle out of the prescaler then clocks the down counter. Eventually, the down counter reaches zero, and two things happen: The counter is designed to hold (stop counting) at zero (and it will remain held until it is next reloaded) and the prescaler is switched back to its normal ratio, P, until the next reload.

Because the technique is widely used, dual-modulus prescaler ICs are widely used and widely available. Devices for use to a few hundred megahertz are cheap, and devices in the 2.5 GHz region are commonly available. Common prescaler IC division ratio pairs are: 8-9, 10-11, 16-17, 32-33, 64-65 and so on. Many ICs containing programmable dividers are available in versions with and without built-in prescaler controllers.

Loop Filter

When designing PLL synthesizers we usually just have to measure and accept the VCO characteristics of K_0 and the PFD output characteristics. Output frequency range and step size are also not flexible. We pull all of these together into a working and stable synthesizer by proper design of the loop filter.

Loop filter design is usually shrouded in mystery, which has given PLL synthesizer design an aura of a "black art." This is not at all warranted because very reliable design algorithms have been around for decades. Unfortunately these have usually been published in obscure places so they are not well known. The best algorithms are presented below. These methods have served extremely well for over 30 years and should provide you with fast design times and very stable PLL synthesizers. No iteration should be needed.

Loop filters come in active and passive structures. In general the easiest designs use passive (RC) loop filters if the output voltage range from the phase detector (including the PD or PFD and its charge pump) is sufficient to tune the VCO over its required frequency range. If the VCO needs a larger tuning voltage range then an active loop filter structure is necessary.

Passive loop filter circuits for current mode charge pump outputs are shown in **Figure 9.48**. The loop filter time constant is set by the charge pump current and C1, independent of R and of the loop filter output voltage. R provides a phase leading zero for PLL stability. The first-order filter in Figure 9.48A has a minimum parts count and results in loop dynamics that are consistent with the output frequency.

A second-order filter has the undesirable characteristic of allowing step and impulse changes in the input to appear at the output. This results in significant reference sidebands — a bad thing. Figure 9.48B shows a third-order filter in which C2 changes step changes at the input to slower ramps by rolling off the high frequency response of the loop filter. This results in a significant reduction in reference sidebands.

Active loop filters offer more structures that work well and are easier to design, though more complicated to build. When a voltage mode charge pump is being used, an active loop filter is strongly desired since it removes the PLL response variations with different loop filter voltage values.

In **Figure 9.49**, the gain of the op-amp isolates the actual loop filter output voltage from the charge pump output voltage, controlling the loop so that the charge pump output voltage is V_{REF}. Each passive component has the same basic function here as in the passive filter.

The third-order active filter in Figure 9.49 adds an additional pole within the feedback loop and reference frequency sidebands are significantly reduced. Charge pump current impulses now cause ramps instead of steps in the output voltage, but they still cause problems at the amplifier inputs. Good design algorithms include this extra pole as part of the fundamental dynamics — not as a disturbance of conventional second-order dynamics.

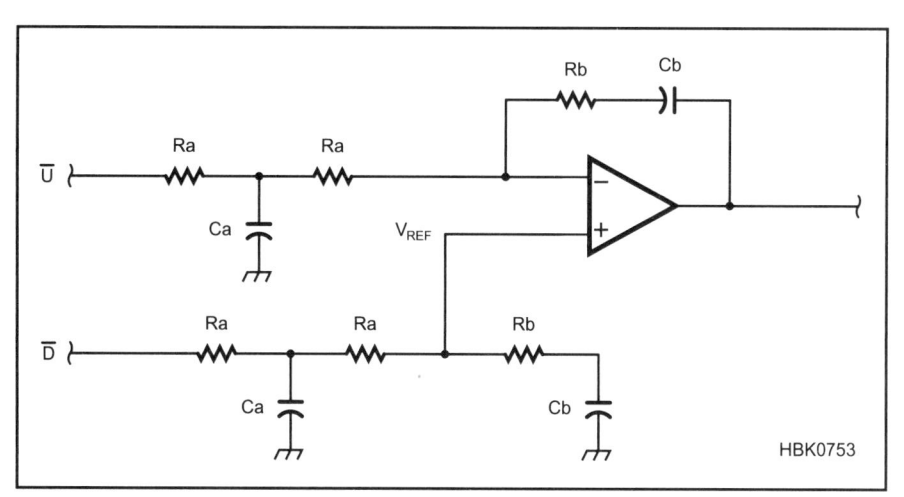

Figure 9.50 — Adding additional low-pass filtering by splitting the input resistor and adding C_A improves loop stability and reduces reference frequency sidebands. This design is well-suited for differential-output PFDs.

$R = f_{XO}/f_{REF}$

$N = f_{OUT}/f_{REF}$

$N_{MIN} = f_{OUT,MIN}/f_{REF}$

$N_{MAX} = f_{OUT,MAX}/f_{REF}$

The best design algorithm for stable PLL design calls for using the geometric mean of the feedback divider value range in the loop filter design. This same idea is used to manage the range of VCO gain values for K_0.

$N_{DESIGN} = \sqrt{N_{MAX} \times N_{MIN}}$

K_0 design target value = $\sqrt{K_{0,MAX} \times K_{0,MIN}}$

PFD gain depends on whether the charge pump is voltage mode or current mode:

(voltage mode) $K_d = (V_H - V_L)/4p$

(current mode) $K_d = I_{QP}/2\pi$

For all of the active loop filter structures use the voltage mode value.

Everything is now ready. Place these design values into the appropriate design equations for the selected loop filter structure. For a passive loop filter use **Figure 9.51**. If you are using an active loop filter the appropriate equations are in **Figure 9.52** or **Figure 9.53**. The resistor and capacitor values from these calculations are not critical. Choose values within 30% of what you calculate and the design will be fine. Truly!

Following any loop filter design, it is always a good idea to check the results by directly calculating the filter time constants from the components chosen. Compare these

Though the design in **Figure 9.50** adds another capacitor by splitting the input resistor, the added complexity is usually well worth it. Charge pumps put out very narrow, spiky signals that are usually of sufficient amplitude and duration to temporarily drive the op-amp input into saturation. If this happens the PLL response becomes non-linear and problems often arise.

The improvement of this design is to low-pass filter the charge pump pulses before being applied to the op-amp input. The op-amp far prefers the resulting ramps, remaining linear and therefore predictable in behavior. This results in further reduction in reference frequency sidebands and is easily adapted to difference-output digital PDs, including the PFD.

Design equations for these loop filters will be presented after the remaining PLL component blocks are discussed.

Reference Oscillator

Any PLL is simply a stability transfer mechanism, so the behavior of the reference oscillator will not be improved on. The fractional frequency error of the overall frequency synthesizer will match that of the reference oscillator. For example if the output of the PLL synthesizer changes 1 kHz at an output frequency of 1 GHz [1000/1,000,000,000 = 1:1 million, or 1 part per million (ppm)] then the reference has changed that same fractional amount. If the crystal reference is 10 MHz (a very common frequency for crystal references) its frequency drift was (1 ppm) × (10 MHz) = 10 Hz. This is not much frequency drift, but it is significant to the ultimate output frequency.

9.6.3 PLL Loop Filter Design

When it is time to design a PLL synthesizer, it is best to do it in steps. Begin with knowing how the hardware you are using behaves:
- VCO tuning characteristics, K_0
- PFD characteristic (with charge pump), K_s
- Crystal reference frequency, f_{XO}

Next, list the requirements of your application
- Output frequency range, f_{OUT}
- Output frequency step size, f_{STEP}

Now you are ready to choose the two main design parameters:
- Loop bandwidth — this should not exceed 5% of $f_{REF} = f_{STEP}$.
- Phase Margin — this sets the overall stability of the PLL and can be any value between 50 and 60 degrees. A good value is 54 degrees.

With all of this information in place it is time to calculate the values for the two frequency dividers and the loop filter components. Begin with the divider values:

$\tau_2 = \dfrac{\sec\phi_0 - \tan\phi_0}{\omega_0} = \dfrac{1 - \sin\phi_0}{\omega_0 \cdot \cos\phi_0}$

$\tau_1 = \dfrac{1}{\omega_0^2 \cdot \tau_2}$

$C_T = \dfrac{K_0 \cdot K_d}{N \cdot \omega_0^2} \cdot \sqrt{\dfrac{1+(\omega_0 \cdot \tau_1)^2}{1+(\omega_0 \cdot \tau_2)^2}} = \dfrac{K_0 \cdot K_d}{N} \cdot \dfrac{\tau_1}{\omega_0}$

$\tau_1 = RC_1$

$\tau_2 = R\left(\dfrac{C_1 \times C_2}{C_1 + C_2}\right)$

$C_T = C_1 + C_2$

$C_2 = \dfrac{\tau_2}{\tau_1} \times C_T$

$C_1 = C_T - C_2$

$R = \dfrac{\tau_1}{C_1}$

ϕ_0 = phase margin (°)
ω_0 = open loop gain crossover frequency (radians/sec)

Figure 9.51 — Design equations for passive loop filters.

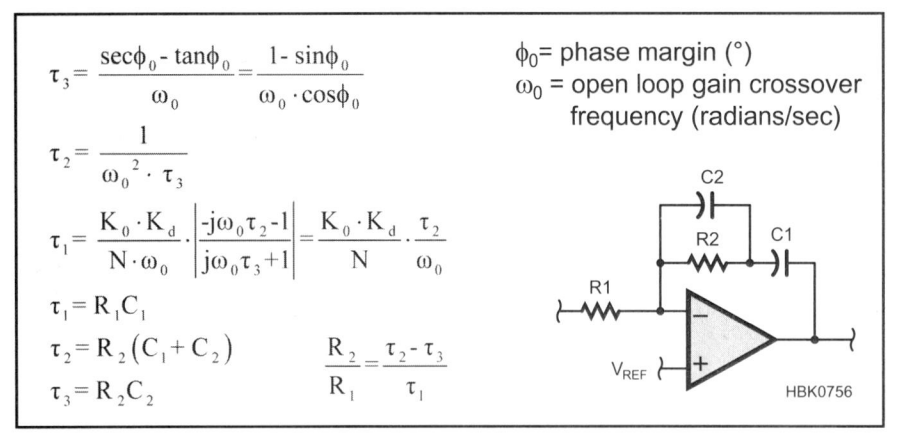

Figure 9.52 — Design equations for third-order active loop filters

$$\tau_3 = \frac{\sec\phi_0 - \tan\phi_0}{\omega_0} = \frac{1-\sin\phi_0}{\omega_0 \cdot \cos\phi_0}$$

$$\tau_2 = \frac{1}{\omega_0^2 \cdot \tau_3}$$

$$\tau_1 = \frac{K_0 \cdot K_d}{N \cdot \omega_0} \cdot \left|\frac{-j\omega_0\tau_2 - 1}{j\omega_0\tau_3 + 1}\right| = \frac{K_0 \cdot K_d}{N} \cdot \frac{\tau_2}{\omega_0}$$

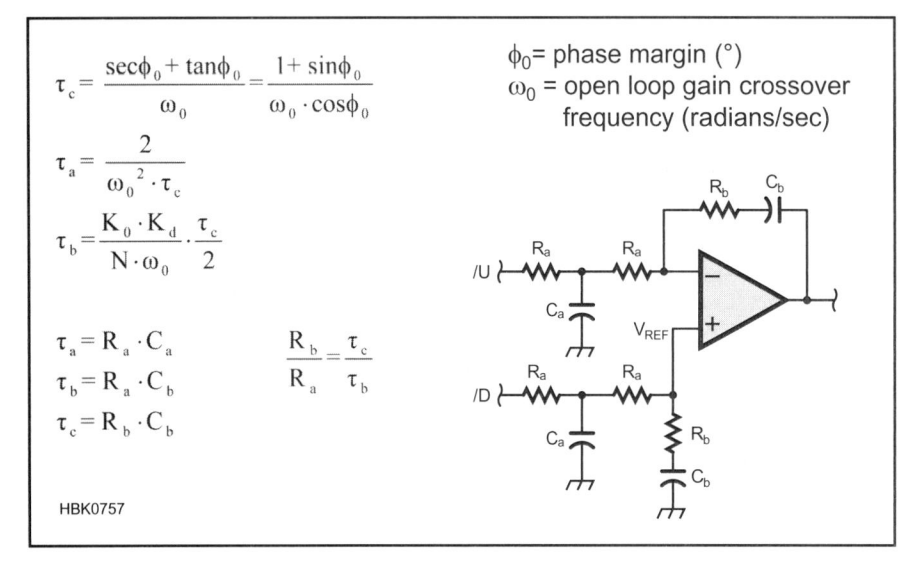

$$\tau_1 = R_1 C_1$$
$$\tau_2 = R_2(C_1 + C_2)$$
$$\tau_3 = R_2 C_2$$
$$\frac{R_2}{R_1} = \frac{\tau_2 - \tau_3}{\tau_1}$$

ϕ_0 = phase margin (°)
ω_0 = open loop gain crossover frequency (radians/sec)

Figure 9.53 — Design equations for differential-input active loop filters

$$\tau_c = \frac{\sec\phi_0 + \tan\phi_0}{\omega_0} = \frac{1+\sin\phi_0}{\omega_0 \cdot \cos\phi_0}$$

$$\tau_a = \frac{2}{\omega_0^2 \cdot \tau_c}$$

$$\tau_b = \frac{K_0 \cdot K_d}{N \cdot \omega_0} \cdot \frac{\tau_c}{2}$$

$$\tau_a = R_a \cdot C_a$$
$$\tau_b = R_a \cdot C_b$$
$$\tau_c = R_b \cdot C_b$$
$$\frac{R_b}{R_a} = \frac{\tau_c}{\tau_b}$$

ϕ_0 = phase margin (°)
ω_0 = open loop gain crossover frequency (radians/sec)

time constants with those derived theoretically. If they match within 10-20%, there should be no problem with loop stability.

The passive third order loop filter design equations of Figure 9.51 look very similar to those of its active filter counterpart. The major difference is that this procedure yields two time constants instead of three, and a term equaling the sum of both filter capacitances.

Unlike the active filter form, there are no arbitrary component choices with the passive filter. From the time constants and the total capacitance, all three loop filter components are uniquely determined.

Since the concepts of natural frequency and damping no longer apply (by definition) in a third-order filter, the more general stability concepts of gain crossover and phase margin are used. A value of 50-60 degrees is usually used for the design phase margin.

The equations for Figure 9.52 and Figure 9.53 include the rolloff pole within the loop dynamics, rather than treating it as a loop perturbation. This allows a greater amount of high frequency rolloff to be achieved as it "kicks in" at a much lower frequency than perturbation techniques would allow.

A usual design strategy is to choose the resistors first to achieve the design ratio. This may provide several possible resistor pairs. Calculate the resulting capacitor values for each resistor pair possibility, and choose the set that provides the closest realizable values.

9.6.4 Fractional-N Synthesizers

The simplest frequency synthesizer is the single PLL with a programmable counter as a frequency divider in the feedback path. It can now all be integrated onto a single semiconductor device, though better performance may be available with some sections done discretely. These synthesizers are well suited to channelized radios where the channel spacing is fairly wide. Millions of them can be found in VHF/UHF radios, cell phones, TV tuners and so on. However, apart from VHF/UHF FM transceivers, most Amateur Radio operation requires fine-resolution synthesizers to simulate the look and feel of a free-tuning VFO.

To this point in the chapter, the PLL synthesizer designs have assumed that the feedback divider operates as a single programmed integer value. This design is referred to as an *integer-N PLL*. These PLLs have an unavoidable trade-off of the step size versus every other performance parameter. Making a fine resolution loop by using a very high value of N forces a very low phase detector frequency and low open loop gain. This leads to extremely slow settling, bad phase noise, and poor suppression of spurs.

Multiple PLL loops can be used to give fine resolution without invoking other performance limitations other than cost, size and power consumption. PLL/DDS hybrids can do the same job and save some cost, size, and power consumption. The holy grail is a fine resolution synthesizer with a clean output, small size, low cost and low power consumption but that has not yet been attained. There is another thread of development particularly suited to high levels of integration, although it, too, has limitations. It is called *fractional-N* or *frac-N synthesis*.

THE ORIGIN

A single PLL would have fine resolution, if the divide-by-N stage in its feedback path weren't constrained to divide only by integers. The dividers are implemented as digital counters, counting cycles of the VCO frequency. Counting in anything smaller than integers would need something running faster than the VCO to act as an interpolator. To get steps much finer than the increments given by integers would need an interpolator running at a very large multiple of the VCO frequency, which is impractical.

One solution is to vary the value of N so that the average value of N, taken over a long enough time period, gives the required resolution. This can be done, and it doesn't need impossibly fast logic. For example, consider the 2 meter synthesizer discussed in the previous section on Frequency Resolution: if N is varied in a repeating pattern of 8 divisions by 1474 followed by 2 divisions by 1475, the average is $(8 \times 1474 + 2 \times 1475)/10 = 1474.2$. A PLL operating with this type of variable division in the feedback loop is called a *fractional-N PLL*.

The resulting problem with such a PLL is that it is never exactly on the desired frequency. It switches between too-high and too-low, even though its average might be just right. We could view this as wide deviation FM, where the modulation is a rectangular pulse of controlled mark-space ratio. Such a spectrum will have high noise levels and huge sidebands which are quite undesirable.

Nevertheless, designers of such systems

have tried to slow the loops so that they could not follow the switching and sat on the average frequency. The problem with obtaining sufficient filtering of the sidebands was that the loop became too slow and all the problems mentioned above appeared, making the solution worse than single-N synthesis.

ANALOG PHASE INTERPOLATION

Variable-N synthesizers were not used in Amateur Radio transceivers, but it was common in test equipment from the 1980s and 1990s without the tuning and noise requirements of radio equipment. This type of synthesizer is described in the context of using or repairing test equipment. (For example, see the HP 3335A Synthesizer service manual's Theory of Operation section.)

PLLs can be phase modulated, quite easily, within their bandwidths by summing in a modulating voltage after the phase detector. The phase effect of the switching of the N number can easily be calculated. A digital system can be made to do this, but an extra analog system must be added to interpolate the results of the digital system. This hybrid circuit can compute a phase modulation waveform which cancels all the effects of the frequency switching, but leaves the average intact. Cancellation is never perfect but manufactured synthesizers were developed that suppressed the unwanted sidebands to around −80 dBc (decibels with respect to the carrier level).

This is a complex system and can be hard to understand. Sometimes a second way of viewing it may be easier: If a ramp waveform is added after a phase detector in a PLL, the loop will be phase modulated with a ramping phase, or in other words, a frequency offset. If the ramp slope is controlled, any amount of resolution is possible. The problem is that ramps cannot go on forever, and the phase detector will soon hit the end of its range. The solution is to increase the N number of the divider just once at the same time that the ramp is reset by a cycle's worth of phase. A sampling system is used to disguise the disturbance of the transient phase shift and ramping resumes.

This is a large system needing careful, individual, trimming to get the analog circuitry to mesh seamlessly with the digital circuitry. The digital parts are integrated into a custom IC, but the discrete analog parts require a lot of board space. The performance was acceptable for mid-range equipment at the time. State of the art equipment used it as part of a hybrid structure as the least significant of three PLLs. The resulting fractional-N loop gave the system much finer resolution than the previous generation of 5-loop hybrids.

NOISE SHAPING

These early schemes switched the PLL divider between N and N+1 in simple, repetitive patterns, so the inevitable sideband energy was concentrated into large, obvious components. One variant of the filtering scheme used "rate multiplier" logic devices to control N to N+1 switching and reduced the amplitude of the unwanted components by spreading them out. While still not clean enough to be generally useful, other technologies were maturing: oversampling 1-bit DACs for audio, pseudo-random binary sequences for simulating telephone traffic for error rate testing, and the addition of dither to ADCs.

An integer-N PLL is a sort of DAC. You put data in as modulation, and the result is a change of frequency rather than voltage. The principles of an extreme oversampling DAC can be applied to it just as much as to the output buffer of a 1-bit DAC in a CD player. These systems scramble the sideband energy and make it much less conspicuous — a good thing. The sideband energy is also spread over a wider frequency range than the bandwidth of the loop filter. This is even better because it means more energy can be filtered out. Further, the scrambling process can be engineered to control the spectrum of the noise-like sidebands, called *noise shaping*, pushing most of the noise energy high enough in frequency that filtering can do a good job. The logic systems which shape the noise are higher-order delta modulators. They take up a lot of logic elements on an IC, but can be highly integrated and are therefore small, cheap, and have low power consumption. As a result, the noise-shaped fractional-N synthesizer looks like a simple PLL with a large amount of logic processing the data fed to its programmable divider.

Delta-modulators above the second order are inherently unstable. Audio converters have various proprietary schemes to stabilize them, and these little subtleties are carefully guarded secrets. The MASH (Multi-stAge noise Shaping) DAC arrangement adds together a series of low-order modulators, rather than trying to make one very high-order modulator. Fixing the stability problem requires that the output doesn't just jump between two states, N and N+1 in PLL terms, but it dances over a limited range.

LIMITATIONS

With the division factor varying in a pseudo-random way, the operating point of the phase detector is also varying over a wide range and the phase detector needs to have a similarly wide operating range. Since filtering only happens *after* the phase detector and large amounts of noise at high offset frequencies are present, the phase detector must be very linear.

The noise-shaping scrambler keeps the close-in frequency range clean, but any nonlinearity in the phase detector allows the strong high frequency noise components to intermodulate. Intermodulation creates products at close-in frequencies, spoiling the noise performance of the close-in range.

This limits how clean the noise-shaping synthesizer can be made. The best examples are useful for many purposes but still aren't good enough for a high-grade HF receiver or any system requiring superior adjacent channel rejection. For such uses, they are combined with a high performance integer-N PLL in a hybrid structure similar to how the original fractional-N loop was used.

AVAILABILITY

Fractional-N synthesizers have been available in chip form for several years. Analog Devices, National Semiconductor, and other manufacturers have offered families of PLL ICs for a long time, and their ranges include devices with all the noise shaping logic on-board. Some even have GHz VCOs on-board as well, with dividers down to more mundane frequency ranges.

These synthesizers have become an RF design building block. The RFMD RFFC2071, for example has a pair of medium-level active mixers with an entire synthesizer all on one die. Handheld transceivers that also receive 0.5 to 999.999999 MHz are likely to be made with these parts. If you are choosing one of these devices, look carefully at the noise sideband performance: the higher frequency version of the RF2071 IC has noise sidebands a few dB lower than the lower frequency version.

WHAT NEXT?

The RF semiconductor industry is currently focused on mass-market applications such as mobile phones, WiFi and so on. The existing fractional-N synthesis parts are adequate for these systems and while there may be progressive increases in the scale of integration, there is little need for higher performance.

Development of fractional-N systems is within the range of the interested amateur, either by using the general-purpose parts on the market, or by developing their own using programmable logic array devices. A moderately-sized FPGA contains enough logic for a number of fractional-N synthesizers. For example, see the July/August 1998 *QEX* article by Ulrich L. Rohde, N1UL "A High-Performance Fractional-N Synthesizer" which describes a design covered by US patent 6509800 (2001).

A figure of merit for a fractional-N system is the maximum frequency at which the phase detector can operate. Higher frequencies allow the scrambled noise to be spread over a greater frequency range, making it easier to filter. The obvious approach is to develop faster and faster logic, but there is an alternative: Several fractional-N dividers with several separate phase detectors may have their outputs combined. The phases of the outputs from the separate dividers may be offset from each other by programming registers differently in each scrambler, and the reference signals to the phase detectors may be offset to match.

Several phase detectors can thus act sequentially over each detector's cycling period, making a system with an effective phase detector frequency several times that of a single phase detector. The effective phase detector frequency can even be higher than the output frequency. A further elaboration would be to seed the pseudo-random noise generators in each divider differently. In this way the noise components from each divider will not correlate, though the tuning components correcting the VCO frequency will correlate. This means that the tuning components add more strongly, as voltages, while the noise components add more weakly as power. Each doubling of the number of dividers has the potential for a 3 dB improvement in noise performance of the system. This multiple divider arrangement is currently covered by a patent, but individuals are free to read them, to experiment and to perhaps find a better way. Patents eventually expire and their technology enters the public domain. Each increase in the density of programmable logic makes it easier.

9.6.5 A PLL Design Example

As our design example, let us consider a synthesized local oscillator chain for a 10 GHz transverter. **Figure 9.54** is a simplified block diagram of this 10 GHz converter. This example is chosen because it is a departure from the traditional multi-stage multiply-and-filter approach. It permits realization of the oscillator system with two simple loops and minimal RF hardware. It is also representative of what is achievable with current hardware, and can fit in a space of 2 to 3 square inches. This example is intended to be a vehicle to explore the loop design aspects and is not offered as a "construction project." The multiple design details required are beyond the scope of this chapter.

Two synthesized frequencies, 10 GHz and 340 MHz, are required. Since 10.368 GHz is one of the popular X-band traffic frequencies, we initially mix this with the 10 GHz LO to produce an IF of 368 MHz. The 368 MHz IF signal is subsequently mixed with the 340 MHz LO to produce a 28 MHz final IF, which can be fed into the 10 meter input of any amateur transceiver. We focus our attention on the design of the 10 GHz synthesizer only. Once this is done, the same principles are applied to the 340 MHz section. Our goal is to design a low-noise LO system (by adopting minimum division ratios) with a loop reference oscillator that is an integer multiple of 10 MHz. Using this technique allows the entire system to be locked at a later time to a 10 MHz standard for precise frequency control.

For the microwave synthesizer we consider using a line of microwave integrated circuits made by Hittite Microwave in gallium-arsenide (GaAs) material. These devices include a selection of prescalers operating to 12 GHz, a 5-bit counter that operates to 2.2 GHz and a phase/frequency detector that operates up to 1.3 GHz. If we use a crystal reference frequency f_{XO} of 100 MHz, and also apply that as f_{REF} into the PFD (therefore R = 1), then the feedback divider number needs to be N = 10,000/100 = 100. One way to realize this in hardware is to represent 100 = 4 × 25, starting with a divide-by-4 prescaler and finishing with the 5 bit counter programmed to divide by 25. The divide-by-4 prescaler output at lock will be 2500 MHz, which is too high for the 2200 MHz limited programmable counter. We need a design change.

The obvious solution is to select a divide-by-8 prescaler, providing a 1250 MHz output from the 10 GHz input. We cannot program the counter to half of 25, so we need to leave it programmed at 25. This makes the output from the feedback divider at 10,000/(8×25) = 50 MHz. We need to set R = 2.

Before even thinking about designing the loop filter, we need to know the VCO gain, VCO noise performance, divider noise performance, phase detector gain, phase detector noise performance and finally reference noise performance. For the 10 GHz VCO, we are always looking for parts that are easily available, useable and economical, so salvaging a dielectric resonator from a Ku band LNB is promising (see "SHF Super Regenerative Reception by Andre Jamet, F9HX, in Jan-Feb 2002 *QEX*). These high-Q oscillators can be fitted with a varactor and tuned over a limited range with good results. The tuning sensitivity of our dielectric resonator VCO is about 10 MHz per volt and the phase noise at 10 kHz offset is –87 dBc/Hz, and –107 dBc/Hz at 100 kHz.

The phase detector and divider information is available from the device data sheets. The HMC363 divide-by-8 operates up to 12 GHz and has a programmable charge pump that sets the phase detector gain K_d. It is usually good to keep this gain high, so we choose to use a 2 mA charge pump current, giving K_d = 0.32 mA/radian. The data sheet also says that this PFD has an output noise floor of –153 dBc/Hz measured at 100 kHz offset. The HMC394 programmable divider operated up to 2.2 GHz with the same output noise floor. The HMC984 PFD operated up to 350 MHz with a noise figure of merit (FOM) of –231 dBc/Hz/Hz-f_{REF}, so with f_{REF} = 50 MHz the PFD output noise floor is –231 + 10 log (50,000,000) = –154 dBc/Hz. Assuming the R divider is implemented in CMOS, the output noise floor from it is –163 + 10 log (50,000,000/125000) = – 137 dBc/Hz. This noise is much higher than the noise from the GaAs dividers, so it is actually better here to use a GaAs divide-by-2 for the R counter instead of using CMOS.

The logic noise floor for the entire PLL is the sum of the individual noises from each divider and the PFD. The result is –147 dBc/Hz. This is determined at the PFD. To calcu-

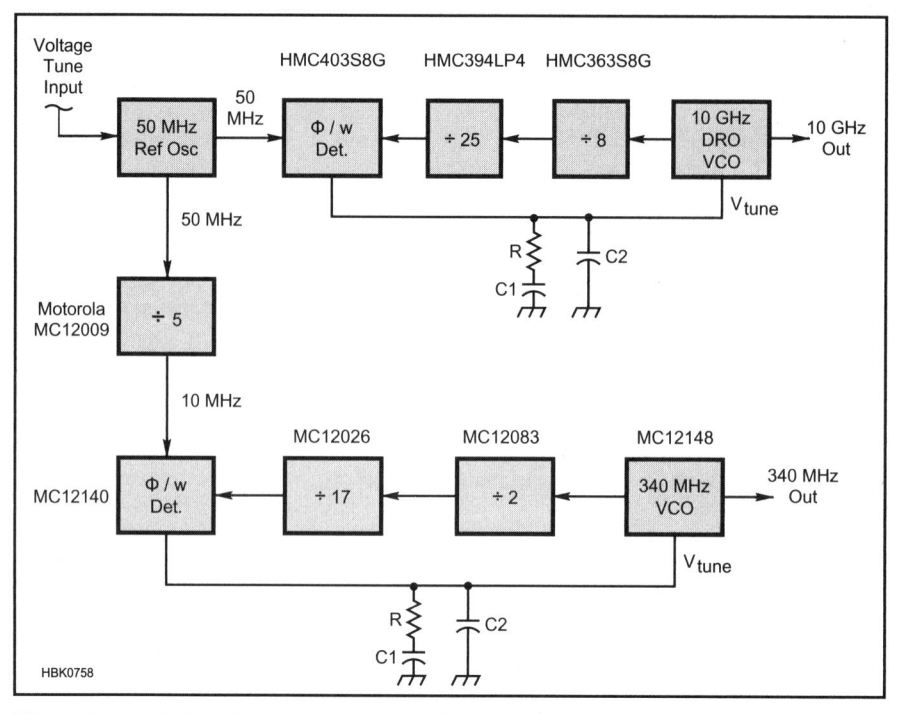

Figure 9.54 — A simplified block diagram of a PLL local oscillator for a 10 GHz converter.

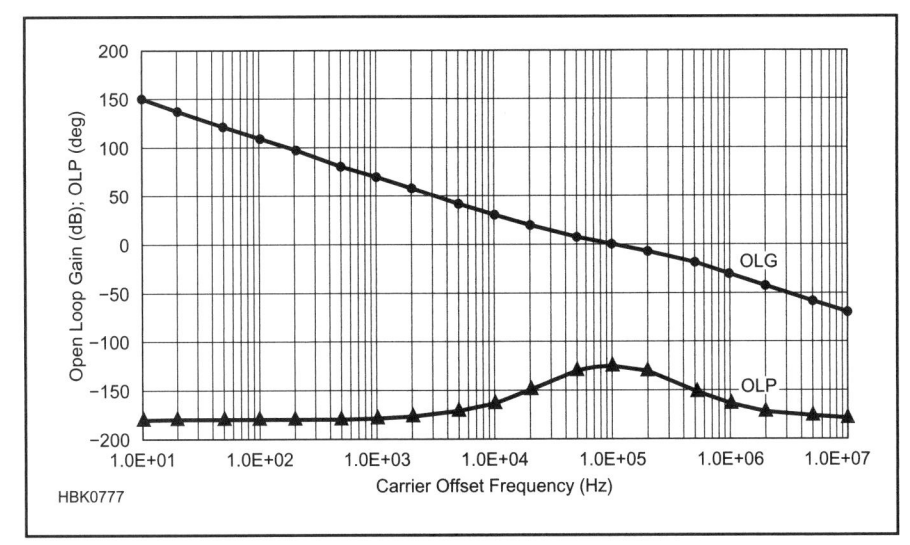

Figure 9.55 — Comparisons of the theoretical and actual PLL dynamics show extremely good correspondence.

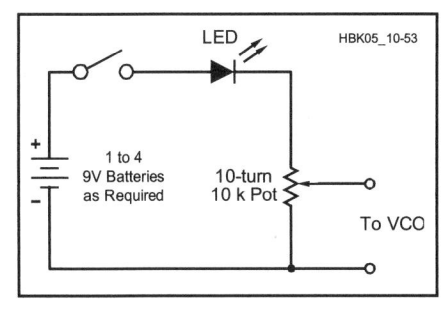

Figure 9.56 — Clean, variable dc voltage source used to measure VCO gain in a PLL design.

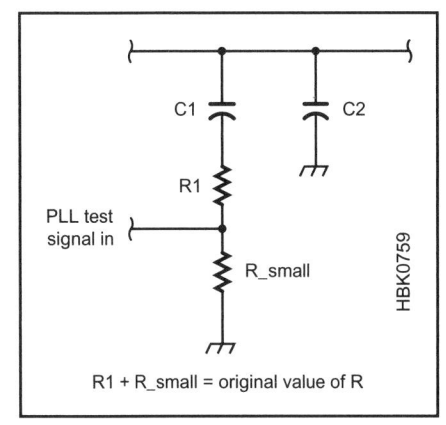

Figure 9.57 — A simple testing structure for PLL dynamics.

late how this noise will measure at the PLL output we need to add 20LogN = 46 dB. Thus the output noise floor due to PLL logic devices is –101 dBc/Hz. This is close to the VCO phase noise at an offset of 100 kHz, so minimum noise design suggests that we select 100 kHz as our loop bandwidth.

An alternative is to eliminate the R counter and directly use a 50 MHz reference. An excellent choice for a low noise reference is the one described by John Stephensen on page 13 in Nov/Dec 1999 QEX. The noise performance of this VCXO is in the order of –160 dBc/Hz at 10 kHz offset at the fundamental frequency. Translating this to the output frequency means adding 20 log N, for a result of –114 dBc/Hz. Eliminating the R counter also lowers the logic noise floor to –104 dBc/Hz at the output. The translated reference oscillator noise is 10 dB below the noise floor from the logic devices, so the logic noise floor dominates.

Using this information we can now design the loop filter. Assuming that the VCO tuning voltage is between 0.5 and 4.5V we can directly use the charge pump included in this PFD and therefore select the passive third order loop filter from Figure 9.48. We use the equations in Figure 9.46 and calculate loop filter component values of R = 6977 ohms, C1 = 724 pF, and C2 = 80 pF. We therefore select 6.8k, 820 pF, and 82 pF for these component values respectively. The Bode plot of the theoretical and actual PLL dynamics is shown in **Figure 9.55**. It is nearly impossible to tell them apart!

If the VCO requires higher tuning voltages, you can insert a non-inverting op-amp gain stage between the output of this loop filter and the VCO. Choose a low input current op-amp to minimize leakage from the loop filter capacitors. Be careful — the gain of this amplifier stage changes the effective VCO gain that the loop experiences. When designing the loop filter components the "design" VCO gain must be replaced by the product of the actual VCO gain and the amplifier gain. It is also essential to assure that the 1 dB bandwidth of the voltage amplifier greatly exceeds the loop bandwidth so that it does not degrade the PLL phase response and hence loop stability.

9.6.6 PLL Measurements and Troubleshooting

VCO GAIN

One of the first things we need to measure when designing a PLL is the VCO gain. The tools needed include a voltmeter, some kind of frequency measuring device like a receiver or frequency counter and a clean source of variable dc voltage. The circuit in **Figure 9.56** containing one or more 9 V batteries and a 10-turn, 10 kΩ pot does nicely. One simply varies the voltage some amount and then records the associated frequency of the VCO. The gain of the VCO is then the change in f divided by the change in voltage (Hz / V).

LOOP BANDWIDTH

Measuring the actual bandwidth of the PLL usually means measuring the entire gain and phase responses of the PLL. There is a much easier way that needs only a square-wave generator and an oscilloscope. This method uses the PLL testing structure of **Figure 9.57** developed by Glenn Ewart that injects a low-value square wave into the loop at a low impedance point so that impulse response can be observed directly. The test signal is also ground-referenced and is independent of the loop locking voltage.

Start by swapping the series RC components in the loop filter so the resistor is connected to ground and the capacitor attaches to the VCO tuning line. Then split the resistor into two resistances that together add up to the total resistance needed by the filter. The bottom resistor connected to ground is very small — 50 Ω is a nice choice when the total resistor value is much greater than 50 Ω. The top resistor is temporarily replaced by a potentiometer that can make up the desired remaining resistance. Across the bottom resistor we connect the square-wave generator and set it to a small amplitude (100 or 200 mV is common) at a frequency a few percent of the loop bandwidth, and operate the PLL. Looking at the VCO tuning line with an oscilloscope we see the impulse response of the PLL.

Now adjust the potentiometer way off-value to the low side. The impulse response will now show ringing. The frequency of this ringing is a good approximation of the PLL loop bandwidth.

SETTLING TIME

Having measured the loop bandwidth, readjust the potentiometer back to its nominal value. The impulse response should look *much* cleaner! It is tempting to look at the settling time of the impulse response and say that this is the settling time of the PLL. This unfortunately is not quite true.

The PLL is not fully settled until capacitor

C1 is fully charged. This usually takes slightly longer than what the impulse response itself shows. Move the scope probe to the "ground" side of C1 and measure when this voltage reaches zero. This means there is no more current flowing through the filter resistors and the capacitor is fully charged.

TROUBLESHOOTING PLLS

Here are some frequently encountered problems in PLL designs:

• The outputs of the phase detector are inverted. This results in the loop slewing to one or the other power supply rails. The loop cannot possibly lock in this condition. Solution: Swap the phase detector outputs.

• The loop cannot comply with the tuning voltage requirements of the VCO. If the loop runs out of tuning voltage before the required voltage for a lock is reached, the locked condition is not possible. Solution: Re-center the VCO at a lower tuning voltage or increase the rail voltages on the op amp.

The loop is very noisy and the tuning voltage is very low. The tuning voltage on the varactor diodes in the VCO should not drop below the RF voltage swing in the oscillator tank circuit. Solution: Adjust the VCO so that the loop locks with a higher tuning voltage.

9.6.7 Commercial Synthesizer ICs

In this section, we explore using commercially available synthesizer chips and the role of DDS in more recent hybrid architectures. The following is not intended to be project oriented, but rather is designed to expose the reader to additional concepts that cannot be fully explored here. The reader, being made aware of these ideas, may wish to examine them in detail using references at the end of this chapter.

Many synthesizer chips have been introduced in recent years for cellular and Wi-Fi applications. One might reasonably ask if any of these devices are well suited to amateur applications. The short answer is — probably not. Applications using these chips strive for a minimum of external components, so they are usually not flexible in design. These chips conform to a strict applications profile in which the communication link is typically sending a few tens of megabits for distances of less than 3 miles (5 km). Some are even designated as "low noise" with respect to other chips of their ilk, but these noise levels are not really low with respect to most amateur requirements. The phase noise, while adequate for their intended application, is not good enough for many HF, VHF and UHF applications without additional measures being taken.

Despite all this, they do have some interesting properties and capabilities that can be exploited with additional design. Some properties that can be exploited are programmable charge pump current, a rich set of division options for creating multiple-loop synthesizers and typically low power consumption.

One of the easiest ways to improve the overall performance is to follow one of these chips with additional frequency division. Consider the following example: One of these chips could be used as a 500 to 550 MHz synthesizer, followed with two cascaded decade dividers for a total division of 100. This division would reduce the phase noise profile by 40 dB, making a reasonably quiet synthesizer for the 5 to 5.5 MHz range. The step size would also be reduced by a factor of 100, making the spacing required in the 500 to 550 MHz range equal to 1 kHz for a step size of 10 Hz at 5 MHz. This would make a good local oscillator for a simple traditional radio that covers 80 and 20 meters using both mixer products against a 9 MHz SSB generator.

There are also other techniques that can prove helpful. Decoupling the VCO from the chip will permit one to avoid much of the "on chip" noise that VCOs are susceptible to at the expense of some more complexity. If the VCO is implemented externally, there is an opportunity to design it with increased operating Q, thereby improving the overall phase noise performance. An external VCO also opens other opportunities.

As mentioned earlier, these chips are designed for operation at a V_{CC} of 3 to 5 V, typically using an internal charge pump to generate the operating voltage. This limits the tuning voltage swing to V_{CC}. One must be able to fit the entire tuning range voltage and the ac voltage excursion in the VCO tank circuit within the V_{CC} range. As mentioned at the end of the earlier section Improving VCO Noise Performance, this problem can be overcome with the addition of voltage gain in an external operational amplifier, running at a higher voltage. This allows the signal-to-noise ratio of the oscillator to be improved by increasing the tank voltage swing and still having adequate voltage range to perform the tuning function. There are certainly more examples of how the performance of these devices could be improved for amateur applications.

USE OF DDS IN HYBRID SYNTHESIZERS

One method of incorporating DDS within a hybrid synthesizer system is to have the DDS supply the least significant digits of the frequency resolution and to sum that DDS output into a conventional divide-by-N loop that supplies the most significant digits. If desired, this signal can be passed through a sufficiently narrow filter to further attenuate any DDS spurious signals. This method is employed in a number of commercial signal generators as well as some of the more modern transceivers.

Another widely used approach is to take advantage of the extremely small step size available from DDS devices and use this as the reference frequency into a conventional PLL synthesizer. The loop bandwidth of the PLL acts now as a tracking band-pass filter to reduce the DDS output spurious signals. Most modern FM broadcast transmitters use the latter technique when broadcasting CD-ROM and other digitized material.

9.6.8 Analog Frequency Synthesis

Even though the term 'analog' seems old-fashioned in the present age, these techniques still have wide use in modern radio designs. They are briefly covered here.

FREQUENCY MULTIPLICATION

It is useful to view frequency multiplication as an increased slope of phase with time, as shown in **Figure 9.58A**. For harmonic

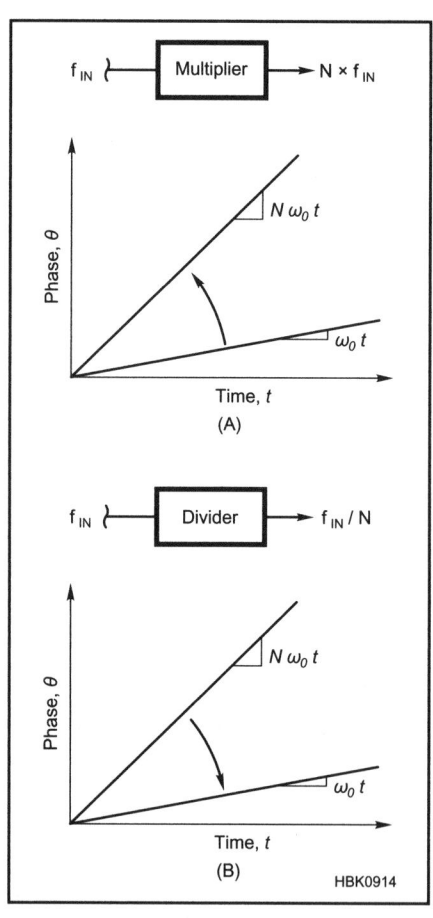

Figure 9.58 — Frequency multiplication and division: A — multiplication increases the rate that signal phase changes with time. This is often an integer (harmonic generation), but it can be non-integer in some applications (PLL); B — frequency division decreases the rate that signal phase changes with time. This is nearly always an integer.

generation, this multiplication factor is an integer. More complicated frequency multipliers, such as phase-locked loops, can readily provide frequency multiplication with non-integer values.

FREQUENCY DIVISION

In the same way, frequency division is usefully viewed as a reduction in the slope of output signal phase with time. This is shown in Figure 9.58B. Frequency multiplication and division are inverse process of each other.

Noise behavior of frequency multipliers and dividers also has an inverse relationship. Phase noise encounters the same processes that the signal phase encounters. **Figure 9.59** shows that the phase noise out of any frequency multiplier is at least $+20\log_{10}(N)$ higher than the phase noise on the input signal. This is unavoidable. It is also a big problem when the multiplication factor N is large. We are motivated to have input signals into a phase multiplier with very low phase noise.

Fortunately the output phase noise of a frequency divider is lower than that on its input signal. This effect is also symmetrical. This effect is often used in very low noise synthesizer design.

FREQUENCY MIXING

Mixers implement frequency addition and subtraction. The problem is that mixers do both at the same time, which means that some filtering is required to intentionally select whether the sum frequency, or the difference frequency, proceeds along to later stages of the radio. In **Figure 9.60** a particular example of frequency mixing is presented. Here the output is a close ratio of the input frequency, such a 2/3 or 3/2 when N = 2, or when N = 8 the outputs can be 7/8 or 9/8.

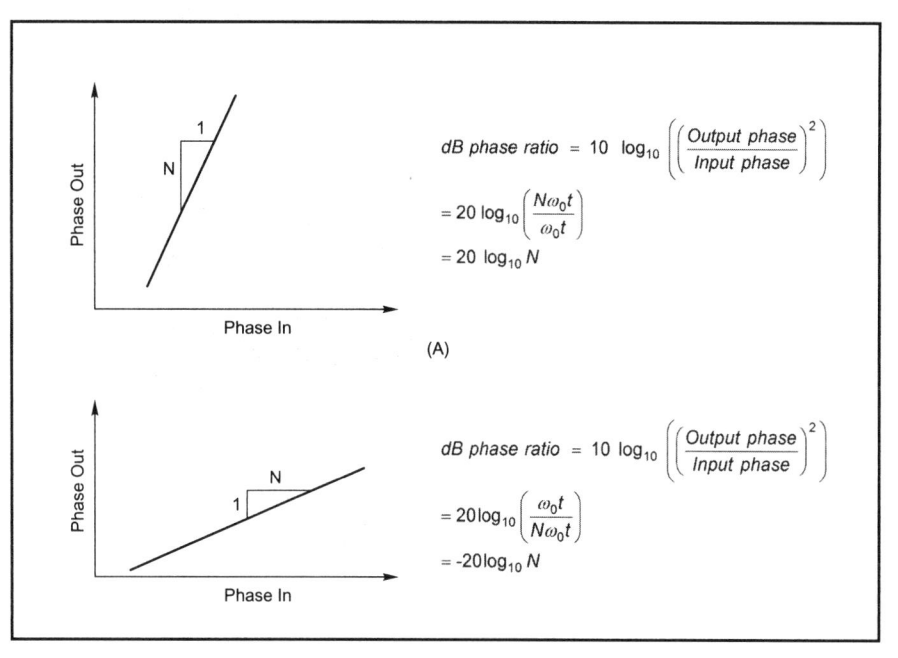

Figure 9.59 — Noise behavior of frequency multipliers and dividers: A — frequency multiplication increases output phase noise; B — frequency multiplication decreases output phase noise.

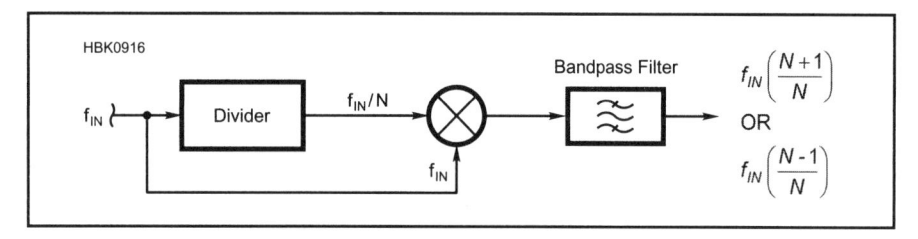

Figure 9.60 — One example of frequency mixing, where a signal is mixed with a divided version of itself to get a frequency ratio.

9.7 Phase Noise

(This section deals specifically with phase noise generated by oscillators. A more general discussion of noise can be found in the **RF Techniques** chapter.) No oscillator output signal is perfect. Viewing an oscillator as a filtered-noise generator is relatively modern. The older approach is to think of an oscillator making a pure sine wave with an added, unwanted noise signal. These are just different ways of visualizing the same thing. They are equally valid views which are used interchangeably, depending on which best makes some point clear.

For example, it is instructive to use the pure-sine-wave-plus-noise view to see relationships between AM (amplitude) noise and PM (phase) noise processes, shown in **Figure 9.61**. Adding Gaussian noise to a pure sine wave is usefully modeled using phasors as shown in Figure 9.61B. This generates both AM due to noise, and PM due to noise as shown in Figure 9.61C. Passing this signal through a limiter process, such as an amplifier in compression or through a switching mixer, leaves only the phase noise depicted in Figure 9.61D. Because it is so easy to remove AM noise but not phase noise, there is essentially no discussion about oscillator AM noise. Phase noise is the critical problem.

Phase modulation (PM) and frequency modulation (FM) are closely related. (See the **Modulation** chapter for a detailed description of each.) Phase is the integral of frequency, so phase modulation resembles frequency modulation, where the frequency deviation increases with increasing modulating frequency. Thus, there is no need to talk of "frequency noise" because phase noise already covers it.

A thorough analysis of oscillator phase noise is beyond the scope of this section. However, a detailed, state-of-the-art treatment by Ulrich Rohde, N1UL, of free-running oscillators using nonlinear harmonic-balance techniques and the sources of noise in the Colpitts oscillator circuit is presented in the downloadable supplemental information accompanying this book.

Because of the dynamic range required to measure phase noise, it is one of the most difficult measurements in all of electrical engineering. The section on ARRL Lab Measurement of Transmitter Phase Noise illustrates the lengths to which one must go to obtain repeatable, reliable measurements. An additional article on measuring receiver

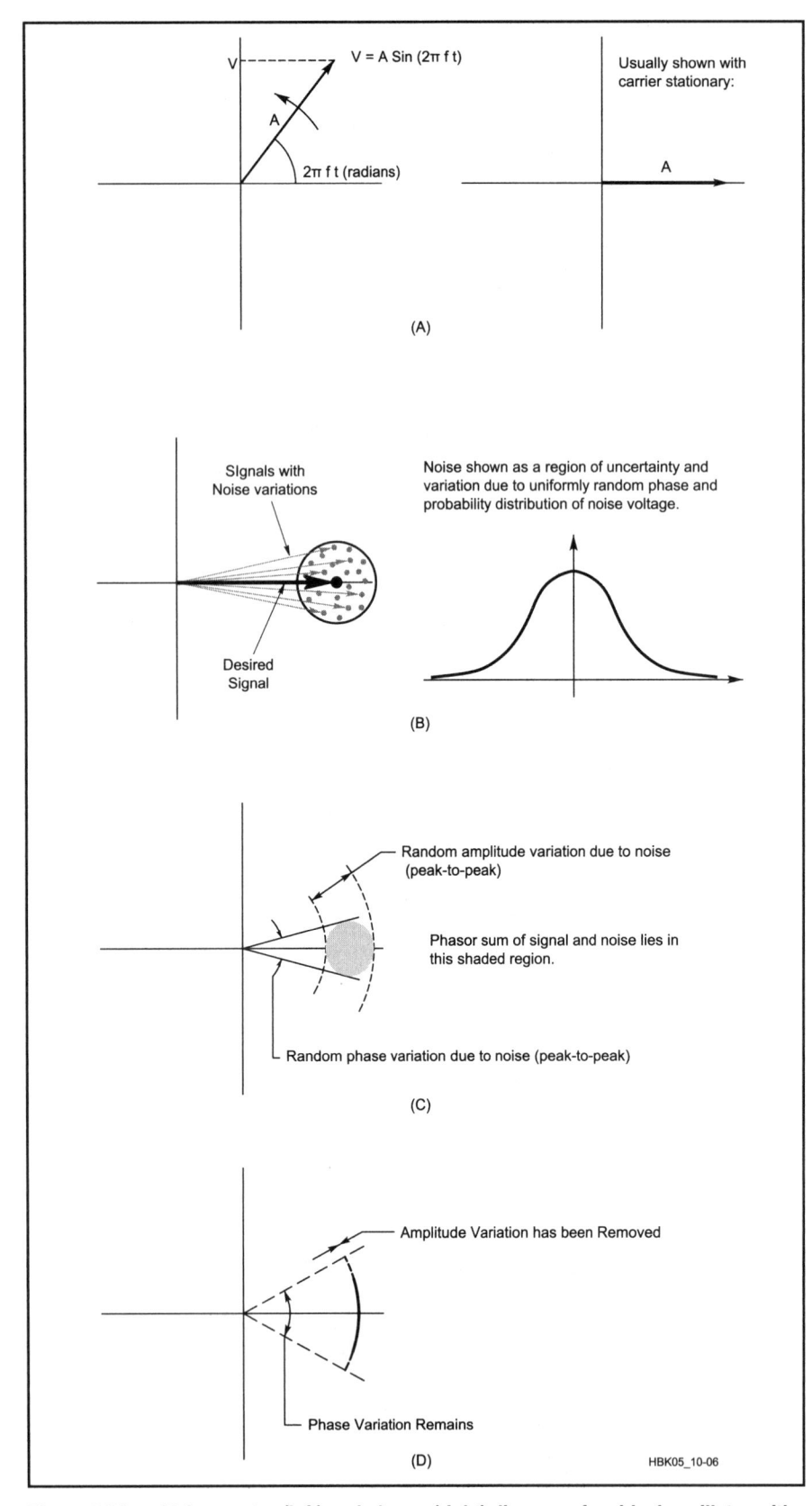

Figure 9.61 — At A, a vector (left) and phasor (right) diagram of an ideal oscillator with no noise. Added noise creates a region of uncertainty in the phasor's length and position (B). AM noise varies the phasor's length; PM noise varies the phasor's relative angular position (C). Limiting a signal that contains both AM and PM noise strips off the AM and leaves the PM (D).

phase noise is included with this book's downloadable supplemental material.

9.7.1 Effects of Phase Noise

Phase noise becomes a problem when it is more noticeable than other limitations. It degrades all signals, but whether it is important or not depends on the application. For voice signals it sounds like background "hiss" in headphones or speakers. It also limits the dynamic range of receivers with closely separated signals, or receiving signals with widely different input powers.

Phase noise became a significant problem for amateurs when the use of frequency synthesizers supplanted conventional LC VFOs in amateur equipment. For reasons discussed in the Frequency Synthesizers section of this chapter, it is a major task to develop a synthesizer that tunes in steps fine enough for use with SSB and CW operation while competing with the phase-noise performance of a reasonable-quality LC VFO. Many synthesizers fall far short of this target. Along with the problems with frequency synthesizers, phase noise always gets worse at higher frequencies.

General-coverage, up-converting receiver architectures require local oscillators to operate at higher and higher frequencies, aggravating phase noise performance. As SDR techniques expand, however, phase noise performance is improving on both receive and transmit.

9.7.2 Reciprocal Mixing

All mixers are symmetrical, meaning that the output IF signal depends on the characteristics of both input signals: the local oscillator (LO) and the desired signal. A change to either signal shows up at the IF, where there is no way of knowing if the signal characteristics seen are from the input signal itself, or from the LO. We usually assume that the LO is very pure so only input signal modulations show up at the IF.

When there is phase noise on the LO signal, the situation changes. Noise on the LO transfers to *all* input signals at the mixer output as if it was originally present on each input signal and the LO was perfectly clean — the IF circuits can't tell the difference. This process is called *reciprocal mixing*, where noise on the LO appears as noise on the desired output signal. This is a serious limitation on a receiver's weak-signal ability.

How reciprocal mixing of LO phase noise can limit receiver dynamic range is shown in **Figure 9.62**. One possible scenario of band activity is shown as the set of input signals in Figure 9.62A. Figure 9.62B shows the phase noise profile for the LO of this receiver. Reciprocal mixing is illustrated in Figure 9.62C, showing that the LO phase noise is

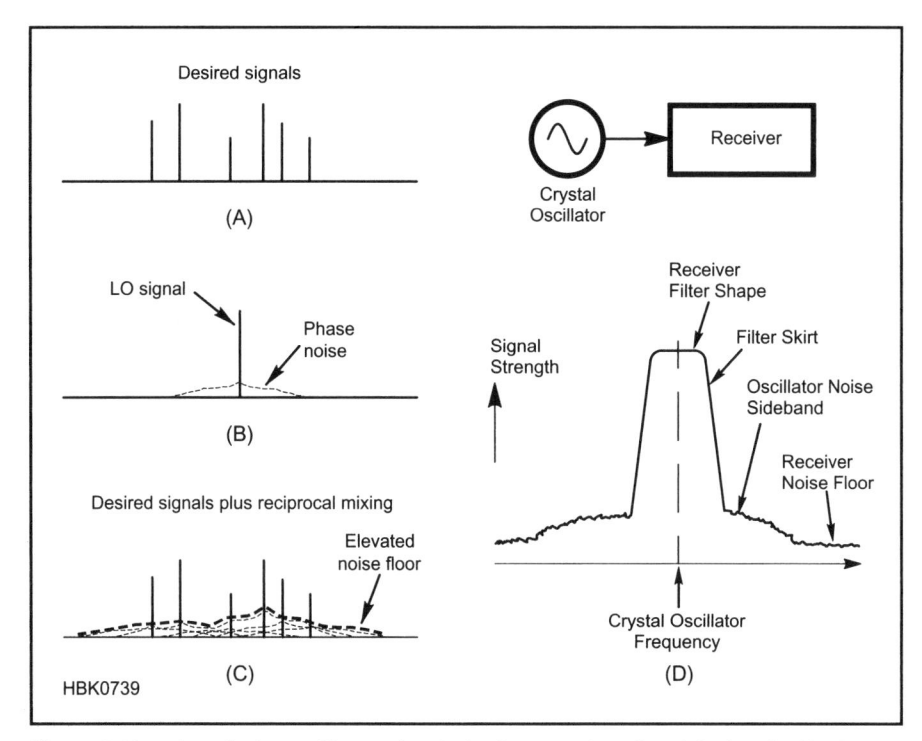

Figure 9.62 — A typical set of input signals is shown at A and an LO signal with phase noise at B. When the LO signal at B is mixed with the input signals at A, the result is a set of mixing products each having phase noise added, raising the noise floor across the band as shown at C. Phase noise in your receiver can be heard by tuning to a strong, clean crystal-oscillator signal as shown in D.

added to each of the signals in the band in proportion to its input power. The total noise seen by the receiver demodulator is the sum of all transferred phase noise profiles at the received frequency. This raises the apparent noise floor of the receiver.

Another receiver problem due to LO phase noise occurs if a very large signal appears in the receiver passband but at a frequency well removed from the desired signal. One example of this is shown in **Figure 9.63**. If the LO phase noise is excessive, then reciprocal mixing with this large signal can completely block the ability to demodulate the desired signals. Indeed, it is possible to make a wide swath of spectrum relatively useless.

Reciprocal mixing in a receiver does not affect the operating ability of other stations. The solution is to reduce the phase noise on the receiver's LO.

9.7.3 A Phase Noise Demonstration

Healthy curiosity demands some form of demonstration so the scale of a problem can be judged "by ear" before measurements are attempted. We need to be able to measure the noise of an oscillator alone (to aid in the development of quieter ones) and we also need to be able to measure the phase noise of the oscillators in a receiver (a transmitter can be treated as an oscillator). Conveniently, a receiver contains most of the functions needed to demonstrate its own phase noise.

Because reciprocal mixing adds the LO's sidebands to clean incoming signals, in the same proportion to the incoming carrier as they exist with respect to the LO carrier, all we need do is to apply a strong, clean signal wherever we want within the receiver's tuning range. This signal's generator must have lower phase noise than the radio being evaluated. A general-purpose signal generator is unlikely to be good enough; a crystal oscillator is needed.

It's appropriate to set the oscillator's signal level into the receiver to about that of a strong broadcast carrier, say S9 + 40 dB. Set the receiver's mode to SSB or CW and tune around the test signal, looking for an increasing noise floor (higher hiss level) as you tune closer toward the signal, as shown in Figure 9.62D. Switching in a narrow CW filter allows you to hear noise closer to the carrier than is possible with an SSB filter. This is also the technique used to measure a receiver's effective selectivity, and some equipment reviewers kindly publish their plots in this format. *QST* reviews, done by the ARRL Lab, often include the results of specific phase-noise measurements.

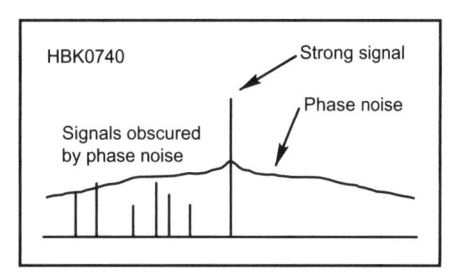

Figure 9.63 — A strong received signal can also cause such severe reciprocal mixing that desired signals are completely obscured by noise. If the signal is transmitted with phase noise from the transmitter LO, the effect is the same as noise covers the desired signals, sometimes across a very wide range of frequencies.

9.7.4 Transmitted Phase Noise

Phase noise on an LO used to generate a transmitted signal will also be amplified and transmitted along with the desired output signal. This obscures reception by raising the noise floor even for receivers with low phase noise because they also receive the noise from the transmitter. In this case, the phase noise is generated externally to the receiver and must be removed at the transmitter.

If the transmitter is operating linearly, the strength of the transmitted noise is of the same proportion to transmitter output power as the phase noise is to the oscillator signal power. The noise may even extend well beyond the band in which the desired signal is transmitted unless the signal passes through narrowband filtering that limits its bandwidth.

This transmitted noise is wasted power that is not useful for communication and unfortunately makes for a noisier band. If you are working a weak station and a nearby transmitter with a noisy oscillator comes on the air with a high power signal on a different frequency, it is possible that the output noise from this off-frequency transmitter may completely block your ability to continue working that weak station.

In bad cases, reception of nearby stations can be blocked over many tens of kilohertz above and below the frequency of the offending station. This is seen in Figure 9.63, where the offending signal and its associated noise are from a nearby transmitter. Frequencies close to that of the nearby transmitter are suddenly useless.

Transmitted phase noise can present serious problems for multi-station operation such as at Field Day or during emergency communications where several transmitters and receivers are in close proximity. This is a particular problem with transceivers that use early PLL-synthesized VFOs. If you are planning such an operation, be sure the level of transmitted phase noise is acceptable for the transceivers you plan on using.

At your receiver there is nothing you can do about transmitted phase noise. When there is noise power present at the same frequency as a weak (far) signal you are receiving, your receiver cannot separate them. The only solution is for the problem station to use a transmitter with a "cleaner" LO (less phase noise). This is a more serious problem than reciprocal mixing since this transmitted noise affects the ability of many other stations to use that band.

9.7.5 PLL Synthesizer Phase Noise

Differences in resonator Q usually make the phase-noise sidebands of a loop's reference oscillator much smaller than those of the VCO. Within its loop bandwidth, a PLL acts toward matching the phase-noise components of its VCO to those of the reference. There are several processes which get in the way of this actually happening, which are outlined here.

Dividing the reference oscillator signal f_{XO} to produce the signal f_{REF} which is applied to the phase detector also divides the deviation of the reference oscillator's phase-noise sidebands. (See the previous section on PLL.) This division results in a 20 dB reduction in phase noise per decade of division. This models as a factor of $-20 \log (R)$ dB, where R is the reference divisor value, since f_{REF} is less than f_{XO}. We also know that within its loop bandwidth the PLL acts as a frequency multiplier and this multiplies the deviation of the phase noise sidebands present at the PFD, again by 20 dB per decade or equivalently by a factor of $20 \log (N)$ dB, where N is the loop divider's value. Between the reference oscillator and the PLL output, the sidebands on the reference signal are increased by $20 \log (N/R)$ dB.

COUNTER AND PFD NOISE

Logic circuits have a noise characteristic that is extremely important to PLL design. Any circuit, when you really get down to it, is always an analog circuit. In this case the switching threshold of the logic circuits has a tiny amount of noise on it. This small amount of noise manifests itself in a very slight variation in when the logic circuit actually switches, even if the input clock is perfectly clean. We can think of this small timing jitter as a small shift in the output signal "zero crossing," which is directly equivalent to a phase modulation.

The amount of this timing jitter is constant, no matter the operating frequency. Thus, the amount of phase shift this represents depends on the operating frequency: 1 nanosecond of jitter at 1 kHz is very small, but represents 36 degrees at 100 MHz. As a result we get different measures of the noise floor from digital circuits that depend on the frequency at which they are operating. This digital noise floor interferes with the PLL action to match the VCO noise to the divided reference oscillator noise as measured at the PFD inputs.

VCO NOISE

The PLL can track only slowly moving noise, well within its bandwidth. Therefore VCO noise components that change slowly enough for the PLL to measure and track will be increasingly canceled successfully. Any VCO noise component that changes at a rate faster than the PLL bandwidth will not be changed at all. At offset frequencies beyond the PLL bandwidth the VCO noise is still present as if the PLL were not even there.

Does this imply that to get a low-noise synthesizer we are encouraged to make the PLL bandwidth very wide? Well, yes, to a certain degree. When we build PLL synthesizers we soon find that the logic noise from the digital section begins to get in the way if the loop bandwidth gets too wide. When this happens the total PLL output noise actually begins to increase as the bandwidth gets wider. There is a range of loop bandwidth values where the total PLL output noise has a minimum. This range is centered at the offset frequency where the logic noise floor, multiplied by $20 \log (f_{OUT}/f_{REF})$, has the same value as the VCO intrinsic phase noise.

Clearly, having a VCO design with minimum phase noise is very important to a good, low-noise PLL synthesizer. Much effort has been expended on this area in industry. A summary of important results from these noise reduction efforts is presented in the section Improving VCO Noise Performance below.

FRACTIONAL DIVISION NOISE

From the brief discussion on fractional-N principles, we note that this whole idea is based on changing the feedback divider value in a semi-randomized way. This inherently jitters the output from the feedback divider, which is a source of phase noise into the PFD. This noise source is algorithmic instead of physical, but the noise is a big problem nonetheless.

OTHER NOISE SOURCES

Phase noise can be introduced into a PLL by other means. Any amplifier stages between the VCO and the circuits that follow it (such as the loop divider) will contribute some noise, as will microphonic effects in loop- and reference-filter components (such as those due to the piezoelectric properties of ceramic capacitors and the crystal filters sometimes used for reference-oscillator filtering). Noise on the power supply to the system's active components can modulate the loop. The fundamental and harmonics of the system's ac line supply can be coupled into the VCO directly or by means of ground loops.

9.7.6 Improving VCO Noise Performance

It is tempting to regard VCO design as a matter of coming up with a suitable oscillator topology with a variable capacitor, simply replacing the variable capacitor with a suitable varactor diode and applying a tuning voltage to the diode. Unfortunately, things are not this simple (as if even this is simple!). There is the matter of applying the tuning voltage to the diode without significantly disturbing the oscillator performance. There is also an issue of not introducing parasitic oscillation with the varactor circuit.

Next, as mentioned earlier, one would not like the tuning voltage to drop below the voltage swing in the oscillator tank. If this is allowed to occur, the tuning diodes go into conduction and the oscillator noise gets worse. A good first approach is to use varactor diodes back to back as shown in **Figure 9.64**. This allows the tank voltage

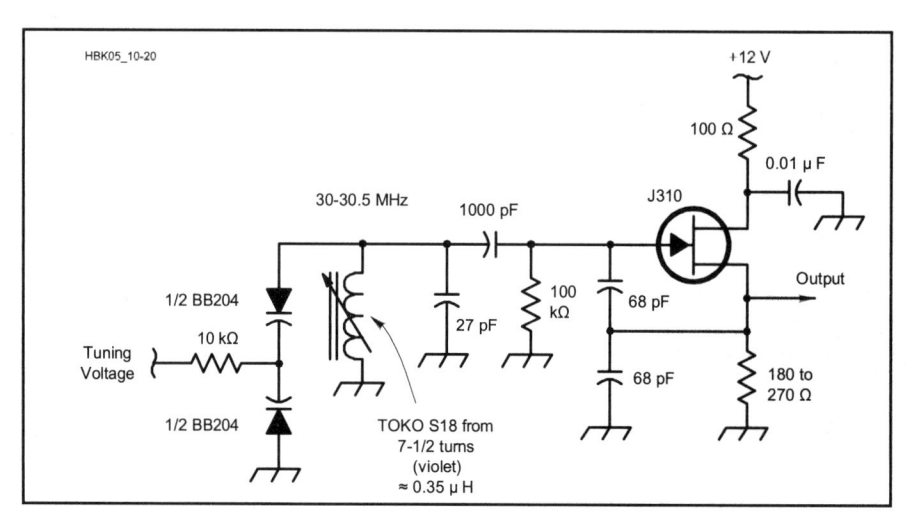

Figure 9.64 — A practical VCO. The tuning diodes are halves of a BB204 dual, common-cathode tuning diode (capacitance per section at 3 V, 39 pF) or equivalent. The ECG617, NTE617 and MV104 are suitable dual-diode substitutes, or use pairs of 1N5451s (39 pF at 4 V) or MV2109s (33 pF at 4 V).

swing to be developed across two diodes instead of one, as well as allow for a more balanced loading of the oscillator's tank. The semiconductor industry has realized this and there are a number of varactors available prepackaged in this configuration today.

IMPROVING VCO OPERATING Q

Often the Q of passive capacitors available for use in an oscillator tank exceeds the Q of available varactors. One way of reducing the influence of the varactor is to use only the amount of varactor capacitance required to tune the oscillator over its desired range. The balance of the capacitance is supplied to the tank in the form of a higher-Q fixed capacitor. This has the advantage of not requiring the varactor to supply all the capacitance needed to make the circuit function, and often allows for the use of a lower capacitance varactor.

Lower capacitance varactors typically exhibit higher Q values than their larger capacitance counterparts. This concept can be extended by splitting the oscillator tuning range, say 70 MHz to 98 MHz (for a typical lower-side up-converter receiver design popular in recent analog architectures), into multiple bands. For this example let us consider four oscillators, each with 7 MHz of tuning range. We desire the varactor Q effects to be swamped by high-Q fixed capacitors. This can be further improved through the use of a "segment-tuned VCO" discussed below. A secondary but important benefit of this is to reduce the effective tuning gain (MHz/volt, K_0) of the oscillators, making them less susceptible to other noise voltage sources in the synthesizer loop. These noise sources can come from a variety of places including, but not limited to, varactor leakage current, varactor tuning drive impedance and output noise of the driving operational amplifier or charge pump.

Segment-tuned VCOs provide the designer with additional benefits, but also with additional challenges. By segmented we mean that circuit elements, which could be both inductance and capacitance, are selected for each range that the VCO is expected to tune. **Figure 9.65** shows the frequency range-switching section of a typical VCO in which several diode switches are used to alter the total tank circuit inductance in small steps. These segments create a type of "coarse tuning" for the VCO, and the output of the PLL loop filter performs "fine tuning" with the varactor diode. Usually the component values are arranged in some sort of binary tree. In some integrated designs, 64 or even 128 subbands are available from the VCO.

Many times the segmented-VCO concept is applied to an oscillator design that is required to cover several octaves in frequency. For example, this would be the case with a single-IF radio with the IF at about 8 MHz. The VCO would be required to cover 8 MHz to 48 MHz for 100 kHz to 50 MHz coverage of a typical transceiver.

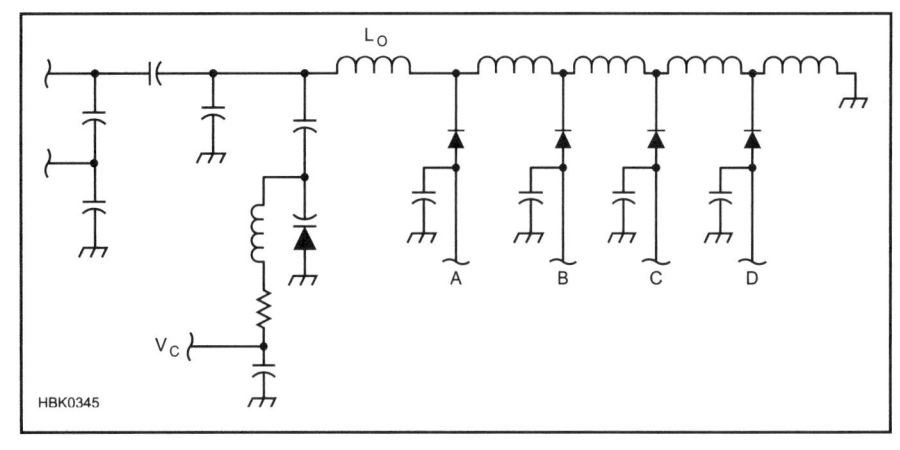

Figure 9.65 — The resonator portion of an inductor-switched segment-tuned VCO. A varactor diode provides tuning over a small range. Diode switches will alter the total inductance, changing the frequency in larger steps. Inductor-switched, capacitor-switched, and combinations are all used in VCO designs. (From Hayward, *Introduction to Radio Frequency Design*, Chapter 7. See references.)

While segmentation allows one to build a multi-octave tunable oscillator, segmentation also imposes some additional constraints. Recalling the earlier section in this chapter on oscillators, the condition for oscillation is an oscillator loop gain of 1 at a phase angle of 0 degrees. Over several octaves, the gain of the oscillating device (typically a transistor) varies, decreasing as operating frequency increases. While conventional limiting in the oscillator circuit will deal with some of this, it is not good practice to let the normal limiting process handle the entire gain variation. This becomes the role of automatic gain control (AGC) in multi-octave oscillator designs. Application of AGC allows for the maintenance of the oscillation criteria, a uniform output and good starting characteristics, and lower noise across the operating bandwidth.

Finally, a properly designed segmented VCO can improve synthesizer switching speed. The segmentation allows the designer to "pre-steer" the PLL system and reduce the time required for the loop filter to slew the VCO to the desired frequency for lock. Frequency-locked loops (FLL) are often employed for this steering operation to be sure that it happens properly.

9.7.7 ARRL Lab Transmitter Phase Noise Measurement

(This section was written by ARRL Lab Staff Engineers, Zack Lau, W1VT, and Bob Allison, WB1GCM.) Receiver performance has improved dramatically over the past generation or two of transceivers. With the widespread use of better filtering and improvements in digital signal processing, the effects of intermodulation distortion (IMD) at close signal spacing have been reduced greatly. Many software defined receivers (SDRs) now experience little to no reciprocal mixing or reduction of audio level on the received frequency from strong adjacent signals. Signals generated within the receiver during reception of one or more strong nearby signals are not the problem they once were, and it's possible to operate effectively in a crowded band.

Although today's receivers can hear weak signals very close to adjacent strong signals, even the best receivers cannot eliminate the effects of a wide signal from an adjacent transmitter. Transmitted signal issues include excessive keying bandwidth on CW, poor suppression of transmitted IMD products (which causes splatter on SSB), or transmitted phase noise (which raises a receiver's noise floor) in the speaker. ARRL Lab Product Review test reports include transmitter IMD products (both typical and worst case), a plot showing keying sidebands, and a plot showing transmitted phase noise.

PHASE NOISE

Phase noise is essentially the noise generated above and below an oscillator's frequency, also called sideband noise. All oscillators generate some level of phase noise. This is most evident when a close adjacent signal is very strong and the receiver's background noise increases. This is due to the mixing of the first local oscillator's phase noise with the incoming signal at the first IF (reciprocal mixing). The Lab reports the effects of reciprocal mixing in the receiver as "reciprocal mixing dynamic range" or RMDR. In many receivers we've tested, RMDR is the limiting dynamic range. In other words, third order IMD dynamic range and blocking dynamic range are better than RMDR. (See the **Receiving** chapter.)

A transmit oscillator, the heart of the transmitter, has phase noise too. A transmitter's

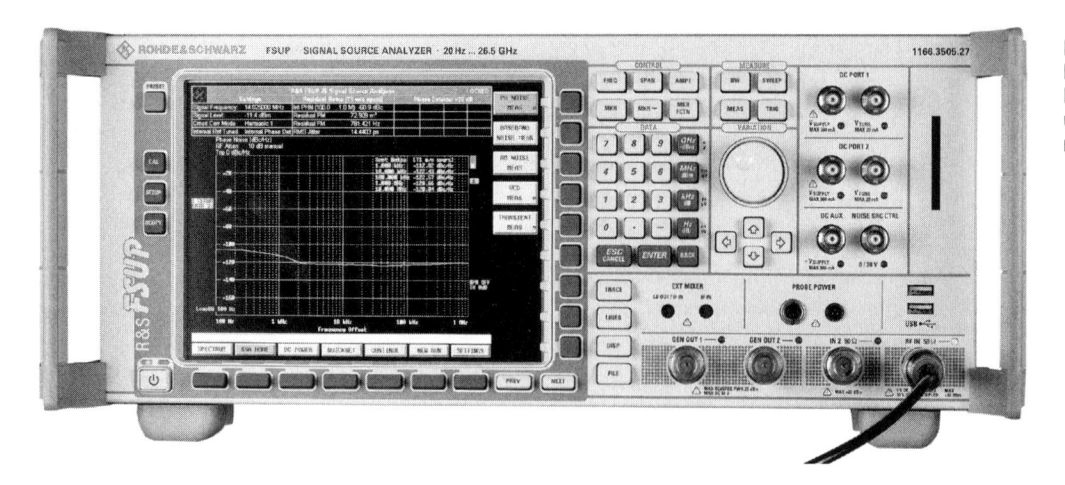

Figure 9.66 — The ARRL Lab's Rohde & Schwarz FSUP 26 Signal Analyzer, used for transmitter phase noise testing.

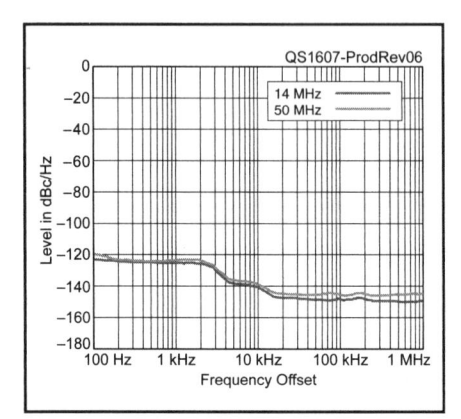

Figure 9.67 — Sample phase noise plot for an amateur HF transceiver as published in Product Review in *QST*. This is the Icom IC-7851.

phase noise is a fixed characteristic and, at times, can be a nuisance to other operators. A good example of observed phase noise can happen at Field Day or other environments where several transmitters are operating in close proximity. When two stations are operating on one band, the CW station blasts the phone operator's ears with bursts of noise, and vice versa. Using a transmitter exhibiting high phase noise with an RF amplifier magnifies the problem.

The solution for the reduction of both transmitted phase noise and receiver reciprocal mixing is the employment of high quality oscillators by the manufacturer. Generally, the better the oscillator (the lower the phase noise), the better the RMDR and the lower the transmitted phase noise.

ARRL LAB TESTING

At the ARRL Laboratory, we use a Rohde & Schwarz FSUP 26 Signal Source Analyzer (**Figure 9.66**), which allows us to measure phase noise on any frequency up to 26.5 GHz. A crystal oscillator with very low phase noise is used to calibrate the system. We use an attenuator after the transmitter to bring the signal down to a suitable level for the phase noise test set.

A sample phase-noise plot for an amateur transceiver is shown in **Figure 9.67**. It was produced with the test setup shown in Figure 9.66. In this case, measurements for 14 MHz and 50 MHz are shown. These plots do not necessarily reflect the phase-noise characteristics of all units of a particular model.

The reference level (the top horizontal line on the scale in the plot) represents 0 dBc/Hz. Because each vertical division represents 20 dB, the plot shows the noise level between 0 dBc/Hz (the top horizontal line) and −180 dBc/Hz (the bottom horizontal line). The horizontal scale is logarithmic, with one decade per division (the first division shows noise from 100 Hz to 1 kHz Hz offset, whereas the last division shows noise from 100 kHz through 1 MHz offset).

WHAT DO THE PHASE-NOISE PLOTS MEAN?

Although they are useful for comparing different radios, plots can also be used to calculate the amount of interference you may receive from a nearby transmitter with known phase-noise characteristics. An approximation is given by

$$A_{QRM} = NL + 10 \times \log(BW)$$

where
A_{QRM} = Interfering signal level, dBc
NL = noise level on the receive frequency, dBc
BW = receiver IF bandwidth, in Hz

For instance, if the noise level is −90 dBc/Hz and you are using a 2.5 kHz SSB filter, the approximate interfering signal will be −56 dBc. In other words, if the transmitted signal is 20 dB over S-9, and each S unit is 6 dB, the interfering signal will be as strong as an S-3 signal.

The measurements made in the ARRL Lab apply only to transmitted signals. It is reasonable to assume that the phase-noise characteristics of most transceivers are similar on transmit and receive because the same oscillators are generally used in the local-oscillator (LO) chain or for generating DDS signals.

In some cases, the receiver may have better phase noise characteristics than the transmitter. Why the possible difference? The most obvious reason is that circuits often perform less than optimally in strong RF fields, as anyone who has experienced RFI problems can tell you. A less obvious reason results from the way that many high-dynamic-range receivers work. To get good dynamic range, a sharp crystal filter called a *roofing filter* is often placed immediately after the first mixer in the receive line. This filter removes all but a small slice of spectrum for further signal processing. If the desired filtered signal is a product of mixing an incoming signal with a noisy oscillator, signals far away from the desired one can end up in this slice. Once this slice of spectrum is obtained, however, unwanted signals cannot be reintroduced, no matter how noisy the oscillators used in further signal processing. As a result, some oscillators in receivers don't affect phase noise.

The difference between this situation and that in transmitters is that crystal filters are seldom used for reduction of phase noise in transmitting because of the high cost involved. Equipment designers have enough trouble getting smooth, click-free break-in operation in transceivers without having to worry about switching crystal filters in and out of circuits at 40 WPM keying speeds!

9.8 Glossary of Oscillator and Synthesizer Terms

Buffer — A circuit that amplifies the output of a circuit while isolating it from the load.

Bypass — Create a low ac impedance to ground at a point in the circuit.

Cavity — A hollow structure used as an electrical resonator.

Closed-loop — Operation under the control of a feedback loop (see also **open-loop**).

Coupling — The transfer of energy between circuits or structures.

Damping (factor) — the characteristics of the decay in a system's response to an input signal. The **damping factor,** ζ, is a numeric value specifying the degree of damping. An **underdamped** system alternately overshoots and undershoots the eventual steady-state output. An **overdamped** system approaches the steady-state output gradually, without overshoot. A **critically-damped** system approaches the steady-state output as quickly as possible without overshoot.

dBc — Decibels with respect to a carrier level.

DC-FM — control of a signal generator's output frequency by a dc voltage.

Decouple — To provide isolation between circuits, usually by means of filtering.

Direct digital synthesis (DDS) — Generation of signals by using counters and accumulators to create an output waveform.

Distributed — Circuit elements that are inherent properties of an extended structure, such as a transmission line.

ESR — Equivalent series resistance.

Free-running — Oscillating without any form of external control.

Fundamental — Lowest frequency of natural vibration or oscillation.

Integrator — A low-pass filter whose output is approximately the integral of the input signal.

Intermodulation — Generation of distortion products from two signals interacting in a nonlinear medium, device, or connection.

Isolation — Preventing signal flow between two circuits or systems. **Reverse isolation** refers to signal flow against the desired signal path.

Jitter (phase jitter) — Random variations of a signal in time, usually refers to random variations in the transition time of digital signals between states.

Linearization — Creation of a linear amplification or frequency characteristic through corrections supplied by an external system.

Loop gain — The total gain applied to a signal traveling around a feedback control loop.

Lumped (element) — Circuit elements whose electrical functions are concentrated at one point in the form of an electronic component.

Match — Equal values of impedance.

Modulus — The number of states of a digital counter or divider.

Motional capacitance (inductance) — The electrical effect of a crystal's mechanical properties, modeled as a capacitance (inductance).

Natural frequency (w_n) — Frequency at which a system oscillates without any external control.

Noise bandwidth — The width of an ideal rectangular filter that would pass the same noise power from white noise as the filter being compared (also called **equivalent noise bandwidth**).

Open-loop — Operation without controlling feedback.

Oscillation — Repetitive mechanical motion or electrical activity created by the application of positive feedback.

Overtones — Vibration or oscillation at frequencies above the **fundamental**, usually harmonically related to the fundamental.

Permeability tuning — Varying the permeability of the core of an inductor used to control an oscillator's frequency.

Phase-lock — Maintain two signals in a fixed phase relationship by means of a control system.

Phase noise — Random variations of a signal in time, expressed as variations in phase of a sinusoidal signal.

Phasor — Representation of a sinusoidal signal as an amplitude and phase, often drawn as a vector.

Power density — Amount of power per unit of frequency, usually specified as dBc/Hz or as RMS voltage/$\sqrt{Hz}$.

Prescaler — A frequency divider used to reduce the frequency of an input signal for processing by slower circuitry.

Preselector — Filters applied at a receiver's input to reject out-of-band signals.

Pull — Change the frequency at which a crystal oscillates by changing reactance of the circuit in which it is installed.

Quadrature — A 90° phase difference maintained between two signals.

Reciprocal mixing — Noise in a mixer's output due to the LO's noise sidebands mixing with those of the desired signal.

Relaxation oscillation — Oscillation produced by a cycle of gradual accumulation of energy followed by its sudden release.

Resonator — Circuit or structure whose resonance acts as a filter.

Simulation — Calculate a circuit's behavior based on mathematical models of the components.

Spurious (spur) — A signal at an undesired frequency, usually unrelated to the frequency of a desired frequency.

Squegg (squeeg) — Chaotic or random jumps in an oscillator's amplitude and/or frequency.

Static (synthesizer) — A synthesizer designed to output a signal whose frequency does not change or that is not changed frequently.

Synthesis (frequency) — The generation of variable-frequency signals by means of nonlinear combination and filtering (direct synthesis) or by using phase-lock or phase-control techniques (indirect synthesis).

TCXO — Temperature-compensated crystal oscillator. A **digitally temperature-compensated oscillator (DTCXO)** is controlled by a microcontroller or computer to maintain a constant frequency. **Oven-controlled crystal oscillators (OCXO)** are placed in a heated enclosure to maintain a constant temperature and frequency.

Temperature coefficient (tempco) — The amount of change in a component's value per degree of change in temperature.

Temperature compensation — Causing a circuit's behavior to change with temperature in such as way as to oppose and cancel the change with temperature of some temperature-sensitive component, such as a crystal.

Varactor (Varicap) — Reverse-biased diode used as a tunable capacitor.

VCO — Voltage-controlled oscillator (also called **voltage-tuned oscillator**).

VFO — Variable-frequency oscillator.

VXO — Variable crystal oscillator, whose frequency is adjustable around that of the crystal.

9.9 References and Bibliography

Agilent application note 5989-9848EN, "Boosting PLL Design Efficiency," — describes the characterization of VCOs using the E5202B Signal Source Analyzer. **literature.cdn.keysight.com/litweb/pdf/5989-9848EN.pdf?id=1548746**

Clarke and Hess, *Communications Circuits; Analysis and Design* (Addison-Wesley, 1971; ISBN 0-201-01040-2). Wide coverage of transistor circuit design, including techniques suited to the design of integrated circuits. Its age shows, but it is especially valuable for its good mathematical treatment of oscillator circuits, covering both frequency- and amplitude-determining mechanisms. Look for a copy at a university library or initiate an interlibrary loan.

F. Gardner, *Phaselock Techniques*, (John Wiley and Sons, 1966, ISBN 0-471-29156-0).

J. Grebenkemper, "Phase Noise and Its Effects on Amateur Communications," *Part 1, QST*. Mar 1988, pp 14-20; *Part 2*, Apr 1988 pp 22-25. Also see Feedback, *QST*, May 1988, p 44.

W. Hayward and D. DeMaw, *Solid State Design for the Radio Amateur* (Newington, CT: ARRL, 1986). Out of print, this is dated but a good source of RF design ideas.

W. Hayward, W7ZOI, R. Campbell, KK7B, and B. Larkin, W7PUA, *Experimental Methods in RF Design* (Newington, CT: ARRL, 2003). A good source of RF design ideas, with good explanation of the reasoning behind design decisions.

W. Hayward, W7ZOI, *Introduction to Radio Frequency Design* (Newington, CT: ARRL, 1994). Out of print, good in-depth treatments of circuits and techniques used at RF.

Hewlett-Packard Application Note 150-4, "Spectrum Analysis…Random Noise Measurements." Source of correction factors for noise measurements using spectrum analyzers. **literature.cdn.keysight.com/litweb/pdf/5952-1147.pdf?id=800596**

I. Keyser, "An Easy to Set Up Amateur Band Synthesizer," *RADCOM* (RSGB), Dec 1993, pp 33-36.

V. Manassewitsch, *Frequency Synthesizers Theory and Design* (Wiley-Interscience, 1987, ISBN 0 471-01116-9).

Mini-Circuits collection of Application Notes on oscillators, synthesizers, and associated components and techniques, **www.minicircuits.com/applications/applications_notes.html**

Motorola Application Note AN-551, "Tuning Diode Design Techniques" No longer supplied by Freescale but available through various on-line sources. A concise explanation of varactor diodes, their characteristics and use.

E.W. Pappenfus. W. Bruene and E.O. Schoenike, *Single Sideband Circuits and Systems*, (McGraw-Hill, 1964). A book on HF SSB transmitters, receivers and accoutrements by Rockwell-Collins staff. Contains chapters on synthesizers and frequency standards. The frequency synthesizer chapter predates the rise of the DDS and other recent techniques, but good information about the effects of synthesizer performance on communications is spread throughout the book.

B. Parzen, A. Ballato. *Design of Crystal and Other Harmonic Oscillators* (Wiley-Interscience, 1983, ISBN 0-471-08819-6). This book shows a thorough treatment of modern crystal oscillators including the optimum design. It is also the only book that looks at the base and collector limiting effect. The second author is affiliated with the US Army Electronics Technology & Devices Laboratory, Fort Monmouth, New Jersey.

B. E. Pontius, "Measurement of Signal Source Phase Noise with Low-Cost Equipment," *QEX,* May-Jun 1998, pp 38-49.

U. Rohde, *Microwave and Wireless Synthesizers Theory and Design* (John Wiley and Sons, 1997, ISBN 0-471-52019-5). This book contains the textbook-standard mathematical analyses of frequency synthesizers combined with unusually good insight into what makes a better synthesizer and *a lot* of practical circuits to entertain serious constructors. A good place to look for low-noise circuits and techniques.

U. Rohde, D. Newkirk, *RF/Microwave Circuit Design for Wireless Applications* (John Wiley and Sons, 2000, ISBN 0-471-29818-2) While giving a deep insight into circuit design for wireless applications, Chapter 5 (RF/Wireless Oscillators) shows a complete treatment of both discrete and integrated circuit based oscillators. Chapter 6 (Wireless Synthesizers) gives more insight in synthesizers and large list of useful references.

U. Rohde, J. Whitaker, *Communications Receivers DSP, Software Radios, and Design*, 3rd ed., (McGraw-Hill, 2001, ISBN 0-07-136121-9). While mostly dedicated to communication receivers, this book has a useful chapter on Frequency Control and Local Oscillators, specifically on Fractional Division Synthesizers.

U. Rohde, A. Poddar, G. Boeck, *The Design of Modern Microwave Oscillators for Wireless Applications Theory and Optimization* (Wiley-Interscience, 2005, ISBN 0-471-72342-8). This is the latest and most advanced textbook on oscillator design for high frequency/microwave application. It shows in detail how to design and optimize high frequency and microwave VCOs. It also contains a thorough analysis of the phase noise as generated in oscillators. While highly mathematical, the appendix gives numerical solutions that can be easily applied to various designs. It covers both bipolar transistors and FETs.

U. Rohde, "All About Phase Noise in Oscillators," Part 1, *QEX*, Dec 1993 pp 3-6; Part 2, *QEX*, Jan 1994 pp 9-16; Part 3, *QEX*, Feb 1994, pp 15-24.

U. Rohde, "Key Components of Modern Receiver Design," Part 1, *QST,* May 1994, pp 29-32; Part 2, *QST,* June 1994, pp 27-31; Part 3, *QST,* Jul 1994, pp 42-45. Includes discussion of phase-noise reduction techniques in synthesizers and oscillators.

U. Rohde, "A High-Performance Hybrid Frequency Synthesizer," *QST*, Mar 1995, pp 30-38.

D. Stockton, "Polyphase noise-shaping fractional-N frequency synthesizer", U.S. Patent 6,509,800.

F. Telewski and E. Drucker, "Noise Reduction Method and Apparatus for Phase-locked Loops," U.S. Patent 5,216,387.

G. Vendelin, A. Pavio, U. Rohde, *Microwave Circuit Design Using Linear and Nonlinear Techniques*, 2nd ed., (Wiley-Interscience, 2005, ISBN 0-471-414479-4). This is a general handbook on microwave circuit design. It covers (in 200 pages) a large variety of oscillator design problems including microwave applications. It provides a step-by-step design guide for both linear and nonlinear oscillator designs.

INTERESTING MODERN JOURNAL PUBLICATIONS

OSCILLATOR REFERENCES

A. D. Berny, A. M. Niknejad, and R. G. Meyer, "A 1.8 GHz LC VCO with 1.3 GHz Tuning Range and Digital Amplitude Calibration," *IEEE Journal of SSC*, vol. 40. no. 4, 2005, pp 909-917.

A. Chenakin, "Phase Noise Reduction in

Microwave Oscillators," *Microwave Journal*, Oct 2009, pp 124-140.

A, P. S. (Paul) Khanna, "Microwave Oscillators: The State of The Technology," *Microwave Journal*, Apr 2006, pp. 22-42.

N. Nomura, M. Itagaki, and Y. Aoyagi, "Small packaged VCSO for 10 Gbit Ethernet Application," *IEEE IUFFCS*, 2004, pp. 418-421.

A. K. Poddar, "A Novel Approach for Designing Integrated Ultra Low Noise Microwave Wideband Voltage-Controlled Oscillators," Dr.-Ing. Dissertation, TU- Berlin, Germany, 14 Dec 2004.

A. Ravi, B. R. Carlton, G. Banerjee, K. Soumyanath, "A 1.4V, 2.4/5.2 GHz, 90 nm CMOS system in a Package Transreceiver for Next Generation WLAN," *IEEE Symp. on VLSI Tech.*, 2005.

U.L. Rohde, "A New Efficient Method of Designing Low Noise Microwave Oscillators," Dr.-Ing. Dissertation, TU-Berlin, Germany, 12 Feb 2004.

U.L. Rohde, "Calculation of FM and AM Noise Signals of Colpitts Oscillators in the Time Domain," *QEX*, Mar/Apr 2016, pp 22-39.

U.L. Rohde, "Some Thoughts on Designing Very High Performance VHF Oscillators," *QEX*, Nov/Dec 2015, pp 32-40.

Sheng Sun and Lei Zhu, "Guided-Wave Characteristics of Periodically Nonuniform Coupled Microstrip Lines-Even and Odd Modes," *IEEE Transaction on MTT*, Vol. 53, No. 4, Apr 2005, pp. 1221-1227.

C.-C. Wei, H.-C. Chiu, and W.-S. Feng, "An Ultra-Wideband CMOS VCO with 3-5 GHz Tuning Range," IEEE, *International Workshop on Radio-Frequency Integration Technology*, Nov 2005, pp 87-90.

M-S Yim, K. K. O., "Switched Resonators and Their Applications in a Dual Band Monolithic CMOS LC Tuned VCO," *IEEE MTT*, Vol. 54, Jan 2006, pp 74-81.

SYNTHESIZER REFERENCES

H. Arora, N. Klemmer, J. C. Morizio, and P. D. Wolf, "Enhanced Phase Noise Modeling of Fractional-N Frequency Synthesizer," IEEE Trans. Circuits and Systems-I: Regular Papers, vol 52, Feb 2005, pp 379-395.

R. van de Beek. D. Leenaerts, G. van der Weide, "A Fast-Hopping Single-PLL 3-band UWB Synthesizer in 0.25um SiGe BiCMOS," Proc. European Solid-State Circuit Conf. 2005, pp 173-176.

R. E. Best, *Phase-Locked Loops: Design, Simulation, and Applications*, 5th ed., McGraw-Hill, 2003.

C. Lam, B. Razavi, "A 2.6/5.2 GHz Frequency Synthesizer in 0.4um CMOS Technology," IEEE JSSC, vol 35, May 2000, pp 788-79.

J. Lee, "A 3-to-8 GHz Fast-Hopping Frequency Synthesizer in 0.18-um CMOS Technology," IEEE Journal of SSC, vol 41, no 3, Mar 2006, pp 566-573.

A. Natrajan, A. Komijani, and A. Hajimiri, "A Fully 24-GHz Phased-Array Transmitter in CMOS," IEEE Journal of SSC, vol 40, no 12, Dec 2005, pp 2502-2514.

W. Rahajandraibe, L. Zaid, V. C. de Beaupre, and G. Bas, "Frequency Synthesizer and FSK Modulator For IEEE 802.15.4 Based Applications," 2007 RFIC Symp. Digest, pp 229-232.

C. Sandner, A. Wiesbauer, "A 3 GHz to 7 GHz Fast-Hopping Frequency Synthesizer For UWB," Proc. Int. Workshop on Ultra Wideband Systems 2004, pp 405-409.

R. B. Staszewski and others, "All Digital PLL and Transmitter for Mobile Phones," IEEE J. Solid-State Circuits, vol 40, no 12, Dec 2005, pp 2469-2482.

Contents

- 10.1 Introduction
- 10.2 Filter Basics
  - 10.2.1 Filter Magnitude Responses
  - 10.2.2 Filter Order
  - 10.2.3 Filter Families
  - 10.2.4 Group Delay
  - 10.2.5 Transient Response
  - 10.2.6 Filter Family Selection
- 10.3 Passive LC Filters
  - 10.3.1 Low-Pass Filters
  - 10.3.2 Low-Pass to Band-Pass Transformation
  - 10.3.3 High-Pass Filters
  - 10.3.4 High-Pass to Band-Stop Transformation
  - 10.3.5 Effect of Component Q
  - 10.3.6 Side Effects of Passband Ripple
  - 10.3.7 Use of Filters at VHF and UHF
  - 10.3.8 Design Software for LC Filters
- 10.4 Active Audio Filters
  - 10.4.1 SCAF Filters
  - 10.4.2 Active RC Filters
  - 10.4.3 Active Filter Responses
  - 10.4.4 Active Filter Design Tools
- 10.5 Digital Filters
  - 10.5.1 FIR Filters
  - 10.5.2 IIR Filters
  - 10.5.3 CIC Filters
  - 10.5.4 Adaptive Filters
- 10.6 Quartz Crystal Filters
  - 10.6.1 Filter Parameters
  - 10.6.2 Crystal Filter Evaluation
- 10.7 SAW Filters
- 10.8 Transmission Line VHF/UHF/Microwave Filters
  - 10.8.1 Stripline and Microstrip Filters
  - 10.8.2 Transmission Line Band-Pass Filters
  - 10.8.3 Quarter-Wave Transmission Line Filters
  - 10.8.4 Emulating LC Filters with Transmission Line Filters
- 10.9 Helical Resonators
  - 10.9.1 Helical Resonator Design
  - 10.9.2 Helical Filter Construction
  - 10.9.3 Helical Resonator Tuning
  - 10.9.4 Helical Resonator Insertion Loss
  - 10.9.5 Coupling Helical Resonators
- 10.10 Filter Projects
  - 10.10.1 Audio Waveshaping Filter for CW Reception
  - 10.10.2 Combline Filters for 50 – 432 MHz
  - 10.10.3 Broadcast-Band Rejection Filters
  - 10.10.4 Optimized Harmonic Transmitting Filters
  - 10.10.5 Diplexer Filter
  - 10.10.6 High-Performance, Low-Cost 1.8 to 54 MHz Low-Pass Filter
  - 10.10.7 Band-Pass Filter for 145 MHz
- 10.11 Filter Glossary
- 10.12 References and Bibliography

Chapter 10 — Downloadable Supplemental Content

Supplemental Files

- "Using Active Filter Design Tools" by Dan Tayloe, N7VE
- "Crystal Parameter Measurements Simplified," by Chuck Adams, K7QO
- "An Improved Audio-Frequency Bandpass Filter for Morse Code Reception" by Jim Tonne, W4ENE
- "HF Yagi Triplexer Especially for Field Day" by Gary Gordon, K6KV
- "An Easy-to-Build, High-Performance Passive CW Filter" by Ed Wetherhold, W3NQN
- "A High Performance, Low Cost 1.8 to 54 MHz Low Pass Filter" by Bill Jones, K8CU
- "Band-Pass Filters for HF Transceivers" by Lew Gordon, K4VX
- "Combline V.H.F. Bandpass Filters," by R. Fisher, W2CQH
- Hands-On Radio Experiments #87 and #88, "*ELSIE* Filter Design — Parts 1 and 2" by Ward Silver, N0AX
- "Altoids Tin Filters" by Paul Wade, W1GHZ
- 6-Meter Filter with Harmonic Suppression, by Paul Wade W1GHZ
- Combline Filters for VHF and UHF, by Paul Wade W1GHZ
- Manual Filter Design Examples by Jim Tonne, W4ENE
- Crystal Filter Design and Crystal Characterization

Design Software

The following *Windows* software by Jim Tonne, W4ENE, is available with the downloadable supplemental content.
- *Diplexer* for design and analysis of diplexer filters
- *Elsie* for design and analysis of lumped-element LC filters
- *Helical* for design and analysis of helical-resonator bandpass filters
- *SVC Filter Designer* for design and analysis of lumped-element high-pass and low-pass filters
- *QuadNet* for design and analysis of active all-pass networks for SSB operation

Chapter 10

Analog and Digital Filtering

This chapter discusses the most common types of filters used by radio amateurs, both analog and digital. Design information is supplied where appropriate or references to software or detailed design procedures are supplied.

The sections describing basic concepts, lumped element filters and some design examples were initially prepared by Jim Tonne, W4ENE, and updated by Ward Silver, NØAX. Digital filter material was updated by Doug Grant, K1DG, based on material originally developed by Alan Bloom, N1AL. Additional digital filter material was based on the SDR: Simplified column in *QEX* by Ray Mack, W5IFS.

The downloadable supplemental information's design example for active filters was provided by Dan Tayloe, N7VE. The downloadable supplemental information's design example for crystal filters was developed by Dave Gordon-Smith, G3UUR.

10.1 Introduction

Electrical filters are circuits used to process signals based on their frequency. For example, most filters are used to pass signals of certain frequencies and reject others. The electronics industry has advanced to its current level in large part because of the successful use of filters. Filters are used in receivers so that the listener can hear only the desired signal; other signals are rejected. Filters are used in transmitters to pass only one signal and reject those that might interfere with other spectrum users. **Table 10.1** shows the usual signal bandwidths for several signal types.

The simplified receivers in **Figure 10.1** show filter use in both an analog, superheterodyne receiver (Figure 10.1A) and a simplified SDR receiver (Figure 10.1B). A *preselector* filter is placed between the antenna and the receiver's front end to pass all frequencies within a given amateur band with low loss. Strong out-of-band signals from broadcast, commercial, or military stations are rejected to prevent them from overloading the receiver input. The preselector filter is almost always built with *lumped-element* or "LC" technology.

In an analog receiver, there are one or more intermediate frequency (IF) filters to select only the desired signal. The IF filter closest to the antenna may be a relatively wide "roofing" filter with a bandwidth of several kHz to reject strong in-band signals not close to the desired signal frequency. Following detection or demodulation, an audio filter is placed somewhere ahead of the AF amplifier and speaker to rejects unwanted products from the noise. The audio filter is often implemented with *active filter* technology. For an SDR receiver, similar preselector and audio filters may be used but the filters which select a single signal are implemented as *digital filters* in the I/Q Processing block.

The complementary transmitter block diagrams are shown in **Figure 10.2** in which a similar array of filters appears in reverse order. In the analog transmitter, an audio filter between the microphone and the balanced mixer rejects noise and unwanted speech components. Since the balanced mixer generates both lower and upper sidebands, an IF filter is placed at the mixer output to pass only the desired lower (or upper) sideband. In the SDR version, the input signals are digitized and processed before the I/Q signals are filtered for transmission.

Finally, a filter at the output of the transmit mixer passes only signals within the amateur band in use rejects unwanted frequencies generated by the mixer to prevent them from being amplified and transmitted. Filters at the transmitter output attenuate the harmonics of the transmitted signals.

Table 10.1
Typical Filter Bandwidths for Typical Signals

Source	Required Bandwidth
Fast-scan analog television (ATV)	4.5 MHz
Broadcast-quality speech and music	15 kHz (from 20 Hz to 15 kHz)
Communications-quality speech	3 kHz (from 300 Hz to 3 kHz)
Slow-scan television (SSTV)	3 kHz (from 300 Hz to 3 kHz)
HF Digital (general)	100 to 1500 Hz (depends on modulation and bit rate)
HF RTTY (standard shift)	250 to 500 Hz
Radiotelegraphy (Morse code, CW)	200 to 500 Hz
PSK31 digital modulation	100 Hz

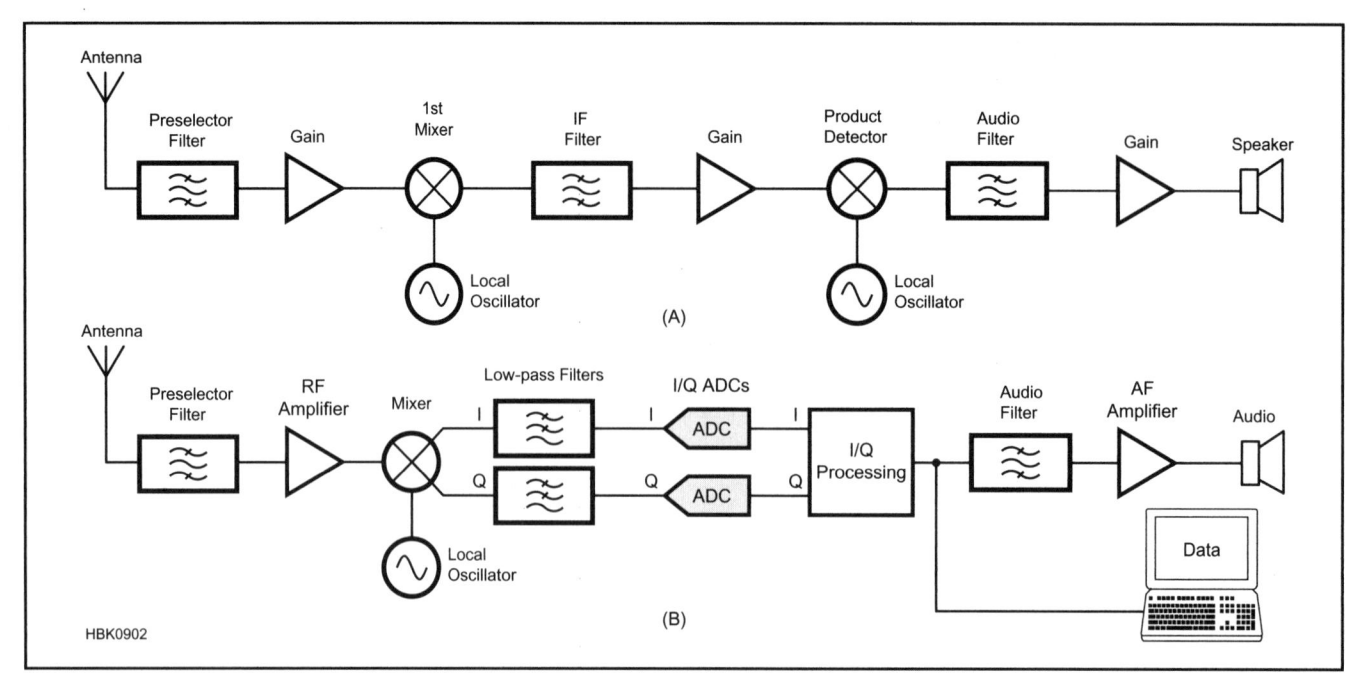

Figure 10.1 — Single-band SSB superheterodyne receiver (A) and SDR SSB/Data receiver (B) showing the filters typically used by each.

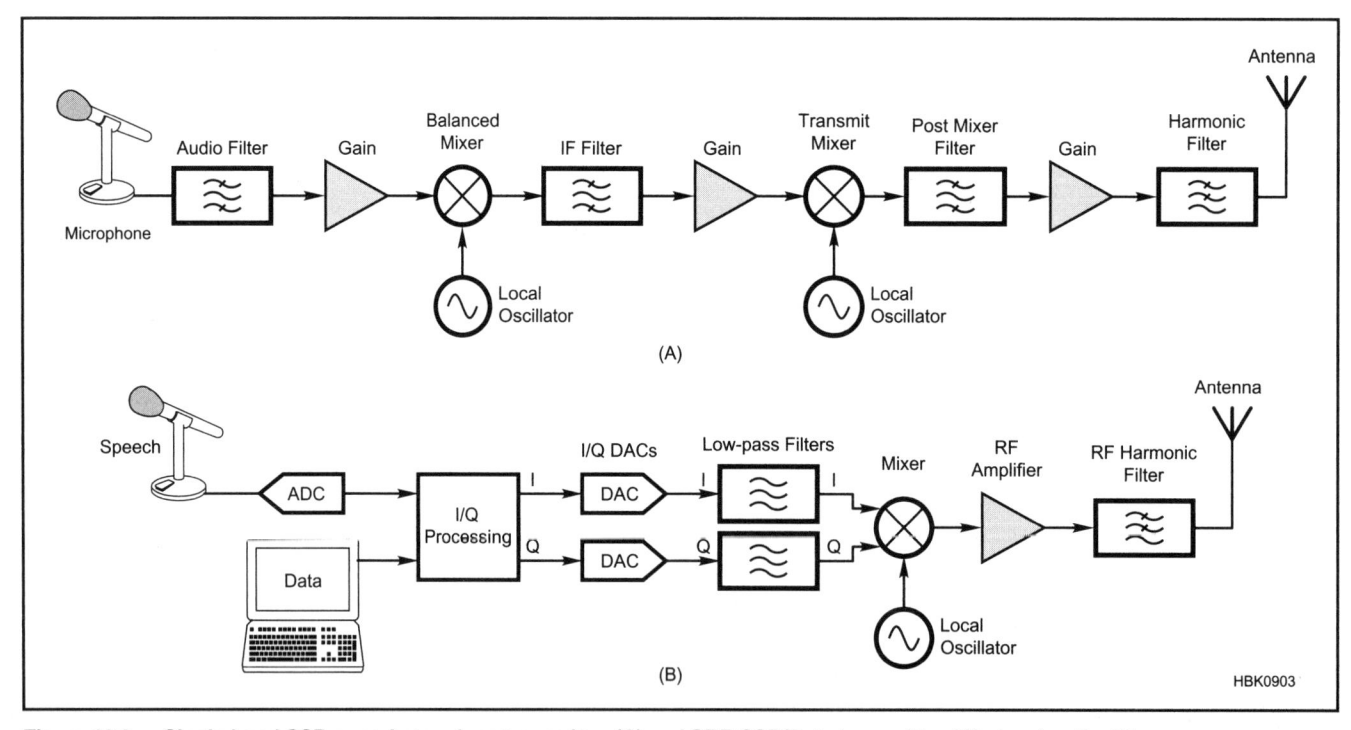

Figure 10.2 — Single-band SSB superheterodyne transmitter (A) and SDR SSB/Data transmitter (B) showing the filters typically used by each.

10.2 Filter Basics

10.2.1 Filter Magnitude Responses

A common type of filter, the *band-pass*, passes signals in a range of frequencies — the *passband* — while rejecting signals outside that range — the *stopband*. To pass signals from dc up to some *cutoff frequency* at which output power is halved (reduced by 3 dB) we would use a *low-pass* filter. To pass signals above a cutoff frequency (also called the "3-dB frequency") we would use a *high-pass* filter. Similarly, to pass signals within a range of frequencies we would use a *band-pass* filter. To pass signals at all frequencies *except* those within a specified range requires a *band-stop* or *notch filter*.

Figure 10.3A illustrates the *magnitude response* of a low-pass filter. Signals lower than the cutoff frequency (3 MHz in this case) are passed with some small amount of attenuation while signals higher than that frequency are attenuated. The degree of attenuation is dependent on several variables, filter complexity being a major factor.

Of the graphs in this chapter that show a filter's magnitude response, the vertical axes are labeled "Transmission (dB)" with 0 dB at the top of the axis and negative values increasing toward the X-axis. Increasingly negative values of transmission in dB are the same as increasingly positive values of attenuation in dB. For example, –40 dB transmission is the same as 40 dB of attenuation.

Figure 10.3B illustrates the magnitude response of a high-pass filter. Signals above the 3 MHz cutoff frequency are passed with minimum attenuation while signals below that frequency are attenuated. Again, the degree of attenuation is dependent on several variables.

Figure 10.3C illustrates the magnitude response of a band-pass filter. Signals within the band-pass range (between the lower and upper cutoff frequencies) are passed with minimum attenuation while signals outside that range are attenuated. In this example the filter was designed with cutoff frequencies of 2 MHz and 4 MHz, for a passband width of 2 MHz.

Figure 10.3D illustrates the magnitude response of a band-stop filter. Signals within the band-stop range are attenuated while all other signals are passed with minimum attenuation. A notch filter is a type of band-stop filter with a narrow stop-band in which the attenuation is a maximum at a single frequency.

An *ideal filter* — a low-pass filter, for example — would pass all frequencies up to some point with no attenuation at all and totally reject everything beyond that point. This is known as a *brick wall* response because the filter's passband and stopband are *flat*, meaning no attenuation, and the rolloff in the transition region is infinitely steep. The magnitude response of such a filter would be drawn as a flat line representing 0 dB attenuation up to the cutoff frequency that then abruptly changes at the cutoff frequency to a flat line at infinite attenuation throughout the stopband to infinite frequency.

Figure 10.4 shows all of the basic para-

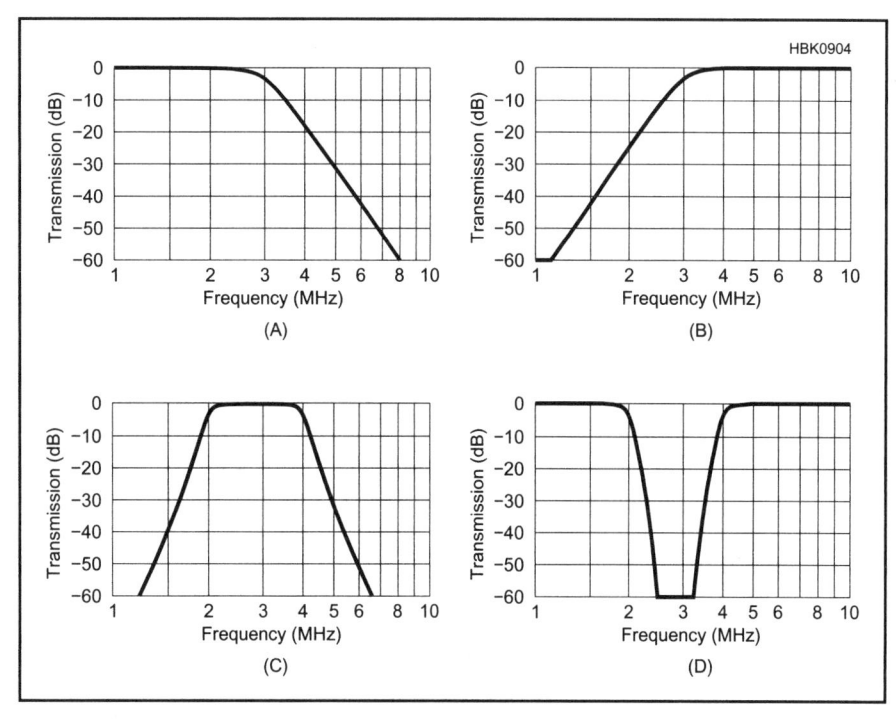

Figure 10.3 — Examples of a low-pass magnitude response (A), high-pass magnitude response (B), band-pass magnitude response (C), and band-stop magnitude response (D).

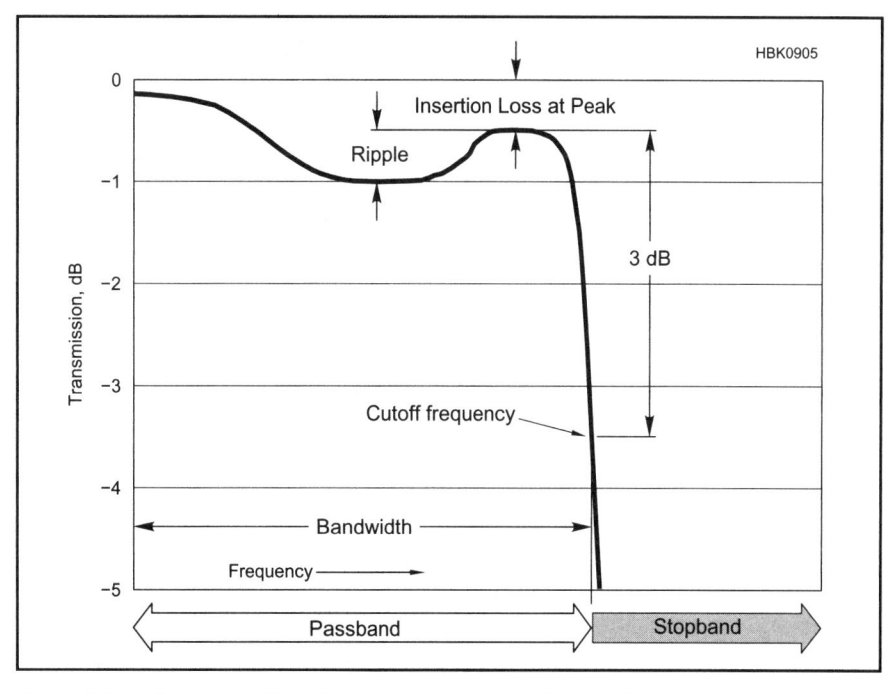

Figure 10.4 — Low-pass filter characteristics showing the passband and stopband, bandwidth, 3 dB cutoff, passband ripple, and insertion loss (IL). This filter has approximately 0.5 dB IL at the frequency of peak response while passband ripple is also 0.5 dB. The vertical axis shows gain (or loss) through the filter, assuming both the input and output are properly terminated. The horizontal axis represents frequency.

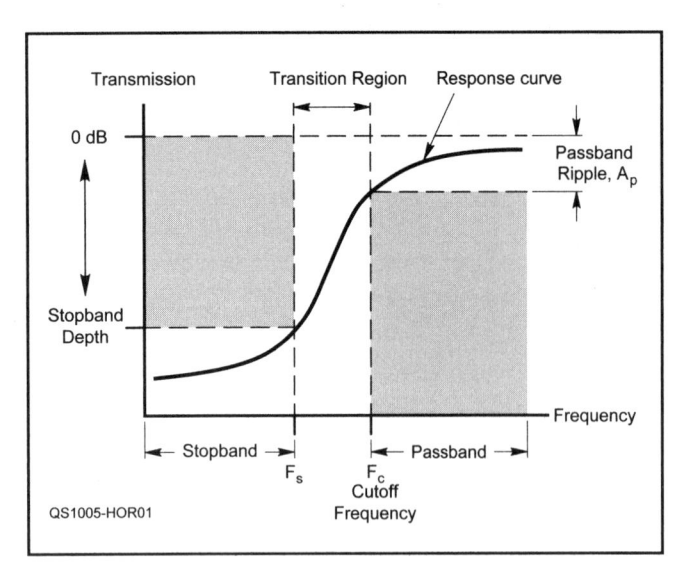

Figure 10.5 — The key specifications for a filter's amplitude response. As long as the filter response curve stays between the light gray boxes, the filter meets the design specification.

meters for a low-pass filter. Variations in amplitude of the response curve in the passband are called *ripple*. (Filters can also have ripple in the stopband for some design families as discussed later.) If the filter is made from passive components, there will be some losses in those components — the amount of loss is called *insertion loss* (IL). The attenuation for signal frequencies in the stopband far from the cutoff frequency is the filter's *ultimate attenuation*.

SPECIFYING A FILTER RESPONSE

Figure 10.5 shows a high-pass filter's *response curve* and some of the terms used to specify the filter's design. On the frequency axis, F_C is the cutoff frequency and F_S defines the *stopband width*. The passband for a high-pass filter consists of all frequencies above F_C. The stopband for a high-pass filter consists of all frequencies below F_S. The *transition region* is the range of frequencies between the stopband and passband. (For a low-pass filter, F_S and F_C are reversed along with the gray boxes they bound.)

The gray boxes leave a space between them through which the filter's response curve must pass. The borders of the gray boxes establish the required performance for the filter. The gray box defining the stopband is bounded on the bottom by the stopband depth. The filter's transmission in the stopband must be equal to or below the stopband depth. The gray box defining the passband is bounded on the top by the passband ripple. The filter's transmission in the passband must be equal to or greater than the passband ripple. Between F_S and F_C is the transition region in which the response curve passes between the stopband and passband. Any response curve that passes through the space between the gray boxes meets the performance requirements for the filter.

As frequency increases through the transition region from the passband into the stopband, the attenuation increases. *Rolloff*, the rate of change of the attenuation for frequencies above cutoff, is expressed in terms of dB of change per octave of frequency. A filter's response with high values of rolloff is called "sharp" or "steep" and "soft" or "shallow" if rolloff is low.

10.2.2 Filter Order

The steepness of the descent from the passband to the region of attenuation — the stopband — is dependent on the complexity of the filter, called the *order*. In a lumped-element filter made from inductors and capacitors, the order is determined by the number of separate energy-storing elements (either L or C) in the filter. For example, an RC filter with one resistor and one capacitor has an order of 1. A notch filter made of a single series-LC circuit has an order of 2. The definition of order for active and digital signal processing filters can be more complex, but the general understanding remains valid that the order of a filter determines how rapidly its response can change with frequency.

For example, **Figures 10.6** and **10.7** shows the magnitude response of one type of low-pass filter (Butterworth family) with orders varying from very simple ("N=2") to the more complex ("N=20"). For each order, frequency has been *normalized* to the ratio of frequency, f, to cutoff frequency, f_C. (i.e. Normalized cutoff frequency is always 1.0.) As the order increases, the rolloff also increases. Figure 10.6 has an expanded vertical scale to show the filter's behavior in the passband more clearly.

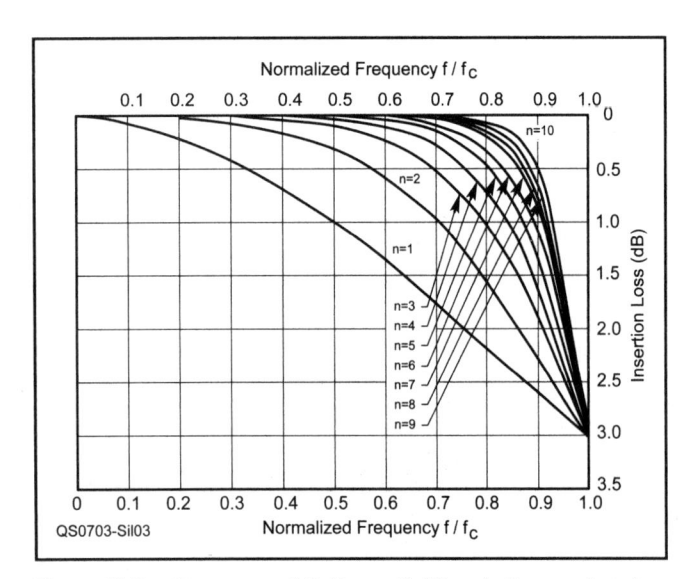

Figure 10.6 — Response of Butterworth filters in the passband below f_C. Frequency is shown as the normalized frequency, f/f_C.

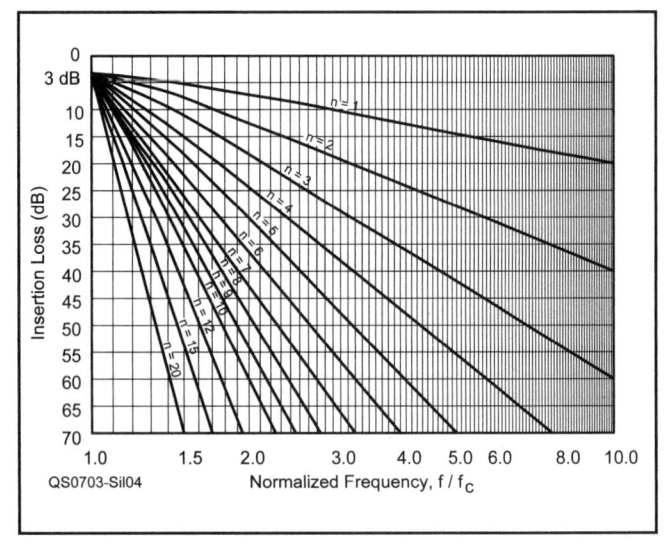

Figure 10.7 — Response of Butterworth filters in the transition and stop-bands above f_C. Frequency is shown as the normalized frequency, f/f_C.

10.2.3 Filter Families

There is no single "best" way to design a filter. Instead we have to decide on some traits and then choose the most appropriate *family* for our design. Different families have different traits, and filter families are commonly named after the mathematician or engineer responsible for defining their behavior mathematically. Each filter family is represented by a specific type of equation that describes the filter's behavior.

Two primary traits of the most importance to amateurs are used to describe the behavior of filter families: ripple (variations in the magnitude response within the passband and stopband) and rolloff. Different families of filters have different degrees of ripple and rolloff (and other characteristics, such as phase response).

With a flat magnitude response (and so no ripples in the passband) we have what is known as a *Butterworth* family design. This family also goes by the name of *Maximally Flat Magnitude* or *Maximally Flat Gain*. An example of the magnitude response of a filter from the Butterworth family is shown in **Figure 10.8**. (Most filter discussions are based on low-pass filters because the same concepts are easily extended to other types of filters and much of the mathematics behind filters is equivalent for the various types of frequency responses.)

By allowing magnitude response ripples in the passband, we can get a somewhat steeper rolloff from the passband into the stopband, particularly just beyond the cutoff frequency. A family that does this is the *Chebyshev* family. **Figure 10.9** illustrates how allowing magnitude ripple in the passband provides a sharper filter rolloff. This plot compares the 1-dB ripple Chebyshev with the no-ripple Butterworth filter down to 12 dB of attenuation.

Figure 10.9 also illustrates the usual definition of bandwidth for a low-pass Butterworth filter — the filter's 3-dB or cutoff frequency. For a low-pass Chebyshev filter, *ripple bandwidth* is used — the frequency range over which the filter's passband ripple is no greater than the specified limit. For example, the ripple bandwidth of a low-pass Chebyshev filter designed to have 1 dB of passband ripple is the highest frequency at which attenuation is 1 dB or less. The 3-dB bandwidth of the frequency of the filter will be somewhat greater.

A Butterworth filter is defined by specifying the order and bandwidth. The Chebyshev filter is defined by specifying the order, the ripple bandwidth, and the amount of passband ripple. In Figure 10.9, the Chebyshev filter has 1 dB of ripple; its ripple bandwidth is 1000 Hz. The Butterworth filter has a 3-dB bandwidth also of 1000 Hz. Some filter textbooks use the 3-dB point to define Chebyshev filters; most use the ripple bandwidth as illustrated here. The schematics (if you ignore parts values) of those two families are identical.

Even small amounts of ripple can be beneficial in terms of increasing a filter's rolloff. **Figure 10.10** compares a Butterworth filter (with the narrow line plot, no ripple in the passband) with a Chebyshev filter (wide line plot, 0.2 dB of ripple in the passband) down to 60 dB of attenuation. (For this comparison the cutoff frequencies at 3 dB of attenuation are the same for each filter.) Even that small amount of ripple in the Chebyshev filter passband allows a noticeably steeper rolloff between the passband and the stopband. As the passband ripple specification is increased, the steepness of the transition from passband to stopband increases, compared to the Butterworth family although the rolloff of the two families eventually becomes equal.

For Chebyshev filters, when the value of the passband ripple is changed, the magnitude response in the stopband region also changes. **Figure 10.11** compares the stopband response of Chebyshev filters with passband ripple ranging from 0.01 to 1 dB.

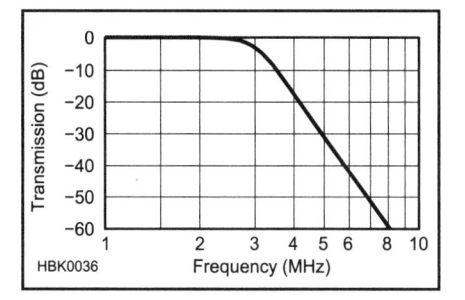

Figure 10.8 — Filters from the Butterworth family exhibit flat magnitude response in the passband.

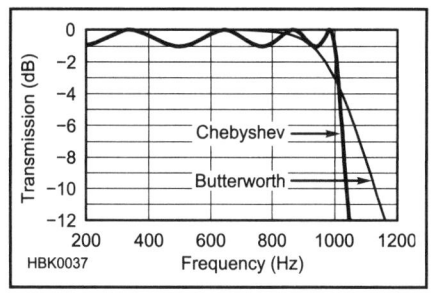

Figure 10.9 — This plot compares the response of a Chebyshev filter with a 1-dB ripple bandwidth of 1000 Hz and a Butterworth filter 3-dB bandwidth of 1000 Hz.

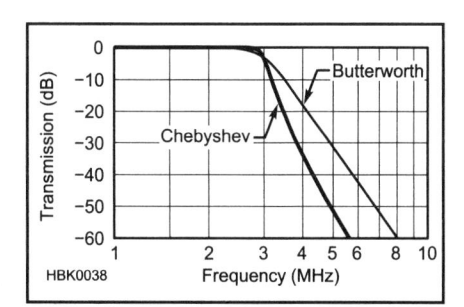

Figure 10.10 — A Chebyshev filter (0.2 dB passband ripple) allows a sharper cutoff than a Butterworth design with no passband ripple.

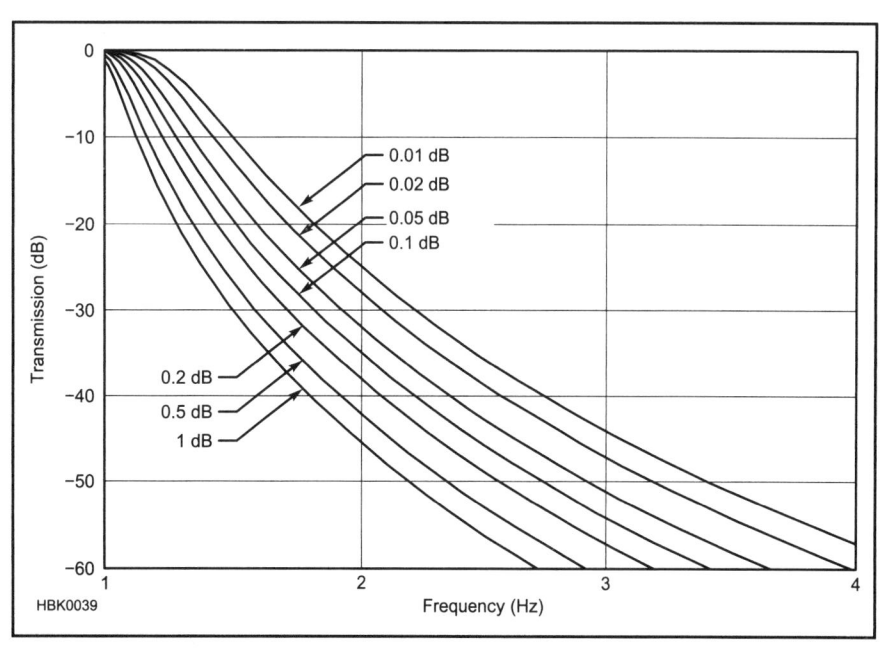

Figure 10.11 — These stop band response plots illustrate the Chebyshev family with various values of passband ripple. These plots are for a seventh-order low-pass design with ripple values from 0.01 to 1 dB. Ignoring the effects in the passband of high ripple values, increasing the ripple will allow somewhat steeper rolloff into the stop band area, and better ultimate attenuation in the stop band.

Analog and Digital Filtering

It is possible to obtain even steeper rolloff into the stopband by adding "traps" whose frequencies are carefully calculated. The resonant frequencies of those traps are in the stopband region and are set to yield best performance. When this is done, we have a *Cauer* family design (also called the *elliptic-function* design). The rolloff of the Cauer filter from the passband into the stopband is the steepest of all analog filter types provided that the behavior in the passband is uniform (either no ripple or a uniform amount of ripple). **Figure 10.12** shows the response of the Chebyshev and Cauer designs for comparison.

The Cauer filter is defined by specifying the order, the ripple bandwidth, and the passband ripple, just as for the Chebyshev. Again, an alternative bandwidth definition is to use the 3-dB frequency instead of the ripple bandwidth. The Cauer family requires one more specification: the *stopband frequency* and/or the *stopband depth*. The stopband frequency is the lowest frequency of a null or notch in the stopband. The stopband depth is the minimum amount of attenuation allowed in the stopband. In Figure 10.12, the stopband frequency is about 3.5 MHz and the stopband depth is 50 dB. For this comparison both designs have the same passband ripple value of 0.2 dB.

A downside to the Cauer filter is that the ultimate attenuation is some chosen value rather than ever increasing, as is the case with the other families. In the far stopband region (where frequency is much greater than the cutoff frequency) the rolloff of Cauer filters ultimately reaches 6 or 12 dB per octave, depending on the order. Odd-ordered Cauer filters have an ultimate rolloff rate of about 6 dB per octave while the even-ordered versions have an ultimate rolloff rate of about 12 dB per octave.

10.2.4 Group Delay

Another trait that can influence the choice of which filter family to use is the way the transit time of signals through the filter varies with frequency. This is known as *group delay*. ("Group" refers to a group of waves of similar frequency and phase moving through a media, in this case, the filter.) The wide line (lower plot) in **Figure 10.13** illustrates the group delay characteristics of a Chebyshev low-pass filter, while the upper plot (narrow line) shows the magnitude response. As shown in Figure 10.13, the group delay of components near the cutoff frequency becomes quite large when compared to that of components at lower and higher frequencies. This is a result of the phase shift of the filter's transmission being nonlinear with frequency; it is usually greater near the cutoff frequency. By delaying signals at different frequencies different amounts, the signal components are "smeared" in time. This

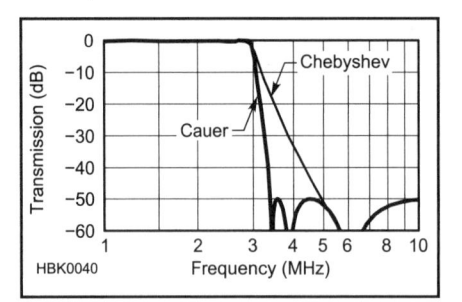

Figure 10.12 — The Cauer family has an even steeper rolloff from the passband into the stop band than the Chebyshev family. Note that the ultimate attenuation in the stop band is a design parameter rather than ever-increasing as is the case with other families.

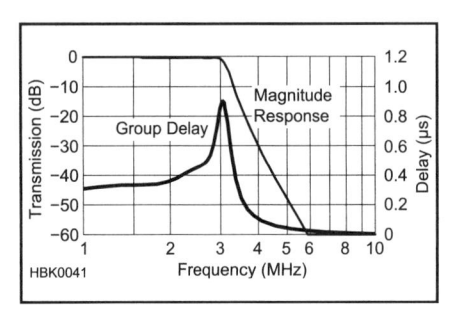

Figure 10.13 — Magnitude response and group delay of a Chebyshev low-pass filter.

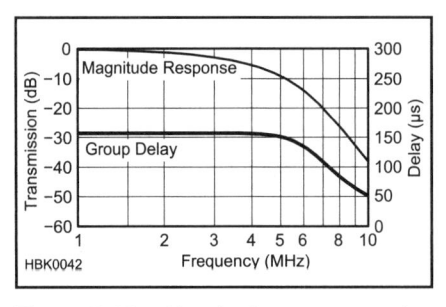

Figure 10.14 — Magnitude response and group delay of a Bessel low-pass filter.

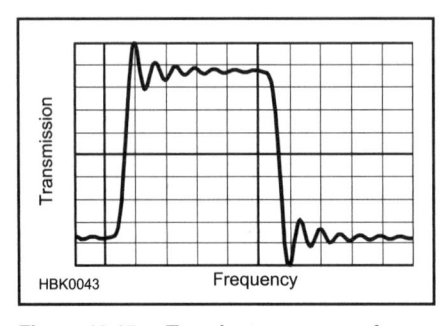

Figure 10.15 — Transient response of a Chebyshev low-pass filter.

causes distortion of the signal and can seriously disrupt high-speed data signals.

If a uniform group delay for signals throughout the passband is needed, then the *Bessel* filter family should be selected. The Bessel filter can be used as a delay-line or time-delay element although the gentle rolloff of the magnitude response may need to be taken into account. The magnitude and delay characteristics for the Bessel family are shown in **Figure 10.14**. Comparing the Bessel filter's response to that of the Butterworth in Figure 10.8 shows the difference in roll off.

A downside of Bessel family filters is that the rolloff characteristic is quite poor; they are not very good as a magnitude-response-shaping filter. The Bessel family is characterized largely by its constant group delay in the passband (for a low- or high-pass filter) shown as the bottom plot in Figure 10.14. The *constant-delay* characteristic of the Bessel extends into the stopband. The Bessel filter bandwidth is commonly defined by its 3-dB point (as with the Butterworth).

Because the Bessel filter is used when phase response is important, it is often characterized by the frequency at which a specific amount of phase shift occurs, usually one radian. (One radian is equal to $360 / 2\pi = 57.3°$.) Since the delay causes the output signal to lag behind the input signal, the filter is specified by its *one-radian lag frequency*.

10.2.5 Transient Response

Some applications require that a signal with sharp rising and falling edges (such as a digital data waveform) applied to the input of a low-pass design have a minimum *overshoot* or *ringing* as seen at the filter's output. Overshoot (and undershoot) occurs when a signal exceeds (falls below) the final amplitude temporarily before settling at its final value. Ringing is a repeated sequence of overshoot and undershoot.

If a sharp-cutoff analog filter is used in such an application, overshoot or ringing will occur. The appearance of a signal such as a square wave with sharp rising and falling edges as it exits from the filter may be as shown in **Figure 10.15**. The scales for both the X- and the Y-axes would depend on the frequency and magnitude of the waveform. (As described later in this chapter, digital filters can be designed not to exhibit this ringing, although they are much more complex than simple analog filters and have other tradeoffs.)

The sharp edge of the square wave is a type of *transient*, an abrupt change in a signal. When a signal at a constant level and changes to another level very rapidly where it remains constant, that type of transient is a *step*. If the signal abruptly changes levels and immediately changes back again, that type of transient is a *pulse*. If the pulse is infinitely narrow, it is called an *impulse* and has interesting mathematical characteristics as discussed below. The output of a circuit a transient occurs at its input is the circuit's *transient response*.

The square wave used in this discussion as a test waveform is composed of a fundamental and an endless series of odd harmonics. If harmonics only up to a certain order are used to create the square wave — that is, if the square wave is passed through a sharp-cutoff low-pass filter that attenuates higher frequencies — then that waveform will have the overshoot or ringing as shown as it exits from the filter. This is the filter's *step response*.

Transients can be repetitive, such as the edges of the square wave, but even a non-periodic waveform can be decomposed into sine waves, although in this case they are not harmonically-related. For example a single pulse of width τ seconds has a frequency spectrum proportional to sinc(fτ) = sin(πfτ)/(πfτ). You can think of this as an infinite number of sine waves spaced infinitely closely together with amplitudes that trace out that spectral shape. It is interesting to note that if τ is decreased, the value of f must increase by the same factor for any given value of sin(πfτ)/(πfτ). In other words, the narrower the pulse the wider the spectrum. Of course that applies to sine waves and other periodic waveforms as well — the smaller the wavelength the higher the frequency. In general, anything that makes the signal "skinnier" in the time domain makes it "fatter" in the frequency domain and vice versa.

As the pulse becomes narrower and narrower, the frequency spectrum spreads out more and more. In the limit, if the pulse is made infinitely narrow (an impulse), the spectrum becomes flat from zero hertz to infinity.

The impulse is a very useful concept because of its flat frequency spectrum. The filter's *impulse response* has a frequency spectrum equal to the frequency response of the filter.

10.2.6 Filter Family Selection

Selecting a filter family is one of the first steps in filter design. To make that choice easier, the following list of filter family attributes is provided:
- Butterworth — No ripple in passband, smooth transition region, shallow rolloff for a given filter order, high ultimate attenuation, smooth group delay change across transition region. The smoothness of the response is particularly apparent near dc for the low-pass response, at the center frequency for a bandpass response, and at infinity for the high-pass response. The resulting magnitude response will also have a relatively gentle transition from the passband into the stop band.
- Chebyshev — Some passband ripple, abrupt transition region, steep rolloff for a given filter order, peak in group delay near cutoff frequency, high ultimate attenuation. The Chebyshev family is used when a sharper cutoff is desired for a given number of components and where at least a small amount of ripple is allowable in the passband.
- Cauer (or Elliptical-function) — Some passband ripple, abrupt transition region, steepest roll off, ripple in stopband due to traps, ultimate attenuation smaller than Butterworth and Chebyshev, group delay peaks near cutoff frequency and in stopband. When steepness of rolloff from passband into stop band is the item of greatest importance, then the Cauer filter family is used. Cauer filters involve a more complicated set of choices. In addition to selecting a passband ripple, the designer must also assign a stop band depth (or stop band frequency). Some of the items interact; they can't all be selected arbitrarily.
- Bessel — No ripple in passband, smooth transition region, constant group delay in passband, shallow rolloff for a given filter order, smooth changes in group delay, high ultimate attenuation

All characterizations such as "steep" and "abrupt" are relative with respect to filter designs from other families with similar orders. Other factors, such as number of components, sensitivity to component value and so on may need to be considered when selecting a filter family for a specific application.

All of the traits mentioned so far in this chapter apply to a filter regardless of how it is implemented, whether it is fabricated using *passive* lumped-element inductors and capacitors or using op amps with resistors and capacitors (an *active* filter) or in software as a digital filter. The traits are general descriptions of filter behavior and can be applied to any type of filter technology. Each type of technology (passive, active, digital) has strong points and tradeoffs.

These four families are the most common, but other families are used as well: for example, Gaussian, Constant-k, and M-derived are all supported by the *ELSIE* filter design package provided with this book's downloadable supplemental information

Digital filters also implement these filter families and others, as well. They also have other classes, such as FIR and IIR, as described in this chapter's section on digital filters. For more information about analog and digital filter design, a list of references and articles is provided at the end of this chapter.

10.3 Passive LC Filters

This part of the chapter deals with passive LC filters fabricated using discrete inductors and capacitors (which gives rise to their name, *lumped-element*). We will begin with a discussion of basic low-pass filters and then generalize to other types of filters.

10.3.1 Low-Pass Filters

A very basic LC filter built using inductors and capacitors is shown in **Figure 10.16**. In the first case (Figure 10.16A), less power is delivered to the load at higher frequencies because the reactance of the inductor in series with the load increases as the test frequency increases. The voltage appearing at the load goes down as the frequency increases. This configuration would pass direct current (dc) and reject higher frequencies, and so it would be a low-pass filter.

With the second case (Figure 10.16B), less power is delivered to the load at higher frequencies because the reactance of the capacitor in parallel with the load decreases as the test frequency increases. Again, the voltage appearing at the load goes down as the frequency increases and so this, too, would be called a low-pass filter. In the real world, combinations of both series and parallel components are used to form a low-pass filter.

A high-pass filter can be made using the opposite configuration — series capacitors and shunt inductors. And a band-pass (or bandstop) filter can be made using pairs of series and parallel tuned circuits. These filters, made from alternating LC elements or LC tuned circuits, are called *ladder filters*.

We spoke of filter order, or complexity, earlier in this chapter. **Figure 10.17** illustrates *capacitor-input* low-pass filters with orders of 3, 4 and 5. Remember that the order corresponds to the number of energy-storing elements. For example, the third-order filter in Figure 10.17A has three energy-storing elements (two capacitors and one inductor), while the fifth-order design in Figure 10.17C has five elements total (three capacitors, two inductors). For comparison, a third-order filter is illustrated in **Figure 10.18**. The filters in Figure 10.17 are *capacitor-input* filters because a capacitor is connected directly across the input source. The filter in Figure 10.18 is an *inductor-input* filter.

As mentioned previously, the Cauer family

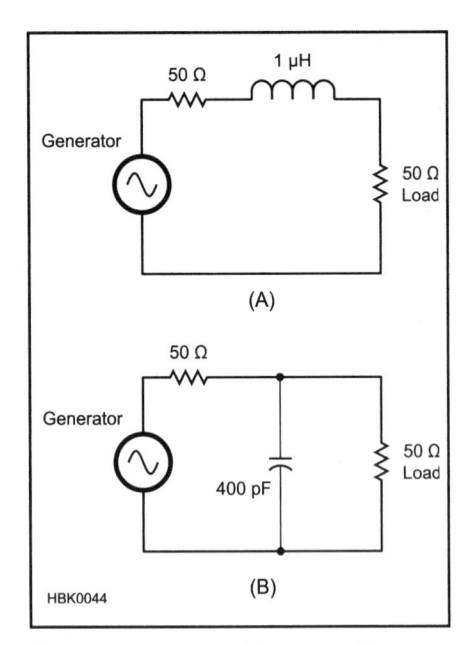

Figure 10.16 — A basic low-pass filter can be formed using a series inductor (A) or a shunt capacitor (B).

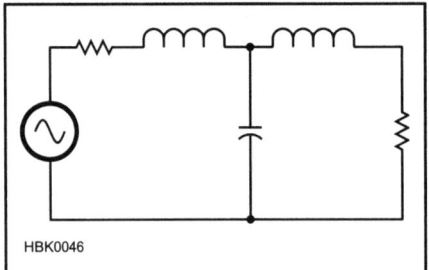

Figure 10.18 — A third-order inductor-input low-pass filter.

has traps (series or parallel tuned circuits) carefully added to produce dips or notches (properly called *zeros*) in the stop band. Schematics for the Cauer versions of capacitor-input low-pass filters with orders of 3, 4 and 5 are shown in **Figure 10.19**. The capacitors in parallel with the series inductors create the notches at calculated frequencies to allow the Cauer filter to be implemented.

The capacitor-input and the inductor-input versions of a given low-pass design have identical characteristics for their magnitude, phase and time responses, but they differ in the impedance seen looking into the filter. The capacitor-input filter has low impedance in the stop band while the inductor-input filter has high impedance in the stop band.

10.3.2 Low-Pass to Band-Pass Transformation

A band-pass filter is defined in part by a *bandwidth* and a *center frequency*. (An alternative method is to specify a lower and an upper cutoff frequency.) A low-pass design such as the one shown in Figure 10.17A can be converted to a band-pass filter by resonating each of the elements at the center frequency. **Figure 10.20** shows a third-order low-pass filter with a design bandwidth of 2 MHz for use in a 50 Ω system. If the shunt elements are now resonated with a parallel component, and if the series elements are resonated with a series component, the result

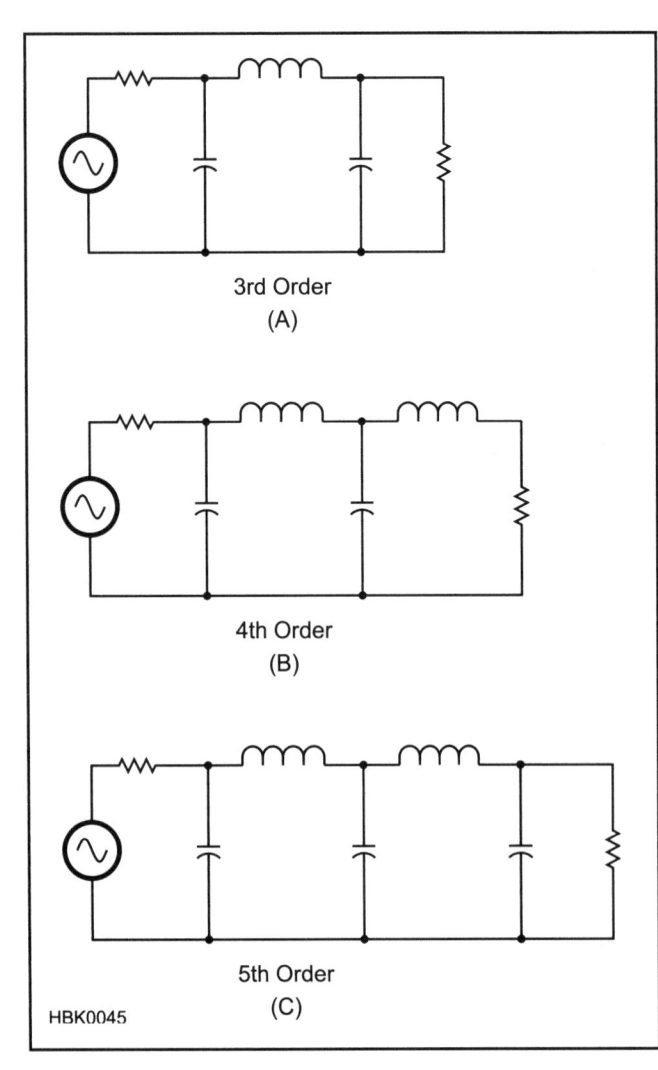

Figure 10.17 — Low-pass, capacitor-input filters for the Butterworth and Chebyshev families with orders 3, 4 and 5.

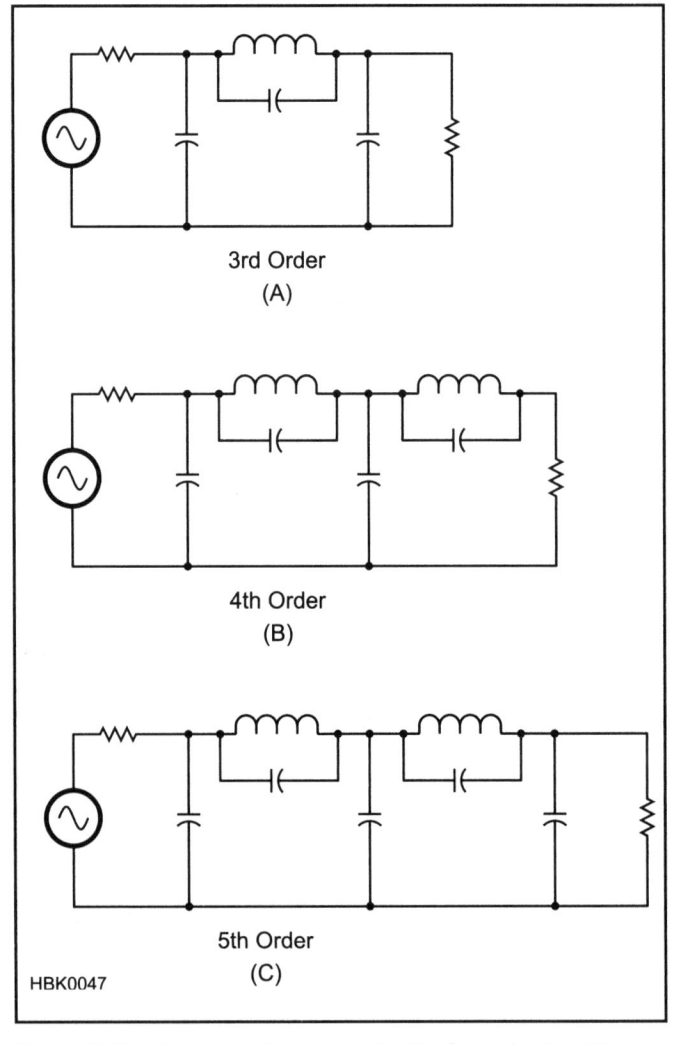

Figure 10.19 — Low-pass topologies for the Cauer family with orders 3, 4 and 5.

10.8 Chapter 10

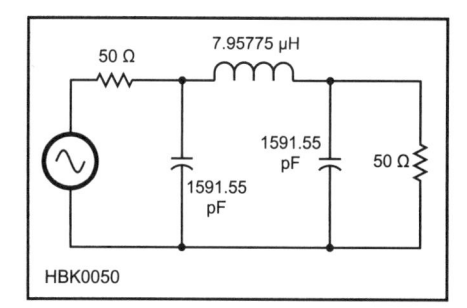

Figure 10.20 — Third-order low-pass filter with a bandwidth of 2 MHz in a 50 Ω system.

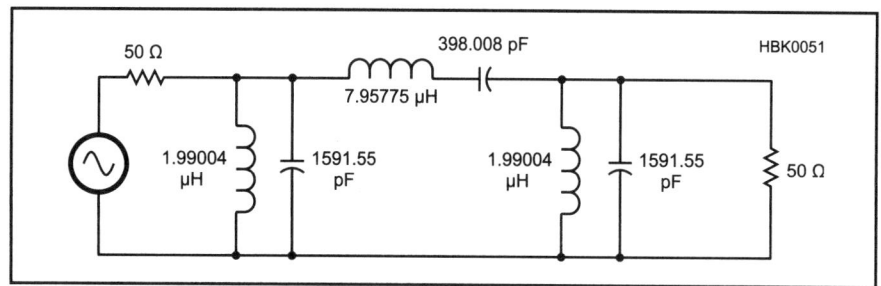

Figure 10.21 — The low-pass filter of Figure 10.20 can be transformed to a band-pass filter by resonating the shunt capacitors with a parallel inductor and resonating the series inductor with a series capacitor. Bandwidth is 2 MHz and the center frequency is 2.828 MHz.

is a band-pass filter as shown in **Figure 10.21**. The series inductor value and the shunt capacitor values are the same as those for the original low-pass design.

10.3.3 High-Pass Filters

A high-pass filter passes signals above its cutoff frequency and attenuates those below. Simple high-pass equivalents of the filters in Figure 10.16 are shown in **Figure 10.22.**

The reactance of the series capacitor in Figure 10.22A increases as the test frequency is lowered and so at lower frequencies there will be less power delivered to the load. Similarly, the reactance of the shunt inductor in Figure 10.22B decreases at lower frequency, with the same effect. Similarly to the low-pass filter designs presented in Figure 10.17, a high-pass filter in a real world design would typically use both series and shunt components but with the positions of inductors and capacitors exchanged.

An example of a high-pass filter application would be a broadcast-reject filter designed to pass amateur-band signals in the range of 3.5 MHz and above while rejecting broadcast signals at 1.7 MHz and below. A high-pass filter with a design cutoff of 2 MHz is illustrated in **Figure 10.23**. It can be implemented as a capacitor-input (Figure 10.23A) or inductor-input (Figure 10.23B) design. In each case, signals above the cutoff are passed with minimum attenuation while signals below the cutoff are attenuated, in a manner similar to the action of a low-pass filter.

10.3.4 High-Pass to Band-Stop Transformation

Just as a low-pass filter can be transformed to a band-pass type, a high-pass filter can be transformed into a band-stop (also called a *band-reject*) filter. The procedures for doing this are similar in nature to those of the transformation from low-pass to band-pass. As with the band-pass filter example, to transform a high-pass to a band-stop we need to specify a center frequency. The bandwidth of a band-stop filter is measured between the frequencies at which the magnitude response drops 3 dB in the transition region into the stop band.

Figure 10.24 shows how to convert the 2 MHz capacitor-input high-pass filter of Figure 10.20A to a band-stop filter centered at

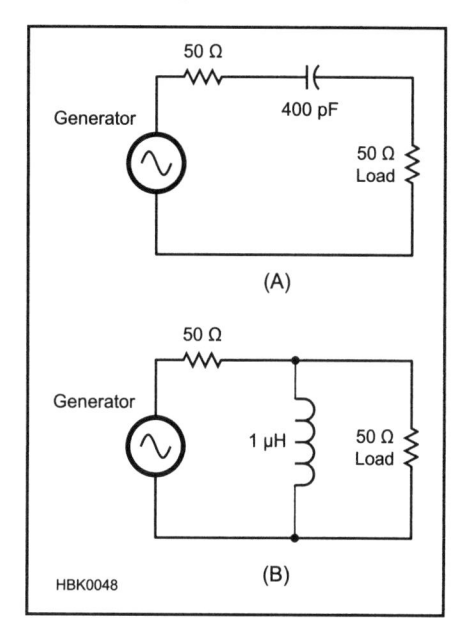

Figure 10.22 — A basic high-pass filter can be formed using a series capacitor (A) or a shunt inductor (B).

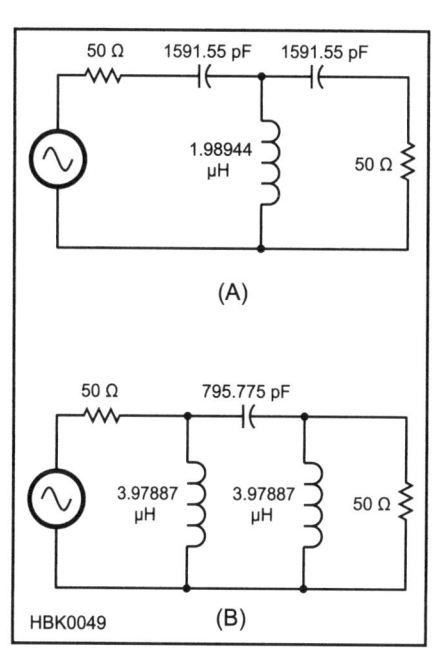

Figure 10.23 — Capacitor-input (A) and inductor-input (B) high-pass filters. Both designs have a 2 MHz cutoff.

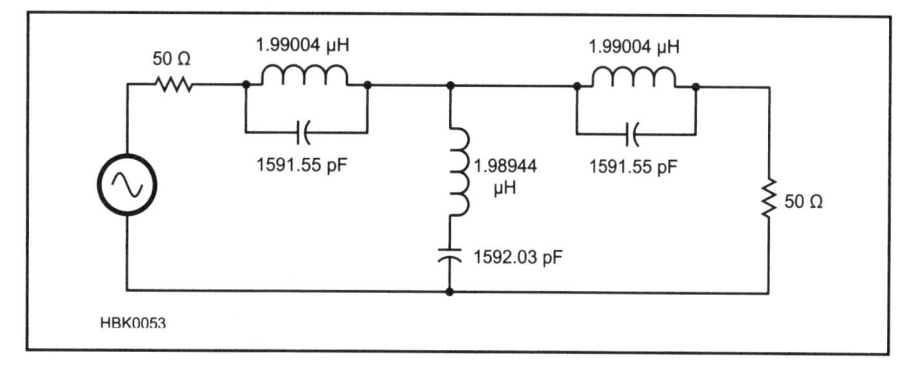

Figure 10.24 — The high-pass filter of Figure 10.23A can be converted to a band-stop filter with a bandwidth of 2 MHz, centered at 2.828 MHz.

2.828 MHz. The original high-pass components are resonated at the chosen center frequency to form a band-stop filter. Either a capacitor-input high-pass or an inductor-input high-pass may be transformed in this manner. In this case the series capacitor values and the shunt inductor values for the band-stop are the same as those for the high-pass. The series elements are resonated with an element in parallel with them. Similarly, the shunt elements are also resonated with an element in series with them. In each case the pair resonate at the center frequency of the band-stop.

10.3.5 Effect of Component Q

When components with less-than-ideal characteristics are used to fabricate a filter, the performance will also be less than ideal. One such item to be concerned about is component "Q." As described in the **Radio Fundamentals** chapter, Q is a measure of the loss in an inductor or capacitor, as determined by its resistive component. Q is the ratio of component's reactance to the loss resistance and is specified at a given test frequency. The loss resistance referred to here includes not only the value as measured by an ohmmeter but includes all sources of loss, such as skin effect, dielectric heating and so on.

The Q values for capacitors are usually greater than 500 and may reach a few thousand. Q values for inductors seldom reach 500 and may be as low as 20 or even worse for miniaturized parts. A good toroidal inductor can have a Q value in the vicinity of 250 to 400.

Q values can affect both the *insertion loss* of signals passing through the filter and the steepness of the filter's rolloff. Band-pass filters (and especially narrowband band-pass filters) are more vulnerable to this problem than low-pass and high-pass filters. **Figure 10.25** shows the effect of finite values of inductor Q values on the response of a low-pass filter. The Q values for each plot are as shown.

Inadequate component Q values introduce loss and more importantly they compromise the filter's response at cutoff, especially problematic in the case of narrowband band-pass filters. **Figure 10.26** illustrates the effect of finite inductor Q values on a narrowband band-pass filter. In the case of a band-pass filter, the Q values required to support a given response shape are much higher than those required for the low-pass or high-pass filter (by the ratio of center to width). Capacitor Q values are generally much high than inductor Q values and so contribute far less to this effect.

In general, component-value adjustment will not be able to fully compensate for inadequate component Q values. However, if the filter is deliberately mismatched (by changing the input and/or output terminations) then a limited amount of *response-shape* correction can sometimes be achieved by network component value optimization ("tweaking"). The loss caused by Q problems (at dc in the case of a low-pass or at the center frequency in the case of a band-pass) may increase if such correction is attempted.

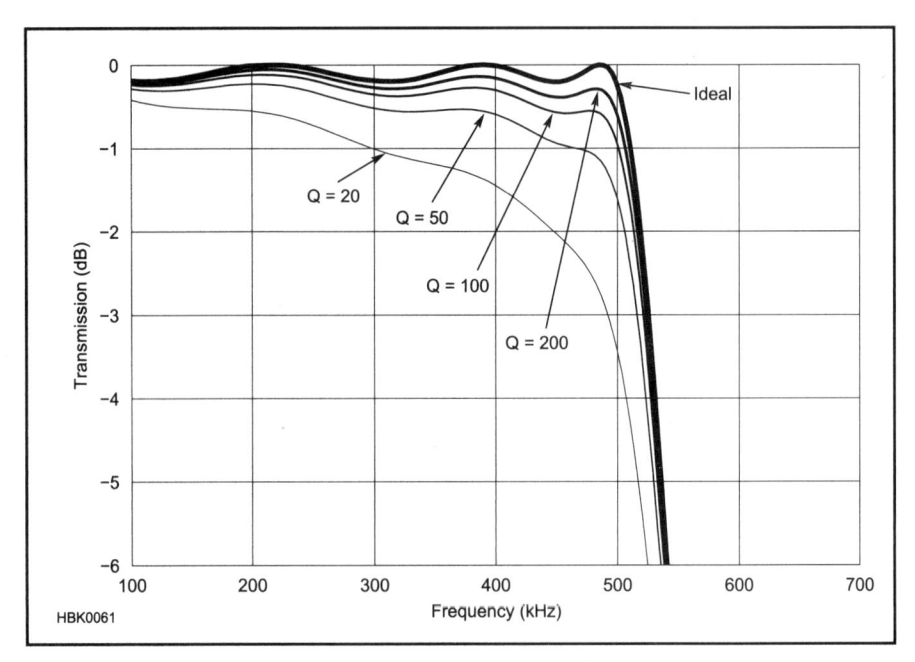

Figure 10.25 — Effect of inductor Q values on a low-pass filter.

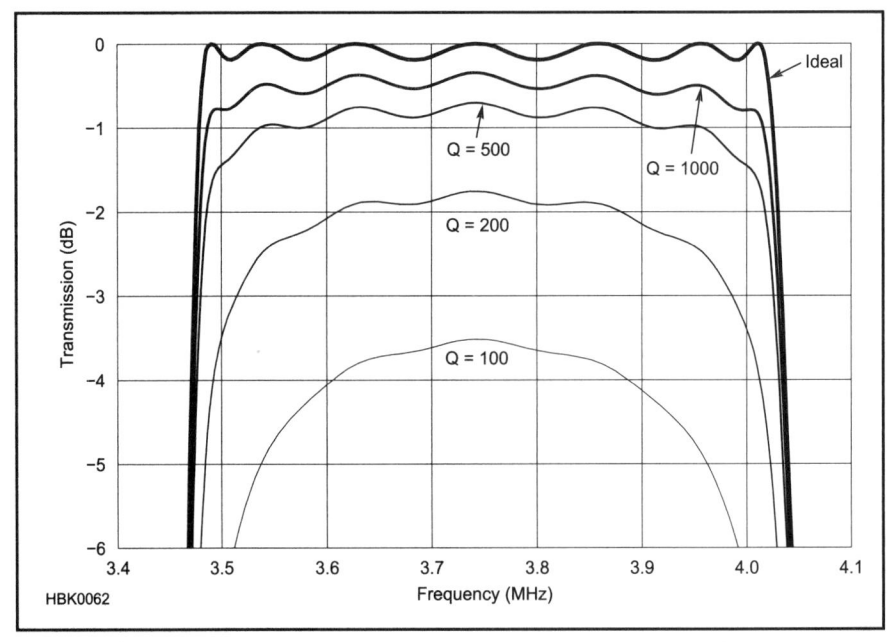

Figure 10.26 — Effect of inductor Q values on a narrowband band-pass filter.

10.3.6 Side Effects of Passband Ripple

Especially in RF applications it is desirable to design a filter such that the impedance seen looking into the input side remains fairly constant over the passband. Increasing the value of passband ripple increases the rate of descent from the passband into the stop band, giving a sharper cutoff. But it also degrades the uniformity of the impedance across the passband as seen looking into the input of the filter. This may be shown in terms of VSWR or return loss; those are simply different ways of stating the same effect. (*Return loss* is explained in the **RF Techniques** chapter.)

Designs using a low value of passband ripple are preferred for RF work. Audio-frequency applications are generally not as critical, and so higher ripple values (up to about 0.2 dB) may be used in audio work.

Table 10.2
Passband Ripple, VSWR and Return Loss

Passband Ripple (dB)	VSWR	Return Loss (dB)
0.0005	1.022	39.38
0.001	1.031	36.37
0.002	1.044	33.36
0.005	1.07	29.39
0.01	1.101	26.38
0.02	1.145	23.37
0.05	1.24	19.41
0.1	1.355	16.42
0.2	1.539	13.46
0.5	1.984	9.636
1	2.66	6.868

Note: As the passband ripple specification is changed so do the other items. Conversely, to limit VSWR to a maximum value or return loss to at least some minimum value, use this table to find the passband ripple that should be used to design the filter.

Table 10.2 shows the maximum value of VSWR and minimum value of return loss for various values of passband ripple. Note that lower values for passband ripple yield better values for VSWR and return loss. Specifying a filter to have a passband ripple value of 0.01 dB will result in that filter's VSWR figure to be about 1.1:1. Or restated, the return loss will be about 26 dB. These values will be a function of frequency and at some test frequencies may be much better.

10.3.7 Use of Filters at VHF and UHF

Even when filters are designed and built properly, they may be rendered totally ineffective if not installed properly. Leakage around a filter can be quite high at VHF and UHF, where wavelengths are short. Proper attention to shielding and good grounding is mandatory for minimum leakage. Poor coaxial cable shield connection into and out of the filter is one of the greatest offenders with regard to filter leakage. Proper dc-lead bypassing throughout the receiving system is good practice, especially at VHF and above. Ferrite beads placed over the dc leads may help to reduce leakage. Proper filter termination is required to minimize loss.

Most VHF RF amplifiers optimized for noise figure do not have a 50 Ω input impedance. As a result, any filter attached to the input of an RF amplifier optimized for noise figure will not be properly terminated and filter loss may rise substantially. As this loss is directly added to the RF amplifier noise figure, carefully choose and place filters in the receiver.

10.3.8 Design Software for LC Filters

Previous editions of this book included an extensive set of design tables and formulas for manual calculation of filter component values. While this method was certainly instructive, it was tedious and error-prone, particularly for higher-order designs. The sections that described this method in previous editions have been extracted as a PDF document that is provided with the downloadable supplemental information for this book.

Filter design is almost universally performed with software today and the *ARRL Handbook* is fortunate to include such a package. Jim Tonne, W4ENE, has made available a version of *ELSIE*, a filter design program, to amateurs at no charge. The latest version of *ELSIE* and related programs are available for downloading with the downloadable supplemental content. The list of software is presented at the beginning of this chapter and the program capabilities are listed below.

Users unfamiliar with *ELSIE* will benefit from following the "walkthrough" accessible from the program's ABOUT menu tab. A presentation by W4ENE explaining *ELSIE* is available at **www.tonnesoftware.com/downloads/FilterTutorial.pdf**. Numerous design examples and tutorials are available as online videos hosted on YouTube.com — search for "elsie filter design tutorial" to locate a good starting set. A two-part step-by-step tutorial for using *ELSIE* from the Hands-On Radio series of columns is available in the downloadable supplemental material for this book as well.

- *ELSIE* — design and analysis of lumped-element LC filters. In addition to providing parts values for filters with various topologies from various families, tools are included to assist with practical construction.
- *SVC Filter Designer* — design of lumped-element high-pass and low-pass filters. The software shows ideal values and also the nearest 5% values for capacitors and inductors. It also analyzes those filters and shows the deviation of key responses from ideal when those 5% values are used.
- *QuadNet* — design and analysis of active quadrature ("90-degree") networks for use in SSB transmitters and receivers. It handles networks with orders from 2 to 10, odd and even, with tuning modes and analysis.
- *Helical* — design and analysis of helical-resonator bandpass filters usually used in the VHF and UHF frequency ranges.
- *Diplexer* — design and analysis of diplexer filters.

10.4 Active Audio Filters

Below RF, in what is broadly referred to as the "audio" range between a few Hz and a few hundred kHz, designers have several choices of filter technology.
- Passive LC
- DSP Digital Filters
- Switched-Capacitor Audio Filter (SCAF)
- Active RC

LC audio filters are not used much in current designs except in high-power audio applications, such as speaker crossover networks, and are not covered here. LC filters were once popular as external audio filters for CW reception. These designs tended to be large and bulky, often using large surplus 44 or 88 mH core inductors. (A classic *ARRL Handbook* project to construct a passive LC CW filter can be found in the downloadable supplemental material for this book.) LC filters used in very low-level receiver applications can be very compact, but these tend to suffer from relatively high insertion loss, which reduces the receiver sensitivity (if no preamp is used ahead of the filter) or its large-signal dynamic range (if a loss-compensating preamp is used ahead of the filter). In addition, LC filters used in low-level receiver applications tend to pick up 60/120 Hz hum from stray magnetic fields from ac power transformers. Even "self shielded" inductors can produce noticeable ac hum pick up when followed by 90 to 120 dB of audio gain!

Digital filtering (see the following section of this chapter) can yield filters that are superior to analog filters. High signal-level DSP-based external audio filters such as the popular Timewave DSP-599 (**www.timewave.com**) and MFJ Enterprises MFJ-784B (**www.mfjenterprises.com**) have been available for some time. In addition, if the filter is coupled to a high-performance audio A/D converter, digital filtering can provide excellent filtering for even very low-level audio signals.

The main drawback to standalone digital filters is that of expense. A low-end DSP external audio filter costs at least $100, while a DSP with a high-end A/D converter (such as an audio sound card front-end to a PC) can run in the $150 to $400+ price range, which does not include the cost of the host PC.

10.4.1 SCAF Filters

Simple SCAF filter designs can produce extremely effective low-power audio filters. The implementation of these filters in practical IC form usually involves small-value capacitors and high-value resistors. The use of high-value resistors tends to generate enough noise to make these filters unsuitable for very low-level audio processing such as the front end of a receiver audio chain. Thus, SCAF filters tend to be limited to filtering at the output end of the audio chain — headphone or speaker level audio applications, an area in which they very much excel. The cutoff frequency of a SCAF filter is set by an external clock signal. Thus, this class of filter naturally lends itself to use in variable frequency filters. For simplicity, excellent frequency selectivity and relatively low cost, SCAF filters are highly recommended when additional audio filtering is desired on the output of an existing receiver.

An example of a very simple, but highly effective SCAF low-pass filter IC is the Maxim MAX7426 (5 V supply) or MAX7427 (3 V supply) in **Figure 10.27**. The filter's cutoff frequency can be set by placing an appropriately sized capacitor across the clock oscillator inputs because the part can generate its own internal clock signal. For example, connecting a 180 pF capacitor across the MAX7426's clock inputs will produce a 1 kHz low-pass filter. The MAX7427 (3-V version) was used in the NC2030 QRP transceiver along with a MVAM108 varactor diode to create a low-pass filter that was tunable from 300 Hz to 1 kHz.

A portion of that schematic is shown in **Figure 10.28**. The SCAF low-pass filter is followed by a 3-V unity-gain headphone amplifier (U14C and U14D) as the filter IC itself cannot directly drive headphones. The low-pass cutoff frequency is tuned by using R83 to vary the voltage applied across the MVAM108 varactor diode D10, thus changing the capacitance across the clock input (pin 8) of the chip. C116 was used to isolate the dc voltage across the varactor diode from the bias voltage on the clock input line. The frequency response of such a filter is shown in **Figure 10.29**.

As can be seen, this is an extremely sharp filter, producing almost 40 dB of attenuation very close to the cut off frequency — not too bad for an inexpensive part. The slightly more expensive MAX7403 gives an even steeper 80 dB cutoff. Both parts are specified for an 80 dB signal-to-noise ratio based on an assumed 4-V_{P-P} signal. Sensitive modern in-ear type headphones require only 20 mV_{P-P} to produce a fairly loud signal. A 20 mV signal is 46 dB below 4 V_{P-P}, so at such headphone levels, the noise floor is actually only 34 dB below the 4 V_{P-P} signal — fairly quiet, but is a lot less noise margin than one would tend to think given the 80 dB specification.

Again, with a noise floor only 34 dB below typical headphone levels, SCAF filters such as these are fine at the end of the receiver chain,

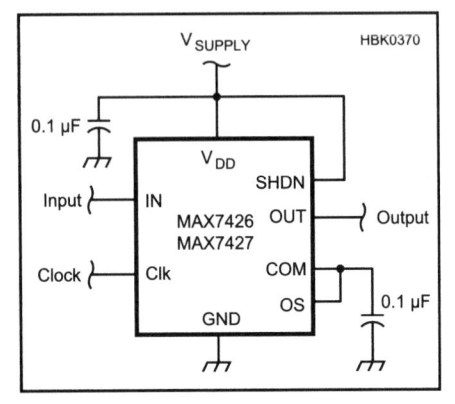

Figure 10.27 — Simple SCAF low pass filter, taken from the MAX7426 data sheet.

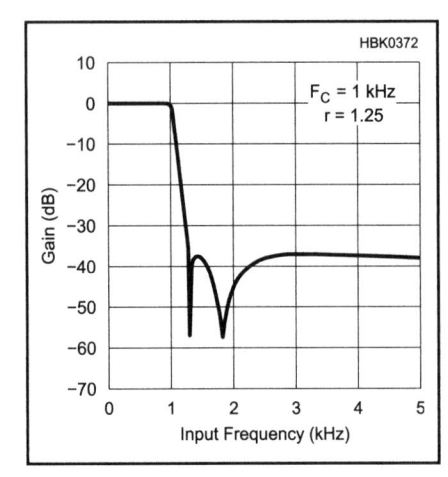

Figure 10.29 — Frequency response of a low-pass filter using the MAX7426 set to a 1 kHz cutoff frequency.

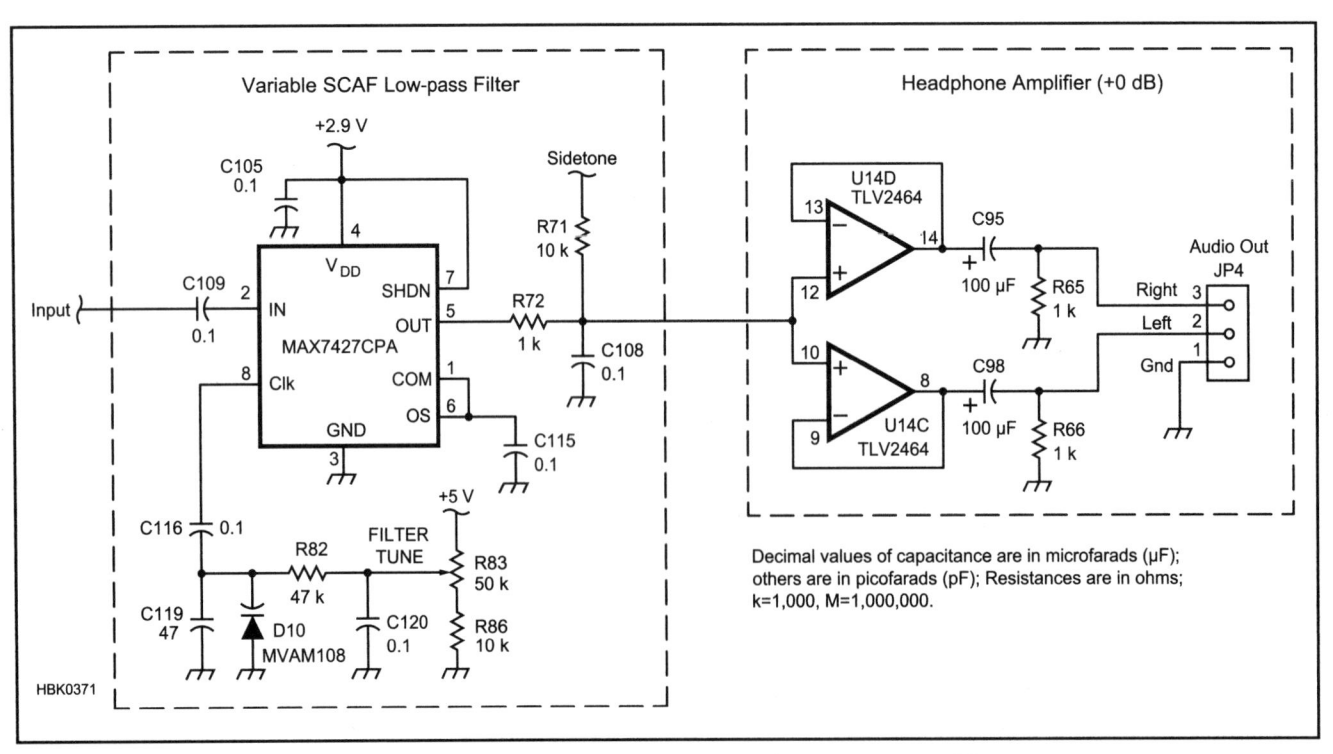

Figure 10.28 — SCAF with variable 300 to 1000 Hz low-pass cutoff and unity-gain headphone amplifier.

but are not useful as an audio filter at very low signal levels early on in a receiver.

Figure 10.30 is an example of a slightly more complex SCAF band-pass filter. This filter features both a variable center frequency (450 Hz to 1000 Hz) and a variable bandwidth (90 Hz to 1500 Hz). This very popular filter, the NESCAF, was designed by the New England QRP Club (**www.newenglandqrp.org**) and is currently offered in kit form in batches. Contact the club if you wish to purchase the kit. The design is included here and is well within the range of a home-builder with intermediate construction skills. There are number of online websites that discuss the filter and how to build it.

The NESCAF filter features both sections of the SCAF10 IC configured as identical band-pass filters. The bandwidth (Q) is adjustable via R7A and R7B, while the center frequency is adjustable by R10 and the trimmer R9 as these resistors set the frequency of the LM555 clock generator.

As in the previous SCAF filter example, this filter also includes an audio amplifier (LM386) for driving either an external speaker or headphones as none of the SCAF filter ICs are capable of driving headphones directly.

10.4.2 Active RC Filters

Active RC filters based on op amp circuits can be used in either high-level audio output or very low-level direct-conversion receiver front-end filtering applications and thus are extremely flexible. Unlike LC filters, active RC filters can provide both filtering and gain at the same time, eliminating the relatively high insertion loss of a physically small, sharp LC filter. In addition, an active RC filter is not susceptible to the same ac hum pickup in low signal level applications as LC filters.

Active filters can be designed for gain and they offer excellent stage-to-stage isolation. The circuits require only resistors and capacitors, avoiding the limitations associated with inductors. By using gain and feedback, filter Q is controllable to a degree unavailable to passive LC filters. Despite the advantages, there are also some limitations. They require power, and performance may be limited by the op amp's finite input and output levels, gain and bandwidth. Active filters that drive speakers or other heavy loads usually employ an audio output amplifier circuit to boost the output power after a low-power filter stage.

A particular advantage of active RC filters for use in receivers is that they can be capable of extremely low noise operation, allowing the filtering of extremely small signals. At the same time they are capable of handling extremely large signals. Op amps are often capable of using ±18-V dual supply voltages or 36-V single supply voltages allowing the construction of a very high performance audio filter/amplifier chain that can handle signals up to 33 V_{P-P}. The ability to provide gain while also providing filtering provides a lot of flexibility in managing the sensitivity of a receiver audio chain.

The main disadvantage of active RC filters is their relatively high parts count compared to other filter types. In addition, active RC filters tend to be fixed-frequency designs unlike SCAF filters whose frequency can be moved simply by changing the clock frequency that drives the SCAF IC.

10.4.3 Active Filter Responses

Active filters can implement any of the passive LC filter responses described in the preceding section: low-pass, high-pass, band-pass, band-stop and all-pass. Filter family responses such as Butterworth, Chebyshev, Bessel and

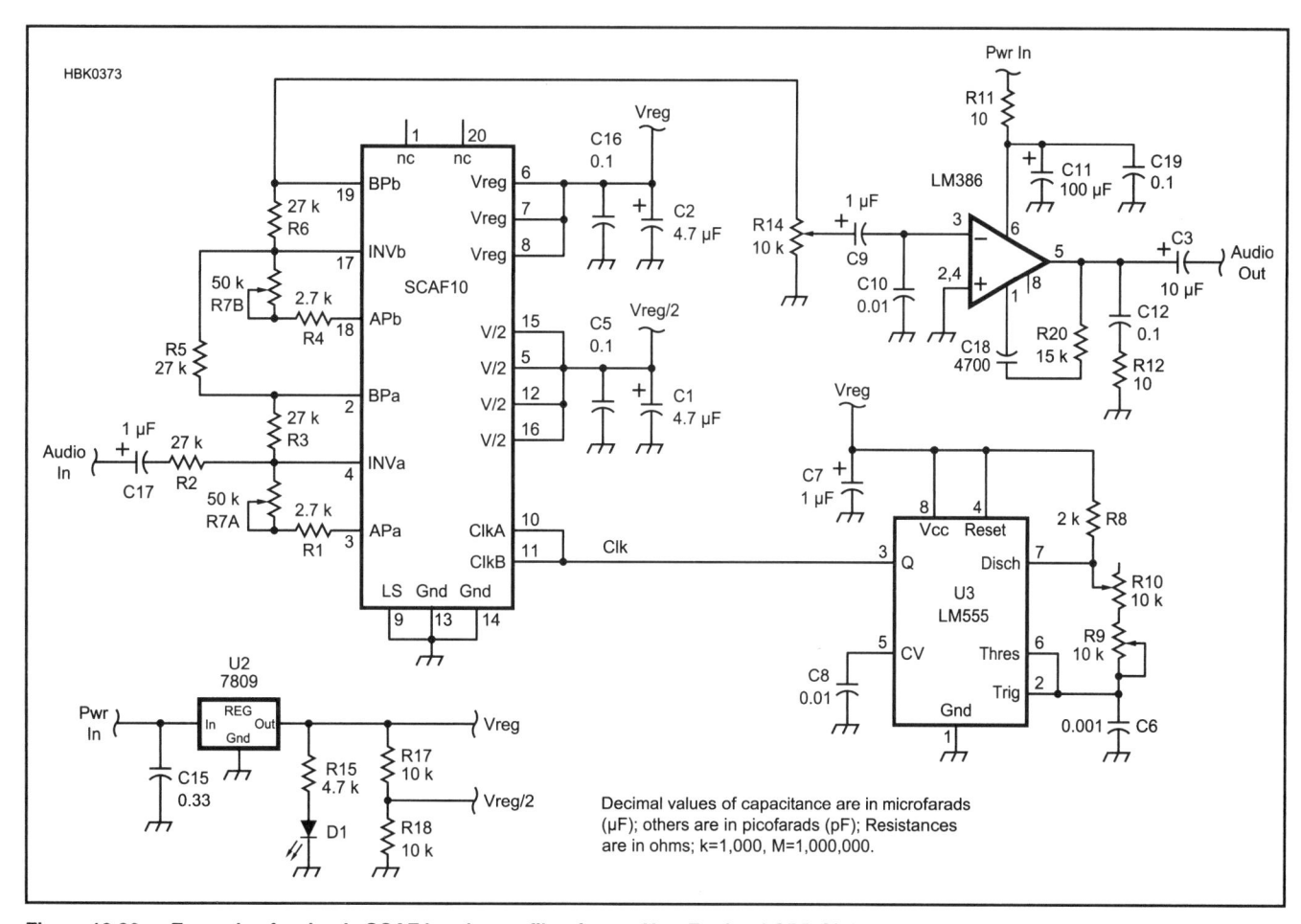

Figure 10.30 — Example of a simple SCAF band-pass filter from a New England QRP Club kit.

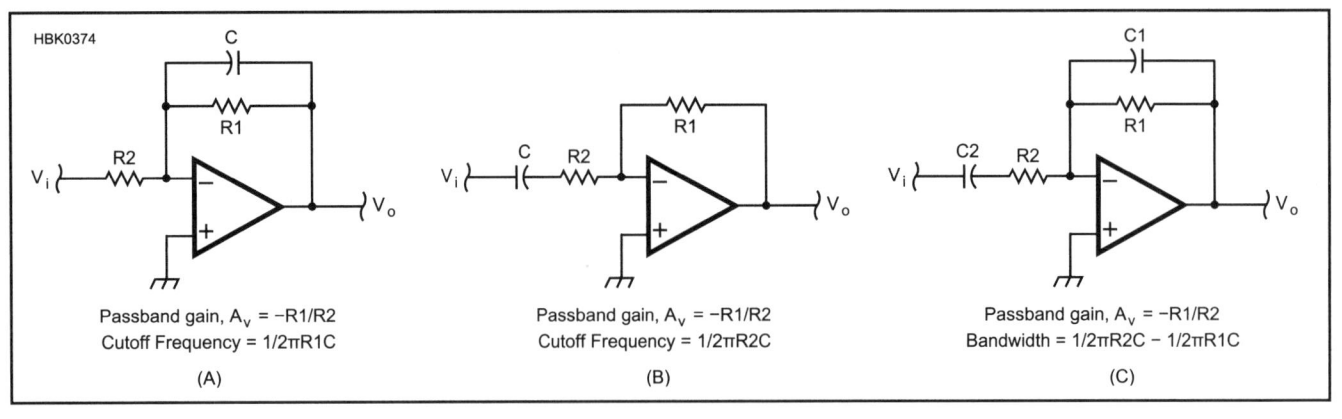

Figure 10.31 — Simple active filters. A low-pass filter is shown at A; B is a high-pass filter. The circuit at C combines the low- and high-pass filters into a wide band-pass filter.

Passband gain, $A_V = -R1/R2$
Cutoff Frequency = $1/2\pi R1C$
(A)

Passband gain, $A_V = -R1/R2$
Cutoff Frequency = $1/2\pi R2C$
(B)

Passband gain, $A_V = -R1/R2$
Bandwidth = $1/2\pi R2C - 1/2\pi R1C$
(C)

Unless otherwise specified, values of R are in ohms, C is in farads, F in hertz and ω in radians per second. Calculations shown here were performed on a scientific calculator.

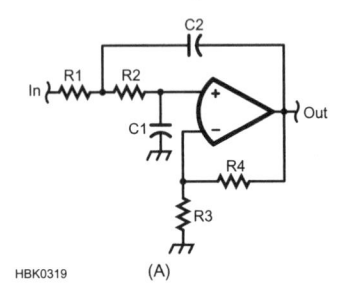

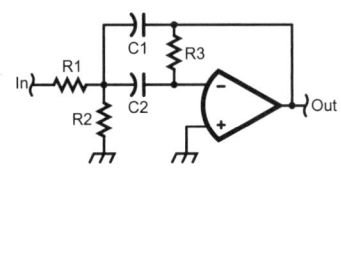

Low-Pass Filter

$$C_1 \leq \frac{[a^2 + 4(K-1)]C_2}{4}$$

$$R_1 = \frac{2}{\left[aC_2 + \sqrt{[a^2 + 4(K-1)]C_2^2 - 4C_1C_2}\right]\omega_C}$$

$$R_2 = \frac{1}{C_1 C_2 R_1 \omega_C^2}$$

$$R_3 = \frac{K(R_1 + R_2)}{K - 1} \quad (K > 1)$$

$$R_4 = K(R_1 + R_2)$$

where
K = gain
f_c = –3 dB cutoff frequency
$\omega_c = 2\pi f_c$
C_2 = a standard value near $10/f_c$ (in µF)
Note: For unity gain, short R4 and omit R3.

Example:
a = 1.414 (see table, one stage)
K = 2
f = 2700 Hz
ω_c = 16,964.6 rad/sec
C_2 = 0.0033 µF
C1 ≤ 0.00495 µF (use 0.0050 µF)
R1 ≤ 25,265.2 Ω (use 24 kΩ)
R2 = 8,420.1 Ω (use 8.2 kΩ)
R3 = 67,370.6 Ω (use 68 kΩ)
R4 = 67,370.6 Ω (use 68 kΩ)

High-Pass Filter

$$R_1 = \frac{4}{\left[a + \sqrt{a^2 + 8(K-1)}\right]\omega_C C}$$

$$R_2 = \frac{1}{\omega_C^2 C^2 R_1}$$

$$R_3 = \frac{KR_1}{K-1} \quad (K > 1)$$

$$R_4 = KR_1$$

where
K = gain
f_c = –3 dB cutoff frequency
$\omega_c = 2\pi f_c$
C = a standard value near $10/f_c$ (in µF)

Note: For unity gain, short R4 and omit R3.

Example:
a = 0.765 (see table, first of two stages)
K = 4
f = 250 Hz
ω_c = 1570.8 rad/sec
C = 0.04 µF (use 0.039 µF)
R1 = 11,123.2 Ω (use 11 kΩ)
R2 = 22,722 Ω (use 22 kΩ)
R3 = 14,830.9 Ω (use 15 kΩ)
R4 = 44,492.8 Ω (use 47 kΩ)

Band-Pass Filter

Pick K, Q, $\omega_0 = 2\pi f_c$
where f_c = center freq.
Choose C
Then

$$R1 = \frac{Q}{K_0 \omega_0 C}$$

$$R2 = \frac{Q}{(2Q^2 - K_0)\omega_0 C}$$

$$R3 = \frac{2Q}{\omega_0 C}$$

Example:
K = 2, f_o = 800 Hz, Q = 5 and C = 0.022 µF
R1 = 22.6 kΩ (use 22 kΩ)
R2 = 942 Ω (use 910 Ω)
R3 = 90.4 kΩ (use 91 kΩ)

Figure 10.32 — Equations for designing a low-pass RC active audio filter are given at A. B, C and D show design information for high-pass, band-pass and band-reject filters, respectively. All of these filters will exhibit a Butterworth response. Values of K and Q should be less than 10. See Table 10.3 for values of "a".

Cauer (elliptic) can be realized. All of the same family characteristics apply equally to passive and active filters and will not be repeated here. (Op amps are discussed in the **Circuits and Components** chapter.)

Figure 10.31 presents circuits for first-order low-pass (Figure 10.31A) and high-pass (Figure 10.31B) active filters. The frequency response of these two circuits is the same as a parallel and series RC circuit, respectively, except that these two circuits can have a passband gain greater than unity. Rolloff is shallow at 6 dB/octave. The two responses can be combined to form a simple band-pass filter (Figure 10.31C). This combination cannot produce sharp band-pass filters because of the shallow rolloff.

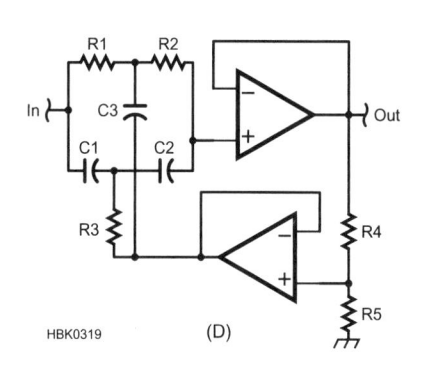

Band-Reject Filter

$$F_0 = \frac{1}{2\pi R1 C1}$$

$$K = 1 - \frac{1}{4Q}$$

$$R \gg (1-K)R1$$

where

$$C1 = C2 = \frac{C3}{2} = \frac{10\,\mu F}{f_0}$$

R1 = R2 = 2R3
R4 = (1 − K)R
R5 = K × R

Example:
f_0 = 500 Hz, Q=10
K = 0.975
C1 = C2 = 0.02 µF (or use 0.022 µF)
C3 = 0.04 µF (or use 0.044 µF)
R1 = R2 = 15.92 kΩ (use 15 kΩ)
R3 = 7.96 kΩ (use 8.2 kΩ)
R >> 1 kΩ
R4 = 25 Ω (use 24 Ω)
R5 = 975 Ω (use 910 Ω)

To achieve high-order responses with steeper rolloff and narrower bandwidths, more complex circuits are required in which combinations of capacitors and resistors create *poles* and *zeroes* in the frequency response. (Poles and zeros are described in the **Radio Fundamentals** chapter.) The various filter response families are created by different combinations of additional poles and zeroes. There are a variety of circuits that can be configured to implement the equations that describe the various families of filter responses. The most common circuits are *Sallen-Key* and *multiple-feedback*, but there are numerous other choices.

There are many types of active filters — this section presents some commonly used circuits as examples. A book on filter design (see the References section) will present more choices and how to develop designs based on the different circuit and filter family types. In addition, op amp manufacturer's publish numerous application notes and tutorials on active filter design. Several are listed in the References section of this chapter. The set of tutorials published by Analog Devices is particularly good.

SECOND-ORDER ACTIVE FILTERS

Figure 10.32 shows circuits for four second-order filters: low-pass (Figure 10.32A), high-pass (Figure 10.32B), band-pass (Figure 10.32C) and band-reject or notch (Figure 10.32D). Sequences of these filters are used to create higher-order circuits by connecting them in series. Two second-order filter stages create a fourth-order filter, and so forth.

The low-pass and high-pass filters use the Sallen-Key circuit. Note that the high-pass circuit is just the low-pass circuit with the positions of R1-R2 and C1-C2 exchanged. R3 and R4 are used to control gain in the low- and high-pass configurations. The band-pass filter is a multiple-feedback design. The notch filter is based on the twin-T circuit. All of the filter design equations and tables will result in a Butterworth family response. (For the Chebyshev and other filter responses, consult the references listed at the end of the chapter.)

The circuits in Figure 10.32 assume the op amp is operating from a balanced, bipolar power supply, such as ±12 V. If a single supply is used (such as +12 V and ground), the circuit must have a dc offset added and blocking capacitors between filter sections to prevent the dc offset from causing the op amp to saturate. The references listed at the end of the chapter provide more detailed information on single-supply circuit design.

Avoid electrolytic or tantalum capacitors as frequency-determining components in active filter design. These capacitors are best used for bypassing and power filtering as their tolerance is generally quite low, they have significant parasitic effects, and are usually polarized. Very small values of capacitance (less than 100 pF) can be affected by stray capacitance to other circuit components and wiring. High-order and high-Q filters require close attention to component tolerance and temperature coefficients, as well.

SECOND-ORDER ACTIVE FILTER DESIGN PROCEDURES

The following simple procedures are used to design filters based on the schematics in Figure 10.32. Equations and a design example are provided in the figure.

Low- and High-Pass Filter Design

To design a low- or high-pass filter using the circuits in Figure 10.32, start by determining your performance requirements for filter order (2, 4, 6, or 8), gain (K) and cutoff frequency (f_C). Calculate $\omega_C = 2\pi f_C$ and C_2 or C as required.

Table 10.3 provides design coefficients to create the Butterworth response from successive Sallen-Key low- and high-pass stages. A different coefficient is used for each stage. Obtain design coefficient "a" from Table 10.3. Calculate the remaining component values from the equations provided.

Band-Pass Filter Design

To design a band-pass filter as shown in Figure 10.32C, begin by determining the filter's required Q, gain, and center frequency, f_0. Choose a value for C and solve for the resistor values. Very high or very low values of resistance (above 1 MΩ or lower than 10 Ω) should be avoided. Change the value of C until suitable values are obtained. High gain and Q may be difficult to obtain in the same stage with reasonable component values. Consider a separate stage for additional gain or to

Table 10.3
Factor "a" for Low- and High-Pass Filters in Figure 10.32

No. of Stages	Stage 1	Stage 2	Stage 3	Stage 4
1	1.414	–	–	–
2	0.765	1.848	–	–
3	0.518	1.414	1.932	–
4	0.390	1.111	1.663	1.962

These values are truncated from those of Appendix C of Williams, *Electronic Filter Design Handbook*, for even-order Butterworth filters narrow the filter bandwidth.

Band-Reject (Notch) Filter Design

Band-reject filter design begins with the selection of center frequency, f_0, and Q. Calculate the value of K. Choose a value for C1 that is approximately 10 μF / f_0. This determines the values of C2 and C3 as shown. Calculate the value for R1 that results in the desired value for f_0. This determines the values of R2 and R3 as shown. Select a convenient value for R4 + R5 that does not load the output amplifier. Calculate R4 and R5 from the value of K.

The depth of the notch depends on how closely the values of the components match the design values. The use of 1%-tolerance resistors is recommended and, if possible, matched values of capacitance. If all identical components are used, two capacitors can be paralleled to create C3 and two resistors in parallel create R3. This helps to minimize thermal drift.

10.4.4 Active Filter Design Tools

While the simple active filter examples presented above can be designed manually, more sophisticated circuits are more easily designed using filter-design software. Follow the same general approach to determining the filter's performance requirements and then the filter family as was presented in the section on LC filters. You can then enter the values or make the necessary selections for the design software. Once a basic design has been calculated, you can then "tweak" the design performance, use standard value components and make other adjustments. The design example presented below shows how a real analog design is assembled by understanding the performance requirements and then using design software to experiment for a "best" configuration.

Op amp manufacturers such as Texas Instruments and National Semiconductor (originally separate companies but now merged) have made available sophisticated "freeware" filter design software. These packages are extremely useful in designing active RC filters. They begin by collecting specifications from the user and then creating a basic circuit. Once the initial circuit has been designed, the user can adjust specifications, component values, and op amp types until satisfied with the final design.

Free online filter design software is available from the following sources:

• Analog Devices — *Analog Filter Wizard 2.0* (**www.analog.com/designtools/en/filter-wizard**)

• Texas Instruments — *FilterPro 3.1* (**www.ti.com**, search for "FilterPro")

Even if a manual design process is followed, using a software tool to double-check the results is a good way to verify the design before building the circuit. A circuit simulator such as *LTSpice* (see the **Computer-Aided Circuit Design** chapter) can also verify a design before building the actual circuit.

An extended design example using the Texas Instruments *FilterPro* software is included in this book's downloadable supplemental information. In the example, Dan Tayloe, N7VE explains the process of designing a high-performance 750 Hz low-pass filter, illustrating the power of using sophisticated interactive tools that enable design changes on-the-fly. The reader is encouraged to follow along and experiment with *FilterPro* as a means of becoming familiar with the software so that it can be used for other filter design tasks. Similar processes apply to other filter design software tools.

10.5 Digital Filters

Where an analog filter operates on a continuous signal in the time domain, digital filters operate on signals that have been converted to a digital stream of data. (See the discussion of digital signals in the **DSP and SDR Fundamentals** chapter.) The usual method of constructing a digital filters is as a series of registers with the stream of samples moving through them in a series of steps called *delays*. At each register (called a *tap*) the amplitude of the signal is modified (by an amount referred to as a *coefficient*) and the result added to the results from other taps. The signal stream is shifted to the next register and the process is repeated. The sum of the results from the taps constitutes the output of the filter.

The value of each coefficient and the configuration of how the filter's taps are added together determine the filter's response to the input signal. This section will discuss two basic filter types, the finite impulse response or FIR, the infinite impulse response or IIR.

The purpose of this section is not to give a tutorial in how each type of filter is designed but explain the characteristics of each type of filter. As with analog filters, the design of digital filter is mostly done by software using validated algorithms that accept performance requirements as inputs and generate design information, in many cases as a data file that can be loaded directly into a DSP processor or subsystem. (The GNU Radio (**gnuradio.org**) toolkit, for example, treats digital filters as one of many functional blocks. The user configures the filter parameters and the software manages the organization of the actual computing elements in the DSP or SDR system.) For the reader interested in a deeper discussion of digital filter theory and design, several excellent references are listed at the end of the chapter.

10.5.1 FIR Filters

The earlier discussion of transient response introduced the impulse, an infinitely narrow pulse. The spectrum of an impulse is infinitely wide, containing all frequencies. If you feed an impulse into the input of a filter (analog or digital), the output of the filter is the filter's impulse response. Because the impulse is made up of all frequencies, it excites the filter at all frequencies. As a result, the impulse response has a frequency spectrum equal to the frequency response of the filter.

One way to design a filter is to determine the impulse response that corresponds to the desired frequency spectrum and then design the filter to have that impulse response. That method is the basis for designing *finite impulse response* (FIR) filters. (Finite refers to time, not amplitude.)

An FIR filter is a filter whose impulse response is finite, ending in some fixed time.

Note that analog filters have an infinite impulse response — the output theoretically rings forever. Even a simple R-C low-pass filter's output decays exponentially toward zero but theoretically never quite reaches it. In contrast, an FIR filter's impulse response becomes exactly zero at some time after receiving the impulse and stays zero forever (or at least until another impulse comes along).

Given that you have somehow figured out the desired impulse response, how would you design a digital filter to have that response? The obvious method would be to pre-calculate a table of impulse response values, sampled at the sample rate. These are called the filter *coefficients*. When an impulse of a certain amplitude is received, you multiply that amplitude by the first entry in the coefficient table and send the result to the output. At the next sample time, multiply the impulse by the second entry, and so on until you have used up all the entries in the table.

A circuit to do that is shown in **Figure 10.33**. The input signal is stored in a shift register. Each block labeled "Delay" represents a delay of one sample time. At each sample time, the signal is shifted one register to the right. Each register feeds a multiplier and the other input to the multiplier comes from one of the coefficient table entries. All the multiplier outputs are added together. Since the input is assumed to be a single impulse, at any given time all

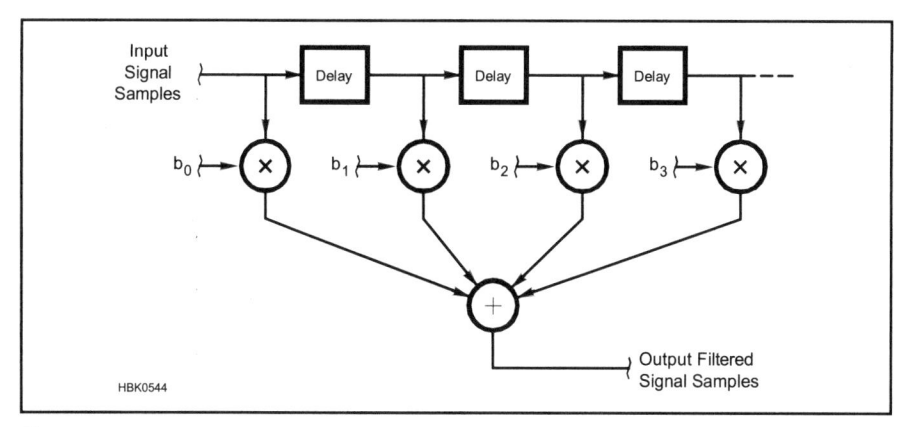

Figure 10.33 — A 4-tap FIR filter. The bn values are the filter coefficients.

the shift registers contain zero except one, which is multiplied by the appropriate table entry and sent to the output.

We've just designed an FIR filter! By using a shift register with a separate multiplier for each tap, the filter works for continuous signals as well as for impulses. Since this is a linear system, the continuing signal is affected by the filter the same as an individual impulse.

It should be obvious from the diagram how to implement an FIR filter in software. You set up two buffers in memory, one for the filter coefficients and one for the data. The length of each buffer is the number of filter taps. (A *tap* is the combination of one filter coefficient, one shift register and one multiplier/accumulator.) Each time a new data value is received, it is stored in the next available position in the data buffer and the accumulator is set to zero. Next, a software loop is executed a number of times equal to the number of taps. During each loop, pointers to the two buffers are incremented, the next coefficient is multiplied by the next data value and the result is added to the current accumulator value. After the last loop, the accumulator contents are the output value. Normally the buffers are implemented as *circular buffers* — when the address pointer gets to the end it is reset back to the beginning.

Now you can see why a hardware multiplier-accumulator (MAC) is such an important feature of a DSP chip. Each tap of the FIR filter involves one multiplication and one addition. With a 1000-tap FIR filter, 1000 multiplications and 1000 additions must be performed during each sample time. The ability to do each MAC operation in a single clock cycle saves a lot of processing time compared to a CPU-type processor.

An FIR filter is a hardware or software implementation of the mathematical operation called *convolution*. We say that the filter *convolves* the input signal with the impulse response of the filter. It turns out that convolution in the time domain is mathematically equivalent to multiplication in the frequency domain. That means that the frequency spectrum of the output equals the frequency spectrum of the input times the frequency spectrum of the filter. Expressed in decibels, the output spectrum equals the input spectrum plus the filter frequency response, all in dB. If at some frequency the input signal is +3 dB and the filter is –10 dB compared to some reference, then the output signal will be 3 – 10 = –7 dB at that frequency.

An FIR filter whose bandwidth is very small compared to the sample rate requires a long impulse response with lot of taps. This is another consequence of the "skinny" versus "fat" relationship between the frequency and time domains. If the filter is narrow in the frequency domain, then its impulse response is wide. Actually, if you want the frequency response to go all the way to zero (minus infinity dB) throughout the stopband, then the impulse response theoretically becomes infinitely wide. Since we're designing a *finite* impulse response filter we have to truncate the impulse response at some point to get it to fit in the coefficient table. When you do that, however, you no longer have infinite attenuation in the stopband. The more heavily you truncate (the narrower the impulse response) the worse the stopband attenuation and the more ripple you get in the passband. Assuming optimum design techniques for selecting coefficients, you can estimate the minimum length L of the impulse response from the following equation:

$$L = 1 - \frac{10\log(\delta_1 \delta_2) - 15}{14\left(\frac{f_T}{f_s}\right)} \text{ taps}$$

where

δ_1 and δ_2 = the passband and stopband ripple expressed as a fraction

f_T = the transition bandwidth (frequency difference between passband and stopband edges)

f_s = the sample rate.

For example, for a low-pass filter with a passband that extends up to 3 kHz, a stopband that starts at 4 kHz (f_T = 4 – 3 = 1 kHz), f_s = 10 kHz sample rate, ±0.1 dB passband ripple ($d_1 = 10^{0.1/20} - 1 = 0.0116$), and 60 dB stopband rejection ($d_2 = 10^{-60/20} = 0.001$), we get

$$L = 1 - \frac{10\log(0.0116 \times 0.001) - 15}{14\left(\frac{1}{10}\right)}$$

$$= 1 - \frac{-49.4 - 15}{1.4} = 47 \text{ taps}$$

Overflow is a potential problem when doing the calculations for an FIR filter. Multiplying two N-bit numbers results in a product with 2N bits, so space must be provided in the accumulator to accommodate that. Although the final result normally will be scaled and truncated back to N bits, it is best to carry through all the intermediate results with full resolution in order not to lose any dynamic range. In addition, the sum of all the taps can be a number with more than 2N bits. For example, if the filter width is 256 taps, then if all coefficients and data are at full scale, the final result could theoretically be 256 times larger, requiring an extra 8 bits in the accumulator. We say "theoretically" because normally most of the filter coefficients are much less than full scale and it is highly unlikely that all 256 data values would ever simultaneously be full-scale values of the correct polarity to cause overflow. The dsPIC processors use 16-bit multipliers with 32-bit results and a 40-bit accumulator, which should handle any reasonable circumstances.

After all taps have been calculated, the final result must be retrieved from the accumulator. Since the accumulator has much more resolution than the processor's data words, normally the result is truncated and scaled to fit. It is up to the circuit designer or programmer to scale by the correct value to avoid overflow. The worst case is when each data value in the shift register is full-scale — positive when it is multiplying a positive coefficient and negative for negative coefficients. That way, all taps add to the maximum value. To calculate the worst-case accumulator amplitude, simply add the absolute values of all the coefficients. However, that normally gives an unrealistically pessimistic value because statistically it is extremely unlikely that such a high peak will ever be reached. For a low-pass filter, a better estimate is to calculate the gain for a dc signal and add a few percent safety margin. The dc gain is just the sum of all the coefficients (not the absolute values). For a band-pass filter, add the sum of all the coefficients multiplied by a sine wave at the center frequency.

Calculating FIR Filter Coefficients

So far we have ignored the question of how to determine the filter coefficients. For an ideal "brick-wall" low-pass filter, the answer turns out to be pretty simple. A "brick-wall" low-

Analog and Digital Filtering   **10.17**

pass filter is one that has a constant response from zero hertz up to the cutoff frequency and zero response above. Its impulse response is proportional to the sinc function:

$$C(n) = C_o \, \text{sinc}(2Bn) = \frac{\sin(2\pi Bn)}{2\pi Bn}$$

where C(n) are the filter coefficients, n is the sample number with n = 0 at the center of the impulse response, C_o is a constant, and B is the single-sided bandwidth normalized to the sample rate, B = bandwidth / sample rate.

It is interesting that this has the same form as the frequency response of a pulse, as was shown in Figure 10.33. That is because a brick-wall response in the frequency domain has the same shape as a pulse in the time domain. A pulse in one domain transforms to a sinc function in the other. This is an example of the general principle that the transformation between time and frequency domains is symmetrical. This is discussed in more detail in the section on Fourier transforms in the **DSP and SDR Fundamentals** chapter.

Normally, the filter coefficients are set up with the peak of the sinc function, sinc(0), at the center of the coefficient table so that there is an equal amount of "tail" on both sides. That points up the principle problem with this method of determining filter coefficients. Theoretically, the sinc function extends from minus infinity to plus infinity. Abruptly terminating the tails causes the frequency response to differ from an ideal brick-wall filter. There is ripple in the passband and non-zero response in the stopband, as shown in the graph in the upper right of **Figure 10.34**. This is mainly caused by the abruptness of the truncation. In effect, all the coefficients outside the limits of the coefficient table have been set to zero. The passband and stopband response can be improved by tapering the edges of the impulse response instead of abruptly transitioning to zero.

The process of tapering the edges of the impulse response is called *windowing*. The impulse response is multiplied by a window, a series of coefficients that smoothly taper to zero at the edges. For example, a rectangular window is equivalent to no window at all. Many different window shapes have been developed over the years — at one time it seemed that every doctoral candidate in the field of signal processing did their dissertation on some new window. Each window has its advantages and disadvantages. A window that transitions slowly and smoothly to zero has excellent passband and stopband response but a wide transition band. A window that has a wider center portion and then transitions more abruptly to zero at the edges has a narrower transition band but poorer passband and stopband response. The equations for the windows in Figure 10.34 are included in a sidebar.

The routine shown in **Table 10.4** is written for a dsPIC processor so it can be used to calculate filter coefficients "on the fly" as the operator adjusts a bandwidth control. The same code should also work using a generic C compiler on a PC so the coefficients could be downloaded into an FIR filter implemented in hardware.

The windowed-sinc method works pretty well for a simple low-pass filter, but what if some more-complicated spectral shape is desired? The same general design approach still applies. You determine the desired spectral shape, transform it to the time domain using an inverse Fourier transform, and apply a window. There is lots of (often free) software available that can calculate the fast Fourier transform

---

Table 10.4
Routine for dsPIC Processor to Calculate Filter Coefficients

```
// Calculate FIR filter coefficients
// using the windowed-sinc method
void set_coef (
 double sample_rate;
 double bandwidth;)
{
extern int c[FIR_LEN]; // Coefficient array
int i; // Coefficient index
double ph; // Phase in radians
double coef; // Filter coefficient
int coef_int; // Digitized coefficient
double bw_ratio; // Normalized bandwidth

bw_ratio = 2 * bandwidth / sample_rate;
for (i = 0; i < (FIR_LEN/2); i++) {
// Brick-wall filter:
ph = PI * (i + 0.5) * bw_ratio;
coef = sin(ph) / ph;
// Hann window:
ph = PI * (i + 0.5) / (FIR_LEN/2);
coef *= (1 + cos(ph)) / 2;
// Convert from floating point to int:
coef *= 1 << (COEF_WIDTH - 1);
coef_int = (int)coef;
// Symmetrical impulse response:
c[i + FIR_LEN/2] = coef_int;
c[FIR_LEN/2 - 1 - i] = coef_int;
}
}
```

Equations for Window Functions

For each window function, the center of the response is considered to be at time t = 0 and the width of the impulse is L. Each window is 1.0 when t = 0 and 0.0 when the |t| > L/2.

Rectangular:

$$w(t) = 1.0$$

Triangular (Bartlett):

$$w(t) = 2\left(\frac{L/2 - |t|}{L}\right)$$

Blackman:

$$w(t) = 0.42 + 0.5\cos\left(\frac{2\pi t}{L}\right) + 0.08\cos\left(\frac{4\pi t}{L}\right)$$

Hamming:

$$w(t) = 0.54 + 0.46\cos\left(\frac{2\pi t}{L}\right)$$

Hanning (Hann):

$$w(t) = 0.5 + 0.5\cos\left(\frac{2\pi t}{L}\right)$$

Rectangular

Triangular

Blackman

Hamming

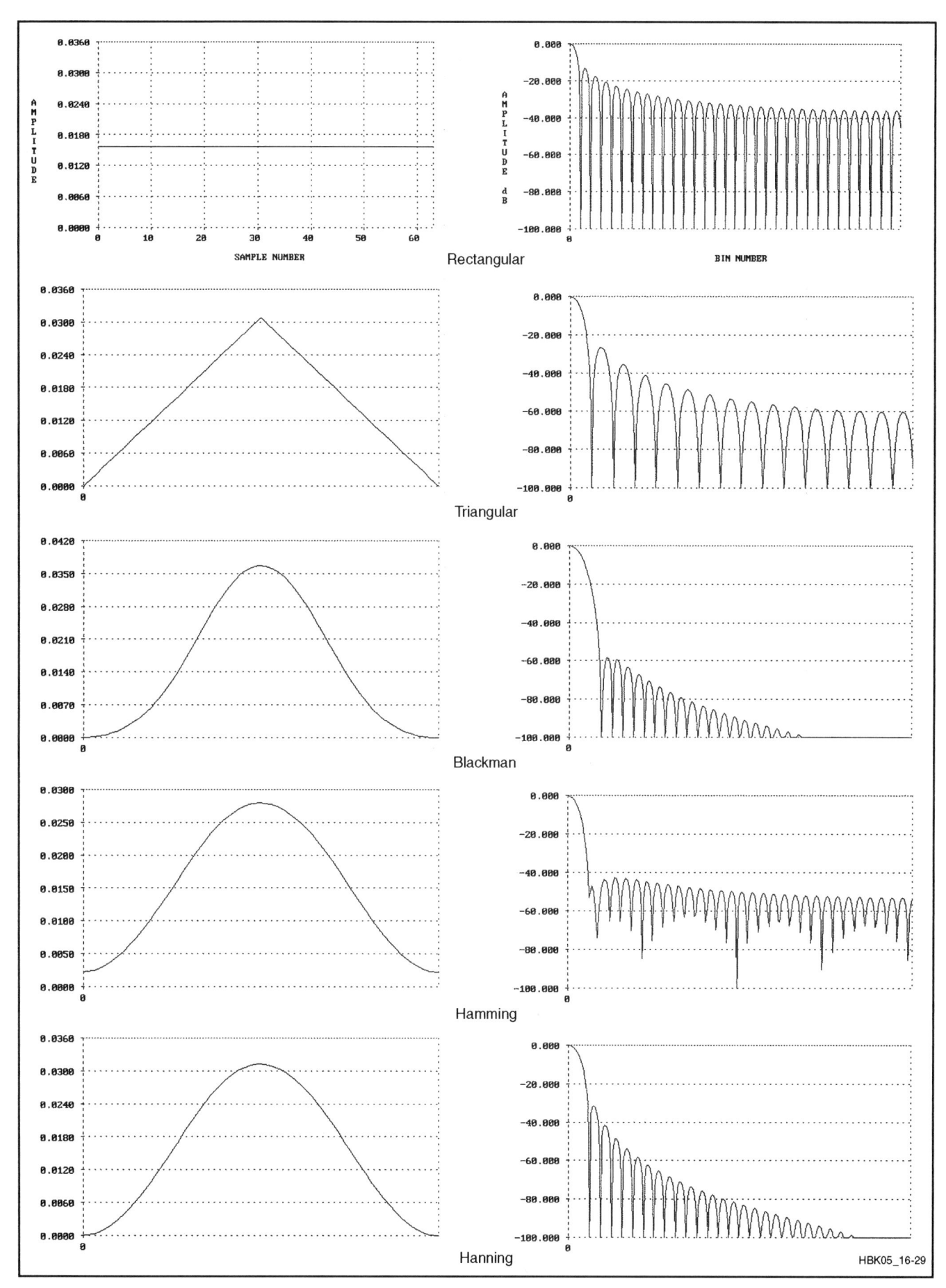

Hanning

Figure 10.34 — Various window functions and their Fourier transforms.

Analog and Digital Filtering 10.19

(FFT) and inverse fast Fourier transform (IFFT). So the technique is to generate the desired spectral shape, transform to the time domain with the IFFT, and multiply the resulting impulse response by the desired window. Then you can transform back to the frequency domain with the FFT to see how the window affected the result. If the result is not satisfactory, you can either choose a different window or modify the original spectral shape and go through the process again.

Windowing methods are useful because they are simple to program and the resulting software routines execute quickly. For example, you can include a bandwidth knob on your DSP filter and calculate filter coefficients "on the fly" as the user turns the knob. However, while the filter performance that results is pretty good, it is not "optimum" in the sense that it does not have minimum passband ripple and maximum stopband attenuation for a given number of filter coefficients. For that, you need what is known as an *equal-ripple*, or *Chebyshev* filter. The calculations to determine Chebyshev filter coefficients are more complicated and time-consuming. For that reason, the coefficients are normally calculated in advance on a PC and stored in DSP program memory for retrieval as needed.

Engineers have not had much success in devising a mathematical algorithm to calculate the Chebyshev coefficients directly, but in 1972 Thomas Parks and James McClellan figured out a method to do it iteratively. The *Parks-McClellan algorithm* is supported in most modern filter-design software, including a number of programs available for free download on the Web. Typically you enter the sample rate, the passband and stopband frequency ranges, the passband ripple and the stopband attenuation. The software then determines the required number of filter coefficients, calculates them and displays a plot of the resulting filter frequency response.

Filter design software typically presents the filter coefficients as floating-point numbers to the full accuracy of the computer. You will need to scale the values and truncate the resolution to the word size of your filter implementation. Truncation of filter coefficients affects the frequency response of the filter but does not add noise in the same manner as truncating the signal data.

As you look at impulse responses for various FIR filters calculated by various methods you soon realize that most of them are symmetrical. If the center of the impulse response is considered to be at time zero, then the value at time t equals the value at time –t for all t. If you know in advance that the filter coefficients are symmetrical, you can take advantage of that in the filter design. By re-arranging the adders and multipliers, the number of multipliers can be reduced by a factor of two, as shown in **Figure 10.35**. This trick is less useful in a software implementation of an FIR filter because the number of additions is the same and many DSPs take the same amount of time to do an addition as a multiply-accumulate.

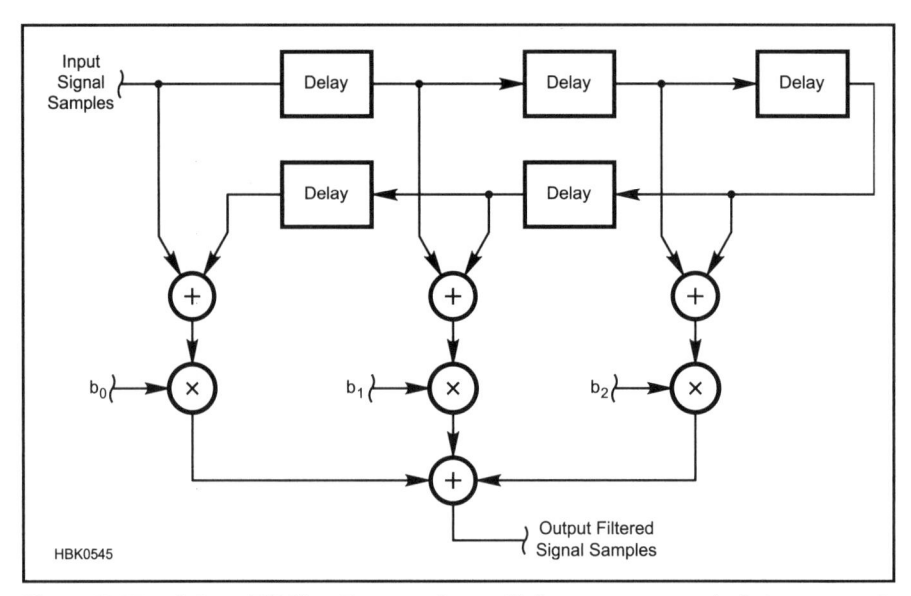

Figure 10.35 — A 6-tap FIR filter. Because the coefficients are symmetrical, the symmetrical taps may be combined before multiplication.

In addition to the computational benefit, a symmetrical impulse response also has the advantage that it is *linear phase*. The time delay through such a filter is one-half the length of the filter for all frequencies. For example, for a 1000-tap filter running at 10 kHz the delay is 500/10,000 = 0.05 second. Since the time delay is constant for all frequencies, the phase delay is directly proportional to the frequency. For example, if the phase delay at 20 Hz is one cycle (0.05 second) it is ten cycles at 200 Hz (still 0.05 second). Linear phase delay is important with digital modulation signals to avoid distortion and inter-symbol interference. It is also desirable with analog modulation where it can result in more natural-sounding audio. All analog filters are non-linear-phase; the phase distortion tends to be worse the more abrupt the transition between passband and stopband. That is why an SSB signal sounds unnatural after being filtered by a crystal filter with a small shape factor even though the passband ripple may be small and distortion minimal.

A band-pass filter can be constructed from a low-pass filter simply by multiplying the impulse response by a sine wave at the desired center frequency. This can be done before or after windowing. The linear-phase property is retained but with reference to the center frequency of the filter, that is, the phase shift is proportional to the difference in frequency from the center frequency. The frequency response is a double-sided version of the low-pass response with the zero-hertz point of the low-pass filter shifted to the frequency of the sine wave.

10.5.2 IIR Filters

An *infinite impulse response* (IIR) filter is a filter whose impulse response is infinite. After an impulse is applied to the input, theoretically the output never goes to zero and stays there. In practice, of course, the signal eventually does decay until it is below the noise level (analog filter) or less than one LSB (digital filter).

Unlike a symmetrical FIR filter, an IIR filter is not generally linear-phase. The delay through the filter is not the same for all frequencies. Also, IIR filters tend to be harder to design than FIR filters. On the other hand, many fewer adders and multipliers are typically required to achieve the same passband and stopband ripple in a given filter, so IIR filters are often used where computations must be minimized.

All analog filters have an infinite impulse response. For a digital filter to be IIR it must have feedback. That means a delayed copy of some internal computation is applied to an earlier stage in the computation. A simple but useful example of an IIR filter is the exponential decay circuit in **Figure 10.36**. In the absence of a signal at the input, the output on the next clock cycle is always (1–δ) times the current output. The time constant (the time for the output to die to 1/e = 36.8% of the initial value) is very nearly

$$\tau = f_s \left(\frac{1}{\delta} - \frac{1}{2} \right)$$

where f_s is the sample rate. The circuit is the digital equivalent of a capacitor with a resistor in parallel and might be useful for example in a digital automatic gain control circuit.

One issue with IIR filters is resolution. Because of the feedback, the number of bits of resolution required for intermediate computations can be much greater than at the input or output. In the previous example, δ is very small for very long time constants. When the value in the register falls below a certain level the multiplication by (1–δ) will no longer be accurate unless the bit width is increased. In practice, the increased resolution required with IIR filters often cancels out part of the savings in the number of circuit elements.

Another issue with IIR filters is stability. Because of the feedback it is possible for the filter to oscillate if care is not taken in the design. Stability can also be affected by nonlinearity at low signal levels. A circuit that is stable with large signals may oscillate with small signals due to the round-off error in certain calculations, which causes faint tones to appear when strong signals are not present. This is known as an unstable *limit cycle*. These issues are part of the reason that IIR filters have a reputation for being hard to design.

Design techniques for IIR filters mostly involve first designing an analog filter using any of the standard techniques and then transforming the design from the analog to the digital domain. The *impulse-invariant* method attempts to duplicate the filter response directly by making the digital impulse response equal the impulse response of the equivalent analog filter. It works fairly well for low-pass filters with bandwidths much less than the sample rate. Its problem is that it tries to duplicate the frequency response all the way to infinity hertz, but that violates the Nyquist criterion resulting in a folding back of the high-frequency response down into low frequencies. It is similar to the aliasing that occurs in a DSP system when the input signal to be sampled is not band-limited below the Nyquist frequency.

The *bilinear transform* method gets around that problem by distorting the frequency axis such that infinity hertz in the analog domain becomes sample rate / 2 in the digital domain. Low frequencies are fairly accurate, but high frequencies are squeezed together more and more the closer you get to the Nyquist frequency. It avoids the aliasing problem at the expense of a change in the spectrum shape, especially at the high-frequency end. For example, when designing a low-pass filter it may be necessary to change the cutoff frequency to compensate. Again, the method works best for filters with passband frequencies much less than the sample rate.

In general, the output of an IIR filter is a combination of the current and previous input values (feed-forward) and previous output values (feed-back). **Figure 10.37A** shows the so-called *direct form I* of an IIR filter. The b_i coefficients represent feed-forward and the a_i coefficients feed-back. For example the previous value of the y output is multiplied by a_1, the second previous value is multiplied by a_2, and so on. Because the filter is linear, it doesn't matter whether the feed forward or feed back stage is performed first. By reversing the order, the number of shift registers is reduced as in Figure 10.37B. There are other equivalent topologies as well. The mathematics for generating the a_i and b_i coefficients for both the impulse-invariant and bilinear transform methods is fairly involved, but fortunately some filter design programs can handle IIR as well as FIR filters.

10.5.3 CIC Filters

(This overview of CIC filters is taken from the 2011 Sep/Oct *QEX* column SDR: Simplified by Ray Mack, W5IFS. Additional background on CIC filters is available in the referenced articles by Donadio and by Lyons.)

The problem with both FIR and IIR filters is that they require a large number of multiply operations, which consume a large number of DSP processor cycles. Eugene Hogenauer (see references) developed a very useful simplification of the sample conversion/filter configuration called a cascaded integrator comb (CIC) filter. The important aspect of CIC filters is

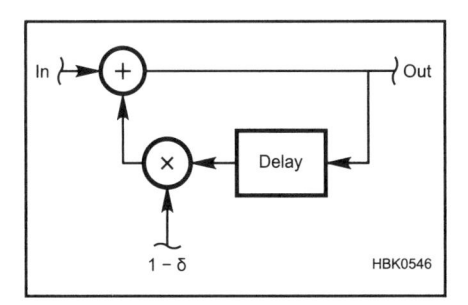

Figure 10.36 — An exponential decay implementation.

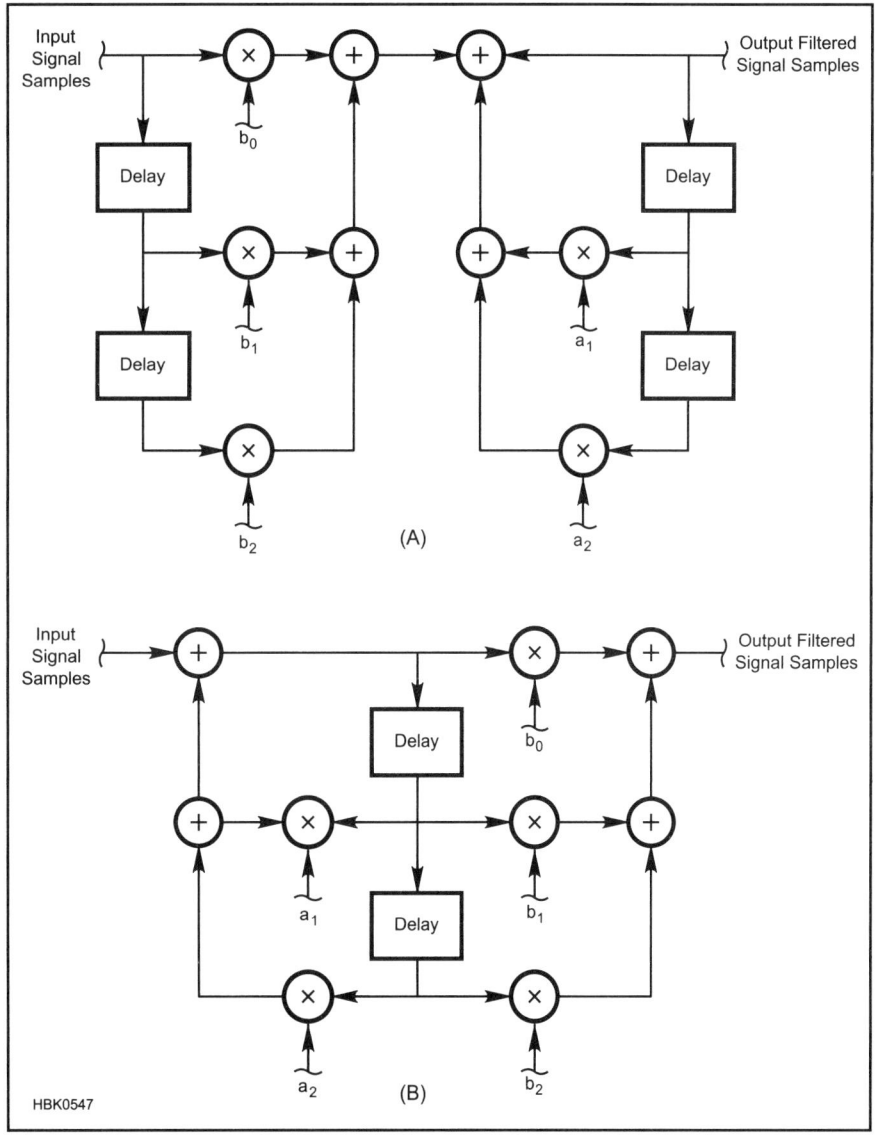

Figure 10.37 — An IIR filter with three feed-forward taps and two feed-back taps. Direct form I (A) and the equivalent direct form II (B).

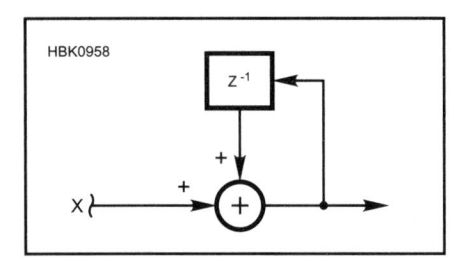

Figure 10.38 — Z transform diagram of an integrator. The new output is the sum of the previous output (represented by Z^{-1}) and the new sample. (The Z transform is explained at en.wikipedia.org/wiki/Z-transform.)

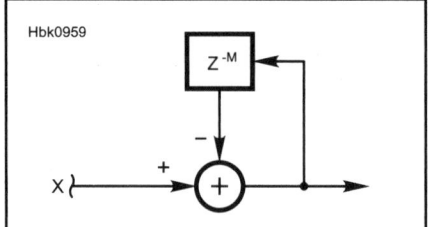

Figure 10.39 — Z transform diagram of a comb. The new output is the difference of the present sample and a delayed sample. The number M designates how many steps happened during the delay.

that only addition, subtraction, and delay operations are required for implementation.

As with most things in life, improving one aspect of a system requires compromise in other aspects. This is also true of CIC filters where we trade the simplification of eliminating multipliers for restricting the filter response: A CIC filter can only have a low-pass response. Additionally, there is a limited subset of possible low-pass responses constrained by the sample rate change and number of stages in the comb and integrator stages. The most important property of a CIC filter is that it can be very easily implemented in hardware either in an FPGA or as part of the dedicated logic of an IC.

The integrator is an infinite impulse response filter. **Figure 10.38** shows how it works and how simple it is. The integrator holds a running total of all previous samples. The integrator adds the last output value (z–1) to the current input value (x). Ordinarily, we would worry about overflow in an integrator because a dc component in the signal will cause the integrator to overflow.

The combination of the comb and the integrator, however, cancels any problems with overflow. The integrator is a single pole low pass filter with infinite gain at dc. (The possibility of overflow doesn't matter as long as the integrators are implemented with adders using two's complement addition (**en.wikipedia.org/wiki/Two's_complement**) that allow wrap around when overflow occurs, and that the number of bits in the word is as big as the expected output word.)

The comb is a finite impulse response stage that subtracts a previous sample from the present sample. The amount of delay between the present sample and the delayed sample is called the differential delay and is denoted as M by most authors. **Figure 10.39** shows the operation of the comb.

An actual CIC filter is composed of multiple integrator-comb sections that are cascaded. A CIC filter has exactly the same number of integrators as combs. According to the associative property you can rearrange the order of the additions in a sequence and the result of the sequence does not change (a + (–b) + c + d + (–e) + (–f) is identical to a + c + d – b – e – f). A CIC filter with a sample rate change uses that property to group all of the integrators together and to group all of the combs together. We place either a downsample or upsample rate changer between the combs and integrators. (See the **DSP and SDR Fundamentals** chapter for a discussion of sample rate changing.)

Figure 10.40 shows that a decimator is an integrator section followed by a down rate change, which is then followed by a comb section. An interpolator turns the system around and puts the comb section first, followed by an up rate changer, which is followed by an integrator section. It is very useful for a hardware implementation that the number of integrators and combs is independent (within reason) from the rate change and that, in general, you can rearrange the inputs, outputs, and rate change to create a decimator and interpolator with the same blocks.

There are three parameters that affect the implementation of a CIC filter. "R" is the up sample rate or down sample rate. "M" is the delay in the comb section and is almost always either one or two. "N" is the number of stages in the comb section (which is required to be the same as the number of integrator sections). The simplification of separating the combs into one section and the integrators into a second section is advantageous for the speed required of the storage elements for the combs. The combs always operate at the low frequency end of the system and the integrators work at the high speed side of the system.

Notice that the associative property would also allow a decimator with the comb first and the integrator after the down converter. Either configuration will give the same results. The reason we always put the comb on the low sample rate side of the system is pragmatic. The comb requires one additional storage element (for the usual M = 1 situation) over what is required for an integrator. Each storage element consumes power when it is clocked. A faster clock and more storage registers translate directly into additional power dissipation. The additional power is an issue when implementing a CIC filter in hardware such as an FPGA.

10.5.4 Adaptive Filters

An *adaptive filter* is one that automatically adjusts its filter coefficients under the control of some algorithm. This is often done in situations where the filter characteristics are not known in advance. For example, an adaptive channel equalizer corrects for the non-flatness in the amplitude and phase spectrum of a com-

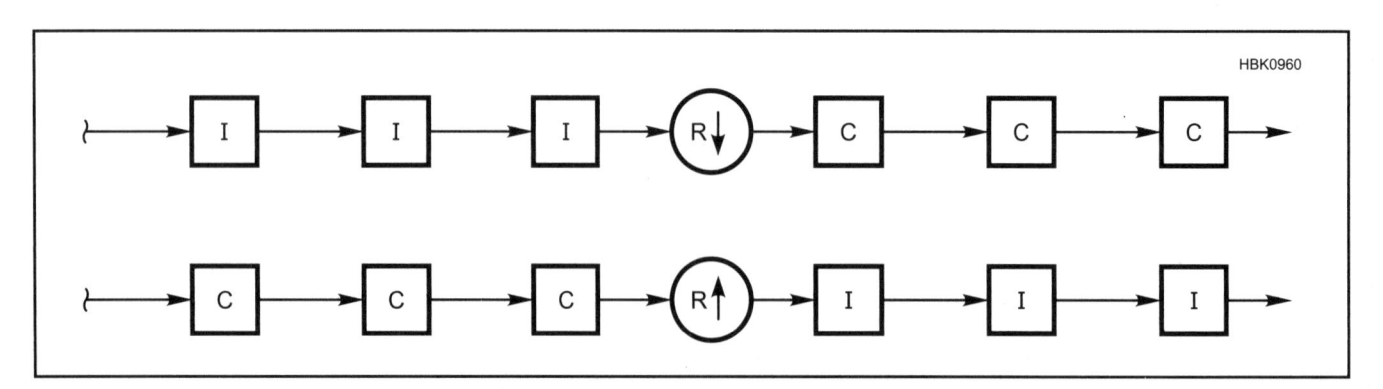

Figure 10.40 — The top CIC filter shows a decimator, where the sample rate is reduced by a value "R." The bottom CIC filter shows an interpolator where the sample rate is increased by a value "R." Note that the difference between the two is the order of the combs and integrators as well as the direction of the rate change. The combs are on the low sample rate side of both systems.

munications channel due to multipath propagation. Typically, the transmitting station periodically sends a known sequence of data, known as a *training sequence*, which is used by the receiver to determine the channel characteristics and adjust its filter coefficients accordingly.

Another example is an automatic notch filter. An algorithm determines the frequency of an interfering tone and automatically adjusts the notch frequency to remove the tone. Noise cancellation is another application. It can be thought of as the opposite of a notch filter. In this case, all the sine-wave tones in the input signal are considered to be desired and the filter coefficients are configured to enhance them. That method works not only for CW signals but for voice as well since the human voice consists largely of discrete frequencies.

A generic block diagram of an adaptive filter is shown in **Figure 10.41**. The variable filter is typically an FIR type with coefficients calculated by the update algorithm. By some means, an estimate of the desired, unimpaired signal, d, is generated and compared to the filter output y. The difference between y and d is the error, e, which is used by the update algorithm to modify the filter coefficients to improve the accuracy of y. The algorithm is capable of acting as a noise-reduction filter and a notch filter simultaneously. Assuming d is in the form of a pure tone (sine wave), the tone is simultaneously optimized in the y output and minimized in the e output.

A common algorithm for minimizing the error signal is called *least mean squares* (LMS). The LMS algorithm includes a performance parameter, μ, which can be adjusted between 0 and 1 to control the tradeoff between adjustment speed and accuracy. A value near 1 results in fast convergence but the convergence is not very accurate. For better accuracy at the cost of slower adjustment, lower the value of μ. Some implementations adjust μ on the fly, using a large value at first to get faster lock-in when the error is large then a smaller value after convergence to reduce the error. That works as long as the signal characteristics are not changing too rapidly.

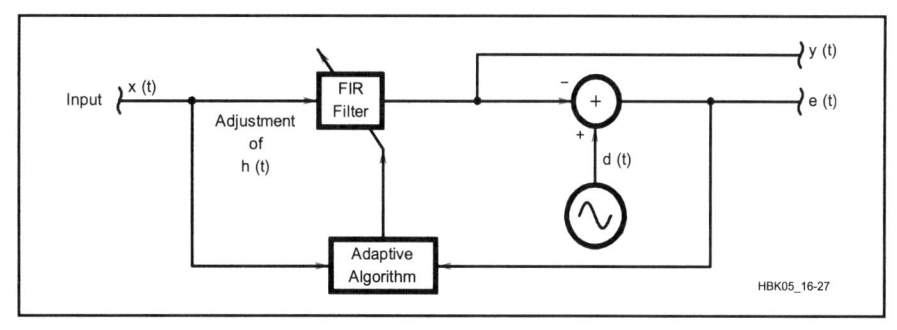

Figure 10.41 — An adaptive filter configuration.

10.6 Quartz Crystal Filters

(The sections on designing and building crystal filters from previous editions are available as a PDF document in the this book's downloadable supplemental material.)

Inductor Q values effectively limit the minimum bandwidth that can be achieved with LC band-pass filters. Higher-Q circuit elements, such as quartz crystal, PLZT ceramic and constant-modulus metal alloy resonators, are required to extend these limits. Quartz crystals offer the highest Q and best stability with time and temperature of all available resonators. They are manufactured for a wide range of frequencies from audio to VHF, using cuts (crystal orientations) that suit the frequency and application of the resonator. The AT cut is favored for HF fundamental and VHF overtone use, whereas other cuts (DT, SL and E) are more convenient for use at lower frequencies.

Each crystal plate has several modes of mechanical vibration. These can be excited electrically thru the piezoelectric effect, but generally resonators are designed so as to maximize their response on a particular operating frequency using a crystal cut that provides low loss and a favorable temperature coefficient. Consequently, for filter design, quartz crystal resonators are modeled using the simplified equivalent circuit shown in **Figure 10.42**. Here L_m, C_m and r_m represent the *motional* parameters of the resonator at the main operating frequency — r_m being the loss resistance, which is also known as the *equivalent series resistance*, or ESR. C_o is a combination of the static capacitance formed between the two metal electrodes with the quartz as dielectric (e_r = 4.54 for AT-cut crystals) and some additional capacitance introduced by the metal case, base and mount. There is a physical relationship between C_m and the static capacitance formed by the resonator electrodes, but, unfortunately, the added holder capacitance masks this direct relationship causing C_o/C_m to vary from 200 to over 500. However, for modern fundamental AT-cut crystals between 1 and 30 MHz, their values of C_m are typically between 0.003 and 0.03 pF. Theoretically, the motional inductance of a quartz crystal should the same whether it is operated on the fundamental or one of its overtones, making the motional capacitance at the nth overtone $1/n^2$ of the value at the fundamental. However, this relationship is modified by the effect of the metal electrodes deposited on either side of the crystal plate and in practice the motional inductance increases with the frequency of the overtone. This makes the motional capacitance at the overtone substantially less than C_m/n^2.

An important parameter for crystal filter design is the unloaded Q at f_s, the resonant frequency of the series arm. This is usually denoted by Q_U.

$Q_u = 2 \pi f_s L_m/r_m$

Q_U is very high, often exceeding 100,000 in the lower HF region. Even VHF overtone crystals can have Q_U values over 20,000, making it possible to design quartz crystal band-pass filters with a tremendously wide range of bandwidths and center frequencies.

The basic filtering action of a crystal can be seen from **Figure 10.43**, which shows a plot of attenuation vs frequency for the test circuit shown in the inset. The series arm of the crystal equivalent circuit forms a series-tuned circuit, which passes signals with little attenuation at its resonant frequency, f_s, but appears inductive above this frequency and parallel resonates with C_o at f_p to produce a deep notch in transmission. The difference between f_s and f_p is known as the pole-zero separation, or PZ spacing, and is dependent on C_m/C_o as well as f_s. Further information on quartz crystal theory and operation can be found in the **Oscillators and Synthesizers** chapter and in the reference for Bottom.

A simple crystal filter developed in the 1930s

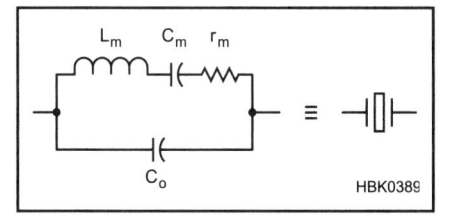

Figure 10.42 — Equivalent circuit of a quartz crystal and its circuit symbol.

Analog and Digital Filtering   10.23

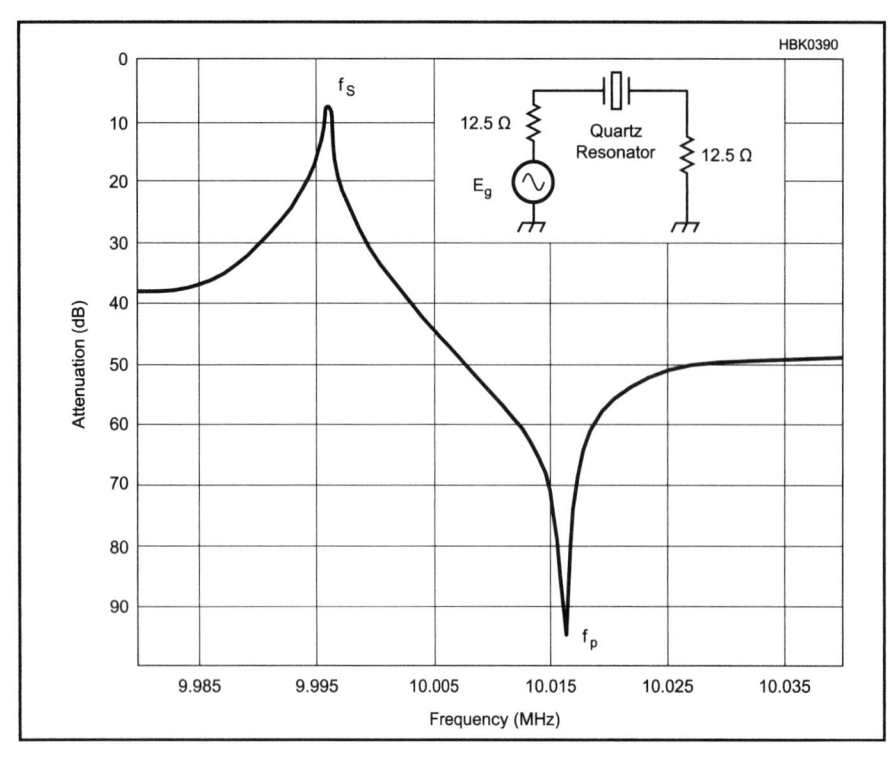

Figure 10.43 — Response of 10 MHz crystal (Cm = 0.0134 pF, Lm = 18.92 mH, ESR = 34 Ω) in a series test circuit (see inset) showing peak of transmission (lowest attenuation) at the series resonant frequency, f_s, and a null (maximum attenuation) caused by the parallel resonance due to C_o at f_p.

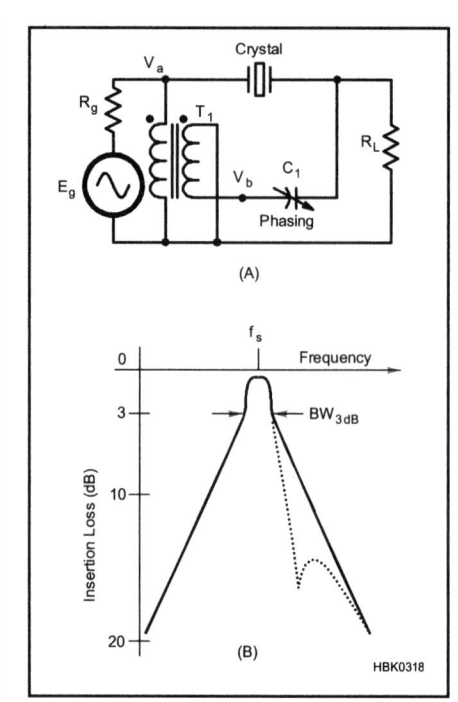

Figure 10.44 — Classic single-crystal filter in A has the response shown in B. The phasing capacitor can be adjusted to balance out C_o (solid line), or set to a lesser or greater value to create a movable null to one side, or other, of the passband (dotted line).

is shown in **Figure 10.44**. The voltage-reversing transformer T1 was usually an IF transformer, but nowadays could be a bifilar winding on a ferrite core. Voltages V_a and V_b have equal magnitude but 180° phase difference. When $C_1 = C_o$, the effect of C_o will disappear and a well-behaved single resonance will occur as indicated by the solid line in Figure 10.44B. However, if C_1 is adjusted to unbalance the circuit, a transmission zero (notch) is produced well away from the pass band and by increasing the amount of imbalance this can be brought back toward the edge of the pass band to attenuate close-by interfering CW signals. If C_1 is reduced in value from the balanced setting, the notch comes in from the high side and if C_1 is increased, it comes in from the low side. The dotted curve in Figure 10.44B illustrates how the notch can be set with C_1 less than C_o to suppress adjacent signals just above the pass band. In practice a notch depth of up to 60 dB can be achieved. This form of "crystal gate" filter, operating at 455 kHz, was present in many high-quality amateur communications receivers from the 1930s through the 1960s. When the filter was switched into the receiver IF amplifier the bandwidth was reduced to a few hundred Hz for CW reception. The close-in range of the notch was sometimes improved by making C_1 part of a differential capacitor that could add extra capacitance to either the C_1 or C_o side of the IF transformer. This design could also be used to good effect at frequencies up to 1.7 MHz with an increased minimum bandwidth. However, any crystal gate requires considerable additional IF filtering to achieve a reasonable ultimate attenuation figure, so it should not be the only form of selectivity used in an IF amplifier.

The half-lattice filter shown in **Figure 10.45** offers an improvement in performance over a single-crystal filter. The quartz crystal static capacitors, C_o, cancel each other. The remaining series-resonant arms, if offset in frequency and terminated properly, will produce an approximate 2-pole Butterworth or Chebyshev response. The crystal spacing for simple Chebyshev designs is usually around two-thirds of the bandwidth. Half-lattice filter sections can be cascaded to produce composite filters with multiple poles. Many of the older commercial filters are coupled half-lattice types using 4, 6 or 8 crystals, and this is still the favored technology for some crystal filters at lower frequencies. Very often extra capacitance was added across one crystal in each half lattice to unbalance C_o and provide deep transmission zeroes on either side of the pass band to sharpen up the close-in response at the expense of the attenuation further out. The reference for Steder and Hardcastle discusses the computer design of half-lattice filters.

Most commercial HF and VHF crystal filters

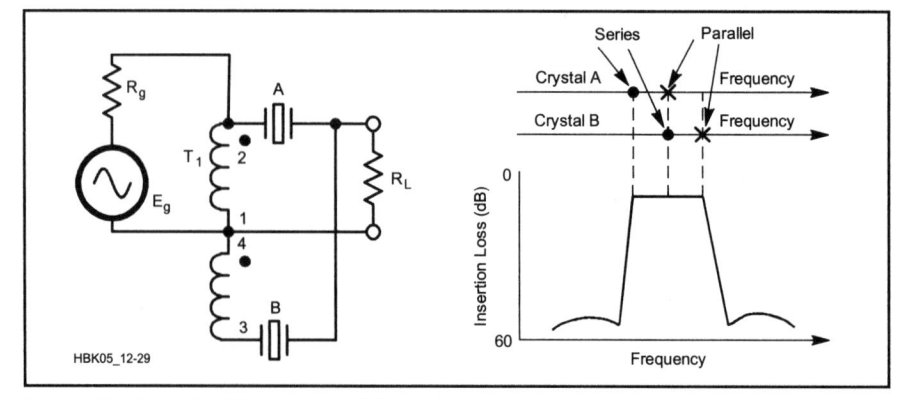

Figure 10.45 — A half-lattice crystal filter. The C_o of one crystal can be made to balance the C_o of the other, or C_o across the higher crystal can be deliberately increased to create nulls on either side of the passband.

10.24 Chapter 10

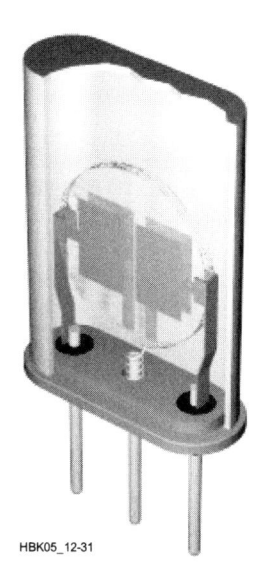

Figure 10.46 — A dual monolithic crystal filter has two sets of electrodes acoustically coupled to provide a two-pole response in a single crystal unit. The center lead is connected to the case and grounded in normal operation.

produced today use dual monolithic structures as their resonant elements. These are a single quartz plate onto which two sets of metal electrodes have been deposited, physically separated to control the acoustic (mechanical) coupling between them. An example of a dual monolithic filter (2-pole) is shown in **Figure 10.46**. These are available with center frequencies from 9 MHz to well over 120 MHz. In effect, the dual monolithic structure behaves just like a pair of coupled crystal resonators. There is a subtle difference, however, because the static capacitance in duals appears across the input and output terminations and doesn't produce a null above the pass band, as it would for two electrically coupled crystal resonators. Multi-pole filters can be built by coupling duals together using external capacitors, the C_o from each dual input and output being absorbed in the coupling capacitors or terminations, or by including more acoustically coupled resonators in the electrode structure on a single quartz plate. Though not common, 3-pole and 4-pole monolithic filters housed in standard, single crystal holders are available from some manufacturers.

10.6.1 Filter Parameters

An ideal band-pass filter would pass the desired signal with no loss and completely attenuate everything else. Practically, it is not possible to achieve such a response with a finite number of resonators, and approximations to this ideal have to be accepted. Greater stop-band attenuation and steeper sides can be achieved if more and more crystals are used, and the response gets nearer to the ideal "brick-wall" one. This feature of a filter is expressed as a *shape factor*, which specifies the ratio of the bandwidth at an attenuation of 60 dB to the bandwidth at 6 dB — both these levels being taken relative to the actual pass band peak to eliminate insertion loss from the calculation. An ideal brickwall filter would have a shape factor of 1, and practical filters have shape factors that depend on the number of crystals used in the design and the type of response chosen for the pass band. A 1 dB Chebyshev design, for example, can typically produce shape factors that vary from about 4.1 for a 4-pole to 1.5 for a 10-pole, but the actual figures obtained in practice are very much dependent on Q_u and how much greater it is than the filter Q, defined by f_o/BW, where f_o is the center frequency and BW the 3 dB bandwidth. The ratio of Q_u to f_o/BW is often quoted as Q_o, or q_o, and this, along with the order and type of response, determines the insertion loss of a crystal filter. Q_o also determines how closely the pass band follows the design response, and how much the passband ripple is smoothed out and the edges of the response rounded off by crystal loss.

Commercial filter manufacturers usually choose the Chebyshev equiripple design for SSB, AM and FM bandwidths because it gives the best compromise between passband response and the steepness of the sides, and 1 dB-ripple Chebyshev designs are pretty standard for speech bandwidths. Tolerances in component values and crystal frequencies can cause the ripple in the pass band to exceed 1 dB, so often the maximum ripple is specified as 2 dB even though the target ripple is lower. Insertion loss, the signal loss going thru the filter, also varies with the type of response and increases as the order of the filter increases. The insertion loss for a given order and bandwidth is higher for high-ripple Chebyshev designs than it is for low-ripple ones, and Butterworth designs have lower insertion loss than any Chebyshev type for a given bandwidth. Pass-band amplitude response and shape factor are important parameters for assessing the performance of filters used for speech communications.

However, group delay is also important for data and narrow bandwidth CW reception. Differential group delay can cause signal distortion on data signals if the variations are greater than the automatic equalizer can handle. Ringing can be an annoying problem when using very narrow CW filters, and the group delay differential across the pass band must be minimized to reduce this effect. When narrow bandwidth filters are being considered, shape factor has to be sacrificed to reduce differential group delay and its associated ringing problems. It's no good having a narrow Chebyshev design with a shape factor of 2 if the filter produces unacceptable ringing and is intolerable to use in practice.

Both Bessel and linear phase (equiripple 0.05°) responses have practically constant, low group delay across the entire pass band and well beyond on either side, making either a good choice for narrow CW or specialized data use. They also have the great advantage of offering the lowest possible insertion loss of all the types of response currently in use, which is important when Q_o is low, as it often is for very narrow bandwidth filters. The insertion loss of the Bessel design is marginally lower than that of the linear phase, but the latter has a superior shape factor giving it the best balance of low group delay and good selectivity. A 6-pole linear phase (equiripple 0.05°) design has a shape factor of 3.39, whereas a 6-pole Bessel has 3.96. The Gaussian-to-12 dB response has a better shape factor than that of either the linear phase or Bessel designs but the group delay across the pass band is not as flat and pronounced peaks (ears) are beginning to appear at the band edges with a 6-pole design. The Gaussian-to-6 dB group delay is reasonably flat for 3- and 4-pole filters, but significant ears appear toward the passband edges in designs with 5 poles or more.

10.6.2 Crystal Filter Evaluation

The simplest means of assessing the performance of a crystal filter is to temporarily install it in a finished transceiver, or receiver, and use a strong on-air signal, or locally generated carrier, to run thru the filter pass band and down either side to see if there are any anomalies. Provided that the filter crystals have been carefully characterized in the first instance, and computer modeling has shown that the design is close to what's required, this may be all that's required to confirm a successful project. However, more elaborate checks on both the pass band and stop band can be made if a DDS signal generator, or vector network analyzer (VNA), is available. A test set-up for evaluating the response of a filter using a DDS generator requires an oscilloscope to display the response, whereas a VNA controlled via the USB port of a PC can display the response on the PC screen with suitable software — see the **Test Equipment and Measurements** chapter. In addition, it can measure the phase and work out the group delay of the filter. VNAs can also be used to characterize the crystals prior to making the filter as well as evaluating filter performance after completion.

10.7 SAW Filters

The resonators in a monolithic crystal filter are coupled together by bulk acoustic waves. These acoustic waves are generated and propagated in the interior of a quartz plate. It is also possible to launch, by an appropriate transducer, acoustic waves that propagate only along the surface of the quartz plate. These are called "surface-acoustic-waves" because they do not appreciably penetrate the interior of the plate.

A *surface-acoustic-wave* (SAW) filter consists of thin aluminum electrodes, or fingers, deposited on the surface of a piezoelectric substrate as shown in **Figure 10.47**. Lithium Niobate ($LiNbO_3$) is usually favored over quartz because it yields less insertion loss. The electrodes make up the filter's transducers. RF voltage is applied to the input transducer and generates electric fields between the fingers. The piezoelectric material vibrates in response, launching an acoustic wave along the surface. When the wave reaches the output transducer it produces an electric field between the fingers. This field generates a voltage across the load resistor.

Since both input and output transducers are not entirely unidirectional, some acoustic power is lost in the acoustic absorbers located behind each transducer. This lost acoustic power produces a mid-band electrical insertion loss typically greater than 10 dB. The SAW filter frequency response is determined by the choice of substrate material and finger pattern. The finger spacing, (usually one-quarter wavelength) determines the filter center frequency. Center frequencies are available from 20 to 1000 MHz. The number and length of fingers determines the filter loaded Q and shape factor.

Loaded Qs are available from 2 to 100, with a shape factor of 1.5 (equivalent to a dozen poles). Thus the SAW filter can be made broadband much like the LC filters that it replaces. The advantage is substantially reduced volume and possibly lower cost. SAW filter research was driven by military needs for exotic amplitude-response and time-delay requirements. Low-cost SAW filters are presently found in television IF amplifiers where high mid-band loss can be tolerated.

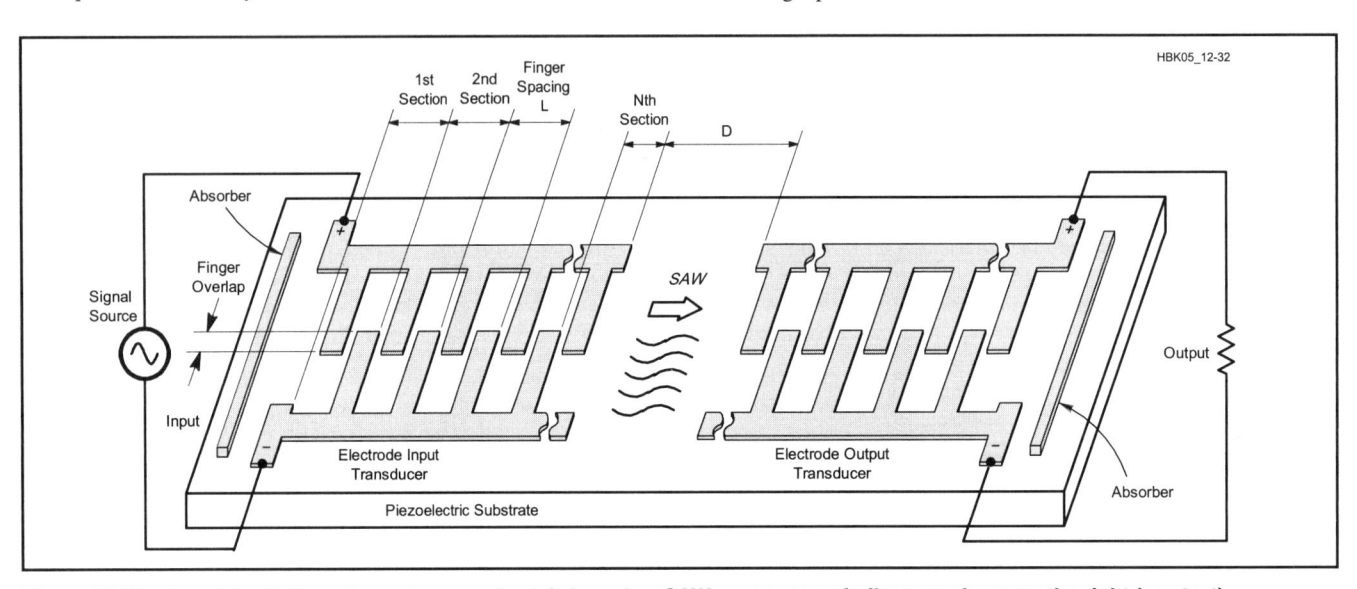

Figure 10.47 — The *interdigitated* transducer, on the left, launches SAW energy to a similar transducer on the right (see text).

10.8 Transmission Line VHF/UHF/Microwave Filters

LC filter calculations are based on the assumption that the reactances are *lumped*— that the physical dimensions of the components are considerably less than the operating wavelength. In such cases the unavoidable inter-turn parasitic capacitance associated with inductors and the unavoidable series parasitic inductance associated with capacitors are neglected as being secondary effects. If careful attention is paid to circuit layout and miniature components are used, lumped LC filter technology can be used up to perhaps 1 GHz.

Replacing lumped reactances with selected short sections of *Transverse Electromagnetic Mode* (TEM) transmission lines results in transmission line filters. (In TEM the electric and magnetic fields associated with a transmission line are at right angles (transverse) to the direction of wave propagation.) Coaxial cable, stripline and microstrip are examples of TEM components. Waveguides and waveguide resonators are not TEM components.

Coaxial cable transmission line filters are often used at HF and VHF frequencies. Stripline and microstrip transmission-line filters predominate from 500 MHz to 10 GHz. In addition they are often used down to 50 MHz when narrowband ($Q_L > 10$) band-pass filtering is required. In this application they exhibit considerably lower loss than their LC counterparts and are useful at frequencies where coaxial transmission lines are too lossy. A detailed treatment of the use of coaxial cable to form transmission line filters is presented in the **Transmission Lines** chapter. This section focuses on stripline and microstrip filters used at VHF and above.

10.8.1 Stripline and Microstrip Filters

Figure 10.48 shows three popular transmission lines used in transmission line filters. The circular coaxial transmission line (*coax*) shown in Figure 10.48A consists of two concentric metal cylinders separated by dielectric (insulating) material. The first transmission-line filters were built from sections of coaxial line. Their mechanical fabrication is expensive and it is difficult to provide electrical coupling between line sections.

Fabrication difficulties are reduced by the use of shielded strip transmission line (*stripline*) shown in Figure 10.48B. The outer conductor of stripline consists of two flat parallel metal plates (ground planes) and the inner conductor is a thin metal strip. Sometimes the inner conductor is a round metal rod. The dielectric between ground planes and strip can be air or a low-loss plastic such as polyethylene. The outer conductors (ground planes or shields) are separated from each other by distance b.

Striplines can be easily coupled together by locating the strips near each other as shown in Figure 10.48B. Stripline Z_0 vs width (w) is plotted in **Figure 10.49**. Air-dielectric stripline technology is best for low bandwidth ($Q_L > 20$) band-pass filters.

The most popular transmission line at UHF and microwave is *microstrip* (unshielded stripline), shown in Figure 10.48C. It can be fabricated with standard printed-circuit processes and is the least expensive configuration. In microstrip the outer conductor is a single flat metal ground-plane. The inner conductor is a thin metal strip separated from the ground-plane by a solid dielectric substrate. Typical substrates are 0.062 inch G-10 fiberglass ($\varepsilon = 4.5$) for the 50 MHz to 1 GHz frequency range and 0.031 inch Teflon ($\varepsilon = 2.3$) for frequencies above 1 GHz. Unfortunately, microstrip has the most loss of the three types of transmission line; therefore it is not suitable for narrow, high-Q, band-pass filters.

Conductor separation must be minimized or radiation from the line and unwanted coupling to adjacent circuits may become problems. Microstrip characteristic impedance and the effective dielectric constant (ε) are shown in **Figure 10.50**. Unlike coax and stripline, the effective dielectric constant is less than that of the substrate since a portion of the electromagnetic wave propagating along the microstrip travels in the air above the substrate.

The characteristic impedance for stripline and microstrip-lines that results in the lowest loss is not 75 Ω as it is for coax. Loss decreases as line width increases, which leads to clumsy, large structures. Therefore, to conserve space, filter sections are often constructed from 50 Ω stripline or microstrip stubs even though the loss at that characteristic impedance is not a minimum for that type of transmission line.

10.8.2 Transmission Line Band-Pass Filters

Band-pass filters can also be constructed from transmission line stubs. (See the **Transmission Lines** chapter for information on stub behavior and their use as filters at HF and VHF.) At VHF the stubs can be considerably shorter than a quarter-wavelength (¼ λ), yielding a compact filter structure with less mid-band loss than its LC counterpart. The single-stage 146 MHz stripline band-pass filter shown in **Figure 10.51** is an example.

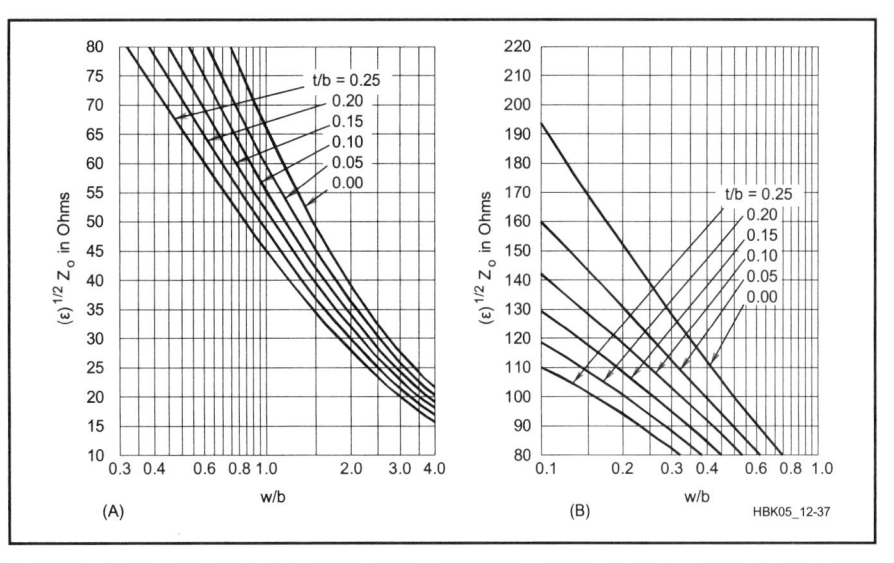

Figure 10.49 — The Z_0 of stripline varies with *w*, *b* and *t* (conductor thickness). See Figure 10.48B. The conductor thickness is *t* and the plots are normalized in terms of *t/b*.

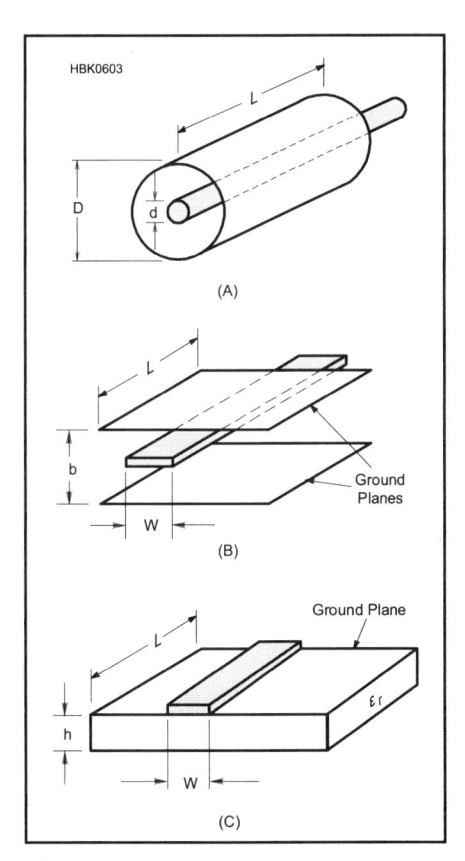

Figure 10.48 — Transmission lines. A: Coaxial line. B: Coupled stripline, which has two ground planes. C: Microstrip has only one ground plane.

Z_0 Ω	$\varepsilon=1$ (AIR) W/h	$\varepsilon=2.3$ (RT/Duroid) W/h	$\sqrt{\varepsilon_e}$	$\varepsilon=4.5$ (G-10) W/h	$\sqrt{\varepsilon_e}$
25	12.5	7.6	1.4	4.9	2.0
50	5.0	3.1	1.36	1.8	1.85
75	2.7	1.6	1.35	0.78	1.8
100	1.7	0.84	1.35	0.39	1.75
	$\sqrt{\varepsilon}=1$				

Figure 10.50 — Microstrip parameters (after H. Wheeler, *IEEE Transactions on MTT*, March 1965, p 132). ε_e is the effective ε.

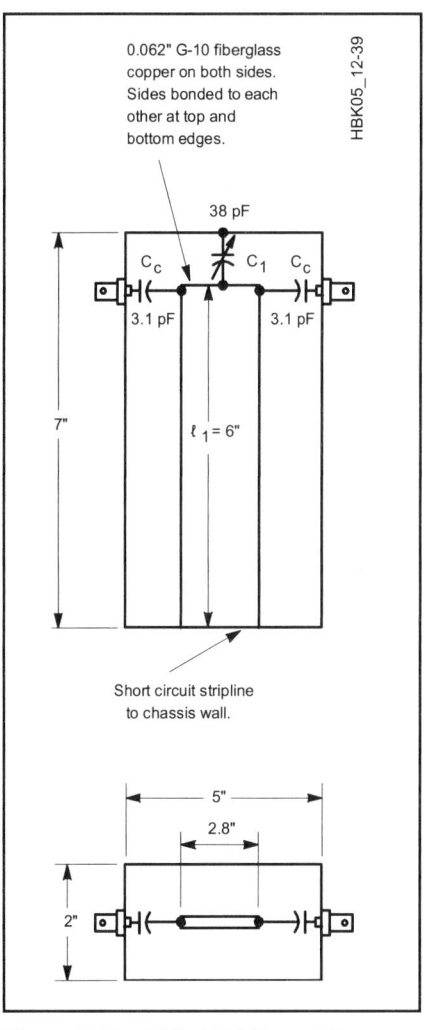

Figure 10.51 — This 146 MHz stripline band-pass filter has been measured to have a Q_L of 63 and a loss of approximately 1 dB.

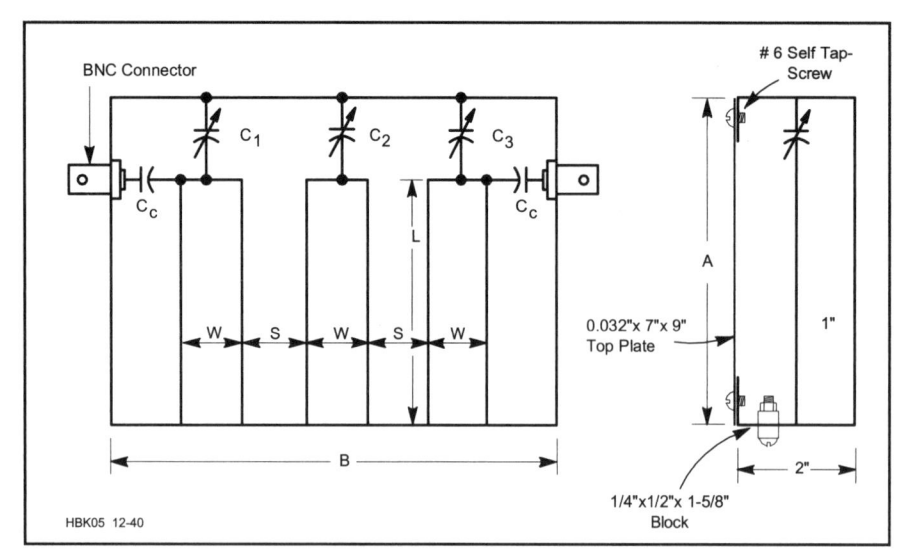

Figure 10.52 — This Butterworth filter is constructed in combline. It was originally discussed by R. Fisher in December 1968 *QST*.

interlaced fingers. Two examples of 3-pole UHF interdigital filters are shown in **Figure 10.53**. Design graphs for round-rod interdigital filters are given in the reference for Metcalf. The ¼ λ resonators may be tuned by physically changing their lengths or by tuning the screw opposite each rod.

If the short-circuited ends of two ¼ λ resonators are connected to each other, the resulting ½ λ stub will remain in resonance, even when the connection to the ground-plane is removed. Such a floating ½ λ microstrip line, when bent into a U-shape, is called a *hairpin* resonator. Closely coupled hairpin resonators can be arranged to form multistage band-pass filters. Microstrip hairpin band-pass filters are popular above 1 GHz because they can be easily fabricated using photo-etching techniques. No connection to the ground-plane is required.

This filter consists of a single inductive 50 Ω strip-line stub mounted into a 2 × 5 × 7 inch aluminum box. The stub is resonated at 146 MHz with the "APC" variable capacitor, C1. Coupling to the 50 Ω generator and load is provided by the coupling capacitors C_c. The measured performance of this filter is: f_o = 146 MHz, BW = 2.3 MHz (Q_L = 63) and mid-band loss = 1 dB.

Single-stage stripline filters can be coupled together to yield multistage filters. One method uses the capacitor coupled band-pass filter synthesis technique to design a 3-pole filter. Another method allows closely spaced inductive stubs to magnetically couple to each other. When the coupled stubs are grounded on the same side of the filter housing, the structure is called a "combline filter." Three examples of combline band-pass filters are shown in **Figure 10.52** and a set of VHF/UHF filter designs by W1GHZ is included in the projects section of this chapter. These filters are constructed in 2 × 7 × 9 inch aluminum boxes. The article describing these filters by Reed Fisher, W2CQH, is available in this book's downloadable supplemental information and is listed in the references, as well.

10.8.3 Quarter-Wave Transmission Line Filters

The reactance of a ¼ λ shorted-stub is infinite, as discussed in the **Transmission Lines** chapter. Thus, a ¼ λ shorted stub behaves like a parallel-resonant LC circuit. Proper input and output coupling to a ¼ λ resonator yields a practical band-pass filter. Closely spaced ¼ λ resonators will couple together to form a multistage band-pass filter. When the resonators are grounded on opposite walls of the filter housing, the structure is called an *interdigital filter* because the resonators look like

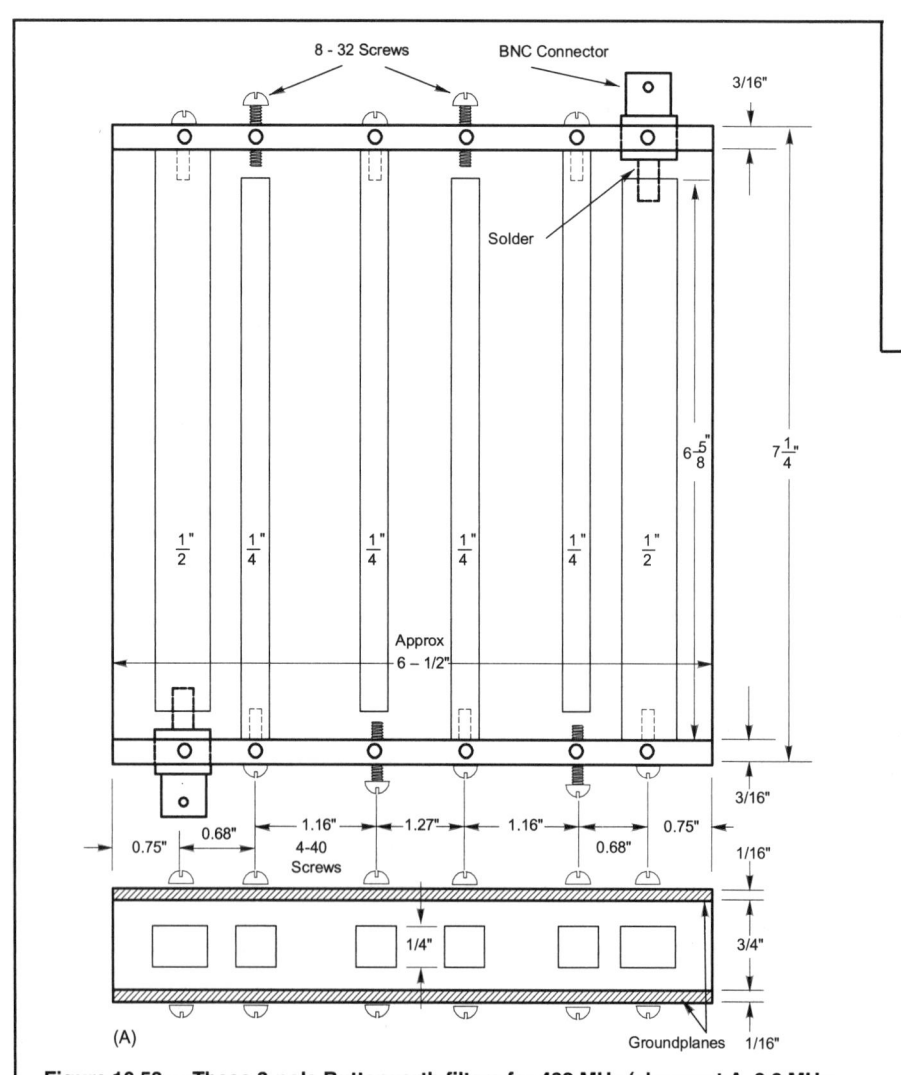

Figure 10.53 — These 3-pole Butterworth filters for 432 MHz (shown at A, 8.6 MHz bandwidth, 1.4 dB passband loss) and 1296 MHz (shown at B, 110 MHz bandwidth, 0.4 dB passband loss) are constructed as interdigitated filters. The material is from R. E. Fisher, March 1968 *QST*.

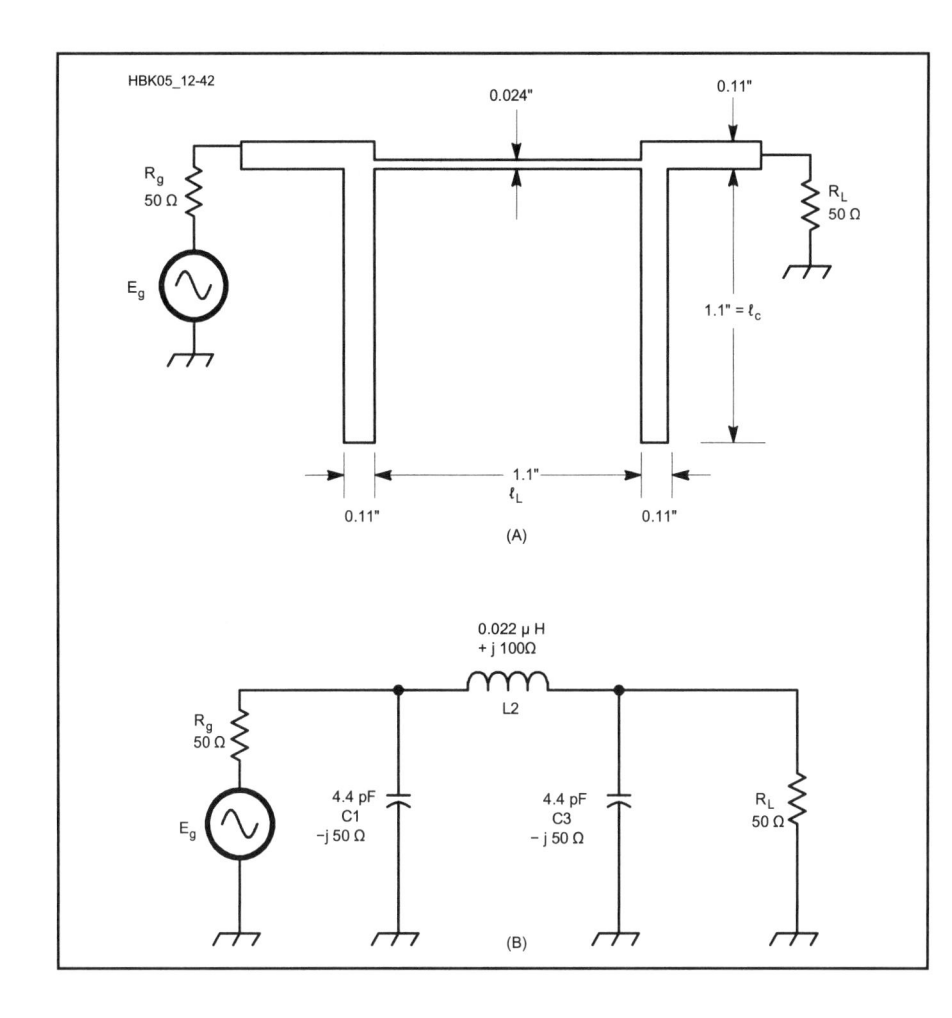

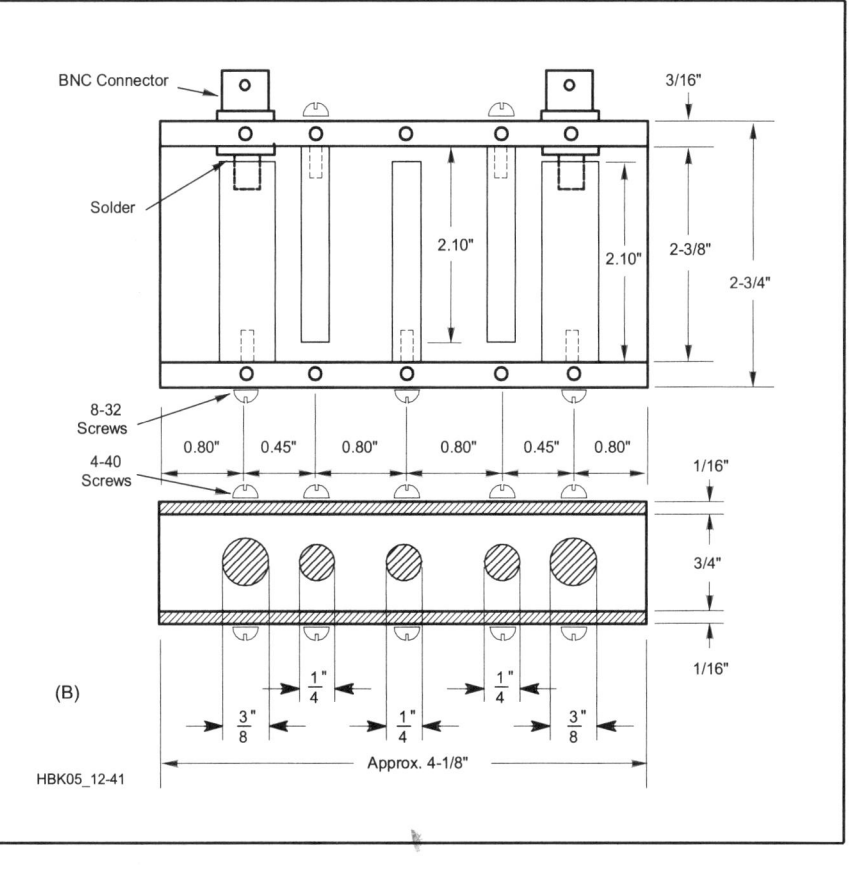

Figure 10.54 — A microstrip 3-pole emulated-Butterworth low-pass filter with a cutoff frequency of 720 MHz. A: Microstrip version built with G-10 fiberglass board ($\varepsilon = 4.5$, h = 0.062 inches). B: Lumped LC version of the same filter. To construct this filter with lumped elements very small values of L and C must be used and stray capacitance and inductance would have to be reduced to a tiny fraction of the component values.

10.8.4 Emulating LC Filters with Transmission Line Filters

Low-pass and high-pass transmission-line filters are usually built from short sections of transmission lines (stubs) that emulate lumped LC reactances. Sometimes low-loss lumped capacitors are mixed with transmission line inductors to form a hybrid component filter. For example, consider the 720 MHz, 3-pole microstrip low-pass filter shown in **Figure 10.54A** that emulates the LC filter shown in Figure 10.54B. C1 and C3 are replaced with 50 Ω open-circuit shunt stubs ℓ_C long. L2 is replaced with a short section of 100-Ω line ℓ_L long. The LC filter, Figure 10.54B, was designed for $f_c = 720$ MHz. Such a filter could be connected between a 432 MHz transmitter and antenna to reduce harmonic and spurious emissions. A reactance chart shows that X_C is 50 Ω, and the inductor reactance is 100 Ω at f_c. The microstrip version is constructed on G-10 fiberglass 0.062 inch thick, with $\varepsilon = 4.5$. Then, from Figure 10.50, w is 0.11 inch and $\ell_C = 0.125\, l_g$ for the 50 Ω capacitive stubs. Also, from Figure 10.50, w is 0.024 inch and ℓ_L is $0.125\, l_g$ for the 100-Ω inductive line. The inductive line length is approximate because the far end is not a short circuit. l_g is $300/(720 \times 1.75) = 0.238$ m, or 9.37 inches Thus ℓ_C is 1.1 inch and ℓ_L is 1.1 inches.

This microstrip filter exhibits about 20 dB of attenuation at 1296 MHz. Its response rises again, however, around 3 GHz. This is because the fixed-length transmission line stubs change in terms of wavelength as the frequency rises. This particular filter was designed to eliminate third-harmonic energy near 1296 MHz from a 432 MHz transmitter and does a better job in this application than the Butterworth filter in Figure 10.53 which has spurious responses in the 1296 MHz band.

Analog and Digital Filtering   10.29

10.9 Helical Resonators

Ever-increasing occupancy of the radio spectrum brings with it a parade of receiver overload and spurious responses. Overload problems can be minimized by using high-dynamic-range receiving techniques, but spurious responses (such as the image frequency) must be filtered out before mixing occurs. Conventional tuned circuits cannot provide the selectivity necessary to eliminate the plethora of signals found in most urban and many suburban environments. Other filtering techniques must be used.

Helical resonators are usually a better choice than ¼ λ cavities on 50, 144 and 222 MHz to eliminate these unwanted inputs because they are smaller and easier to build than coaxial cavity resonators, although their Q is not as high as that of cavities. In the frequency range from 30 to 100 MHz it is difficult to build high-Q inductors, and coaxial cavities are very large. In this frequency range the helical resonator is an excellent choice. At 50 MHz for example, a capacitively tuned, ¼ λ coaxial cavity with an unloaded Q of 3000 would be about 4 inches in diameter and nearly 5 ft long. On the other hand, a helical resonator with the same unloaded Q is about 8.5 inches in diameter and 11.3 inches long. Even at 432 MHz, where coaxial cavities are common, the use of helical resonators results in substantial size reductions.

The helical resonator was described by the late Jim Fisk, W1HR, in a June 1976 *QST* article. (see the **Reference** section) The resonator is described as a coil surrounded by a shield, but it is actually a shielded, resonant section of helically wound transmission line with relatively high characteristic impedance and low propagation velocity along the axis of the helix. The electrical length is about 94% of an axial ¼ λ or 84.6°. One lead of the helical winding is connected directly to the shield and the other end is open circuited as shown in **Figure 10.55**. Although the shield may be any shape, only round and square shields will be considered here.

10.9.1 Helical Resonator Design

The unloaded Q of a helical resonator is determined primarily by the size of the shield. For a round resonator with a copper coil on a low-loss form, mounted in a copper shield, the unloaded Q is given by

$$Q_U = 50D\sqrt{f_0}$$

where
 D = inside diameter of the shield, in inches
 f_0 = frequency, in MHz.

D is assumed to be 1.2 times the width of

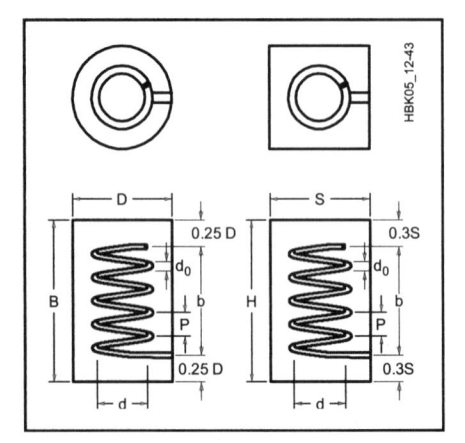

Figure 10.55 — Dimensions of round and square helical resonators. The diameter, D (or side, S) is determined by the desired unloaded Q. Other dimensions are expressed in terms of D or S (see text).

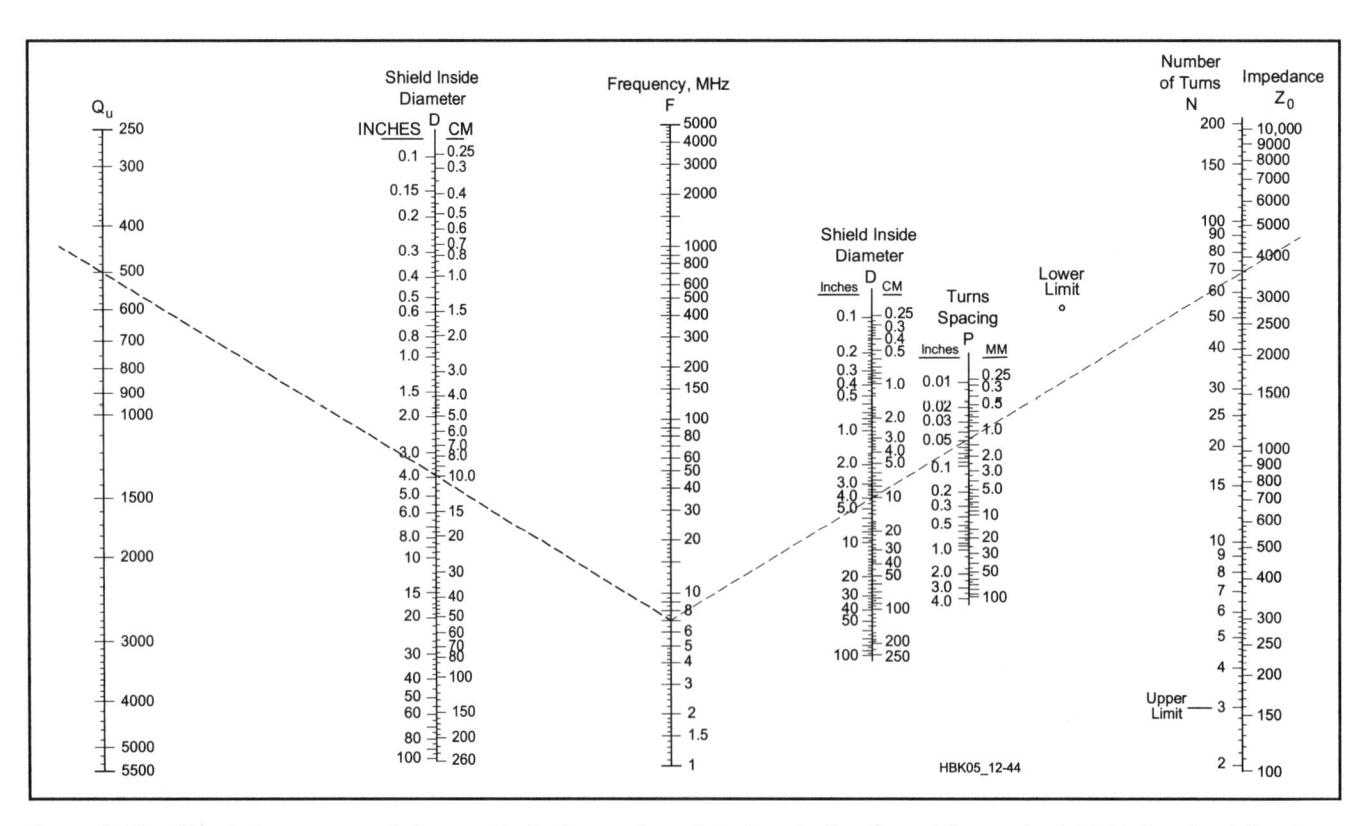

Figure 10.56 — The design nomograph for round helical resonators starts by selecting Q_U and the required shield diameter. A line is drawn connecting these two values and extended to the frequency scale (example here is for a shield of about 3.8 inches and Q_U of 500 at 7 MHz). Finally the number of turns, N, winding pitch, P, and characteristic impedance, Z_0, are determined by drawing a line from the frequency scale through selected shield diameter (but this time to the scale on the right-hand side). For the example shown, the dashed line shows P ≈ 0.047 inch, N = 70 turns, and Z_n = 3600 Ω).

one side for square shield cans. This formula includes the effects of losses and imperfections in practical materials. It yields values of unloaded Q that are easily attained in practice. Silver plating the shield and coil increases the unloaded Q by about 3% over that predicted by the equation. At VHF and UHF, however, it is more practical to increase the shield size slightly (that is, increase the selected QU by about 3% before making the calculation). The fringing capacitance at the open-circuit end of the helix is about 0.15D pF (that is, approximately 0.3 pF for a shield 2 inches in diameter). Once the required shield size has been determined, the total number of turns, N, winding pitch, P and characteristic impedance, Z_0, for round and square helical resonators with air dielectric between the helix and shield, are given by:

$$N = \frac{1908}{f_0 D}$$

$$P = \frac{f_0 D^2}{2312}$$

$$Z_0 = \frac{99,000}{f_0 D}$$

$$N = \frac{1590}{f_0 S}$$

$$P = \frac{f_0 S^2}{1606}$$

$$Z_0 = \frac{82,500}{f_0 S}$$

In these equations, dimensions D and S are in inches and f_0 is in megahertz. The design nomograph for round helical resonators in **Figure 10.56** is based on these formulas.

Although there are many variables to consider when designing helical resonators, certain ratios of shield size to length and coil diameter to length, provide optimum results. For helix diameter, d = 0.55 D or d = 0.66 S. For helix length, b = 0.825D or b = 0.99S. For shield length, B = 1.325 D and H = 1.60 S.

Design of filter dimensions can be done using the nomographs in this section or with computer software. The program *Helical* for designing and analyzing helical filters is available with the downloadable supplemental content. Use of the nomographs is described in the following paragraphs.

Figure 10.57 simplifies calculation of these dimensions. Note that these ratios result in a helix with a length 1.5 times its diameter, the condition for maximum Q. The shield is about 60% longer than the helix — although it can be made longer — to completely contain the electric field at the top of the helix and the magnetic field at the bottom.

The winding pitch, P, is used primarily to determine the required conductor size. Adjust the length of the coil to that given by the equations during construction. Conductor size ranges from 0.4 P to 0.6 P for both round and square resonators and are plotted graphically in **Figure 10.58**.

Obviously, an area exists (in terms of frequency and unloaded Q) where the designer must make a choice between a conventional cavity (or lumped LC circuit) and a helical resonator. The choice is affected by physical shape at higher frequencies. Cavities are long and relatively small in diameter, while the length of a helical resonator is not much greater than its diameter. A second consideration is that point where the winding pitch, P, is less than the radius of the helix (otherwise the structure tends to be non-helical). This condition occurs when the helix has fewer than three turns (the "upper limit" on the design nomograph of Figure 10.56).

10.9.2 Helical Filter Construction

The shield should not have any seams parallel to the helix axis to obtain as high an unloaded Q as possible. This is usually not a problem with round resonators because large-diameter copper tubing is used for the shield, but square resonators require at least one seam

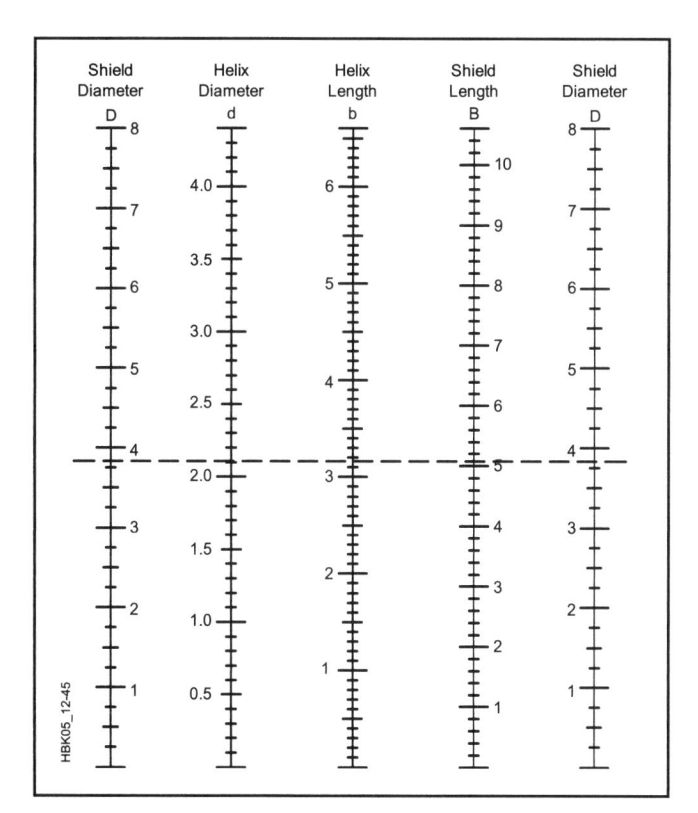

Figure 10.57 — The helical resonator is scaled from this design nomograph. Starting with the shield diameter, the helix diameter, d, helix length, b, and shield length, B, can be determined with this graph. The example shown has a shield diameter of 3.8 inches. This requires a helix mean diameter of 2.1 inches, helix length of 3.1 inches, and shield length of 5 inches.

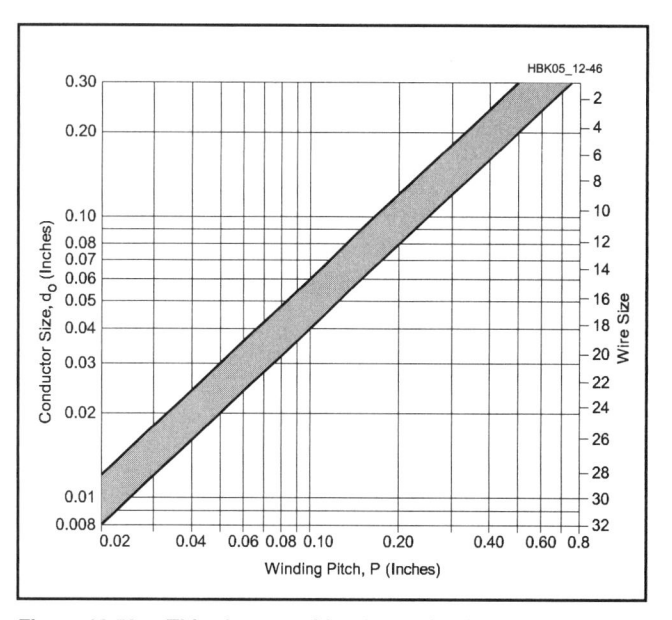

Figure 10.58 — This chart provides the design information of helix conductor size vs winding pitch, P. For example, a winding pitch of 0.047 inch results in a conductor diameter between 0.019 and 0.028 inch (#22 or #24 AWG).

and usually more. The effect on unloaded Q is minimized if the seam is silver soldered carefully from one end to the other.

Results are best when little or no dielectric is used inside the shield. This is usually no problem at VHF and UHF because the conductors are large enough that a supporting coil form is not required. The lower end of the helix should be soldered to the nearest point on the inside of the shield.

Although the external field is minimized by the use of top and bottom shield covers, the top and bottom of the shield may be left open with negligible effect on frequency or unloaded Q. Covers, if provided, should make electrical contact with the shield. In those resonators where the helix is connected to the bottom cover, that cover must be soldered solidly to the shield to minimize losses.

10.9.3 Helical Resonator Tuning

A carefully built helical resonator designed from the nomograph of Figure 10.56 will resonate very close to the design frequency. Slightly compress or expand the helix to adjust resonance over a small range. If the helix is made slightly longer than that called for in Figure 10.57, the resonator can be tuned by pruning the open end of the coil. However, neither of these methods is recommended for wide frequency excursions because any major deviation in helix length will degrade the unloaded Q of the resonator.

Most helical resonators are tuned by means of a brass tuning screw or high-quality air-variable capacitor across the open end of the helix. Piston capacitors also work well, but the Q of the tuning capacitor should ideally be several times the unloaded Q of the resonator. Varactor diodes have sometimes been used where remote tuning is required, but varactors can generate unwanted harmonics and other spurious signals if they are excited by strong, nearby signals.

When a helical resonator is to be tuned by a variable capacitor, the shield size is based on the chosen unloaded Q at the operating frequency. Then the number of turns, N and the winding pitch, P, are based on resonance at 1.5 f_0. Tune the resonator to the desired operating frequency, f_0.

10.9.4 Helical Resonator Insertion Loss

The insertion loss (dissipation loss), I_L, in decibels, of all single-resonator circuits is given by

$$I_L = 20 \log_{10}\left(\frac{1}{1 - \frac{Q_L}{Q_U}}\right)$$

where
Q_L = loaded Q
Q_U = unloaded Q

This is plotted in **Figure 10.59**. For the most practical cases ($Q_L > 5$), this can be closely approximated by $I_L \approx 9.0\ (Q_L/Q_U)$ dB. The selection of Q_L for a tuned circuit is dictated primarily by the required selectivity of the circuit. However, to keep dissipation loss to 0.5 dB or less (as is the case for low-noise VHF receivers), the unloaded Q must be at least 18 times the Q_L.

10.9.5 Coupling Helical Resonators

Signals are coupled into and out of helical resonators with inductive loops at the bottom of the helix, direct taps on the coil or a combination of both. Although the correct tap point can be calculated easily, coupling by loops and probes must be determined experimentally.

The input and output coupling is often provided by probes when only one resonator is used. The probes are positioned on opposite sides of the resonator for maximum isolation. When coupling loops are used, the plane of the loop should be perpendicular to the axis of the helix and separated a small distance from the bottom of the coil. For resonators with only a few turns, the plane of the loop can be tilted slightly so it is parallel with the slope of the adjacent conductor.

Helical resonators with inductive coupling (loops) exhibit more attenuation to signals above the resonant frequency (as compared to attenuation below resonance), whereas resonators with capacitive coupling (probes) exhibit more attenuation below the passband, as shown for a typical 432 MHz resonator in **Figure 10.60**. Consider this characteristic when choosing a coupling method. The passband can be made more symmetrical by using a combination of coupling methods (inductive input and capacitive output, for example).

If more than one helical resonator is required to obtain a desired band-pass characteristic, adjacent resonators may be coupled through apertures in the shield wall between the two resonators. Unfortunately, the size and location of the aperture must be found empirically, so this method of coupling is not very practical unless you're building a large number of identical units.

Since the loaded Q of a resonator is determined by the external loading, this must be considered when selecting a tap (or position of a loop or probe). The ratio of this external loading, R_b, to the characteristic impedance, Z_0, for a ¼ λ resonator is calculated from:

$$K = \frac{R_b}{Z_0} = 0.785\left(\frac{1}{Q_L} - \frac{1}{Q_U}\right)$$

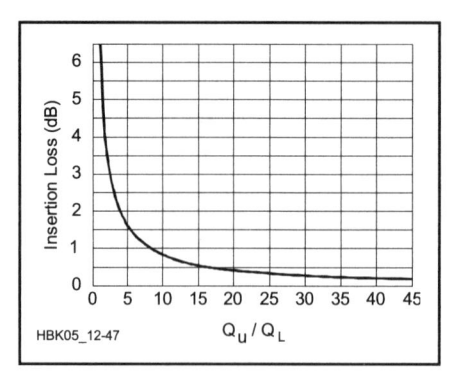

Figure 10.59 — The ratio of loaded (Q_L) to unloaded (Q_U) Q determines the insertion loss of a tuned resonant circuit.

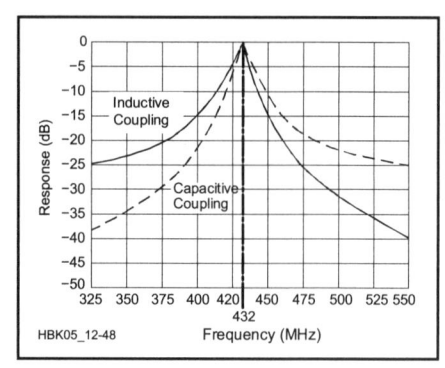

Figure 10.60 — This response curve for a single-resonator 432 MHz filter shows the effects of capacitive and inductive input/output coupling. The response curve can be made symmetrical on each side of resonance by combining the two methods (inductive input and capacitive output, or vice versa).

10.10 Filter Projects

The filter projects to follow are by no means the only filter projects in this book. Filters for specific applications may be found in other chapters of this *Handbook* and in the downloadable supplemental material. Receiver input filters, transmitter filters, inter-stage filters and others can be extracted from the various projects and built for other applications. Since filters are a first line of defense against *electromagnetic interference* (EMI) problems, additional filter methods appear in the **RF Interference** chapter.

10.10.1 Audio Waveshaping Filter for CW Reception

This project is condensed from the Mar/Apr 2017 *QEX* article, "An Improved Audio-Frequency Bandpass Filter for Morse Code Reception," by Jim Tonne, W4ENE. That article is included in the downloadable supplemental information for this book.

The IF response of the superheterodyne receiver used by a typical CW operator has a flat top with a width of typically 400 Hz. If the center frequency is set to 500 Hz, the filter bandwidth extends from about 300 to 700 Hz, dropping off abruptly beyond those limits. In most of these receivers, the filter characteristics result in distortion of the leading and trailing edge of the CW audio. The distortion (primarily ringing) is strong enough to become objectionable at sending speeds beginning above 20 WPM. The cause is the group delay characteristics typical of filters with sharp bandpass edges or "skirts". (The original article contains several measured and simulated waveforms showing the cause and effect relationship.)

Short of replacing the filter circuit in the receiver, one way to improve the situation is to modify the entire system response of the receiver by adding a waveshaping filter. (SDR receiver filters can be redesigned or modified to eliminate these effects without hardware circuit changes.) The author has designed this add-on filter to have a slightly narrower bandwidth than the IF filter and has a smoother ("more gentle") response at the band edges, both in magnitude and phase. As a result, the original filter's overshoot and ringing are greatly reduced in the final audio output. Field testers report that the filter "sounds better" which is the ultimate goal for CW reception by ear.

The filter can be constructed either from passive components (**Figure 10.61**) or an equivalent active design (**Figure 10.62**). The passive filter has a center frequency of about 500 Hz and shows optional input and output matching transformers for 8 Ω to the filter's input and output 125Ω impedance. (That value was chosen to use the 77.5 mH inductors available as surplus from Ed Wetherhold, W3NQN, **w3nqn@comcast.net** and other sources.) All inductor values are the same to ease construction. Components with 5% tolerance can be used with some loss of performance or components could be selected from a batch by using an L-C meter. Transformers are optional (performance degrades somewhat if connected directly to 8 Ω inputs or loads) but should be high-quality and able to handle the expected signal levels. If driven into saturation, the signal will be distorted, eliminating any benefit provided by the filter. The active version does not require transformers but the high-impedance input should be shielded from RF pickup. The output op-amp may not be able to drive larger headphones, so an audio output amplifier IC may need to be added.

10.10.2 Combline Filters for 50 – 432 MHz

(This project description is condensed from the paper "Combline Filters for VHF and UHF" by Paul Wade, W1GHZ, at the 41st Eastern VHF Conference in 2015. The full paper is available in the downloadable supplemental information for this book.)

RF pollution is rampant at good portable locations on mountaintops and other high places — anywhere accessible is populated with cell phone towers, TV and FM broadcast stations, two-way radio and pager transmitters, and even amateur repeaters. Most of these are high power, producing signals strong enough to seriously overload the VHF and UHF transceivers we use for contest operation or microwave liaison. The advent of broadband MMIC preamps acerbates the problem. The problem often manifests itself as a very high noise level.

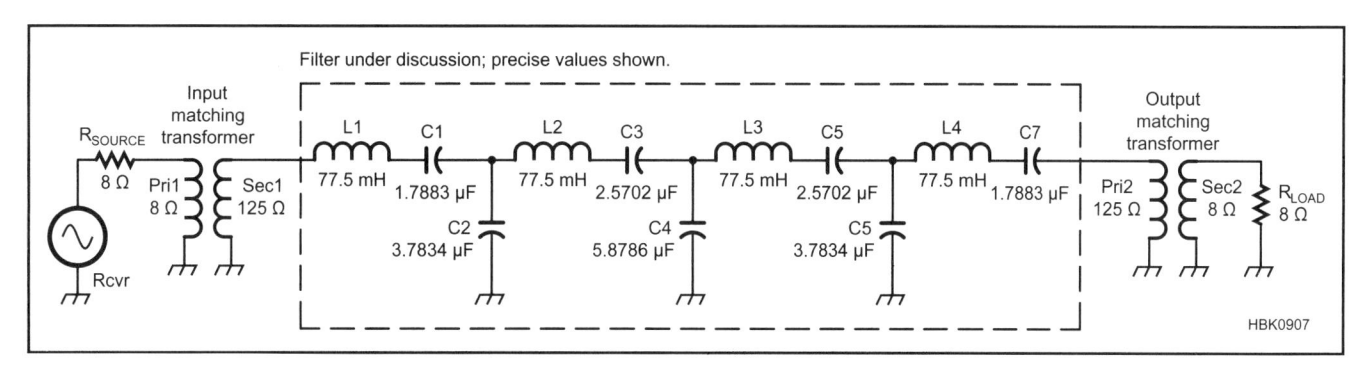

Figure 10.61 — Schematic of the passive waveshaping add-on filter.

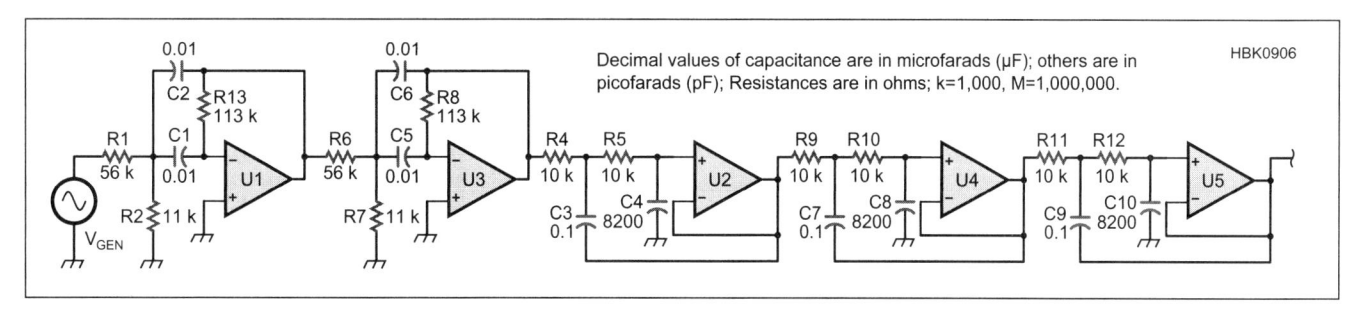

Figure 10.62 — Schematic of the active waveshaping add-on filter.

A combline filter uses parallel transmission line resonators less than a quarter-wave long, loaded by capacitance at the open end. This allows tuning over a range of frequencies by varying the capacitance. Typical electrical length of the resonators is between 30 and 60 electrical degrees; a quarter-wavelength is 90 degrees. These filters use stripline construction with tapped input and output coupling, as sketched in **Figure 10.63**, and the design procedure is given in the full paper.

A good, sharp filter must be mechanically robust to stay on frequency, especially for rover work. For low loss, high Q is important, requiring wide striplines with good contact to ground at the bottom, the high-current point. The filter uses all-aluminum construction to prevent dissimilar metal corrosion. All connections are made with #4 tinned solder lugs and stainless-steel hardware, metals that are least likely to interact with aluminum. An inexpensive aluminum enclosure of 220 × 145 × 60 mm was used for the 144 MHz filter in **Figure 10.64**. Dimensions for all of the filters are included in **Table 10.5**. Enclosure model numbers can be searched online to find sources for the boxes. A close match is sufficient.

The full paper includes construction guidelines, including selecting parts, metalworking, and assembly details. Tuning instructions are given and require the use of a sweep generator or a vector network analyzer can be used. The performance curves in **Figure 10.65** are indic-

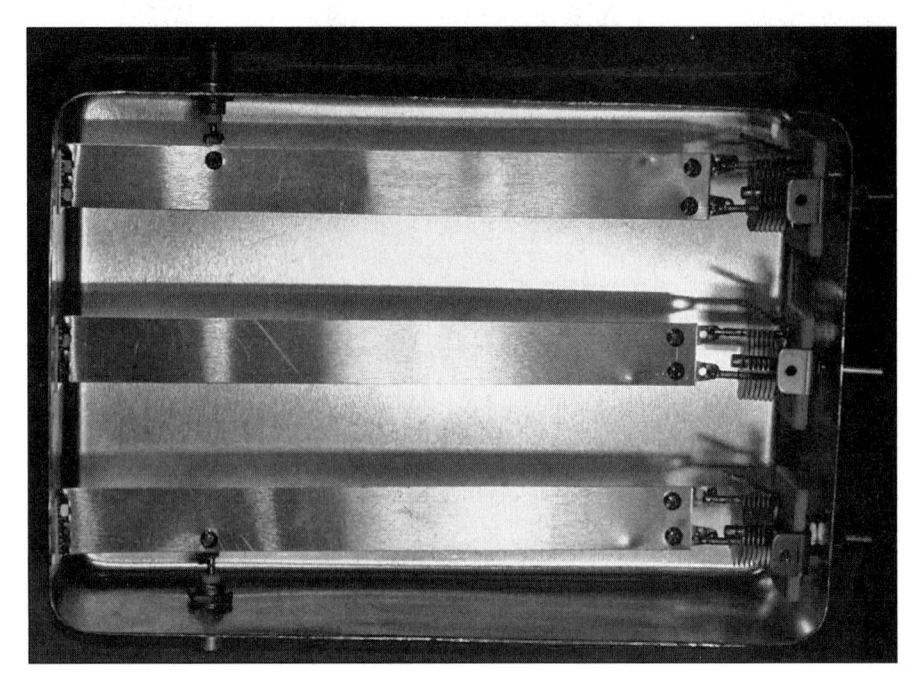

Figure 10.64 — Combline filter for 144 MHz

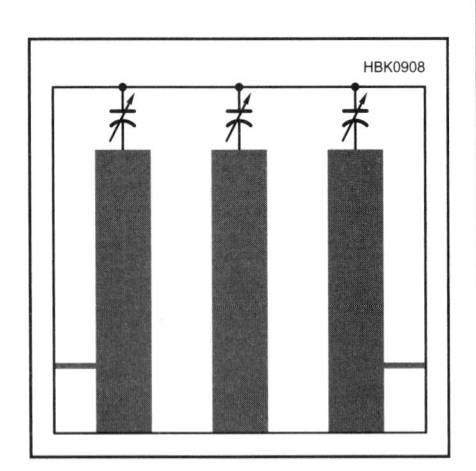

Figure 10.63 — Sketch of combline filter in stripline.

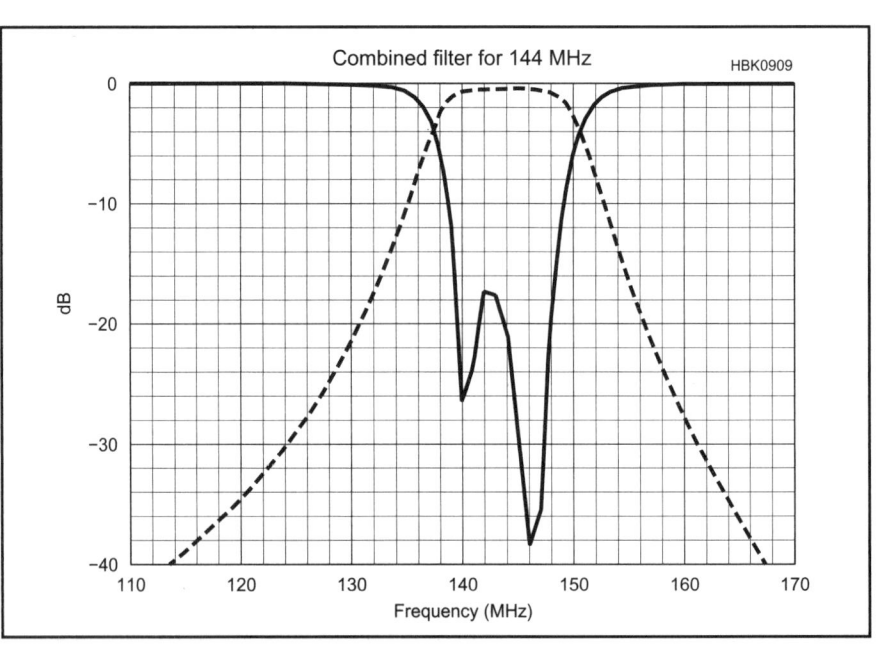

Figure 10.65 — Performance of 144 MHz combline filter. The solid line is Return Loss and the dashed line is Insertion Loss.

Table 10.5 - Dimensions for Combline Filter in Stripline

| Band (MHz) | Bandwidth (MHz) | BoxModel | Length (mm) | Width (mm) | Depth (mm) | Strip |
width (mm)	Strip spacing (mm)	Strip c to c (mm)	Tap point (mm)	Capacitor (pF)		
144	2.5	AC-406	9 in / 7 in	2 in / 33	44 / 77	22 / 24
222	8	U3879 mid	202 / 129	54 / 34	40 / 74	30 / 15
432	11	1590-BB	115 / 90	30 / 16	25 / 41	16 / 5
432	13	U3879 sm	176 / 99	43 / 29	35 / 64	15 / 5
50	3	AC-1418	8 in / 10 in	2.5 in / 30	40 / 70	90 / 150

ative of completed filter performance. If that equipment is not available, the filters can be optimized at one frequency and used as narrowband filters.

10.10.3 Broadcast-Band Rejection Filters

Inadequate front-end selectivity or poorly performing RF amplifier and mixer stages often result in unwanted cross-talk and overloading from adjacent commercial or amateur stations. Two passive receive-only filters are described here — a high-pass, multi-section filter and a simple series wave trap.

BROADCAST-BAND REJECTION HIGH-PASS FILTER

The filter shown is inserted between the antenna and receiver. It attenuates the out-of-band signals from broadcast stations but passes signals of interest (1.8 to 30 MHz) with little or no attenuation.

The high signal strength of local broadcast stations requires that the stop-band attenuation of the high-pass filter also be high. This filter provides about 60 dB of stop-band attenuation with less than 1 dB of attenuation above 1.8 MHz. The filter input and output ports match 50 Ω with a maximum SWR of 1.353:1 (reflection coefficient = 0.15). A 10-element filter yields adequate stop-band attenuation and a reasonable rate of attenuation rise. The design uses only standard-value capacitors.

The filter parts layout, schematic diagram, response curve and component values are shown in **Figure 10.66**. The standard capacitor values listed are within 2.8% of the design values. If the attenuation peaks (f2, f4 and f6) do not fall at 0.677, 1.293 and 1.111 MHz, tune the series-resonant circuits by slightly squeezing or separating the inductor windings.

Construction of the filter is shown in **Figure 10.67**. Use polypropylene film-type capacitors. These capacitors are available through Digi-Key and other suppliers. The powdered-iron T50-2 toroidal cores are available through Amidon, Palomar Engineers and others.

For a 3.4 MHz cutoff frequency, divide the L and C values by 2. (This effectively doubles the frequency-label values in Figure 10.66.)

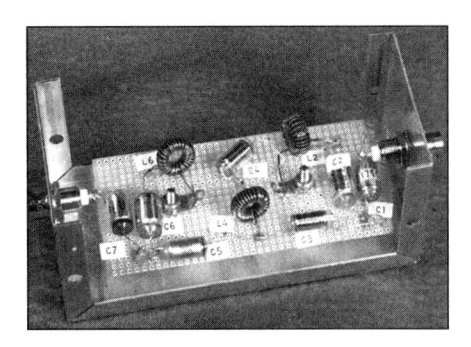

Figure 10.67 — The filter fits easily in a 2 × 2 × 5 inch enclosure. The version in the photo was built on a piece of perfboard.

For the 80 meter version, L2 through L6 should be 20 to 25 turns each, wound on T50-6 cores. The actual turns required may vary one or two from the calculated values. Parallel-connect capacitors as needed to achieve the nonstandard capacitor values required for this filter.

The measured filter performance is shown in Figure 10.66. The stop-band attenuation is more than 58 dB. The measured cutoff frequency (less than 1 dB attenuation) is under 1.8 MHz. The measured passband loss is less than 0.8 dB from 1.8 to 10 MHz. Between 10 and 100 MHz, the insertion loss of the filter gradually increases to 2 dB. Input impedance was measured between 1.7 and 4.2 MHz. Over the range tested, the input impedance of the filter remained within the 37- to 67.7-Ω input-impedance window (equivalent to a maximum SWR of 1.353:1).

WAVE TRAP FOR BROADCAST STATIONS

Nearby medium-wave broadcast stations can sometimes cause interference to HF receivers over a broad range of frequencies. A wave trap can catch the unwanted frequencies and keep them out of your receiver.

The way the circuit works is quite simple. Referring to **Figure 10.68**, you can see that it consists essentially of only two components, a coil L1 and a variable capacitor C1. This series-tuned circuit is connected in parallel with the antenna circuit of the receiver. The characteristic of a series-tuned circuit is that the coil and capacitor have a very low impedance (resistance) to frequencies very close to the frequency to which the circuit is tuned. All other frequencies are almost unaffected. If the circuit is tuned to 1530 kHz, for example, the signals from a broadcast station on that frequency will flow through the filter to ground, rather than go on into the receiver. All other frequencies will pass straight into the receiver. In this way, any interference caused in the receiver by the station on 1530 kHz is significantly reduced.

This is a series-tuned circuit that is adjustable from about 540 kHz to 1600 kHz. It is built into a metal box, **Figure 10.69**, to shield it from other unwanted signals and is connected as shown in Figure 10.68. To make the inductor, first make a *former* by winding two layers of paper on the ferrite rod. Fix this in place with black electrical tape. Next, lay one end of the wire for the coil on top of the former, leaving about an inch of wire protruding beyond the end of the ferrite rod. Use several turns of electrical tape to secure the wire to the former. Now, wind the coil along the former, making sure the turns are in a single layer and close together. Leave an inch or so of wire free at the end of the coil. Once again, use a couple of turns of electrical tape

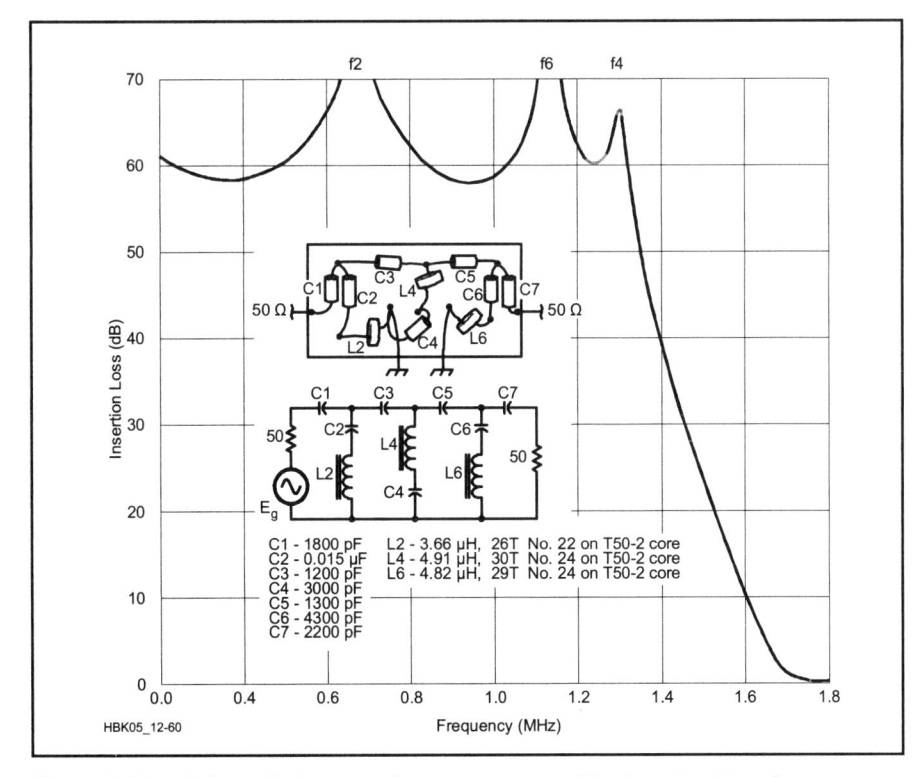

Figure 10.66 — Schematic, layout and response curve of the broadcast band rejection filter.

C1 - 1800 pF
C2 - 0.015 µF
C3 - 1200 pF
C4 - 3000 pF
C5 - 1300 pF
C6 - 4300 pF
C7 - 2200 pF

L2 - 3.66 µH, 26T No. 22 on T50-2 core
L4 - 4.91 µH, 30T No. 24 on T50-2 core
L6 - 4.82 µH, 29T No. 24 on T50-2 core

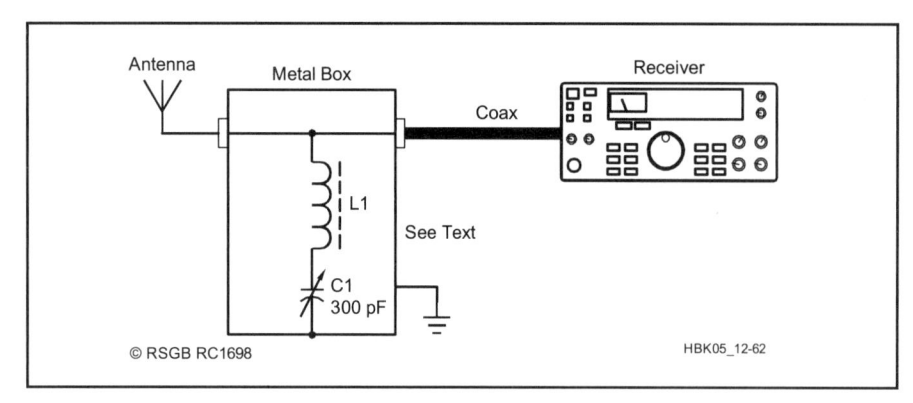

Figure 10.68 — The wave trap consists of a series tuned circuit, which 'shunts' signals on an unwanted frequency to ground.

Figure 10.69 — The wave trap can be roughly calibrated to indicate the frequency to which it is tuned.

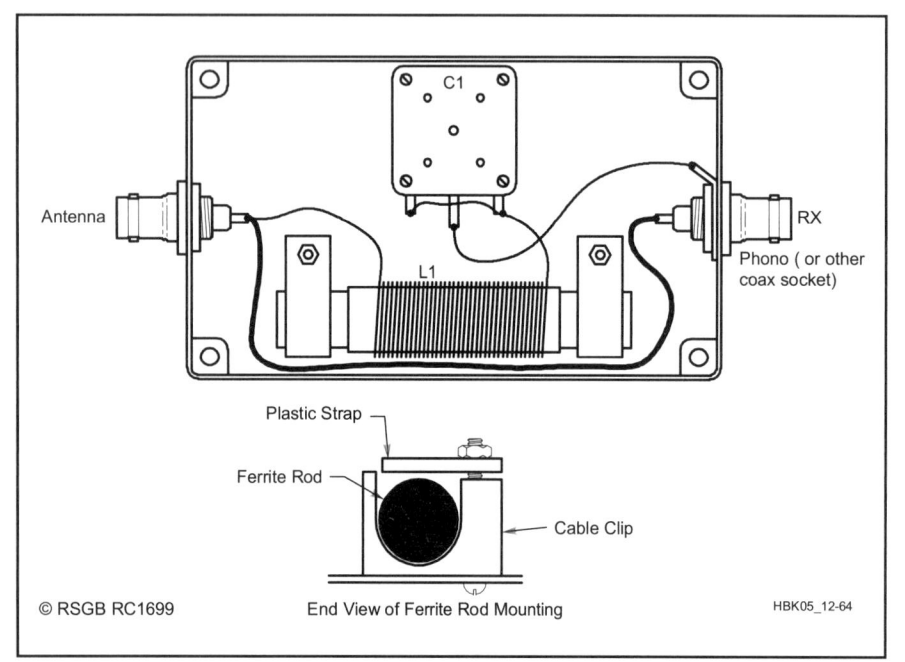

Figure 10.70 — Wiring of the wave trap. The ferrite rod is held in place with cable clips.
C1 — 300 pF polyvaricon variable.
L1 — 80 turns of 30 SWG enameled wire, wound on a ferrite rod.
Associated items: Case (die-cast box), knobs to suit, connectors to suit, nuts and bolts, plastic cable clips.

to secure the wire to the former. Finally, remove half an inch of enamel from each end of the wire.

Alternatively, if you have an old AM transistor radio, a suitable coil can usually be recovered already wound on a ferrite rod. Ignore any small coupling coils. Drill the box to take the components, then fit them in and solder together as shown in **Figure 10.70**. Make sure the lid of the box is fixed securely in place, or the wave trap's performance will be adversely affected by pick-up on the components.

Connect the wave trap between the antenna and the receiver, then tune C1 until the interference from the offending broad-cast station is a minimum. You may not be able to elim-inate interference completely, but this handy little device should reduce it enough to listen to the amateur bands. Let's say you live near an AM transmitter on 1530 kHz, and the signals break through on your 1.8 MHz receiver. By tuning the trap to 1530 kHz, the problem is greatly reduced. If you have problems from more than one broadcast station, the problem needs a more complex solution.

10.10.4 Optimized Harmonic Transmitting Filters

Low-pass filters should be placed at the output of transmitters to ensure that they meet the various regulatory agency requirements for harmonic suppression. These are commonly designed to pass a single amateur band and provide attenuation at harmonics of that band sufficient to meet the requirements. The material presented here by Jim Tonne, W4ENE, is based on material originally published in the September/October 1998 issue of *QEX*. The basic approach is to use a computer to optimize the performance in the passband (a single amateur band) while simultaneously maximizing the attenuation at the second and third harmonic of that same band. When this is done, the higher harmonics will also be well within spec.

The schematic of this filter along with parts values for the 3.5 to 4.0 MHz amateur band

Table 10.6
Values for the Optimized Harmonic Filters

Band (meters)	C1 (pF)	L2, 5% (μH)	L2, Exact (μH)	C2 (pF)	C3 (pF)	L4, 5% (μH)	L4, Exact (μH)	C4 (pF)	C5 (pF)
160	2400	3.0	2.88	360	4700	2.4	2.46	820	2200
80	1300	1.5	1.437	180	2400	1.3	1.29	390	1100
60	910	1.0	1.029	120	1600	0.91	0.8897	270	750
40	680	0.75	0.7834	91	1300	0.62	0.6305	220	560
30	470	0.56	0.5626	68	910	0.47	0.4652	160	430
20	330	0.39	0.3805	47	620	0.33	0.3163	110	300
17	270	0.30	0.3063	36	510	0.27	0.2617	82	240
15	220	0.27	0.2615	30	430	0.22	0.2245	68	200
12	200	0.24	0.241	27	390	0.20	0.2042	62	180
10	180	0.20	0.2063	24	330	0.18	0.1721	56	150
6	91	0.11	0.108	13	180	0.091	0.0911	30	82

is shown in **Figure 10.71**. The responses of that filter are shown in **Figure 10.72**.

Component values for the 160 meter through the 6 meter amateur bands are shown in **Table 10.6**. The capacitors are shown in pF and the inductors in µH. The capacitors are the nearest 5% values; both the nearest 5% and the exact inductor values are shown.

Using the nearest-5% inductor values will result in satisfactory operation. If the construction method is such that exact-value (adjustable) inductors can be used then the "Exact" values are preferred. These values were obtained from the program *SVC Filter Designer* which is available with the downloadable supplemental content.

An example of how to construct 100-W class transmitting filters using simple PC techniques is provided in the downloadable supplemental information. See the article "Band-Pass Filters for HF Transceivers," by Lew Gordon, K4VX which includes a series of alternate designs for the 1.8, 3.5, 7, 14, 21, and 28 MHz bands.

10.10.5 Diplexer Filter

This section, covering diplexer filters, was written by William E. Sabin, WØIYH. The diplexer is helpful in certain applications, such as frequency mixer terminations.

The terms "diplexer" and "duplexer" are often confused. A duplexer is a device such as a circulator that allows a transmitter and a receiver to use the same antenna *without* the use of filters. Diplexers use filters so that the signal frequencies must be far apart, such as on different bands. Diplexers have a constant filter-input resistance that extends to the stop band as well as the passband. Ordinary filters that become highly reactive or have an open or short-circuit input impedance outside the passband may degrade performance of the devices to which they are attached. (For example, impedances far from 50 Ω outside the operating frequency range may cause an amplifier to develop parasitic oscillations.)

Figure 10.73 shows a *normalized* prototype 5-element, 0.1-dB Chebyshev low-pass/high-pass (LP/HP) filter. This idealized filter is driven by a voltage generator with zero internal resistance, has load resistors of 1.0 Ω and a cutoff frequency of 1.0 radian per second (0.1592 Hz). The LP prototype values are taken from standard filter tables.[1] The first element is a series inductor. The HP prototype is found by:

a) replacing the series L (LP) with a series C (HP) whose value is 1/L, and

b) replacing the shunt C (LP) with a shunt L (HP) whose value is 1/C.

For the Chebyshev filter, the return loss is improved several dB by multiplying the prototype LP values by an experimentally derived number, K, and dividing the HP values by the same K. You can calculate the LP values in henrys and farads for a 50 Ω RF application with the following formulas:

$$L_{LP} = \frac{KL_{P(LP)}R}{2\pi f_{CO}}; C_{LP} = \frac{KC_{P(LP)}}{2\pi f_{CO}R}$$

where

$L_{P(LP)}$ and $C_{P(LP)}$ are LP prototype values

K = 1.005 (in this specific example)

R = 50 Ω

f_{CO} = the cutoff (–3 dB response) frequency in Hz.

For the HP segment:

$$L_{HP} = \frac{L_{P(HP)}R}{2\pi f_{CO}K}; C_{HP} = \frac{C_{P(HP)}}{2\pi f_{CO}KR}$$

where $L_{P(HP)}$ and $C_{P(HP)}$ are HP prototype values.

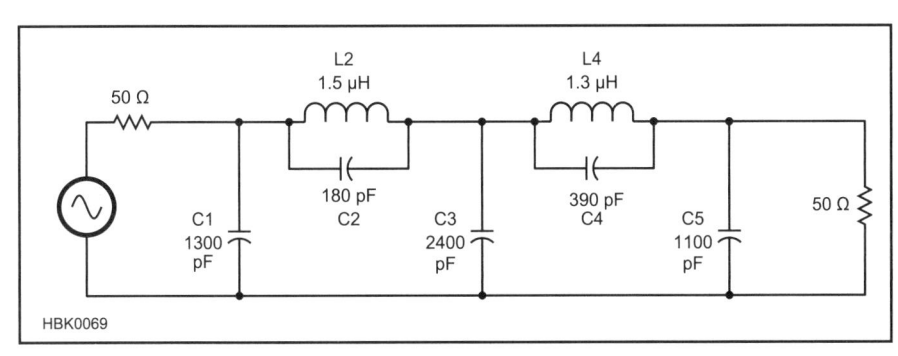

Figure 10.71 — Optimized low-pass filter. This design is for the 80 meter amateur band. It is similar to a Cauer design but the parts values have been optimized as described in the text and in the Sep/Oct 1998 issue of *QEX*.

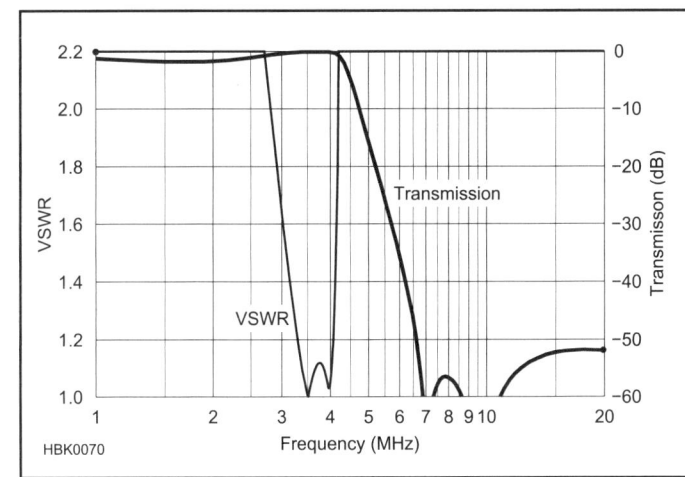

Figure 10.72 — Responses of the filter shown in Figure 10.71. Note the low values of SWR from 3.5 to 4 MHz. At the same time the harmonics are attenuated to meet regulations. Responses for the other amateur bands are very similar except for the frequency scaling.

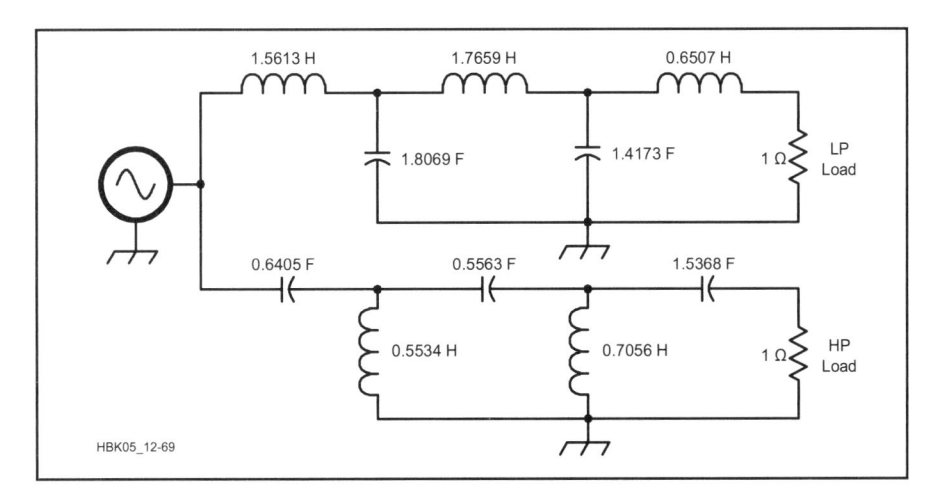

Figure 10.73 — Low-pass and high-pass prototype diplexer filter design. The low-pass portion is at the top, and the high-pass at the bottom of the drawing. See text.

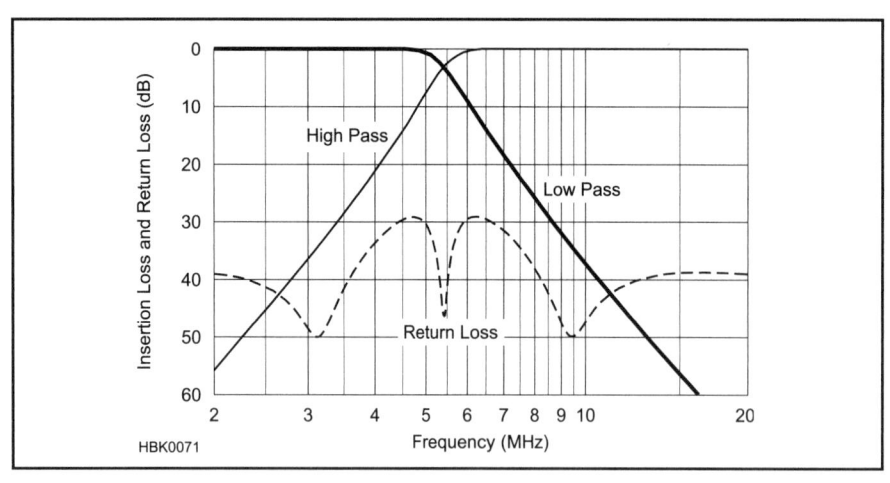

Figure 10.74 — Response for the low-pass and high-pass portions of the 80 meter diplexer filter. Also shown is the return loss of the filter.

Figure 10.74 shows the LP and HP responses of a diplexer filter for the 80 meter band. The following items are to be noted:
• The 3 dB responses of the LP and HP meet at 5.45 MHz.
• The input impedance is close to 50 Ω at all frequencies, as indicated by the high value of return loss (SWR <1.07:1).
• At and near 5.45 MHz, the LP input reactance and the HP input reactance are conjugates; therefore, they cancel and produce an almost perfect 50 Ω input resistance in that region.
• Because of the way the diplexer filter is derived from synthesis procedures, the transfer characteristic of the filter is mostly independent of the actual value of the amplifier dynamic output impedance.[2] This is a useful feature, since the RF power amplifier output impedance is usually not known or specified.
• The 80 meter band is well within the LP response.
• The HP response is down more than 20 dB at 4 MHz.
• The second harmonic of 3.5 MHz is down only 18 dB at 7.0 MHz. Because the second harmonic attenuation of the LP is not great, it is necessary that the amplifier itself be a well-balanced push-pull design that greatly rejects the second harmonic. In practice this is not a difficult task.
• The third harmonic of 3.5 MHz is down almost 40 dB at 10.5 MHz.

Figure 10.75A shows the unfiltered output of a solid-state push-pull power amplifier for the 80 meter band. In the figure you can see that:
• The second harmonic has been suppressed by a proper push-pull design.
• The third harmonic is typically only 15 dB or less below the fundamental.

The amplifier output goes through our diplexer filter. The desired output comes from the LP side, and is shown in Figure 10.75B. In it we see that:

• The fundamental is attenuated only about 0.2 dB.
• The LP has some harmonic content; however, the attenuation exceeds FCC requirements for a 100 W amplifier.

Figure 10.75C shows the HP output of the diplexer that terminates in the HP load or *dump* resistor. A small amount of the fundamental frequency (about 1%) is also lost in this resistor. Within the 3.5 to 4.0 MHz band, the filter input resistance is almost exactly the correct 50 Ω load resistance value. This is because power that would otherwise be *reflected* back to the amplifier is absorbed in the dump resistor.

Solid state power amplifiers tend to have stability problems that can be difficult to debug.[3] These problems may be evidenced by level changes in: load impedance, drive, gate or base bias, supply voltage, etc. Problems may arise from:
• The reactance of the low-pass filter outside the desired passband. This is especially true for transistors that are designed for high-frequency operation.
• Self-resonance of a series inductor at some high frequency.
• A stop band impedance that causes voltage, current and impedance reflections back to the amplifier, creating instabilities within the output transistors.

Intermodulation performance can also be degraded by these reflections. The strong third harmonic is especially bothersome for these problems.

The diplexer filter is an approach that can greatly simplify the design process, especially for the amateur with limited PA-design experience and with limited home-lab facilities. For these reasons, the amateur homebrew enthusiast may want to consider this solution, despite its slightly greater parts count and expense.

The diplexer is a good technique for narrowband applications such as the HF amateur bands.[4] From Figure 10.74, we see that if the

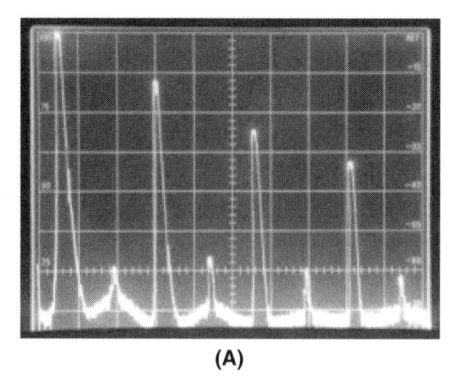

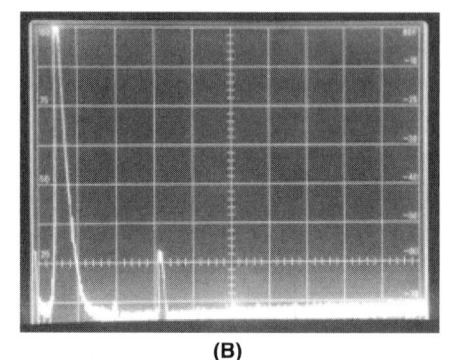

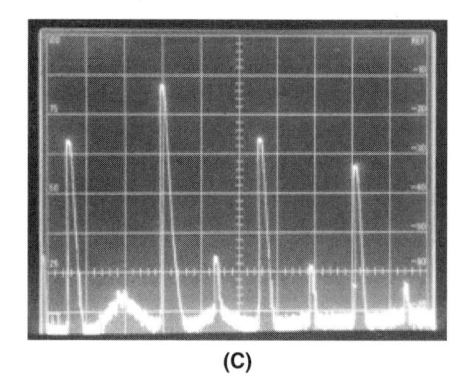

Figure 10.75 — At A, the output spectrum of a push-pull 80 meter amplifier. At B, the spectrum after passing through the low-pass filter. At C, the spectrum after passing through the high-pass filter.

signal frequency is moved beyond 4.0 MHz the amount of desired signal lost in the dump resistor becomes large. For signal frequencies below 3.5 MHz the harmonic reduction may be inadequate. A single filter will not suffice for all the HF amateur bands.

This treatment provides you with the information to calculate your own filters. A *QEX* article has detailed instructions for building and testing a set of six filters for a 120 W amplifier. These filters cover all nine of the MF/HF amateur bands.[5]

You can use this technique for other filters such as Bessel, Butterworth, linear phase, Chebyshev 0.5, 1.0, etc.[6] However, the diplexer idea does *not* apply to the elliptic function types.

The diplexer approach is a resource that can

be used in any application where a constant value of filter input resistance over a wide range of passband and stop band frequencies is desirable for some reason. Computer modeling is an ideal way to finalize the design before the actual construction. The coil dimensions and the dump resistor wattage need to be determined from a consideration of the power levels involved.

Another significant application of the diplexer is for elimination of EMI, RFI and TVI energy. Instead of being reflected and very possibly escaping by some other route, the unwanted energy is dissipated in the dump resistor.[7]

See the discussion "Design Software for LC Filters" at the end of the Passive LC Filters section of this chapter. The software package provided by Jim Tonne, W4ENE, of Tonne Software (**www.tonnesoftware.com**) includes *Diplexer* which greatly simplifies the process of designing diplexer filters. The software is part of the downloadable supplemental information for this book.

Notes

[1]Williams, A. and Taylor, F., *Electronic Filter Design Handbook*, any edition, McGraw-Hill.

[2]Storer, J.E., *Passive Network Synthesis*, McGraw-Hill 1957, pp 168-170. This book shows that the input resistance is ideally constant in the passband and the stop band and that the filter transfer characteristic is ideally independent of the generator impedance.

[3]Sabin, W. and Schoenike, E., *HF Radio Systems and Circuits*, Chapter 12, Noble Publishing, 1998. Also the previous edition of this book, *Single-Sideband Systems and Circuits*, McGraw-Hill, 1987 or 1995.

[4]Dye, N. and Granberg, H., *Radio Frequency Transistors, Principles and Applications*, Butterworth-Heinemann, 1993, p 151.

[5]Sabin, W.E. WØIYH, "Diplexer Filters for the HF MOSFET Power Amplifier," *QEX*, Jul/Aug, 1999. Also check the ARRL website at **www.arrl.org/qex**.

[6]See note 1. *Electronic Filter Design Handbook* has LP prototype values for various filter types, and for complexities from 2 to 10 components.

[7]Weinrich, R. and Carroll, R.W., "Absorptive Filters for TV Harmonics," *QST*, Nov 1968, pp 10-25.

10.10.6 High-Performance, Low-Cost 1.8 to 54 MHz Low-Pass Filter

The low-pass filter shown in **Figure 10.76** offers low insertion loss, mechanical simplicity, easy construction and operation on all amateur bands from 160 through 6 meters. Originally built as an accessory filter for a 1500 W 6 meter amplifier, the filter easily handles legal limit power. No complicated test equipment is necessary for alignment. It was originally described by Bill Jones, K8CU, in November 2002 *QST*. The complete original *QST* article for this project is included with the downloadable supplemental content. The article supplies complete assembly and alignment drawings.

Although primarily intended for coverage of the 6 meter band, this filter has low insertion loss and presents excellent SWR characteristics for all HF bands. Although harmonic attenuation at low VHF frequencies near TV channels 2, 3 and 4 does not compare to filters designed only for HF operation, the use of this filter on HF is a bonus to 6 meter operators who also use the HF bands. Six meter operators may easily tune this filter for low insertion loss and SWR in any favorite band segment, including the higher frequency FM portion of the band.

ELECTRICAL DESIGN

The software tool used to design this low-pass filter is *Elsie* by Jim Tonne, W4ENE, which is available with the downloadable supplemental content. The *Elsie* format data file for this filter, DC54.lct, may be downloaded for your own evaluation from the author's website at **www.realhamradio.com**.

Figure 10.77 is a schematic diagram of the filter. The use of low self-inductance capacitors with Teflon dielectric easily allows legal limit high power operation and aids in the ultimate stop band attenuation of this filter. Capacitors with essentially zero lead length will not introduce significant series inductance that upsets filter operation. This filter also uses a trap that greatly attenuates second harmonic frequencies of the 6 meter band. The parts list for the filter is given in **Table 10.7**.

PERFORMANCE DISCUSSION

Assuming the 6 meter SWR is set to a low value for a favorite part of the band, the worst case calculated forward filter loss is about 0.18 dB. The forward loss is better in the HF

Table 10.7
Low-Pass Filter Parts List

Qty	Description
1	Miniature brass strip, 1 × 12 in., 0.032 in. thick (C3)
1	Miniature brass strip, 2 × 12 in., 0.064 in. thick (C1, C2)
5 ft	⅛ inch diameter soft copper tubing
4	¼ × 20 × ½ in. long hex head bolt
4	Plastic spacer or washer, 0.5 in. OD, 0.25 in. ID, 0.0625 in. thick
6	¼ × 20 hex nut with integral tooth lock washer
1	¼ × 20 × 4 in. long bolt
1	¼ × 20 threaded nut insert, PEM nut, or "Nutsert"
1	1 × 0.375 in. diameter nylon spacer. ID smaller than 0.25 in. (used for C3 plunger).
4	Nylon spacer, 0.875 in. OD, 0.25 to 0.34 in. ID, approx. 0.065 in. or greater thickness (used to attach brass capacitor plates).

Aluminum diecast enclosure is available from Jameco Electronics (www.jameco.com) part no. 11973. The box dimensions are 7.5 × 4.3 × 2.4 in. The 0.03125 in. thick Teflon sheet is available from McMaster-Carr Supply Co (www.mcmaster.com), item #8545K21 is available as a 12 × 12 in. sheet.

Figure 10.76 — The 1.8 to 54 MHz low-pass filter is housed in a die-cast box.

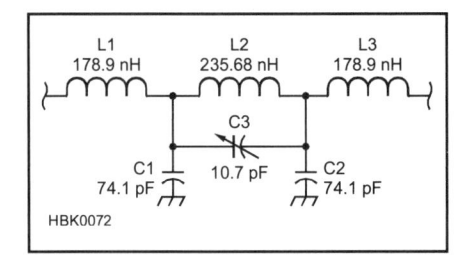

Figure 10.77 — The low-pass filter schematic. See construction details in the article with the downloadable supplemental content.

C1, C2 — 74.1 pF. 2 × 2.65 inch brass plate sandwiched with 0.03125 inch thick Teflon sheet. The metal enclosure is the remaining grounded terminal of this capacitor.

C3 — Homemade variable using brass and Teflon.

L1, L3 — 178.9 nH. Wind with ⅛ inch OD soft copper tubing, 3.5 turns, 0.75 inch diameter form, 0.625 inch long, ¼ inch lead length for soldering to brass plate. The length of the other lead to RF connector as required.

L2 — 235.68 nH. Wind with ⅛ inch OD soft copper tubing, 5 turns, 0.75 inch diameter form, 1.75 inches long. Leave ¼ inch lead length for soldering.

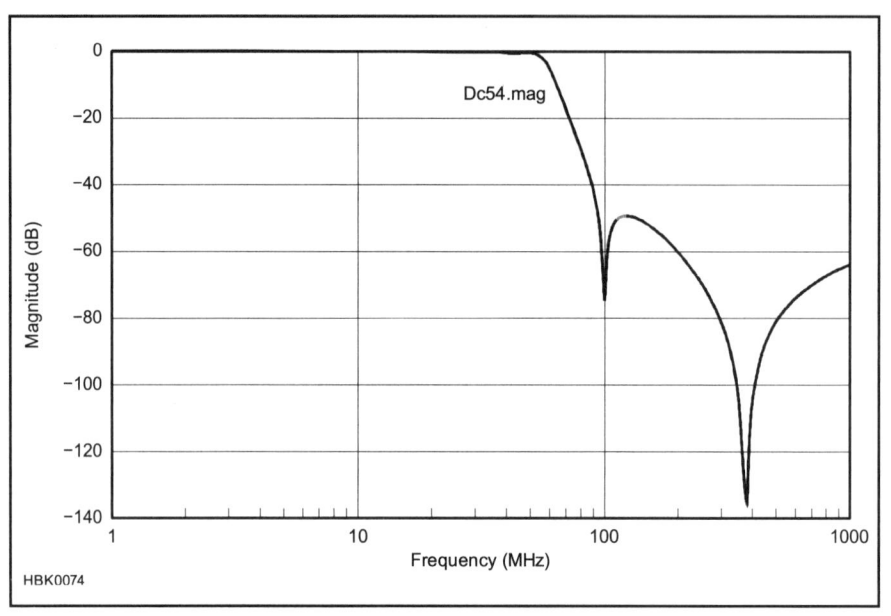

Figure 10.78 — Modeled filter response from 1 to 1000 MHz.

bands, with a calculated loss of only 0.05 dB from 1.8 through 30 MHz. The filter cutoff frequency is about 56 MHz, and the filter response drops sharply above this.

Figure 10.78 shows the calculated filter response from 1 to 1000 MHz. The impressive notch near 365 MHz is because of these inherent stray capacitances across each of the coils. Slight variations in each coil will make slightly different tuned traps. This will introduce a stagger-tuned effect that results in a broader notch.

10.10.7 Band-Pass Filter for 145 MHz

The following project is based on a design from the RSGB *Radio Communication Handbook, 11th edition*. This filter is intended to reduce harmonics and other out-of-band spurious emissions when transmitting and suppress strong out-of-band incoming signals which could overload the receiver. The filter's schematic and response curve are shown in **Figure 10.79**. This filter design is not suitable for use as a repeater duplexer for in-band signals sharing a common antenna — a high-Q cavity resonator is required.

Direct inductive coupling from the proximity of the coils is used between the first two and the last two resonant circuits. C_C performs "top coupling" between the center two sections where a shield prevents stray coupling. The input and output connections are tapped down on their respective coils to transform the 50 Ω source and load into the proper impedances for terminating the filter

At VHF, self-supporting coils and mica, ceramic or air-dielectric trimmer capacitors give adequate results for most applications. Piston ceramic trimmers can be used for receiving or for low-power signals of a few watts. At higher power, use an air-variable capacitor. The filter is assembled in a 4 × 2½ × 1½ inch die-cast aluminum box so there is room for either piston or air-variable capacitors.

The band-pass filter is made from four parallel resonant circuits formed by the inductance of the coils and their associated parasitic inter-turn capacitance described in the **RF Techniques** chapter. A 1-6 pF series capacitor (C in Figure 10.79) connected to ground adjusts the resonant frequency of each coil. A ceramic capacitor should be used for C_C which has a value of 0.5 pF.

The dimensions of the coils are important to control the self-resonant frequency. Each coil is constructed from 6-½ turns of #17 AWG solid, bare wire (1.15 mm dia), ⅜ inch (9.5 mm) in diameter. Each turn is spaced 1 wire diameter apart. The original design used British #18 SWG wire which is slightly thicker (1.22 mm) so coils made with #17 AWG wire will have a slightly higher resonant frequency. The taps for the coils are made 1 turn from the grounded end of the coil as shown in the figure.

Adjustment will be required after assembly to tune out the stray capacitances and inductances. A sweep generator and oscilloscope (see the **Test Equipment and Measurements** chapter) provide the most practical adjustment method. A variable oscillator with frequency counter and a voltmeter with RF probe, plus a good deal of patience, can also do the job.

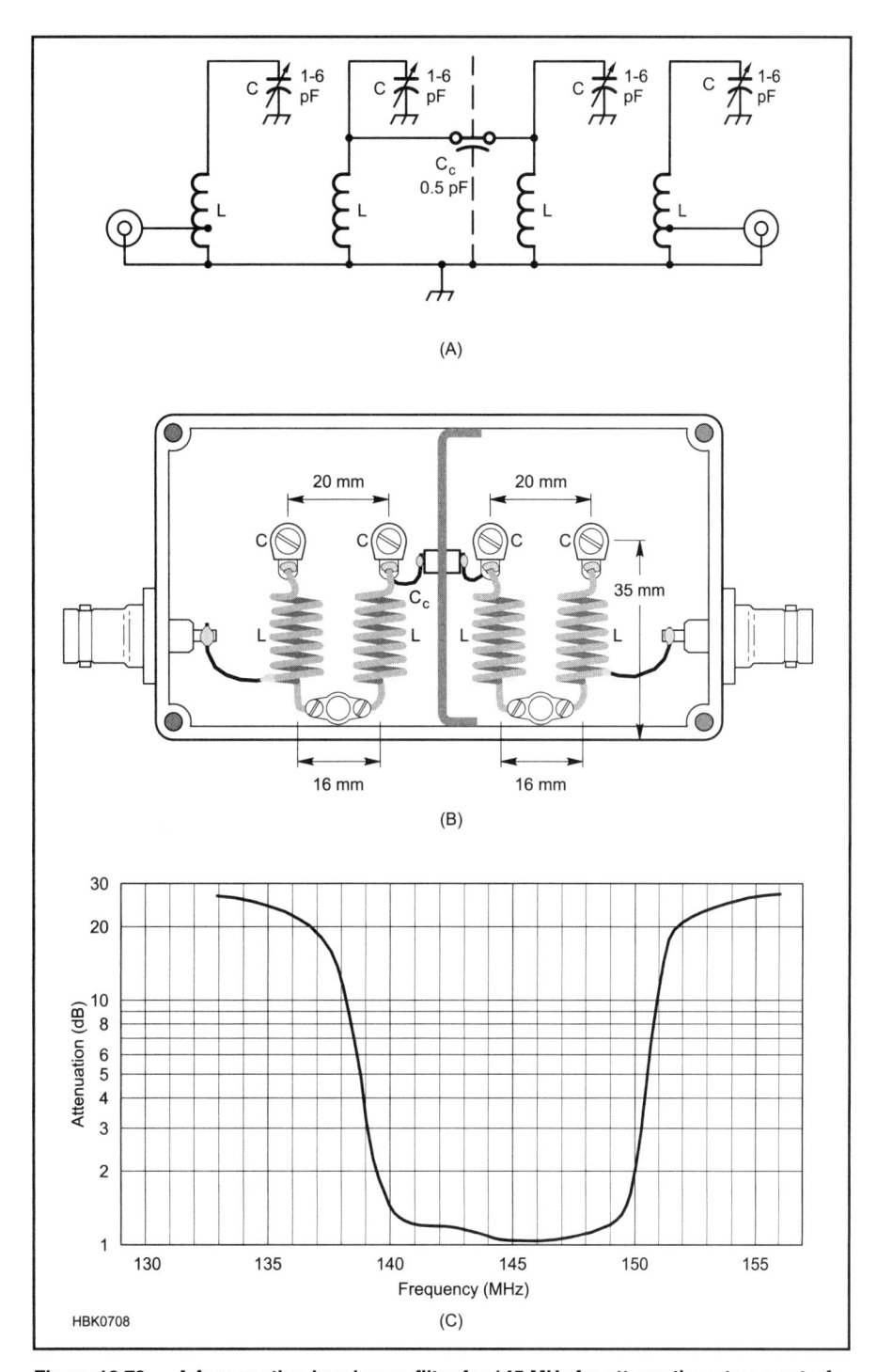

Figure 10.79 — A four-section band-pass filter for 145 MHz for attenuating strong out-of-band signals and reducing harmonics or other out-of-band spurious emissions.

10.11 Filter Glossary

Active filter — A filter that uses active (powered) devices to implement its function.

Adaptive filter — A filter whose coefficients can be changed automatically.

All-pass — Filter response in which the magnitude response does not change with frequency, but the phase response does change with frequency.

Amplitude response — see **magnitude response**

Band-pass — Filter response in which signals are passed in a range of frequencies and rejected outside that range.

Band-stop — Filter response in which signals are rejected in a range of frequencies and passed outside that range (also called *band-reject* or *notch* filter).

Bandwidth — Range of frequencies over which signals are passed (low-pass, high-pass, band-pass) or rejected (band-stop).

Brick wall response — An ideal filter response in which signals are either passed with no attenuation or attenuated completely.

Chebyshev filter — A filter with equal ripple in the passband, stopband or both.

Cutoff frequency — Frequency at which a filter's output is 3 dB below its passband output (also called *corner frequency* or *3 dB frequency*).

Decade — A ratio of 10 in frequency.

Decimation — Reduction of sample rate by an integer factor.

Equiripple — Equalized ripple in a filter's magnitude response across the passband, stopband, or both.

Filter coefficient — One of a series of numbers that define the transfer function of a filter.

Finite impulse response (FIR) — An impulse response that is zero for all time that is greater than some finite amount from the time of the impulse.

Flat — Refers to a filter's magnitude response that is constant across a range of frequencies.

Group delay — The transit time of signals through a filter.

High-pass — Filter response in which signals above the cutoff frequency are passed and rejected at lower frequencies.

Ideal filter — Filter that passes signals without loss or attenuates them completely. An ideal filter has no transition regions. (See also **brick wall response**).

Impulse — A pulse of finite energy with a width that approaches zero.

Impulse-invariant — A design technique for IIR filters in which the impulse response is the same as the impulse response of a certain analog filter.

Impulse response — The response versus time of a filter to an impulse.

Infinite impulse response (IIR) — An impulse response that theoretically never goes to and remains at zero.

Insertion loss — The loss incurred by signals in a filter's passband.

Interpolation — Increasing the sample rate by an integer factor.

Low-pass — Filter response in which signals below the cutoff frequency are passed and rejected at higher frequencies.

Lumped elements — Discrete inductors and capacitors; a lumped-element filter made from discrete inductors and capacitors.

Magnitude response — Graph of a filter's output amplitude versus frequency.

Microstrip — A type of transmission line made from a strip of metal separated from a ground plane by a layer of insulating material, such as on a printed-circuit board.

Normalize — The technique of converting numeric values to their ratio with respect to some reference value. (To denormalize is to reverse the normalization, converting the ratios back to the original values.)

Notch filter — see **band-stop filter**.

Octave — A ratio of two in frequency (see also **decade**).

Overshoot — The condition in which the output of a circuit, in responding to a change in its input, temporarily exceeds the steady-state value that the input should cause.

Overtone — Vibration mode at a higher frequency than the fundamental mode, usually harmonically related.

Passband — The range of frequencies passed by a filter.

Passive filter — A filter that does not require power to perform its function (see also **lumped element**).

Phase response — Graph of the difference in angular units (degrees or radians) between a filter's input and output versus frequency.

Radian — Unit of angular measurement equal to $1/2\pi$ of a circle, equal to $360/2\pi$ degrees

Ringing — The condition in which the output of a circuit, in responding to a change in its input, exhibits a damped alternating sequence of exceeding and falling below the steady-state value that the input should cause before settling at the steady-state value.

Ripple — A regular variation with frequency in a filter's magnitude response.

Rolloff — The rate of change in a filter's magnitude response in the transition region and stopband.

Scaling — Changing a filter's impedance or frequency characteristics through multiplication or division by a constant.

Shape factor — The ratio of a filter's bandwidth between the points at which its magnitude response is 6 dB and 60 dB below the response in the filter's passband.

Stopband — The range of frequencies that are rejected by a filter.

Stripline — A transmission line consisting of a metal strip suspended between two ground planes.

Tap — One processing block, consisting of a coefficient memory, signal register, multiplier and adder, of an FIR filter.

TEM — Transverse electromagnetic mode in which the electric and magnetic fields of electromagnetic energy are aligned perpendicularly to the direction of motion.

Topology — The arrangement of connections of components in the filter. For example, "capacitor-input" and "inductor-input" are two different topologies.

Transition region — Range of frequencies between a filter's passband and stopband.

10.12 References and Bibliography

REFERENCES

Analog Devices. "Using the Analog Devices Active Filter Design Tool"

Applied Radio Labs, Design Note DN004, "Group Delay Explanations and Applications," **www.radiolab.com.au**

Virgil E. Bottom, "Introduction to Quartz Crystal Unit Design," Van Nostrand Reinhold Company, 1982, ISBN 0-442-26201-9.

S. Butterworth, "On the Theory of Filter Amplifiers," *Experimental Wireless and Wireless Engineer*, Oct 1930, pp 536-541.

Laplace Transforms: P. Chirlian, *Basic Network Theory,* McGraw Hill, 1969.

S. Darlington, "Synthesis of Reactance 4-Poles Which Produce Prescribed Insertion Loss Characteristics," *Journal of Mathematics and Physics*, Sep 1939, pp 257-353.

M. Dishal, "Top Coupled Band-pass Filters," *IT&T Handbook*, 4th edition, American Book, Inc, 1956, p 216.

M. Donadio, "CIC Filter Introduction",

18 July 2000, **dspguru.com/dsp/tutorials/cic-filter-introduction**.

J. Fisk W1DTY, "Helical-Resonator Design Techniques," *QST*, June 1976, pp 11-14.

Fourier Transforms: *Reference Data for Engineers*, Chapter 7, 7th edition, Howard Sams, 1985.

Phillip R. Geffe, *Simplified Modern Filter Design* (New York: John F. Rider, 1963, OCLC: 2470870).

D. Gordon-Smith, G3UUR, "Extended Bandwidth Crystal Ladder Filters With Almost Symmetrical Responses," *QEX*, Jul/Aug 2011, pp 36-44.

W. Hayward, R. Campbell, R. Larkin, *Experimental Methods in RF Design*, Chapter 3, ARRL, 2003.

E. B. Hogenauer, "An Economical Class of Digital Filters For Decimation and Interpolation," *IEEE Transactions on Acoustics, Speech and Signal Processing*, Volume 29, April 1981 pp.155-162.

R. Lyons, "Understanding Cascaded Integrator-Comb Filters," *EE Times*, March 31, 2005.

R. Lyons, Understanding Digital Signal Processing, Pearson, 2011.

R. Mack, "SDR: Simplified" *QEX* columns from 2009.

Maxim Integrated, Tutorial 733, "A Filter Primer," 2008.

W. S. Metcalf, "Graphs Speed Interdigitated Filter Design," *Microwaves*, Feb 1967.

Randall W. Rhea, *HF Filter Design and Computer Simulation* (New York: McGraw-Hill, ISBN 0070520550, OCLC 32013486).

Cauer Elliptic Filters: R. Saal, *The Design of Filters Using the Catalogue of Normalized Low-Pass Filters*,(German; brief introduction in English) (AEH Telefunken, 1968, OCLC 13988270). Also *Reference Data for Radio Engineers*, pp 9-5 to 9-11.

W. Silver, "Hands-On Radio," Experiments 50, 51, 87, 88, **www.arrl.org/hands-on-radio**.

H. Steder, DJ6EV, and J. Hardcastle, G3JIR, "Crystal Ladder Filters for All," *QEX*, Nov-Dec 2009, pp 14-18.

L. Weinberg, "Network Design by use of Modern Synthesis Techniques and Tables," *Proceedings of the National Electronics Conference*, vol 12, 1956.

Donald R.J. White, *A Handbook on Electrical Filters (Synthesis, Design and Applications)* (White Electromagnetics, 1980, ISBN 0932263070).

A. B. Williams, *Electronic Filter Design Handbook* (New York: McGraw-Hill, 1981).

O. Zobel, "Theory and Design of Electric Wave Filters," *Bell System Technical Journal*, Jan 1923.

H. Zumbahlen, AN-281 "Passive and Active Filtering," Analog Devices.

H. Zumbahlen, Mini-tutorial MT-202, "Allpass Filters," Analog Devices, 2012.

H. Zumbahlen, Mini-tutorial MT-204, "The Bessel Response," Analog Devices, 2012.

H. Zumbahlen, Mini-tutorial MT-205, "Biquadratic (Biquad) Filters," Analog Devices, 2012.

H. Zumbahlen, Mini-tutorial MT-206, "The Chebyshev Response," Analog Devices, 2012.

H. Zumbahlen, Mini-tutorial MT-210, "F_0 and Q in Filters," Analog Devices, 2012.

H. Zumbahlen, Mini-tutorial MT-215 "Low-Pass to Band-Pass Filter Transformation," Analog Devices, 2012.

H. Zumbahlen, Mini-tutorial MT-216 "Low-Pass to Band-Stop (Notch) Filter Transformation," Analog Devices, 2012.

H. Zumbahlen, Mini-tutorial MT-217 "Low-Pass to High-Pass Filter Transformation," Analog Devices, 2012.

H. Zumbahlen, Mini-tutorial MT-220, "Multiple Feedback Filters," Analog Devices, 2012.

H. Zumbahlen, Mini-tutorial MT-222, "Sallen-Key Filters," Analog Devices, 2012.

H. Zumbahlen, Mini-tutorial MT-223, "State Variable Filters," Analog Devices, 2012.

H. Zumbahlen, Mini-tutorial MT-224, "The Butterworth Response," Analog Devices, 2012.

H. Zumbahlen, Mini-tutorial MT-225, "Twin T Notch Filter," Analog Devices, 2012.

A.I. Zverev, *Handbook of Filter Synthesis* (New York: John Wiley and Sons, 1967, ISBN 0471986801, OCLC 972252).

Practical Filter Designs

P. Antoniazzi, IW2ACD and M. Arecco, IK2WAQ, "Easy Microwave Filters Using Waveguides and Cavities," *QEX*, Sep/Oct 2006, pp 37-42.

B. Bartlett, VK4UW and J. Loftus, VK4EMM, "Band-Pass Filters for Contesting," *National Contest Journal*, Jan 2000, pp 11-15.

T. Cefalo Jr, WA1SPI, "Diplexers, Some Practical Applications," *Communications Quarterly*, Fall 1997, pp 19-24.

P.R. Cope, W2GOM/7, "The Twin-T Filter," *QEX*, July/Aug 1998, pp 45-49.

R. Fisher, W2CQH, "Combline V.H.F. Bandpass Filters," QST, December 1968, pp. 44-45.

R. Fisher, W2CQH, "Interdigital Bandpass Filters for Amateur VHF/UHF Applications," *QST*, Mar 1968, p 32.

D. Gordon-Smith, G3UUR, "Seventh-Order Unequal-Ripple Low-pass Filter Design," *QEX*, Nov/Dec 2006, pp 31-34.

D. Gordon-Smith, G3UUR, "Fifth-Order Unequal-Ripple Low-pass Filter Design," *QEX*, Nov/Dec 2010, pp 42-47.

W. Hayward, W7ZOI, "Extending the Double-Tuned Circuit to Three Resonators," *QEX*, Mar/Apr 1998, pp 41-46.

F. Heemstra, KT3J, "A Double-Tuned Active Filter with Interactive Coupling," *QEX*, Mar/Apr 1999, pp 25-29.

D. Jansson, WD4FAB and E. Wetherhold, W3NQN, "High-Pass Filters to Combat TVI," *QEX*, Feb 1987, pp 7-8 and 13.

Z. Lau, W1VT, "A Narrow 80-Meter Band-Pass Filter," *QEX*, Sept/Oct 1998, p 57.

R. Lumachi, WB2CQM. "How to Silverplate RF Tank Circuits," *73 Amateur Radio Today*, Dec 1997, pp 18-23.

T. Moliere, DL7AV, "Band-Reject Filters for Multi-Multi Contest Operations," *CQ Contest*, Feb 1996, pp 14-22.

W. Rahe, DC8NR, "High Performance Audio Speech Low-Pass and CW Band-Pass Filters in SVL Design," *QEX*, Jul/Aug 2007, pp 31-39.

W. Sabin, WØIYH, "Diplexer Filters for the HF MOSFET Power Amplifier," *QEX*, July/Aug 1999, pp 20-26.

W. Sabin, WØIYH, "Narrow Band-Pass Filters for HF," *QEX*, Sept/Oct 2000, pp 13-17.

J. Tonne, WB6BLD, "Harmonic Filters, Improved," *QEX*, Sept/Oct 1998, pp 50-53.

E. Wetherhold, W3NQN, "Modern Design of a CW Filter Using 88 and 44-mH Surplus Inductors," *QST*, Dec 1980, pp 14-19. See also Feedback in Jan 1981 *QST*, p 43.

E. Wetherhold, W3NQN, "Band-Stop Filters for Attenuating High-Level Broadcast-Band Signals," *QEX*, Nov 1995, pp 3-12.

E. Wetherhold, W3NQN, " CW and SSB Audio Filters Using 88-mH Inductors," *QEX*, Dec 1988, pp 3-10; *Radio Handbook*, 23rd edition, W. Orr, editor, p 13-4, Howard W. Sams and Co., 1987; and, "A CW Filter for the Radio Amateur Newcomer," *Radio Communication* (RSGB) Jan 1985, pp 26-31.

E. Wetherhold, W3NQN, "Clean Up Your Signals with Band-Pass Filters," Parts 1 and 2, *QST*, May and June 1998, pp 44-48 and 39-42.

E. Wetherhold, W3NQN, "Second-Harmonic-Optimized Low-Pass Filters," *QST*, Feb 1999, pp 44-46.

E. Wetherhold, W3NQN, "Receiver Band-Pass Filters Having Maximum Attenuation in Adjacent Bands," *QEX*, July/Aug 1999, pp 27-33.

Contents

11.1 Introduction
    11.1.1 Emission Designators
    11.1.2 Bandwidth Definition
11.2 Amplitude Modulation (AM)
    11.2.1 Double-Sideband, Full-Carrier AM
    11.2.2 Double-Sideband, Suppressed Carrier (DSB-SC) AM
    11.2.3 Single-Sideband (SSB-SC)
    11.2.4 Amplitude-Modulated On-Off Keying (OOK)
11.3 Angle Modulation
    11.3.1 Angle-Modulated Modulation Index
    11.3.2 Angle Modulation Audio Frequency Response
    11.3.3 Angle Modulation Bandwidth
    11.3.4 Carson's Rule
    11.3.5 AM Noise and FM Signals
11.4 FSK and PSK
    11.4.1 Multi-carrier Modulation
    11.4.2 Audio Frequency-Shift Keying (AFSK)
11.5 Quadrature Modulation
11.6 Analytic Signals and Modulation
    11.6.1 I/Q Modulation and Demodulation
    11.6.2 SSB Using I/Q Modulators and Demodulators
    11.6.3 Uses for I/Q Modulators and Demodulators
11.7 Image Modulation
    11.7.1 Fast-Scan Television
    11.7.2 Slow-Scan Television
11.8 Spread Spectrum Modulation
    11.8.1 Frequency Hopping Spread Spectrum
    11.8.2 Direct Sequence Spread Spectrum
    11.8.3 Code-Division Multiple-Access (CDMA)
11.9 Pulse Modulation
11.10 Modulation Bandwidth and Impairments
    11.10.1 Filtering and Bandwidth of Digital Signals
    11.10.2 Intermodulation Distortion
    11.10.3 Transmitted Bandwidth
    11.10.4 Modulation Accuracy
11.11 Modulation Glossary
11.12 References and Bibliography

Chapter 11 — Downloadable Supplemental Content
- SDR: Simplified, columns from *QEX* by Ray Mack, W5IFS
- "About FM" and "About SSB" by Ward Silver, NØAX
- Emission Designators table

Chapter 11

Modulation

Radio amateurs use a wide variety of modulations to convey information. This chapter, updated from Alan Bloom, N1AL's original material by Doug Grant, K1DG, explores various characteristics of modulation commonly used by amateurs. Traditional modulation types used for analog signals are discussed, as well as techniques suited for digital transmissions. Pulse and image modulations are also included. Methods of modulating and demodulating these signals are presented in the chapters on **Receiving** and **Transmitting**. The chapter concludes with a discussion of modulation impairments and a glossary of terms and suggestions for additional reading.

11.1 Introduction

The purpose of Amateur Radio transmissions is to send information via radio. The one possible exception to that is a beacon station that transmits an unmodulated carrier for propagation testing. In that case the only information being sent is, "I am transmitting (or not) from this location." One can think of it as a single data bit with two states, *on* or *off*. However, in reality even a beacon station or test transmission must periodically identify with the station call sign! Modulation is what allows the signal to carry the information, no matter how much or little.

To represent the information being sent, the radio signal must periodically change its characteristics (or *state*) in some way that can be detected by the receiver. In the early days of radio, the only way to do that was on-off keying using Morse code. By alternating the on and off states with the proper sequence and rhythm, a pair of highly-skilled operators can exchange textual data at rates up to perhaps 60 WPM.

Later, engineers figured out how to amplify the signal from a microphone and use it to vary the power of the radio signal continuously. Thus was born amplitude modulation, which allowed transmitting voices at full speaking speeds, that is, up to about 200 WPM. That led to analog modes such as television with even faster information rates. Today's digital radio systems are capable of transferring tens of megabits of information per second, equivalent to tens of millions of words per minute.

Modulation is but one component of any transmission mode. For example AM voice and NTSC television (the old analog TV system) both use amplitude modulation, but the transmission protocol and type of information sent are very different. Digital modes also are generally defined not only by the modulation but also by multiple layers of protocol and data coding. Of the three components of a mode (modulation, protocol and information), this chapter will concentrate on the first. The **Digital Protocols and Modes** chapter covers digital transmission protocols and the **Digital Communications** operating chapter with the downloadable supplemental content covers practical aspects of operating using the various digital modes.

Types of modulation are often referred to as "analog" or "digital." There is really no distinction between the two. What is usually meant is whether the modulating signal itself is an analog (continuously varying) or digital (some number of fixed states) signal.

The type of modulation is the choice of the radio system designer. The combination of modulation and a protocol create a mode. Modes can be analog or digital, again referring to whether they carry a continuously varying signal or not.

As an example of the difference between mode and modulation, consider HF and VHF packet radio. Both modes use the same AX.25 protocol to control how the data packets are formed and how the stations establish, conduct, and terminate the contact. Both modes also encode data as a pair of audio tones. On HF, however, the audio tones modulate an SSB transceiver to create an AFSK signal. On VHF, the tones modulate an FM transceiver, creating a very different type of signal. Both transceivers (SSB and FM) don't "know" whether the audio tones represent speech or data. If the audio is speech, the result is an "analog" mode. If the audio tones represent data, the result a "digital" mode.

11.1.1 Emission Designators

We tend to think of a radio signal as being "on" a particular frequency. In reality, any modulated signal occupies a band of frequencies. The bandwidth depends on the type of modulation and the data rate. A Morse code signal can be sent within a bandwidth of a couple hundred Hz at 60 WPM, or less at lower speeds. An AM voice signal requires about 6 kHz. For high-fidelity music, more bandwidth is needed; in the United States, an FM broadcast signal occupies a 200-kHz channel. Television signals need about 6 MHz, while 802.11ad, the latest generation of "WiFi" wireless LAN, uses up to 2 GHz for data transmission at its maximum transfer rate.

The International Telecommunication Union (ITU) has specified a system for designating radio emissions based on the bandwidth, modulation type and information to be transmitted. The emission designator begins with the bandwidth, expressed as a maximum of five numerals and one letter. The letter occupies the position of the decimal point and represents the unit of bandwidth, as follows: H = hertz, K = kilohertz, M = megahertz and G = gigahertz. The bandwidth is followed by three to five emission classification symbols, as defined in the table of emission designators available with the dowloadable supplemental content. The first three symbols are mandatory; the fourth and fifth symbols are supplemental. These designators are found in Appendix 1 of the ITU Radio Regulations, ITU-R Recommendation SM.1138 and in the FCC rules §2.201. More information on emissions designators is also available on the FCC website at **fcced.io/Emissions-Designator**.

For example, the designator for a CW signal might be 150H0A1A, which means 150 Hz bandwidth, double sideband, digital information without subcarrier, and telegraphy for aural reception. SSB would be 2K5J3E, or 2.5 kHz bandwidth, single sideband with suppressed carrier, analog information, and telephony. The designator for a PSK31 digital signal is 60H0J2B, which means 60 Hz bandwidth, single sideband with suppressed carrier, digital information using a modulating subcarrier, and telegraphy for automatic reception.

Authorized modulation modes for Amateur Radio operators depend on frequency, license class, and geographical location, as specified in the FCC regulations §97.305. Technical standards for amateur emissions are specified in §97.307. Among other things, they require that no amateur station transmission shall occupy more bandwidth than necessary for the information rate and emission type being transmitted, in accordance with good amateur practice. We will discuss the necessary bandwidth for each type of modulation as it is covered in the following sections.

11.1.2 Bandwidth Definition

The general definition of bandwidth for a tuned circuit or filter are not used for the legal definition of signal bandwidth. The FCC regulations are more concerned with the amount of spectrum a signal consumes. This leads to the concept of *occupied bandwidth*. This is the range of frequencies within which a specified percentage of the total power occurs. A common percentage used is 99%. This means that the total signal power outside the occupied bandwidth must be less than 20 dB less than the total signal power. For a properly-adjusted, low-distortion transmitting system, the occupied bandwidth is determined mainly by the modulation type and filtering and, in the case of digital modulation, the symbol rate.

FCC Rule §97.3(a)(8) provides the legal definition of a signal's bandwidth as "The width of a frequency band outside of which the mean power of the transmitted signal is attenuated at least 26 dB below the mean power of the transmitted signal with the band." The 26 dB limit is equivalent to 1/400th of the signal's power. **Figure 11.1** illustrates this relationship.

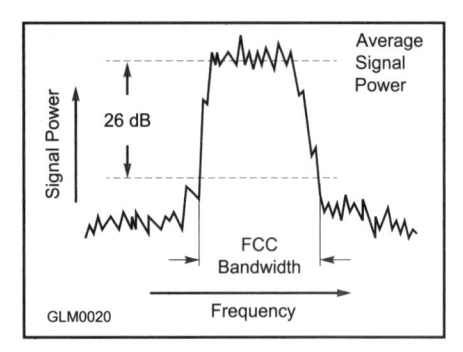

Figure 11.1 — The FCC definition of bandwidth (see text).

11.2 Amplitude Modulation (AM)

Of the various properties of a signal that can be modulated to transmit voice information, amplitude was the first to be used. Not only are modulation and demodulation of AM signals simple in concept, but they are simple to implement as well.

11.2.1 Double-Sideband, Full-Carrier AM

An AM signal is created from two signals; the RF signal that can be transmitted and the modulating signal that will be combined with the RF signal. The RF signal is called the *carrier*, c(t), which is a single-frequency sinusoid at a frequency of f_C.

$$c(t) = C \sin(2\pi f_C t)$$

The modulating signal is represented by m(t) and may be a sine wave or a complex signal like speech. The modulating signal is also referred to as *baseband modulation*.

$$m(t) = M \cos(2\pi f_M t)$$

(The use of sine and cosine are to help identify which signal is which — there is no requirement for the carrier and modulating signal to have a specific phase relationship.)

Amplitude modulation is performed when c(t) is multiplied by m(t). Mathematically, the process of amplitude modulation is easiest

Figure 11.2 — Graphical representation of amplitude modulation. In the unmodulated carrier (A) each RF cycle has the same amplitude. When the modulating signal (B) is applied, the RF amplitude is increased or decreased according to the amplitude of the modulating signal (C). A modulation index of approximately 75% is shown. With 100% modulation the RF power would just reach zero on negative peaks of the modulating signal.

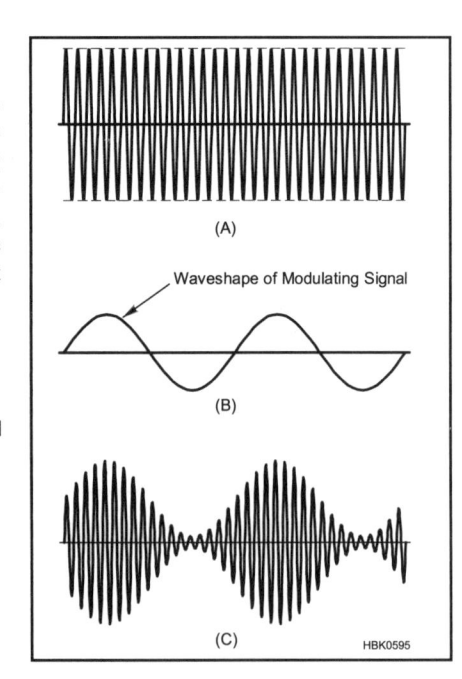

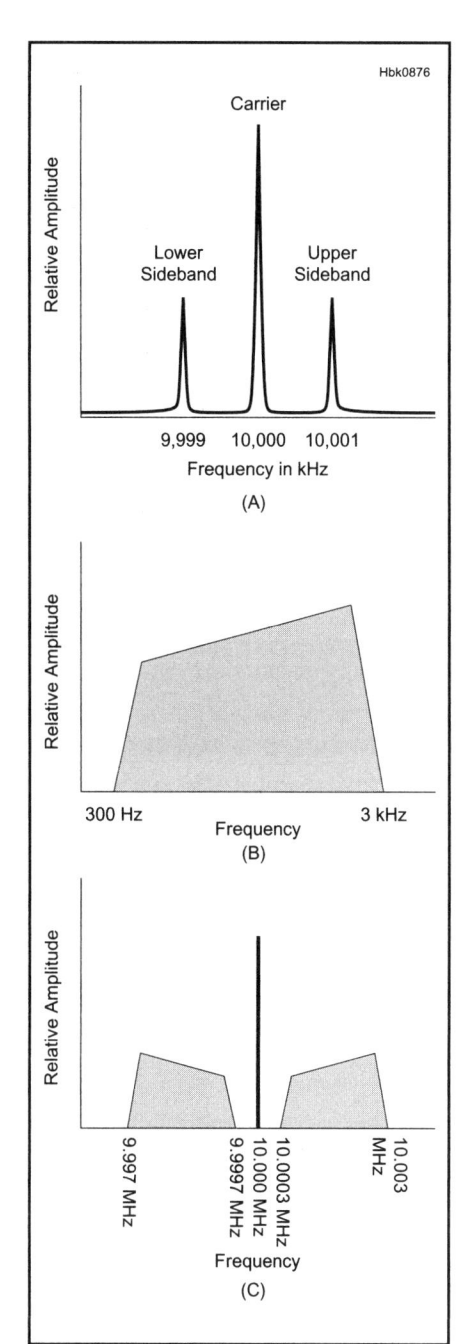

Figure 11.3 — AM with a single 1 kHz tone modulating a 10 MHz carrier (A) and a speech waveform (B) modulating the same carrier in (C).

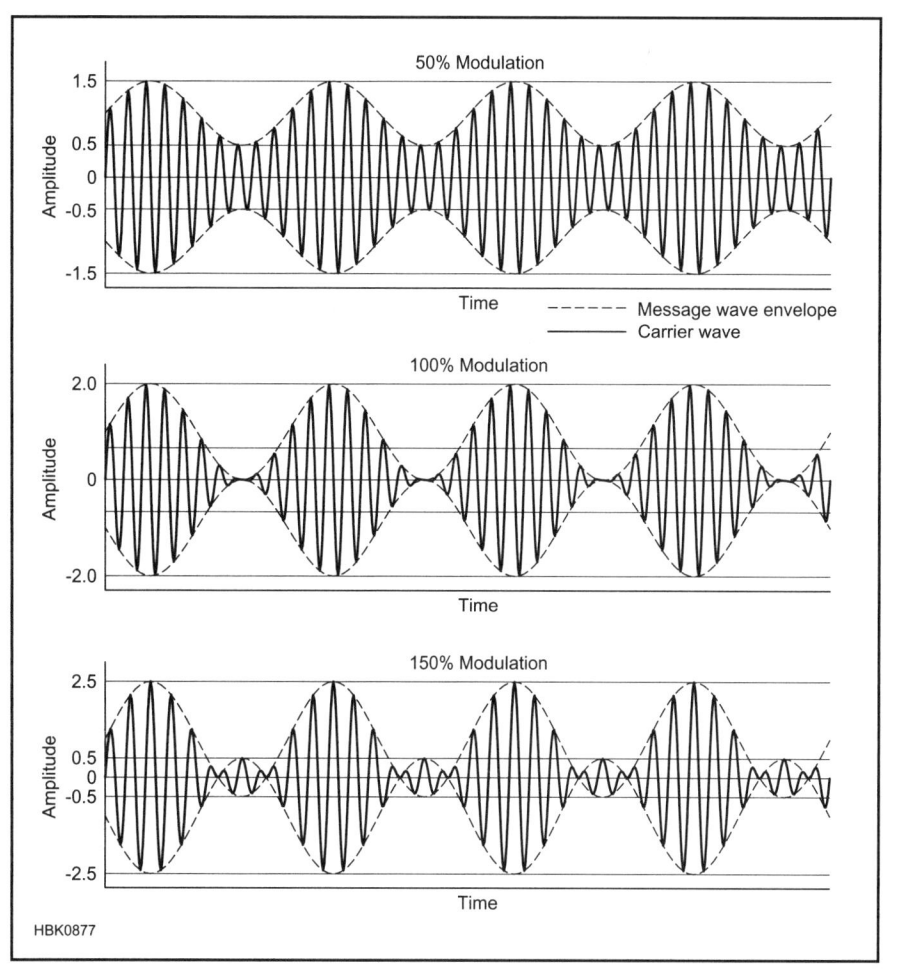

Figure 11.4 — AM waveforms showing 50% modulation (A) and 100% modulation (B). Overmodulation (C) causes distortion of the envelope and reversal of the RF carrier's phase, creating spurious emissions and interference on adjacent channels.

to envision if the modulating signal, m(t) is a single audio tone with a frequency of f_M.

$$c(t) \times [1 + m(t)] = [1+M \cos(2\pi f_M t)] \times C \sin(2\pi f_C t)$$

The constant 1 represents a dc component which is necessary to allow the *envelope* of the AM signal to both increase and decrease as in **Figure 11.2**. Note that if the modulating signal is zero (such as when there is no speech or tone) then the result is just the original carrier, c(t). If M=1, the value of 1 + m(t) can vary from zero to 2 and the signal would just go to zero on the peaks of the modulating signal. Figure 11.2C shows a case very similar to this where the signal's envelope almost goes to zero but not quite.

Mathematically, the resulting AM signal is:

$$C\sin(2\pi f_C t) + \frac{C \times M}{2}\sin(2\pi(f_C + f_M)t) + \frac{C \times M}{2}\sin(2\pi(f_C - f_M)t)$$

This expression describes a signal with three components represented by the three terms: first, the carrier; second, an *upper sideband* with a frequency of $f_C + f_M$; and third, a *lower sideband* with a frequency of $f_C - f_M$. This is *double-sideband, full-carrier* (DSB-FC) AM.

If M=1, each sideband's amplitude (C/2) has half the amplitude of the carrier (C). This means each sideband has one-quarter of the carrier's power level or is 6 dB weaker than the carrier. Adding the two sidebands together means that ⅓ of the total signal power is in the sidebands and 2/3 in the carrier. For example, if the carrier power is 100 watts, each sideband will have 100 × ¼ = 25 watts. The total signal power is 100 + 2 × 25 = 150 watts.

AM SPECTRUM

Figure 11.3A shows the spectrum of a 10-MHz signal modulated with a 1-kHz sine wave. The upper sideband is a single frequency at 10 MHz + 1 kHz = 10.001 MHz. The spectrum of the lower sideband is inverted, so it is at 10 MHz − 1 kHz = 9.999 MHz.

When the modulating signal is speech, instead of a single tone, the result is shown in Figure 11.3B and 11.3C. The speech signal is represented by the shaded region in Figure 11.3B extending from 300 Hz to 3 kHz with the higher frequency speech components having a slightly higher amplitude. When the 10 MHz carrier is modulated with the speech signal, the resulting sidebands are shown in Figure 11.3C. Each speech component behaves like a separate tone, creating its

Modulation 11.3

own sideband. The set of components in speech create the set of sidebands shown by the shaded regions. Note that the upper and lower sideband spectra are "mirror images" of each other with the lower components closest to the carrier.

With both sidebands and the carrier, the AM signal's total bandwidth is twice the bandwidth of the baseband modulation signal. (A single tone's bandwidth is considered to be the frequency of the tone.) The bandwidth of an AM signal modulated by communications-quality speech with a frequency range of 300 Hz to 3 kHz is 2 × 3 kHz = 6 kHz. Note that the AM signal's bandwidth does not depend on the lower limit of the baseband modulation signal.

AM MODULATION INDEX

If the AM signal's envelope is zero on negative peaks of the modulating signal, that corresponds to 100% modulation. For the case where the modulation signal is zero leaving just the steady carrier signal, that is 0% modulation. Expressed as a value from 0 to 1, this is the *modulation index*:

Modulation index = M / C

Modulation percentage = (M / C) × 100%

Figure 11.4A and 11.4B show the AM signal waveform when M = C/2 (50% modulation or a modulation index of 0.5) and when M = C (100% modulation or a modulation index of 1.0.) If M is greater than C, the envelope of the AM signal can go "below zero" as shown in Figure 11.4C, causing the envelope of the signal to be distorted on negative peaks (and possibly positive peaks depending on the design of the modulator circuit). This is the condition of *overmodulation* and the distortion is known as "flat-topping" because of the shape of the envelope which often exhibits a flattening of peaks during overmodution. This also results in spurious emissions the extend beyond the upper and lower sideband, causing interference on adjacent channels.

11.2.2 Double-Sideband, Suppressed Carrier (DSB-SC) AM

Another way of seeing how an AM signal is constructed is illustrated in **Figure 11.5**. Figure 11.5A shows the carrier and the sidebands from a modulating tone are shown in 11.5B and 11.5C. If you look closely, you can see that the waveforms in Figure 11.5B and 11.5C have slightly different frequencies than the carrier. If the two sidebands are added together, the signal of Figure 11.5D is produced. This is a *double-sideband, suppressed carrier* (DSB-SC) signal and its spectrum is shown in **Figure 11.6**, assuming the same 10 MHz carrier and 300-3000 Hz sidebands.

When the carrier signal is added, the full AM signal is produced in Figure 11.5D. When all of the signals are in-phase, the resulting signal has its maximum amplitude. When all of the signals are out of phase, the resulting signal goes to zero. If the carrier's phase is used as our reference, the phase of each sideband can be viewed as slipping behind (lower sideband) or moving ahead (upper sideband) of the carrier. The sidebands are out of phase with each other at the frequency of the tone so the resulting envelope reproduces the modulating tone's sine wave.

11.2.3 Single-Sideband (SSB-SC)

As we have seen, since the carrier itself contains no modulation, it does not need to be transmitted, which saves at least 67% of the transmitted power. Since the two sidebands carry identical information, one of them may be eliminated as well, saving half the bandwidth. The result is *single sideband, suppressed carrier* (SSB-SC), which is commonly referred to simply as "SSB." If the lower sideband is eliminated, the result is called *upper sideband* (USB). If the upper sideband is eliminated, you're left with *lower sideband* (LSB). **Figure 11.7** shows the result of removing one of the sidebands in Figure 11.6.

The effect of SSB modulation is that

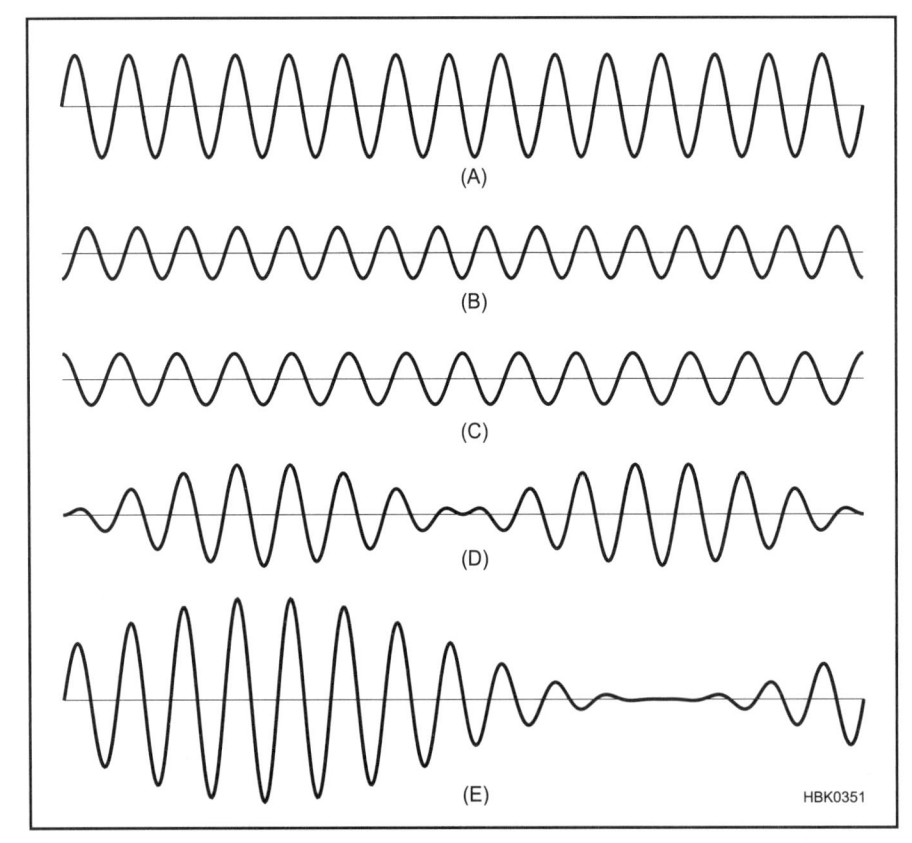

Figure 11.5 — At A is an unmodulated carrier. If the upper (B) and lower (C) sidebands are added together a double-sideband suppressed carrier (DSB-SC) signal results (D). If each sideband has half the amplitude of the carrier, then the combination of the carrier with the two sidebands results in a 100%-modulated AM signal (E). Whenever the two sidebands are out of phase with the carrier, the three signals sum to zero. Whenever the two sidebands are in phase with the carrier, the resulting signal has twice the amplitude of the unmodulated carrier.

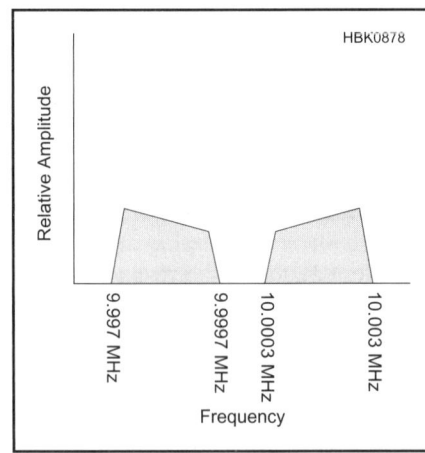

Figure 11.6 — The spectrum of a double-sideband, suppressed-carrier (DSB-SC) signal created from the signal shown in Figure 11.3.

the baseband modulation signal is simply frequency-shifted to the RF carrier frequency (whether the carrier is transmitted or not.) The spectrum of the modulation may be inverted during the shifting process, requiring the demodulation process to re-invert the signal as it is translated back to the baseband frequency range. Aside from that technical consideration, there is no difference between the information in the LSB and USB signals.

The bandwidth of an SSB signal is a little less than half that of an equivalent AM signal. Using the same 300 Hz to 3 kHz speech bandwidth, the SSB signal has a bandwidth of 3000 − 300 = 2700 Hz = 2.7 kHz. In practice, SSB transmitters have an overall audio response from 300 Hz to 2.8 kHz, resulting in 2.5 kHz bandwidth.

Compared to most other analog modulation modes, SSB has excellent power efficiency because the transmitted power is proportional to the modulating signal and no power at all is transmitted during pauses in speech. Another advantage is that the lack of a carrier results in less interference to other stations.

SSB transceivers also are well-suited for the narrowband digital modes. Because an SSB transceiver simply frequency-translates the baseband audio signal to RF in the transmitter and back to audio again in the receiver, digital modulation may be generated and detected at audio frequencies using the sound card in a personal computer.

11.2.4 Amplitude-Modulated On-Off Keying (OOK)

On-off keying (OOK) is a special case of *amplitude-shift keying* (ASK) and is normally used for sending Morse code. For historical reasons dating from the days of spark transmitters, amateurs often refer to this as *continuous wave* (CW) even though the signal is actually keyed on and off.

You can think of OOK as being the same as analog AM that is modulated with a two-level signal that switches between full power and zero power. For example, imagine that the modulation is a 10 Hz square wave, equivalent to sending a series of dits at 24 WPM. A square wave may be decomposed into a sine wave of the same frequency and a theoretically infinite succession of odd harmonics. Recall that the lower and upper sidebands of an AM signal are simply the inverted and non-inverted spectra of the baseband modulation. The RF spectrum therefore contains sidebands at the carrier frequency ±10 Hz, ±30 Hz, ±50 Hz, and so on to plus and minus infinity. This phenomenon is called *key clicks*. Stations listening on nearby frequencies hear a click upon every key closure and opening.

To prevent interference to other stations, the modulation must be low-pass filtered, which slows down the transition times between the on and off states. See **Figure 11.8**. If the transitions are too fast, then excessive key clicks occur. If the transitions are too slow, then at high speeds the previous transition may not have finished before the next one starts, which makes the signal sound mushy and hard to read. Traditionally, filtering was done with a simple resistor-capacitor low-pass filter on the keying line, but using a transition with a raised-cosine shape allows faster transition times without excessive key clicks. Some modern transceivers use DSP techniques to generate such a controlled transition shape.

The optimum transition time, and thus bandwidth, depends on keying speed. It also depends on propagation conditions. When the signal is fading, the transitions must be sharper to allow good copy. **Figure 11.9** gives recommended keying characteristics based on sending speed and propagation. As a compromise, many transmitters use a 5 ms rise and fall time. That limits the bandwidth

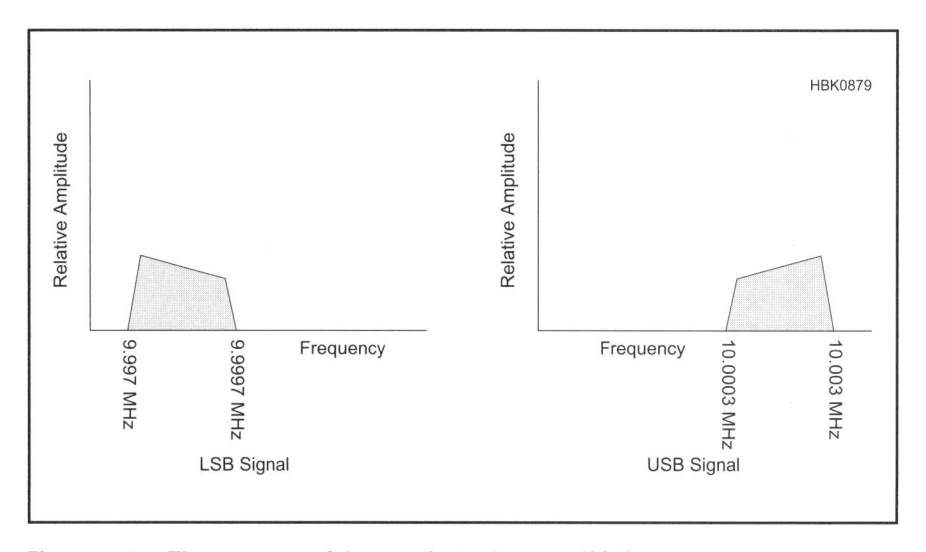

Figure 11.7 — The spectrum of the two single sideband (SSB) signals that could be created from the signal shown in Figure 11.6.

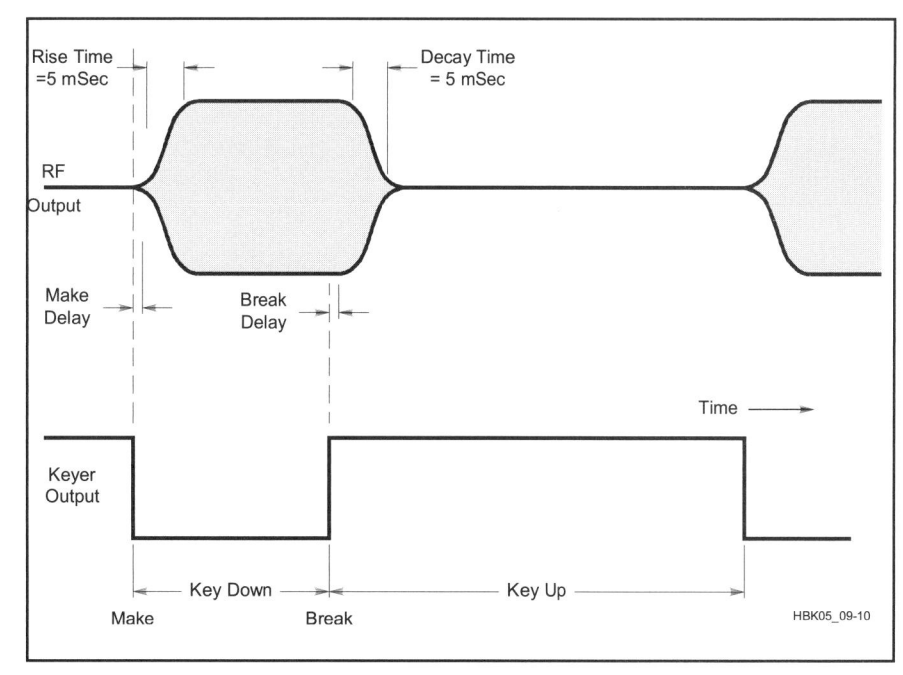

Figure 11.8 — A filtered CW keying waveform. The on-off transitions of the RF envelope should be as smooth as possible while transitioning as quickly as possible. The shape of the RF Output waveform is nearly optimum in that respect.

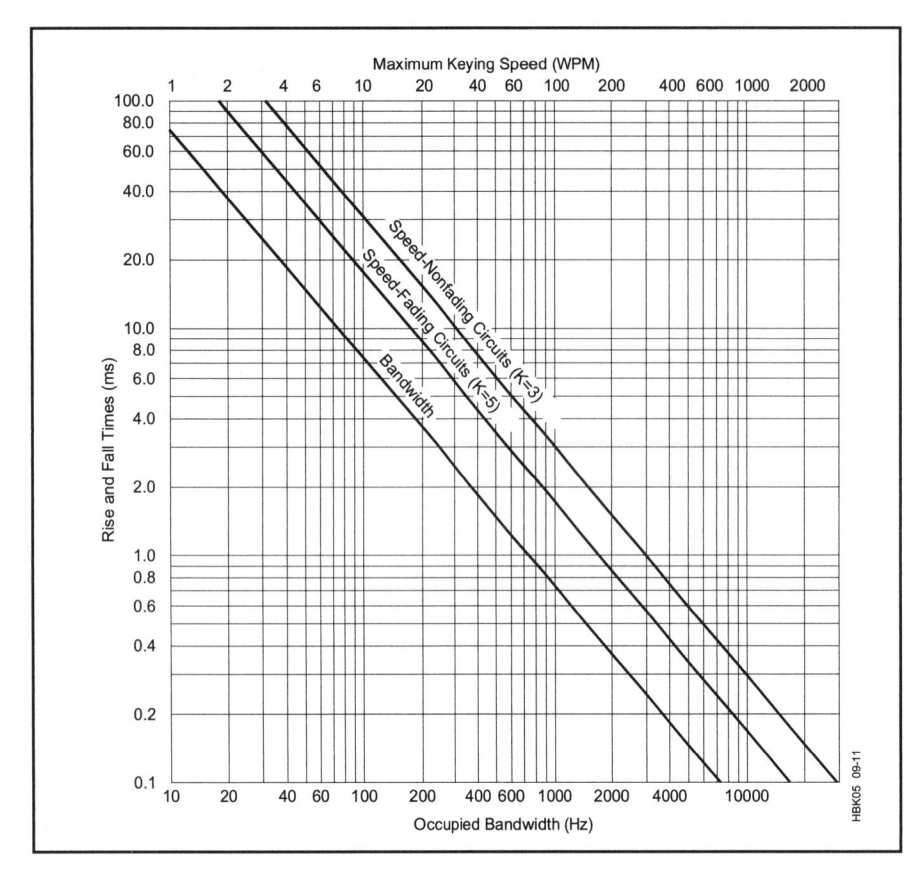

Figure 11.9 — Keying speed vs rise and fall times vs bandwidth for fading and non-fading communications circuits. For example, to optimize transmitter timing for 20 WPM on a non-fading circuit, draw a vertical line from the WPM axis to the K = 3 line. From there draw a horizontal line to the rise/fall axis (approximately 15 ms). Draw a vertical line from where the horizontal line crosses the bandwidth line and see that the bandwidth is about 50 Hz. Harder (more abrupt) keying is required to maintain copying ability in the presence of fading.

to approximately 150 Hz while allowing good copy up to 60 WPM on non-fading channels and 35 WPM on fading channels, which covers most requirements.

With any digital system, the number of changes of state per second is called the *baud rate* or the *symbol rate*, measured in *bauds* or *symbols per second*. Sending a single Morse code dit requires two equal-length states, or symbols: *on* for the length of the dit and *off* for the space between dits. Thus, a string of dits sent at a rate of 10 dits per second has a symbol rate of 20 bauds.

Refer to **Figure 11.10**. A Morse code dash is on for three times the length of a dit. Including one symbol for the off time, the total time to send a dash is four symbols, twice the time to send a dit. For example, at a baud rate of 20 bauds, there are 10 dits per second or 5 dashes per second. The spacing between characters within a word is three symbols, two more than the normal space between dits and dashes. The spacing between words is seven symbols.

For purposes of computing sending speed, a standard word is considered to have five characters, plus the inter-word spacing. On average, that results in 50 symbols per word. From that, the speed in words per minute may be computed from the baud rate:

$$\text{WPM} = \frac{60 \,(\text{sec}/\text{min})}{50 \,(\text{symbols}/\text{word})} \times \text{bauds}$$
$$= 1.2 \times \text{bauds} = 2.4 \times \text{dits}/\text{sec}$$

Characters in Morse code do not all have the same length. Longer codes are used for characters that are used less frequently while the shortest codes are reserved for the most common characters. For example, the most common letter in the English language, E, is sent as a single dit. In that way, the average character length is reduced, resulting in a faster sending speed for a given baud rate. Such a variable-length code is known as *varicode*, a technique that has been copied in some modern digital modes (see the **Digital Protocols and Modes** chapter).

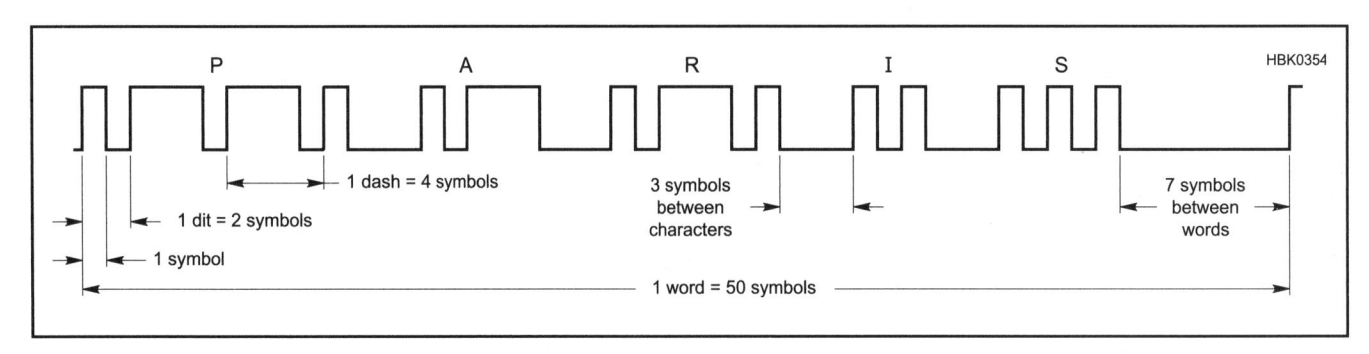

Figure 11.10 — CW timing of the word PARIS, which happens to have a length equal to the standard 50 symbols per word. By programming it multiple times into a memory keyer, the speed may be calibrated simply by counting the number of times the word is completed in one minute.

11.3 Angle Modulation

Angle modulation varies the phase angle of an RF signal in response to the modulating signal. In this context, "phase" means the phase of the modulated RF sine wave with respect to the unmodulated carrier. Angle modulation includes both frequency modulation and phase modulation because any change in frequency results in a change in phase. For example, the way to smoothly ramp the phase from one value to another is to change the frequency and wait. If the frequency is changed by +1 Hz, then after 1 second the phase will have changed by +360°. After 2 seconds, the phase will have changed by +720°, and so on. Change the frequency in the other direction and the phase moves in the opposite direction as well. With sine-wave modulation, the frequency and phase both vary in a sinusoidal fashion. See **Figure 11.11**.

For angle modulation, the modulation signal, m(t) is applied to the frequency or phase of the carrier, not its amplitude:

$$\sin(2\pi f_C t + k_P m(t)) \text{ or } \sin(2\pi f_C t \times f_d m(t))$$

Mathematically, these are equivalent and most texts work with the second form. The constants k_P and f_d are described below in the discussion on modulation index.

Since any change in frequency results in a change in phase and vice versa, *frequency modulation* (FM) and *phase modulation* (PM) are fundamentally the same. The term *frequency deviation* means the amount the RF frequency deviates from the center (carrier) frequency with a given modulating signal. The instantaneous deviation of an FM signal is proportional to the instantaneous amplitude of the modulating signal. The instantaneous deviation of a PM signal is proportional to the instantaneous *rate of change* of the modulating signal. Since the rate of change of a sine wave is proportional to its frequency as well as its amplitude, the deviation of a PM signal is proportional to both the amplitude and the frequency of the modulating signal.

11.3.1 Angle-Modulated Modulation Index

The *modulation index* is the ratio of the peak deviation to the highest audio frequency. The *deviation ratio* is the ratio of maximum permitted peak deviation to the maximum permitted modulating frequency. The modulation index is a measure of the maximum amount of phase change (ϕ_{MAX}) the modulation signal can cause. For a single-tone modulating signal:

Modulation index = $A \times f_d / f_M$ (for FM)

Modulation index = $(\phi_{MAX}) = k_P \times A$ (for PM)

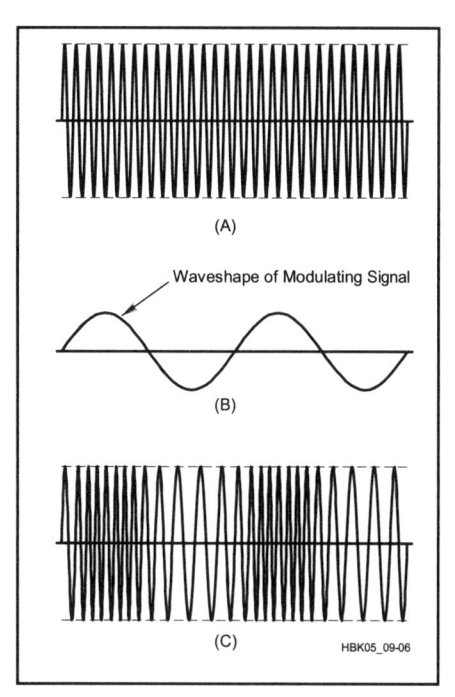

Figure 11.11 — Graphical representation of frequency modulation. In the unmodulated carrier (A) each RF cycle occupies the same amount of time. When the modulating signal (B) is applied, the radio frequency is increased or decreased according to the amplitude and polarity of the modulating signal (C).

where the modulation index is calculated in radians and there are 180/ϖ radians in the 360° of one complete sine wave cycle (1 radian ≈ 57.3°). In addition,

A is the amplitude of the modulation signal in volts

f_M is the frequency of the message signal in hertz

f_d is the *frequency deviation constant* that represents the sensitivity of the modulator in hertz of deviation per volt of the modulating signal

$A \times f_d$ is the *peak deviation*

ϕ_{MAX} is the maximum value of phase change caused by the modulation signal

k_P is the *phase deviation constant* and is similar to f_d in that it specifies the sensitivity of the phase modulator in radians of phase change per volt of the modulating signal.

For PM, the modulation index doesn't depend on message frequency at all. For an FM signal, m will be larger if the peak deviation gets larger or if f_M gets smaller. For example, loud low-frequency signals can cause the modulation index to become quite large unless the transmitter limits deviation and microphone gain or frequency response.

FCC regulations limit the modulation index at the highest modulating frequency to a maximum of 1.0 for frequencies below 29 MHz. If the audio is low-pass filtered to 3 kHz, then the deviation may be no more than 3 kHz. For that reason, FM transmitters for frequencies below 29 MHz are usually set for 3 kHz deviation while FM transmitters at higher frequencies are typically set for about 5 kHz deviation. The term *narrowband FM* generally refers to deviation of no more than 3 kHz and *wideband FM* refers to deviation greater than 3 kHz.

11.3.2 Angle Modulation Audio Frequency Response

The only difference between FM and PM is the audio frequency response. An FM transmitter with 6 dB/octave pre-emphasis of the modulating signal is indistinguishable from a PM transmitter. A PM transmitter with 6 dB/octave de-emphasis is indistinguishable from an FM transmitter. The reverse happens at the receiver. A frequency detector followed by a 6 dB/octave de-emphasis network acts like a phase detector. It is interesting to note that most VHF and UHF amateur "FM" transceivers should really be called "PM" transceivers due to the pre-emphasis and de-emphasis networks used in the transmitters and receivers respectively.

Most FM and PM transmitters include some kind of audio compressor before the modulator to limit the maximum deviation. Common usage of the term *deviation* is that it refers to the maximum peak deviation allowed by the audio compressor. If the frequency swings a maximum of 5 kHz above the center frequency and 5 kHz below the center frequency, we say the deviation is 5 kHz.

11.3.3 Angle Modulation Bandwidth

The spectrum of an angle-modulated signal is fairly complex. With sine-wave modulation, the RF frequency spectrum from an angle-modulated transmitter consists of the carrier and a series of sideband pairs, each spaced by the frequency of the modulation. For example, with 3 kHz sine-wave modulation, the spectrum includes tones at ±3 kHz, ±6 kHz, ±9 kHz and so on with respect to the carrier. When the modulation index is much less than 1.0, only the first sideband pair is significant, and the spectrum looks similar to that of an AM signal (although the phases of the sidebands are different).

As the modulation index is increased, more

and more sidebands appear. Unlike with AM, the carrier amplitude also changes with deviation and actually disappears altogether for certain modulation indices. Because the amplitude of an angle-modulated signal does not vary with modulation, the total power of the carrier and all sidebands is constant. **Figure 11.12** shows several graphs of an FM signal with a 1 kHz modulation signal at different modulation indexes. Note how the sidebands increase and decrease as modulation index changes. All of these spectra have the same total power.

The amplitudes of the carrier and the various sidebands are described by a series of mathematical equations called Bessel functions, which are illustrated graphically in **Figure 11.13**. Note that the carrier disappears when the modulation index equals 2.405 and 5.52. That fact can be used to set the deviation of an FM transmitter. For example, to set 5 kHz deviation, connect the microphone input to a sine-wave generator set for a frequency of 5 / 2.405 = 2.079 kHz, listen to the carrier on a narrowband receiver, and adjust the deviation until the carrier disappears.

11.3.4 Carson's Rule

Unlike amplitude modulation, angle modulation is nonlinear. Recall that with amplitude modulation, the shape of the RF spectrum is the same as that of the modulation spectrum, single-sided with SSB and double-sided with DSB. That is not true with angle modulation. A double-sideband AM signal with audio band-limited to 3 kHz has 6 kHz RF bandwidth. It is easy to see that an FM transmitter with the same audio characteristics but with, say, 5 kHz deviation must have a bandwidth of at least 10 kHz. While you might think that the bandwidth equals twice the deviation, in reality the transmitted spectrum theoretically extends to infinity, although it does become vanishingly small beyond a certain point. As a rule of thumb, approximately 98% of the spectral energy is contained within the bandwidth defined by *Carson's rule*:

$$BW = 2(f_d + f_m)$$

where
f_d = the peak deviation, and
f_m = the highest modulating frequency.

For example, if the deviation is 5 kHz and the audio is limited to 3 kHz, the bandwidth is approximately 2 (5 + 3) = 16 kHz.

Be careful not to "over apply" Carson's Rule. It is just a method of estimating the bandwidth in which a certain amount (98%) of the signal power is contained. This is not as strict a definition as the FCC definition cited earlier in this chapter. Limiting the modulation index and stating the bandwidth in the rules defines a single FM or PM "channel" and how much energy is allowed to be outside that channel. **Figure 11.14** shows a typical 2 meter FM repeater output and compares Carson's Rule and the FCC bandwidth limits. The bandwidths derived from the two rules are "close" but not equivalent. The FCC would judge the signal to be wider than what Carson's Rule predicts. Relying on Carson's Rule is not sufficient to guarantee that there will be no interference to adjacent channels at minimum spacing.

11.3.5 AM Noise and FM Signals

Since the amplitude carries no information, FM receivers are designed to be as insensitive to amplitude variations as possible. Because noise tends to be mostly AM in nature, that results in a quieter demodulated signal. Typically the receiver includes a *limiter*, which is a very high-gain amplifier that causes the signal to clip, removing any amplitude variations, before being applied to the detector. Unlike with AM, as an FM signal gets stronger the volume of the demodulated audio stays the same, but the noise is reduced.

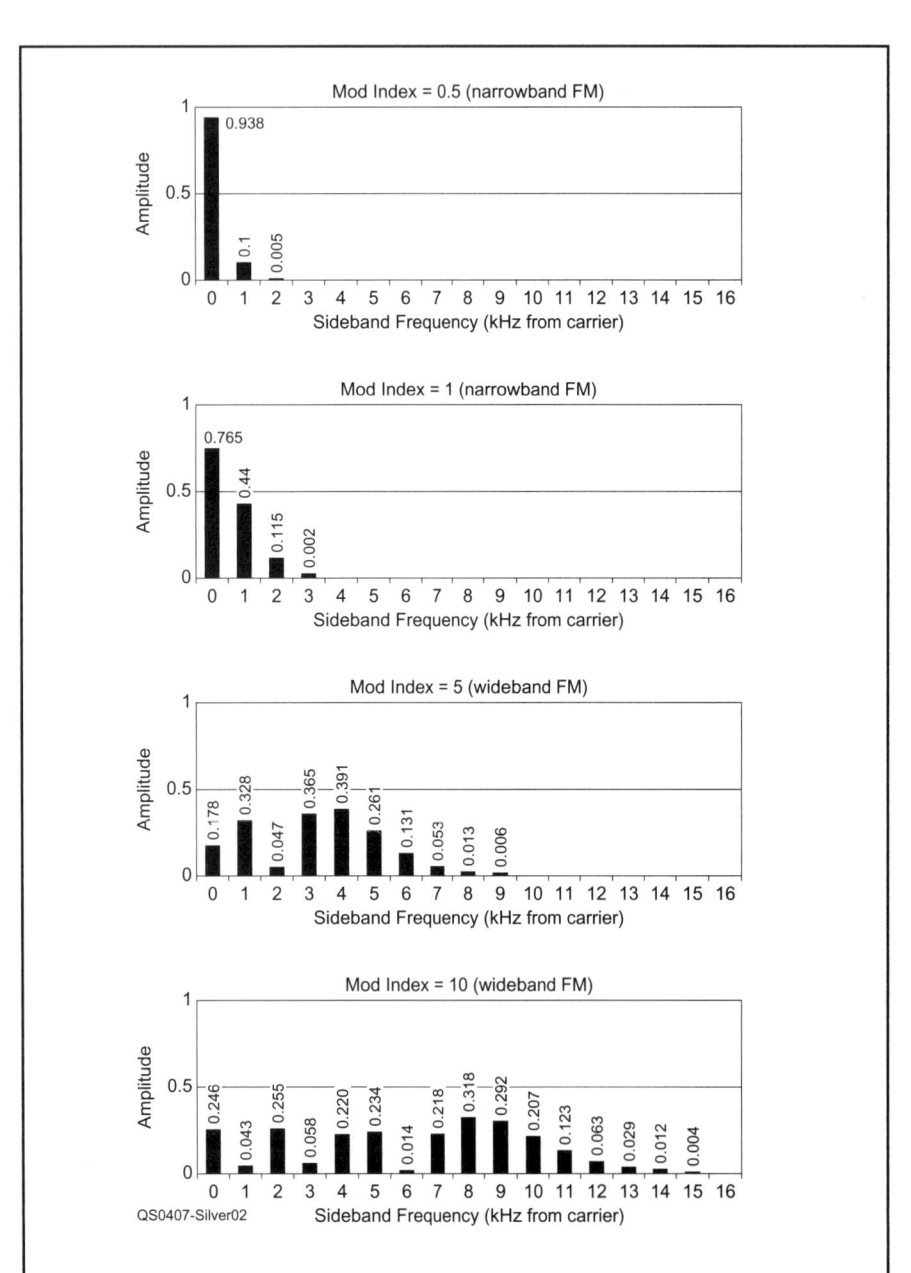

Figure 11.12 — Charts showing one-half of an FM signal's sidebands for a modulating signal frequency of 1 kHz at different modulation indexes.

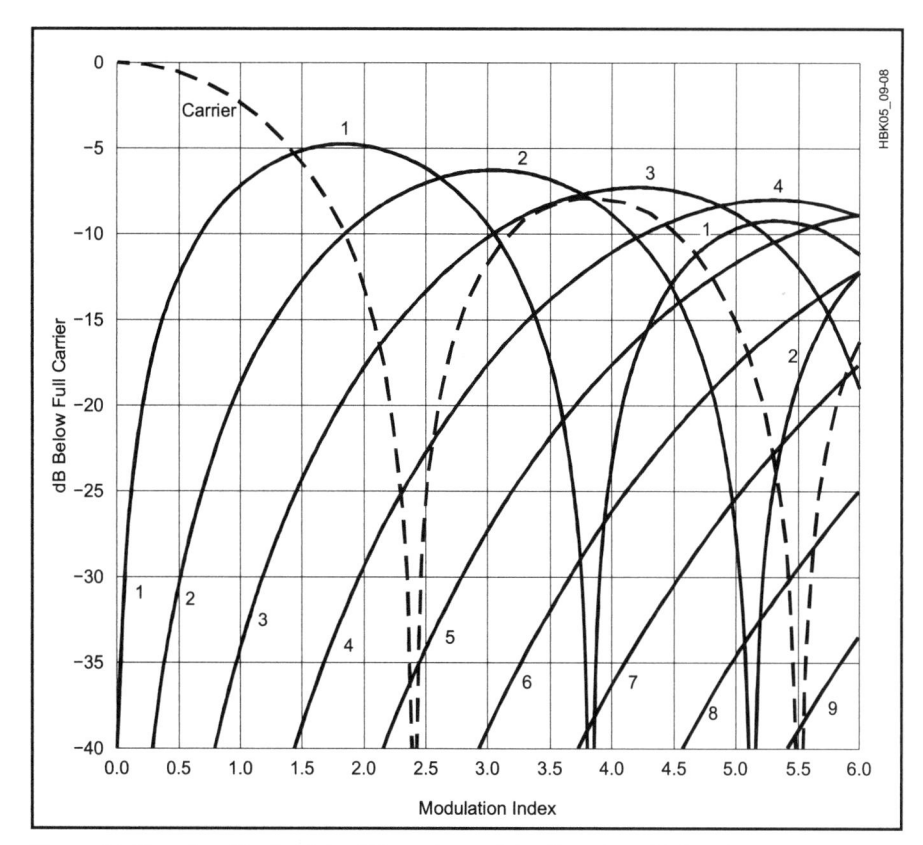

Figure 11.13 — Amplitude of the FM carrier and the first nine sidebands versus modulation index. This is a graphical representation of mathematical functions developed by F. W. Bessel. Note that the carrier completely disappears at modulation indices of 2.405 and 5.52.

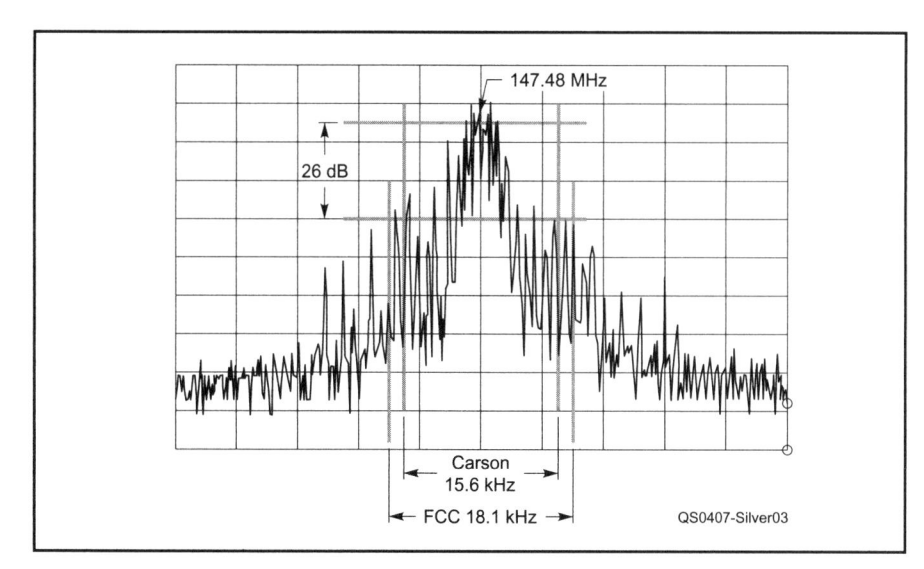

Figure 11.14 — Spectrum analyzer display for a typical 2 meter FM repeater. The bandwidths and amplitudes for Carson's Rule and the FCC's bandwidth definition are overlaid on the spectrum.

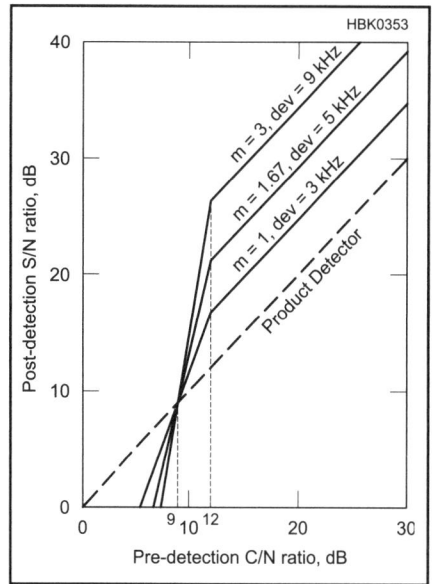

Figure 11.15 — A plot of post-detection signal-to-noise ratio (S/N) versus input carrier-to-noise ratio (C/N) for an FM detector at various modulation indices, m. For each modulation index the deviation is also noted assuming a maximum modulating frequency of 3 kHz. For comparison, the performance of an SSB product detector is also shown.

Receiver sensitivity is often specified by how much the noise is suppressed for a certain input signal level. For example, if a 0.25 µV signal causes the noise to be reduced by 20 dB, then we say the receiver sensitivity is "0.25 µV for 20 dB of quieting."

The limiter also causes a phenomenon known as *capture effect*. If more than one signal is present at the same time, the limiter tends to reduce the weaker signal relative to the stronger one. We say that the stronger signal "captures" the receiver. The effect is very useful in reducing on-channel interference.

The suppression of both noise and interference is greater the wider the deviation. FM signals with wider deviation do take up more bandwidth and actually have a poorer signal-to-noise (S/N) ratio at the detector output for weak signals but have better S/N ratio and interference rejection for signal levels above a certain threshold. See **Figure 11.15**.

In addition to the noise and interference-reduction advantage, angle-modulated signals share with full-carrier AM the advantages of non-critical frequency accuracy and the continuous presence of a signal, which eases the task of the automatic gain control system in the receiver. In addition, since the signal is constant-amplitude, the transmitter does not need a linear amplifier. Class C amplifiers may be used, which have greater power efficiency.

Modulation 11.9

11.4 FSK and PSK

While technically types of angle modulation, frequency-shift keying (FSK) and phase-shift keying are more easily discussed on their own terms. The technique of shifting a signal's frequency or phase to signify the 0 and 1 bit values of digital data is the dominant form of communications outside of Amateur Radio. Amateurs are making wider use of these techniques as they adopt more digital techniques, especially at and above UHF allocations where symbol rate and bandwidth limits are much more favorable than at VHF and below.

Frequency-shift keying (FSK) was the first digital angle-modulated format to come into common use. FSK can be thought of as being the same as analog FM that is modulated with a binary (two-level) signal that causes the RF signal to switch between two frequencies. It can also be thought of as equivalent to two on-off-keyed (OOK) signals on two nearby frequencies that are keyed in such a way that whenever one is on the other is off. Just as with OOK, if the transitions between states are instantaneous, then excessive bandwidth occurs — causing interference on nearby channels similar to key clicks. For that reason, the modulating signal must be low-pass filtered to slow down the speed at which the RF signal moves from one frequency to the other.

Although FSK is normally transmitted as a true constant-amplitude signal with only the frequency changing between symbols, it does not have to be received that way. The receiver can treat the signal as two OOK signals and demodulate each one separately. This is an advantage when HF propagation conditions exhibit selective fading — even if one frequency fades out completely the receiver can continue to copy the other, a form of *frequency diversity*. To take advantage of it, wide shift (850 Hz) must normally be used. With narrow-shift FSK (170 Hz), the two tones are generally too close to exhibit selective fading.

As previously discussed, selective fading is caused by the signal arriving at the receiver antenna by two or more paths simultaneously. The same phenomenon can cause another signal impairment known as *inter-symbol interference*. See **Figure 11.16**. If the difference in the two path lengths is great enough, then the signal from one path may arrive delayed by one entire symbol time with respect to the other. The receiver sees two copies of the signal that are time-shifted by one symbol. In effect, the signal interferes with itself. One solution is to slow down the baud rate so that the symbols do not overlap. It is for this reason that symbol rates employed on HF are usually no more than 50 to 100 bauds.

Multi-level FSK (MFSK) is one method to reduce the symbol rate. Unlike with conventional binary FSK, more than two shift frequencies are allowed. For example, with eight frequencies, each symbol can have eight possible states. Since three bits are required to represent eight states, three bits are transmitted per symbol. That means you get three times the data rate without increasing the baud rate. The disadvantage is a reduced signal to noise and signal to interference ratio. If the maximum deviation is the same, then the frequencies are seven times closer with 8FSK than with binary FSK and the receiver is theoretically seven times (16.9 dB) more susceptible to noise and interference. However the IF limiter stage removes most amplitude variations before the signal arrives at the FSK detector, so the actual increase in susceptibility is less for signal levels above a certain threshold.

With any type of FSK, you can theoretically make the shift as narrow as you like. The main disadvantage is that the receiver becomes more susceptible to noise and interference, as explained above. In addition, the bandwidth is not reduced as much as you might expect. Just as with analog FM, you still get sidebands whose extent depends on the symbol rate, no matter how small the deviation.

Minimum-shift keying (MSK) is FSK with a deviation that is at the minimum practical level, taking bandwidth and signal-to-noise ratio into account. That turns out to be a frequency shift from the center frequency of 0.25 times the baud rate or, using the common definition of frequency shift, a difference between the two tones of 0.5 times the baud rate. If, on a given symbol, the frequency is shifted to the upper tone, then the phase of the RF signal will change by 0.25 cycles, or 90°, during the symbol period. If the lower tone is selected, the phase shift is –90°. Thus, MSK may be regarded as either FSK with a frequency shift of 0.5 times the symbol rate, or as *differential phase-shift keying* (DPSK) with a phase shift of ±90°. The binary data cause the phase to change by either +90 or –90° from one symbol to the next.

Gaussian minimum-shift keying (GMSK) refers to MSK where the modulating signal has been filtered with a low-pass filter that has a Gaussian frequency response. As mentioned before, with any type of angle modulation the spectrum of the modulation is not duplicated at RF, but spreads out into an increased bandwidth. For that reason, there is no point in using a modulation filter with a sharp cutoff since the RF spectrum will be wider anyway. It turns out that a Gaussian filter, with its gradual transition from passband to stopband, has the optimum shape for an angle-modulated digital system. However, a Gaussian filter also has a gradual transition from symbol-to-symbol in the time domain as well. The transition is not totally completed by the time of the next symbol, which means that there is some inter-symbol interference in the transmitted signal, even in the absence of propagation impairments. With the proper choice of filter bandwidth, however, the ISI is small enough not to seriously affect performance.

Binary phase-shift keying (BPSK), often referred to simply as phase-shift keying (PSK), is included in this section because the name suggests that it is true constant-amplitude angle modulation. It is possible to implement it that way. An example is MSK which, as described above, can be considered to be differential BPSK with a ±90° phase shift. However the term BPSK is normally understood to refer to phase-shift keying with a 180° phase difference between symbols. To transition from one state to the other, the modulation filter smoothly reduces the amplitude to zero where the polarity reverses (phase changes 180°) before smoothly ramping up to full amplitude again. For that reason, BPSK as usually implemented really should not be considered to be PSK, but rather a form of amplitude-shift keying (ASK) with two modulation amplitudes, +1 and –1. Unlike true angle modulation, it is linear so that the spectrum of the modulation filter is duplicated at RF. The transmitter must use a linear amplifier to prevent distortion and excessive bandwidth similar to the splatter that results from an over-driven SSB transmitter.

11.4.1 Multi-carrier Modulation

An effective method to fit more data bits into each symbol is to use more than one separately-modulated signal at a time, each on its own carrier frequency spaced an appropriate distance from the frequencies of the other carriers. An example is multi-carrier FSK. This is not to be confused with MFSK which also uses multiple frequencies, but only one at a time. With multi-carrier FSK, each carrier is present continuously and is frequency-shifted in response to a separate data stream. The total data rate equals the

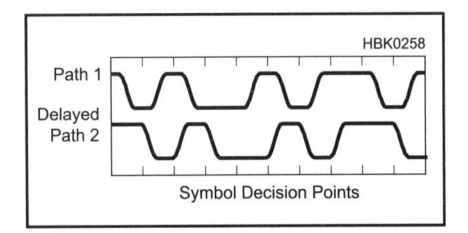

Figure 11.16 — Multipath propagation can cause inter-symbol interference (ISI). At the symbol decision points, which is where the receiver decoder samples the signal, the path 2 data is often opposing the data on path 1.

data rate of one carrier times the number of carriers. A disadvantage of multi-carrier FSK is that the resulting signal is no longer constant-amplitude—a linear amplifier must be used. In general, multi-carrier signals using any modulation type on each carrier tend to have high peak-to-average power ratios.

In the presence of selective fading, one or more of the carriers may disappear while the others are still present. An advantage of multi-carrier modulation is that error-correcting coding can use the unaffected carriers to reconstruct the missing data. Also, since each carrier signal is relatively narrowband, propagation conditions are essentially constant within that bandwidth. That makes it easier for the receiver to correct for other frequency-selective propagation impairments such as phase distortion. If a single-carrier signal of the same total bandwidth had been used instead, the receiver would need an adaptive equalizer to correct for the amplitude and phase variations across the transmission channel.

By using multiple carriers each with multiple-bit-per-symbol modulation it is possible to obtain quite high data rates while maintaining the low symbol rates that are required to combat the effects of multi-path propagation on the HF bands. For example, PACTOR-III achieves a raw data rate of 3600 bits per second with a 100-baud symbol rate using 18 carriers of DQPSK. (100 bauds × 2 bits/symbol × 18 carriers = 3600 bits per second.) Similarly, Clover-2000 modulation gets 3000 bits per second with a 62.5-baud symbol rate using eight carriers of 16-DPSK combined with 4-level DASK. (62.5 bauds x (4+2) bits/symbol × 8 carriers = 3000 bits per second.) Decoding is rather fragile using these complex modulation techniques, so PACTOR and Clover include means to automatically switch to simpler, more-robust modulation types as propagation conditions deteriorate.

What is the minimum carrier spacing that can be used without excessive interference between signals on adjacent frequencies? The answer depends on the symbol rate and the filtering. It turns out that it is easy to design the filtering to be insensitive to interference on frequencies that are spaced at integer multiples of the symbol rate. (See the following section on filtering and bandwidth.) For that reason, it is common to use a carrier spacing equal to the symbol rate. The carriers are said to be *orthogonal* to each other since each theoretically has zero correlation with the others.

Orthogonal frequency-division multiplexing (OFDM), sometimes called *coded OFDM* (COFDM), refers to the multiplexing of multiple data streams onto a series of such orthogonal carriers. The term usually implies a system with a large number of carriers. In that case, an efficient decoding method is to use a DSP algorithm called the fast Fourier transform (FFT). (See the **DSP and SDR Fundamentals** chapter) The FFT is the software equivalent of a hardware spectrum analyzer. It gathers a series of samples of a signal taken at regular time intervals and outputs another series of samples representing the frequency spectrum of the signal. See **Figure 11.17**. If the length of the series of

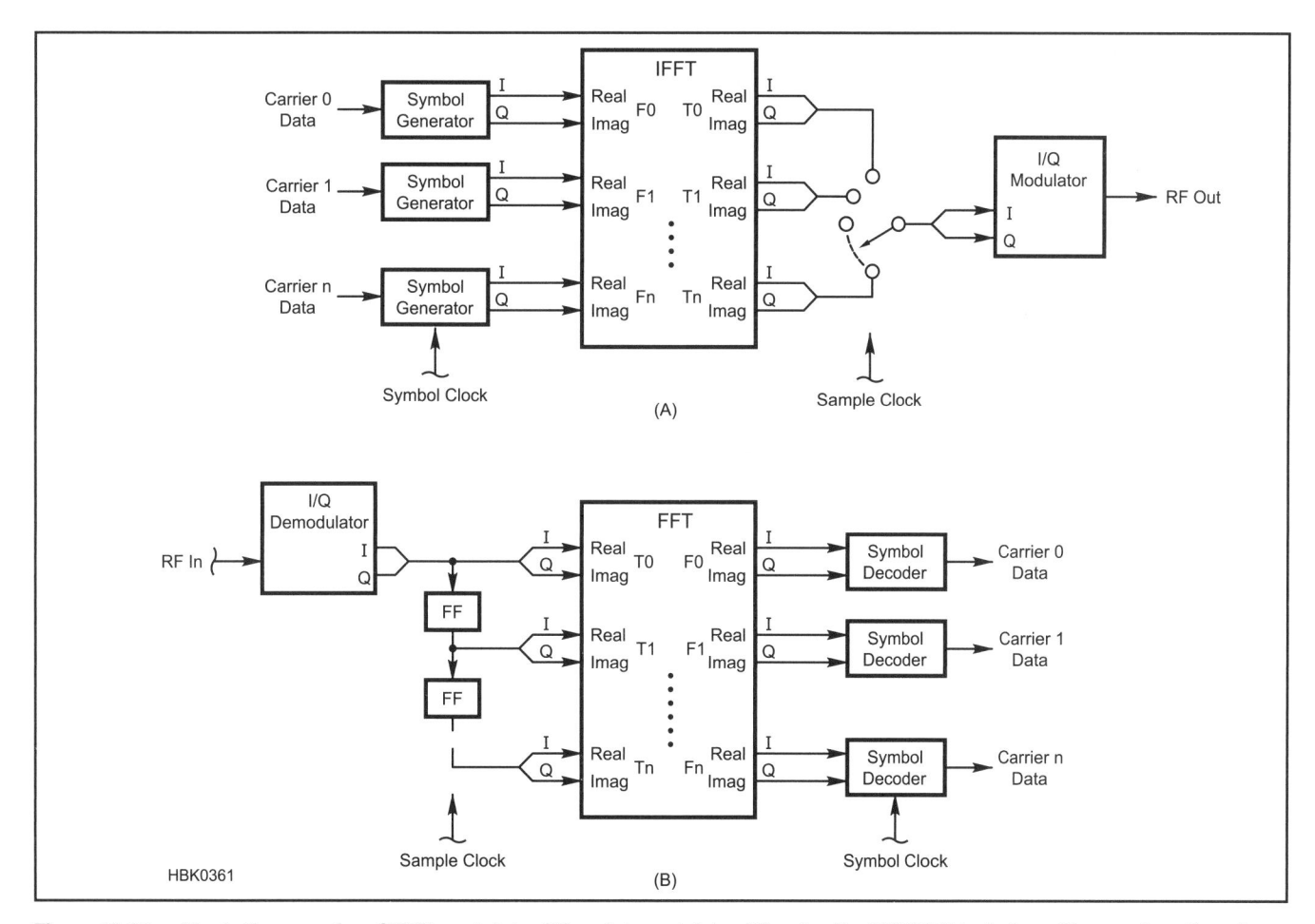

Figure 11.17 — Block diagram of an OFDM modulator (A) and demodulator (B) using the FFT/IFFT technique. The number of carriers is n, and the sample rate is n times the symbol rate. Once per symbol, all the symbol generators in the modulator are loaded with new data and the inverse fast-Fourier transform (IFFT) generates n output samples, which are selected in succession by the switch. In the demodulator, n samples are stored in a shift register (string of flip-flops) for each symbol, then the FFT generates one "frequency" output for each carrier frequency. From the amplitude and phase of each frequency, the symbol decoders can determine the symbol locations and thus the data.

input samples equals one symbol time and if the sample rate is selected properly, then each frequency sample of the FFT output corresponds to one carrier. Each frequency sample is a complex number (containing a "real" and "imaginary" part) that represents the amplitude and phase of one of the carriers during that symbol period. Knowing the amplitude and phase of a carrier is all the information required to determine the symbol location in the I/Q diagram and thus decode the data. At the transmitter end of the circuit, an inverse FFT (IFFT) can be used to encode the data, that is, to convert the amplitudes and phases of each of the carriers into a series of I and Q time samples to send to the I/Q modulator. See Figure 11.17A.

One advantage of OFDM is high spectral efficiency. The carriers are spaced as closely as theoretically possible and, because of the narrow bandwidth of each carrier, the overall spectrum is very square in shape with a sharp drop-off at the passband edges. One disadvantage is that the receiver must be tuned very accurately to the transmitter's frequency to avoid loss of orthogonality, which causes cross-talk between the carriers.

11.4.2 Audio Frequency-Shift Keying (AFSK)

Audio frequency-shift keying (AFSK) is the generation of radio-frequency FSK using an audio-frequency FSK signal fed into the microphone input of an SSB transmitter. Assume the SSB transmitter is tuned to 14.000 MHz, USB. If the audio signal consists of a sine wave that shifts between 2125 Hz and 2295 Hz (170-Hz frequency shift), then the RF signal is a sine wave shifting between 14.002125 and 14.002295 MHz. The frequency shift and spectral characteristics are theoretically unchanged, other than being translated 14 MHz upward in frequency. The RF signal should be indistinguishable from one generated by varying the frequency of an RF oscillator directly.

This technique works not only for FSK but also for nearly any modulation type with a bandwidth narrow enough to fit within the passband of an SSB transmitter and receiver. The most common non-voice analog modulation type to use this technique on the amateur bands is *slow-scan television* (SSTV), which uses frequency modulation for the video signal. In addition, nearly all narrowband digital signals today are generated in this manner. The audio is generated and received either from a dedicated hardware modulator/demodulator (modem) or using the sound card that is found in virtually all personal computers.

Whatever the method, it is important to ensure that unwanted interference is not caused by audio distortion or by insufficient suppression of the carrier and unwanted sideband. For example, with the AFSK tone frequencies mentioned above, 2125 and 2295 Hz, the tone harmonics cause no trouble because they fall outside of the transmitter's passband. However, some AFSK modems use 1275 and 1445 Hz (to accommodate 850-Hz shift without changing the 1275-Hz mark frequency). In that case, the second harmonics at 2550 and 2890 Hz must be suppressed since those frequencies are not well-attenuated by the transmitter. With non-constant-envelope modulation types such as QPSK or the various multi-carrier modes, it is important to set the amplitude of the audio input to the SSB transmitter below the level that activates the transmitter's automatic level control (ALC). That is because the ALC circuit itself generates distortion of signals within the bandwidth of its feedback loop.

11.5 Quadrature Modulation

Quadrature modulation encodes digital signals using a combination of amplitude and phase modulation. With two types of modulation to work with, it is possible to cram more data bits into each modulation symbol, which allows more throughput for a given bandwidth. Modulation formats in use today have up to 8 or more bits per symbol which would be impractical for ASK, FSK or PSK alone.

Since quadrature-modulated symbols are defined by both amplitude and phase, the most common way to represent symbol states is with a polar plot, called a *constellation diagram*. See **Figure 11.18**, which shows a *four-level quadrature amplitude modulation* (4-QAM) signal, often referred to simply as QAM. The distance of each state from the origin represents the amplitude. The phase angle with respect to the +I axis represents the phase. The four states shown have phase angles of +45°, +135°, −45° and −135°. Normally, the receiver has no absolute phase information and can only detect phase differences between the states. For that reason, we could just as easily have drawn

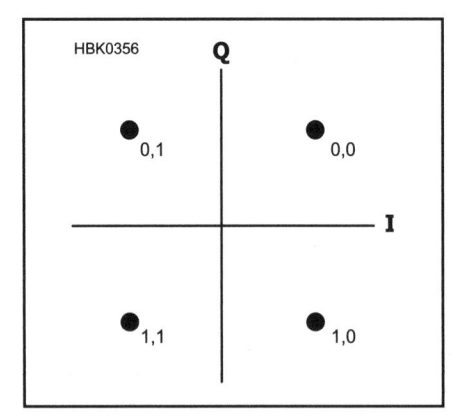

Figure 11.18 — Constellation diagram of a 4-QAM signal, also known as QPSK. The four symbol locations all have the same amplitude and have phase angles of 45°, 135°, −135° and −45°. 4-QAM is a two-bits-per-symbol format. The four symbols are selected by the four possible states of the two data bits, which can be assigned in any order. With the assignment shown, the Q value depends only on the first bit and the I value depends only on the second, an arrangement that can simplify symbol encoding.

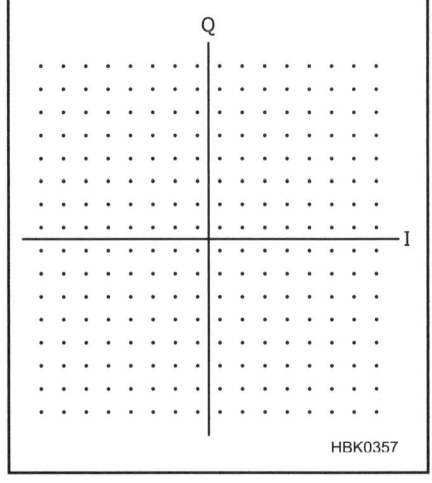

Figure 11.19 — Constellation diagram of a 256-QAM signal. Since an 8-bit number has 256 possible states, each symbol represents 8 bits of data.

the four states directly on the I and Q axes, at 0°, +90°, 180° and –90°. Note that each of the four states has the same amplitude, differing only in phase. For that reason 4-QAM is often referred to as *quadrature phase-shift keying* (QPSK), in the same manner that two-level ASK is normally referred to as BPSK.

Since 4-QAM has four possible states, there are two data bits per symbol. However QAM is not limited to four states. **Figure 11.19** illustrates a 256-QAM signal. It takes 8 bits to represent 256 states, so 256-QAM packs 8 data bits into each symbol. The disadvantage of using lots of states is that the effect of noise and interference is worse at the receiver. Since, for the same peak power, the states of a 256-QAM signal are 15 times closer together than with 4-QAM, the receiver's decoder has to determine each symbol's location to 15 times greater accuracy. That means the ratio of peak power to noise and interference must be 20 log(15) = 23.5 dB greater for accurate decoding. That is why QAM with a large number of states is normally not used on the HF bands where fading, noise and interference are common. A more common application is digital cable television where the coaxial-cable transmission channel is much cleaner. For example, the European DVB-C standard provides for 16-QAM through 256-QAM, depending on bandwidth and data rate.

There are at least two ways to generate a QAM signal. One is to combine a phase modulator and an amplitude modulator. The phase modulator places the symbol location at the correct phase angle and the amplitude modulator adjusts the amplitude so the symbol is the correct distance from the origin. That method is seldom used, both because of the circuit complexity and because the nonlinear phase modulator makes the signal difficult to filter so as to limit the bandwidth.

A much more common method of generating QAM is with an *I/Q modulator*. See **Figure 11.20**. By using two modulators (mixers) fed with RF sine waves in quadrature (90° out of phase with each other), any amplitude and phase may be obtained by varying the amplitudes of the two modulation inputs. The input labeled I (for in-phase) moves the symbol location horizontally in the constellation diagram and the one labeled Q (for quadrature) moves it vertically. For example, to obtain an amplitude of 1 and a phase angle of –45°, set I to +0.707 and set Q to –0.707.

It is possible to generate virtually any type of modulation using an I/Q modulator. For example, to generate BPSK or on-off keying, simply disconnect the Q input and apply the modulation to I. For angle modulation, such as FM or PM, a waveform generator applies a varying signal to I and Q in such a manner to cause the symbol to rotate at constant amplitude with the correct phase and frequency (rotation rate). Even a multi-carrier signal may be generated with a single I/Q modulator by applying the sum of a number of signals, each representing one carrier, to the I and Q inputs. The phase of each signal rotates at a rate equal to the frequency offset of its carrier from the center.

One problem with QAM is that whenever the signal trajectory between two symbol states passes through the origin, the signal amplitude momentarily goes to zero. That imposes stringent linearity requirements on the RF power amplifier, since many amplifiers exhibit their worst linearity near zero power. One solution is *offset QPSK* (OQPSK) modulation. In this case, the symbol transitions of the I and Q channels are offset by half a symbol. That is, for each symbol, the I channel changes state first then the Q channel changes half a symbol time later. That allows the symbol trajectory to sidestep around the origin, allowing use of a higher-efficiency or lower-cost power amplifier that has worse linearity.

Another solution to the zero-crossing problem is called *PI over 4 differential QPSK* (π/4 DQPSK). See **Figure 11.21**. This is actually a form of 8-PSK, where the eight symbol locations are located every 45° around a constant-amplitude circle. On any given symbol, however, only four of the symbol locations are used. The symbol location always changes by an odd multiple of 45° (π/4 radians). If the current symbol is located on the I or Q axis, then on the next symbol only the four non-axis locations are available and vice versa. As with OQPSK, that avoids transitions that pass through the origin.

Another advantage of π/4 DQPSK which is shared with other types of differential modulation is that absolute phase doesn't matter. The information is encoded only in the *difference* in the phase of successive symbols. That greatly simplifies the job of the receiver's demodulator.

The block diagram of an I/Q demodulator looks like an I/Q modulator drawn backward. See **Figure 11.22**. If the local oscillator is not tuned to exactly the same frequency as the one in the transmitter (after downconversion to the IF, assuming a superhet receiver) then the demodulated signal will rotate in the I/Q plane at a rate equal to the frequency error. Most receivers include a *carrier-recovery* circuit, which phase-locks the local oscillator to the average frequency of the incoming signal to obtain stable demodulation. While that corrects the frequency error, it does not correct the phase, which must be accounted for in some other manner such as by using differential modulation or some kind of symbol-recovery mechanism.

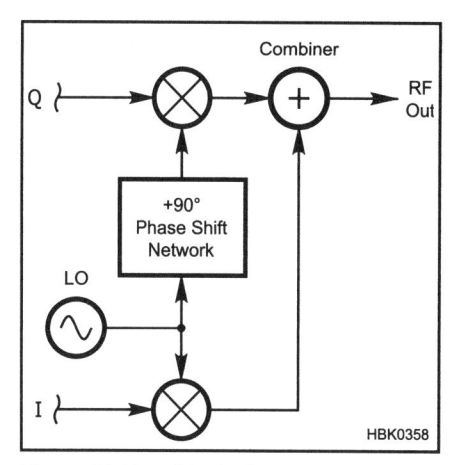

Figure 11.20 — Block diagram of an I/Q modulator. By connecting an audio 90° phase-shift network to the I and Q inputs, an I/Q modulator can generate an analog SSB signal by the phasing method.

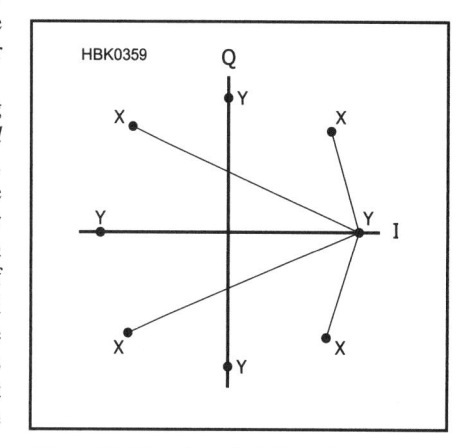

Figure 11.21 — Constellation diagram of a π/4 DQPSK signal. There are eight possible symbol locations. If the current symbol location is at one of the four positions labeled "X" then the next symbol will be at one of the four locations labeled "Y" and vice versa. That guarantees that no possible symbol trajectories (the lines between symbol locations) can ever pass through the origin.

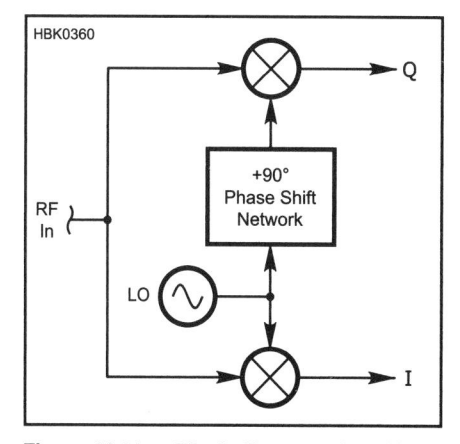

Figure 11.22 — Block diagram of an I/Q demodulator.

11.6 Analytic Signals and Modulation

In the area of modulation, the topic that seems to give people the most trouble is the concept of negative frequency. What in the world is meant by that? Consider a single-frequency signal oscillating at ω radians per second. (Recall that $\omega = 2\pi f$, where f is frequency in Hz.) Let's represent the signal by a cosine wave with a peak amplitude of 1.0, $x(t) = \cos(\omega t)$, where t is time. Changing the sign of the frequency is equivalent to running time backwards because $(-\omega)t = \omega(-t)$. By examining **Figure 11.23A** you can see that, because a cosine wave is symmetrical about the time t = 0 point, a negative frequency results in exactly the same signal. That is, as you may remember from high-school trigonometry, $\cos(-\omega t) = \cos(\omega t)$. If, for example, you add a positive-frequency cosine wave to its negative-frequency twin, you get the same signal with twice the amplitude.

That assumes that the phase of the signal is such that it reaches a peak at t = 0. What if instead we had a sine wave, which is zero at t = 0? From Figure 11.23B you can see that running time backwards results in a reversal of polarity, $\sin(-\omega t) = -\sin(\omega t)$. If you add positive and negative-frequency sine waves of the same frequency and amplitude, they cancel, resulting in zero net signal.

A sinusoidal wave of any arbitrary amplitude and phase may be represented by the weighted sum of a sine and cosine wave:

$x(t) = I \cos(\omega t) + Q \sin(\omega t)$

For computational purposes, it is convenient to consider the *in-phase (I)* and *quadrature (Q)* components separately. Since the I and Q components are 90° out of phase in the time domain, they are often plotted on a polar graph at a 90° angle from each other. See **Figure 11.24**. For example if Q = 0, then as time increases the signal oscillates along the I (horizontal) axis, tracing out the path back and forth between I = +1 and I = –1 in a sinusoidal fashion. Conversely, if I = 0, then the signal oscillates along the Q axis.

What if both I and Q are non-zero, for example I = Q = 1? Recall that the cosine and sine are 90° out of phase. When t = 0, $\cos(\omega t) = 1$ and $\sin(\omega t) = 0$. A quarter cycle later, $\cos(\omega t) = 0$ and $\sin(\omega t) = 1$. Comparing Figure 11.24 with Figure 11.23 it should not be hard to convince yourself that the signal is tracing out a circle in the counter-clockwise direction.

What about negative frequency? Again, it should not be hard to convince yourself that changing ω to –ω results in a signal that circles the origin in the clockwise direction. If you combine equal-amplitude signals of opposite frequency, the sine portions cancel out and you are left with a simple cosine wave of twice the amplitude:

$x(t) = [\cos(\omega t) + \sin(\omega t)] + [\cos(-\omega t) + \sin(-\omega t)] = 2\cos(\omega t)$

You can see that graphically in **Figure 11.25**. Imagine the two vectors rotating in opposite directions. If you mentally add them by placing the tail of one vector on the head of the other, as shown by the dotted line, the result always lies on the I axis and oscillates between +2 and –2.

That is why we say that a single scalar sinusoidal signal, $\cos(\omega t)$, actually contains two frequencies, +ω and –ω. It also offers a logical explanation of why a mixer or modulator produces the sum and difference of the frequencies of the two inputs. For example, an AM modulator produces sidebands at the carrier frequency plus and minus the modulating frequency precisely because those positive and negative frequencies are actually already present in the modulating signal.

For many purposes, it is useful to separate the portion of the signal that specifies the amplitude and phase (I and Q) from the oscillating part ($\sin(\omega t)$ and $\cos(\omega t)$). For mathematical convenience, the I/Q part is represented by a complex number, $x = I + jQ$. The oscillating part is also a complex number $e^{-j\omega t} = \cos(\omega t) - j\sin(\omega t)$. (Don't worry if you don't know where that equation comes from — concentrate on the part to the right of the equals sign.[4]) In the equations, $j = \sqrt{}$ of –1. Of course, –1 does not have a real square root (any real number multiplied by itself is positive) so j, or any real number multiplied by j, is called an *imaginary number*. A number with both real and imaginary parts is called a *complex number*. The total *analytic signal* is a complex number equal to

$x(t) = xe^{-j\omega t} = (I + jQ)(\cos(\omega t) - j\sin(\omega t))$

In the above equation, the $\cos(\omega t) - \sin(\omega t)$ portion generally represents an RF carrier, with ω being the carrier frequency (a positive or negative value). The I + jQ part is the modulation. The *scalar* value of a modulated signal (what you would measure with an oscilloscope) is just the real (Re) part of the analytic signal. Using the fact that $j^2 = -1$,

$Re[x(t)] = Re[(I + jQ)(\cos(\omega t) - j\sin(\omega t))]$

$Re[x(t)] = Re[(I\cos(\omega t) + Q\sin(\omega t)) + j(Q\cos(\omega t) - I\sin(\omega t))]$

$Re[x(t)] = I\cos(\omega t) + Q\sin(\omega t)$

Note that if the modulation (I and Q) var-

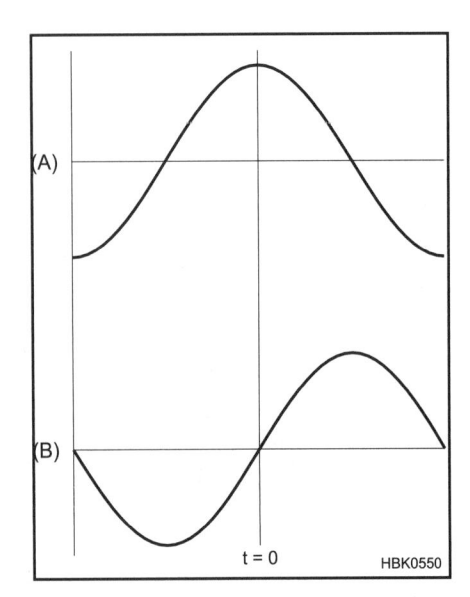

Figure 11.23 — Cosine wave (A) and sine wave (B).

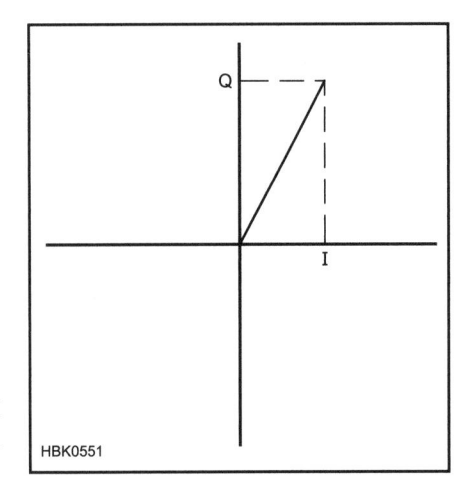

Figure 11.24 — In-phase (I) and quadrature (Q) portions of a signal.

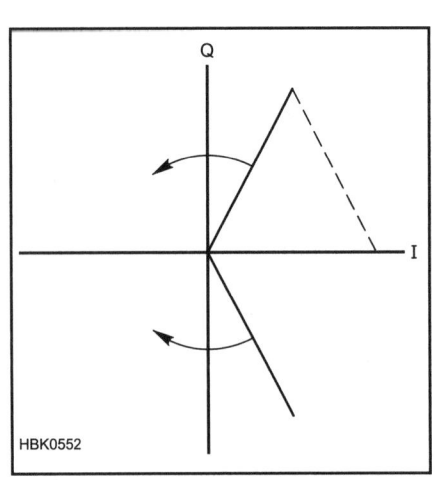

Figure 11.25 — A real frequency is the sum of a positive and negative analytic frequency.

ies with time, the above equation assumes that the modulated signal does not overlap zero Hz. That is, I and Q have no frequency components greater than ω.

Normally the I/Q diagram shows only I and Q (the modulation) and not the oscillating part. We call such a representation a *phasor diagram*. The I/Q vector represents the *difference* in phase and amplitude of the RF signal compared to the unmodulated carrier. For example, if the I/Q vector is at 90°, that means the carrier has been phase-shifted by 90° from what it otherwise would have been. If the I/Q vector is rotating counter-clockwise 10 times per second, then the carrier frequency has been increased by 10 Hz.

It is worth noting that the modulation can be specified either by the in-phase and quadrature (I and Q) values as shown or alternatively by the amplitude and phase. The amplitude is the length of the I/Q vector in the phasor diagram,

$$A = \sqrt{I^2 + Q^2}$$

The phase is the angle of the vector with respect to the +I axis,

$$\varphi = \arctan\left[\frac{Q}{I}\right]$$

An alternative expression for the modulated analytic signal using amplitude and phase is

$$x(t) = Ae^{-j(\varphi + \omega t)}$$
$$= A\left[\cos(\varphi + \omega t) + j\sin(\varphi + \omega t)\right]$$

and for the scalar signal

$$\text{Re}[x(t)] = A\cos(\varphi + \omega t)$$

One final comment. So far we have been looking at signals that consist of a single sinusoidal frequency. In any linear system, anything that is true for a single frequency is also true for a combination of many frequencies. Each frequency is affected by the system as though the others were not present. Since any complicated signal can be broken down into a (perhaps large) number of single-frequency sinusoids, all our previous conclusions apply to multi-frequency signals as well.

11.6.1 I/Q Modulation and Demodulation

An *I/Q modulator* is just a device that controls the amplitude and phase of an RF signal directly from the in-phase (I) and quadrature (Q) components. See **Figure 11.26A**. An *I/Q demodulator* is basically the same circuit in reverse. It puts out I and Q signals that represent the in-phase and quadrature components of the incoming RF signal. See Figure 11.26B. Assuming the demodulator's

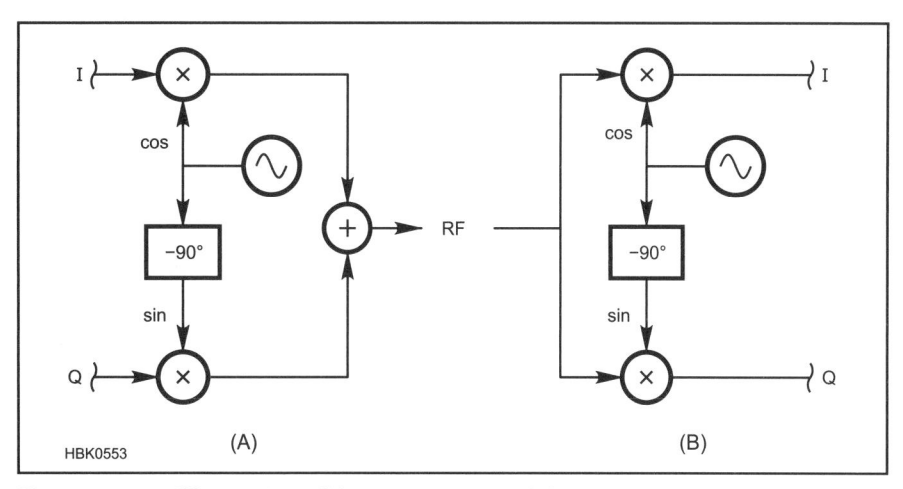

Figure 11.26 — I/Q modulator (A) and demodulator (B).

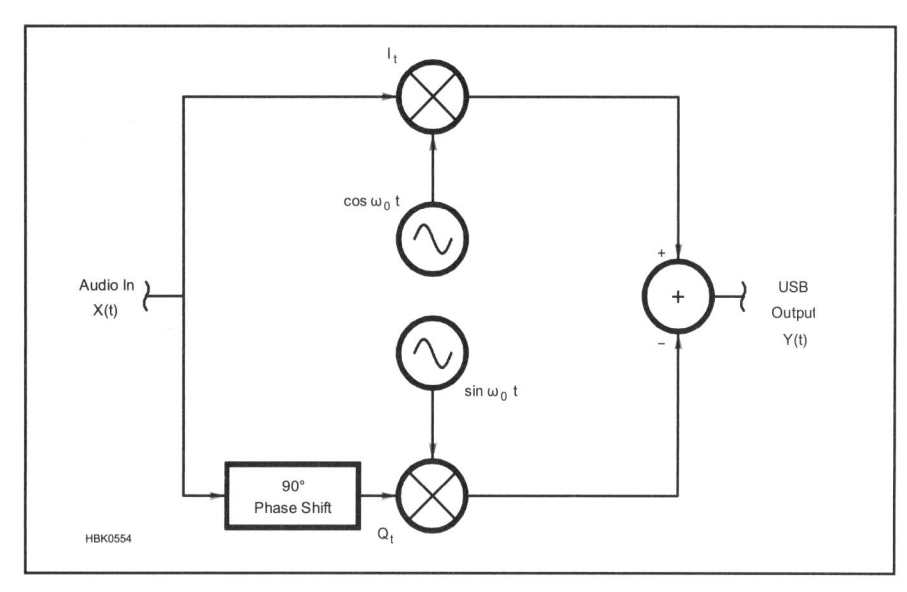

Figure 11.27 — Generating a USB signal with an I/Q modulator.

local oscillator is on the same frequency and is in phase with the carrier of the signal being received then the I/Q output of the receiver's demodulator is theoretically identical to the I/Q input at the transmitter end.

I/Q modulators and demodulators can be built with analog components. The LO could be a transistor oscillator and the 90° phase-shift network could be implemented with coils and capacitors. The circles with the multiplication symbol would be double-balanced mixers. Not shown in the diagram are trim adjustments to balance the amplitude between the I and Q channels and to adjust the phase shift as close as possible to 90°.

No analog circuit is perfect, however. If the 90° phase-shift network is not exactly 90° or the amplitudes of the I and Q channels are not perfectly balanced, you don't get perfect opposite-sideband rejection. The modulator output includes a little bit of signal on the unwanted sideband and the I/Q signal from the demodulator includes a small signal rotating in the wrong direction. If there is a small dc offset in the amplifiers feeding the modulator's I/Q inputs, that shows up as carrier feedthrough. On receive, a dc offset makes the demodulator think there is a small signal at a constant amplitude and phase angle that is always there even when no actual signal is being received. Nor is analog circuitry distortion-free, especially the mixers. Intermodulation distortion shows up as out-of-channel "splatter" on transmit and unwanted out-of channel responses on receive.

All those problems can be avoided by going digital. If the analog I/Q inputs to the modulator are converted to streams of digital numbers with a pair of ADCs, then the mixers, oscillator, phase-shift network and summer can all be digital. In many systems, the I and Q signals are also generated digitally, so that the digital output signal has perfect unwanted sideband rejection, no carrier feedthrough

Modulation   11.15

and no distortion within the dynamic range afforded by the number of bits in the data words. A similar argument holds for a digital demodulator. If the incoming RF signal is first digitized with an ADC, then the demodulation can be done digitally without any of the artifacts caused by imperfections in the analog circuitry.

You can think of an I/Q modulator as a device that converts the analytic signal $I + jQ$ into a scalar signal at some RF frequency. The spectrum of the I/Q signal, both positive and negative frequencies, is translated upward in frequency so that it is centered on the carrier frequency. Thinking in terms of the phasor diagram, any components of the I/Q signal that are rotating counter-clockwise appear above the carrier frequency and clockwise components appear below.

11.6.2 SSB Using I/Q Modulators and Demodulators

As an example of how this works, let's walk through the process of generating an upper-sideband signal using an I/Q modulator. See **Figure 11.27**. We'll first describe the mathematics in the following paragraph and then give the equivalent explanation using the phasor diagram.

The modulating signal is a sine wave at a frequency of ω_m radians per second ($\omega_m / 2\pi$ cycles per second). Because ω_m is a positive frequency the signals applied to the I/Q inputs are $I(t) = \cos(\omega_m t)$ and $Q(t) = \sin(\omega_m t)$. Assume the modulating frequency ω_m is much less than the RF frequency ω. The analytic signal is

$$x(t) = \left[\cos(\omega_m t) + j\sin(\omega_m t)\right]$$
$$\times \left[\cos(\omega t) - j\sin(\omega t)\right]$$

so that the real, scalar signal that appears at the modulator output is

$$\mathrm{Re}\left[x(t)\right] = \cos(\omega_m t)\cos(\omega t) + \sin(\omega_m t)\sin(\omega t)$$

At the moment when $t = 0$, then $\cos(\omega_m t) = 1$ and $\sin(\omega_m t) = 0$, so the real signal is just $\cos(\omega t)$, the RF signal with zero phase. One quarter of a modulation cycle later $\omega_m t = \pi/2$, so $\cos(\omega_m t) = 0$ and $\sin(\omega_m t) = 1$, and the real signal is now $\sin(\omega t)$, the RF signal with a phase of $+\pi/2$, or $+90°$. Every quarter cycle of the modulating signal, the RF phase, increases by $90°$. That means that the RF phase increases by one full cycle for every cycle of the modulation, which is another way of saying the frequency has shifted by ω_m. We have an upper sideband at a frequency of $\omega + \omega_m$.

On the phasor diagram, the I/Q signal is rotating counterclockwise at a frequency of ω_m radians per second. As it rotates it is increasing the phase of the RF signal at the same rate, which causes the frequency to increase by ω_m radians per second. To cause the phasor to rotate in the opposite direction, you could change the polarity of either I or Q or you could swap the I and Q inputs. In that case you would have a lower sideband.

For that to work, the baseband signals applied to the I and Q inputs must be $90°$ out of phase. That's not hard to do for a single sine wave, but to generate a voice SSB signal, all frequencies in the audio range must be simultaneously phase-shifted by $90°$ without changing their amplitudes. To do that with analog components requires a broadband phase-shift network consisting of an array of precision resistors and capacitors and a number of operational amplifiers.

THE HILBERT TRANSFORMER

To do that with DSP requires a *Hilbert transformer*, an FIR filter with a constant $90°$ phase shift at all frequencies. Recall that a symmetrical FIR filter has a constant *delay* at all frequencies. That means that the phase shift is not constant — it increases linearly with frequency. It turns out that with an *antisymmetrical* filter, in which the top half of the coefficients are the negative of the mirror image of the lower half, the phase shift is $90°$ at all frequencies, which is exactly what we need to generate an SSB signal.

The Hilbert transformer is connected in series with either the I or Q input, depending on whether USB or LSB is desired. Just as with any FIR filter, a Hilbert transformer has a delay equal to half its length, so an equal delay must be included in the other I/Q channel as shown in **Figure 11.28**. It is possible to combine the Hilbert transformer with the normal FIR filter that may be needed anyway to filter the baseband signal. The other I/Q channel then simply uses a similar filter with the same delay but without the $90°$ phase shift.

Because the RF output of the modulator is normally at a much higher frequency than the audio signal, it is customary to use a higher sample rate for the output signal than for the input. The FIR filters can still run at the lower rate to save processing time, and their output is then upsampled to a higher rate with an interpolator. It is convenient to use an output sample rate that is exactly four times the carrier frequency because each sample advances the RF phase by exactly $90°$. The sequence of values for the sine wave is 0, 1, 0 and –1. To generate the $90°$ phase shift for the cosine wave, simply start the sequence at the second sample: 1, 0, –1, 0. The complete block diagram is shown in **Figure 11.29**.

Amateurs who have been in the hobby for many years may recognize this as the "phasing method" of SSB generation[7]. It was popular when SSB first became common on the amateur bands back in the 1950s because suitable crystal filters were expensive or difficult to obtain. The phasing method had the reputation of producing signals with excellent-quality audio, no doubt due to the lack of the phase distortion caused by crystal filters.

A Hilbert transformer may also be used in an SSB demodulator at the receiver end of the communications system. It is basically the same block diagram drawn backwards, as illustrated in **Figure 11.30**.

It is important to note that an ideal Hilbert transformer is impossible to construct because it theoretically has an infinitely-long impulse response. However, with a sufficiently-long impulse response, the accuracy

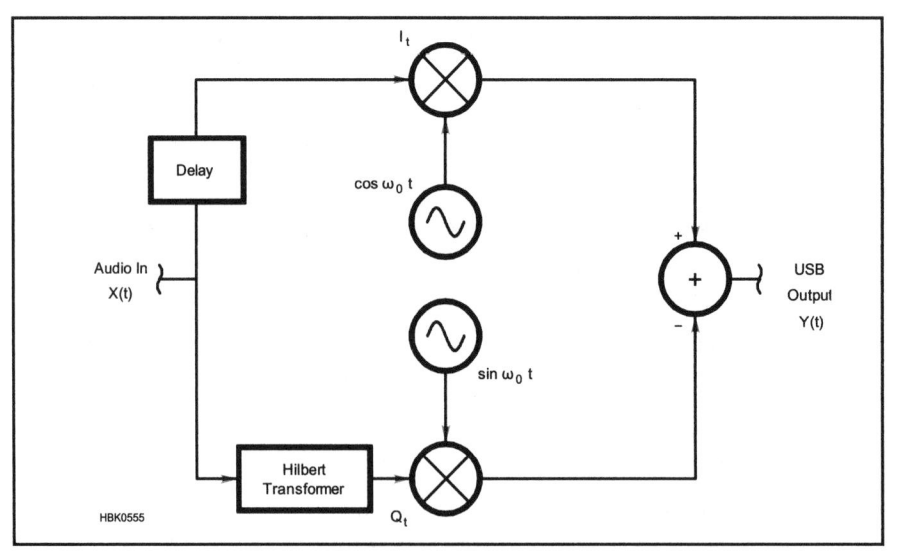

Figure 11.28 — Generating a non-sinusoidal USB signal with an I/Q modulator.

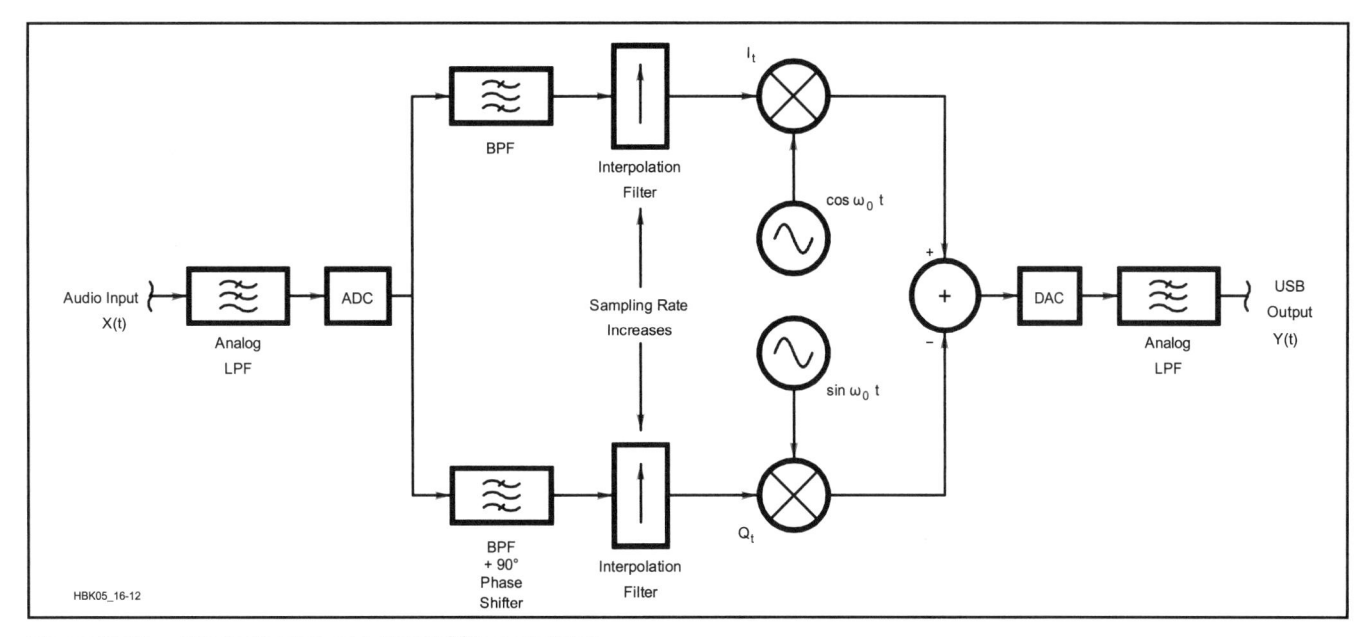

Figure 11.29 — Block diagram of a digital SSB modulator.

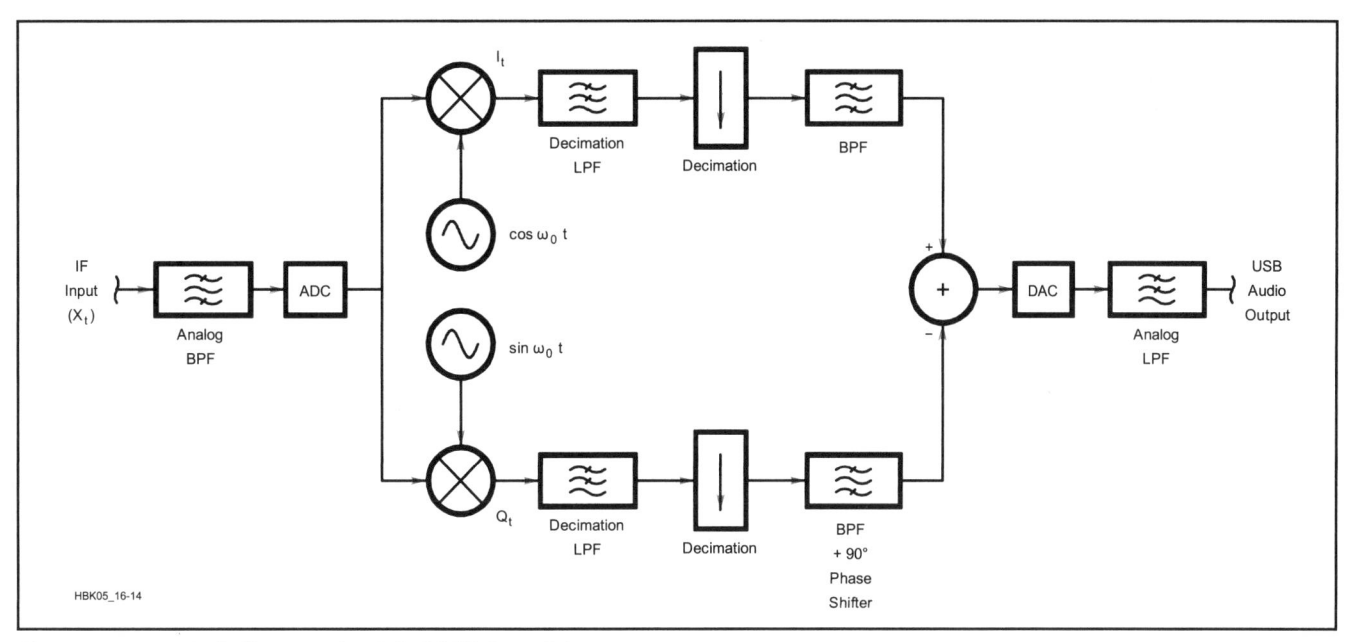

Figure 11.30 — Block diagram of a digital SSB demodulator.

is much better than an analog phase-shift network. Just as with an analog network, the frequency passband must be limited both at the low end as well as the high end. That is, the audio must be band-pass filtered before the 90° phase shift. Actually, the filtering and phase shifting can be combined into one operation using the following method.

First design a low-pass FIR filter with a bandwidth one-half the desired audio bandwidth. For example, if the desired passband is 300 to 2700 Hz, the low-pass filter bandwidth should be (2700 − 300)/2 = 1200 Hz. Then multiply the impulse response coefficients with a sine wave of a frequency equal to the center frequency of the desired passband, (2700 + 300)/2 = 1500 Hz in this case. That results in a band-pass filter with the desired 300 – 2700 Hz response. By using sine waves 90° out of phase for the I and Q channels, you end up with two band-pass filters with the same amplitude response and delay but a 90° phase difference at all frequencies. Multiply by a cosine for zero phase and by a sine for a 90° phase shift.

This bears a striking resemblance to the Weaver method, the so-called "third method" of SSB generation (after "filter" and "phasing"). It was originally used back in the late 1950s to eliminate the need for a wide-band audio phase-shift network.[6,7] It is almost as if there is no such thing as truly new technology, just old ideas coming back with new terminology!

THE FILTER METHOD IN DSP

As DSP hardware has grown more powerful, it has also become possible to implement the filter method of SSB generation in software. In fact, the DSP filters that can be constructed in software are quite a bit better than the best analog filters. The result is a very simple system as shown in **Figure 11.31** that is equivalent to the analog method. Ray Mack, W5IFS, discusses the various tradeoffs and

Modulation 11.17

filter characteristics required of this method in his Sep/Oct 2012 *QEX* SDR Simplified column.

Phil Karn, KA9Q, uses a DSP-based filter method for SSB generation because it avoids the need for a Hilbert transformer function. He performs his filtering by converting the signal to the frequency domain with an FFT (see the **DSP and SDR Fundamentals** chapter), multiplies each frequency component by a constant that defines the desired filter shape, and then converts back to the time domain with the inverse FFT. The windowing functions discussed with the FFT material can be applied to this filtering operation as well, with the Kaiser window recommended as supporting smooth trade-offs for sharp response against stop-band attenuation.

Karn has developed a fairly general purpose package in C that downconverts, filters, and detects a range of modulation/demodulates methods. The package is available at **github.com/ka9q/ka9q-radio** along with a WWV emulator at **github.com/ka9q/WWV**. It currently demodulates AM, CAM (coherent AM), LSB, USB, FM, ISB (independent sideband) and IQ (straight IQ pass through). The software should work on processors that support C and floating point operations. It's not yet a polished product for the end user, but rather a set of building blocks for the experimenter.

11.6.3 Uses for I/Q Modulators and Demodulators

While I/Q modulators and demodulators can be used for analog modes such as SSB, they really shine when used with digital modulation modes. The modulation states of the various digital formats map to positions in the phasor diagram, what is called a *constellation diagram* (see this chapter's section on Quadrature Modulation). The transmitter can generate the correct modulation states simply by placing the correct values on the I and Q inputs to the I/Q modulator. In the receiver, the filtered I and Q values are sampled at the symbol decision times to determine which modulation state they most closely match.

I/Q modulators and demodulators can also be used as so-called *imageless mixers*. A normal mixer with inputs at f_1 and f_2 produces outputs at f_1, f_2, $f_1 + f_2$, and $f_1 - f_2$. A balanced mixer eliminates the f_1 and f_2 terms but both the sum and difference terms remain, even though normally only one is desired. By feeding an RF instead of AF signal into the input of an SSB modulator, we can choose the sum or difference frequency in the same way as choosing the upper or lower sideband. If the input signal is a sine wave, the Hilbert transformer can be replaced by a simple 90° phase shifter. Similarly, a mixer with the same architecture as an SSB demodulator can be used

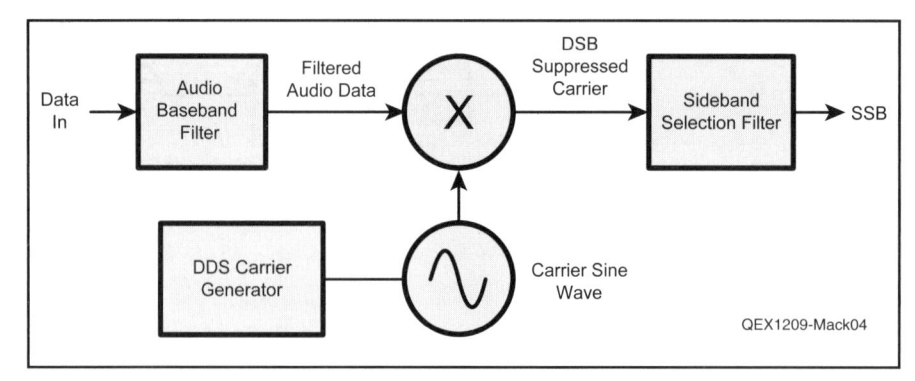

Figure 11.31 — The DSP method of using filters to create a SSB signal is simple and equivalent to the analog filter method.

Table 11.1
Software AM Detector

```
static long int carrier;
long int am;
int i, q, signal;

/* Code that generates i and q
omitted */
am = (long int)sqrt((long int)
i*i + (long int)q*q);
signal = am - carrier;
// Divide signal by 2^10:
carrier += signal >> 10;
// Audio output to DAC via SPI
bus:
```

to downconvert an RF signal to IF with zero image response. Analog imageless mixers are covered in the **Receiving** chapter. They are sometimes used in microwave receivers and transmitters where it is difficult to build filters narrow enough to reject the image response, but they typically only achieve image rejection in the 20-30 dB range. With a digital imageless mixer, the image rejection is "perfect" within the dynamic range of the bit resolution.

SOFTWARE AM MODULATORS AND DEMODULATORS

In this chapter we've already covered many of the algorithms needed for a software-defined radio. For example, we know how to make I/Q modulators and demodulators and use them to build an SSB modulator and detector. Let's say we want our software-defined transceiver to operate on AM voice as well. How do you make an AM modulator and demodulator using DSP and software?

The modulator is easy. Simply add a constant value, representing the carrier, to the audio signal and multiply the result by a sine wave at the carrier frequency, as shown in **Figure 11.32**.

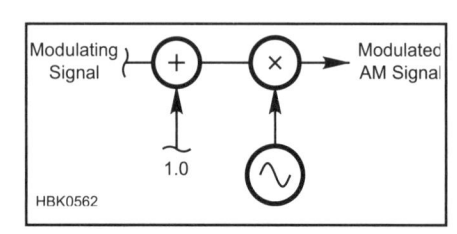

Figure 11.32 — A digital AM modulator

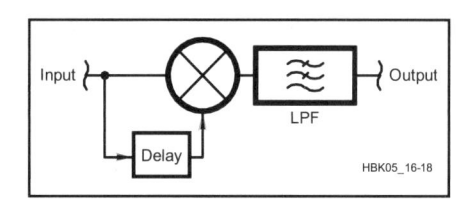

Figure 11.33 — A digital quadrature detector.

Demodulation is almost as easy. We could just simulate a full-wave rectifier by taking the absolute value of the signal, as mentioned previously, and low-pass filter the result to remove the RF energy. If the signal to be demodulated is complex, with I and Q components, then instead of absolute value we take the magnitude

$$A = \sqrt{I^2 + Q^2}$$

The dc bias can be removed by adding a "series blocking capacitor" — a high-pass filter with a suitable cut-off frequency.

A little more elegant way to do it would be to include the AM detector as part of the AGC loop. In the C code snippet shown in **Table 11.1**, the variable "carrier" is the average AM carrier level. It is passed to another subroutine to control the gain.

Note that no "series capacitor" is needed since the audio signal is computed by subtracting the average historical value, carrier, from the magnitude of the current I/Q signal, am. A small fraction of its value is added to the historical value so that the AGC tracks the average AM carrier level. AGC speed is controlled by that fraction. Dividing by 2^{10} = 1024 gives a time constant of about 1024 clock cycles.

Another type of detector we haven't discussed yet is for frequency modulation. For a scalar signal, the *quadrature detector* shown in **Figure 11.33** is one elegant solution. This is the same circuit whose analog equivalent has been used in millions of FM receivers around the world. In the digital implementation, the delay block is a FIFO buffer constructed from a series of shift registers. Multiplying the signal by a delayed version of itself gives an output with a cosinusoidal response versus frequency. The response crosses zero whenever the carrier frequency is $f = N/(4\tau)$, where N is an odd integer and the delay in seconds is $\tau = n/f_s$, where n is the number of samples of delay and f_s is the sample frequency. As the carrier deviates above and below the zero-crossing frequency the output varies above and below zero, just what we want for an FM detector.

For an I/Q signal, probably the most straightforward FM detector is a phase detector followed by a differentiator to remove the 6 dB per octave rolloff caused by the phase detector. The phase is just

$$\varphi = \arctan\left(\frac{Q}{I}\right)$$

You have to be a little careful since there is a 180° phase ambiguity in the arctangent function. For example,

$$\arctan\left(\frac{1}{1}\right) = \arctan\left(\frac{-1}{-1}\right)$$

Software will have to check which quadrant of the phasor diagram the I/Q signal is in and add 180° when necessary. If there is no arctan function in the library, one can be constructed using a look-up table. Frequency is the derivative of the phase. A differentiator is nothing more than a subtractor that takes the difference between successive samples.

$$f = \frac{\varphi_n - \varphi_{n-1}}{2\pi f_s}$$

where n is the sample number and f_s is the sample rate. It is important to make sure that the difference equation functions properly around 360°. If the phase variable is scaled so that 360° equals the difference between the highest and lowest representable numbers, then standard two's complement subtraction should roll over to the right value at the 360° / 0° transition. Another thing to watch out for is that the derivative of the phase may be a rather small signal, so it might be necessary to carry through all the calculations using long integers or floating point numbers.

11.7 Image Modulation

The following section covers the modulation aspects of amateur television and facsimile communications. More detailed information on protocols and operating standards can be found in the **Image Communications** operating chapter in this book's downloadable supplemental information.

11.7.1 Fast-Scan Television

Amateur fast-scan television (ATV) is a wideband mode used in the amateur bands above 420 MHz. It is called "fast scan" to differentiate it from slow-scan TV.

NTSC

NTSC is named after the National Television Standards Committee that developed the modulation standard. It was released initially in 1941 (black-and-white only) and again in 1953 (color). It remained the dominant television standard until the late 1990s.

Although obsolete commercially, there is much ATV activity using NTSC, the same technical standard used by commercial analog television stations in the United States before most switched to digital TV in 2009. **Figure 11.34** shows the spectrum of an NTSC analog TV channel. It's basically a full-carrier, double-sideband AM signal, with filtering to partially remove the lower sideband. The partially-filtered *vestigial sideband* (VSB) extends 1.25 MHz below the carrier frequency. The channel is 6 MHz wide to accommodate the composite video and two subcarriers, one at 3.58 MHz for the color burst and the other an FM-modulated signal at 4.5 MHz for the sound. For simplicity, amateur stations often transmit unfiltered full-DSB AM, but the normally-removed portion of the lower sideband is unused by the TV receiver. Since less than 5% of the video energy appears more than 1 MHz below the carrier, little of the transmitter power is wasted. If needed, to reduce interference to other band users, a VSB filter in the antenna line can attenuate the lower sideband color and sound subcarrier frequencies by 20-30 dB.

The video signal includes pulses to synchronize the vertical and horizontal scan oscillators in the receiver. See **Figure 11.35**. The sync pulses and the "front porch" and "back porch" areas that bracket them are "blacker than black" so that the signal is

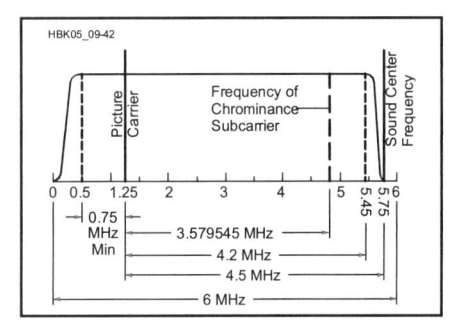

Figure 11.34 — An analog NTSC 6-MHz video channel with the video carrier 1.25 MHz up from the lower edge. The color subcarrier is at 3.58 MHz and the sound subcarrier at 4.5 MHz above the video subcarrier.

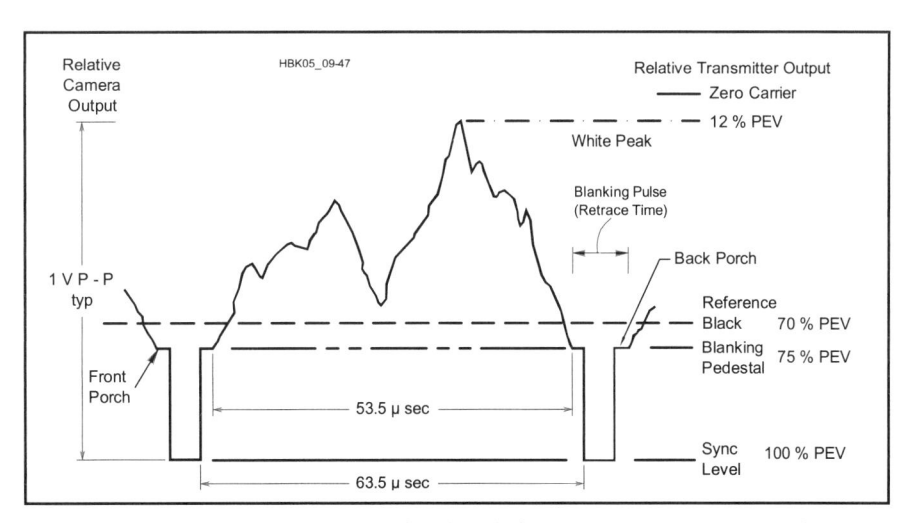

Figure 11.35 — An ATV waveform, showing the relative camera output as well as the transmitter output RF power during one horizontal line scan for black-and-white TV. (A color camera would generate a "burst" of 8 cycles at 3.58 MHz on the back porch of the blanking pedestal.) Note that "black" corresponds to a higher transmitter power than "white."

blanked during retrace. The video-to-sync ratio must remain constant throughout all of the linear amplifiers in the transmit chain as the video level from the camera changes. To maintain the sync tips at 100% of peak power, the modulator usually contains a clamp circuit that also acts as a sync stretcher to compensate for amplifier gain compression.

Given NTSC's 525 horizontal lines and its 30 frames per second scan rate, the resulting horizontal resolution bandwidth is 80 lines per MHz. Therefore, with the typical TV set's 3-dB rolloff at 3 MHz (primarily in the IF filter), up to 240 vertical black lines can be seen, corresponding to 480 pixels per line. Color bandwidth in a TV set is less than that, resulting in up to 100 color lines. (Lines of resolution should not be confused with the number of horizontal scan lines per frame.)

The PAL analog TV system is an AM system based on NTSC. The SECAM system uses FM color subcarriers. As described previously, FM achieves superior noise and interference suppression for signal levels above a certain threshold, although AM seems to work better for receiver signal levels below about 5 μV. FM ATV in the United States typically uses 4 MHz deviation with NTSC video and a 5.5-MHz sound subcarrier set to 15 dB below the video level. Using Carson's rule, the occupied bandwidth comes out to just under 20 MHz. Most available FM ATV equipment is made for the 1.2, 2.4 and 10.25-GHz bands.

DIGITAL TV MODULATION

Digital fast-scan TV has been explored by amateurs in Europe and the US using the commercial DVB-S satellite digital video broadcasting standard. It uses MPEG2 audio and video data compression and QPSK modulation with symbol rates up to 20 Mbaud. Much of work has been on the 23 cm band since inexpensive set-top boxes are available that cover that frequency range.

DTV operates on the same 6 MHz-wide channels used for analog TV. However, instead of each channel slot carrying an analog NTSC television signal (visual carrier, color subcarrier and aural carrier), the channel slot carries an 8-VSB digitally modulated signal. The 6 MHz-wide over-the-air channel slots themselves didn't change, just the signals carried in them! So, channel 2 is still 54-60 MHz, channel 3 is 60-66 MHz, and so forth, up to channel 51. Channels 2-6 have largely been abandoned in the US as stations moved to broadcast digital TV on UHF channels. UHF channels 52-69 will be reallocated to other uses.

The designation "8-VSB" refers to 8-level vestigial sideband modulation. This is similar to 256-QAM, which means 256-state *quadrature amplitude modulation* — the 256 "states" are 256 combinations of signal phase

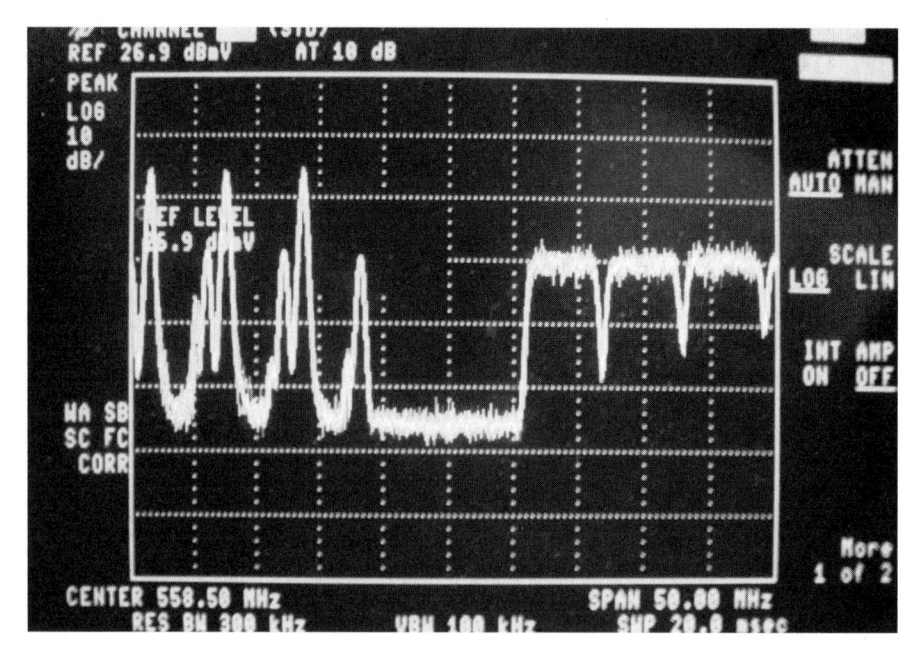

Figure 11.36 — The spectrum of three analog NTSC TV channels (left of center) and three QAM signals (right of center). The digital channel power of the QAM "haystacks" is about 6 dB below the analog visual carrier PEP.

and amplitude values that represent the 256 different transmitted symbols — a digital format used in cable TV networks (64-QAM is also used by cable companies). In the case of 8-VSB, the "8" refers to the eight-level baseband DTV signal that amplitude modulates an IF signal. For more info about 8-VSB modulation, see the online article, "What Exactly Is 8-VSB Anyway?" by David Sparano at **www.arrl.org/files/file/ Technology/TV_Channels/8_Bit_VSB. pdf** and other references at **www.arrl.org/ tv-channels-air-catv**.

The eight levels result in three bits per symbol, resulting in approximately 32 Mbits/second raw data rate with a 10.76 Mbaud symbol rate. The net data rate with error correction and other overhead is 19.39 Mbits/second. The DTV signal fits into the same 6 MHz channel as analog TV.

Digitally modulated signals used to transport video — whether 8-VSB for over-the-air or 64-QAM or 256-QAM in cable networks — are noise-like signals over their 6 MHz bandwidth. If a digital TV signal interferes with analog radio communications such as FM or SSB, the effect is similar to degraded signal-to-noise ratio. Indeed, a digital TV signal can be thought of as a 6 MHz wide "pile of noise." On a spectrum analyzer, it looks like a "haystack" as shown in **Figure 11.36**. Of course, the IF bandwidth of the amateur receiver is quite narrow relative to the 6 MHz-wide digital TV channel, so the actual noise level seen by the receiver (assuming no overload or IMD problems) will in part be determined by the receiver's IF bandwidth. Still, the effect on the

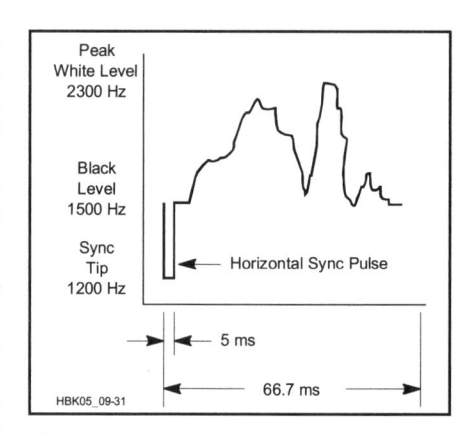

Figure 11.37 — The basic 8-second black and white transmission format developed by early SSTV experimenters. The sync pulses are "blacker than black" to blank the signal during retrace. A complete frame has 120 lines (8 seconds at 15 lines per second). Horizontal sync pulses occur at the beginning of every line; a 30-ms vertical sync pulse precedes each frame.

receiver is what amounts to an elevated noise floor, similar to the effects of wide-spectrum broadband noise.

11.7.2 Slow-Scan Television

Despite its name, so-called *slow-scan television* (SSTV) is actually a method for sending still images, like facsimile. The original monochrome analog SSTV format illustrated in **Figure 11.37** takes approximately 8 seconds to send one complete frame. The 1500 to 2300-Hz frequency-modulated audio tone resembles that of a fax signal, but is sent at a faster rate and includes pulses at 1200 Hz for synchronization.

Color may be sent using any of several methods. The first to be used was the *frame-sequential* method, in which each of the three primary colors (red, green and blue) is sent sequentially, as a complete frame. That has the disadvantage that you have to wait for the third frame to begin before colors start to become correct, and any noise or interference is three times more likely to corrupt the image and risks ruining the image registration (the overlay of the frames) and thus spoil the picture.

In the *line-sequential* method, each line is electronically scanned three times: once each for red, green and blue. Pictures scan down the screen in full color as they are received and registration problems are reduced. The Wraase SC-1 modes are examples of early line-sequential color transmission. They have a horizontal sync pulse for each of the color component scans. The major weakness of this method is that if the receiving system gets out of step, it doesn't know which scan represents which color.

Rather than sending color images with the usual RGB (red, green, blue) components, Robot Research decided to use luminance and chrominance signals for their 1200C modes. The first half or two thirds of each scan line contains the luminance information, which is a weighted average of the R, G and B components. The remainder of each line contains the chrominance signal with the color information. Existing black-and-white equipment could display the B&W-compatible image on the first part of each scan line and the rest would go off the edge of the screen. That compatibility was very beneficial when most people still had only B&W equipment.

The luminance-chrominance encoding makes more efficient use of the transmission time. A 120-line color image can be sent in 12 seconds, rather than the usual 24. Our eyes are more sensitive to details in changes of brightness than color, so the time is used more efficiently by devoting more time to luminance than chrominance. The NTSC and PAL broadcast standards also take advantage of this vision characteristic and use less bandwidth for the color part of the signal. For SSTV, luminance-chrominance encoding offers some benefits, but image quality suffers. It is acceptable for most natural images but looks bad for sharp, high-contrast edges, which are more and more common as images are altered via computer graphics. As a result, all newer modes have returned to RGB encoding.

The 1200C introduced another innovation, called *vertical interval signaling* (VIS). It encodes the transmission mode in the vertical sync interval. By using narrow FSK encoding around the sync frequency, compatibility is maintained. This new signal just looks like an extra-long vertical sync to older equipment.

The Martin and Scottie modes are essentially the same except for the timings. They have a single horizontal sync pulse for each set of RGB scans. Therefore, the receiving end can easily get back in step if synchronization is temporarily lost. Although they have horizontal sync, some implementations ignore them on receive. Instead, they rely on very accurate time bases at the transmitting and receiving stations to keep in step. The advantage of this "synchronous" strategy is that missing or corrupted sync pulses won't disturb the received image. The disadvantage is that even slight timing inaccuracies produce slanted pictures.

In the late 1980s, yet another incompatible mode was introduced. The AVT mode is different from all the rest in that it has *no horizontal sync*. It relies on very accurate oscillators at the sending and receiving stations to maintain synchronization. If the beginning-of-frame sync is missed, it's all over. There is no way to determine where a scan line begins. However, it's much harder to miss the 5-s header than the 300-ms VIS code. Redundant information is encoded 32 times and a more powerful error-detection scheme is used. It's only necessary to receive a small part of the AVT header in order to achieve synchronization. After this, noise can wipe out parts of the image, but image alignment and colors remain correct.

Digital images may be sent over Amateur Radio using any of the standard digital modulation formats that support binary file transfer. *Digital SSTV* (DSSTV) is one method of transmitting computer image files, such as JPEG or GIF, as described in an article by Ralph Taggart, WB8DQT, in the Feb 2004 issue of *QST*. This format phase-modulates a total of eight subcarriers (ranging from 590 to 2200 Hz) at intervals of 230 Hz. Each subcarrier has nine possible modulation states. This signal modulation format is known as *redundant digital file transfer* (RDFT) developed by Barry Sanderson, KB9VAK.

Most digital SSTV transmission has switched to using Digital Radio Mondiale (DRM), derived from a system developed for shortwave digital voice broadcasting. The DRM digital SSTV signal occupies the bandwidth between 350 and 2750 Hz. As many as 57 subcarriers may be sent simultaneously, all at the same level. Three pilot carriers are sent at twice the level of the other subcarriers. The subcarriers are modulated using OFDM and QAM, which were described earlier in this chapter. DRM SSTV includes several methods of error correction.

11.8 Spread Spectrum Modulation

A *spread-spectrum* (SS) system is one that intentionally increases the bandwidth of a digital signal beyond that normally required by means of a special spreading code that is independent of the data sequence. There are several reasons for spreading the spectrum in that way.

Spread spectrum was first used in military systems, where the purpose was to encrypt the transmissions to make it harder for the enemy to intercept or jam them. Amateurs are not allowed to encrypt transmissions for the purpose of concealing the information, but reducing interference, intentional or otherwise, is an obvious benefit. The signal is normally spread in such a fashion that it appears like random noise to a receiver not designed to receive it, so other users of the band may not even be aware that an SS signal is present.

Another advantage to spreading the spectrum is that it can make frequency accuracy less critical. In addition, the wide bandwidth means that expensive narrow-bandwidth filters are not required in the receiver. It also provides a measure of frequency diversity. If certain frequencies are unusable because of interference or selective fading, the signal can often be reconstructed using information in the rest of the bandwidth.

There are several ways to spread the spectrum — we will cover the two most common methods below — but they all share certain characteristics. Imagine that the unspread signal occupies a 10 kHz bandwidth and it is spread by a factor of 100. The resulting SS signal is 1000 kHz (1 MHz) wide. Each 10-kHz channel contains 1/100 of the total signal power, or –20 dB. That means that any narrowband stations using one of those 10-kHz channels experience a 20 dB reduction in interference, but also are more likely to be interfered with because of the 100-times greater bandwidth of the SS station's emissions.

How is the spread-spectrum station affected by interference from narrowband stations? In effect, the SS receiver attenuates the signal received on each 10 kHz channel by 20 dB in order to obtain a full-power signal when all 100 channels are added together. That means that the interference from a narrowband station is reduced by 20 dB but, again, the interference is more likely to occur because of the 100-times greater bandwidth of the SS station's receiver.

How is the spread-spectrum station affected by interference from another SS station on the same frequency? It turns out that if the other station is using a different orthogonal spreading code then, once again, the interference reduction is 20 dB for 100-times spreading. That means that many SS stations can share the same channel without interference as long as they are all received at roughly the same signal level. Commercial mobile-telephone SS networks use an elaborate system of power control with real-time feedback to ensure that the signals from all the mobile stations arrive at the base station at approximately the same level.

That scheme works well in a one-to-many (base station to mobile stations) system architecture but would be much more difficult to implement in a typical amateur many-to-many arrangement because of the different distances and thus path losses between each pair of stations in the network. On the HF bands it is not uncommon to see differences in signal levels of 80 to 90 dB or more. (For example, the difference between S1 and 40 dB over S9 is 88 dB, assuming 6 dB per S-unit.) A spread spectrum signal at S9 + 40 dB with a spreading ratio of 100 times would interfere with any other signals below about S9 + 20 dB. It works the same in the other direction as well. The SS signal would experience interference from any other stations that are more than 20 dB louder than the desired signal.

Normally, increasing the bandwidth of a transmission degrades the signal-to-noise (S/N) ratio at the receiver. A 100-times greater bandwidth contains 100 times as much noise, which causes a 20 dB reduction in S/N ratio. However SS receivers benefit from a phenomenon known as processing gain. Just as the receiver is insensitive to other SS signals with different orthogonal spreading codes, so it is insensitive to random noise. The improvement in S/N ratio due to processing gain is:

Processing gain =
$$10 \times \log\left(\frac{\text{spread bandwidth}}{\text{unspread bandwidth}}\right) \text{dB}$$

That is exactly equal to the reduction in S/N ratio due to the increased bandwidth. The net result is that an SS signal has neither an advantage nor a disadvantage in signal-to-noise ratio compared to the unspread version of the same signal. When someone states that, because of processing gain, an SS receiver can receive signals that are below the noise level (signals that have a negative S/N ratio), that is a true statement. However, it does not imply better S/N performance than could be obtained if the signal were not spread.

11.8.1 Frequency Hopping Spread Spectrum

One simple way to spread the spectrum

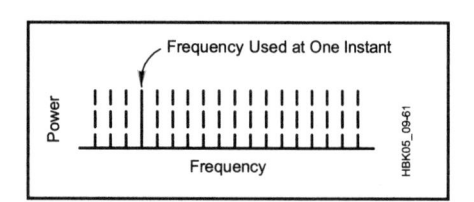

Figure 11.38 — Power versus frequency for a frequency-hopping spread spectrum signal. Emissions jump around to discrete frequencies in pseudo-random fashion. Normally the spacing of the frequencies is approximately equal to the bandwidth of the unspread signal so that the average spectrum is approximately flat.

of a narrowband signal is to repetitively sweep it across the frequency range of the wider spectrum, either continuously or in a series of steps at discrete frequencies. That technique, called *chirp modulation*, can be considered a special case of *frequency-hopping spread spectrum* (FHSS), in which the narrowband signal covers the expanded spectrum by rapidly hopping back and forth from frequency to frequency in a pseudo-random manner. On average, each frequency is used the same percentage of time so that the average spectrum is flat across the bandwidth of the FHSS signal. See **Figure 11.38**.

If the receiver hops in step with the transmitter, using the same pseudo-random sequence synchronized to the one in the transmitter, then the transmitter and receiver are always tuned to the same frequency and the receiver's detector sees a continuous, non-hopped narrowband signal which can be demodulated in the normal way. We say that the signal has been *de-spread*, that is, returned to its normal narrowband form. Synchronization between the receiver and transmitter is one of the challenges in an FHSS system. If the timing of the two sequences differs by even one hop, then the receiver is always tuned to the wrong frequency, unless the same frequency happens to occur twice in succession in the pseudo-random sequence. Any signal with an unsynchronized sequence, or with a different sequence, is reduced in amplitude by the processing gain.

There are two types of FHSS based on the rate at which the frequency hops take place. *Slow-frequency hopping* refers to a hop rate slower than the baud rate. Several symbols are sent per hop. With *fast-frequency hopping*, the hop rate is faster than the baud rate. Several hops occur during each symbol. The term *chip* refers to the shortest-duration modulation state in the system. For slow-frequency hopping, that is the baud rate. For fast-frequency hopping it is the hop rate. Fast-

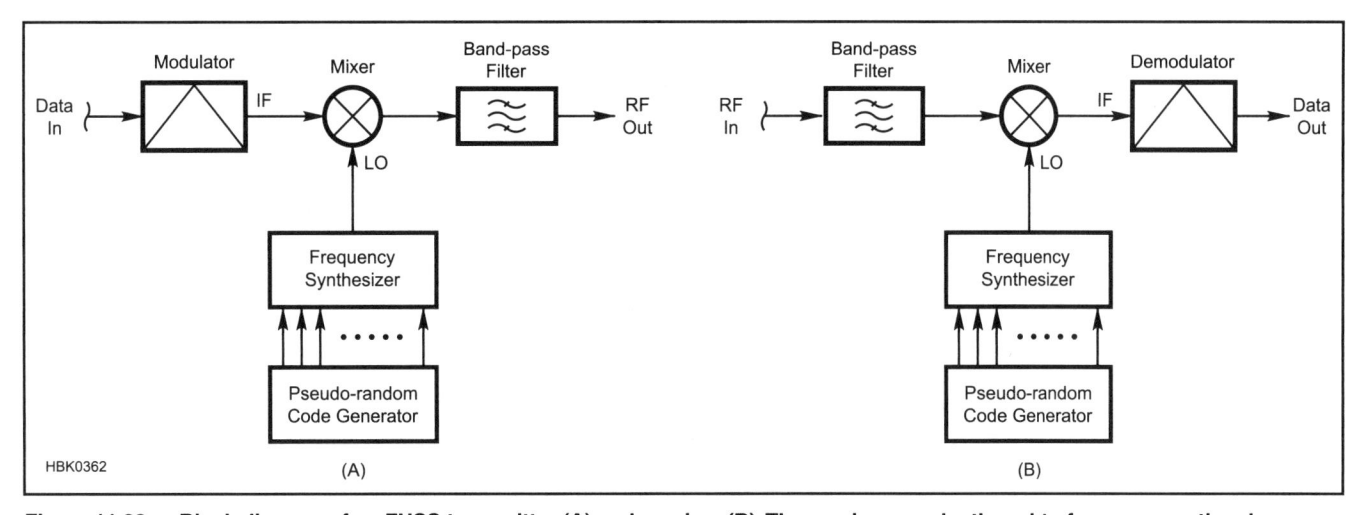

Figure 11.39 — Block diagram of an FHSS transmitter (A) and receiver (B). The receiver may be thought of as a conventional superhet with a local oscillator (LO) that is continually hopping its frequency in response to a pseudo-random code generator. The transmitter has a similar architecture to up-convert a conventionally-modulated intermediate frequency (IF) to a frequency-hopped radio frequency (RF).

frequency hopping can be useful in reducing the effects of multi-path propagation. If the hop period is less than the typical time delay of secondary propagation paths, then those signals are uncorrelated to the main path and are attenuated by the processing gain.

A diagram of a frequency-hopping spread spectrum system is shown in **Figure 11.39**. In both the transmitter and the receiver, a pseudo-random code generator controls a frequency synthesizer to hop between frequencies in the correct order. In this way, the narrowband signal is first spread by the transmitter, then sent over the radio channel, and finally de-spread at the receiver to obtain the original narrowband signal again. One issue with FHSS is that many synthesizers do not maintain phase coherence over successive frequency hops. That means the basic (non-spread) modulation must be a type that does not depend on phase information. That rules out PSK, QPSK and QAM. That is the reason that modulation types that do not depend on phase, such as FSK and MFSK with non-coherent detection, are frequently used as the base modulation type in FHSS systems.

11.8.2 Direct Sequence Spread Spectrum

Whereas an FHSS system hops through a pseudo-random sequence of frequencies to spread the signal, a *direct-sequence spread spectrum* (DSSS) system applies the pseudo-random sequence directly to the data in order to spread the signal. See **Figure 11.40**. The binary data is considered to be in *polar* form, that is, the two possible states of each bit are represented by −1 and +1. The data bits are multiplied by a higher-bit-rate pseudo-random sequence, also in polar form, which chops the data into smaller time increments called *chips*. The ratio of the chip rate to the data's bit rate equals the ratio of the spread bandwidth to the unspread bandwidth, which is just the processing gain:

Processing gain =
$$10 \times \log\left(\frac{\text{chip rate}}{\text{bit rate}}\right) \text{dB}$$

Although it doesn't have to, DSSS normally uses a one-bit-per-symbol modulation type such as BPSK. In that case, the modulator and demodulator in Figure 11.40 would consist simply of a mixer, which multiplies the RF local oscillator by the bipolar DSSS modulating signal. Since unfiltered BPSK is constant-envelope, a nonlinear class-C power amplifier may be used for high efficiency. The demodulator in the receiver would also be a mixer, which multiplies the RF signal by a local oscillator to regenerate the DSSS modulating signal. Not shown are additional mixers and filters that would be used in a superheterodyne receiver to convert the received signal to an intermediate frequency before demodulation and decoding.

The unfiltered spectrum has the form of a sinc function. That shows up clearly in the spectrum of an actual DSSS signal in **Figure 11.41A**, which is plotted on a logarithmic scale calibrated in decibels. The humps in the response to the left and right (and additional ones not shown off scale) are not needed for communications and should be filtered out to avoid excessive occupied bandwidth. Figure 11.41B shows the DSSS signal in the presence of noise at the input to the receiver, and Figure 11.41C illustrates the improvement in signal-to-noise ratio of the de-spread narrowband signal.

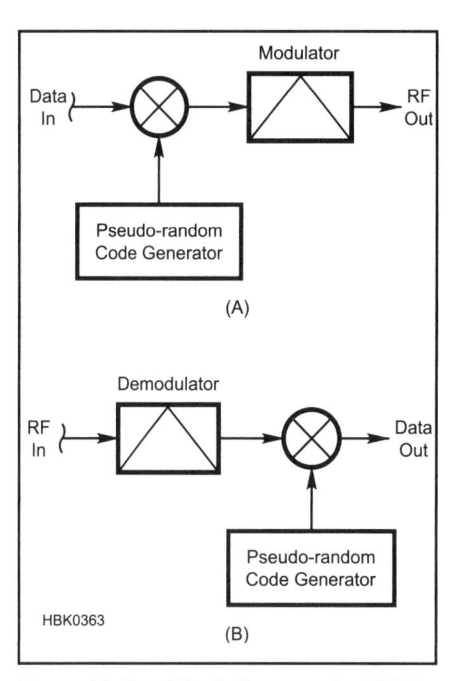

Figure 11.40 — Block diagram of a DSSS transmitter (A) and receiver (B). For BPSK modulation, the modulation has the same format as the bipolar data (±1), so the modulator and demodulator could be moved to the other side of the multiplier if desired.

11.8.3 Code-Division Multiple-Access (CDMA)

As mentioned before, to receive an SS signal, the de-spreading sequence in the receiver must match the spreading sequence in the transmitter. The term *orthogonal* refers to two sequences that are coded in such a way that they are completely uncorrelated. The receiver's response to an orthogonal

Modulation 11.23

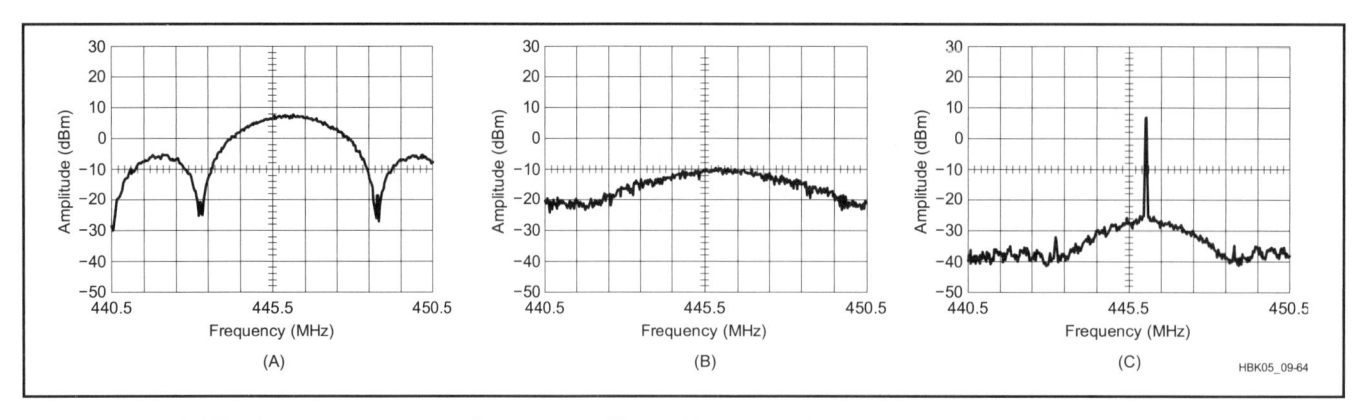

Figure 11.41 — (A) The frequency spectrum of an actual unfiltered biphase-modulated spread spectrum signal as viewed on a spectrum analyzer. In this practical system, band-pass filtering is used to confine the spread spectrum signal to the amateur band. (B) At the receiver end of the line, the filtered spread spectrum signal is apparent only as a 10-dB hump in the noise floor. (C) The signal at the output of the receiver de-spreader. The original carrier — and any modulation components that accompany it — has been recovered. The peak carrier is about 45 dB above the noise floor — more than 30 dB above the hump shown at B. (These spectrograms were made at a sweep rate of 0.1 s/division and an analyzer bandwidth of 30 kHz; the horizontal scale is 1 MHz/division.)

code is the same as to random noise, that is, it is suppressed by a factor equal to the processing gain. One can take advantage of this property to allow multiple SS stations to access the same frequency simultaneously, a technique known as *code-division multiple access* (CDMA). Each transmitter is assigned a different orthogonal code. A receiver can "tune in" any transmitter's signal by selecting the correct code for de-spreading.

If multiple stations want to be able to transmit simultaneously without using spread spectrum, they must resort to either *frequency-division multiple access* (FDMA), where each station transmits on a different frequency channel, or *time-division multiple access* (TDMA), where each transmission is broken up into short time slots which are interleaved with the time slots of the other stations. Compared to TDMA, CDMA has the advantage that it does not require an external synchronization network to make sure that different stations' time slots do not overlap. Compared to both TDMA and FDMA, CDMA has the further advantage that it experiences a gradual degradation in performance as the number of stations on the channel increases. It is relatively easy to add new users to the system. Also CDMA has inherent resistance to interference due to multi-path propagation or intentional jamming. The primary disadvantages of CDMA are the relative complexity and the necessity for accurate power-level control to make sure that unwanted signals do not exceed the level that can be rejected through processing gain.

11.9 Pulse Modulation

Another type of digital amplitude modulation comes under the general category of *pulse modulation*. The RF signal is broken up into a series of pulses, which are usually equally-spaced in time and separated by periods of no signal. We will discuss three types of pulse modulation, PAM, PWM and PPM.

Pulse-amplitude modulation (PAM) consists of a series of pulses of varying amplitude that correspond directly to the amplitude of the modulating signal. See **Figure 11.42B**. The pulses can be positive or negative, depending on the polarity of the signal. The modulating signal can be recovered simply by low-pass filtering the pulse train. The effect of the negative pulses is to reverse the polarity of the RF signal. The result is very similar to a double-sideband, suppressed-carrier signal that is rapidly turned on and off at the pulse rate of the PAM. In other words, the DSBSC signal is periodically sampled at a certain pulse repetition rate.

For the signal to be properly represented, its highest modulating frequency must be less than the *Nyquist frequency*, which is one-half the sample rate. That condition, known as the *Nyquist criterion*, applies not only to PAM but to any digital modulation technique.

There are two variations of PAM that should be mentioned. *Natural sampling* does not hold the amplitude of each pulse constant throughout the pulse as shown in Figure 11.42B, but rather follows the shape of the analog modulation. The *single-polarity method* adds a fixed offset, or pedestal, to the modulating signal before the PAM modulator. As long as the pedestal is greater than or equal to the peak negative modulation, then the RF phase never changes and the signal is equivalent to sampled full-carrier AM rather than DSB-SC.

PAM is rarely used on the amateur bands because it increases the transmitted bandwidth and adds circuit complexity with no improvement in signal-to-noise ratio for most types of noise and interference. The concept is useful, however, because PAM is similar to the signal generated by the sample-and-hold circuit that is used at the input to an analog-to-digital converter (ADC). An ADC is used in virtually every digital transmitter to convert the analog voice signal to a digital signal suitable for digital signal processing.

Pulse-width modulation (PWM) is a series of pulses whose width varies in proportion to the amplitude of the modulating signal. Figure 11.42C shows the pulses centered on the sample times, but in some systems the sample times may correspond to the leading or trailing pulse edges. With either method, the modulating signal can be recovered by low-pass filtering the pulse train and passing it through a coupling capacitor to remove the dc component.

Pulse-position modulation (PPM), Figure 11.42D, varies the position, or phase, of the pulses in proportion to the amplitude of the modulating signal. With both PWM and PPM, the peak amplitude of the signal is constant. That allows the receiver to be designed to be insensitive to amplitude variations, which can result in a better post-detection signal-to-noise ratio, in a manner similar to analog angle modulation.

Figure 11.42 — Three types of pulse-code modulation. A sine-wave modulating signal (A) is shown at the top. Pulse-amplitude modulation (B) varies the amplitude of the pulses, pulse-width modulation (C) varies the pulse width, and pulse-position modulation (D) varies the pulse position, proportional to the modulating signal. The tic marks show the nominal pulse times. The RF signal is created by an AM modulator using (B), (C) or (D) as the modulating signal.

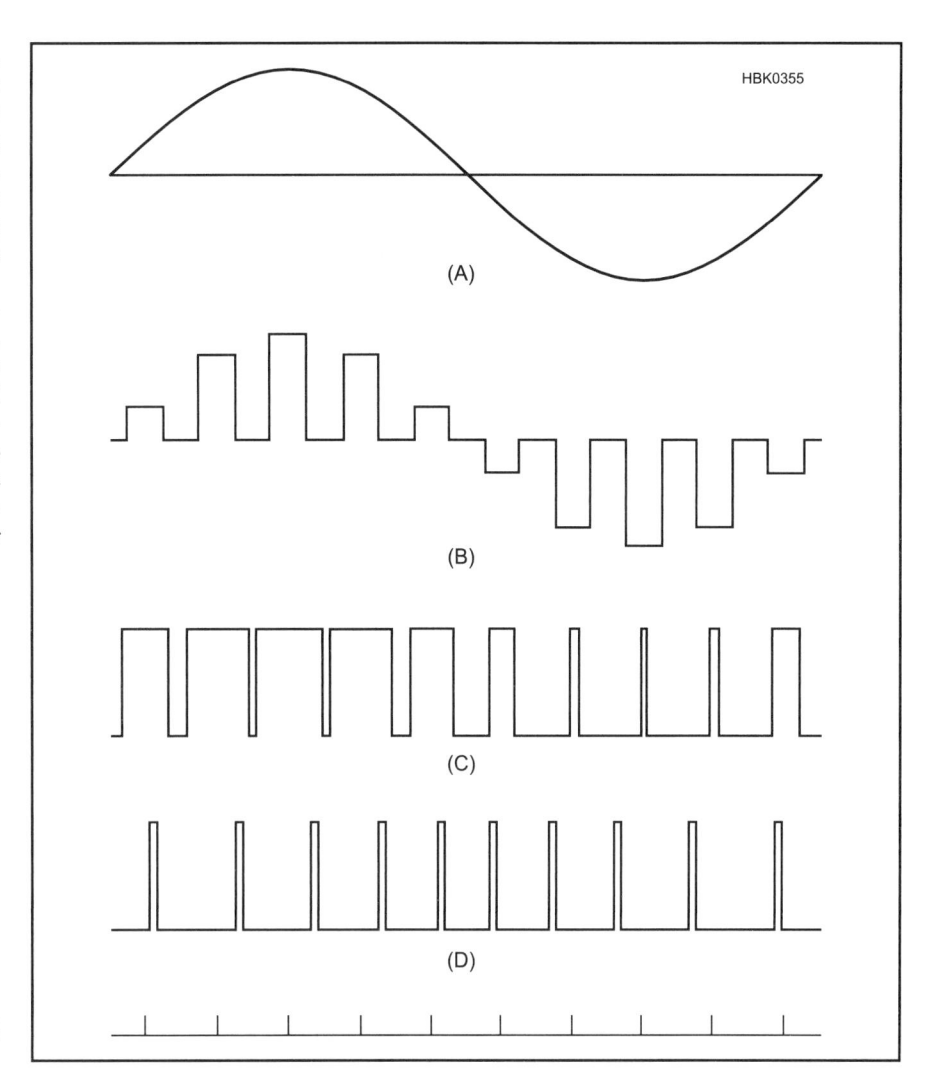

11.10 Modulation Bandwidth and Impairments

Most of the previous discussion of the various modulation types has assumed the modulation is perfect. With analog modulation, that means the audio or video modulating signal is perfectly reproduced in the RF waveform without distortion, spurious frequencies or other unwanted artifacts. With digital modulation, the symbol timing and the locations and trajectories in the I/Q constellation are perfectly accurate. In all cases, the RF power amplifier is perfectly linear, if so required by the modulation type, and it introduces no noise or other spurious signals close to the carrier frequency.

In the real world, of course, such perfection can never be achieved. Some modulation impairments are caused by the transmitting system, some by the transmission medium through which the signal propagates, and some in the receiving system. This section will concentrate on impairments caused by the circuitry in the transmitter and, to some extent, in the receiver. Signal impairments due to propagation are covered in detail in the **Propagation of Radio Signals** chapter.

11.10.1 Filtering and Bandwidth of Digital Signals

We have already touched on this topic in previous sections, but let us now cover it a little more systematically. The bandwidth required by a digital signal depends on the filtering of the modulation, the symbol rate and the type of modulation. For linear modulation types such as OOK, BPSK, QPSK and QAM, the bandwidth depends only on the symbol rate and the modulation filter.

As an example, an unfiltered BPSK modulating signal with alternating ones and zeroes for data (10101010...) is a square wave at one-half the symbol rate. Like any square wave, its spectrum can be broken down into a series of sine waves at the fundamental frequency (symbol rate / 2) and all the odd harmonics. If the data consists of alternating pairs of ones and pairs of zeroes (11001100...) then we have a square wave at one-fourth the symbol rate and the spectrum is a series of sine waves at one-fourth the symbol rate and all its odd harmonics. Random data contains energy at all frequencies from zero to half the symbol rate and all the odd harmonics of those frequencies. The harmonics are not needed for proper demodulation of the signal, so they can be filtered out with a low-pass filter with a cutoff frequency of one-half the symbol rate.

With random data, the shape of the unfiltered spectrum is a sinc function,

$$\text{sinc}(f / f_s) = \frac{\sin(\pi f / f_s)}{\pi f / f_s}$$

Modulation 11.25

where f_s is the symbol rate. See **Figure 11.43**. Note that the response is zero (minus infinity dB) whenever f is an integer multiple of the symbol rate. That is why multi-carrier modulation generally uses a carrier spacing equal to the symbol rate.

The previous discussion applies to the baseband signal, before it modulates the RF carrier. BPSK is a double-sideband-type modulation so the baseband spectrum appears above and below the RF carrier frequency, doubling the bandwidth to 2 × (symbol rate / 2) = symbol rate. In reality, since no practical filter has an infinitely-sharp cutoff, the occupied bandwidth of a BPSK signal must be somewhat greater than the symbol rate. That is also true for all other double-sideband linear modulation types, such as OOK and the various forms of QPSK and QAM.

If the low-pass filtering is not done properly, it may slow down the transition between symbols to the point where one symbol starts to run into another, causing *inter-symbol interference* (ISI). A type of filter that avoids that problem is called a *Nyquist filter*. It ensures that each symbol's contribution to the modulating signal passes through zero at the center of all other symbols, so that no ISI occurs. The most common type of Nyquist filter is the *raised-cosine* filter, so-called because the frequency response (plotted on a linear scale) in the passband-to-stopband transition region follows a raised-cosine curve. See **Figure 11.44**. The sharpness of the frequency cutoff is specified by a parameter called *alpha*. If alpha is 1.0, then the transition from passband to stopband is very gradual — it starts to roll off right at zero hertz and finally reaches zero response at two times the nominal cutoff frequency. An alpha of 0.0 specifies an ideal "brick-wall" filter that transitions instantaneously from full response to zero right at the cutoff frequency. Values in the range of 0.3 to 0.5 are common in communications systems.

Unfortunately, if any additional filter is placed before or after the Nyquist filter it destroys the anti-ISI property. In order to allow filtering in both the transmitter and the receiver many systems effectively place half the Nyquist filter in each place. Because the frequency response of each filter is the square root of the response of a Nyquist filter, they are called *root-Nyquist* filters. The *root-raised-cosine* filter is an example. While a Nyquist or root-Nyquist response theoretically could be approximated with an analog filter, they are almost always implemented as digital filters. More information on digital filters appears in the **DSP and SDR Fundamentals** and the **Analog and Digital Filtering** chapters.

As mentioned before, filtering is more difficult with angle modulation because it is nonlinear. The RF spectrum is not a linear transposition of the baseband spectrum as it is with linear modes and Nyquist filtering doesn't work. Old-fashioned RTTY transmitters traditionally just used an R-C low-pass filter to slow down the transitions between mark and space. While that does not limit the bandwidth to the minimum value possible, the baud rate is low enough that the resulting bandwidth is acceptable anyway. In more modern systems, there is a tradeoff between making the filter bandwidth as narrow as possible for interference reduction and widening the bandwidth to reduce inter-symbol interference. For example, the GSM (Global System for Mobile communications) standard, used for some cellular telephone systems, uses minimum-shift keying and a Gaussian filter with a BT (bandwidth symbol-time product) of 0.3. A 0.3 Gaussian filter has a 0.3 ratio of 3-dB bandwidth to baud rate, which results in a small but acceptable amount of ISI and a moderate amount of adjacent-channel interference.

CHANNEL CAPACITY

It is possible to increase the quantity of error-free data that can be transmitted over a communications channel by using an error-correcting code. That involves adding additional error-correction bits to the transmitted data. The more bits that are added, the greater the errors that can be corrected. However, the extra bits increase the data rate, which requires additional bandwidth, which increases the amount of noise. For that reason, as you add more and more error-correction bits, requiring more and more bandwidth, you eventually reach a point of limited additional return. In the 1940s, Claude Shannon worked out a formula (called the *Shannon-Hartley theorem*) for the maximum capacity possible over a communications channel, assuming a theoretically-perfect error-correction code:

$$C = B \log_2 \left(1 + \frac{S}{N}\right) \text{bit/s}$$

where
- C = the net channel capacity, not including error-correcting bits,
- B = the bandwidth in Hz, and
- S/N = the signal-to-noise ratio, expressed as a power ratio.

Note that as B increases, N increases in the same proportion. **Figure 11.45** is a plot of channel capacity versus bandwidth based on the formula. As bandwidth is increased, channel capacity increases rapidly until the point where the S/N ratio drops to unity (labeled Bandwidth = 1 in the graph) after which channel capacity increases much more slowly.

11.10.2 Intermodulation Distortion

To minimize distortion of the modulation, each stage in the signal chain must be linear,

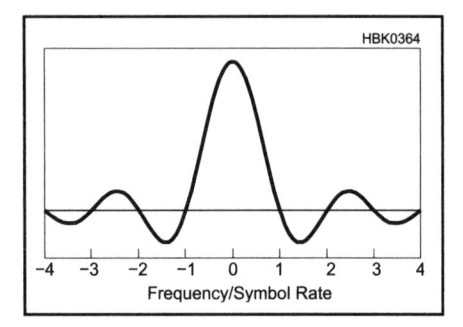

Figure 11.43 — The sinc function, which is the spectrum of an unfiltered BPSK modulating signal with random data, plotted with a linear vertical scale. The center (zero) point corresponds to the RF carrier frequency. To see what the double-sided RF spectrum looks like on a logarithmic (dB) scale, see Figure 11.41A.

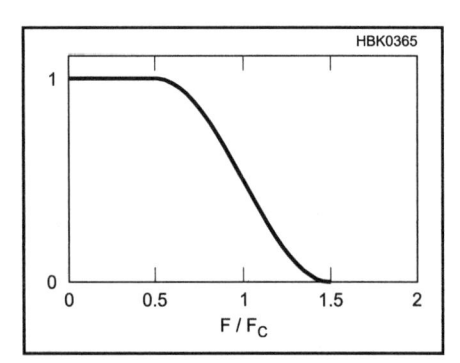

Figure 11.44 — Amplitude versus frequency for a 0.5-alpha, raised-cosine filter. The vertical scale is linear, not logarithmic as would be seen on a spectrum analyzer. The amplitude is 0.5 (–6 dB) at the cutoff frequency, Fc. The amplitude is 1.0 for frequencies less than Fc × (1 – alpha) and is 0.0 for frequencies above Fc × (1 + alpha).

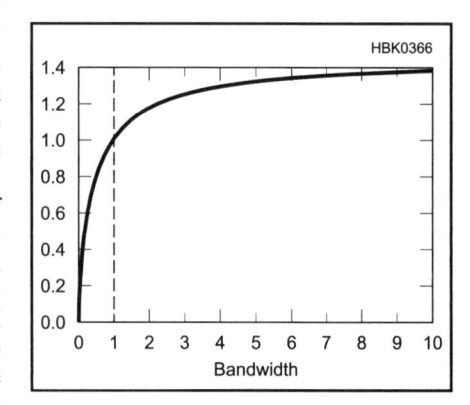

Figure 11.45 — Plot of channel capacity versus bandwidth, calculated by the Shannon-Hartley theorem. The S/N ratio has been selected to be unity at Bandwidth = 1.

from the microphone or modem, through all the intermediate amplifiers and processors, to the modulator itself. For the linear modulation types, all the amplifiers and other stages between the modulator and the antenna must be linear as well.

If the modulation consists of a single sine wave, then nonlinearity causes only harmonic distortion, which produces new frequencies at integer multiples of the sine-wave frequency. If multiple frequencies are present in the modulation, however, then *intermodulation distortion* (IMD) products are produced. IMD occurs when a nonlinear amplifier or other device acts as a mixer, producing sum and difference frequencies of all the pairs of frequencies and their harmonics. For example if two frequencies, F1 and F2 > F1, are present, then IMD will cause spurious frequencies to appear at F1 + F2, F2 – F1, 2F1, 2F2, 2F1 – F2, 2F2 – F1, 2F2 – 2F1, 3F1, 3F2, and so on. *Odd-order* products are those that include the original frequencies an odd number of times, such as 3F1, 2F1 + F2, 3F1 – 2F2, and so on. *Even-order* products contain an even number of the original frequencies, such as 2F2, F1 + F2, 3F1 + F2, and so on. If more than two frequencies are present in the undistorted modulation, then the number of unwanted frequencies increases exponentially.

Although intermodulation distortion that occurs before modulation is fundamentally the same as IMD that occurs after the modulator (at the intermediate or radio frequency), the effects are quite different. Consider two frequency components of a modulating signal at, for example, 1000 Hz and 1200 Hz that modulate an SSB transmitter tuned to 14.000 MHz, USB. The desired RF signal has components at 14.001 and 14.0012 MHz. If the IMD occurs before modulation, then the F1 + F2 distortion product occurs at 1000 + 1200 = 2200 Hz. Since that is well within the audio passband of the SSB transmitter, there is no way to filter it out so it shows up at 14.0022 MHz at the RF output. However, if the distortion had occurred after the modulator, the F1 + F2 product would be at 14.001 + 14.0012 = 28.0022 MHz which is easily filtered out by the transmitter's low-pass filter.

That explains why RF speech processors work better than audio processors. A speech processor clips or limits the peak amplitude of the modulating signal to prevent over-modulation in the transmitter. However, the limiting process typically produces considerable intermodulation distortion. If the limiter is located after the modulator rather than before it, then it is an RF signal being clipped, rather than audio. If the RF limiter is followed by a band-pass filter then many of the distortion products are removed, resulting in a less-distorted signal.

If the distortion is perfectly symmetrical (for example equal clipping of positive and negative peaks) then only odd-order products are produced. Most distortion is not symmetrical so that both even and odd-order products appear. However, the odd-order products are of particular interest when measuring the linearity of an RF power amplifier. The reason is that even-order products that occur after the modulator occur only near harmonics of the RF frequency where they are easy to filter out. Odd-order products can fall within the desired channel, where they cause distortion of the modulation, or at nearby frequencies, where they cause interference to other stations.

The informal term for such IMD that interferes with other stations outside the desired channel is *splatter*. It becomes severe if the linear amplifier is over-driven, which causes clipping of the modulation envelope with the resulting odd-order IMD products.

The method commonly used to test the linearity of an SSB transmitter or RF power amplifier is the *two-tone test*. Two equal-amplitude audio-frequency tones are fed into the microphone input, the transmitter and/or amplifier is adjusted for the desired power level, and the output signal is observed on a spectrum analyzer. See **Figure 11.46**. The third-order products that occur near the desired signal are at 2F1 – F2 and 2F2 – F1. The fifth-order products occur at 3F1 – 2F2 and 3F2 – 2F1. If, for example, the two tones are spaced 1 kHz apart, then the two third-order products show up at 1 kHz above the high tone and 1 kHz below the low tone. The fifth-order products are at 2 kHz above and below the high and low tones respectively.

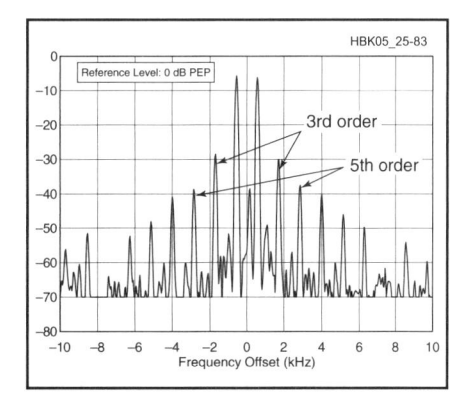

Figure 11.46 — Intermodulation products from an SSB transmitter. The two signals at the center are the desired frequencies. The frequencies of the third-order products are separated from the frequencies of the desired tones by the tone spacing. The fifth-order frequencies are separated by two times the tone spacing, and so on for higher-order products.

11.10.3 Transmitted Bandwidth

We have already discussed the necessary bandwidth for each of the various modulation types. The previous section explained how intermodulation distortion is one phenomenon that can cause unwanted emissions outside of the desired communications channel. Another is failing to properly low-pass filter the modulating signal to the minimum necessary bandwidth. That is especially a concern for linear modulation modes such as SSB, AM, OOK (CW), BPSK and QAM. For angle-modulated modes like FM and FSK, excessive bandwidth can result from simply setting the deviation too high.

There are other modulation impairments that cause emissions outside the desired bandwidth. For example, in an SSB transmitter, if the unwanted sideband is not sufficiently suppressed, the occupied bandwidth is up to twice as large as it should be. Also, an excessively strong suppressed carrier causes particularly-annoying heterodyne interference to stations tuned near that frequency. In some SSB modulators, there is an adjustment provided to optimize carrier suppression.

The carrier suppression may be degraded by a modulating signal that is too low in amplitude. For example, if the signal from the microphone to an SSB transmitter is one-tenth (–20 dB) of the proper amplitude, and if the gain of the RF amplifier stages is increased to compensate, then the carrier suppression is degraded by 20 dB.

The term *adjacent-channel power* (ACP) refers to the amount of transmitted power that falls into an adjacent communications channel above or below the desired channel. Normally the unwanted out-of channel power is worse for the immediately-adjacent channels than for those that are two channels away, the so-called *alternate* channels. ACP is normally specified as a power ratio in dB. It is measured with a spectrum analyzer that can measure the total power within the desired channel and the total power in an adjacent channel, so that the dB difference can be calculated.

The *occupied bandwidth* is the bandwidth within which a specified percentage of the total power occurs. A common percentage used is 99%. For a properly-adjusted, low-distortion transmitting system, the occupied bandwidth is determined mainly by the modulation type and filtering and, in the case of digital modulation, the symbol rate. For example, the IS-54 TDMA format that has been used in some US digital cellular networks has about 30 kHz occupied bandwidth using 24.3-kilosymbols/sec, π/4-DQPSK modulation with a 0.35-alpha root-raised-cosine filter. The GSM cellular standard requires about a 350-kHz occupied bandwidth for its 270.833-kilosymbols/sec, 0.3 Gaussian-filtered MSK signal.

11.10.4 Modulation Accuracy

For analog modes, modulation accuracy is mainly a question of maintaining the proper frequency response across the desired bandwidth with minimal distortion and unwanted signal artifacts. In-band artifacts like noise and spurious signals should not be a problem with any reasonably-well-designed system. Maintaining modulation peaks near 100% for AM signals or the proper deviation for FM signals is facilitated by an audio compressor. It can be either the type that uses a detector and an automatic-gain-control feedback loop to vary the gain in the modulation path or a clipper-type compressor that limits the peak amplitude and then filters the clipped signal to remove the harmonics and intermodulation products that result. SSB transmitters can also use audio speech compression to maintain the proper peak power level although, as explained previously, clipping of the signal before it reaches the modulator can cause unacceptable distortion unless special techniques are used.

For digital signals, there are a number of other possible sources of modulation inaccuracy. For modes that use Nyquist filtering, the cutoff frequency and filter shape must be accurate to ensure no inter-symbol interference (ISI). Fortunately, that is easy to do with digital filters. However any additional filtering in the signal path can degrade the ISI. For example, most HF digital modes use an analog SSB transceiver to up-convert the signal from audio to RF for transmission and to down-convert from RF to audio again at the receiver end. The crystal filters used in the transmitter and receiver can significantly degrade group delay flatness, especially near the edges of the filter passband. That is why most HF digital modes use a bandwidth substantially less than a typical transceiver's passband and attempt to center the signal near the crystal filters' center frequency.

Distortion can also impair the proper decoding of digital signals, especially formats with closely-spaced symbols such as 256-QAM. Any "flat-topping" in the final amplifier causes the symbols at the outermost corners of the constellation to be closer together than they should be. The accuracy of the symbol clock is critical in formats like JT65 that integrate the detection process over a large number of symbols. Perhaps surprisingly, the clock rate on some inexpensive computer sound cards can be off on the order of a percent, which results in a similar error in symbol rate.

The modulation accuracy of an FSK signal is normally characterized by the frequency shift at the center of each symbol time, the point at which the receiver usually makes the decision of which symbol is being received. For other digital formats, the modulation accuracy is normally characterized by the amplitude and phase at the symbol decision points. Amplitude error is typically measured as a percentage of the largest symbol amplitude. The phase error is quoted in degrees. In both cases one can specify either the average RMS value or the peak error that was detected over the measurement period. Amplitude error is the most important consideration for modulation types such as BPSK where the information is encoded as an amplitude. For a constant-envelope format like MSK, phase error is a more important metric.

For formats like QPSK and QAM, both amplitude and phase are important in determining symbol location. A measurement that includes both is called *error vector magnitude* (EVM). It is the RMS average distance between the ideal symbol location

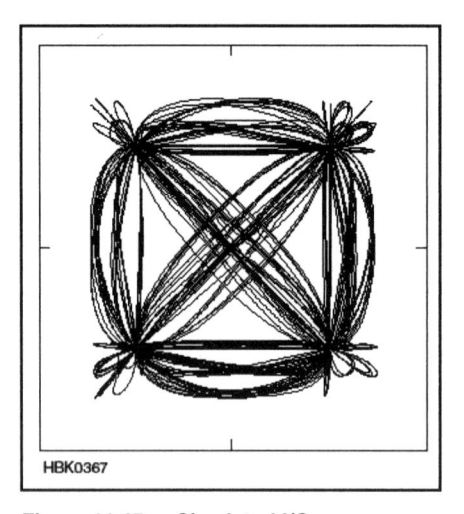

Figure 11.47 — Simulated I/Q constellation display of the trajectory of a QPSK signal over an extended period. A 0.5-alpha raised-cosine filter was used. Because it is a Nyquist filter, the trajectories pass exactly through each symbol location.

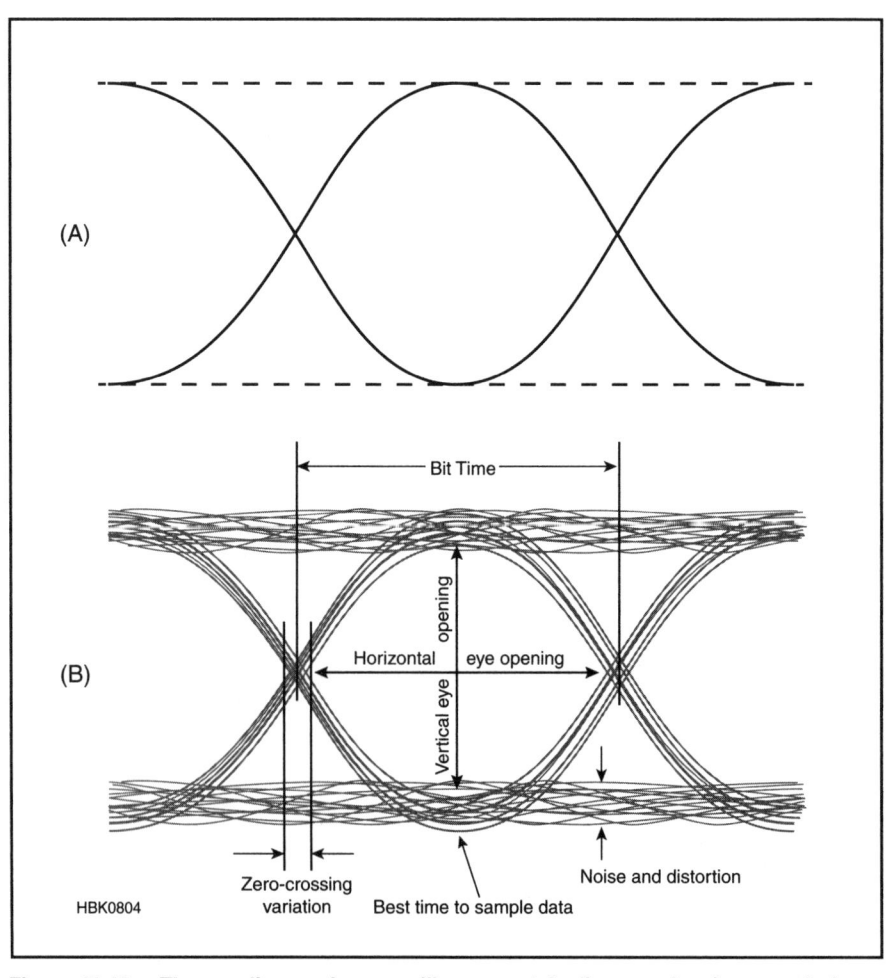

Figure 11.48 — The eye diagram is an oscilloscope-style diagram showing repeated samples of the digital signal as it transitions between points in the constellation. The eye diagram at A is for a perfect, undistorted signal. The eye diagram in B shows a signal with noise, distortion, and timing variations.

in the constellation diagram and the actual signal value at the symbol decision point, expressed as a percentage of either the RMS signal power or the maximum symbol amplitude. This is a measurement that requires specialized test equipment not generally available to home experimenters. However it is possible to estimate the effect on EVM of various design choices using computer simulations.

Previously, we have plotted constellation diagrams with the transitions between symbol locations indicated by straight lines. In an actual system, both the I and Q signals are low-pass filtered which makes the symbol transitions smoother, with no abrupt changes of direction at the symbol locations. **Figure 11.47** shows the actual symbol trajectories for a QPSK signal using a 0.5-alpha raised-cosine filter with random data. Since a raised-cosine is a type of Nyquist filter, the trajectories pass exactly through each symbol location. This is what you would see if you connected the I and Q outputs from a QPSK baseband generator to the X (horizontal) and Y (vertical) inputs of an oscilloscope. It is also what you would see in a receiver at the input to the symbol detector after the carrier and clock-recovery circuits have stabilized the signal. If the symbol trajectories were not accurate, then the dark areas at the symbol points would be less distinct and more spread out. Such a constellation diagram is also a good troubleshooting tool for other purposes, for example to check for amplitude distortion or to see if a faulty symbol encoder is missing some symbols or placing them at the wrong location.

In a system where a root-Nyquist filter is used in both the transmitter and receiver to obtain a net Nyquist response, the transmitter output will not display sharply defined symbol locations as in the figure. In that case, the measuring instrument must supply the missing root-Nyquist filter that is normally in the receiver, in order to obtain a clean display. Professional modulation analyzers normally include a means of selecting the proper matching filter.

Another way to view modulation accuracy is with an *eye diagram*. See **Figures 11.48** and **11.49**. In this case the oscilloscope's horizontal axis is driven by its internal sweep generator, triggered by the symbol clock. The two vertical channels of the oscilloscope are connected to the I and Q outputs of the baseband generator. The "eye" is the empty area at the center of the I and Q traces in between the symbol decision points, where all the traces come together. The eye should be as "open" as possible to make the job of the receiver's symbol decoder as easy as possible. The oscilloscope would typically be set for infinite persistence, so that the worst-case excursions from the ideal symbol trajectory are recorded. QPSK has four symbol locations, one in each quadrant, such that I and Q each only have two possible values and there is only one "eye" for each. 16-QAM has 16 symbol locations with four possible locations for I and Q, which forms three "eyes."

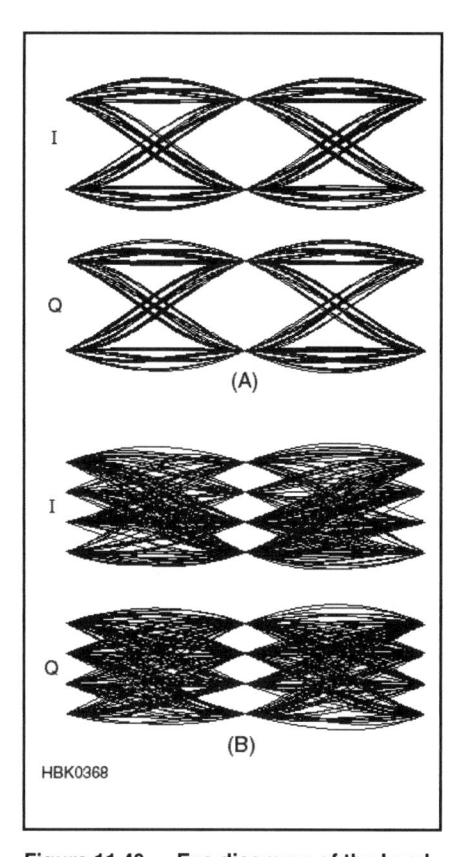

Figure 11.49 — Eye diagrams of the I and Q outputs of a QPSK generator (A) and a 16-QAM generator (B). The "eye" is the empty area between the symbol decision points, visible as the points where all the symbol trajectories come together. The bigger the "eye" the easier the signal is to decode.

11.11 Modulation Glossary

GENERAL

AM — Amplitude modulation.

Angle modulation — Modulation of an RF carrier by varying the phase or frequency.

Emission designator — Official ITU code to specify the bandwidth and modulation type of a radio transmission.

Frequency diversity — The use of a wideband signal to compensate for selective fading. While one band of frequencies is faded, the data can be reconstructed from other frequencies that are not faded.

FM — Frequency modulation.

IMD — Intermodulation distortion. Unwanted frequencies that occur at the sum and difference of the desired frequencies and their harmonics.

ITU — International Telecommunications Union. An agency of the United Nations that coordinates and recommends technical standards for electronic communications.

Modulation — The periodic alteration of some parameter of a carrier wave in order to transmit information.

PM — Phase modulation.

Protocol — A formal set of rules and procedures for the exchange of information within a communications network.

Selective fading — A propagation phenomenon in which closely-spaced frequencies experience markedly different fading at the same time.

Telemetry — The use of telecommunication for automatically indicating or recording measurements at a distance from the measuring instrument.

Telephony — A form of telecommunication primarily intended for the exchange of information in the form of speech.

Telegraphy — A form of telecommunication in which the transmitted information is intended to be recorded on arrival as a graphic document; the transmitted information may sometimes be presented in an alternative form or may be stored for subsequent use.

Television — A form of telecommunication for the transmission of transient images of fixed or moving objects.

AMPLITUDE AND ANGLE MODULATION (INCLUDING IMAGE)

ATV — Amateur fast-scan television.

BFO — Beat frequency oscillator. In an SSB or DSBSC receiver, the intermediate-frequency oscillator in the receiver that re-inserts the suppressed carrier.

Carson's rule — A rule of thumb to calculate FM bandwidth that says that 98% of the energy is typically contained within a bandwidth equal to two times the sum of the peak frequency deviation and the highest modulating frequency.

Capture effect — The tendency of the strongest signal to suppress other signals in an FM detector, which improves the signal-to-noise and signal-to-interference ratio.

Deviation ratio — The ratio of the maximum permitted peak deviation of an angle-modulated signal to the maximum permitted modulating frequency.

DSB-SC — Double sideband, suppressed carrier. An AM signal in which the carrier has been removed but both sidebands remain.

Frame — In television, one complete scanned image. On systems with interlaced scanning, there are two vertical scans per frame.

Frequency deviation — The amount the RF frequency of an angle-modulated signal deviates from the center (carrier) frequency in response to the modulating signal. The term is often understood to mean the maximum deviation available in a given system.

Limiter — A high-gain amplifier in an FM receiver that limits the peak amplitude of the signal in order to eliminate any AM component.

LSB — Lower sideband. An SSB signal with the upper sideband removed.

Martin — A series of analog SSTV formats, especially popular in Europe.

Modulation index (AM) — The ratio of the peak value of the modulation of an AM signal to the value that just causes the modulation envelope of the RF signal to reach zero on negative peaks and twice the average value on positive peaks.

Modulation index (FM) — The ratio of the peak deviation of an angle-modulated signal to the highest modulating frequency.

Narrowband FM — An FM signal with a modulation index less than or equal to 1.0.

NTSC — National Television System Committee. The analog television standard used in the US, Japan and several other countries.

PAL — Phase alteration line. The analog television standard used in many parts of Europe.

Phasing method — A method of generating an SSBSC signal that does not require a filter to remove the unwanted sideband.

Pixel — Picture element. The dots that make up images on a computer's monitor.

Product detector — A detector that multiplies a BFO signal with the received signal, typically SSB or DSBSC-modulated.

RGB — Red, green and blue. The three primary colors required to transmit a full-color image in many television and facsimile systems.

Scottie — A series of analog SSTV formats, especially popular in the US.

SSB — Single sideband. An AM signal in which one sideband has been removed. The term is usually understood to mean SSBSC.

SSB-SC — Single sideband, suppressed carrier. An AM signal in which one sideband and the carrier have been removed.

SSTV — Slow scan TV, a system for sending and receiving still images.

Sync — Modulation pulses used in ATV and SSTV to synchronize the horizontal and/or vertical scanning.

Synchronous detector — A type of AM detector in which the carrier is regenerated in the receiver.

Two-tone test — A procedure for testing the IMD of an SSB transmitter. Two equal-amplitude tones are fed to the microphone input and the transmitter RF output is examined with a spectrum analyzer to determine the amplitudes of the IMD products.

USB — Upper sideband. An SSB signal with the lower sideband removed.

Vestigial sideband — The filtering of all but the bottom MHz or so of the lower sideband of an ATV or NTSC television signal.

VIS — Vertical interval signaling. Digital encoding of the transmission mode during the vertical sync interval of an SSTV frame.

Wideband FM — An FM signal with a modulation index greater than 1.0.

DIGITAL MODULATION

AFSK — Audio FSK. The use of an SSB transceiver to transmit and receive FSK using an audio-frequency modem.

ASK — Amplitude-shift keying. Digital amplitude modulation in which the amplitude depends on the modulating code.

Baud — The rate at which a digital signal transitions between symbol states. Symbol rate. Symbols per second. Unit of symbol rate.

Bit rate — The total number of physically transferred bits per second over a communication link. Bit rate can be used interchangeably with **baud rate** only when each modulation transition carries exactly one bit of data.

BPSK — Binary PSK. PSK with only two possible states. The term is usually understood to mean a non-constant-envelope signal in which the two states differ by 180°.

Chirp — Incidental frequency modulation of a carrier as a result of oscillator instability during keying.

CW — Continuous wave. The term used for on-off keying using Morse code.

Constellation diagram — A diagram showing the constellation of possible symbol locations on a polar plot of modulation amplitude and phase.

DBPSK — Differential BPSK.

Decision point — The point, typically in the center of a symbol time, at which the receiver decides which symbol is being sent.

Differential modulation — A modulation technique that encodes the information in the difference between subsequent symbols, rather than in the symbols themselves.

Equalization — Correction for variations in amplitude and/or phase versus frequency across a communications channel.

DQPSK — Differential QPSK.

Eye diagram — An oscilloscope measurement of a digital modulating signal with the horizontal sweep synchronized to the symbol times. With Nyquist filtering, there should be a clear separation, or "eye", in the trajectories at the symbol decision points.

EVM — Error vector magnitude. A measure of the RMS error in the symbol locations at the symbol decision points in the constellation plot of a digital signal.

FFT — Fast Fourier transform. The Fourier transform is a mathematical function that calculates the frequency spectrum of a signal. The FFT is a software algorithm that does the calculations very efficiently.

FSK — Frequency-shift keying. A form of digital frequency modulation in which the frequency deviation depends on the modulating data.

GMSK — Gaussian MSK. MSK with a Gaussian modulation filter.

I/Q modulation — Quadrature modulation implemented with an I/Q modulator, one that uses in-phase (I) and quadrature (Q) modulating signals to generate the zero-degree and 90° components of the RF signal.

ISI — Inter-symbol interference. Interference of a signal with itself, caused when energy from one symbol is delayed long enough to interfere with a subsequent symbol.

MFSK — Multi-level FSK. FSK with more than two states represented by different frequency deviations.

Modem — Modulator/demodulator. A device that generates and demodulates digital modulation signals, usually at audio frequencies. It connects between the data terminal (usually a computer) and the radio.

MSK — Minimum-shift keying. A form of FSK with a frequency shift equal to one-half the symbol rate.

Nyquist criterion — A principle that states that the sampling frequency must be greater than twice the highest frequency in the sampled signal.

Nyquist frequency — One-half the sampling frequency.

OFDM — Orthogonal frequency-division multiplexing. A transmission mode that uses multiple carriers, spaced such that modulation on each carrier is orthogonal with the others.

OOK — On-off keying. A type of ASK with only two states, on and off.

OQPSK — Offset QPSK. By offsetting in time the symbol transitions of the I and Q channels, symbol trajectories through the origin are eliminated.

Orthogonal — Refers to streams of data that are uncorrelated with each other such that there is no mutual interference.

PAM — Pulse amplitude modulation. A type of pulse modulation where the modulating signal is encoded in the pulse amplitude.

π/4 DQPSK — PI-over-four differential QPSK. A form of differential 8PSK in which the only allowed transitions are ±45 and ±135°, resulting in four allowed states per symbol.

PPM — Pulse position modulation. A type of pulse modulation where the modulating signal is encoded in the pulse position.

PSK — Phase-shift keying. A form of digital phase modulation in which the phase of the RF signal depends on the modulating code. The term often is understood to refer to BPSK.

Pulse modulation — The modulating signal is sampled at regular intervals to generate a series of modulation symbols in the form of pulses.

PWM — Pulse width modulation. A type of pulse modulation where the modulating signal is encoded in the pulse width.

QAM — Quadrature amplitude modulation. A digital modulation type in which both amplitude and phase are varied. The number that precedes it, for example 64QAM, is the number of different possible states of the amplitude and phase.

QPSK — PSK with four possible states. The term is usually understood to be equivalent to four-level QAM, in which the four states have the same amplitude and differ in phase by 90°.

Quadrature modulation — Refers to modulation using two RF carriers in phase quadrature, that is, 90° out of phase.

Symbol rate — The rate at which a digital signal transitions between different states. Baud rate.

Varicode — A coding method in which the length of each character code depends on its frequency of occurrence. It is used to optimize the ratio of characters per second to baud rate.

SPREAD SPECTRUM

CDMA — Code-division multiple access. A method of allowing several stations to use the same frequency band simultaneously by assigning each station a different orthogonal spreading code.

Chip — The shortest-duration modulation state in a SS system.

De-spreading — Conversion of an SS signal back to its narrowband equivalent by convolving it with the spreading code.

DSSS — Direct-sequence SS. Spreading of a signal by multiplying the data stream by a higher-rate pseudo-random digital sequence.

FHSS — Frequency-hopping SS. Spreading of a signal by means of pseudo-random frequency-hopping of the unspread signal.

Processing gain — The increase in signal-to-noise ratio that occurs when an SS signal is de-spread.

SS — Spread spectrum. A system that intentionally increases the bandwidth of a digital signal by means of a special spreading code.

FILTERING AND BANDWIDTH

ACP — Adjacent channel power. The amount of transmitted power that falls into a communications channel immediately adjacent to the desired one.

Alpha — A design parameter for a Nyquist or root Nyquist filter. The smaller the alpha, the sharper the passband-to-stopband transition at the cutoff frequency.

Cutoff frequency — The frequency at which a filter response changes from the passband to the stopband.

Gaussian filter — A modulation filter with a Gaussian frequency response. The transition between passband and stopband is more gradual than with most Nyquist filters.

Key clicks — Out-of-channel interference from an OOK signal caused by too-sharp transitions between the on and off states.

Nyquist filter — A filter that causes no inter-symbol interference (ISI). It is so-called because the cutoff frequency is at one-half the symbol rate, the Nyquist frequency.

Nyquist criterion — The rule that states that the sample rate must be greater than twice the highest frequency to be sampled.

Occupied bandwidth — The bandwidth within which a specified percentage of the total power occurs, typically 99%.

Raised-cosine filter — A type of Nyquist filter whose passband-to-stopband transition region has the shape of the first half-cycle of a cosine raised so that the negative peak is at zero.

Root Nyquist filter — A filter that, when cascaded with another identical filter, forms a Nyquist filter. The frequency response is the square root of that of the Nyquist filter.

Root raised-cosine filter — A root Nyquist filter with a frequency response that is the square root of a raised-cosine filter.

Shannon-Hartley theorem — A formula that predicts the maximum channel capacity that is theoretically possible over a channel of given bandwidth and signal-to-noise ratio.

Sinc function — The spectrum of a pulse or random series of pulses, equal to $\sin(x)/x$.

Splatter — Out-of-channel interference from an amplitude-modulated signal such as SSB or QPSK caused by distortion, typically in the power amplifier stages.

11.12 References and Bibliography

"A Brief Introduction to Sigma-Delta Conversion," AN9504, Intersil. **www.intersil.com/content/dam/Intersil/documents/an95/an9504.pdf**

Agilent Technologies, "Digital Modulation in Communications Systems — An Introduction" Application Note 1298. **literature.cdn.keysight.com/litweb/pdf/5965-7160E.pdf?id=1817805**

Costas, J. P., "Poisson, Shannon, and the Radio Amateur," *Proceedings of the IRE*, vol 47, pp 2058-2068, Dec 1959.

Ford, S., WB8IMY, *Get On the Air with HF Digital* (ARRL, 2011)

Ford, S., WB8IMY, *ARRL's VHF Digital Handbook* (ARRL, 2008)

Haykin, S., *Digital Communications* (Wiley, 1988)

Langner, J. WB2OSZ, "SSTV Transmission Modes," **www.comunicacio.net/digigrup/ccdd/sstv.htm**

Mack, R., W5IFS, SDR: Simplified column, *QEX*, from 2009.

"Manual of Transmission Methods – Reference Document," Rohde & Schwarz, 2014, available at **resources.rohde-schwarz-usa.com/c/manual-of-transmissi-2**

Nagle, J., K4KJ, "Diversity Reception: an Answer to High Frequency Signal Fading," *Ham Radio*, Nov 1979, pp 48-55.

Sabin, W., et al, *Single-Sideband Systems and Circuits* (McGraw Hill, 1987)

Shavkoplyas, A., VE3NEA, "CW Shaping in DSP Software," *QEX*, May/Jun 2006, pp 3-7.

Seiler, T., HB9JNX/AE4WA, et al, "Digital Amateur TeleVision (D-ATV)," proc. 2001 ARRL/TAPR Digital Communications Conference, **www.tapr.org/pdf/DCC2001-Digital-ATV-HB9JNX-DF9IC-DG8FAC-DL8SDL.pdf**

Silver, W., NØAX, "About FM," *QST*, Jul 2004, pp 38-42.

Silver, W., NØAX, "About SSB," *QST*, Jan 2016, pp 51-54.

Smith, D., KF6DX, "Distortion and Noise in OFDM Systems," *QEX*, Mar/Apr 2005, pp 57-59.

Smith, D., KF6DX, "Digital Voice: The Next New Mode?," *QST*, Jan 2002, pp 28-32.

Stanley, J., K4ERO, "Observing Selective Fading in Real Time with Dream Software," *QEX*, Jan/Feb 2007, pp 18-22.

Taggart, R., WB8DQT, "An Introduction to Amateur Television," *QST*, Apr, May and Jun 1993.

Taggart, R., WB8DQT, *Image Communications Handbook* (ARRL, 2002)

Taggart, R., WB8DQT, "Digital Slow-Scan Television," *QST*, Feb 2004, pp 47-51.

Van Valkenburg, M., et al, *Reference Data for Engineers: Radio, Electronics, Computer and Communications*, chapters 23, 24 and 25, 9th Ed. (Newnes, 2001)

Notes

Notes

Notes

Notes

Notes

Notes